STUDENT'S SOLUTIONS MANUAL

CINDY TRIMBLE & ASSOCIATES

PREALGEBRA & INTRODUCTORY ALGEBRA
THIRD EDITION

Elayn Martin-Gay
University of New Orleans

Prentice Hall
is an imprint of

D1372128

Reproduced by Pearson Prentice Hall from electronic files supplied by the author.

ISBN-13: 978-0-321-64943-0   Standalone
ISBN-10: 0-321-64943-5   Standalone

ISBN-13: 978-0-321-64944-7   Component
ISBN-10: 0-321-64944-3   Component

3 4 5 6 BRR 14 13 12 11 10

Prentice Hall
is an imprint of

www.pearsonhighered.com

Contents

Chapter 1

Practice Problems

1. The place value of the 8 in 38,760,005 is millions.

2. The place value of the 8 in 67,890 is hundreds.

3. The place value of the 8 in 481,922 is ten-thousands.

4. 54 is written as fifty-four.

5. 678 is written as six hundred seventy-eight.

6. 93,205 is written as ninety-three thousand, two hundred five.

7. 679,430,105 is written as six hundred seventy-nine million, four hundred thirty thousand, one hundred five.

8. Thirty-seven in standard form is 37.

9. Two hundred twelve in standard form is 212.

10. Eight thousand, two hundred seventy-four in standard form is 8,274 or 8274.

11. Five million, fifty-seven thousand, twenty-six in standard form is 5,057,026.

12. 4,026,301
    = 4,000,000 + 20,000 + 6000 + 300 + 1

13. **a.** Find Great Britain in the left-hand column. Read from left to right until the "bronze" column is reached. Great Britain won 15 bronze medals.

    b. Find the countries for which the entry in the last column (The United States and China) is greater than 90. The United States and China won more than 90 medals.

Vocabulary and Readiness Check

1. The numbers 0, 1, 2, 3, 4, 5, 6, 7, 8, 9, 10, 11, 12, ... are called whole numbers.

2. The number 1,286 is written in standard form.

3. The number "twenty-one" is written in words.

4. The number 900 + 60 + 5 is written in expanded form.

5. In a whole number, each group of 3 digits is called a period.

6. The place value of the digit 4 in the whole number 264 is ones.

Exercise Set 1.2

1. The place value of the 5 in 657 is tens.

3. The place value of the 5 in 5423 is thousands.

5. The place value of the 5 in 43,526,000 is hundred-thousands.

7. The place value of the 5 in 5,408,092 is millions.

9. 354 is written as three hundred fifty-four.

11. 8279 is written as eight thousand, two hundred seventy-nine.

13. 26,990 is written as twenty-six thousand, nine hundred ninety.

15. 2,388,000 is written as two million, three hundred eighty-eight thousand.

17. 24,350,185 is written as twenty-four million, three hundred fifty thousand, one hundred eighty-five.

19. 304,367 is written as three hundred four thousand, three hundred sixty-seven.

21. 2600 is written as two thousand, six hundred.

23. 15,800,000 is written as fifteen million, eight hundred thousand.

25. 14,433 is written as fourteen thousand, four hundred thirty-three.

27. 13,000,000 is written as thirteen million.

29. Six thousand, five hundred eighty-seven in standard form is 6587.

31. Fifty-nine thousand, eight hundred in standard form is 59,800.

1

33. Thirteen million, six hundred one thousand, eleven in standard form is 13,601,011.

35. Seven million, seventeen in standard form is 7,000,017.

37. Two hundred sixty thousand, nine hundred ninety-seven in standard form is 260,997.

39. Three hundred ninety-five in standard form is 395.

41. Thirty thousand, seven hundred fifty in standard form is 30,750.

43. Sixty-six million, four hundred thousand in standard form is 66,400,000.

45. Five hundred sixty-five in standard form is 565.

47. $209 = 200 + 9$

49. $3470 = 3000 + 400 + 70$

51. $80,774 = 80,000 + 700 + 70 + 4$

53. $66,049 = 60,000 + 6000 + 40 + 9$

55. 39,680,000
$= 30,000,000 + 9,000,000 + 600,000 + 80,000$

57. Mount Shasta erupted in 1786, which is in standard form.

59. Mount Baker has four eruptions listed, which is more eruptions than any other volcano listed in the table.

61. Glacier Peak has an eruption listed in approximately 1750. All other eruptions listed in the table occurred after this one.

63. Boxer has fewer dogs registered than Dachshund.

65. Labrador Retrievers have the most registrations; 123,760 is written as one hundred twenty-three thousand, seven hundred sixty.

67. The maximum weight of an average-size Dachshund is 25 pounds.

69. The largest number is 9861.

71. No; 105.00 should be written as one hundred five.

73. answers may vary

75. 1000 trillion in standard form is 1,000,000,000,000,000.

Section 1.3

Practice Problems

1.
$$\begin{array}{r} 4135 \\ + 252 \\ \hline 4387 \end{array}$$

2.
$$\begin{array}{r} {\scriptstyle 1\;1\;11} \\ 47,364 \\ + 135,898 \\ \hline 183,262 \end{array}$$

3. Notice $12 + 8 = 20$ and $4 + 6 = 10$.
$12 + 4 + 8 + 6 + 5 = 20 + 10 + 5 = 35$

4.
$$\begin{array}{r} {\scriptstyle 1\;2\;2} \\ 6432 \\ 789 \\ 54 \\ + 28 \\ \hline 7303 \end{array}$$

5. a. $14 - 6 = 8$ because $8 + 6 = 14$.

   b. $20 - 8 = 12$ because $12 + 8 = 20$

   c. $93 - 93 = 0$ because $0 + 93 = 93$.

   d. $42 - 0 = 42$ because $42 + 0 = 42$.

6. a.
$$\begin{array}{r} 9143 \\ - 122 \\ \hline 9021 \end{array} \qquad \textit{Check:} \begin{array}{r} 9021 \\ + 122 \\ \hline 9143 \end{array}$$

   b.
$$\begin{array}{r} 978 \\ - 851 \\ \hline 127 \end{array} \qquad \textit{Check:} \begin{array}{r} 127 \\ + 851 \\ \hline 978 \end{array}$$

7. a.
$$\begin{array}{r} {\scriptstyle 8\;17} \\ 6\cancel{9}\,\cancel{7} \\ - 4\,9 \\ \hline 64\,8 \end{array} \qquad \textit{Check:} \begin{array}{r} 648 \\ + 49 \\ \hline 697 \end{array}$$

   b.
$$\begin{array}{r} {\scriptstyle 2\;12} \\ \cancel{3}\cancel{2}6 \\ - 245 \\ \hline 81 \end{array} \qquad \textit{Check:} \begin{array}{r} 81 \\ + 245 \\ \hline 326 \end{array}$$

c.
$$\begin{array}{r} 1234 \\ -\ 822 \\ \hline 412 \end{array}$$
Check:
$$\begin{array}{r} 412 \\ +\ 822 \\ \hline 1234 \end{array}$$

8. a.
$$\begin{array}{r} \overset{9}{\cancel{3}}\overset{10}{\cancel{10}}0 \\ \cancel{4}\ \cancel{0}\ \cancel{0} \\ -1\ 6\ 4 \\ \hline 2\ 3\ 6 \end{array}$$
Check:
$$\begin{array}{r} 236 \\ +\ 164 \\ \hline 400 \end{array}$$

b.
$$\begin{array}{r} \overset{9}{\cancel{9}}\overset{10}{\cancel{10}}0 \\ 1\cancel{0}\ \cancel{0}\ \cancel{0} \\ -\ 7\ 6\ 2 \\ \hline 2\ 3\ 8 \end{array}$$
Check:
$$\begin{array}{r} 238 \\ +\ 762 \\ \hline 1000 \end{array}$$

9. 2 cm + 8 cm + 15 cm + 5 cm = 30 cm
The perimeter is 30 centimeters.

10. 647 + 647 + 647 = 1941
The perimeter is 1941 feet.

11.
$$\begin{array}{r} 15,759 \\ -\ \ \ \ 458 \\ \hline 15,301 \end{array}$$
The radius of Neptune is 15,301 miles.

12. a. The country with the fewest endangered species corresponds to the shortest bar, which is Australia.

    b. To find the total number of endangered species for Brazil, India, and Mexico, we add.
$$\begin{array}{r} 73 \\ 89 \\ +\ 72 \\ \hline 234 \end{array}$$
The total number of endangered species for Brazil, India, and Mexico is 234.

Calculator Explorations

1. 89 + 45 = 134

2. 76 + 97 = 173

3. 285 + 55 = 340

4. 8773 + 652 = 9425

5. 985 + 1210 + 562 + 77 = 2834

6. 465 + 9888 + 620 + 1550 = 12,523

7. 865 − 95 = 770

8. 76 − 27 = 49

9. 147 − 38 = 109

10. 366 − 87 = 279

11. 9625 − 647 = 8978

12. 10,711 − 8925 = 1786

Vocabulary and Readiness Check

1. The sum of 0 and any number is the same <u>number</u>.

2. In 35 + 20 = 55, the number 55 is called the <u>sum</u> and 35 and 20 are each called an <u>addend</u>.

3. The difference of any number and that same number is <u>0</u>.

4. The difference of any number and 0 is the same <u>number</u>.

5. In 37 − 19 = 18, the number 37 is the <u>minuend</u>, the 19 is the <u>subtrahend</u>, and the 18 is the <u>difference</u>.

6. The distance around a polygon is called its <u>perimeter</u>.

7. Since 7 + 10 = 10 + 7, we say that changing the <u>order</u> in addition does not change the sum. This property is called the <u>commutative</u> property of addition.

8. Since (3 + 1) + 20 = 3 + (1 + 20), we say that changing the <u>grouping</u> in addition does not change the sum. This property is called the <u>associative</u> property of addition.

Exercise Set 1.3

1.
$$\begin{array}{r} 14 \\ +\ 22 \\ \hline 36 \end{array}$$

3.
$$\begin{array}{r} 62 \\ +\ 230 \\ \hline 292 \end{array}$$

5.   12
           13
        + 24
        ‾‾‾‾
           49

7.   5267
        + 132
        ‾‾‾‾‾
         5399

       1 1 1
9.   22,781
        + 186,297
        ‾‾‾‾‾‾‾‾‾
         209,078

11.   8
            9
            2
            5
          + 1
          ‾‾‾
           25

     2 2
13.   81
           17
           23
           79
         + 12
         ‾‾‾‾
          212

     1 1 2
15.   24
          9006
           489
        + 2407
        ‾‾‾‾‾‾
         11,926

     1 1 1
17.   6 820
           4 271
         + 5 626
         ‾‾‾‾‾‾
          16,717

     1 1 2 2
19.   49
             628
           5 762
         + 29,462
         ‾‾‾‾‾‾‾
          35,901

       1 22 2 1
21.   121,742
            57,279
            26,586
         + 426,782
         ‾‾‾‾‾‾‾‾
          632,389

23.   749   *Check:*   600
         − 149   + 149
         ‾‾‾‾   ‾‾‾‾
           600   749

                    1
25.   62   *Check:*   25
          −37   + 37
          ‾‾‾   ‾‾‾
           25   62

                    1 1
27.   922   *Check:*   288
         −634   + 634
         ‾‾‾‾   ‾‾‾‾
          288   922

                    1 1
29.   600   *Check:*   168
         − 432   + 432
         ‾‾‾‾   ‾‾‾‾
           168   600

                    1
31.   6283   *Check:*   5723
         − 560   + 560
         ‾‾‾‾   ‾‾‾‾
          5723   6283

                    1
33.   533   *Check:*   504
         − 29   + 29
         ‾‾‾‾   ‾‾‾‾
           504   533

                    1
35.   1983   *Check:*   79
         − 1904   + 1904
         ‾‾‾‾   ‾‾‾‾‾
            79   1983

                    1 1 11
37.   50,000   *Check:*   32,711
         − 17,289   + 17,289
         ‾‾‾‾‾‾   ‾‾‾‾‾‾
          32,711   50,000

                    1 1 1
39.   7020   *Check:*   5041
         − 1979   + 1979
         ‾‾‾‾   ‾‾‾‾
          5041   7020

4

41.
$$\begin{array}{r} 51{,}111 \\ -\,19{,}898 \\ \hline 31{,}213 \end{array}$$

$$\textit{Check:}\quad \overset{11\ 11}{\begin{array}{r} 31{,}213 \\ +\,19{,}898 \\ \hline 51{,}111 \end{array}}$$

43.
$$\begin{array}{r} 986 \\ +\,48 \\ \hline 1034 \end{array}$$

45.
$$\begin{array}{r} 76 \\ -\,67 \\ \hline 9 \end{array}$$

47.
$$\begin{array}{r} 9000 \\ -\,482 \\ \hline 8518 \end{array}$$

49.
$$\overset{11\ 1}{\begin{array}{r} 10{,}962 \\ 4\ 851 \\ +\,7\ 063 \\ \hline 22{,}876 \end{array}}$$

51. $7 + 8 + 10 = 25$
The perimeter is 25 feet.

53. Opposite sides of a rectangle have the same length.
$4 + 8 + 4 + 8 = 12 + 12 = 24$
The perimeter is 24 inches.

55. $8 + 3 + 5 + 7 + 5 + 1 = 29$
The perimeter is 29 inches.

57. The unknown vertical side has length
$12 - 5 = 7$ meters. The unknown horizontal side
has length $10 - 5 = 5$ meters.
$10 + 12 + 5 + 7 + 5 + 5 = 44$
The perimeter is 44 meters.

59. "Find the sum" indicates addition.
$$\overset{1\ 1\ 1}{\begin{array}{r} 297 \\ +\,1796 \\ \hline 2093 \end{array}}$$
The sum of 297 and 1796 is 2093.

61. "Find the total" indicates addition.
$$\overset{1\ 3}{\begin{array}{r} 76 \\ 39 \\ 8 \\ 17 \\ +\,126 \\ \hline 266 \end{array}}$$
The total of 76, 39, 8, 17, and 126 is 266.

63. "Find the difference" indicates subtraction.
$$\begin{array}{r} 41 \\ -\,21 \\ \hline 20 \end{array}$$
The difference of 41 and 21 is 20.

65. "Increased by" indicates addition.
$$\overset{1}{\begin{array}{r} 452 \\ +\,92 \\ \hline 544 \end{array}}$$
452 increased by 92 is 544.

67. "Less" indicates subtraction.
$$\begin{array}{r} 108 \\ -\,36 \\ \hline 72 \end{array}$$
108 less 36 is 72.

69. "Subtracted from" indicates subtraction.
$$\begin{array}{r} 100 \\ -\,12 \\ \hline 88 \end{array}$$
12 subtracted from 100 is 88.

71. Subtract 19,308 thousand from 22,478 thousand.
$$\begin{array}{r} 22{,}478 \\ -\,19{,}308 \\ \hline 3\ 170 \end{array}$$
Florida's projected population increase is
3170 thousand.

73. Subtract the cost of the DVD player from the amount in her savings account.
$$\begin{array}{r} 914 \\ -\,295 \\ \hline 619 \end{array}$$
She will have $619 left.

75.
$$\begin{array}{r} 189,000 \\ +\ 75,000 \\ \hline 264,000 \end{array}$$
The total U.S. land area drained by the Upper Mississippi and Lower Mississippi sub-basins is 264,000 square miles.

77.
$$\begin{array}{r} 530,000 \\ -\ 247,000 \\ \hline 283,000 \end{array}$$
The Missouri sub-basin drains 283,000 square miles more than the Arkansas Red-White sub-basin.

79. $70 + 78 + 90 + 102 = 340$
The homeowner needs 340 feet of fencing.

81.
$$\begin{array}{r} 503 \\ -\ 239 \\ \hline 264 \end{array}$$
She must read 264 more pages.

83.
$$\begin{array}{r} 4,280,031 \\ +\ 29,719,969 \\ \hline 34,000,000 \end{array}$$
The sheep population was 34,000,000.

85. Live rock music has a decibel level of 100 dB.

87.
$$\begin{array}{r} 88 \\ -\ 30 \\ \hline 58 \end{array}$$
The sound of snoring is 58 dB louder than normal conversation.

89.
$$\begin{array}{r} 2677 \\ +\ 493 \\ \hline 3170 \end{array}$$
There were 3170 stores worldwide.

91. Each side of a square has the same length.
$31 + 31 + 31 + 31 = 124$
The perimeter of the playing board is 124 feet.

93. California has the most Target stores.

95.
$$\begin{array}{r} 225 \\ 136 \\ +\ 115 \\ \hline 476 \end{array}$$
The total number of Target stores in California, Texas, and Florida is 476 stores.

97. Florida and Georgia:
$$\begin{array}{r} 115 \\ +\ 51 \\ \hline 166 \end{array}$$
Michigan and Ohio:
$$\begin{array}{r} 57 \\ +\ 63 \\ \hline 120 \end{array}$$
Florida and Georgia have more Target stores.

99.
$$\begin{array}{r} \overset{1}{}2029 \\ +\ 3865 \\ \hline 5894 \end{array}$$
The total highway mileage in Delaware is 5894 miles.

101. The minuend is 48 and the subtrahend is 1.

103. The minuend is 70 and the subtrahend is 7.

105. answers may vary

107.
$$\begin{array}{r} \overset{1}{}566 \\ 932 \\ +\ 871 \\ \hline 2369 \end{array}$$
The given sum is correct.

109.
$$\begin{array}{r} \overset{2\ 2}{}14 \\ 173 \\ 86 \\ +\ 257 \\ \hline 530 \end{array}$$
The given sum is incorrect, the correct sum is 530.

111.
$$\begin{array}{r} \overset{1\ 1}{}675 \\ +\ 56 \\ \hline 731 \end{array}$$
The given difference is incorrect.
$$\begin{array}{r} 741 \\ -\ 56 \\ \hline 685 \end{array}$$

113.
$$\begin{array}{r} 141 \\ +\ 888 \\ \hline 1029 \end{array}$$
The given difference is correct.

115.

$$
\begin{array}{r}
5269 \\
- 2385 \\
\hline
2884
\end{array}
$$

117. answers may vary

119.

$$
\begin{array}{r}
{\scriptstyle 1\,2\,1\ 3\,2} \\
289,462 \\
369,477 \\
218,287 \\
+ 121,685 \\
\hline
998,911
\end{array}
$$

Since 998,911 is less than one million, they did not reach their goal.

$$
\begin{array}{r}
1,000,000 \\
-\ 998,911 \\
\hline
1\ 089
\end{array}
$$

They need to read 1089 more pages.

Section 1.4

Practice Problems

1. a. To round 57 to the nearest ten, observe that the digit in the ones place is 7. Since the digit is at least 5, we add 1 to the digit in the tens place. The number 57 rounded to the nearest ten is 60.

b. To round 641 to the nearest ten, observe that the digit in the ones place is 1. Since the digit is less than 5, we do not add 1 to the digit in the tens place. The number 641 rounded to the nearest ten is 640.

c. To round 325 to the nearest ten observe that the digit in the ones place is 5. Since the digit is at least 5, we add 1 to the digit in the tens place. The number 325 rounded to the nearest ten is 330.

2. a. To round 72,304 to the nearest thousand, observe that the digit in the hundreds place is 3. Since the digit is less than 5, we do not add 1 to the digit in the thousands place. The number 72,304 rounded to the nearest thousand is 72,000.

b. To round 9222 to the nearest thousand, observe that the digit in the hundreds place is 2. Since the digit is less than 5, we do not add 1 to the digit in the thousands place. The number 9222 rounded to the nearest thousand is 9000.

c. To round 671,800 to the nearest thousand, observe that the digit in the hundreds place is 8. Since this digit is at least 5, we add 1 to the digit in the thousands place. The number 671,800 rounded to the nearest thousand is 672,000.

3. a. To round 3474 to the nearest hundred, observe that the digit in the tens place is 7. Since this digit is at least 5, we add 1 to the digit in the hundreds place. The number 3474 rounded to the nearest hundred is 3500.

b. To round 76,243 to the nearest hundred, observe that the digit in the tens place is 4. Since this digit is less than 5, we do not add 1 to the digit in the hundreds place. The number 76,243 rounded to the nearest hundred is 76,200.

c. To round 978,965 to the nearest hundred, observe that the digit in the tens place is 6. Since this digit is at least 5, we add 1 to the digit in the hundreds place. The number 978,865 rounded to the nearest hundred is 979,000.

4.

49	rounds to	50
25	rounds to	30
32	rounds to	30
51	rounds to	50
98	rounds to	+ 100
		260

5.

3785	rounds to	4000
− 2479	rounds to	− 2000
		2000

6.

11	rounds to	10
16	rounds to	20
19	rounds to	20
+ 31	rounds to	+ 30
		80

The total distance is approximately 80 miles.

7.

48,445	rounds to	48,000
6,584	rounds to	7,000
+ 15,632	rounds to	+ 16,000
		71,000

The total number of cases is approximately 71,000.

Vocabulary and Readiness Check

1. To <u>graph</u> a number on a number line, darken the point representing the location of the number.

2. Another word for approximating a whole number is <u>rounding</u>.

3. The number 65 rounded to the nearest ten is <u>70</u> but the number 61 rounded to the nearest ten is <u>60</u>.

4. An <u>exact</u> number of products is 1265, but an <u>estimate</u> is 1000.

Exercise Set 1.4

1. To round 423 to the nearest ten, observe that the digit in the ones place is 3. Since this digit is less than 5, we do not add 1 to the digit in the tens place. The number 423 rounded to the nearest ten is 420.

3. To round 635 to the nearest ten, observe that the digit in the ones place is 5. Since this digit is at least 5, we add 1 to the digit in the tens place. The number 635 rounded to the nearest ten is 640.

5. To round 2791 to the nearest hundred, observe that the digit in the tens place is 9. Since this digit is at least 5, we add 1 to the digit in the hundreds place. The number 2791 rounded to the nearest hundred is 2800.

7. To round 495 to the nearest ten, observe that the digit in the ones place is 5. Since this digit is at least 5, we add 1 to the digit in the tens place. The number 495 rounded to the nearest ten is 500.

9. To round 21,094 to the nearest thousand, observe that the digit in the hundreds place is 0. Since this digit is less than 5, we do not add 1 to the digit in the thousands place. The number 21,094 rounded to the nearest thousand is 21,000.

11. To round 33,762 to the nearest thousand, observe that the digit in the hundreds place is 7. Since this digit is at least 5, we add 1 to the digit in the thousands place. The number 33,762 rounded to the nearest thousand is 34,000.

13. To round 328,495 to the nearest hundred, observe that the digit in the tens place is 9. Since this digit is at least 5, we add 1 to the digit in the hundreds place. The number 328,495 rounded to the nearest hundred is 328,500.

15. To round 36,499 to the nearest thousand, observe that the digit in the hundreds place is 4. Since this digit is less than 5, we do not add 1 to the digit in the thousands place. The number 36,499 rounded to the nearest thousand is 36,000.

17. To round 39,994 to the nearest ten, observe that the digit in the ones place is 4. Since this digit is less than 5, we do not add 1 to the digit in the tens place. The number 39,994 rounded to the nearest ten is 39,990.

19. To round 29,834,235 to the nearest ten-million, observe that the digit in the millions place is 9. Since this digit is at least 5, we add 1 to the digit in the ten-millions place. The number 29,834,235 rounded to the nearest ten-million is 30,000,000.

21. Estimate 5281 to a given place value by rounding it to that place value. 5281 rounded to the tens place is 5280, to the hundreds place is 5300, and to the thousands place is 5000.

23. Estimate 9444 to a given place value by rounding it to that place value. 9444 rounded to the tens place is 9440, to the hundreds place is 9400, and to the thousands place is 9000.

25. Estimate 14,876 to a given place value by rounding it to that place value. 14,876 rounded to the tens place is 14,880, to the hundreds place is 14,900, and to the thousands place is 15,000.

27. To round 39,786 to the nearest thousand, observe that the digit in the hundreds place is 7. Since this digit is greater than 5, we add 1 to the digit in the thousands place. Therefore, 39,786 rounded to the nearest thousand is 40,000.

29. To round 38,387 to the nearest thousand, observe that the digit in the hundreds place is 3. Since this digit is less than 5, we do not add 1 to the digit in the thousands place. Therefore, 38,387 points rounded to the nearest thousand is 38,000 points.

31. To round 42,570,000,000 to the nearest billion, observe that the digit in the hundred-millions place is 5. Since this digit is at least 5, we add 1 to the digit in the billions place. Therefore, $42,570,000,000 rounded to the nearest billion is $43,000,000,000.

33. To round 4,934,078 to the nearest hundred-thousand, observe that the digit in the ten-thousands place is 3. Since this digit is less than 5, we do not add 1 to the digit in the hundred-thousands place. Therefore, $4,934,078 rounded to the nearest hundred-thousand is $4,900,000.

35. U.S.: To round 262,700,000 to the nearest million, observe that the digit in the hundred-thousands place is 7. Since this digit is at least 5, we add 1 to the digit in the millions place. The number 262,700,000 rounded to the nearest million is 263,000,000.
India: To round 296,886,000 to the nearest million, observe that the digit in the hundred-thousands place is 8. Since this digit is at least 5, we add 1 to the digit in the millions place. The number 296,886,000 rounded to the nearest million is 297,000,000.

37.
39	rounds to	40
45	rounds to	50
22	rounds to	20
+ 17	rounds to	+ 20
		130

39.
449	rounds to	450
− 373	rounds to	− 370
		80

41.
1913	rounds to	1900
1886	rounds to	1900
+ 1925	rounds to	+ 1900
		5700

43.
1774	rounds to	1800
− 1492	rounds to	− 1500
		300

45.
3995	rounds to	4000
2549	rounds to	2500
+ 4944	rounds to	+ 4900
		11,400

47. 463 + 219 is approximately 460 + 220 = 680. The answer of 600 is incorrect.

49. 229 + 443 + 606 is approximately 230 + 440 + 610 = 1280. The answer of 1278 is correct.

51. 7806 + 5150 is approximately 7800 + 5200 = 13,000. The answer of 12,956 is correct.

53.
899	rounds to	900
1499	rounds to	1500
+ 999	rounds to	+ 1000
		3400

The total cost is approximately $3400.

55.
1429	rounds to	1400
− 530	rounds to	− 500
		900

Boston in approximately 900 miles farther from Kansas City than Chicago is.

57.
20,320	rounds to	20,000
− 14,410	rounds to	− 14,000
		6 000

The difference in elevation is approximately 6000 feet.

59.
142,702	rounds to	140,000
− 75,543	rounds to	− 80,000
		60,000

Joliet was approximately 60,000 larger than Evanston.

61.
908,412	rounds to	908,000
− 905,851	rounds to	− 906,000
		2 000

The increase in enrollment is approximately 2000 children.

63. 761 hundred-thousands is 76,100,000 in standard form. 76,100,000 rounded to the nearest million is 76,000,000. 76,100,000 rounded to the nearest ten-million is 80,000,000.

65. 598 hundred-thousands is 59,800,000 in standard form. 59,800,000 rounded to the nearest million is 60,000,000. 59,800,000 rounded to the nearest ten-million is 60,000,000.

67. 5723, for example, rounded to the nearest hundred is 5700.

69. a. The smallest possible number that rounds to 8600 is 8550.

b. The largest possible number that rounds to 8600 is 8649.

71. answers may vary

73. 54 rounds to 50
17 rounds to 20
50 + 20 + 50 + 20 = 140
The perimeter is approximately 140 meters.

Section 1.5

Practice Problems

1. a. $6 \times 0 = 0$

b. $(1)8 = 8$

c. $(50)(0) = 0$

d. $75 \cdot 1 = 75$

2. a. $6(4 + 5) = 6 \cdot 4 + 6 \cdot 5$

b. $30(2 + 3) = 30 \cdot 2 + 30 \cdot 3$

c. $7(2 + 8) = 7 \cdot 2 + 7 \cdot 8$

3. a.
$$\begin{array}{r} {}^{5} \\ 29 \\ \times\ 6 \\ \hline 174 \end{array}$$

b.
$$\begin{array}{r} {}^{44} \\ 648 \\ \times\ 5 \\ \hline 3240 \end{array}$$

4.
$$\begin{array}{r} 306 \\ \times\ 81 \\ \hline 306 \\ 24\ 480 \\ \hline 24,786 \end{array}$$

5.
$$\begin{array}{r} 726 \\ \times\ 142 \\ \hline 1\ 452 \\ 29\ 040 \\ 72\ 600 \\ \hline 103,092 \end{array}$$

6. Area = length · width
= (360 miles)(280 miles)
= 100,800 square miles
The area of Wyoming is 100,800 square miles.

7.
$$\begin{array}{r} 16 \\ \times\ 45 \\ \hline 80 \\ 640 \\ \hline 720 \end{array}$$
The printer can print 720 pages in 45 minutes.

8. $8 \times 11 = 88$
$5 \times 9 = 45$
$$\begin{array}{r} {}^{1} \\ 88 \\ +\ 45 \\ \hline 133 \end{array}$$
The total cost is $133.

9.
$$\begin{array}{rll} 163 & \text{rounds to} & 200 \\ \times\ 391 & \text{rounds to} & \times\ 400 \\ \hline & & 80,000 \end{array}$$
There are approximately 80,000 words on 391 pages.

Calculator Explorations

1. $72 \times 48 = 3456$

2. $81 \times 92 = 7452$

3. $163 \cdot 94 = 15,322$

4. $285 \cdot 144 = 41,040$

5. $983(277) = 272,291$

6. $1562(843) = 1,316,766$

Vocabulary and Readiness Check

1. The product of 0 and any number is 0.

2. The product of 1 and any number is the number.

3. In $8 \cdot 12 = 96$, the 96 is called the product and 8 and 12 are each called a factor.

4. Since $9 \cdot 10 = 10 \cdot 9$, we say that changing the order in multiplication does not change the product. This property is called the commutative property of multiplication.

5. Since $(3 \cdot 4) \cdot 6 = 3 \cdot (4 \cdot 6)$, we say that changing the grouping in multiplication does not change the product. This property is called the associative property of multiplication.

6. Area measures the amount of surface of a region.

7. Area of a rectangle = length · width.

8. We know $9(10 + 8) = 9 \cdot 10 + 9 \cdot 8$ by the <u>distributive</u> property.

Exercise Set 1.5

1. $1 \cdot 24 = 24$

3. $0 \cdot 19 = 0$

5. $8 \cdot 0 \cdot 9 = 0$

7. $87 \cdot 1 = 87$

9. $6(3 + 8) = 6 \cdot 3 + 6 \cdot 8$

11. $4(3 + 9) = 4 \cdot 3 + 4 \cdot 9$

13. $20(14 + 6) = 20 \cdot 14 + 20 \cdot 6$

15.
$$\begin{array}{r} 64 \\ \times\ 8 \\ \hline 512 \end{array}$$

17.
$$\begin{array}{r} 613 \\ \times\ 6 \\ \hline 3678 \end{array}$$

19.
$$\begin{array}{r} 277 \\ \times\ 6 \\ \hline 1662 \end{array}$$

21.
$$\begin{array}{r} 1074 \\ \times\ 6 \\ \hline 6444 \end{array}$$

23.
$$\begin{array}{r} 89 \\ \times\ 13 \\ \hline 267 \\ 890 \\ \hline 1157 \end{array}$$

25.
$$\begin{array}{r} 421 \\ \times\ 58 \\ \hline 3\,368 \\ 21\,050 \\ \hline 24{,}418 \end{array}$$

27.
$$\begin{array}{r} 306 \\ \times\ 81 \\ \hline 306 \\ 24\,480 \\ \hline 24{,}786 \end{array}$$

29.
$$\begin{array}{r} 780 \\ \times\ 20 \\ \hline 15{,}600 \end{array}$$

31. $(495)(13)(0) = 0$

33. $(640)(1)(10) = (640)(10) = 6400$

35.
$$\begin{array}{r} 1234 \\ \times\ 39 \\ \hline 11\,106 \\ 37\,020 \\ \hline 48{,}126 \end{array}$$

37.
$$\begin{array}{r} 609 \\ \times\ 234 \\ \hline 2\,436 \\ 18\,270 \\ 121\,800 \\ \hline 142{,}506 \end{array}$$

39.
$$\begin{array}{r} 8649 \\ \times\ 274 \\ \hline 34\,596 \\ 605\,430 \\ 1\,729\,800 \\ \hline 2{,}369{,}826 \end{array}$$

41.
$$\begin{array}{r} 589 \\ \times\ 110 \\ \hline 5\,890 \\ 58\,900 \\ \hline 64{,}790 \end{array}$$

43.
$$\begin{array}{r} 1941 \\ \times\ 2035 \\ \hline 9\,705 \\ 58\,230 \\ 3\,882\,000 \\ \hline 3{,}949{,}935 \end{array}$$

45. Area = (length)(width)
= (9 meters)(7 meters)
= 63 square meters

Perimeter = length + width + length + width
= 9 + 7 + 9 + 7
= 32 meters

47. Area = (length)(width)
$$= (40 \text{ feet})(17 \text{ feet})$$
$$= 680 \text{ square feet}$$

Perimeter = length + width + length + width
$$= 40 + 17 + 40 + 17$$
$$= 114 \text{ feet}$$

49.

576	rounds to	600
× 354	rounds to	× 400
		240,000

51.

604	rounds to	600
× 451	rounds to	× 500
		300,000

53. 38×42 is approximately 40×40, which is 1600. The best estimate is c.

55. 612×29 is approximately 600×30, which is 18,000.
The best estimate is c.

57. $80 \times 11 = (8 \times 10) \times 11$
$$= 8 \times (10 \times 11)$$
$$= 8 \times 110$$
$$= 880$$

59. $6 \times 700 = 4200$

61.

$$\begin{array}{r} 2240 \\ \times\ \ \ 2 \\ \hline 4480 \end{array}$$

63.

$$\begin{array}{r} 125 \\ \times\ \ \ 3 \\ \hline 375 \end{array}$$

There are 375 calories in 3 tablespoons of olive oil.

65.

$$\begin{array}{r} 94 \\ \times 35 \\ \hline 470 \\ 2820 \\ \hline 3290 \end{array}$$

The total cost is $3290.

67. a. $4 \times 5 = 20$
There are 20 boxes in one layer.

b.

$$\begin{array}{r} 20 \\ \times\ 5 \\ \hline 100 \end{array}$$

There are 100 boxes on the pallet.

c.

$$\begin{array}{r} 100 \\ \times\ 20 \\ \hline 2000 \end{array}$$

The weight of the cheese on the pallet is 2000 pounds.

69. Area = (length)(width)
$$= (110 \text{ feet})(80 \text{ feet})$$
$$= 8800 \text{ square feet}$$
The area is 8800 square feet.

71. Area = (length)(width)
$$= (350 \text{ feet})(160 \text{ feet})$$
$$= 56,000 \text{ square feet}$$
The area is 56,000 square feet.

73.

$$\begin{array}{r} 94 \\ \times 62 \\ \hline 188 \\ 5640 \\ \hline 5828 \end{array}$$

There are 5828 pixels on the screen.

75.

$$\begin{array}{r} 60 \\ \times\ 35 \\ \hline 300 \\ 1\ 800 \\ \hline 2\ 100 \end{array}$$

There are 2100 characters in 35 lines.

77.

$$\begin{array}{r} 160 \\ \times\ \ 8 \\ \hline 1280 \end{array}$$

There are 1280 calories in 8 ounces.

79.

T-Shirt Size	Number of Shirts Ordered	Cost per Shirt	Cost per Size Ordered
S	4	$10	$40
M	6	$10	$60
L	20	$10	$200
XL	3	$12	$36
XXL	3	$12	$36
Total Cost			$372

81. There are 60 minutes in one hour.
$24 \times 60 \times 1000 = 1440 \times 1000 = 1,440,000$
1,440,000 tea bags are produced in one day.

83.
$$\begin{array}{r} 128 \\ +\ \ 7 \\ \hline 135 \end{array}$$

85.
$$\begin{array}{r} 134 \\ \times 16 \\ \hline 804 \\ 1340 \\ \hline 2144 \end{array}$$

87.
$$\begin{array}{r} 19 \\ +\ \ 4 \\ \hline 23 \end{array}$$
The sum of 19 and 4 is 23.

89.
$$\begin{array}{r} 19 \\ -\ \ 4 \\ \hline 15 \end{array}$$
The difference of 19 and 4 is 15.

91. $6 + 6 + 6 + 6 + 6 = 5 \cdot 6$ or $6 \cdot 5$

93. a. $3 \cdot 5 = 5 + 5 + 5$ or $3 + 3 + 3 + 3 + 3$

    b. answers may vary

95.
$$\begin{array}{r} 203 \\ \times\ 14 \\ \hline 812 \\ 2030 \\ \hline 2842 \end{array}$$

97. $42 \times 3 = 126$
$42 \times 9 = 378$
The problem is
$$\begin{array}{r} 42 \\ \times 93 \\ \hline \end{array}$$

99. answers may vary

101. On a side with 7 windows per row, there are $7 \times 23 = 161$ windows. On a side with 4 windows per row, there are $4 \times 23 = 92$ windows.
$161 + 161 + 92 + 92 = 506$
There are 506 windows on the building.

Section 1.6

Practice Problems

1. a. $9\overline{)72}$ with quotient 8 because $8 \cdot 9 = 72$.

    b. $40 \div 5 = 8$ because $8 \cdot 5 = 40$.

    c. $\dfrac{24}{6} = 4$ because $4 \cdot 6 = 24$.

2. a. $\dfrac{7}{7} = 1$ because $1 \cdot 7 = 7$.

    b. $5 \div 1 = 5$ because $5 \cdot 1 = 5$.

    c. $1\overline{)11}$ with quotient 11 because $11 \cdot 1 = 11$.

    d. $4 \div 1 = 4$ because $4 \cdot 1 = 4$.

    e. $\dfrac{10}{1} = 10$ because $10 \cdot 1 = 10$.

    f. $21 \div 21 = 1$ because $1 \cdot 21 = 21$.

3. a. $\dfrac{0}{7} = 0$ because $0 \cdot 7 = 0$.

    b. $8\overline{)0}$ with quotient 0 because $0 \cdot 8 = 0$.

    c. $7 \div 0$ is undefined because if $7 \div 0$ is a number, then the number times 0 would be 7.

    d. $0 \div 14 = 0$ because $0 \cdot 14 = 0$.

4. a.
$$
\begin{array}{r}
818 \\
6\overline{)4908} \\
-48 \\
\hline
10 \\
-6 \\
\hline
48 \\
-48 \\
\hline
0
\end{array}
$$

Check:
$$
\begin{array}{r}
818 \\
\times\ 6 \\
\hline
4908
\end{array}
$$

b.
$$
\begin{array}{r}
553 \\
4\overline{)2212} \\
-20 \\
\hline
21 \\
-20 \\
\hline
12 \\
-12 \\
\hline
0
\end{array}
$$

Check:
$$
\begin{array}{r}
553 \\
\times\ 4 \\
\hline
2212
\end{array}
$$

c.
$$
\begin{array}{r}
251 \\
3\overline{)753} \\
-6 \\
\hline
15 \\
-15 \\
\hline
03 \\
-3 \\
\hline
0
\end{array}
$$

Check:
$$
\begin{array}{r}
251 \\
\times\ 3 \\
\hline
753
\end{array}
$$

5. a.
$$
\begin{array}{r}
304 \\
7\overline{)2128} \\
-21 \\
\hline
02 \\
-0 \\
\hline
28 \\
-28 \\
\hline
0
\end{array}
$$

Check: $304 \times 7 = 2128$

b.
$$
\begin{array}{r}
5\,100 \\
9\overline{)45{,}900} \\
-45 \\
\hline
0\,9 \\
-9 \\
\hline
000
\end{array}
$$

Check: $5100 \times 9 = 45{,}900$

6. a.
$$
\begin{array}{r}
234 \text{ R } 3 \\
4\overline{)939} \\
-8 \\
\hline
13 \\
-12 \\
\hline
19 \\
-16 \\
\hline
3
\end{array}
$$

Check: $234 \cdot 4 + 3 = 939$

b.
$$
\begin{array}{r}
657 \text{ R } 2 \\
5\overline{)3287} \\
-30 \\
\hline
28 \\
-25 \\
\hline
37 \\
-35 \\
\hline
2
\end{array}
$$

Check: $657 \cdot 5 + 2 = 3287$

7. a.
$$
\begin{array}{r}
9067 \text{ R } 2 \\
9\overline{)81{,}605} \\
-81 \\
\hline
0\,6 \\
-0 \\
\hline
60 \\
-54 \\
\hline
65 \\
-63 \\
\hline
2
\end{array}
$$

Check: $9067 \cdot 9 + 2 = 81{,}605$

b.

$$
\begin{array}{r}
5827 \text{ R } 2 \\
4\overline{)\ 23{,}310} \\
-20 \\
\hline
3\ 3 \\
-3\ 2 \\
\hline
11 \\
-8 \\
\hline
30 \\
-28 \\
\hline
2
\end{array}
$$

Check: $5827 \cdot 4 + 2 = 23{,}310$

8.

$$
\begin{array}{r}
524 \text{ R } 12 \\
17\overline{)\ 8920} \\
-85 \\
\hline
42 \\
-34 \\
\hline
80 \\
-68 \\
\hline
12
\end{array}
$$

9.

$$
\begin{array}{r}
49 \text{ R } 60 \\
678\overline{)\ 33{,}282} \\
-27\ 12 \\
\hline
6\ 162 \\
-6\ 102 \\
\hline
60
\end{array}
$$

10.

$$
\begin{array}{r}
57 \\
3\overline{)\ 171} \\
-15 \\
\hline
21 \\
-21 \\
\hline
0
\end{array}
$$

Each student got 57 CDs.

11.

$$
\begin{array}{r}
44 \\
12\overline{)\ 532} \\
-48 \\
\hline
52 \\
-48 \\
\hline
4
\end{array}
$$

There will be 44 full boxes and 4 printers left over.

12. Find the sum and divide by 7.

$$
\begin{array}{r}
4 \\
7 \\
35 \\
16 \\
9 \\
3 \\
+\ 52 \\
\hline
126
\end{array}
\qquad
\begin{array}{r}
18 \\
7\overline{)\ 126} \\
-7 \\
\hline
56 \\
-56 \\
\hline
0
\end{array}
$$

The average time is 18 minutes.

Calculator Explorations

1. $848 \div 16 = 53$

2. $564 \div 12 = 47$

3. $5890 \div 95 = 62$

4. $1053 \div 27 = 39$

5. $\dfrac{32{,}886}{126} = 261$

6. $\dfrac{143{,}088}{264} = 542$

7. $0 \div 315 = 0$

8. $315 \div 0$ is an error.

Vocabulary and Readiness Check

1. In $90 \div 2 = 45$, the answer 45 is called the quotient, 90 is called the dividend, and 2 is called the divisor.

2. The quotient of any number and 1 is the same number.

3. The quotient of any number (except 0) and the same number is 1.

4. The quotient of 0 and any number (except 0) is 0.

5. The quotient of any number and 0 is undefined.

6. The average of a list of numbers is the sum of the numbers divided by the number of numbers.

Exercise Set 1.6

1. $54 \div 9 = 6$

3. $36 \div 3 = 12$

5. $0 \div 8 = 0$

7. $31 \div 1 = 31$

9. $\dfrac{18}{18} = 1$

11. $\dfrac{24}{3} = 8$

13. $26 \div 0$ is undefined

15. $26 \div 26 = 1$

17. $0 \div 14 = 0$

19. $18 \div 2 = 9$

21.
$$\begin{array}{r}
29 \\
3\overline{)\,87} \\
-6 \\
\hline
27 \\
-27 \\
\hline
0
\end{array}$$
Check: $3 \cdot 29 = 87$

23.
$$\begin{array}{r}
74 \\
3\overline{)\,222} \\
-21 \\
\hline
12 \\
-12 \\
\hline
0
\end{array}$$
Check: $74 \cdot 3 = 222$

25.
$$\begin{array}{r}
338 \\
3\overline{)\,1014} \\
-9 \\
\hline
11 \\
-9 \\
\hline
24 \\
-24 \\
\hline
0
\end{array}$$
Check: $3 \cdot 338 = 1014$

27. $\dfrac{30}{0}$ is undefined.

29.
$$\begin{array}{r}
9 \\
7\overline{)\,63} \\
-63 \\
\hline
0
\end{array}$$
Check: $7 \cdot 9 = 63$

31.
$$\begin{array}{r}
25 \\
6\overline{)\,150} \\
-12 \\
\hline
30 \\
-30 \\
\hline
0
\end{array}$$
Check: $25 \cdot 6 = 150$

33.
$$\begin{array}{r}
68 \text{ R } 3 \\
7\overline{)\,479} \\
-42 \\
\hline
59 \\
-56 \\
\hline
3
\end{array}$$
Check: $7 \cdot 68 + 3 = 479$

35.
$$\begin{array}{r}
236 \text{ R } 5 \\
6\overline{)\,1421} \\
-12 \\
\hline
22 \\
-18 \\
\hline
41 \\
-36 \\
\hline
5
\end{array}$$
Check: $236 \cdot 6 + 5 = 1421$

37.
$$\begin{array}{r}
38 \text{ R } 1 \\
8\overline{)\,305} \\
-24 \\
\hline
65 \\
-64 \\
\hline
1
\end{array}$$
Check: $8 \cdot 38 + 1 = 305$

39.
$$\begin{array}{r}
326 \text{ R } 4 \\
7\overline{)\,2286} \\
-21 \\
\hline
18 \\
-14 \\
\hline
46 \\
-42 \\
\hline
4
\end{array}$$
Check: $326 \cdot 7 + 4 = 2286$

41.
$$
\begin{array}{r}
13 \\
55\overline{)\,715} \\
\underline{-55} \\
165 \\
\underline{-165} \\
0
\end{array}
$$
Check: $55 \cdot 13 = 715$

43.
$$
\begin{array}{r}
49 \\
23\overline{)\,1127} \\
\underline{-92} \\
207 \\
\underline{-207} \\
0
\end{array}
$$
Check: $49 \cdot 23 = 1127$

45.
$$
\begin{array}{r}
97 \text{ R } 8 \\
97\overline{)\,9417} \\
\underline{-873} \\
687 \\
\underline{-679} \\
8
\end{array}
$$
Check: $97 \cdot 97 + 8 = 9417$

47.
$$
\begin{array}{r}
209 \text{ R } 11 \\
15\overline{)\,3146} \\
\underline{-30} \\
14 \\
\underline{-0} \\
146 \\
\underline{-135} \\
11
\end{array}
$$
Check: $209 \cdot 15 + 11 = 3146$

49.
$$
\begin{array}{r}
506 \\
13\overline{)\,6578} \\
\underline{-65} \\
07 \\
\underline{-0} \\
78 \\
\underline{-78} \\
0
\end{array}
$$
Check: $13 \cdot 506 = 6578$

51.
$$
\begin{array}{r}
202 \text{ R } 7 \\
46\overline{)\,9299} \\
\underline{-92} \\
09 \\
\underline{-0} \\
99 \\
\underline{-92} \\
7
\end{array}
$$
Check: $202 \cdot 46 + 7 = 9299$

53.
$$
\begin{array}{r}
54 \\
236\overline{)\,12744} \\
\underline{-1180} \\
944 \\
\underline{-944} \\
0
\end{array}
$$
Check: $236 \cdot 54 = 12{,}744$

55.
$$
\begin{array}{r}
99 \text{ R } 100 \\
103\overline{)\,10{,}297} \\
\underline{-9\ 27} \\
1\ 027 \\
\underline{-927} \\
100
\end{array}
$$
Check: $99 \cdot 103 + 100 = 10{,}297$

57.
$$
\begin{array}{r}
202 \text{ R } 15 \\
102\overline{)\,20619} \\
\underline{-204} \\
21 \\
\underline{-0} \\
219 \\
\underline{-204} \\
15
\end{array}
$$
Check: $102 \cdot 202 + 15 = 20{,}619$

59.
$$
\begin{array}{r}
579 \text{ R } 72 \\
423\overline{)\,244{,}989} \\
\underline{-211\ 5} \\
33\ 48 \\
\underline{-29\ 61} \\
3\ 879 \\
\underline{-3\ 807} \\
72
\end{array}
$$
Check: $579 \cdot 423 + 72 = 244{,}989$

61.
$$
\begin{array}{r}
17 \\
7\overline{)119} \\
\underline{-7} \\
49 \\
\underline{-49} \\
0
\end{array}
$$

63.
$$
\begin{array}{r}
511\ \text{R}\ 3 \\
7\overline{)3580} \\
\underline{-35} \\
08 \\
\underline{-7} \\
10 \\
\underline{-7} \\
3
\end{array}
$$

65.
$$
\begin{array}{r}
2132\ \text{R}\ 32 \\
40\overline{)85312} \\
\underline{-80} \\
53 \\
\underline{-40} \\
131 \\
\underline{-120} \\
112 \\
\underline{-80} \\
32
\end{array}
$$

67.
$$
\begin{array}{r}
6\ 080 \\
142\overline{)863,360} \\
\underline{-852} \\
11\ 3 \\
\underline{-0} \\
11\ 36 \\
\underline{-11\ 36} \\
00 \\
\underline{-0} \\
0
\end{array}
$$

69.
$$
\begin{array}{r}
23\ \text{R}\ 2 \\
5\overline{)117} \\
\underline{-10} \\
17 \\
\underline{-15} \\
2
\end{array}
$$
The quotient is 23 R 2.

71.
$$
\begin{array}{r}
5\ \text{R}\ 25 \\
35\overline{)200} \\
\underline{-175} \\
25
\end{array}
$$
200 divided by 35 is 5 R 25.

73.
$$
\begin{array}{r}
20\ \text{R}\ 2 \\
3\overline{)62} \\
\underline{-6} \\
02 \\
\underline{-0} \\
2
\end{array}
$$
The quotient is 20 R 2.

75.
$$
\begin{array}{r}
33 \\
65\overline{)2145} \\
\underline{-195} \\
195 \\
\underline{-195} \\
0
\end{array}
$$
There are 33 students in the group.

77.
$$
\begin{array}{r}
165 \\
318\overline{)52470} \\
\underline{-318} \\
2067 \\
\underline{-1908} \\
1590 \\
\underline{-1590} \\
0
\end{array}
$$
The person weighs 165 pounds on Earth.

79.
$$
\begin{array}{r}
310 \\
18\overline{)5580} \\
\underline{-54} \\
18 \\
\underline{-18} \\
0
\end{array}
$$
The distance is 310 yards.

81.
$$
\begin{array}{r}
88\ \text{R}\ 1 \\
3\overline{)265} \\
\underline{-24} \\
25 \\
\underline{-24} \\
1
\end{array}
$$
There are 88 bridges every 3 miles over the 265 miles, plus the first bridge, for a total of 89 bridges.

83.
$$492 \overline{)\begin{array}{r} 10 \\ 5280 \end{array}}$$
$$\underline{-492}$$
$$360$$

There should be 10 poles, plus the first pole for a total of 11 light poles.

85.
$$5280 \overline{)\begin{array}{r} 5 \\ 26400 \end{array}}$$
$$\underline{-26400}$$
$$0$$

Broad Peak is 5 miles tall.

87.
$$3 \overline{)\begin{array}{r} 1760 \\ 5280 \end{array}}$$
$$\underline{-3}$$
$$22$$
$$\underline{-21}$$
$$18$$
$$\underline{-18}$$
$$0$$

There are 1760 yards in 1 mile.

89.
$$\begin{array}{r} 2 \\ 10 \\ 24 \\ 35 \\ 22 \\ 17 \\ +12 \\ \hline 120 \end{array}$$
$$6 \overline{)\begin{array}{r} 20 \\ 120 \end{array}}$$
$$\underline{-12}$$
$$00$$

$$\text{Average} = \frac{120}{6} = 20$$

91.
$$\begin{array}{r} 1 \\ 205 \\ 972 \\ 210 \\ +161 \\ \hline 1548 \end{array}$$
$$4 \overline{)\begin{array}{r} 387 \\ 1548 \end{array}}$$
$$\underline{-12}$$
$$34$$
$$\underline{-32}$$
$$28$$
$$\underline{-28}$$
$$0$$

$$\text{Average} = \frac{1548}{4} = 387$$

93.
$$\begin{array}{r} 2 \\ 86 \\ 79 \\ 81 \\ 69 \\ +80 \\ \hline 395 \end{array}$$
$$5 \overline{)\begin{array}{r} 79 \\ 395 \end{array}}$$
$$\underline{-35}$$
$$45$$
$$\underline{-45}$$
$$0$$

$$\text{Average} = \frac{395}{5} = 79$$

95.
$$\begin{array}{r} 2 \\ 69 \\ 77 \\ +76 \\ \hline 222 \end{array}$$
$$3 \overline{)\begin{array}{r} 74 \\ 222 \end{array}}$$
$$\underline{-21}$$
$$12$$
$$\underline{-12}$$
$$0$$

The average temperature is 74°.

97.
$$\begin{array}{r} 111 \\ 82 \\ 463 \\ 29 \\ +8704 \\ \hline 9278 \end{array}$$

99.
$$\begin{array}{r} 546 \\ \times \quad 28 \\ \hline 4\ 368 \\ 10\ 920 \\ \hline 15,288 \end{array}$$

101.
$$\begin{array}{r} 722 \\ -43 \\ \hline 679 \end{array}$$

103. $\dfrac{45}{0}$ is undefined.

105.
$$24 \overline{)\begin{array}{r} 9 \text{ R } 12 \\ 228 \end{array}}$$
$$\underline{-216}$$
$$12$$

107. The quotient of 40 and 8 is $40 \div 8$, which is choice c.

109. 200 divided by 20 is $200 \div 20$, which is choice b.

111.
$$\begin{array}{r} 443{,}135{,}000 \\ +\,391{,}390{,}600 \\ \hline 834{,}525{,}600 \end{array}$$

$$\begin{array}{r} 417{,}262{,}800 \\ 2\overline{)\,834{,}525{,}600} \\ \underline{-8} \\ 03 \\ \underline{-2} \\ 14 \\ \underline{-14} \\ 0\;5 \\ \underline{-4} \\ 12 \\ \underline{-12} \\ 05 \\ \underline{-4} \\ 1\;6 \\ \underline{-1\;6} \\ 0 \end{array}$$

The top two advertisers spent an average of $417,262,800.

113. The average will increase; answers may vary.

115. No; answers may vary
Possible answer: The average cannot be less than each of the four numbers.

117.
$$\begin{array}{r} 12 \\ 5\overline{)\,60} \\ \underline{-5} \\ 10 \\ \underline{-10} \\ 0 \end{array}$$

The length is 12 feet.
Notice that Area = length × width = $12 \times 5 = 60$.

119. answers may vary

121.
$$\begin{array}{r} 26 \\ \underline{-5} \\ 21 \\ \underline{-5} \\ 16 \\ \underline{-5} \\ 11 \\ \underline{-5} \\ 6 \\ \underline{-5} \\ 1 \end{array}$$

Therefore, $26 \div 5 = 5$ R 1

Integrated Review

1.
$$\begin{array}{r} {\scriptstyle 1} \\ 42 \\ 63 \\ +\,89 \\ \hline 194 \end{array}$$

2.
$$\begin{array}{r} 7006 \\ -\;\;451 \\ \hline 6555 \end{array}$$

3.
$$\begin{array}{r} 87 \\ \times\;52 \\ \hline 174 \\ 4350 \\ \hline 4524 \end{array}$$

4.
$$\begin{array}{r} 562 \\ 8\overline{)\,4496} \\ \underline{-40} \\ 49 \\ \underline{-48} \\ 16 \\ \underline{-16} \\ 0 \end{array}$$

5. $1 \cdot 67 = 67$

6. $\dfrac{36}{0}$ is undefined.

7. $16 \div 16 = 1$

8. $5 \div 1 = 5$

9. $0 \cdot 21 = 0$

10. $7 \cdot 0 \cdot 8 = 0$

11. $0 \div 7 = 0$

12. $12 \div 4 = 3$

13. $9 \cdot 7 = 63$

14. $45 \div 5 = 9$

15.
$$\begin{array}{r} 207 \\ -\;\;69 \\ \hline 138 \end{array}$$

16.
$$\begin{array}{r} \overset{1}{}207 \\ +\ \ 69 \\ \hline 276 \end{array}$$

17.
$$\begin{array}{r} 3718 \\ -\ 2549 \\ \hline 1169 \end{array}$$

18.
$$\begin{array}{r} \overset{11}{1861} \\ +\ 7965 \\ \hline 9826 \end{array}$$

19.
$$\begin{array}{r} 182\ \text{R}\ 4 \\ 7\overline{)1278} \\ \underline{-7} \\ 57 \\ \underline{-56} \\ 18 \\ \underline{-14} \\ 4 \end{array}$$

20.
$$\begin{array}{r} 1259 \\ \times\ \ \ \ 63 \\ \hline 3\ 777 \\ 75\ 540 \\ \hline 79,317 \end{array}$$

21.
$$\begin{array}{r} 1099\ \text{R}\ 2 \\ 7\overline{)7695} \\ \underline{-7} \\ 06 \\ \underline{-0} \\ 69 \\ \underline{-63} \\ 65 \\ \underline{-63} \\ 2 \end{array}$$

22.
$$\begin{array}{r} 111\ \text{R}\ 1 \\ 9\overline{)1000} \\ \underline{-9} \\ 10 \\ \underline{-9} \\ 10 \\ \underline{-9} \\ 1 \end{array}$$

23.
$$\begin{array}{r} 663\ \text{R}\ 24 \\ 32\overline{)21,240} \\ \underline{-19\ 2} \\ 2\ 04 \\ \underline{-1\ 92} \\ 120 \\ \underline{-96} \\ 24 \end{array}$$

24.
$$\begin{array}{r} 1\ 076\ \text{R}\ 60 \\ 65\overline{)70,000} \\ \underline{-65} \\ 5\ 0 \\ \underline{-\ 0} \\ 5\ 00 \\ \underline{-4\ 55} \\ 450 \\ \underline{-390} \\ 60 \end{array}$$

25.
$$\begin{array}{r} 4000 \\ -\ 2963 \\ \hline 1037 \end{array}$$

26.
$$\begin{array}{r} 10,000 \\ -\ \ \ 101 \\ \hline 9\ 899 \end{array}$$

27.
$$\begin{array}{r} 303 \\ \times\ \ 101 \\ \hline 303 \\ 30\ 300 \\ \hline 30,603 \end{array}$$

28. $(475)(100) = 47,500$

29.
$$\begin{array}{r} \overset{1}{}62 \\ +\ \ 9 \\ \hline 71 \end{array}$$
The total of 62 and 9 is 71.

30.
$$\begin{array}{r} 62 \\ \times\ \ 9 \\ \hline 558 \end{array}$$
The product of 62 and 9 is 558.

31.

$$\begin{array}{r} 6 \text{ R } 8 \\ 9\overline{)\ 62} \\ \underline{-54} \\ 8 \end{array}$$

The quotient of 62 and 9 is 6 R 8.

32.

$$\begin{array}{r} 62 \\ -\ 9 \\ \hline 53 \end{array}$$

The difference of 62 and 9 is 53.

33.

$$\begin{array}{r} 200 \\ -\ 17 \\ \hline 183 \end{array}$$

17 subtracted from 200 is 183.

34.

$$\begin{array}{r} 432 \\ -\ 201 \\ \hline 231 \end{array}$$

The difference of 432 and 201 is 231.

35. 9735 rounded to the nearest ten is 9740.
9735 rounded to the nearest hundred is 9700.
9735 rounded to the nearest thousand is 10,000.

36. 1429 rounded to the nearest ten is 1430.
1429 rounded to the nearest hundred is 1400.
1429 rounded to the nearest thousand is 1000.

37. 20,801 rounded to the nearest ten is 20,800.
20,801 rounded to the nearest hundred is 20,800.
20,801 rounded to the nearest thousand is 21,000.

38. 432,198 rounded to the nearest ten is 432,200.
432,198 rounded to the nearest hundred is 432,200.
432,198 rounded to the nearest thousand is 432,000.

39. $6 + 6 + 6 + 6 = 24$
$6 \times 6 = 36$
The perimeter is 24 feet and the area is 36 square feet.

40. $14 + 7 + 14 + 7 = 42$

$$\begin{array}{r} 14 \\ \times\ 7 \\ \hline 98 \end{array}$$

The perimeter is 42 inches and the area is 98 square inches.

41.

$$\begin{array}{r} 13 \\ 9 \\ +\ 6 \\ \hline 28 \end{array}$$

The perimeter is 28 miles.

42. The unknown vertical side has length $4 + 3 = 7$ meters. The unknown horizontal side has length $3 + 3 = 6$ meters.

$$\begin{array}{r} 3 \\ 4 \\ 3 \\ 7 \\ 6 \\ +\ 3 \\ \hline 26 \end{array}$$

The perimeter is 26 meters.

43.

$$\begin{array}{r} 3 \\ 19 \\ 15 \\ 25 \\ 37 \\ +\ 24 \\ \hline 120 \end{array} \qquad \begin{array}{r} 24 \\ 5\overline{)\ 120} \\ \underline{-10} \\ 20 \\ \underline{-20} \\ 0 \end{array}$$

$\text{Average} = \dfrac{120}{5} = 24$

44.

$$\begin{array}{r} 1\ 2 \\ 108 \\ 131 \\ 98 \\ +\ 159 \\ \hline 496 \end{array} \qquad \begin{array}{r} 124 \\ 4\overline{)\ 496} \\ \underline{-4} \\ 09 \\ \underline{-8} \\ 16 \\ \underline{-16} \\ 0 \end{array}$$

$\text{Average} = \dfrac{496}{4} = 124$

45.

$$\begin{array}{r} 28,547 \\ -\ 26,372 \\ \hline 2\ 175 \end{array}$$

The Lake Pontchartrain Bridge is longer by 2175 feet.

46.

$$\begin{array}{r} 485 \\ \times\ 18 \\ \hline 3880 \\ 4850 \\ \hline 8730 \end{array}$$

The amount spent on toys is $8730.

Section 1.7

Practice Problems

1. $8 \cdot 8 \cdot 8 \cdot 8 = 8^4$

2. $3 \cdot 3 \cdot 3 = 3^3$

3. $10 \cdot 10 \cdot 10 \cdot 10 \cdot 10 = 10^5$

4. $5 \cdot 5 \cdot 4 \cdot 4 \cdot 4 \cdot 4 \cdot 4 \cdot 4 = 5^2 \cdot 4^6$

5. $4^2 = 4 \cdot 4 = 16$

6. $7^3 = 7 \cdot 7 \cdot 7 = 343$

7. $11^1 = 11$

8. $2 \cdot 3^2 = 2 \cdot 3 \cdot 3 = 18$

9. $9 \cdot 3 - 8 \div 4 = 27 - 8 \div 4 = 27 - 2 = 25$

10. $48 \div 3 \cdot 2^2 = 48 \div 3 \cdot 4 = 16 \cdot 4 = 64$

11. $(10 - 7)^4 + 2 \cdot 3^2 = 3^4 + 2 \cdot 3^2$
$$\begin{aligned} &= 81 + 2 \cdot 9 \\ &= 81 + 18 \\ &= 99 \end{aligned}$$

12. $36 \div [20 - (4 \cdot 2)] + 4^3 - 6 = 36 \div [20 - 8] + 4^3 - 6$
$$\begin{aligned} &= 36 \div 12 + 4^3 - 6 \\ &= 36 \div 12 + 64 - 6 \\ &= 3 + 64 - 6 \\ &= 61 \end{aligned}$$

13. $\dfrac{25 + 8 \cdot 2 - 3^3}{2(3 - 2)} = \dfrac{25 + 8 \cdot 2 - 27}{2(1)}$
$$\begin{aligned} &= \frac{25 + 16 - 27}{2} \\ &= \frac{14}{2} \\ &= 7 \end{aligned}$$

14. $36 \div 6 \cdot 3 + 5 = 6 \cdot 3 + 5 = 18 + 5 = 23$

15. Area $= (\text{side})^2$
$$\begin{aligned} &= (12 \text{ centimeters})^2 \\ &= 144 \text{ square centimeters} \end{aligned}$$
The area of the square is 144 square centimeters.

Calculator Explorations

1. $4^6 = 4096$

2. $5^6 = 15{,}625$

3. $5^5 = 3125$

4. $7^6 = 117{,}649$

5. $2^{11} = 2048$

6. $6^8 = 1{,}679{,}616$

7. $7^4 + 5^3 = 2526$

8. $12^4 - 8^4 = 16{,}640$

9. $63 \cdot 75 - 43 \cdot 10 = 4295$

10. $8 \cdot 22 + 7 \cdot 16 = 288$

11. $4(15 \div 3 + 2) - 10 \cdot 2 = 8$

12. $155 - 2(17 + 3) + 185 = 300$

Vocabulary and Readiness Check

1. In $2^5 = 32,$ the 2 is called the <u>base</u> and the 5 is called the <u>exponent</u>.

2. To simplify $8 + 2 \cdot 6$, which operation should be performed first? <u>multiplication</u>

3. To simplify $(8 + 2) \cdot 6$, which operation should be performed first? <u>addition</u>

4. To simplify $9(3 - 2) \div 3 + 6$, which operation should be performed first? <u>subtraction</u>

5. To simplify $8 \div 2 \cdot 6$, which operation should be performed first? <u>division</u>

Exercise Set 1.7

1. $4 \cdot 4 \cdot 4 = 4^3$

3. $7 \cdot 7 \cdot 7 \cdot 7 \cdot 7 \cdot 7 = 7^6$

5. $12 \cdot 12 \cdot 12 = 12^3$

7. $6 \cdot 6 \cdot 5 \cdot 5 \cdot 5 = 6^2 \cdot 5^3$

9. $9 \cdot 8 \cdot 8 = 9 \cdot 8^2$

11. $3 \cdot 2 \cdot 2 \cdot 2 \cdot 2 = 3 \cdot 2^4$

13. $3 \cdot 2 \cdot 2 \cdot 2 \cdot 2 \cdot 5 \cdot 5 \cdot 5 \cdot 5 \cdot 5 = 3 \cdot 2^4 \cdot 5^5$

15. $8^2 = 8 \cdot 8 = 64$

17. $5^3 = 5 \cdot 5 \cdot 5 = 125$

19. $2^5 = 2 \cdot 2 \cdot 2 \cdot 2 \cdot 2 = 32$

21. $1^{10} = 1 \cdot 1 \cdot 1 \cdot 1 \cdot 1 \cdot 1 \cdot 1 \cdot 1 \cdot 1 \cdot 1 = 1$

23. $7^1 = 7$

25. $2^7 = 2 \cdot 2 \cdot 2 \cdot 2 \cdot 2 \cdot 2 \cdot 2 = 128$

27. $2^8 = 2 \cdot 2 \cdot 2 \cdot 2 \cdot 2 \cdot 2 \cdot 2 \cdot 2 = 256$

29. $4^4 = 4 \cdot 4 \cdot 4 \cdot 4 = 256$

31. $9^3 = 9 \cdot 9 \cdot 9 = 729$

33. $12^2 = 12 \cdot 12 = 144$

35. $10^2 = 10 \cdot 10 = 100$

37. $20^1 = 20$

39. $3^6 = 3 \cdot 3 \cdot 3 \cdot 3 \cdot 3 \cdot 3 = 729$

41. $3 \cdot 2^6 = 3 \cdot 2 \cdot 2 \cdot 2 \cdot 2 \cdot 2 \cdot 2 = 192$

43. $2 \cdot 3^4 = 2 \cdot 3 \cdot 3 \cdot 3 \cdot 3 = 162$

45. $15 + 3 \cdot 2 = 15 + 6 = 21$

47. $14 \div 7 \cdot 2 + 3 = 2 \cdot 2 + 3 = 4 + 3 = 7$

49. $32 \div 4 - 3 = 8 - 3 = 5$

51. $13 + \dfrac{24}{8} = 13 + 3 = 16$

53. $6 \cdot 5 + 8 \cdot 2 = 30 + 16 = 46$

55. $\dfrac{5 + 12 \div 4}{1^7} = \dfrac{5 + 3}{1} = \dfrac{8}{1} = 8$

57. $(7 + 5^2) \div 4 \cdot 2^3 = (7 + 25) \div 4 \cdot 2^3$
$$= 32 \div 4 \cdot 2^3$$
$$= 32 \div 4 \cdot 8$$
$$= 8 \cdot 8$$
$$= 64$$

59. $5^2 \cdot (10 - 8) + 2^3 + 5^2 = 5^2 \cdot 2 + 2^3 + 5^2$
$$= 25 \cdot 2 + 8 + 25$$
$$= 50 + 8 + 25$$
$$= 83$$

61. $\dfrac{18 + 6}{2^4 - 2^2} = \dfrac{24}{16 - 4} = \dfrac{24}{12} = 2$

63. $(3 + 5) \cdot (9 - 3) = 8 \cdot 6 = 48$

65. $\dfrac{7(9 - 6) + 3}{3^2 - 3} = \dfrac{7(3) + 3}{9 - 3} = \dfrac{21 + 3}{6} = \dfrac{24}{6} = 4$

67. $8 \div 0 + 37 = $ undefined

69. $2^4 \cdot 4 - (25 \div 5) = 2^4 \cdot 4 - 5$
$$= 16 \cdot 4 - 5$$
$$= 64 - 5$$
$$= 59$$

71. $3^4 - [35 - (12 - 6)] = 3^4 - [35 - 6]$
$$= 3^4 - 29$$
$$= 81 - 29$$
$$= 52$$

73. $(7 \cdot 5) + [9 \div (3 \div 3)] = (7 \cdot 5) + [9 \div (1)]$
$$= 35 + 9$$
$$= 44$$

75.
$$\begin{aligned}
8 \cdot [2^2 + (6-1) \cdot 2] - 50 \cdot 2 &= 8 \cdot (2^2 + 5 \cdot 2) - 50 \cdot 2 \\
&= 8 \cdot (4 + 5 \cdot 2) - 50 \cdot 2 \\
&= 8 \cdot (4 + 10) - 50 \cdot 2 \\
&= 8 \cdot 14 - 50 \cdot 2 \\
&= 112 - 50 \cdot 2 \\
&= 112 - 100 \\
&= 12
\end{aligned}$$

77.
$$\begin{aligned}
\frac{9^2 + 2^2 - 1^2}{8 \div 2 \cdot 3 \cdot 1 \div 3} &= \frac{81 + 4 - 1}{4 \cdot 3 \cdot 1 \div 3} \\
&= \frac{85 - 1}{12 \cdot 1 \div 3} \\
&= \frac{84}{12 \div 3} \\
&= \frac{84}{4} \\
&= 21
\end{aligned}$$

79.
$$\begin{aligned}
\frac{2 + 4^2}{5(20 - 16) - 3^2 - 5} &= \frac{2 + 16}{5(4) - 3^2 - 5} \\
&= \frac{18}{5(4) - 9 - 5} \\
&= \frac{18}{20 - 9 - 5} \\
&= \frac{18}{11 - 5} \\
&= \frac{18}{6} \\
&= 3
\end{aligned}$$

81.
$$\begin{aligned}
9 \div 3 + 5^2 \cdot 2 - 10 &= 9 \div 3 + 25 \cdot 2 - 10 \\
&= 3 + 25 \cdot 2 - 10 \\
&= 3 + 50 - 10 \\
&= 43
\end{aligned}$$

83.
$$\begin{aligned}
[13 \div (20 - 7) + 2^5] - (2 + 3)^2 &= [13 \div 13 + 2^5] - 5^2 \\
&= [13 \div 13 + 32] - 5^2 \\
&= [1 + 32] - 5^2 \\
&= 33 - 5^2 \\
&= 33 - 25 \\
&= 8
\end{aligned}$$

85.
$$\begin{aligned}
7^2 - \{18 - [40 \div (5 \cdot 1) + 2] + 5^2\} &= 7^2 - \{18 - [40 \div 5 + 2] + 5^2\} \\
&= 7^2 - \{18 - [8 + 2] + 5^2\} \\
&= 7^2 - \{18 - 10 + 5^2\} \\
&= 7^2 - \{18 - 10 + 25\} \\
&= 7^2 - 33 \\
&= 49 - 33 \\
&= 16
\end{aligned}$$

87.
$$\begin{aligned}
\text{Area of a square} &= (\text{side})^2 \\
&= (7 \text{ meters})^2 \\
&= 49 \text{ square meters}
\end{aligned}$$
Perimeter = 4(side) = 4(7 meters) = 28 meters

89.
$$\begin{aligned}
\text{Area of a square} &= (\text{side})^2 \\
&= (23 \text{ miles})^2 \\
&= 529 \text{ square miles}
\end{aligned}$$
Perimeter = 4(side) = 4(23 miles) = 92 miles

91. The statement is true.

93. $2^5 = 2 \cdot 2 \cdot 2 \cdot 2 \cdot 2$
The statement is false.

95. $(2 + 3) \cdot 6 - 2 = 5 \cdot 6 - 2 = 30 - 2 = 28$

97. $24 \div (3 \cdot 2) + 2 \cdot 5 = 24 \div 6 + 2 \cdot 5 = 4 + 10 = 14$

99. The unknown vertical length is
$30 - 12 = 18$ feet. The unknown horizontal
length is $60 - 40 = 20$ feet.
Perimeter = $60 + 30 + 40 + 18 + 20 + 12 = 180$
The total perimeter of seven homes is
$7(180) = 1260$ feet.

101.
$$\begin{aligned}
(7 + 2^4)^5 - (3^5 - 2^4)^2 &= (7 + 16)^5 - (243 - 16)^2 \\
&= 23^5 - 227^2 \\
&= 6,436,343 - 51,529 \\
&= 6,384,814
\end{aligned}$$

103. answers may vary; possible answer:
$$\begin{aligned}
(20 - 10) \cdot 5 \div 25 + 3 &= 10 \cdot 5 \div 25 + 3 \\
&= 50 \div 25 + 3 \\
&= 2 + 3 \\
&= 5
\end{aligned}$$

Section 1.8

Practice Problems

1. $x - 2 = 7 - 2 = 5$

2. $y(x - 3) = 4(8 - 3) = 4(5) = 20$

3. $\dfrac{y+6}{x} = \dfrac{18+6}{6} = \dfrac{24}{6} = 4$

4. $25 - z^3 + x = 25 - 2^3 + 1 = 25 - 8 + 1 = 18$

5. $\dfrac{5(F - 32)}{9} = \dfrac{5(41 - 32)}{9} = \dfrac{5(9)}{9} = \dfrac{45}{9} = 5$

6. $3(y - 6) = 6$
   $3(8 - 6) \overset{?}{=} 6$
   $3(2) \overset{?}{=} 6$
   $6 = 6$ True
   Yes, 8 is a solution.

7. $5n + 4 = 34$
   Let n be 10.
   $5(10) + 4 \overset{?}{=} 34$
   $50 + 4 \overset{?}{=} 34$
   $54 = 34$ False
   No, 10 is not a solution.
   Let n be 6.
   $5(6) + 4 \overset{?}{=} 34$
   $30 + 4 \overset{?}{=} 34$
   $34 = 34$ True
   Yes, 6 is a solution.
   Let n be 8.
   $5(8) + 4 \overset{?}{=} 34$
   $40 + 4 \overset{?}{=} 34$
   $44 = 34$ False
   No, 8 is not a solution.

8. a. Twice a number is $2x$.

   b. 8 increased by a number is $8 + x$ or $x + 8$.

   c. 10 minus a number is $10 - x$.

   d. 10 subtracted from a number is $x - 10$.

   e. The quotient of 6 and a number is $6 \div x$ or $\dfrac{6}{x}$.

Vocabulary and Readiness Check

1. A combination of operations on letters (variables) and numbers is an <u>expression</u>.

2. A letter that represents a number is a <u>variable</u>.

3. $3x - 2y$ is called an <u>expression</u> and the letters x and y are <u>variables</u>.

4. Replacing a variable in an expression by a number and then finding the value of the expression is called <u>evaluating the expression</u>.

5. A statement of the form "expression = expression" is called an <u>equation</u>.

6. A value for the variable that makes the equation a true statement is called a <u>solution</u>.

Exercise Set 1.8

1.

a	b	$a + b$	$a - b$	$a \cdot b$	$a \div b$
21	7	$21 + 7 = 28$	$21 - 7 = 14$	$21 \cdot 7 = 147$	$21 \div 7 = 3$

3.

a	b	$a + b$	$a - b$	$a \cdot b$	$a \div b$
152	0	$152 + 0 = 152$	$152 - 0 = 152$	$152 \cdot 0 = 0$	$152 \div 0$ is undefined.

5.

a	b	$a + b$	$a - b$	$a \cdot b$	$a \div b$
56	1	$56 + 1 = 57$	$56 - 1 = 55$	$56 \cdot 1 = 56$	$56 \div 1 = 56$

7. $3 + 2z = 3 + 2(3) = 3 + 6 = 9$

9. $3xz - 5x = 3(2)(3) - 5(2) = 18 - 10 = 8$

11. $z - x + y = 3 - 2 + 5 = 1 + 5 = 6$

13. $4x - z = 4(2) - 3 = 8 - 3 = 5$

15. $y^3 - 4x = 5^3 - 4(2) = 125 - 4(2) = 125 - 8 = 117$

17. $2xy^2 - 6 = 2(2)(5)^2 - 6$
$= 2 \cdot 2 \cdot 25 - 6$
$= 100 - 6$
$= 94$

19. $8 - (y - x) = 8 - (5 - 2) = 8 - 3 = 5$

21. $x^5 + (y - z) = 2^5 + (5 - 3)$
$= 2^5 + 2$
$= 32 + 2$
$= 34$

23. $\dfrac{6xy}{z} = \dfrac{6 \cdot 2 \cdot 5}{3} = \dfrac{60}{3} = 20$

25. $\dfrac{2y-2}{x} = \dfrac{2(5)-2}{2} = \dfrac{10-2}{2} = \dfrac{8}{2} = 4$

27. $\dfrac{x+2y}{z} = \dfrac{2+2\cdot5}{3} = \dfrac{2+10}{3} = \dfrac{12}{3} = 4$

29. $\dfrac{5x}{y} - \dfrac{10}{y} = \dfrac{5(2)}{5} - \dfrac{10}{5} = \dfrac{10}{5} - 2 = 2 - 2 = 0$

31. $\begin{aligned} 2y^2 - 4y + 3 &= 2\cdot5^2 - 4\cdot5 + 3 \\ &= 2\cdot25 - 4\cdot5 + 3 \\ &= 50 - 20 + 3 \\ &= 33 \end{aligned}$

33. $\begin{aligned} (4y-5z)^3 &= (4\cdot5 - 5\cdot3)^3 \\ &= (20-15)^3 \\ &= (5)^3 \\ &= 125 \end{aligned}$

35. $(xy+1)^2 = (2\cdot5+1)^2 = (10+1)^2 = 11^2 = 121$

37. $\begin{aligned} 2y(4z-x) &= 2\cdot5(4\cdot3-2) \\ &= 2\cdot5(12-2) \\ &= 2\cdot5(10) \\ &= 10(10) \\ &= 100 \end{aligned}$

39. $\begin{aligned} xy(5+z-x) &= 2\cdot5(5+3-2) \\ &= 2\cdot5(6) \\ &= 10(6) \\ &= 60 \end{aligned}$

41. $\dfrac{7x+2y}{3x} = \dfrac{7(2)+2(5)}{3(2)} = \dfrac{14+10}{6} = \dfrac{24}{6} = 4$

43.

t	1	2	3	4
$16t^2$	$16\cdot1^2 = 16\cdot1 = 16$	$16\cdot2^2 = 16\cdot4 = 64$	$16\cdot3^2 = 16\cdot9 = 144$	$16\cdot4^2 = 16\cdot16 = 256$

45. Let n be 10.
$n - 8 = 2$
$10 - 8 \overset{?}{=} 2$
$\qquad 2 = 2$ True
Yes, 10 is a solution.

47. Let n be 3.
$$24 = 80n$$
$$24 \stackrel{?}{=} 80 \cdot 3$$
$$24 = 240 \quad \text{False}$$
No, 3 is not a solution.

49. Let n be 7.
$$3n - 5 = 10$$
$$3(7) - 5 \stackrel{?}{=} 10$$
$$21 - 5 \stackrel{?}{=} 10$$
$$16 = 10 \quad \text{False}$$
No, 7 is not a solution.

51. Let n be 20.
$$2(n - 17) = 6$$
$$2(20 - 17) \stackrel{?}{=} 6$$
$$2(3) \stackrel{?}{=} 6$$
$$6 = 6 \quad \text{True}$$
Yes, 20 is a solution.

53. Let x be 0.
$$5x + 3 = 4x + 13$$
$$5(0) + 3 \stackrel{?}{=} 4(0) + 13$$
$$0 + 3 \stackrel{?}{=} 0 + 13$$
$$3 = 13 \quad \text{False}$$
No, 0 is not a solution.

55. Let f be 8.
$$7f = 64 - f$$
$$7(8) \stackrel{?}{=} 64 - 8$$
$$56 = 56 \quad \text{True}$$
Yes, 8 is a solution.

57. $n - 2 = 10$
Let n be 10.
$$10 - 2 \stackrel{?}{=} 10$$
$$8 = 10 \quad \text{False}$$
Let n be 12.
$$12 - 2 \stackrel{?}{=} 10$$
$$10 = 10 \quad \text{True}$$
Let n be 14.
$$14 - 2 \stackrel{?}{=} 10$$
$$12 = 10 \quad \text{False}$$
12 is a solution.

59. $5n = 30$
Let n be 6.
$$5 \cdot 6 \stackrel{?}{=} 30$$
$$30 = 30 \quad \text{True}$$
Let n be 25.
$$5 \cdot 25 \stackrel{?}{=} 30$$
$$125 = 30 \quad \text{False}$$

Let n be 30.
$$5 \cdot 30 \stackrel{?}{=} 30$$
$$150 = 30 \quad \text{False}$$
6 is a solution.

61. $6n + 2 = 26$
Let n be 0.
$$6(0) + 2 \stackrel{?}{=} 26$$
$$0 + 2 \stackrel{?}{=} 26$$
$$2 = 26 \quad \text{False}$$
Let n be 2.
$$6(2) + 2 \stackrel{?}{=} 26$$
$$12 + 2 \stackrel{?}{=} 26$$
$$14 = 26 \quad \text{False}$$
Let n be 4.
$$6(4) + 2 \stackrel{?}{=} 26$$
$$24 + 2 \stackrel{?}{=} 26$$
$$26 = 26 \quad \text{True}$$
4 is a solution.

63. $3(n - 4) = 10$
Let n be 5.
$$3(5 - 4) \stackrel{?}{=} 10$$
$$3(1) \stackrel{?}{=} 10$$
$$3 = 10 \quad \text{False}$$
Let n be 7.
$$3(7 - 4) \stackrel{?}{=} 10$$
$$3(3) \stackrel{?}{=} 10$$
$$9 = 10 \quad \text{False}$$
Let n be 10.
$$3(10 - 4) \stackrel{?}{=} 10$$
$$3(6) \stackrel{?}{=} 10$$
$$18 = 10 \quad \text{False}$$
None are solutions.

65. $7x - 9 = 5x + 13$
Let x be 3.
$$7(3) - 9 \stackrel{?}{=} 5(3) + 13$$
$$21 - 9 \stackrel{?}{=} 15 + 13$$
$$12 = 28 \quad \text{False}$$
Let x be 7.
$$7(7) - 9 \stackrel{?}{=} 5(7) + 13$$
$$49 - 9 \stackrel{?}{=} 35 + 13$$
$$40 = 48 \quad \text{False}$$
Let x be 11.
$$7(11) - 9 \stackrel{?}{=} 5(11) + 13$$
$$77 - 9 \stackrel{?}{=} 55 + 13$$
$$68 = 68 \quad \text{True}$$
11 is a solution.

67. Eight more than a number is $x + 8$.

69. The total of a number and 8 is $x + 8$.

71. Twenty decreased by a number is $20 - x$.

73. The product of 512 and a number is $512x$.

75. The quotient of eight and a number is $\dfrac{8}{x}$.

77. The sum of seventeen and a number added to the product of five and the number is $5x + (17 + x)$.

79. The product of five and a number is $5x$.

81. A number subtracted from 11 is $11 - x$.

83. A number less 5 is $x - 5$.

85. 6 divided by a number is $6 \div x$ or $\dfrac{6}{x}$.

87. Fifty decreased by eight times a number is $50 - 8x$.

89. $x^4 - y^2 = 23^4 - 72^2$
$= 279{,}841 - 5184$
$= 274{,}657$

91. $x^2 + 5y - 112 = 23^2 + 5(72) - 112$
$= 529 + 360 - 112$
$= 777$

93. $5x$ is the largest; answers may vary.

95. As t gets larger, $16t^2$ gets larger.

Chapter 1 Vocabulary Check

1. The <u>whole numbers</u> are 0, 1, 2, 3, ...

2. The <u>perimeter</u> of a polygon is its distance around or the sum of the lengths of its sides.

3. The position of each digit in a number determines its <u>place value</u>.

4. An <u>exponent</u> is a shorthand notation for repeated multiplication of the same factor.

5. To find the <u>area</u> of a rectangle, multiply length times width.

6. The <u>digits</u> used to write numbers are 0, 1, 2, 3, 4, 5, 6, 7, 8, and 9.

7. A letter used to represent a number is called a <u>variable</u>.

8. An <u>equation</u> can be written in the form "expression = expression."

9. A combination of operations on variables and numbers is called an <u>expression</u>.

10. A <u>solution</u> of an equation is a value of the variable that makes the equation a true statement.

11. A collection of numbers (or objects) enclosed by braces is called a <u>set</u>.

12. The 21 above is called the <u>sum</u>.

13. The 5 above is called the <u>divisor</u>.

14. The 35 above is called the <u>dividend</u>.

15. The 7 above is called the <u>quotient</u>.

16. The 3 above is called a <u>factor</u>.

17. The 6 above is called the <u>product</u>.

18. The 20 above is called the <u>minuend</u>.

19. The 9 above is called the <u>subtrahend</u>.

20. The 11 above is called the <u>difference</u>.

21. The 4 above is called an <u>addend</u>.

Chapter 1 Review

1. The place value of 4 in 7640 is tens.

2. The place value of 4 in 46,200,120 is ten-millions.

3. 7640 is written as seven thousand, six hundred forty.

4. 46,200,120 is written as forty-six million, two hundred thousand, one hundred twenty.

5. $3158 = 3000 + 100 + 50 + 8$

6. $403{,}225{,}000 = 400{,}000{,}000 + 3{,}000{,}000 + 200{,}000 + 20{,}000 + 5000$

7. Eighty-one thousand, nine hundred in standard form is 81,900.

8. Six billion, three hundred four million in standard form is 6,304,000,000.

9. Locate Europe in the first column and read across to the number in the 2008 column. There were 384,633,765 Internet users in Europe in 2008.

10. Locate Oceania/Australia in the first column and read across to the number in the 2004 column. There were 11,805,500 Internet users in Oceania/Australia in 2004.

11. Locate the smallest number in the 2000 column. Middle East had the fewest Internet users in 2000.

12. Locate the biggest number in the 2008 column. Asia had the greatest number of Internet users in 2008.

13.
$$\begin{array}{r} 1 \\ 18 \\ + 49 \\ \hline 67 \end{array}$$

14.
$$\begin{array}{r} 1 \\ 28 \\ + 39 \\ \hline 67 \end{array}$$

15.
$$\begin{array}{r} 462 \\ - 397 \\ \hline 65 \end{array}$$

16.
$$\begin{array}{r} 583 \\ - 279 \\ \hline 304 \end{array}$$

17.
$$\begin{array}{r} 428 \\ + 21 \\ \hline 449 \end{array}$$

18.
$$\begin{array}{r} 1 \\ 819 \\ + 21 \\ \hline 840 \end{array}$$

19.
$$\begin{array}{r} 4000 \\ - 86 \\ \hline 3914 \end{array}$$

20.
$$\begin{array}{r} 8000 \\ - 92 \\ \hline 7908 \end{array}$$

21.
$$\begin{array}{r} 1\,2\,1 \\ 91 \\ 3623 \\ + 497 \\ \hline 4211 \end{array}$$

22.
$$\begin{array}{r} 11 \\ 82 \\ 1647 \\ + 238 \\ \hline 1967 \end{array}$$

23.
$$\begin{array}{r} 11 \\ 74 \\ 342 \\ + 918 \\ \hline 1334 \end{array}$$
The sum of 74, 342, and 918 is 1334.

24.
$$\begin{array}{r} 2 \\ 49 \\ 529 \\ + 308 \\ \hline 886 \end{array}$$
The sum of 49, 529, and 308 is 886.

25.
$$\begin{array}{r} 25,862 \\ - 7\,965 \\ \hline 17,897 \end{array}$$
7965 subtracted from 25,862 is 17,897.

26.
$$\begin{array}{r} 39,007 \\ - 4\,349 \\ \hline 34,658 \end{array}$$
4349 subtracted from 39,007 is 34,658.

27.
$$\begin{array}{r} 1 \\ 205 \\ + 7318 \\ \hline 7523 \end{array}$$
The total distance is 7523 miles.

28.
$$
\begin{array}{r}
{\scriptstyle 1\ 1\ 1}\\
62{,}589\\
65{,}340\\
+\ 69{,}770\\
\hline
197{,}699
\end{array}
$$
Her total earnings were $197,699.

29. $40 + 52 + 52 + 72 = 216$
The perimeter is 216 feet.

30. $11 + 20 + 35 = 66$
The perimeter is 66 kilometers.

31.
$$
\begin{array}{r}
384{,}633{,}765\\
-\ 241{,}208{,}100\\
\hline
143{,}425{,}665
\end{array}
$$
The number of Internet users in Europe increased by 143,425,665.

32.
$$
\begin{array}{r}
41{,}939{,}200\\
-\ 20{,}204{,}331\\
\hline
21{,}734{,}869
\end{array}
$$
There were 21,734,869 more Internet users in the Middle East than in Oceania/Australia in 2008.

33. Find the shortest bar. The balance was the least in May.

34. Find the tallest bar. The balance was the greatest in August.

35.
$$
\begin{array}{r}
280\\
-\ 170\\
\hline
110
\end{array}
$$
The balance decreased by $110 from February to April.

36.
$$
\begin{array}{r}
490\\
-\ 250\\
\hline
240
\end{array}
$$
The balance increased by $240 from June to August.

37. To round 43 to the nearest ten, observe that the digit in the ones place is 3. Since this digit is less than 5, we do not add 1 to the digit in the tens place. The number 43 rounded to the nearest ten is 40.

38. To round 45 to the nearest ten, observe that the digit in the ones place is 5. Since this digit is at least 5, we add 1 to the digit in the tens place. The number 45 rounded to the nearest ten is 50.

39. To round 876 to the nearest ten, observe that the digit in the ones place is 6. Since this digit is at least 5, we add 1 to the digit in the tens place. The number 876 rounded to the nearest ten is 880.

40. To round 493 to the nearest hundred, observe that the digit in the tens place is 9. Since this digit is at least 5, we add 1 to the digit in the hundreds place. The number 493 rounded to the nearest hundred is 500.

41. To round 3829 to the nearest hundred, observe that the digit in the tens place is 2. Since this digit is less than 5, we do not add 1 to the digit in the hundreds place. The number 3829 rounded to the nearest hundred is 3800.

42. To round 57,534 to the nearest thousand, observe that the digit in the hundreds place is 5. Since this digit is at least 5, we add 1 to the digit in the thousands place. The number 57,534 rounded to the nearest thousand is 58,000.

43. To round 39,583,819 to the nearest million, observe that the digit in the hundred-thousands place is 5. Since this digit is at least 5, we add 1 to the digit in the millions place. The number 39,583,819 rounded to the nearest million is 40,000,000.

44. To round 768,542 to the nearest hundred-thousand, observe that the digit in the ten-thousands place is 6. Since this digit is at least 5, we add 1 to the digit in the hundred-thousands place. The number 768,542 rounded to the nearest hundred-thousand is 800,000.

45.
$$
\begin{array}{rll}
3785 & \text{rounds to} & \overset{2}{3800}\\
648 & \text{rounds to} & 600\\
+\ 2866 & \text{rounds to} & +\ 2900\\
\hline
& & 7300
\end{array}
$$

46.
$$
\begin{array}{rll}
5925 & \text{rounds to} & 5900\\
-\ 1787 & \text{rounds to} & -\ 1800\\
\hline
& & 4100
\end{array}
$$

47.

630	rounds to	600
192	rounds to	200
271	rounds to	300
56	rounds to	100
703	rounds to	700
454	rounds to	500
+ 329	rounds to	+ 300
		2700

They traveled approximately 2700 miles.

48.

139,009,209	rounds to	139,000,000
− 51,065,630	rounds to	− 51,000,000
		88,000,000

There were approximately 88,000,000 more Internet users in Latin America/Caribbean than in Africa in 2008.

49.
$$\begin{array}{r} 276 \\ \times\ \ 8 \\ \hline 2208 \end{array}$$

50.
$$\begin{array}{r} 349 \\ \times\ \ 4 \\ \hline 1396 \end{array}$$

51.
$$\begin{array}{r} 57 \\ \times\ 40 \\ \hline 2280 \end{array}$$

52.
$$\begin{array}{r} 69 \\ \times\ 42 \\ \hline 138 \\ 2760 \\ \hline 2898 \end{array}$$

53. $20(7)(4) = 140(4) = 560$

54. $25(9)(4) = 225(4) = 900$
or
$25(4)(9) = 100(9) = 900$

55. $26 \cdot 34 \cdot 0 = 0$

56. $62 \cdot 88 \cdot 0 = 0$

57.
$$\begin{array}{r} 586 \\ \times\ \ 29 \\ \hline 5\ 274 \\ 11\ 720 \\ \hline 16,994 \end{array}$$

58.
$$\begin{array}{r} 242 \\ \times\ 37 \\ \hline 1694 \\ 7260 \\ \hline 8954 \end{array}$$

59.
$$\begin{array}{r} 642 \\ \times\ \ 177 \\ \hline 4\ 494 \\ 44\ 940 \\ 64\ 200 \\ \hline 113,634 \end{array}$$

60.
$$\begin{array}{r} 347 \\ \times\ 129 \\ \hline 3\ 123 \\ 6\ 940 \\ 34\ 700 \\ \hline 44,763 \end{array}$$

61.
$$\begin{array}{r} 1026 \\ \times\ \ \ 401 \\ \hline 1\ 026 \\ 410\ 400 \\ \hline 411,426 \end{array}$$

62.
$$\begin{array}{r} 2107 \\ \times\ \ \ 302 \\ \hline 4\ 214 \\ 632\ 100 \\ \hline 636,314 \end{array}$$

63. "Product" indicates multiplication.
$$\begin{array}{r} 250 \\ \times\ \ 6 \\ \hline 1500 \end{array}$$
The product of 6 and 250 is 1500.

64. "Product" indicates multiplication.
$$\begin{array}{r} 820 \\ \times\ \ 6 \\ \hline 4920 \end{array}$$
The product of 6 and 820 is 4920.

65.

$$
\begin{array}{r}
32 \\
\times\ 15 \\
\hline
160 \\
320 \\
\hline
480
\end{array}
\qquad
\begin{array}{r}
38 \\
\times\ 11 \\
\hline
38 \\
380 \\
\hline
418
\end{array}
$$

$$
\begin{array}{r}
480 \\
+\ 418 \\
\hline
898
\end{array}
$$

The total cost is $898.

66.

$$
\begin{array}{r}
6112 \\
\times\ \ \ 20 \\
\hline
122,240
\end{array}
$$

The total cost is $122,240.

67. Area = (length)(width)
= (13 miles)(7 miles)
= 91 square miles

68. Area = (length)(width)
= (25 centimeters)(20 centimeters)
= 500 square centimeters

69. $\dfrac{49}{7} = 7$ Check:
$$\begin{array}{r} 7 \\ \times\ 7 \\ \hline 49 \end{array}$$

70. $\dfrac{36}{9} = 4$ Check:
$$\begin{array}{r} 9 \\ \times\ 4 \\ \hline 36 \end{array}$$

71.
$$
\begin{array}{r}
5\ R\ 2 \\
5\overline{)\ 27} \\
-25 \\
\hline
2
\end{array}
$$
Check: $5 \times 5 + 2 = 27$

72.
$$
\begin{array}{r}
4\ R\ 2 \\
4\overline{)\ 18} \\
-16 \\
\hline
2
\end{array}
$$
Check: $4 \times 4 + 2 = 18$

73. $918 \div 0$ is undefined.

74. $0 \div 668 = 0$ Check: $0 \cdot 668 = 0$

75.
$$
\begin{array}{r}
33\ R\ 2 \\
5\overline{)\ 167} \\
-15 \\
\hline
17 \\
-15 \\
\hline
2
\end{array}
$$
Check: $33 \times 5 + 2 = 167$

76.
$$
\begin{array}{r}
19\ R\ 7 \\
8\overline{)\ 159} \\
-8 \\
\hline
79 \\
-72 \\
\hline
7
\end{array}
$$
Check: $19 \times 8 + 7 = 159$

77.
$$
\begin{array}{r}
24\ R\ 2 \\
26\overline{)\ 626} \\
-52 \\
\hline
106 \\
-104 \\
\hline
2
\end{array}
$$
Check: $24 \times 26 + 2 = 626$

78.
$$
\begin{array}{r}
35\ R\ 15 \\
19\overline{)\ 680} \\
-57 \\
\hline
110 \\
-95 \\
\hline
15
\end{array}
$$
Check: $35 \times 19 + 15 = 680$

79.
$$
\begin{array}{r}
506\ R\ 10 \\
47\overline{)\ 23,792} \\
-23\ 5 \\
\hline
29 \\
-0 \\
\hline
292 \\
-282 \\
\hline
10
\end{array}
$$
Check: $506 \times 47 + 10 = 23,792$

34

80.
$$
\begin{array}{r}
907 \ \text{R } 40 \\
53\overline{)48,111} \\
-47\ 7 \\
\hline
41 \\
-0 \\
\hline
411 \\
-371 \\
\hline
40
\end{array}
$$
Check: $907 \times 53 + 40 = 48,111$

81.
$$
\begin{array}{r}
2793 \ \text{R } 140 \\
207\overline{)578,291} \\
-414 \\
\hline
164\ 2 \\
-144\ 9 \\
\hline
19\ 39 \\
-18\ 63 \\
\hline
761 \\
-621 \\
\hline
140
\end{array}
$$
Check: $2793 \times 207 + 140 = 578,291$

82.
$$
\begin{array}{r}
2012 \ \text{R } 60 \\
306\overline{)615,732} \\
-612 \\
\hline
3\ 7 \\
-0 \\
\hline
3\ 73 \\
-3\ 06 \\
\hline
672 \\
-612 \\
\hline
60
\end{array}
$$
Check: $2012 \times 306 + 60 = 615,732$

83.
$$
\begin{array}{r}
18 \ \text{R } 2 \\
5\overline{)92} \\
-5 \\
\hline
42 \\
-40 \\
\hline
2
\end{array}
$$
The quotient of 92 and 5 is 18 R 2.

84.
$$
\begin{array}{r}
21 \ \text{R } 2 \\
4\overline{)86} \\
-8 \\
\hline
06 \\
-4 \\
\hline
2
\end{array}
$$
The quotient of 86 and 4 is 21 R 2.

85.
$$
\begin{array}{r}
27 \\
24\overline{)648} \\
-48 \\
\hline
168 \\
-168 \\
\hline
0
\end{array}
$$
27 boxes can be filled with cans of corn.

86.
$$
\begin{array}{r}
13 \\
1760\overline{)22,880} \\
-17\ 60 \\
\hline
5\ 280 \\
-5\ 280 \\
\hline
0
\end{array}
$$
There are 13 miles in 22,880 yards.

87. Divide the sum by 4.

$$
\begin{array}{r}
76 \\
49 \\
32 \\
+\ 47 \\
\hline
204
\end{array}
\qquad
\begin{array}{r}
51 \\
4\overline{)204} \\
-20 \\
\hline
04 \\
-4 \\
\hline
0
\end{array}
$$
The average is 51.

88. Divide the sum by 4.

$$
\begin{array}{r}
23 \\
85 \\
62 \\
+\ 66 \\
\hline
236
\end{array}
\qquad
\begin{array}{r}
59 \\
4\overline{)236} \\
-20 \\
\hline
36 \\
-36 \\
\hline
0
\end{array}
$$
The average is 59.

89. $8^2 = 8 \cdot 8 = 64$

90. $5^3 = 5 \cdot 5 \cdot 5 = 125$

91. $5 \cdot 9^2 = 5 \cdot 9 \cdot 9 = 405$

92. $4 \cdot 10^2 = 4 \cdot 10 \cdot 10 = 400$

93. $18 \div 2 + 7 = 9 + 7 = 16$

94. $12 - 8 \div 4 = 12 - 2 = 10$

95. $\dfrac{5(6^2 - 3)}{3^2 + 2} = \dfrac{5(36 - 3)}{9 + 2} = \dfrac{5(33)}{11} = \dfrac{165}{11} = 15$

96. $\dfrac{7(16 - 8)}{2^3} = \dfrac{7(8)}{8} = \dfrac{56}{8} = 7$

97. $48 \div 8 \cdot 2 = 6 \cdot 2 = 12$

98. $27 \div 9 \cdot 3 = 3 \cdot 3 = 9$

99. $2 + 3[1^5 + (20 - 17) \cdot 3] + 5 \cdot 2$
$= 2 + 3[1^5 + 3 \cdot 3] + 5 \cdot 2$
$= 2 + 3[1 + 3 \cdot 3] + 5 \cdot 2$
$= 2 + 3[1 + 9] + 5 \cdot 2$
$= 2 + 3 \cdot 10 + 5 \cdot 2$
$= 2 + 30 + 10$
$= 42$

100. $21 - [2^4 - (7 - 5) - 10] + 8 \cdot 2$
$= 21 - [2^4 - 2 - 10] + 8 \cdot 2$
$= 21 - [16 - 2 - 10] + 8 \cdot 2$
$= 21 - 4 + 8 \cdot 2$
$= 21 - 4 + 16$
$= 33$

101. $19 - 2(3^2 - 2^2) = 19 - 2(9 - 4)$
$= 19 - 2(5)$
$= 19 - 10$
$= 9$

102. $16 - 2(4^2 - 3^2) = 16 - 2(16 - 9)$
$= 16 - 2(7)$
$= 16 - 14$
$= 2$

103. $4 \cdot 5 - 2 \cdot 7 = 20 - 14 = 6$

104. $8 \cdot 7 - 3 \cdot 9 = 56 - 27 = 29$

105. $(6 - 4)^3 \cdot [10^2 \div (3 + 17)] = (6 - 4)^3 \cdot [10^2 \div 20]$
$= (6 - 4)^3 \cdot [100 \div 20]$
$= 2^3 \cdot 5$
$= 8 \cdot 5$
$= 40$

106. $(7 - 5)^3 \cdot [9^2 \div (2 + 7)] = (7 - 5)^3 \cdot [9^2 \div 9]$
$= (7 - 5)^3 \cdot [81 \div 9]$
$= 2^3 \cdot 9$
$= 8 \cdot 9$
$= 72$

107. $\dfrac{5 \cdot 7 - 3 \cdot 5}{2(11 - 3^2)} = \dfrac{35 - 15}{2(11 - 9)} = \dfrac{20}{2(2)} = \dfrac{20}{4} = 5$

108. $\dfrac{4 \cdot 8 - 1 \cdot 11}{3(9 - 2^3)} = \dfrac{32 - 11}{3(9 - 8)} = \dfrac{21}{3(1)} = \dfrac{21}{3} = 7$

109. Area $= (\text{side})^2 = (7 \text{ meters})^2 = 49$ square meters

110. Area $= (\text{side})^2 = (3 \text{ inches})^2 = 9$ square inches

111. $\dfrac{2x}{z} = \dfrac{2 \cdot 5}{2} = \dfrac{10}{2} = 5$

112. $4x - 3 = 4 \cdot 5 - 3 = 20 - 3 = 17$

113. $\dfrac{x + 7}{y} = \dfrac{5 + 7}{0}$ is undefined.

114. $\dfrac{y}{5x} = \dfrac{0}{5 \cdot 5} = \dfrac{0}{25} = 0$

115. $x^3 - 2z = 5^3 - 2 \cdot 2 = 125 - 2 \cdot 2 = 125 - 4 = 121$

116. $\dfrac{7 + x}{3z} = \dfrac{7 + 5}{3 \cdot 2} = \dfrac{12}{6} = 2$

117. $(y + z)^2 = (0 + 2)^2 = 2^2 = 4$

118. $\dfrac{100}{x} + \dfrac{y}{3} = \dfrac{100}{5} + \dfrac{0}{3} = 20 + 0 = 20$

119. Five subtracted from a number is $x - 5$.

120. Seven more than a number is $x + 7$.

121. Ten divided by a number is $10 \div x$ or $\dfrac{10}{x}$.

122. The product of 5 and a number is $5x$.

123. Let n be 5.

$n + 12 = 20 - 3$

$5 + 12 \overset{?}{=} 20 - 3$

    $17 = 17$ True

Yes, 5 is a solution.

124. Let n be 23.

$n - 8 = 10 + 6$

$23 - 8 \overset{?}{=} 10 + 6$

    $15 = 16$ False

No, 23 is not a solution.

125. Let $n = 14$.

$30 = 3(n - 3)$

$30 \overset{?}{=} 3(14 - 3)$

$30 \overset{?}{=} 3(11)$

    $30 = 33$ False

No, 14 is not a solution.

126. Let n be 20.

$5(n - 7) = 65$

$5(20 - 7) \overset{?}{=} 65$

    $5(13) \overset{?}{=} 65$

        $65 = 65$ True

Yes, 20 is a solution.

127. $7n = 77$

Let n be 6.

$7 \cdot 6 \overset{?}{=} 77$

  $42 = 77$ False

Let n be 11.

$7 \cdot 11 \overset{?}{=} 77$

  $77 = 77$ True

Let n be 20.

$7 \cdot 20 \overset{?}{=} 77$

  $140 = 77$ False

11 is a solution.

128. $n - 25 = 150$

Let n be 125.

$125 - 25 \overset{?}{=} 150$

    $100 = 150$ False

Let n be 145.

$145 - 25 \overset{?}{=} 150$

    $120 = 150$ False

Let n be 175.

$175 - 25 \overset{?}{=} 150$

    $150 = 150$ True

175 is a solution.

129. $5(n + 4) = 90$

Let n be 14.

$5(14 + 4) \overset{?}{=} 90$

  $5(18) \overset{?}{=} 90$

    $90 = 90$ True

Let n be 16.

$5(16 + 4) \overset{?}{=} 90$

  $5(20) \overset{?}{=} 90$

    $100 = 90$ False

Let n be 26.

$5(26 + 4) \overset{?}{=} 90$

  $5(30) \overset{?}{=} 90$

    $150 = 90$ False

14 is a solution.

130. $3n - 8 = 28$

Let n be 3.

$3(3) - 8 \overset{?}{=} 28$

  $9 - 8 \overset{?}{=} 28$

    $1 = 28$ False

Let n be 7.

$3(7) - 8 \overset{?}{=} 28$

  $21 - 8 \overset{?}{=} 28$

    $13 = 28$ False

Let n be 15.

$3(15) - 8 \overset{?}{=} 28$

  $45 - 8 \overset{?}{=} 28$

    $37 = 28$ False

None are solutions.

131.
$$\begin{array}{r} 485 \\ -\ \ 68 \\ \hline 417 \end{array}$$

132.
$$\begin{array}{r} 729 \\ -\ \ 47 \\ \hline 682 \end{array}$$

133.
$$\begin{array}{r} 732 \\ \times\ \ \ 3 \\ \hline 2196 \end{array}$$

134.
$$\begin{array}{r} 629 \\ \times\ \ \ 4 \\ \hline 2516 \end{array}$$

135.
$$\begin{array}{r} {}^{2\ 2} \\ 374 \\ 29 \\ +\ 698 \\ \hline 1101 \end{array}$$

136.
$$
\begin{array}{r}
2\,1\\
593\\
52\\
+\,766\\
\hline
1411
\end{array}
$$

137.
$$
\begin{array}{r}
458\text{ R }8\\
13\overline{)5962}\\
-52\\
\hline
76\\
-65\\
\hline
112\\
-104\\
\hline
8
\end{array}
$$

138.
$$
\begin{array}{r}
237\text{ R }1\\
18\overline{)4267}\\
-36\\
\hline
66\\
-54\\
\hline
127\\
-126\\
\hline
1
\end{array}
$$

139.
$$
\begin{array}{r}
1968\\
\times\ \ 36\\
\hline
11\,808\\
59\,040\\
\hline
70{,}848
\end{array}
$$

140.
$$
\begin{array}{r}
5324\\
\times\ \ 18\\
\hline
42\,592\\
53\,240\\
\hline
95{,}832
\end{array}
$$

141.
$$
\begin{array}{r}
2000\\
-\ 356\\
\hline
1644
\end{array}
$$

142.
$$
\begin{array}{r}
9000\\
-\ 519\\
\hline
8481
\end{array}
$$

143. To round 842 to the nearest ten, observe that the digit in the ones place is 2. Since this digit is less than 5, we do not add 1 to the digit in the tens place. The number 842 rounded to the nearest ten is 840.

144. To round 258,371 to the nearest hundred-thousand, observe that the digit in the ten-thousands place is 5. Since this digit is at least 5, we add 1 to the digit in the hundred-thousands place. The number 258,371 rounded to the nearest hundred-thousand is 300,000.

145. $24 \div 4 \cdot 2 = 6 \cdot 2 = 12$

146. $\dfrac{(15+3)\cdot(8-5)}{2^3+1} = \dfrac{(18)(3)}{8+1} = \dfrac{54}{9} = 6$

147. Let n be 9.
$$5n - 6 = 40$$
$$5 \cdot 9 - 6 \overset{?}{=} 40$$
$$45 - 6 \overset{?}{=} 40$$
$$39 = 40 \quad \text{False}$$
No, 9 is not a solution.

148. Let n be 3.
$$2n - 6 = 5n - 15$$
$$2(3) - 6 \overset{?}{=} 5(3) - 15$$
$$6 - 6 \overset{?}{=} 15 - 15$$
$$0 = 0 \quad \text{True}$$
Yes, 3 is a solution.

149.
$$
\begin{array}{r}
53\\
32\overline{)1714}\\
-160\\
\hline
114\\
-96\\
\hline
18
\end{array}
$$
There are 53 full boxes with 18 left over.

150.
$$
\begin{array}{r}
27\\
\times\ 2\\
\hline
54
\end{array}
\qquad
\begin{array}{r}
8\\
\times\,4\\
\hline
32
\end{array}
$$
$$
\begin{array}{r}
54\\
+\,32\\
\hline
86
\end{array}
$$
The total bill before taxes is $86.

Chapter 1 Test

1. 82,426 in words is eighty-two thousand, four hundred twenty-six.

2. Four hundred two thousand, five hundred fifty in standard form is 402,550.

3.
$$\begin{array}{r} \overset{1}{}59 \\ +\,82 \\ \hline 141 \end{array}$$

4.
$$\begin{array}{r} 600 \\ -\,487 \\ \hline 113 \end{array}$$

5.
$$\begin{array}{r} 496 \\ \times\ \ 30 \\ \hline 14{,}880 \end{array}$$

6.
$$\begin{array}{r} 766\ \text{R}\ 42 \\ 69\overline{)\,52{,}896} \\ -48\ 3 \\ \hline 4\ 59 \\ -4\ 14 \\ \hline 456 \\ -414 \\ \hline 42 \end{array}$$

7. $2^3 \cdot 5^2 = 2 \cdot 2 \cdot 2 \cdot 5 \cdot 5 = 200$

8. $98 \div 1 = 98$

9. $0 \div 49 = 0$

10. $62 \div 0$ is undefined.

11. $(2^4 - 5) \cdot 3 = (16 - 5) \cdot 3 = 11 \cdot 3 = 33$

12. $\begin{aligned}[t] 16 + 9 \div 3 \cdot 4 - 7 &= 16 + 3 \cdot 4 - 7 \\ &= 16 + 12 - 7 \\ &= 28 - 7 \\ &= 21 \end{aligned}$

13. $6^1 \cdot 2^3 = 6 \cdot 2 \cdot 2 \cdot 2 = 48$

14. $\begin{aligned}[t] 2[(6-4)^2 + (22-19)^2] + 10 &= 2[2^2 + 3^2] + 10 \\ &= 2[4 + 9] + 10 \\ &= 2[13] + 10 \\ &= 26 + 10 \\ &= 36 \end{aligned}$

15. $5698 \cdot 1000 = 5{,}698{,}000$

16. Divide the sum by 5.

$$\begin{array}{r} \overset{2}{}\\ 62 \\ 79 \\ 84 \\ 90 \\ +\,95 \\ \hline 410 \end{array} \qquad \begin{array}{r} 82 \\ 5\overline{)\,410} \\ -40 \\ \hline 10 \\ -10 \\ \hline 0 \end{array}$$

The average is 82.

17. To round 52,369 to the nearest thousand, observe that the digit in the hundreds place is 3. Since this digit is less than 5, we do not add 1 to the digit in the thousands place. The number 52,369 rounded to the nearest thousand is 52,000.

18.
6289	rounds to	6 300
5403	rounds to	5 400
+ 1957	rounds to	+ 2 000
		13,700

19.
4267	rounds to	4300
− 2738	rounds to	− 2700
		1600

20.
$$\begin{array}{r} 107 \\ -\ 15 \\ \hline 92 \end{array}$$

21.
$$\begin{array}{r} 15 \\ +\,107 \\ \hline 122 \end{array}$$

22.
$$\begin{array}{r} 107 \\ \times\ 15 \\ \hline 535 \\ 1070 \\ \hline 1605 \end{array}$$

23.
$$\begin{array}{r} 7\ \text{R}\ 2 \\ 15\overline{)\,107} \\ -105 \\ \hline 2 \end{array}$$

24.
$$
\begin{array}{r}
17 \\
29\overline{)493} \\
\underline{-29} \\
203 \\
\underline{-203} \\
0
\end{array}
$$
Each can cost $17.

25.
$$
\begin{array}{r}
725 \\
-599 \\
\hline
126
\end{array}
$$
The higher-priced one is $126 more.

26.
$$
\begin{array}{r}
45 \\
\times\ 8 \\
\hline
360
\end{array}
$$
There are 360 calories in 8 tablespoons of white granulated sugar.

27.
$$
\begin{array}{r}
430 \\
\times\ 16 \\
\hline
2580 \\
4300 \\
\hline
6880
\end{array}
\qquad
\begin{array}{r}
205 \\
\times\ 5 \\
\hline
1025
\end{array}
$$

$$
\begin{array}{r}
6880 \\
+\ 1025 \\
\hline
7905
\end{array}
$$
The total cost is $7905.

28. Perimeter $= (5 + 5 + 5 + 5)$ centimeters
$\qquad\qquad = 20$ centimeters

$\quad$ Area $= (\text{side})^2$
$\qquad\ = (5 \text{ centimeters})^2$
$\qquad\ = 25$ square centimeters

29. Perimeter $= (20 + 10 + 20 + 10)$ yards $= 60$ yards

$\quad$ Area $= (\text{length})(\text{width})$
$\qquad\ = (20 \text{ yards})(10 \text{ yards})$
$\qquad\ = 200$ square yards

30. Let x be 2.
$$5(x^3 - 2) = 5(2^3 - 2) = 5(8 - 2) = 5(6) = 30$$

31. Let x be 7 and y be 8.
$$\frac{3x - 5}{2y} = \frac{3(7) - 5}{2 \cdot 8} = \frac{21 - 5}{16} = \frac{16}{16} = 1$$

32. a. The quotient of a number and 17 is $x \div 17$ or
$\dfrac{x}{17}$.

$\quad$ **b.** Twice a number, decreased by 20 is $2x - 20$.

33. Let n be 6.
$$
\begin{aligned}
5n - 11 &= 19 \\
5(6) - 11 &\overset{?}{=} 19 \\
30 - 11 &\overset{?}{=} 19 \\
19 &= 19 \quad \text{True}
\end{aligned}
$$
6 is a solution.

34. $n + 20 = 4n - 10$
$\quad$ Let n be 0.
$$
\begin{aligned}
0 + 20 &\overset{?}{=} 4 \cdot 0 - 10 \\
20 &\overset{?}{=} 0 - 10 \\
20 &= -10 \quad \text{False}
\end{aligned}
$$
$\quad$ Let n be 10.
$$
\begin{aligned}
10 + 20 &\overset{?}{=} 4 \cdot 10 - 10 \\
30 &\overset{?}{=} 40 - 10 \\
30 &= 30 \quad \text{True}
\end{aligned}
$$
$\quad$ Let n be 20.
$$
\begin{aligned}
20 + 20 &\overset{?}{=} 4 \cdot 20 - 10 \\
40 &\overset{?}{=} 80 - 10 \\
40 &= 70 \quad \text{False}
\end{aligned}
$$
10 is a solution.

Chapter 2

Section 2.1

Practice Problems

1. **a.** If 0 represents the surface of the earth, then 3805 below the surface of the earth is −3805.

   b. If zero degrees Fahrenheit is represented by 0°F, then 85 degrees below zero, Fahrenheit is represented by −85°F.

2.

3. **a.** $0 > -5$ since 0 is to the right of −5 on a number line.

   b. $-3 < 3$ since −3 is to the left of 3 on a number line.

   c. $-7 > -12$ since −7 is to the right of −12 on a number line.

4. **a.** $|-6| = 6$ because −6 is 6 units from 0.

   b. $|4| = 4$ because 4 is 4 units from 0.

   c. $|-12| = 12$ because −12 is 12 units from 0.

5. **a.** The opposite of 14 is −14.

   b. The opposite of −9 is −(−9) or 9.

6. **a.** $-|-7| = -7$

   b. $-|4| = -4$

   c. $-(-12) = 12$

7. $-|x| = -|-6| = -6$

8. The planet with the highest average temperature is the one that corresponds to the bar that extends the furthest in the positive direction (upward). Venus has the highest average temperature.

Vocabulary and Readiness Check

1. The numbers ...−3, −2, −1, 0, 1, 2, 3, ... are called <u>integers</u>.

2. Positive numbers, negative numbers, and zero, together are called <u>signed</u> numbers.

3. The symbols "<" and ">" are called <u>inequality symbols</u>.

4. Numbers greater than 0 are called <u>positive</u> numbers while numbers less than 0 are called <u>negative</u> numbers.

5. The sign "<" means <u>is less than</u> and ">" means <u>is greater than</u>.

6. On a number line, the greater number is to the <u>right</u> of the lesser number.

7. A number's distance from 0 on the number line is the number's <u>absolute value</u>.

8. The numbers −5 and 5 are called <u>opposites</u>.

Exercise Set 2.1

1. If 0 represents ground level, then 1235 feet underground is −1235.

3. If 0 represents sea level, then 14,433 feet above sea level is +14,433.

5. If 0 represents zero degrees Fahrenheit, then 118 degrees above zero is +118.

7. If 0 represents the surface of the ocean, then 13,000 feet below the surface of the ocean is −13,000.

9. If 0 represents a loss of $0, then a loss of $2723 million is −2723 million.

11. If 0 represents the surface of the ocean, then 160 feet below the surface is −160 and 147 feet below the surface is −147. Since −160 extends further in the negative direction, Guillermo is deeper.

13. If 0 represents a decrease of 0%, then a 13 percent decrease is −13.

41

15.

17.

19.

21.

23. $0 > -7$ since 0 is to the right of -7 on a number line.

25. $-7 < -5$ since -7 is to the left of -5 on a number line.

27. $-30 > -35$ since -30 is to the right of -35 on a number line.

29. $-26 < 26$ since -26 is to the left of 26 on a number line.

31. $|5| = 5$ since 5 is 5 units from 0 on a number line.

33. $|-8| = 8$ since -8 is 8 units from 0 on a number line.

35. $|0| = 0$ since 0 is 0 units from 0 on a number line.

37. $|-55| = 55$ since -55 is 55 units from 0 on a number line.

39. The opposite of 5 is negative 5.
$-(5) = -5$

41. The opposite of negative 4 is 4.
$-(-4) = 4$

43. The opposite of 23 is negative 23.
$-(23) = -23$

45. The opposite of negative 85 is 85.
$-(-85) = 85$

47. $|-7| = 7$

49. $-|20| = -20$

51. $-|-3| = -3$

53. $-(-43) = 43$

55. $|-15| = 15$

57. $-(-33) = 33$

59. $|-x| = |-(-6)| = |6| = 6$

61. $-|-x| = -|-2| = -2$

63. $|x| = |-32| = 32$

65. $-|x| = -|7| = -7$

67. $-12 < -6$ since -12 is to the left of -6 on a number line.

69. $|-8| = 8$
$|-11| = 11$
Since $8 < 11$, $|-8| < |-11|$.

71. $|-47| = 47$
$-(-47) = 47$
Since $47 = 47$, $|-47| = -(-47)$.

73. $-|-12| = -12$
$-(-12) = 12$
Since $-12 < 12$, $-|-12| < -(-12)$.

75. $0 > -9$ since 0 is to the right of -9 on a number line.

77. $|0| = 0$
$|-9| = 9$
Since $0 < 9$, $|0| < |-9|$.

79. $-|-2| = -2$
$-|-10| = -10$
Since $-2 > -10$, $-|-2| > -|-10|$.

81. $-(-12) = 12$
$-(-18) = 18$
Since $12 < 18$, $-(-12) < -(-18)$.

83. If the number is 31, then the absolute value of 31 is 31 and the opposite of 31 is -31.

85. If the opposite of a number is -28, then the number is 28, and its absolute value is 28.

87. The bar that extends the farthest in the negative direction corresponds to the Caspian Sea, so the Caspian Sea has the lowest elevation.

89. The tallest bar on the graph corresponds to Lake Superior, so Lake Superior has the highest elevation.

91. The positive number on the graph closest to $100°C$ is $184°C$, which corresponds to iodine.

93. The number on the graph closest to $-200°C$ is $-186°C$, which corresponds to oxygen.

95. $0 + 13 = 13$

97.
$$\begin{array}{r} 15 \\ + 20 \\ \hline 35 \end{array}$$

99.
$$\begin{array}{r} 1\ 2 \\ 47 \\ 236 \\ + 77 \\ \hline 360 \end{array}$$

101. $2^2 = 4$, $-|3| = -3$, $-(-5) = 5$, and $-|-8| = -8$, so the numbers in order from least to greatest are $-|-8|$, $-|3|$, 2^2, $-(-5)$.

103. $|-1| = 1$, $-|-6| = -6$, $-(-6) = 6$, and $-|1| = -1$, so the numbers in order from least to greatest are $-|-6|$, $-|1|$, $|-1|$, $-(-6)$.

105. $-(-2) = 2$, $5^2 = 25$, $-10 = -10$, $-|-9| = -9$, and $|-12| = 12$, so the numbers in order from least to greatest are -10, $-|-9|$, $-(-2)$, $|-12|$, 5^2.

107. **a.** $|-9| = 9$; since $9 > 8$, then $|-9| > 8$ is true.

    b. $|-5| = 5$; since $5 < 8$, then $|-5| > 8$ is false.

    c. $|8| = 8$; since $8 = 8$, then $|8| > 8$ is false.

    d. $|-12| = 12$; since $12 > 8$, then $|-12| > 8$ is true.

109. $-(-|-8|) = -(-8) = 8$

111. False; consider $a = -2$ and $b = -3$, then $-2 > -3$.

113. True; a positive number will always be to the right of a negative number on a number line.

115. False; consider $a = -5$, then the opposite of -5 is 5, which is a positive number.

117. answers may vary

119. no; answers may vary

Section 2.2

Practice Problems

1.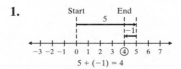
$5 + (-1) = 4$

2.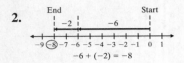

$$-6 + (-2) = -8$$

3.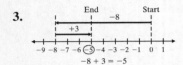

$$-8 + 3 = -5$$

4. $|-3| + |-19| = 3 + 19 = 22$
The common sign is negative, so $(-3) + (-19) = -22$.

5. $-12 + (-30) = -42$

6. $9 + 4 = 13$

7. $|-1| = 1$, $|26| = 26$, and $26 - 1 = 25$
$26 > 1$, so the answer is positive.
$-1 + 26 = 25$

8. $|2| = 2$, $|-18| = 18$, and $18 - 2 = 16$
$18 > 2$, so the answer is negative.
$2 + (-18) = -16$

9. $-54 + 20 = -34$

10. $7 + (-2) = 5$

11. $-3 + 0 = -3$

12. $18 + (-18) = 0$

13. $-64 + 64 = 0$

14. $6 + (-2) + (-15) = 4 + (-15) = -11$

15. $5 + (-3) + 12 + (-14) = 2 + 12 + (-14)$
$$= 14 + (-14)$$
$$= 0$$

16. $x + 3y = -6 + 3(2) = -6 + 6 = 0$

17. $x + y = -13 + (-9) = -22$

18. Temperature at 8 a.m. $= -7 + (+4) + (+7)$
$$= -3 + (+7)$$
$$= 4$$
The temperature was $4°F$ at 8 a.m.

Calculator Explorations

1. $-256 + 97 = -159$

2. $811 + (-1058) = -247$

3. $6(15) + (-46) = 44$

4. $-129 + 10(48) = 351$

5. $-108,650 + (-786,205) = -894,855$

6. $-196,662 + (-129,856) = -326,518$

Vocabulary and Readiness Check

1. If n is a number, then $-n + n = \underline{0}$.

2. Since $x + n = n + x$, we say that addition is <u>commutative</u>.

3. If a is a number, then $-(-a) = \underline{a}$.

4. Since $n + (x + a) = (n + x) + a$, we say that addition is <u>associative</u>.

Exercise Set 2.2

1.

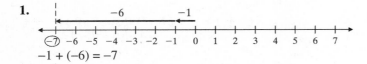

$-1 + (-6) = -7$

3.

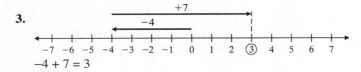

$-4 + 7 = 3$

5.

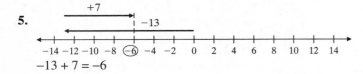

$-13 + 7 = -6$

7. $46 + 21 = 67$

9. $|-8| + |-2| = 8 + 2 = 10$
The common sign is negative, so $(-8) + (-2) = -10$.

11. $-43 + 43 = 0$

13. $|6| - |-2| = 6 - 2 = 4$
$6 > 2$, so the answer is positive.
$6 + (-2) = 4$

15. $-6 + 0 = -6$

17. $|-5| - |3| = 5 - 3 = 2$
$5 > 3$, so the answer is negative.
$3 + (-5) = -2$

19. $|-2| + |-7| = 2 + 7 = 9$
The common sign is negative, so $-2 + (-7) = -9$.

21. $|-12| + |-12| = 12 + 12 = 24$
The common sign is negative, so
$-12 + (-12) = -24$.

23. $|-640| + |-200| = 640 + 200 = 840$
The common sign is negative, so
$-640 + (-200) = -840$.

25. $|12| - |-5| = 12 - 5 = 7$
$12 > 5$, so the answer is positive.
$12 + (-5) = 7$

27. $|-6| - |3| = 6 - 3 = 3$
$6 > 3$, so the answer is negative.
$-6 + 3 = -3$

29. $|-56| - |26| = 56 - 26 = 30$
$56 > 26$, so the answer is negative.
$-56 + 26 = -30$

31. $|85| - |-45| = 85 - 45 = 40$
$85 > 45$, so the answer is positive.
$-45 + 85 = 40$

33. $|-144| - |124| = 144 - 124 = 20$
$144 > 124$, so the answer is negative.
$124 + (-144) = -20$

35. $|-82| + |-43| = 82 + 43 = 125$
The common sign is negative, so
$-82 + (-43) = -125$.

37. $-4 + 2 + (-5) = -2 + (-5) = -7$

39. $-52 + (-77) + (-117) = -129 + (-117) = -246$

41. $12 + (-4) + (-4) + 12 = 8 + (-4) + 12$
$\qquad\qquad\qquad\qquad = 4 + 12$
$\qquad\qquad\qquad\qquad = 16$

43. $(-10) + 14 + 25 + (-16) = 4 + 25 + (-16)$
$\qquad\qquad\qquad\qquad\qquad = 29 + (-16)$
$\qquad\qquad\qquad\qquad\qquad = 13$

45. $-6 + (-15) + (-7) = -21 + (-7) = -28$

47. $-26 + 15 = -11$

49. $5 + (-2) + 17 = 3 + 17 = 20$

51. $-13 + (-21) = -34$

53. $3 + 14 + (-18) = 17 + (-18) = -1$

55. $-92 + 92 = 0$

57. $-13 + 8 + (-10) + (-27) = -5 + (-10) + (-27)$
$\qquad\qquad\qquad\qquad\qquad\quad = -15 + (-27)$
$\qquad\qquad\qquad\qquad\qquad\quad = -42$

59. $x + y = -20 + (-50) = -70$

61. $3x + y = 3(2) + (-3) = 6 + (-3) = 3$

63. $3x + y = 3(3) + (-30) = 9 + (-30) = -21$

65. The sum of -6 and 25 is $-6 + 25 = 19$.

67. The sum of -31, -9, and 30 is
$-31 + (-9) + 30 = -40 + 30 = -10$.

69. $0 + (-215) + (-16) = -215 + (-16) = -231$
The diver's final depth is 231 feet below the surface.

71. Stanford:
$0 + 0 + 0 + (-1) + 0 + 0 + 0 + 1 + 0 + 1 + 0 + 0$
$\quad + (-1) + (-1) + (-1) + 0 + 0 + 0 = -2$
Wie:
$0 + 0 + 0 + (-1) + 0 + 0 + 0 + 0 + (-1) + 0 + 2$
$\quad + 0 + 0 + 0 + 0 + 0 + 1 + 0 = +1$

73. The bar for 2007 has a height of 3496, so the net income in 2007 was \$3,496,000,000.

75. $69 + 1328 = 1397$
The total net income for years 2003 and 2005 was \$1,397,000,000.

77. $-10 + 12 = 2$
The temperature at 11 p.m. was 2°C.

79. $-1786 + 15,395 = 13,609$
The sum of the net incomes for 2006 and 2007 is \$13,609.

81. $-55 + 8 = -47$
West Virginia's record low temperature is -47°F.

83. $-10,924 + 3245 = -7679$
The depth of the Aleutian Trench is -7679 meters.

85. $44 - 0 = 44$

87. $\begin{array}{r} 200 \\ -\ 59 \\ \hline 141 \end{array}$

89. answers may vary

91. $7 + (-10) = -3$

93. $-10 + (-12) = -22$

95. True

97. False; for example, $4 + (-2) = 2 > 0$.

99. answers may vary

Section 2.3

Practice Problems

1. $13 - 4 = 13 + (-4) = 9$

2. $-8 - 2 = -8 + (-2) = -10$

3. $11 - (-15) = 11 + 15 = 26$

4. $-9 - (-1) = -9 + 1 = -8$

5. $6 - 9 = 6 + (-9) = -3$

6. $-14 - 5 = -14 + (-5) = -19$

7. $-3 - (-4) = -3 + 4 = 1$

8. $-15 - 6 = -15 + (-6) = -21$

9. $\begin{aligned} -6 - 5 - 2 - (-3) &= -6 + (-5) + (-2) + 3 \\ &= -11 + (-2) + 3 \\ &= -13 + 3 \\ &= -10 \end{aligned}$

10. $\begin{aligned} 8 + (-2) - 9 - (-7) &= 8 + (-2) + (-9) + 7 \\ &= 6 + (-9) + 7 \\ &= -3 + 7 \\ &= 4 \end{aligned}$

11. $x - y = -5 - 13 = -5 + (-13) = -18$

12. $3y - z = 3(9) - (-4) = 27 + 4 = 31$

13. $29{,}028 - (-1312) = 29{,}028 + 1312 = 30{,}340$
Mount Everest is 30,340 feet higher than the Dead Sea.

Vocabulary and Readiness Check

1. It is true that $a - b = \underline{a + (-b)}$.   b

2. The opposite of n is $\underline{-n}$.   a

3. To evaluate $x - y$ for $x = -10$ and $y = -14$, we replace x with -10 and y with -14 and evaluate $\underline{-10 - (-14)}$.   d

4. The expression $-5 - 10$ equals $\underline{-5 + (-10)}$.   c

Exercise Set 2.3

1. $-8 - (-8) = -8 + 8 = 0$

3. $19 - 16 = 19 + (-16) = 3$

5. $3 - 8 = 3 + (-8) = -5$

7. $11 - (-11) = 11 + 11 = 22$

9. $-4 - (-7) = -4 + 7 = 3$

11. $-16 - 4 = -16 + (-4) = -20$

13. $3 - 15 = 3 + (-15) = -12$

15. $42 - 55 = 42 + (-55) = -13$

17. $478 - (-30) = 478 + 30 = 508$

19. $-4 - 10 = -4 + (-10) = -14$

21. $-7 - (-3) = -7 + 3 = -4$

23. $17 - 29 = 17 + (-29) = -12$

25. $-25 - 17 = -25 + (-17) = -42$

27. $-22 - (-3) = -22 + 3 = -19$

29. $2 - (-12) = 2 + 12 = 14$

31. $-37 + (-19) = -56$

33. $8 - 13 = 8 + (-13) = -5$

35. $-56 - 89 = -56 + (-89) = -145$

37. $30 - 67 = 30 + (-67) = -37$

39. $8 - 3 - 2 = 8 + (-3) + (-2) = 5 + (-2) = 3$

41. $13 - 5 - 7 = 13 + (-5) + (-7) = 8 + (-7) = 1$

43. $-5 - 8 - (-12) = -5 + (-8) + 12 = -13 + 12 = -1$

45. $\begin{aligned} -11 + (-6) - 14 &= -11 + (-6) + (-14) \\ &= -17 + (-14) \\ &= -31 \end{aligned}$

47. $18 - (-32) + (-6) = 18 + 32 + (-6)$
$\qquad\qquad\qquad\quad = 50 + (-6)$
$\qquad\qquad\qquad\quad = 44$

49. $-(-5) - 21 + (-16) = 5 + (-21) + (-16)$
$\qquad\qquad\qquad\qquad = -16 + (-16)$
$\qquad\qquad\qquad\qquad = -32$

51. $-10 - (-12) + (-7) - 4 = -10 + 12 + (-7) + (-4)$
$\qquad\qquad\qquad\qquad\qquad = 2 + (-7) + (-4)$
$\qquad\qquad\qquad\qquad\qquad = -5 + (-4)$
$\qquad\qquad\qquad\qquad\qquad = -9$

53. $-3 + 4 - (-23) - 10 = -3 + 4 + 23 + (-10)$
$\qquad\qquad\qquad\qquad\quad = 1 + 23 + (-10)$
$\qquad\qquad\qquad\qquad\quad = 24 + (-10)$
$\qquad\qquad\qquad\qquad\quad = 14$

55. $x - y = -4 - 7 = -4 + (-7) = -11$

57. $x - y = 8 - (-23) = 8 + 23 = 31$

59. $2x - y = 2(4) - (-4) = 8 + 4 = 12$

61. $2x - y = 2(1) - (-18) = 2 + 18 = 20$

63. The temperature in March is 11°F and in February is −4°F.
$11 - (-4) = 11 + 4 = 15$
The difference is 15°F.

65. The two months with the lowest temperatures are January, −10°F, and December, −6°F.
$-6 - (-10) = -6 + 10 = 4$
The difference is 4°F.

67. $136 - (-129) = 136 + 129 = 265$
Therefore, 136°F is 265°F warmer than −129°F.

69. $14 - (-8) = 14 + 8 = 22$
There was a difference of 22 strokes.

71. $-4 - 3 + 4 - 7 = -4 + (-3) + 4 + (-7)$
$\qquad\qquad\qquad = -7 + 4 + (-7)$
$\qquad\qquad\qquad = -3 + (-7)$
$\qquad\qquad\qquad = -10$
The temperature at 9 a.m. is −10°C.

73. $-282 - (-436) = -282 + 436 = 154$
The difference in elevation is 154 feet.

75. $-436 - (-505) = -436 + 505 = 69$
The difference in elevation is 69 feet.

77. $600 - (-52) = 600 + 52 = 652$
The difference in elevation is 652 feet.

79. $144 - 0 = 144$
The difference in elevation is 144 feet.

81. $867 - (-330) = 867 + 330 = 1197$
The difference in temperatures is 1197°F.

83. $1646 - 2346 = 1646 + (-2346) = -700$
The trade balance was −$700 billion.

85. The sum of −5 and a number is $-5 + x$.

87. Subtract a number from −20 is $-20 - x$.

89. $\dfrac{100}{20} = 5$

91.
$\begin{array}{r} 23 \\ \times\ 46 \\ \hline 138 \\ 920\ \\ \hline 1058 \end{array}$

93. answers may vary

95. $9 - (-7) = 9 + 7 = 16$

97. $10 - 30 = 10 + (-30) = -20$

99. $|-3| - |-7| = 3 - 7 = 3 + (-7) = -4$

101. $|-5| - |5| = 5 - 5 = 0$

103. $|-15| - |-29| = 15 - 29 = 15 + (-29) = -14$

105. $|-8 - 3| = |-8 + (-3)| = |-11| = 11$
$8 - 3 = 8 + (-3) = 5$
Since $11 \neq 5$, the statement is false.

107. answers may vary

Section 2.4

Practice Problems

1. $-3 \cdot 8 = -24$

2. $-5(-2) = 10$

3. $0 \cdot (-20) = 0$

4. $10(-5) = -50$

5. $8(-6)(-2) = -48(-2) = 96$

6. $(-9)(-2)(-1) = 18(-1) = -18$

7. $(-3)(-4)(-5)(-1) = 12(-5)(-1) = -60(-1) = 60$

8. $(-2)^4 = (-2)(-2)(-2)(-2)$
$= 4(-2)(-2)$
$= -8(-2)$
$= 16$

9. $-8^2 = -(8 \cdot 8) = -64$

10. $\dfrac{42}{-7} = -6$

11. $-16 \div (-2) = 8$

12. $\dfrac{-80}{10} = -8$

13. $\dfrac{-6}{0}$ is undefined.

14. $\dfrac{0}{-7} = 0$

15. $xy = 5 \cdot (-8) = -40$

16. $\dfrac{x}{y} = \dfrac{-12}{-3} = 4$

17. total score $= 4 \cdot (-13) = -52$
The card player's total score was -52.

Vocabulary and Readiness Check

1. The product of a negative number and a positive number is a <u>negative</u> number.

2. The product of two negative numbers is a <u>positive</u> number.

3. The quotient of two negative numbers is a <u>positive</u> number.

4. The quotient of a negative number and a positive number is a <u>negative</u> number.

5. The product of a negative number and zero is <u>0</u>.

6. The quotient of 0 and a negative number is <u>0</u>.

7. The quotient of a negative number and 0 is <u>undefined</u>.

Exercise Set 2.4

1. $-6(-2) = 12$

3. $-4(9) = -36$

5. $9(-9) = -81$

7. $0(-11) = 0$

9. $6(-2)(-4) = -12(-4) = 48$

11. $-1(-3)(-4) = 3(-4) = -12$

13. $-4(4)(-5) = -16(-5) = 80$

15. $10(-5)(0)(-7) = 0$

17. $-5(3)(-1)(-1) = -15(-1)(-1) = 15(-1) = -15$

19. $-3^2 = -(3 \cdot 3) = -9$

21. $(-3)^3 = (-3)(-3)(-3) = 9(-3) = -27$

23. $-6^2 = -(6 \cdot 6) = -36$

25. $(-4)^3 = (-4)(-4)(-4) = 16(-4) = -64$

27. $-24 \div 3 = -8$

29. $\dfrac{-30}{6} = -5$

31. $\dfrac{-77}{-11} = 7$

33. $\dfrac{0}{-21} = 0$

35. $\dfrac{-10}{0}$ is undefined.

37. $\dfrac{56}{-4} = -14$

39. $-14(0) = 0$

41. $-5(3) = -15$

43. $-9 \cdot 7 = -63$

45. $-7(-6) = 42$

47. $-3(-4)(-2) = 12(-2) = -24$

49. $(-7)^2 = (-7)(-7) = 49$

51. $-\dfrac{25}{5} = -5$

53. $-\dfrac{72}{8} = -9$

55. $-18 \div 3 = -6$

57. $4(-10)(-3) = -40(-3) = 120$

59. $-30(6)(-2)(-3) = -180(-2)(-3)$
$\qquad\qquad = 360(-3)$
$\qquad\qquad = -1080$

61. $\dfrac{-25}{0}$ is undefined.

63. $\dfrac{120}{-20} = -6$

65. $280 \div (-40) = \dfrac{280}{-40} = -7$

67. $\dfrac{-12}{-4} = 3$

69. $-1^4 = -(1 \cdot 1 \cdot 1 \cdot 1) = -1$

71. $(-2)^5 = (-2)(-2)(-2)(-2)(-2)$
$\qquad\quad = 4(-2)(-2)(-2)$
$\qquad\quad = -8(-2)(-2)$
$\qquad\quad = 16(-2)$
$\qquad\quad = -32$

73. $-2(3)(5)(-6) = -6(5)(-6) = -30(-6) = 180$

75. $(-1)^{32} = 1$, since there are an even number of factors.

77. $-2(-3)(-5) = 6(-5) = -30$

79.
$$\begin{array}{r} 48 \\ \times\ 23 \\ \hline 144 \\ 960 \\ \hline 1104 \end{array}$$
$-48 \cdot 23 = -1104$

81.
$$\begin{array}{r} 35 \\ \times\ 82 \\ \hline 70 \\ 2800 \\ \hline 2870 \end{array}$$
$35 \cdot (-82) = -2870$

83. $ab = -8 \cdot 7 = -56$

85. $ab = 9(-2) = -18$

87. $ab = (-7)(-5) = 35$

89. $\dfrac{x}{y} = \dfrac{5}{-5} = -1$

91. $\dfrac{x}{y} = \dfrac{-15}{0}$ is undefined.

93. $\dfrac{x}{y} = \dfrac{-36}{-6} = 6$

95. $xy = -8 \cdot (-2) = 16$
$\dfrac{x}{y} = \dfrac{-8}{-2} = 4$

97. $xy = 0(-8) = 0$
$\dfrac{x}{y} = \dfrac{0}{-8} = 0$

99. $\dfrac{-54}{9} = -6$

The quotient of -54 and 9 is -6.

101.
$$\begin{array}{r} 42 \\ \times\ 6 \\ \hline 252 \end{array}$$
$-42(-6) = 252$
The product of -42 and -6 is 252.

103. The product of -71 and a number is $-71 \cdot x$ or $-71x$.

50

105. Subtract a number from -16 is $-16 - x$.

107. -29 increased by a number is $-29 + x$.

109. Divide a number by -33 is $\dfrac{x}{-33}$ or $x \div (-33)$.

111. A loss of 4 yards is represented by -4.
$3 \cdot (-4) = -12$
The team had a total loss of 12 yards.

113. Each move of 20 feet down is represented by -20.
$5 \cdot (-20) = -100$
The diver is at a depth of 100 feet.

115. $3 \cdot (-70) = -210$
The melting point of nitrogen is $-210°C$.

117. $-3 \cdot 63 = -189$
The melting point of argon is $-189°C$.

119. $3 \cdot (-2.1) = -6.3$
The reduction in sales will be $-\$6.3$ million after three months.

121. a. $13{,}922 - 12{,}050 = 1872$
1872 fewer movie titles were released to DVD in 2007 than in 2005. This is a change of -1872 movies.

    b. This is a period of 2 years.
$\dfrac{-1872}{2} = -936$
The average change was -936 movies per year.

123. $90 + 12^2 - 5^3 = 90 + 144 - 125$
$= 90 + 144 + (-125)$
$= 234 + (-125)$
$= 109$

125. $12 \div 4 - 2 + 7 = 3 - 2 + 7 = 1 + 7 = 8$

127. $-57 \div 3 = -19$

129. $-8 - 20 = -8 + (-20) = -28$

131. $-4 - 15 - (-11) = -4 + (-15) + 11$
$= -19 + 11$
$= -8$

133. The product of an odd number of negative numbers is negative, so the product of seven negative numbers is negative.

135. $(-2)^{12}$ and $(-5)^{12}$ are positive since there are an even number of factors. Note that $(-5)^{12}$ will be the larger of the two since $|-5| > |-2|$ and the exponent on each is the same.
$(-2)^{17}$ and $(-5)^{17}$ are negative since there are an odd number of factors. Note that $\left|(-5)^{17}\right| > \left|(-2)^{17}\right|$ since $|-5| > |-2|$ and the exponent on each is the same. The numbers from least to greatest are $(-5)^{17}$, $(-2)^{17}$, $(-2)^{12}$, $(-5)^{12}$.

137. answers may vary

Integrated Review

1. Let 0 represent $0°F$. Then 50 degrees below zero is represented by -50 and 122 degrees above zero is represented by $+122$ or 122.

2.

3. $0 > -10$ since 0 is to the right of -10 on a number line.

4. $-4 < 4$ since -4 is to the left of 4 on a number line.

5. $-15 < -5$ since -15 is to the left of -5 on a number line.

6. $-2 > -7$ since -2 is to the right of -7 on a number line.

7. $|-3| = 3$ because -3 is 3 units from 0.

8. $|-9| = 9$ because -9 is 9 units from 0.

9. $-|-4| = -4$

10. $-(-5) = 5$

11. The opposite of 11 is -11.

12. The opposite of -3 is $-(-3) = 3$.

13. The opposite of 64 is -64.

14. The opposite of 0 is $-0 = 0$.

15. $-3 + 15 = 12$

16. $-9 + (-11) = -20$

17. $-8(-6)(-1) = 48(-1) = -48$

18. $-18 \div 2 = -9$

19. $65 + (-55) = 10$

20. $1000 - 1002 = 1000 + (-1002) = -2$

21. $53 - (-53) = 53 + 53 = 106$

22. $-2 - 1 = -2 + (-1) = -3$

23. $\dfrac{0}{-47} = 0$

24. $\dfrac{-36}{-9} = 4$

25. $-17 - (-59) = -17 + 59 = 42$

26. $-8 + (-6) + 20 = -14 + 20 = 6$

27. $\dfrac{-95}{-5} = 19$

28. $-9(100) = -900$

29. $-12 - 6 - (-6) = -12 + (-6) + 6 = -18 + 6 = -12$

30. $-4 + (-8) - 16 - (-9) = -4 + (-8) + (-16) + 9$
$$= -12 + (-16) + 9$$
$$= -28 + 9$$
$$= -19$$

31. $\dfrac{-105}{0}$ is undefined.

32. $7(-16)(0)(-3) = 0$ (since one factor is 0)

33. Subtract -8 from -12 is
$-12 - (-8) = -12 + 8 = -4$.

34. The sum of -17 and -27 is $-17 + (-27) = -44$.

35. The product of -5 and -25 is $-5(-25) = 125$.

36. The quotient of -100 and -5 is $\dfrac{-100}{-5} = 20$.

37. Divide a number by -17 is $\dfrac{x}{-17}$ or $x \div (-17)$.

38. The sum of -3 and a number is $-3 + x$.

39. A number decreased by -18 is $x - (-18)$.

40. The product of -7 and a number is $-7 \cdot x$ or $-7x$.

41. $x + y = -3 + 12 = 9$

42. $x - y = -3 - 12 = -3 + (-12) = -15$

43. $2y - x = 2(12) - (-3) = 24 - (-3) = 24 + 3 = 27$

44. $3y + x = 3(12) + (-3) = 36 + (-3) = 33$

45. $5x = 5(-3) = -15$

46. $\dfrac{y}{x} = \dfrac{12}{-3} = -4$

Section 2.5

Practice Problems

1. $(-2)^4 = (-2)(-2)(-2)(-2) = 16$

2. $-2^4 = -(2)(2)(2)(2) = -16$

3. $3 \cdot 6^2 = 3 \cdot (6 \cdot 6) = 3 \cdot 36 = 108$

4. $\dfrac{-25}{5(-1)} = \dfrac{-25}{-5} = 5$

5. $\dfrac{-18 + 6}{-3 - 1} = \dfrac{-12}{-4} = 3$

6. $30 + 50 + (-4)^3 = 30 + 50 + (-64)$
$$= 80 + (-64)$$
$$= 16$$

7. $-2^3 + (-4)^2 + 1^5 = -8 + 16 + 1 = 8 + 1 = 9$

8. $2(2 - 9) + (-12) - 3 = 2(-7) + (-12) - 3$
$$= -14 + (-12) - 3$$
$$= -26 - 3$$
$$= -29$$

9. $(-5) \cdot |-8| + (-3) + 2^3 = (-5) \cdot 8 + (-3) + 2^3$
$$= (-5) \cdot 8 + (-3) + 8$$
$$= -40 + (-3) + 8$$
$$= -43 + 8$$
$$= -35$$

10. $-4[-6 + 5(-3 + 5)] - 7 = -4[-6 + 5(2)] - 7$
$$= -4[-6 + 10] - 7$$
$$= -4(4) - 7$$
$$= -16 - 7$$
$$= -23$$

11. $x^2 = (-15)^2 = (-15)(-15) = 225$

$-x^2 = -(-15)^2 = -(-15)(-15) = -225$

12. $5y^2 = 5(4)^2 = 5(16) = 80$

$5y^2 = 5(-4)^2 = 5(16) = 80$

13. $x^2 + y = (-6)^2 + (-3) = 36 + (-3) = 33$

14. $4 - x^2 = 4 - (-8)^2 = 4 - 64 = -60$

15. average
$$= \frac{\text{sum of numbers}}{\text{number of numbers}}$$
$$= \frac{15 + (-1) + (-11) + (-14) + (-16) + (-14) + (-1)}{7}$$
$$= \frac{-42}{7}$$
$$= -6$$
The average of the temperatures is $-6°F$.

Calculator Explorations

1. $\dfrac{-120 - 360}{-10} = 48$

2. $\dfrac{4750}{-2 + (-17)} = -250$

3. $\dfrac{-316 + (-458)}{28 + (-25)} = -258$

4. $\dfrac{-234 + 86}{-18 + 16} = 74$

Vocabulary and Readiness Check

1. To simplify $-2 \div 2 \cdot (3)$ which operation should be performed first? <u>division</u>

2. To simplify $-9 - 3 \cdot 4$, which operation should be performed first? <u>multiplication</u>

3. The <u>average</u> of a list of numbers is $\dfrac{\text{sum of numbers}}{\textit{number} \text{ of numbers}}$.

4. To simplify $5[-9 + (-3)] \div 4$, which operation should be performed first? <u>addition</u>

5. To simplify $-2 + 3(10 - 12) \cdot (-8)$, which operation should be performed first? <u>subtraction</u>

6. To evaluate $x - 3y$ for $x = -7$ and $y = -1$, replace x with -7 and y with -1 and evaluate $\underline{-7 - 3(-1)}$.

Exercise Set 2.5

1. $(-5)^3 = (-5)(-5)(-5) = -125$

3. $-4^3 = -(4)(4)(4) = -64$

5. $8 \cdot 2^2 = 8 \cdot 4 = 32$

7. $8 - 12 - 4 = -4 - 4 = -8$

9. $7 + 3(-6) = 7 + (-18) = -11$

11. $5(-9) + 2 = -45 + 2 = -43$

13. $-10 + 4 \div 2 = -10 + 2 = -8$

15. $6 + 7 \cdot 3 - 10 = 6 + 21 - 10$
$$= 27 - 10$$
$$= 17$$

17. $\dfrac{16 - 13}{-3} = \dfrac{3}{-3} = -1$

19. $\dfrac{24}{10 + (-4)} = \dfrac{24}{6} = 4$

21. $5(-3) - (-12) = -15 - (-12) = -15 + 12 = -3$

23. $[8 + (-4)]^2 = [4]^2 = 16$

25. $8 \cdot 6 - 3 \cdot 5 + (-20) = 48 - 3 \cdot 5 + (-20)$
$= 48 - 15 + (-20)$
$= 33 + (-20)$
$= 13$

27. $4 - (-3)^4 = 4 - 81 = -77$

29. $|7+3| \cdot 2^3 = |10| \cdot 2^3 = 10 \cdot 2^3 = 10 \cdot 8 = 80$

31. $7 \cdot 6^2 + 4 = 7 \cdot 36 + 4 = 252 + 4 = 256$

33. $7^2 - (4 - 2^3) = 7^2 - (4 - 8)$
$= 7^2 - (-4)$
$= 49 - (-4)$
$= 49 + 4$
$= 53$

35. $|3 - 15| \div 3 = |-12| \div 3 = 12 \div 3 = 4$

37. $-(-2)^6 = -64$

39. $(5-9)^2 \div (4-2)^2 = (-4)^2 \div (2)^2 = 16 \div 4 = 4$

41. $|8 - 24| \cdot (-2) \div (-2) = |-16| \cdot (-2) \div (-2)$
$= 16 \cdot (-2) \div (-2)$
$= -32 \div (-2)$
$= 16$

43. $(-12 - 20) \div 16 - 25 = (-32) \div 16 - 25$
$= -2 - 25$
$= -27$

45. $5(5-2) + (-5)^2 - 6 = 5(3) + (-5)^2 - 6$
$= 5(3) + 25 - 6$
$= 15 + 25 - 6$
$= 40 - 6$
$= 34$

47. $(2-7) \cdot (6-19) = (-5) \cdot (-13)$
$= 65$

49. $(-36 \div 6) - (4 \div 4) = -6 - 1 = -7$

51. $(10 - 4^2)^2 = (10 - 16)^2 = (-6)^2 = 36$

53. $2(8-10)^2 - 5(1-6)^2 = 2(-2)^2 - 5(-5)^2$
$= 2(4) - 5(25)$
$= 8 - 125$
$= -117$

55. $3(-10) \div [5(-3) - 7(-2)] = 3(-10) \div [-15 + 14]$
$= 3(-10) \div (-1)$
$= -30 \div (-1)$
$= 30$

57. $\dfrac{(-7)(-3) - (4)(3)}{3[7 \div (3-10)]} = \dfrac{21 - 12}{3[7 \div (-7)]}$
$= \dfrac{9}{3(-1)}$
$= \dfrac{9}{-3}$
$= -3$

59. $-3[5 + 2(-4+9)] + 15 = -3[5 + 2(5)] + 15$
$= -3[5 + 10] + 15$
$= -3(15) + 15$
$= -45 + 15$
$= -30$

61. $x + y + z = -2 + 4 + (-1) = 2 + (-1) = 1$

63. $2x - 3y - 4z = 2(-2) - 3(4) - 4(-1)$
$= -4 - 12 + 4$
$= -16 + 4$
$= -12$

65. $x^2 - y = (-2)^2 - 4 = 4 - 4 = 0$

67. $\dfrac{5y}{z} = \dfrac{5(4)}{-1} = \dfrac{20}{-1} = -20$

69. $x^2 = (-3)^2 = 9$

71. $-z^2 = -(-4)^2 = -16$

73. $2z^3 = 2(-4)^3 = 2(-64) = -128$

75. $10 - x^2 = 10 - (-3)^2 = 10 - 9 = 1$

77. $2x^3 - z = 2(-3)^3 - (-4)$
$= 2(-27) - (-4)$
$= -54 - (-4)$
$= -54 + 4$
$= -50$

79. average $= \dfrac{-10 + 8 + (-4) + 2 + 7 + (-5) + (-12)}{7}$

$\qquad\qquad = \dfrac{-14}{7}$

$\qquad\qquad = -2$

81. average $= \dfrac{-17 + (-26) + (-20) + (-13)}{4}$

$\qquad\qquad = \dfrac{-76}{4}$

$\qquad\qquad = -19$

83. The lowest score is -11 and the highest is 8.
$8 - (-11) = 8 + 11 = 19$
The difference between the lowest score and the highest score is 19.

85. average $= \dfrac{-11 + (-7) + 3}{3} = \dfrac{-15}{3} = -5$
The average of the scores is -5.

87. no; answers may vary

89. $\quad\begin{array}{r} 45 \\ \times\ 90 \\ \hline 4050 \end{array}$

91. $\quad\begin{array}{r} 90 \\ -\ 45 \\ \hline 45 \end{array}$

93. $8 + 8 + 8 + 8 = 32$
The perimeter is 32 inches.

95. $9 + 6 + 9 + 6 = 30$
The perimeter is 30 feet.

97. $2 \cdot (7 - 5) \cdot 3 = 2 \cdot 2 \cdot 3 = 4 \cdot 3 = 12$

99. $-6 \cdot (10 - 4) = -6 \cdot 6 = -36$

101. answers may vary

103. answers may vary

105. $(-12)^4 = (-12)(-12)(-12)(-12) = 20{,}736$

107. $x^3 - y^2 = (21)^3 - (-19)^2 = 9261 - 361 = 8900$

109. $(xy + z)^x = [2(-5) + 7]^2$
$\qquad\qquad\quad = [-10 + 7]^2$
$\qquad\qquad\quad = [-3]^2$
$\qquad\qquad\quad = 9$

Section 2.6

Practice Problems

1. $\quad -4x - 3 = 5$
$\quad -4(-2) - 3 \overset{?}{=} 5$
$\qquad\quad 8 - 3 \overset{?}{=} 5$
$\qquad\qquad\quad 5 = 5 \quad$ True
Since $5 = 5$ is true, -2 is a solution of the equation.

2. $\qquad y - 6 = -2$
$\quad y - 6 + 6 = -2 + 6$
$\qquad\qquad y = 4$
Check: $y - 6 = -2$
$\qquad\qquad 4 - 6 \overset{?}{=} -2$
$\qquad\qquad\quad -2 = -2 \quad$ True
The solution is 4.

3. $\qquad -2 = z + 8$
$\quad -2 - 8 = z + 8 - 8$
$\qquad -10 = z$
Check: $-2 = z + 8$
$\qquad\qquad -2 \overset{?}{=} -10 + 8$
$\qquad\qquad -2 = -2 \quad$ True
The solution is -10.

4. $\qquad 10x = -2 + 9x$
$\quad 10x - 9x = -2 + 9x - 9x$
$\qquad\qquad x = -2$
Check: $\qquad 10x = -2 + 9x$
$\qquad 10(-2) \overset{?}{=} -2 + 9(-2)$
$\qquad\quad -20 \overset{?}{=} -2 + (-18)$
$\qquad\quad -20 = -20 \quad$ True
The solution is -2.

5. $\quad 3y = -18$
$\quad \dfrac{3y}{3} = \dfrac{-18}{3}$
$\quad \dfrac{3}{3} \cdot y = \dfrac{-18}{3}$
$\qquad y = -6$
Check: $\qquad 3y = -18$
$\qquad 3(-6) \overset{?}{=} -18$
$\qquad\quad -18 = -18 \quad$ True
The solution is -6.

6. $-32 = 8x$

$$\frac{-32}{8} = \frac{8x}{8}$$

$$\frac{-32}{8} = \frac{8}{8} \cdot x$$

$$-4 = x$$

Check: $-32 = 8x$

$$-32 \stackrel{?}{=} 8(-4)$$

$$-32 = -32 \quad \text{True}$$

The solution is -4.

7. $-3y = -27$

$$\frac{-3y}{-3} = \frac{-27}{-3}$$

$$\frac{-3}{-3} \cdot y = \frac{-27}{-3}$$

$$y = 9$$

Check: $-3y = -27$

$$-3 \cdot 9 \stackrel{?}{=} -27$$

$$-27 = -27 \quad \text{True}$$

The solution is 9.

8. $\dfrac{x}{-4} = 7$

$$-4 \cdot \frac{x}{-4} = -4 \cdot 7$$

$$\frac{-4}{-4} \cdot x = -4 \cdot 7$$

$$x = -28$$

Check: $\dfrac{x}{-4} = 7$

$$\frac{-28}{-4} \stackrel{?}{=} 7$$

$$7 = 7 \quad \text{True}$$

The solution is -28.

Vocabulary and Readiness Check

1. A combination of operations on variables and numbers is called an <u>expression</u>.

2. A statement of the form "expression = expression" is called an <u>equation</u>.

3. An <u>equation</u> contains an equal sign (=) while an <u>expression</u> does not.

4. An <u>expression</u> may be simplified and evaluated while an <u>equation</u> may be solved.

5. A <u>solution</u> of an equation is a number that when substituted for a variable makes the equation a true statement.

6. <u>Equivalent</u> equations have the same solution.

7. By the <u>addition</u> property of equality, the same number may be added to or subtracted from both sides of an equation without changing the solution of the equation.

8. By the <u>multiplication</u> property of equality, the same nonzero number may be multiplied or divided by both sides of an equation without changing the solution of the equation.

Exercise Set 2.6

1. $x - 8 = -2$

$$6 - 8 \stackrel{?}{=} -2$$

$$-2 = -2 \quad \text{True}$$

Since $-2 = -2$ is true, 6 is a solution of the equation.

3. $x + 12 = 17$

$$-5 + 12 \stackrel{?}{=} 17$$

$$7 = 17 \quad \text{False}$$

Since $7 = 17$ is false, -5 is not a solution of the equation.

5. $-9f = 64 - f$

$$-9(-8) \stackrel{?}{=} 64 - (-8)$$

$$72 \stackrel{?}{=} 64 + 8$$

$$72 = 72 \quad \text{True}$$

Since $72 = 72$ is true, -8 is a solution of the equation.

7. $5(c - 5) = -10$

$$5(3 - 5) \stackrel{?}{=} -10$$

$$5(-2) \stackrel{?}{=} -10$$

$$-10 = -10 \quad \text{True}$$

Since $-10 = -10$ is true, 3 is a solution of the equation.

9. $a + 5 = 23$

$$a + 5 - 5 = 23 - 5$$

$$a = 18$$

Check: $a + 5 = 23$

$$18 + 5 \stackrel{?}{=} 23$$

$$23 = 23 \quad \text{True}$$

The solution is 18.

11.
$$d - 9 = -21$$
$$d - 9 + 9 = -21 + 9$$
$$d = -12$$
Check: $\quad d - 9 = -21$
$$-12 - 9 \overset{?}{=} -21$$
$$-21 = -21 \quad \text{True}$$
The solution is -12.

13.
$$7 = y - 2$$
$$7 + 2 = y - 2 + 2$$
$$9 = y$$
Check: $7 = y - 2$
$$7 \overset{?}{=} 9 - 2$$
$$7 = 7 \quad \text{True}$$
The solution is 9.

15.
$$11x = 10x - 17$$
$$11x - 10x = 10x - 10x - 17$$
$$1x = -17$$
$$x = -17$$
Check: $\quad 11x = 10x - 17$
$$11(-17) \overset{?}{=} 10(-17) - 17$$
$$-187 \overset{?}{=} -170 - 17$$
$$-187 = -187 \quad \text{True}$$
The solution is -17.

17.
$$5x = 20$$
$$\frac{5x}{5} = \frac{20}{5}$$
$$\frac{5}{5} \cdot x = \frac{20}{5}$$
$$x = 4$$
Check: $\quad 5x = 20$
$$5(4) \overset{?}{=} 20$$
$$20 = 20 \quad \text{True}$$
The solution is 4.

19.
$$-3z = 12$$
$$\frac{-3z}{-3} = \frac{12}{-3}$$
$$\frac{-3}{-3} \cdot z = \frac{12}{-3}$$
$$z = -4$$
Check: $\quad -3z = 12$
$$-3(-4) \overset{?}{=} 12$$
$$12 = 12 \quad \text{True}$$
The solution is -4.

21.
$$\frac{n}{7} = -2$$
$$7 \cdot \frac{n}{7} = 7 \cdot (-2)$$
$$\frac{7}{7} \cdot n = 7 \cdot (-2)$$
$$n = -14$$
Check: $\quad \frac{n}{7} = -2$
$$\frac{-14}{7} \overset{?}{=} -2$$
$$-2 = -2 \quad \text{True}$$
The solution is -14.

23.
$$2z = -34$$
$$\frac{2z}{2} = \frac{-34}{2}$$
$$\frac{2}{2} \cdot z = \frac{-34}{2}$$
$$z = -17$$
Check: $\quad 2z = -34$
$$2 \cdot (-17) \overset{?}{=} -34$$
$$-34 = -34 \quad \text{True}$$
The solution is -17.

25.
$$-4y = 0$$
$$\frac{-4y}{-4} = \frac{0}{-4}$$
$$\frac{-4}{-4} \cdot y = \frac{0}{-4}$$
$$y = 0$$
Check: $\quad -4y = 0$
$$-4(0) \overset{?}{=} 0$$
$$0 = 0 \quad \text{True}$$
The solution is 0.

27.
$$-10x = -10$$
$$\frac{-10x}{-10} = \frac{-10}{-10}$$
$$\frac{-10}{-10} \cdot x = \frac{-10}{-10}$$
$$x = 1$$
Check: $\quad -10x = -10$
$$-10 \cdot 1 \overset{?}{=} -10$$
$$-10 = -10 \quad \text{True}$$
The solution is 1.

29. $5x = -35$

$$\frac{5x}{5} = \frac{-35}{5}$$

$$\frac{5}{5} \cdot x = \frac{-35}{5}$$

$$x = -7$$

The solution is -7.

31. $n - 5 = -55$

$n - 5 + 5 = -55 + 5$

$$n = -50$$

The solution is -50.

33. $-15 = y + 10$

$-15 - 10 = y + 10 - 10$

$$-25 = y$$

The solution is -25.

35. $\dfrac{x}{-6} = -6$

$$-6 \cdot \frac{x}{-6} = -6 \cdot (-6)$$

$$\frac{-6}{-6} \cdot x = -6 \cdot (-6)$$

$$x = 36$$

The solution is 36.

37. $11n = 10n + 21$

$11n - 10n = 10n - 10n + 21$

$$1n = 21$$

$$n = 21$$

The solution is 21.

39. $-12y = -144$

$$\frac{-12y}{-12} = \frac{-144}{-12}$$

$$\frac{-12}{-12} \cdot y = \frac{-144}{-12}$$

$$y = 12$$

The solution is 12.

41. $\dfrac{n}{4} = -20$

$$4 \cdot \frac{n}{4} = 4 \cdot (-20)$$

$$\frac{4}{4} \cdot n = 4 \cdot (-20)$$

$$n = -80$$

The solution is -80.

43. $-64 = 32y$

$$\frac{-64}{32} = \frac{32y}{32}$$

$$\frac{-64}{32} = \frac{32}{32} \cdot y$$

$$-2 = y$$

The solution is -2.

45. A number decreased by -2 is $x - (-2)$.

47. The product of -6 and a number is $-6 \cdot x$ or $-6x$.

49. The sum of -15 and a number is $-15 + x$.

51. -8 divided by a number is $-8 \div x$ or $\dfrac{-8}{x}$.

53. $n - 42,860 = -1286$

$n - 42,860 + 42,860 = -1286 + 42,860$

$$n = 41,574$$

The solution is $41,574$.

55. $-38x = 15,542$

$$\frac{-38x}{-38} = \frac{15,542}{-38}$$

$$\frac{-38}{-38} \cdot x = \frac{15,542}{-38}$$

$$x = -409$$

The solution is -409.

57. answers may vary

59. answers may vary

Chapter 2 Vocabulary Check

1. Two numbers that are the same distance from 0 on the number line but are on opposite sides of 0 are called <u>opposites</u>.

2. The <u>absolute value</u> of a number is that number's distance from 0 on a number line.

3. The <u>integers</u> are ..., $-3, -2, -1, 0, 1, 2, 3, \ldots$.

4. The <u>negative</u> numbers are numbers less than zero.

5. The <u>positive</u> numbers are numbers greater than zero.

6. The symbols "<" and ">" are called <u>inequality symbols</u>.

7. A <u>solution</u> of an equation is a number that when substituted for a variable makes the equation a true statement.

8. The <u>average</u> of a list of numbers is $\dfrac{sum\ of\ numbers}{number\ of\ numbers}$.

9. A combination of operations on variables and numbers is called an <u>expression</u>.

10. A statement of the form "expression = expression" is called an <u>equation</u>.

11. The sign "<" means <u>is less than</u> and ">" means <u>is greater than</u>.

12. By the <u>addition</u> property of equality, the same number may be added to or subtracted from both sides of an equation without changing the solution of the equation.

13. By the <u>multiplication</u> property of equality, the same nonzero number may be multiplied or divided by both sides of an equation without changing the solution of the equation.

Chapter 2 Review

1. If 0 represents ground level, then 1572 feet below the ground is −1572.

2. If 0 represents sea level, then an elevation of 11,239 feet is +11,239.

3.

4.
-7 -6 -5 -4 -3 -2 -1 0 1 2 3 4 5 6 7

5. $|-11| = 11$ since −11 is 11 units from 0 on a number line.

6. $|0| = 0$ since 0 is 0 units from 0 on a number line.

7. $-|8| = -8$

8. $-(-9) = 9$

9. $-|-16| = -16$

10. $-(-2) = 2$

11. $-18 > -20$ since −18 is to the right of −20 on a number line.

12. $-5 < 5$ since −5 is to the left of 5 on a number line.

13. $|-123| = 123$
    $-|-198| = -198$
    Since $123 > -198$, $|-123| > -|-198|$.

14. $|-12| = 12$
    $-|-16| = -16$
    Since $12 > -16$, $|-12| > -|-16|$.

15. The opposite of −18 is 18.
    $-(-18) = 18$

16. The opposite of 42 is negative 42.
$-(42) = -42$

17. False; consider $a = 1$ and $b = 2$, then $1 < 2$.

18. True

19. True

20. True

21. $|y| = |-2| = 2$

22. $|-x| = |-(-3)| = |3| = 3$

23. $-|-z| = -|-(-5)| = -|5| = -5$

24. $-|-n| = -|-(-10)| = -|10| = -10$

25. The bar that extends the farthest in the negative direction corresponds to Elevator D, so Elevator D extends the farthest below ground.

26. The bar that extends the farthest in the positive direction corresponds to Elevator B, so Elevator B extends the highest above ground.

27. $|5| - |-3| = 5 - 3 = 2$
$5 > 3$, so the answer is positive.
$5 + (-3) = 2$

28. $|18| - |-4| = 18 - 4 = 14$
$18 > 4$, so the answer is positive.
$18 + (-4) = 14$

29. $|16| - |-12| = 16 - 12 = 4$
$16 > 12$, so the answer is positive.
$-12 + 16 = 4$

30. $|40| - |-23| = 40 - 23 = 17$
$40 > 23$, so the answer is positive.
$-23 + 40 = 17$

31. $|-8| + |-15| = 8 + 15 = 23$
The common sign is negative, so
$-8 + (-15) = -23$.

32. $|-5| + |-17| = 5 + 17 = 22$
The common sign is negative, so
$-5 + (-17) = -22$.

33. $|-24| - |3| = 24 - 3 = 21$
$24 > 3$, so the answer is negative.
$-24 + 3 = -21$

34. $|-89| - |19| = 89 - 19 = 70$
$89 > 19$, so the answer is negative.
$-89 + 19 = -70$

35. $15 + (-15) = 0$

36. $-24 + 24 = 0$

37. $|-43| + |-108| = 43 + 108 = 151$
The common sign is negative, so
$-43 + (-108) = -151$.

38. $|-100| + |-506| = 100 + 506 = 606$
The common sign is negative, so
$-100 + (-506) = -606$.

39. $-15 + (-5) = -20$
The temperature at 6 a.m. is $-20°$C.

40. $-127 + (-23) = -150$
The diver's current depth is -150 feet.

41. $-6 + (-9) + (-4) + (-2) = -15 + (-4) + (-2)$
$= -19 + (-2)$
$= -21$
His total score was -21.

42. $16 - 4 = 16 + (-4) = 12$
The team's score was 12.

43. $12 - 4 = 12 + (-4) = 8$

44. $-12 - 4 = -12 + (-4) = -16$

45. $-7 - 17 = -7 + (-17) = -24$

46. $7 - 17 = 7 + (-17) = -10$

47. $7 - (-13) = 7 + 13 = 20$

48. $-6 - (-14) = -6 + 14 = 8$

49. $16 - 16 = 16 + (-16) = 0$

50. $-16 - 16 = -16 + (-16) = -32$

51. $-12 - (-12) = -12 + 12 = 0$

52. $-5 - (-12) = -5 + 12 = 7$

53. $-(-5) - 12 + (-3) = 5 + (-12) + (-3)$
$= -7 + (-3)$
$= -10$

60

54. $-8+(-12)-10-(-3) = -8+(-12)+(-10)+3$
$$= -20+(-10)+3$$
$$= -30+3$$
$$= -27$$

55. $600-(-92) = 600+92 = 692$
The difference in elevations is 692 feet.

56. $142-125+43-85 = 142+(-125)+43+(-85)$
$$= 17+43+(-85)$$
$$= 60+(-85)$$
$$= -25$$
The balance in his account is -25.

57. $85 - 99 = 85 + (-99) = -14$
You are -14 feet or 14 feet below ground at the end of the drop.

58. $66 - (-16) = 66 + 16 = 82$
The total length of the elevator shaft for Elevator C is 82 feet.

59. $|-5| - |-6| = 5 - 6 = 5 + (-6) = -1$
$5 - 6 = 5 + (-6) = -1$
$|-5| - |-6| = 5 - 6$ is true.

60. $|-5 - (-6)| = |-5 + 6| = |1| = 1$
$5 + 6 = 11$
Since $1 \neq 11$, the statement is false.

61. $-3(-7) = 21$

62. $-6(3) = -18$

63. $-4(16) = -64$

64. $-5(-12) = 60$

65. $(-5)^2 = (-5)(-5) = 25$

66. $(-1)^5 = (-1)(-1)(-1)(-1)(-1) = -1$

67. $12(-3)(0) = 0$

68. $-1(6)(2)(-2) = -6(2)(-2) = -12(-2) = 24$

69. $-15 \div 3 = -5$

70. $\dfrac{-24}{-8} = 3$

71. $\dfrac{0}{-3} = 0$

72. $\dfrac{-46}{0}$ is undefined.

73. $\dfrac{100}{-5} = -20$

74. $\dfrac{-72}{8} = -9$

75. $\dfrac{-38}{-1} = 38$

76. $\dfrac{45}{-9} = -5$

77. A loss of 5 yards is represented by -5.
$(-5)(2) = -10$
The total loss is 10 yards.

78. A loss of $50 is represented by -50.
$(-50)(4) = -200$
The total loss is $200.

79. A debt of $1024 is represented by -1024.
$-1024 \div 4 = -256$
Each payment is $256.

80. A drop of 45 degrees is represented by -45.
$$\dfrac{-45}{9} = -5 \text{ or } -45 \div 9 = -5$$
The average drop each hour is $5°F$.

81. $(-7)^2 = (-7)(-7) = 49$

82. $-7^2 = -(7 \cdot 7) = -49$

83. $5 - 8 + 3 = -3 + 3 = 0$

84. $-3+12+(-7)-10 = 9+(-7)-10 = 2-10 = -8$

85. $-10 + 3 \cdot (-2) = -10 + (-6) = -16$

86. $5 - 10 \cdot (-3) = 5 - (-30) = 5 + 30 = 35$

87. $16 \div (-2) \cdot 4 = -8 \cdot 4 = -32$

88. $-20 \div 5 \cdot 2 = -4 \cdot 2 = -8$

89. $16+(-3) \cdot 12 \div 4 = 16+(-36) \div 4$
$$= 16+(-9)$$
$$= 7$$

90. $-12 + 10 \div (-5) = -12 + (-2) = -14$

91. $4^3 - (8-3)^2 = 4^3 - (5)^2 = 64 - 25 = 39$

92. $(-3)^3 - 90 = -27 - 90 = -117$

93. $\dfrac{(-4)(-3) - (-2)(-1)}{-10 + 5} = \dfrac{12 - 2}{-5} = \dfrac{10}{-5} = -2$

94. $\dfrac{4(12-18)}{-10 \div (-2-3)} = \dfrac{4(-6)}{-10 \div (-5)} = \dfrac{-24}{2} = -12$

95. $\begin{aligned} \text{average} &= \dfrac{-18 + 25 + (-30) + 7 + 0 + (-2)}{6} \\ &= \dfrac{-18}{6} \\ &= -3 \end{aligned}$

96. $\begin{aligned} \text{average} &= \dfrac{-45 + (-40) + (-30) + (-25)}{4} \\ &= \dfrac{-140}{4} \\ &= -35 \end{aligned}$

97. $2x - y = 2(-2) - 1 = -4 - 1 = -5$

98. $y^2 + x^2 = 1^2 + (-2)^2 = 1 + 4 = 5$

99. $\dfrac{3x}{6} = \dfrac{3(-2)}{6} = \dfrac{-6}{6} = -1$

100. $\dfrac{5y - x}{-y} = \dfrac{5(1) - (-2)}{-1} = \dfrac{5 + 2}{-1} = \dfrac{7}{-1} = -7$

101. $\begin{aligned} 2n - 6 &= 16 \\ 2(-5) - 6 &\overset{?}{=} 16 \\ -10 - 6 &\overset{?}{=} 16 \\ -16 &= 16 \quad \text{False} \end{aligned}$
Since $-16 = 16$ is false, -5 is not a solution of the equation.

102. $\begin{aligned} 2(c - 8) &= -20 \\ 2(-2 - 8) &\overset{?}{=} -20 \\ 2(-10) &\overset{?}{=} -20 \\ -20 &= -20 \quad \text{True} \end{aligned}$
Since $-20 = -20$ is true, -2 is a solution of the equation.

103. $\begin{aligned} n - 7 &= -20 \\ n - 7 + 7 &= -20 + 7 \\ n &= -13 \end{aligned}$
The solution is -13.

104. $\begin{aligned} -5 &= n + 15 \\ -5 - 15 &= n + 15 - 15 \\ -20 &= n \end{aligned}$
The solution is -20.

105. $\begin{aligned} 10x &= -30 \\ \dfrac{10x}{10} &= \dfrac{-30}{10} \\ \dfrac{10}{10} \cdot x &= \dfrac{-30}{10} \\ x &= -3 \end{aligned}$
The solution is -3.

106. $\begin{aligned} -8x &= 72 \\ \dfrac{-8x}{-8} &= \dfrac{72}{-8} \\ \dfrac{-8}{-8} \cdot x &= \dfrac{72}{-8} \\ x &= -9 \end{aligned}$
The solution is -9.

107. $\begin{aligned} 9y &= 8y - 13 \\ 9y - 8y &= 8y - 8y - 13 \\ 1y &= -13 \\ y &= -13 \end{aligned}$
The solution is -13.

108. $\begin{aligned} 6x - 31 &= 7x \\ 6x - 6x - 31 &= 7x - 6x \\ -31 &= 1x \\ -31 &= x \end{aligned}$
The solution is -31.

109. $\begin{aligned} \dfrac{n}{-4} &= -11 \\ -4 \cdot \dfrac{n}{-4} &= -4 \cdot (-11) \\ \dfrac{-4}{-4} \cdot n &= -4 \cdot (-11) \\ n &= 44 \end{aligned}$
The solution is 44.

110.
$$\frac{x}{-2} = 13$$
$$-2 \cdot \frac{x}{-2} = -2 \cdot 13$$
$$\frac{-2}{-2} \cdot x = -2 \cdot 13$$
$$x = -26$$
The solution is -26.

111.
$$n + 12 = -7$$
$$n + 12 - 12 = -7 - 12$$
$$n = -19$$
The solution is -19.

112.
$$n - 40 = -2$$
$$n - 40 + 40 = -2 + 40$$
$$n = 38$$
The solution is 38.

113.
$$-36 = -6x$$
$$\frac{-36}{-6} = \frac{-6x}{-6}$$
$$\frac{-36}{-6} = \frac{-6}{-6} \cdot x$$
$$6 = x$$
The solution is 6.

114.
$$-40 = 8y$$
$$\frac{-40}{8} = \frac{8y}{8}$$
$$\frac{-40}{8} = \frac{8}{8} \cdot y$$
$$-5 = y$$
The solution is -5.

115. $-6 + (-9) = -15$

116. $-16 - 3 = -16 + (-3) = -19$

117. $-4(-12) = 48$

118. $\dfrac{84}{-4} = -21$

119. $-76 - (-97) = -76 + 97 = 21$

120. $-9 + 4 = -5$

121. $-32 + 23 = -9$
His financial situation can be represented by $-\$9$.

122. $-11 + 17 = 6$
The temperature at noon on Tuesday was $6°C$.

123. $12{,}923 - (-195) = 12{,}923 + 195 = 13{,}118$
The difference in elevations is 13,118 feet.

124. $-18 - 9 = -27$
The temperature on Friday was $-27°C$.

125. $(3 - 7)^2 \div (6 - 4)^3 = (-4)^2 \div (2)^3 = 16 \div 8 = 2$

126. $3(4 + 2) + (-6) - 3^2 = 3(6) + (-6) - 3^2$
$$= 3(6) + (-6) - 9$$
$$= 18 + (-6) - 9$$
$$= 12 - 9$$
$$= 3$$

127. $2 - 4 \cdot 3 + 5 = 2 - 12 + 5 = -10 + 5 = -5$

128. $4 - 6 \cdot 5 + 1 = 4 - 30 + 1 = -26 + 1 = -25$

129. $\dfrac{-|-14| - 6}{7 + 2(-3)} = \dfrac{-14 - 6}{7 + (-6)} = \dfrac{-20}{1} = -20$

130. $5(7 - 6)^3 - 4(2 - 3)^2 + 2^4 = 5(1)^3 - 4(-1)^2 + 2^4$
$$= 5(1) - 4(1) + 16$$
$$= 5 - 4 + 16$$
$$= 1 + 16$$
$$= 17$$

131.
$$n - 9 = -30$$
$$n - 9 + 9 = -30 + 9$$
$$n = -21$$
The solution is -21.

132.
$$n + 18 = 1$$
$$n + 18 - 18 = 1 - 18$$
$$n = -17$$
The solution is -17.

133.
$$-4x = -48$$
$$\frac{-4x}{-4} = \frac{-48}{-4}$$
$$\frac{-4}{-4} \cdot x = \frac{-48}{-4}$$
$$x = 12$$
The solution is 12.

134. $9x = -81$

$$\frac{9x}{9} = \frac{-81}{9}$$

$$\frac{9}{9} \cdot x = \frac{-81}{9}$$

$$x = -9$$

The solution is -9.

135. $\dfrac{n}{-2} = 100$

$$-2 \cdot \frac{n}{-2} = -2 \cdot 100$$

$$\frac{-2}{-2} \cdot n = -2 \cdot 100$$

$$n = -200$$

The solution is -200.

136. $\dfrac{y}{-1} = -3$

$$-1 \cdot \frac{y}{-1} = -1(-3)$$

$$\frac{-1}{-1} \cdot y = -1 \cdot (-3)$$

$$y = 3$$

The solution is 3.

Chapter 2 Test

1. $-5 + 8 = 3$

2. $18 - 24 = 18 + (-24) = -6$

3. $5 \cdot (-20) = -100$

4. $-16 \div (-4) = 4$

5. $-18 + (-12) = -30$

6. $-7 - (-19) = -7 + 19 = 12$

7. $-5 \cdot (-13) = 65$

8. $\dfrac{-25}{-5} = 5$

9. $|-25| + (-13) = 25 + (-13) = 12$

10. $14 - |-20| = 14 - 20 = 14 + (-20) = -6$

11. $|5| \cdot |-10| = 5 \cdot 10 = 50$

12. $\dfrac{|-10|}{-|-5|} = \dfrac{10}{-5} = -2$

13. $-8 + 9 \div (-3) = -8 + (-3) = -11$

14. $-7 + (-32) - 12 + 5 = -7 + (-32) + (-12) + 5$
$$= -39 + (-12) + 5$$
$$= -51 + 5$$
$$= -46$$

15. $(-5)^3 - 24 \div (-3) = -125 - 24 \div (-3)$
$$= -125 - (-8)$$
$$= -125 + 8$$
$$= -117$$

16. $(5-9)^2 \cdot (8-2)^3 = (-4)^2 \cdot (6)^3 = 16 \cdot 216 = 3456$

17. $-(-7)^2 \div 7 \cdot (-4) = -49 \div 7 \cdot (-4) = -7 \cdot (-4) = 28$

18. $3 - (8-2)^3 = 3 - 6^3$
$$= 3 - 216$$
$$= 3 + (-216)$$
$$= -213$$

19. $\dfrac{4}{2} - \dfrac{8^2}{16} = \dfrac{4}{2} - \dfrac{64}{16} = 2 - 4 = 2 + (-4) = -2$

20. $\dfrac{-3(-2)+12}{-1(-4-5)} = \dfrac{6+12}{-1(-9)} = \dfrac{18}{9} = 2$

21. $\dfrac{|25-30|^2}{2(-6)+7} = \dfrac{|-5|^2}{-12+7} = \dfrac{(5)^2}{-5} = \dfrac{25}{-5} = -5$

22. $5(-8) - [6 - (2-4)] + (12-16)^2$
$$= 5(-8) - [6 - (-2)] + (12-16)^2$$
$$= 5(-8) - (6+2) + (-4)^2$$
$$= 5(-8) - 8 + (-4)^2$$
$$= 5(-8) - 8 + 16$$
$$= -40 - 8 + 16$$
$$= -48 + 16$$
$$= -32$$

23. $7x + 3y - 4z = 7(0) + 3(-3) - 4(2)$
$$= 0 + (-9) - 8$$
$$= -9 - 8$$
$$= -17$$

24. $10 - y^2 = 10 - (-3)^2 = 10 - 9 = 1$

25. $\dfrac{3z}{2y} = \dfrac{3(2)}{2(-3)} = \dfrac{6}{-6} = -1$

26. A descent of 22 feet is represented by −22.
$4(-22) = -88$
Mary is 88 feet below sea level.

27. $129 + (-79) + (-40) + 35 = 50 + (-40) + 35$
$$= 10 + 35$$
$$= 45$$
His new balance can be represented by 45.

28. Subtract the elevation of the Romanche Gap from the elevation of Mt. Washington.
$6288 - (-25,354) = 6288 + 25,354 = 31,642$
The difference in elevations is 31,642 feet.

29. Subtract the depth of the lake from the elevation of the surface.
$1495 - 5315 = 1495 + (-5315) = -3820$
The deepest point of the lake is 3820 feet below sea level.

30. average $= \dfrac{-12 + (-13) + 0 + 9}{4} = \dfrac{-16}{4} = -4$

31. a. The product of a number and 17 is $17x$.

    b. Twice a number subtracted from 20 is $20 - 2x$.

32. $-9n = -45$
$$\dfrac{-9n}{-9} = \dfrac{-45}{-9}$$
$$\dfrac{-9}{-9} \cdot n = \dfrac{-45}{-9}$$
$$n = 5$$
The solution is 5.

33. $\dfrac{n}{-7} = 4$
$$-7 \cdot \dfrac{n}{-7} = -7 \cdot 4$$
$$\dfrac{-7}{-7} \cdot n = -7 \cdot 4$$
$$n = -28$$
The solution is −28.

34. $x - 16 = -36$
$$x - 16 + 16 = -36 + 16$$
$$x = -20$$
The solution is −20.

35. $9x = 8x - 4$
$$9x - 8x = 8x - 8x - 4$$
$$1x = -4$$
$$x = -4$$
The solution is −4.

Cumulative Review Chapters 1–2

1. The place value of 3 in 396,418 is hundred-thousands.

2. The place value of 3 in 4308 is hundreds.

3. The place value of 3 in 93,192 is thousands.

4. The place value of 3 is 693,298 is thousands.

5. The place value of 3 in 534,275,866 is ten-millions.

6. The place value of 3 in 267,301,818 is hundred-thousands.

7. a. $-7 < 7$ since −7 is to the left of 7 on a number line.

    b. $0 > -4$ since 0 is to the right of −4 on a number line.

    c. $-9 > -11$ since −9 is to the right of −11 on a number line.

8. a. $12 > -4$ since 12 is to the right of −4 on a number line.

    b. $-13 > -31$ since −13 is to the right of −31 on a number line.

    c. $-82 < 79$ since −82 is to the left of 79 on a number line.

9. $13 + 2 + 7 + 8 + 9 = (13 + 7) + (2 + 8) + 9$
$$= 20 + 10 + 9$$
$$= 39$$

10. $11 + 3 + 9 + 16 = (11 + 9) + (3 + 16) = 20 + 19 = 39$

11.
```
   7826
 −  505
 ──────
   7321
```
Check:
```
   7321
 +  505
 ──────
   7826
```

12.
```
  3285
-  272
  3013
```
Check:
```
  3013
+  272
  3285
```

13. Subtract 7257 from the radius of Jupiter.
```
 43,441
- 7 257
 36,184
```
The radius of Saturn is 36,184 miles.

14. Subtract the cost of the camera from the amount in her account.
```
  762
- 237
  525
```
She will have $525 left in her account after buying the camera.

15. To round 568 to the nearest ten, observe that the digit in the ones place is 8. Since this digit is at least 5, we add 1 to the digit in the tens place. The number 568 rounded to the nearest ten is 570.

16. To round 568 to the nearest hundred, observe that the digit in the tens place is 6. Since this digit is at least 5, we add 1 to the digit in the hundreds place. The number 568 rounded to the nearest hundred is 600.

17.
```
  4725   rounds to      4700
- 2879   rounds to    - 2900
                        1800
```

18.
```
  8394   rounds to      8000
- 2913   rounds to    - 3000
                        5000
```

19. a. $5(6 + 5) = 5 \cdot 6 + 5 \cdot 5$

   b. $20(4 + 7) = 20 \cdot 4 + 20 \cdot 7$

   c. $2(7 + 9) = 2 \cdot 7 + 2 \cdot 9$

20. a. $5(2 + 12) = 5 \cdot 2 + 5 \cdot 12$

   b. $9(3 + 6) = 9 \cdot 3 + 9 \cdot 6$

   c. $4(8 + 1) = 4 \cdot 8 + 4 \cdot 1$

21.
```
    631
 ×  125
  3 155
 12 620
 63 100
 78,875
```

22.
```
    299
 ×  104
  1 196
 29 900
 31,096
```

23. a. $42 \div 7 = 6$ because $6 \cdot 7 = 42$.

   b. $\dfrac{64}{8} = 8$ because $8 \cdot 8 = 64$.

   c. $3\overline{)21}$ with quotient 7 because $7 \cdot 3 = 21$.

24. a. $\dfrac{35}{5} = 7$ because $7 \cdot 5 = 35$.

   b. $64 \div 8 = 8$ because $8 \cdot 8 = 64$.

   c. $4\overline{)48}$ with quotient 12 because $12 \cdot 4 = 48$.

25.
```
      741
 5) 3705
   -35
    20
   -20
    05
    -5
     0
```
Check:
```
  741
×   5
 3705
```

26.
$$8\overline{)3648}$$

$$\begin{array}{r} 456 \\ 8\overline{)3648} \\ \underline{-32} \\ 44 \\ \underline{-40} \\ 48 \\ \underline{-48} \\ 0 \end{array}$$

Check:
$$\begin{array}{r} 456 \\ \times \;\; 8 \\ \hline 3648 \end{array}$$

27. $\dfrac{\text{number of cards}}{\text{for each person}} = \dfrac{\text{number of}}{\text{cards}} \div \dfrac{\text{number of}}{\text{friends}}$

$$= 238 \div 19$$

$$\begin{array}{r} 12 \text{ R } 10 \\ 19\overline{)238} \\ \underline{-19} \\ 48 \\ \underline{-38} \\ 10 \end{array}$$

Each friend will receive 12 cards. There will be 10 cards left over.

28. $\dfrac{\text{Cost of each}}{\text{ticket}} = \dfrac{\text{total}}{\text{cost}} \div \text{number of tickets}$

$$= 324 \div 36$$

$$\begin{array}{r} 9 \\ 36\overline{)324} \\ \underline{-324} \\ 0 \end{array}$$

Each ticket cost $9.

29. $9^2 = 9 \cdot 9 = 81$

30. $5^3 = 5 \cdot 5 \cdot 5 = 125$

31. $6^1 = 6$

32. $4^1 = 4$

33. $5 \cdot 6^2 = 5 \cdot 6 \cdot 6 = 180$

34. $2^3 \cdot 7 = 2 \cdot 2 \cdot 2 \cdot 7 = 56$

35. $\dfrac{7 - 2 \cdot 3 + 3^2}{5(2-1)} = \dfrac{7 - 2 \cdot 3 + 9}{5(1)} = \dfrac{7 - 6 + 9}{5} = \dfrac{10}{5} = 2$

36.
$$\dfrac{6^2 + 4 \cdot 4 + 2^3}{37 - 5^2} = \dfrac{36 + 4 \cdot 4 + 8}{37 - 25}$$
$$= \dfrac{36 + 16 + 8}{12}$$
$$= \dfrac{60}{12}$$
$$= 5$$

37. $x + 6 = 8 + 6 = 14$

38. $5 + x = 5 + 9 = 14$

39. a. $|-9| = 9$ because -9 is 9 units from 0.

    b. $|8| = 8$ because 8 is 8 units from 0.

    c. $|0| = 0$ because 0 is 0 units from 0.

40. a. $|4| = 4$ because 4 is 4 units from 0.

    b. $|-7| = 7$ because -7 is 7 units from 0.

41. $-2 + 25 = 23$

42. $8 + (-3) = 5$

43. $2a - b = 2(8) - (-6) = 16 - (-6) = 16 + 6 = 22$

44. $x - y = -2 - (-7) = -2 + 7 = 5$

45. $-7 \cdot 3 = -21$

46. $5(-2) = -10$

47. $0 \cdot (-4) = 0$

48. $-6 \cdot 9 = -54$

49. $3(4-7) + (-2) - 5 = 3(-3) + (-2) - 5$
$$= -9 + (-2) - 5$$
$$= -11 - 5$$
$$= -16$$

50. $4 - 8(7-3) - (-1) = 4 - 8(4) - (-1)$
$$= 4 - 32 - (-1)$$
$$= 4 - 32 + 1$$
$$= -28 + 1$$
$$= -27$$

Chapter 3

Practice Problems

1. **a.** $8m - 14m = (8 - 14)m = -6m$

   b. $6a + a = 6a + 1a = (6 + 1)a = 7a$

   c. $-y^2 + 3y^2 + 7 = -1y^2 + 3y^2 + 7$
   $$= (-1 + 3)y^2 + 7$$
   $$= 2y^2 + 7$$

2. $6z + 5 + z - 4 = 6z + 5 + 1z + (-4)$
   $$= 6z + 1z + 5 + (-4)$$
   $$= (6 + 1)z + 5 + (-4)$$
   $$= 7z + 1$$

3. $6y + 12y - 6 = 18y - 6$

4. $7y - 5 + y + 8 = 7y + (-5) + 1y + 8$
   $$= 7y + 1y + (-5) + 8$$
   $$= 8y + 3$$

5. $-7y + 2 - 2y - 9x + 12 - x$
   $$= -7y + 2 + (-2y) + (-9x) + 12 + (-1x)$$
   $$= -7y + (-2y) + (-9x) + (-1x) + 2 + 12$$
   $$= -9y - 10x + 14$$

6. $6(4a) = (6 \cdot 4)a = 24a$

7. $-8(9x) = (-8 \cdot 9)x = -72x$

8. $8(y + 2) = 8 \cdot y + 8 \cdot 2 = 8y + 16$

9. $3(7a - 5) = 3 \cdot 7a - 3 \cdot 5 = 21a - 15$

10. $6(5 - y) = 6 \cdot 5 - 6 \cdot y = 30 - 6y$

11. $5(2y - 3) - 8 = 5(2y) - 5(3) - 8$
    $$= 10y - 15 - 8$$
    $$= 10y - 23$$

12. $-7(x - 1) + 5(2x + 3)$
    $$= -7(x) - (-7)(1) + 5(2x) + 5(3)$$
    $$= -7x + 7 + 10x + 15$$
    $$= 3x + 22$$

13. $-(y + 1) + 3y - 12 = -1(y + 1) + 3y - 12$
    $$= -1 \cdot y + (-1)(1) + 3y - 12$$
    $$= -y - 1 + 3y - 12$$
    $$= 2y - 13$$

14. $4(2x) = (4 \cdot 2)x = 8x$
    The perimeter is $8x$ centimeters.

15. $3(12y + 9) = 3 \cdot 12y + 3 \cdot 9 = 36y + 27$
    The area of the garden is $(36y + 27)$ square yards.

Vocabulary and Readiness Check

1. $14y^2 + 2x - 23$ is called an <u>expression</u> while $14y^2$, $2x$, and -23 are each called a <u>term</u>.

2. To multiply $3(-7x + 1)$, we use the <u>distributive</u> property.

3. To simplify an expression like $y + 7y$, we <u>combine like terms</u>.

4. By the <u>commutative</u> properties, the *order* of adding or multiplying two numbers can be changed without changing their sum or product.

5. The term $5x$ is called a <u>variable</u> term while the term 7 is called a <u>constant</u> term.

6. The term z has an understood <u>numerical coefficient</u> of 1.

7. By the <u>associative</u> properties, the grouping of adding or multiplying numbers can be changed without changing their sum or product.

8. The terms $-x$ and $5x$ are <u>like</u> terms and the terms $5x$ and $5y$ are <u>unlike</u> terms.

9. For the term $-3x^2y$, -3 is called the <u>numerical coefficient</u>.

Exercise Set 3.1

1. $3x + 5x = (3 + 5)x = 8x$

3. $2n - 3n = (2 - 3)n = -1n = -n$

5. $4c + c - 7c = (4 + 1 - 7)c = -2c$

7. $4x - 6x + x - 5x = (4 - 6 + 1 - 5)x = -6x$

9. $3a + 2a + 7a - 5 = (3 + 2 + 7)a - 5 = 12a - 5$

11. $6(7x) = (6 \cdot 7)x = 42x$

13. $-3(11y) = (-3 \cdot 11)y = -33y$

15. $12(6a) = (12 \cdot 6)a = 72a$

17. $2(y + 3) = 2 \cdot y + 2 \cdot 3 = 2y + 6$

19. $3(a - 6) = 3 \cdot a - 3 \cdot 6 = 3a - 18$

21. $-4(3x + 7) = -4 \cdot 3x + (-4) \cdot 7 = -12x - 28$

23. $\begin{aligned} 2(x + 4) - 7 &= 2 \cdot x + 2 \cdot 4 - 7 \\ &= 2x + 8 - 7 \\ &= 2x + 1 \end{aligned}$

25. $\begin{aligned} 8 + 5(3c - 1) &= 8 + 5 \cdot 3c - 5 \cdot 1 \\ &= 8 + 15c - 5 \\ &= 15c + 8 - 5 \\ &= 15c + 3 \end{aligned}$

27. $\begin{aligned} -4(6n - 5) + 3n &= -4 \cdot 6n - (-4) \cdot 5 + 3n \\ &= -24n + 20 + 3n \\ &= -24n + 3n + 20 \\ &= -21n + 20 \end{aligned}$

29. $\begin{aligned} 3 + 6(w + 2) + w &= 3 + 6 \cdot w + 6 \cdot 2 + w \\ &= 3 + 6w + 12 + w \\ &= 6w + w + 3 + 12 \\ &= 7w + 15 \end{aligned}$

31. $\begin{aligned} 2(3x + 1) + 5(x - 2) &= 2(3x) + 2(1) + 5(x) - 5(2) \\ &= 6x + 2 + 5x - 10 \\ &= 6x + 5x + 2 - 10 \\ &= 11x - 8 \end{aligned}$

33. $\begin{aligned} -(2y - 6) + 10 &= -1(2y - 6) + 10 \\ &= -1 \cdot 2y - (-1) \cdot (6) + 10 \\ &= -2y + 6 + 10 \\ &= -2y + 16 \end{aligned}$

35. $18y - 20y = (18 - 20)y = -2y$

37. $z - 8z = (1 - 8)z = -7z$

39. $\begin{aligned} 9d - 3c - d &= 9d - d - 3c \\ &= (9 - 1)d - 3c \\ &= 8d - 3c \end{aligned}$

41. $\begin{aligned} 2y - 6 + 4y - 8 &= 2y + 4y - 6 - 8 \\ &= (2 + 4)y - 6 - 8 \\ &= 6y - 14 \end{aligned}$

43. $\begin{aligned} 5q + p - 6q - p &= 5q - 6q + p - p \\ &= (5 - 6)q + (1 - 1)p \\ &= -1q + 0p \\ &= -q \end{aligned}$

45. $\begin{aligned} 2(x + 1) + 20 &= 2 \cdot x + 2 \cdot 1 + 20 \\ &= 2x + 2 + 20 \\ &= 2x + 22 \end{aligned}$

47. $\begin{aligned} 5(x - 7) - 8x &= 5 \cdot x - 5 \cdot 7 - 8x \\ &= 5x - 35 - 8x \\ &= 5x - 8x - 35 \\ &= -3x - 35 \end{aligned}$

49. $\begin{aligned} -5(z + 3) + 2z &= -5 \cdot z + (-5) \cdot 3 + 2z \\ &= -5z - 15 + 2z \\ &= -5z + 2z - 15 \\ &= -3z - 15 \end{aligned}$

51. $\begin{aligned} 8 - x + 4x - 2 - 9x &= -x + 4x - 9x + 8 - 2 \\ &= (-1 + 4 - 9)x + 8 - 2 \\ &= -6x + 6 \end{aligned}$

53. $\begin{aligned} -7(x + 5) &+ 5(2x + 1) \\ &= -7 \cdot x + (-7) \cdot 5 + 5 \cdot 2x + 5 \cdot 1 \\ &= -7x - 35 + 10x + 5 \\ &= -7x + 10x - 35 + 5 \\ &= 3x - 30 \end{aligned}$

55. $\begin{aligned} 3r - 5r + 8 + r &= 3r - 5r + r + 8 \\ &= (3 - 5 + 1)r + 8 \\ &= -1r + 8 \\ &= -r + 8 \end{aligned}$

57. $\begin{aligned} -3(n - 1) - 4n &= -3 \cdot n - (-3) \cdot 1 - 4n \\ &= -3n + 3 - 4n \\ &= -3n - 4n + 3 \\ &= -7n + 3 \end{aligned}$

59. $\begin{aligned} 4(z - 3) + 5z - 2 &= 4 \cdot z - 4 \cdot 3 + 5z - 2 \\ &= 4z - 12 + 5z - 2 \\ &= 4z + 5z - 12 - 2 \\ &= 9z - 14 \end{aligned}$

61. $\begin{aligned} 6(2x - 1) - 12x &= 6 \cdot 2x - 6 \cdot 1 - 12x \\ &= 12x - 6 - 12x \\ &= 12x - 12x - 6 \\ &= -6 \end{aligned}$

63. $-(4x-5)+5 = -1(4x-5)+5$
$\qquad = -1 \cdot 4x - (-1)(5) + 5$
$\qquad = -4x + 5 + 5$
$\qquad = -4x + 10$

65. $-(4x-10) + 2(3x+5)$
$\quad = -1(4x-10) + 2(3x+5)$
$\quad = -1 \cdot 4x - (-1) \cdot 10 + 2 \cdot 3x + 2 \cdot 5$
$\quad = -4x + 10 + 6x + 10$
$\quad = -4x + 6x + 10 + 10$
$\quad = 2x + 20$

67. $3a + 4(a+3) = 3a + 4 \cdot a + 4 \cdot 3$
$\qquad = 3a + 4a + 12$
$\qquad = 7a + 12$

69. $5y - 2(y-1) + 3 = 5y + (-2)(y) - (-2)(1) + 3$
$\qquad = 5y - 2y + 2 + 3$
$\qquad = 3y + 5$

71. $3y + 4y + 2y + 6 + 5y + 16$
$\quad = 3y + 4y + 2y + 5y + 6 + 16$
$\quad = (3 + 4 + 2 + 5)y + 6 + 16$
$\quad = 14y + 22$
The perimeter is $(14y + 22)$ meters.

73. $2a + 2a + 6 + 5a + 6 + 2a$
$\quad = 2a + 2a + 5a + 2a + 6 + 6$
$\quad = (2 + 2 + 5 + 2)a + 6 + 6$
$\quad = 11a + 12$
The perimeter is $(11a + 12)$ feet.

75. $5(-5x + 11) = 5 \cdot (-5x) + 5 \cdot 11 = -25x + 55$
The perimeter is $(-25x + 55)$ inches.

77. Area $= (\text{length}) \cdot (\text{width})$
$\qquad = (4y) \cdot (9)$
$\qquad = (4 \cdot 9)y$
$\qquad = 36y$
The area is $36y$ square inches.

79. Area $= (\text{length}) \cdot (\text{width})$
$\qquad = (x-2) \cdot (32)$
$\qquad = x \cdot 32 - 2 \cdot 32$
$\qquad = 32x - 64$
The area is $(32x - 64)$ square kilometers.

81. Area $= (\text{length}) \cdot (\text{width})$
$\qquad = (3y+1) \cdot (20)$
$\qquad = 3y \cdot 20 + 1 \cdot 20$
$\qquad = (3 \cdot 20)y + 20$
$\qquad = 60y + 20$
The area is $(60y + 20)$ square miles.

83. Area $= (\text{length}) \cdot (\text{width}) = 94 \cdot 50 = 4700$
The area is 4700 square feet.

85. Perimeter $= 2 \cdot (\text{length}) + 2 \cdot (\text{width})$
$\qquad = 2 \cdot (18) + 2 \cdot (14)$
$\qquad = 36 + 28$
$\qquad = 64$
The perimeter is 64 feet.

87. $5 + x + 2x + 1 = x + 2x + 5 + 1$
$\qquad = (1 + 2)x + 5 + 1$
$\qquad = 3x + 6$
The perimeter is $(3x + 6)$ feet.

89. $-13 + 10 = -3$

91. $-4 - (-12) = -4 + 12 = 8$

93. $-4 + 4 = 0$

95. $5(3x - 2) = 5 \cdot 3x - 5 \cdot 2 = 15x - 10$
The expressions are not equivalent.

97. $7x - (x+2) = 7x + (-1) \cdot (x+2)$
$\qquad = 7x + (-1) \cdot x + (-1) \cdot 2$
$\qquad = 7x - x - 2$
The expressions are equivalent.

99. Since multiplication is distributed over subtraction in $6(2x - 3) = 12x - 18$, this is the distributive property.

101. The order of the terms is not changed, but the grouping is. This is the associative property of addition.

103. Add the areas of each rectangle.
$7(2x+1) + 3(2x+3) = 7 \cdot 2x + 7 \cdot 1 + 3 \cdot 2x + 3 \cdot 3$
$\qquad = 14x + 7 + 6x + 9$
$\qquad = 14x + 6x + 7 + 9$
$\qquad = 20x + 16$
The total area is $(20x + 16)$ square miles.

105. $9684q - 686 - 4860q + 12{,}960$
$= 9684q - 4860q - 686 + 12{,}960$
$= 4824q + 12{,}274$

107. answers may vary

109. answers may vary

Section 3.2

Practice Problems

1. $x + 6 = 1 - 3$
$x + 6 = -2$
$x + 6 - 6 = -2 - 6$
$x = -8$

2. $10 = 2m - 4m$
$10 = -2m$
$\dfrac{10}{-2} = \dfrac{-2m}{-2}$
$-5 = m$

3. $-8 + 6 = \dfrac{a}{3}$
$-2 = \dfrac{a}{3}$
$3 \cdot (-2) = 3 \cdot \dfrac{a}{3}$
$3 \cdot (-2) = \dfrac{3}{3} \cdot a$
$-6 = a$

4. $-6y - 1 + 7y = 17 + 2$
$-6y + 7y - 1 = 17 + 2$
$y - 1 = 19$
$y - 1 + 1 = 19 + 1$
$y = 20$

5. $-4 - 10 = 4y - 5y$
$-14 = -y$
$\dfrac{-14}{-1} = \dfrac{-1y}{-1}$
$14 = y$

6. $13x = 4(3x - 1)$
$13x = 4 \cdot 3x - 4 \cdot 1$
$13x = 12x - 4$
$13x - 12x = 12x - 4 - 12x$
$x = -4$

7. $5y + 2 = 17$
$5y + 2 - 2 = 17 - 2$
$5y = 15$
$\dfrac{5y}{5} = \dfrac{15}{5}$
$y = 3$

8. $-4(x + 2) - 60 = 2 - 10$
$-4x - 8 - 60 = 2 - 10$
$-4x - 68 = -8$
$-4x - 68 + 68 = -8 + 68$
$-4x = 60$
$\dfrac{-4x}{-4} = \dfrac{60}{-4}$
$x = -15$

9. a. The sum of -3 and a number is $-3 + x$.

   b. -5 decreased by a number is $-5 - x$.

   c. Three times a number is $3x$.

   d. A number subtracted from 83 is $83 - x$.

   e. The quotient of a number and -4 is $\dfrac{x}{-4}$ or $-\dfrac{x}{4}$.

10. a. The product of 5 and a number, decreased by 25, is $5x - 25$.

   b. Twice the sum of a number and 3 is $2(x + 3)$.

   c. The quotient of 39 and twice a number is $39 \div (2x)$ or $\dfrac{39}{2x}$.

Vocabulary and Readiness Check

1. The equations $-3x = 51$ and $\dfrac{-3x}{-3} = \dfrac{51}{-3}$ are called <u>equivalent</u> equations.

2. The difference between an equation and an expression is that an <u>equation</u> contains an equal sign, while an <u>expression</u> does not.

3. The process of writing $-3x + 10x$ as $7x$ is called <u>simplifying</u> the expression.

4. For the equation $-5x - 1 = -21$, the process of finding that 4 is the solution is called <u>solving</u> the equation.

5. By the <u>addition</u> property of equality, $x = -2$ and $x + 7 = -2 + 7$ are equivalent equations.

6. By the <u>multiplication</u> property of equality, $y = 8$ and $3 \cdot y = 3 \cdot 8$ are equivalent equations.

Exercise Set 3.2

1. $x - 3 = -1 + 4$
$x - 3 = 3$
$x - 3 + 3 = 3 + 3$
$x = 6$

3. $-7 + 10 = m - 5$
$3 = m - 5$
$3 + 5 = m - 5 + 5$
$8 = m$

5. $2w - 12w = 40$
$-10w = 40$
$\dfrac{-10w}{-10} = \dfrac{40}{-10}$
$w = -4$

7. $24 = t + 3t$
$24 = 4t$
$\dfrac{24}{4} = \dfrac{4t}{4}$
$6 = t$

9. $2z = 12 - 14$
$2z = -2$
$\dfrac{2z}{2} = \dfrac{-2}{2}$
$z = -1$

11. $4 - 10 = \dfrac{z}{-3}$
$-6 = \dfrac{z}{-3}$
$-3 \cdot (-6) = -3 \cdot \dfrac{z}{-3}$
$18 = z$

13. $-3x - 3x = 50 - 2$
$-6x = 48$
$\dfrac{-6x}{-6} = \dfrac{48}{-6}$
$x = -8$

15. $\dfrac{x}{5} = -26 + 16$
$\dfrac{x}{5} = -10$
$5 \cdot \dfrac{x}{5} = 5 \cdot (-10)$
$x = -50$

17. $7x + 7 - 6x = 10$
$7x - 6x + 7 = 10$
$x + 7 = 10$
$x + 7 - 7 = 10 - 7$
$x = 3$

19. $-8 - 9 = 3x + 5 - 2x$
$-17 = x + 5$
$-17 - 5 = x + 5 - 5$
$-22 = x$

21. $2(5x - 3) = 11x$
$2 \cdot 5x - 2 \cdot 3 = 11x$
$10x - 6 = 11x$
$10x - 10x - 6 = 11x - 10x$
$-6 = x$

23. $3y = 2(y + 12)$
$3y = 2 \cdot y + 2 \cdot 12$
$3y = 2y + 24$
$3y - 2y = 2y - 2y + 24$
$y = 24$

25. $21y = 5(4y - 6)$
$21y = 5 \cdot 4y - 5 \cdot 6$
$21y = 20y - 30$
$21y - 20y = 20y - 20y - 30$
$y = -30$

27. $-3(-4 - 2z) = 7z$
$-3 \cdot (-4) - (-3)(2z) = 7z$
$12 + 6z = 7z$
$12 + 6z - 6z = 7z - 6z$
$12 = z$

29. $2x - 8 = 0$
$2x - 8 + 8 = 0 + 8$
$2x = 8$
$\dfrac{2x}{2} = \dfrac{8}{2}$
$x = 4$

31.
$$7y + 3 = 24$$
$$7y + 3 - 3 = 24 - 3$$
$$7y = 21$$
$$\frac{7y}{7} = \frac{21}{7}$$
$$y = 3$$

33.
$$-7 = 2x - 1$$
$$-7 + 1 = 2x - 1 + 1$$
$$-6 = 2x$$
$$\frac{-6}{2} = \frac{2x}{2}$$
$$-3 = x$$

35.
$$6(6 - 4y) = 12y$$
$$6 \cdot 6 - 6 \cdot 4y = 12y$$
$$36 - 24y = 12y$$
$$36 - 24y + 24y = 12y + 24y$$
$$36 = 36y$$
$$\frac{36}{36} = \frac{36y}{36}$$
$$1 = y$$

37.
$$11(x - 6) = -4 - 7$$
$$11 \cdot x - 11 \cdot 6 = -11$$
$$11x - 66 = -11$$
$$11x - 66 + 66 = -11 + 66$$
$$11x = 55$$
$$\frac{11x}{11} = \frac{55}{11}$$
$$x = 5$$

39.
$$-3(x + 1) - 10 = 12 + 8$$
$$-3 \cdot x - 3 \cdot 1 - 10 = 20$$
$$-3x - 3 - 10 = 20$$
$$-3x - 13 = 20$$
$$-3x - 13 + 13 = 20 + 13$$
$$-3x = 33$$
$$\frac{-3x}{-3} = \frac{33}{-3}$$
$$x = -11$$

41.
$$y - 20 = 6y$$
$$y - y - 20 = 6y - y$$
$$-20 = 5y$$
$$\frac{-20}{5} = \frac{5y}{5}$$
$$-4 = y$$

43.
$$22 - 42 = 4(x - 1) - 4$$
$$-20 = 4 \cdot x - 4 \cdot 1 - 4$$
$$-20 = 4x - 4 - 4$$
$$-20 = 4x - 8$$
$$-20 + 8 = 4x - 8 + 8$$
$$-12 = 4x$$
$$\frac{-12}{4} = \frac{4x}{4}$$
$$-3 = x$$

45.
$$-2 - 3 = -4 + x$$
$$-5 = -4 + x$$
$$-5 + 4 = -4 + 4 + x$$
$$-1 = x$$

47.
$$y + 1 = -3 + 4$$
$$y + 1 = 1$$
$$y + 1 - 1 = 1 - 1$$
$$y = 0$$

49.
$$3w - 12w = -27$$
$$-9w = -27$$
$$\frac{-9w}{-9} = \frac{-27}{-9}$$
$$w = 3$$

51.
$$-4x = 20 - (-4)$$
$$-4x = 20 + 4$$
$$-4x = 24$$
$$\frac{-4x}{-4} = \frac{24}{-4}$$
$$x = -6$$

53.
$$18 - 11 = \frac{x}{-5}$$
$$7 = \frac{x}{-5}$$
$$-5 \cdot 7 = -5 \cdot \frac{x}{-5}$$
$$-5 \cdot 7 = \frac{-5}{-5} \cdot x$$
$$-35 = x$$

55.
$$9x - 12 = 78$$
$$9x - 12 + 12 = 78 + 12$$
$$9x = 90$$
$$\frac{9x}{9} = \frac{90}{9}$$
$$x = 10$$

57. $10 = 7t - 12t$

$10 = -5t$

$\dfrac{10}{-5} = \dfrac{-5t}{-5}$

$-2 = t$

59. $5 - 5 = 3x + 2x$

$0 = 5x$

$\dfrac{0}{5} = \dfrac{5x}{5}$

$0 = x$

61. $50y = 7(7y + 4)$

$50y = 7 \cdot 7y + 7 \cdot 4$

$50y = 49y + 28$

$50y - 49y = 49y - 49y + 28$

$y = 28$

63. $8x = 2(6x + 10)$

$8x = 2 \cdot 6x + 2 \cdot 10$

$8x = 12x + 20$

$8x - 12x = 12x - 12x + 20$

$-4x = 20$

$\dfrac{-4x}{-4} = \dfrac{20}{-4}$

$x = -5$

65. $7x + 14 - 6x = -4 - 10$

$7x - 6x + 14 = -14$

$x + 14 = -14$

$x + 14 - 14 = -14 - 14$

$x = -28$

67. $\dfrac{x}{-4} = -1 - (-8)$

$\dfrac{x}{-4} = -1 + 8$

$\dfrac{x}{-4} = 7$

$-4 \cdot \dfrac{x}{-4} = -4 \cdot 7$

$x = -28$

69. $23x + 8 - 25x = 7 - 9$

$23x - 25x + 8 = -2$

$-2x + 8 = -2$

$-2x + 8 - 8 = -2 - 8$

$-2x = -10$

$\dfrac{-2x}{-2} = \dfrac{-10}{-2}$

$x = 5$

71. $-3(x + 9) - 41 = 4 - 60$

$-3 \cdot x - 3 \cdot 9 - 41 = 4 - 60$

$-3x - 27 - 41 = -56$

$-3x - 68 = -56$

$-3x - 68 + 68 = -56 + 68$

$-3x = 12$

$\dfrac{-3x}{-3} = \dfrac{12}{-3}$

$x = -4$

73. The sum of -7 and a number is $-7 + x$.

75. Eleven subtracted from a number is $x - 11$.

77. The product of -13 and a number is $-13x$.

79. A number divided by -12 is $\dfrac{x}{-12}$ or $-\dfrac{x}{12}$.

81. The product of -11 and a number, increased by 5 is $-11x + 5$.

83. Negative ten decreased by 7 times a number is $-10 - 7x$.

85. Seven added to the product of 4 and a number is $4x + 7$.

87. Twice a number, decreased by 17 is $2x - 17$.

89. The product of -6 and the sum of a number and 15 is $-6(x + 15)$.

91. The quotient of 45 and the product of a number and -5 is $\dfrac{45}{-5x}$ or $-\dfrac{45}{5x}$.

93. The quotient of seventeen and a number, increased by -15 is $\dfrac{17}{x} + (-15)$ or $\dfrac{17}{x} - 15$.

95. The longest bar corresponds to the year in which the number of trumpeter swans was the greatest. The year is 2005.

97. From the length of the bar, there were approximately 35,000 trumpeter swans in 2005.

99. answers may vary

101. no; answers may vary

103. answers may vary

105.

$$\frac{y}{72} = -86 - (-1029)$$

$$\frac{y}{72} = -86 + 1029$$

$$\frac{y}{72} = 943$$

$$72 \cdot \frac{y}{72} = 72 \cdot 943$$

$$\frac{72}{72} \cdot y = 72 \cdot 943$$

$$y = 67{,}896$$

107.

$$\frac{x}{-2} = 5^2 - |-10| - (-9)$$

$$\frac{x}{-2} = 25 - |-10| - (-9)$$

$$\frac{x}{-2} = 25 - 10 - (-9)$$

$$\frac{x}{-2} = 25 - 10 + 9$$

$$\frac{x}{-2} = 24$$

$$-2 \cdot \frac{x}{-2} = -2 \cdot 24$$

$$\frac{-2}{-2} \cdot x = -2 \cdot 24$$

$$x = -48$$

109.

$$|-13| + 3^2 = 100y - |-20| - 99y$$

$$13 + 3^2 = 100y - 20 - 99y$$

$$13 + 9 = 100y - 99y - 20$$

$$22 = y - 20$$

$$22 + 20 = y - 20 + 20$$

$$42 = y$$

Integrated Review

1. $7x - 5y + 14$ is an expression because it does not contain an equal sign.

2. $7x = 35 + 14$ is an equation because it contains an equal sign.

3. $3(x - 2) = 5(x + 1) - 17$ is an equation because it contains an equal sign.

4. $-9(2x + 1) - 4(x - 2) + 14$ is an expression because it does not contain an equal sign.

5. To <u>simplify</u> an expression, we combine any like terms.

6. To <u>solve</u> an equation, we use properties of equality to find any value of the variable that makes the equation a true statement.

7. $7x + x = (7 + 1)x = 8x$

8. $6y - 10y = (6 - 10)y = -4y$

9. $2a + 5a - 9a - 2 = (2 + 5 - 9)a - 2 = -2a - 2$

10. $6a - 12 - a - 14 = 6a - a - 12 - 14$
$$= (6 - 1)a - 12 - 14$$
$$= 5a - 26$$

11. $-2(4x + 7) = -2 \cdot 4x + (-2) \cdot 7 = -8x - 14$

12. $-3(2x - 10) = -3(2x) - (-3)(10) = -6x + 30$

13. $5(y + 2) - 20 = 5 \cdot y + 5 \cdot 2 - 20$
$$= 5y + 10 - 20$$
$$= 5y - 10$$

14. $12x + 3(x - 6) - 13 = 12x + 3 \cdot x - 3 \cdot 6 - 13$
$$= 12x + 3x - 18 - 13$$
$$= (12 + 3)x - 18 - 13$$
$$= 15x - 31$$

15. Area = (length) $\cdot$ (width)
$$= 3(4x - 2)$$
$$= 3 \cdot 4x - 3 \cdot 2$$
$$= 12x - 6$$
The area is $(12x - 6)$ square meters.

16. Perimeter $= x + x + 2 + 7 = 2x + 9$
The perimeter is $(2x + 9)$ feet.

17.

$$12 = 11x - 14x$$

$$12 = -3x$$

$$\frac{12}{-3} = \frac{-3x}{-3}$$

$$-4 = x$$

Check: $12 = 11x - 14x$
$$12 \overset{?}{=} 11(-4) - 14(-4)$$
$$12 \overset{?}{=} -44 + 56$$
$$12 = 12 \quad \text{True}$$
The solution is -4.

18. $8y + 7y = -45$

$15y = -45$

$\dfrac{15y}{15} = \dfrac{-45}{15}$

$y = -3$

Check: $8y + 7y = -45$

$8(-3) + 7(-3) \overset{?}{=} -45$

$-24 + (-21) \overset{?}{=} -45$

$-45 = -45$ True

The solution is -3.

19. $x - 12 = -45 + 23$

$x - 12 = -22$

$x - 12 + 12 = -22 + 12$

$x = -10$

Check: $x - 12 = -45 + 23$

$-10 - 12 \overset{?}{=} -45 + 23$

$-22 = -22$ True

The solution is -10.

20. $6 - (-5) = x + 5$

$6 + 5 = x + 5$

$11 = x + 5$

$11 - 5 = x + 5 - 5$

$6 = x$

Check: $6 - (-5) = x + 5$

$6 - (-5) \overset{?}{=} 6 + 5$

$6 + 5 \overset{?}{=} 6 + 5$

$11 = 11$ True

The solution is 6.

21. $\dfrac{x}{3} = -14 + 9$

$\dfrac{x}{3} = -5$

$3 \cdot \dfrac{x}{3} = 3(-5)$

$x = -15$

Check: $\dfrac{x}{3} = -14 + 9$

$\dfrac{-15}{3} \overset{?}{=} -14 + 9$

$-5 = -5$ True

The solution is -15.

22. $\dfrac{z}{4} = -23 - 7$

$\dfrac{z}{4} = -30$

$4 \cdot \dfrac{z}{4} = 4 \cdot (-30)$

$z = -120$

Check: $\dfrac{z}{4} = -23 - 7$

$\dfrac{-120}{4} \overset{?}{=} -23 - 7$

$-30 = -30$ True

The solution is -120.

23. $-6 + 2 = 4x + 1 - 3x$

$-4 = x + 1$

$-4 - 1 = x + 1 - 1$

$-5 = x$

Check: $-6 + 2 = 4x + 1 - 3x$

$-6 + 2 \overset{?}{=} 4(-5) + 1 - 3(-5)$

$-4 \overset{?}{=} -20 + 1 + 15$

$-4 = -4$ True

The solution is -5.

24. $5 - 8 = 5x + 10 - 4x$

$-3 = x + 10$

$-3 - 10 = x + 10 - 10$

$-13 = x$

Check: $5 - 8 = 5x + 10 - 4x$

$5 - 8 \overset{?}{=} 5(-13) + 10 - 4(-13)$

$-3 \overset{?}{=} -65 + 10 + 52$

$-3 = -3$ True

The solution is -13.

25. $6(3x - 4) = 19x$

$6 \cdot 3x - 6 \cdot 4 = 19x$

$18x - 24 = 19x$

$18x - 18x - 24 = 19x - 18x$

$-24 = x$

Check: $6(3x - 4) = 19x$

$6[3(-24) - 4] \overset{?}{=} 19(-24)$

$6(-72 - 4) \overset{?}{=} -456$

$6(-76) \overset{?}{=} -456$

$-456 = -456$ True

The solution is -24.

26.
$$25x = 6(4x - 9)$$
$$25x = 6 \cdot 4x - 6 \cdot 9$$
$$25x = 24x - 54$$
$$25x - 24x = 24x - 24x - 54$$
$$x = -54$$

Check:
$$25x = 6(4x - 9)$$
$$25(-54) \overset{?}{=} 6[4(-54) - 9]$$
$$-1350 \overset{?}{=} 6(-216 - 9)$$
$$-1350 \overset{?}{=} 6(-225)$$
$$-1350 = -1350 \quad \text{True}$$

The solution is -54.

27.
$$-36x - 10 + 37x = -12 - (-14)$$
$$x - 10 = -12 + 14$$
$$x - 10 = 2$$
$$x - 10 + 10 = 2 + 10$$
$$x = 12$$

Check:
$$-36x - 10 + 37x = -12 - (-14)$$
$$-36(12) - 10 + 37(12) \overset{?}{=} -12 - (-14)$$
$$-432 - 10 + 444 \overset{?}{=} -12 + 14$$
$$2 = 2 \quad \text{True}$$

The solution is 12.

28.
$$-8 + (-14) = -80y + 20 + 81y$$
$$-22 = y + 20$$
$$-22 - 20 = y + 20 - 20$$
$$-42 = y$$

Check: $-8 + (-14) = -80y + 20 + 81y$
$$-8 + (-14) \overset{?}{=} -80(-42) + 20 + 81(-42)$$
$$-22 \overset{?}{=} 3360 + 20 - 3402$$
$$-22 = -22 \quad \text{True}$$

The solution is -42.

29.
$$3x - 16 = -10$$
$$3x - 16 + 16 = -10 + 16$$
$$3x = 6$$
$$\frac{3x}{3} = \frac{6}{3}$$
$$x = 2$$

Check:
$$3x - 16 = -10$$
$$3(2) - 16 \overset{?}{=} -10$$
$$6 - 16 \overset{?}{=} -10$$
$$-10 = -10 \quad \text{True}$$

The solution is 2.

30.
$$4x - 21 = -13$$
$$4x - 21 + 21 = -13 + 21$$
$$4x = 8$$
$$\frac{4x}{4} = \frac{8}{4}$$
$$x = 2$$

Check: $4x - 21 = -13$
$$4 \cdot 2 - 21 \overset{?}{=} -13$$
$$8 - 21 \overset{?}{=} -13$$
$$-13 = -13 \quad \text{True}$$

The solution is 2.

31.
$$-8z - 2z = 26 - (-4)$$
$$-10z = 26 + 4$$
$$-10z = 30$$
$$\frac{-10z}{-10} = \frac{30}{-10}$$
$$z = -3$$

Check: $-8z - 2z = 26 - (-4)$
$$-8(-3) - 2(-3) \overset{?}{=} 26 - (-4)$$
$$24 + 6 \overset{?}{=} 26 + 4$$
$$30 = 30 \quad \text{True}$$

The solution is -3.

32.
$$-12 + (-13) = 5x - 10x$$
$$-25 = -5x$$
$$\frac{-25}{-5} = \frac{-5x}{-5}$$
$$5 = x$$

Check: $-12 + (-13) = 5x - 10x$
$$-12 + (-13) \overset{?}{=} 5(5) - 10(5)$$
$$-25 \overset{?}{=} 25 - 50$$
$$-25 = -25 \quad \text{True}$$

The solution is 5.

33.
$$-4(x + 8) - 11 = 3 - 26$$
$$-4 \cdot x + (-4) \cdot 8 - 11 = 3 - 26$$
$$-4x - 32 - 11 = -23$$
$$-4x - 43 = -23$$
$$-4x - 43 + 43 = -23 + 43$$
$$-4x = 20$$
$$\frac{-4x}{-4} = \frac{20}{-4}$$
$$x = -5$$

Check: $-4(x + 8) - 11 = 3 - 26$
$$-4(-5 + 8) - 11 \overset{?}{=} 3 - 26$$
$$-4(3) - 11 \overset{?}{=} -23$$
$$-12 - 11 \overset{?}{=} -23$$
$$-23 = -23 \quad \text{True}$$

The solution is -5.

34.
$$-6(x-2)+10 = -4-10$$
$$-6 \cdot x - (-6)(2)+10 = -4-10$$
$$-6x+12+10 = -14$$
$$-6x+22 = -14$$
$$-6x+22-22 = -14-22$$
$$-6x = -36$$
$$\frac{-6x}{-6} = \frac{-36}{-6}$$
$$x = 6$$

Check: $-6(x-2)+10 = -4-10$
$$-6(6-2)+10 \stackrel{?}{=} -4-10$$
$$-6(4)+10 \stackrel{?}{=} -14$$
$$-24+10 \stackrel{?}{=} -14$$
$$-14 = -14 \quad \text{True}$$

The solution is 6.

35. The difference of a number and 10 is $x - 10$.

36. The sum of -20 and a number is $-20 + x$.

37. The product of 10 and a number is $10x$.

38. The quotient of 10 and a number is $\dfrac{10}{x}$.

39. Five added to the product of -2 and a number is $-2x + 5$.

40. The product of -4 and the difference of a number and 1 is $-4(x - 1)$.

Section 3.3

Practice Problems

1.
$$7x+12 = 3x-4$$
$$7x+12-12 = 3x-4-12$$
$$7x = 3x-16$$
$$7x-3x = 3x-16-3x$$
$$4x = -16$$
$$\frac{4x}{4} = \frac{-16}{4}$$
$$x = -4$$

2.
$$40-5y+5 = -2y-10-4y$$
$$45-5y = -6y-10$$
$$45-5y-45 = -6y-10-45$$
$$-5y = -6y-55$$
$$-5y+6y = -6y-55+6y$$
$$y = -55$$

3.
$$6(a-5) = 4a+4$$
$$6a-30 = 4a+4$$
$$6a-30-4a = 4a+4-4a$$
$$2a-30 = 4$$
$$2a-30+30 = 4+30$$
$$2a = 34$$
$$\frac{2a}{2} = \frac{34}{2}$$
$$a = 17$$

4.
$$4(x+3)+1 = 13$$
$$4x+12+1 = 13$$
$$4x+13 = 13$$
$$4x+13-13 = 13-13$$
$$4x = 0$$
$$\frac{4x}{4} = \frac{0}{4}$$
$$x = 0$$

5. a. The difference of 110 and 80 is 30 translates to $110 - 80 = 30$.

b. The product of 3 and the sum of -9 and 11 amounts to 6 translates to $3(-9 + 11) = 6$.

c. The quotient of 24 and -6 yields -4 translates to $\dfrac{24}{-6} = -4$.

Calculator Explorations

1. Replace x with 12.
$76(12 - 25) = -988$
Yes

2. Replace x with 35.
$-47 \cdot 35 + 862 = -783$
Yes

3. Replace x with -170.
$-170 + 562 = 392$
$3 \cdot (-170) + 900 = 390$
No

4. Replace x with -18.
$55(-18 + 10) = -440$
$75 \cdot (-18) + 910 = -440$
Yes

5. Replace x with -21.
$29 \cdot (-21) - 1034 = -1643$
$61 \cdot (-21) - 362 = -1643$
Yes

6. Replace x with 25.

$-38 \cdot 25 + 205 = -745$

$25 \cdot 25 + 120 = 745$

No

Vocabulary and Readiness Check

1. An example of an expression is $\underline{3x - 9 + x - 16}$ while an example of an equation is $\underline{5(2x + 6) - 1 = 39}$.

2. To solve $\dfrac{x}{-7} = -10$, we use the <u>multiplication</u> property of equality.

3. To solve $x - 7 = -10$, we use the <u>addition</u> property of equality.

4. To solve $9x - 6x = 10 + 6$, first <u>combine like terms</u>.

5. To solve $5(x - 1) = 25$, first use the <u>distributive</u> property.

6. To solve $4x + 3 = 19$, first use the <u>addition</u> property of equality.

Exercise Set 3.3

1.
$$3x - 7 = 4x + 5$$
$$3x - 3x - 7 = 4x - 3x + 5$$
$$-7 = x + 5$$
$$-7 - 5 = x + 5 - 5$$
$$-12 = x$$

3.
$$10x + 15 = 6x + 3$$
$$10x + 15 - 15 = 6x + 3 - 15$$
$$10x = 6x - 12$$
$$10x - 6x = 6x - 6x - 12$$
$$4x = -12$$
$$\frac{4x}{4} = \frac{-12}{4}$$
$$x = -3$$

5.
$$19 - 3x = 14 + 2x$$
$$19 - 3x + 3x = 14 + 2x + 3x$$
$$19 = 14 + 5x$$
$$19 - 14 = 14 - 14 + 5x$$
$$5 = 5x$$
$$\frac{5}{5} = \frac{5x}{5}$$
$$1 = x$$

7.
$$-14x - 20 = -12x + 70$$
$$-14x + 12x - 20 = -12x + 12x + 70$$
$$-2x - 20 = 70$$
$$-2x - 20 + 20 = 70 + 20$$
$$-2x = 90$$
$$\frac{-2x}{-2} = \frac{90}{-2}$$
$$x = -45$$

9.
$$x + 20 + 2x = -10 - 2x - 15$$
$$x + 2x + 20 = -10 - 15 - 2x$$
$$3x + 20 = -25 - 2x$$
$$3x + 2x + 20 = -25 - 2x + 2x$$
$$5x + 20 = -25$$
$$5x + 20 - 20 = -25 - 20$$
$$5x = -45$$
$$\frac{5x}{5} = \frac{-45}{5}$$
$$x = -9$$

11.
$$40 + 4y - 16 = 13y - 12 - 3y$$
$$40 - 16 + 4y = 13y - 3y - 12$$
$$24 + 4y = 10y - 12$$
$$24 + 4y - 4y = 10y - 4y - 12$$
$$24 = 6y - 12$$
$$24 + 12 = 6y - 12 + 12$$
$$36 = 6y$$
$$\frac{36}{6} = \frac{6y}{6}$$
$$6 = y$$

13.
$$35 - 17 = 3(x - 2)$$
$$18 = 3x - 6$$
$$18 + 6 = 3x - 6 + 6$$
$$24 = 3x$$
$$\frac{24}{3} = \frac{3x}{3}$$
$$8 = x$$

15.
$$3(x - 1) - 12 = 0$$
$$3x - 3 - 12 = 0$$
$$3x - 15 = 0$$
$$3x - 15 + 15 = 0 + 15$$
$$3x = 15$$
$$\frac{3x}{3} = \frac{15}{3}$$
$$x = 5$$

17. $2(y-3) = y-6$
$2y-6 = y-6$
$2y-y-6 = y-y-6$
$y-6 = -6$
$y-6+6 = -6+6$
$y = 0$

19. $-2(y+4) = 2$
$-2y-8 = 2$
$-2y-8+8 = 2+8$
$-2y = 10$
$\dfrac{-2y}{-2} = \dfrac{10}{-2}$
$y = -5$

21. $2t-1 = 3(t+7)$
$2t-1 = 3t+21$
$2t-2t-1 = 3t-2t+21$
$-1 = t+21$
$-1-21 = t+21-21$
$-22 = t$

23. $3(5c+1)-12 = 13c+3$
$15c+3-12 = 13c+3$
$15c-9 = 13c+3$
$15c-13c-9 = 13c-13c+3$
$2c-9 = 3$
$2c-9+9 = 3+9$
$2c = 12$
$\dfrac{2c}{2} = \dfrac{12}{2}$
$c = 6$

25. $-4x = 44$
$\dfrac{-4x}{-4} = \dfrac{44}{-4}$
$x = -11$

27. $x+9 = 2$
$x+9-9 = 2-9$
$x = -7$

29. $8-b = 13$
$8-8-b = 13-8$
$-b = 5$
$\dfrac{-b}{-1} = \dfrac{5}{-1}$
$b = -5$

31. $-20-(-50) = \dfrac{x}{9}$
$-20+50 = \dfrac{x}{9}$
$30 = \dfrac{x}{9}$
$9 \cdot 30 = 9 \cdot \dfrac{x}{9}$
$270 = x$

33. $3r+4 = 19$
$3r+4-4 = 19-4$
$3r = 15$
$\dfrac{3r}{3} = \dfrac{15}{3}$
$r = 5$

35. $-7c+1 = -20$
$-7c+1-1 = -20-1$
$-7c = -21$
$\dfrac{-7c}{-7} = \dfrac{-21}{-7}$
$c = 3$

37. $8y-13y = -20-25$
$-5y = -45$
$\dfrac{-5y}{-5} = \dfrac{-45}{-5}$
$y = 9$

39. $6(7x-1) = 43x$
$42x-6 = 43x$
$42x-42x-6 = 43x-42x$
$-6 = x$

41. $-4+12 = 16x-3-15x$
$8 = x-3$
$8+3 = x-3+3$
$11 = x$

43. $-10(x+3)+28 = -16-16$
$-10x-30+28 = -32$
$-10x-2 = -32$
$-10x-2+2 = -32+2$
$-10x = -30$
$\dfrac{-10x}{-10} = \dfrac{-30}{-10}$
$x = 3$

45.
$$4x + 3 = 2x + 11$$
$$4x - 2x + 3 = 2x - 2x + 11$$
$$2x + 3 = 11$$
$$2x + 3 - 3 = 11 - 3$$
$$2x = 8$$
$$\frac{2x}{2} = \frac{8}{2}$$
$$x = 4$$

47.
$$-2y - 10 = 5y + 18$$
$$-2y - 10 - 5y = 5y + 18 - 5y$$
$$-7y - 10 = 18$$
$$-7y - 10 + 10 = 18 + 10$$
$$-7y = 28$$
$$\frac{-7y}{-7} = \frac{28}{-7}$$
$$y = -4$$

49.
$$-8n + 1 = -6n - 5$$
$$-8n + 8n + 1 = -6n + 8n - 5$$
$$1 = 2n - 5$$
$$1 + 5 = 2n - 5 + 5$$
$$6 = 2n$$
$$\frac{6}{2} = \frac{2n}{2}$$
$$3 = n$$

51.
$$9 - 3x = 14 + 2x$$
$$9 - 3x - 2x = 14 + 2x - 2x$$
$$9 - 5x = 14$$
$$9 - 5x - 9 = 14 - 9$$
$$-5x = 5$$
$$\frac{-5x}{-5} = \frac{5}{-5}$$
$$x = -1$$

53.
$$9a + 29 + 7 = 0$$
$$9a + 36 = 0$$
$$9a + 36 - 36 = 0 - 36$$
$$9a = -36$$
$$\frac{9a}{9} = \frac{-36}{9}$$
$$a = -4$$

55.
$$7(y - 2) = 4y - 29$$
$$7y - 14 = 4y - 29$$
$$7y - 4y - 14 = 4y - 4y - 29$$
$$3y - 14 = -29$$
$$3y - 14 + 14 = -29 + 14$$
$$3y = -15$$
$$\frac{3y}{3} = \frac{-15}{3}$$
$$y = -5$$

57.
$$12 + 5t = 6(t + 2)$$
$$12 + 5t = 6t + 12$$
$$12 + 5t - 5t = 6t - 5t + 12$$
$$12 = t + 12$$
$$12 - 12 = t + 12 - 12$$
$$0 = t$$

59.
$$3(5c - 1) - 2 = 13c + 3$$
$$15c - 3 - 2 = 13c + 3$$
$$15c - 5 = 13c + 3$$
$$15c - 13c - 5 = 13c - 13c + 3$$
$$2c - 5 = 3$$
$$2c - 5 + 5 = 3 + 5$$
$$2c = 8$$
$$\frac{2c}{2} = \frac{8}{2}$$
$$c = 4$$

61.
$$10 + 5(z - 2) = 4z + 1$$
$$10 + 5z - 10 = 4z + 1$$
$$5z = 4z + 1$$
$$5z - 4z = 4z - 4z + 1$$
$$z = 1$$

63.
$$7(6 + w) = 6(2 + w)$$
$$42 + 7w = 12 + 6w$$
$$42 + 7w - 6w = 12 + 6w - 6w$$
$$42 + w = 12$$
$$42 - 42 + w = 12 - 42$$
$$w = -30$$

65. The sum of −42 and 16 is −26 translates to
$$-42 + 16 = -26.$$

67. The product of −5 and −29 gives 145 translates
to $-5(-29) = 145.$

69. Three times the difference of −14 and 2 amounts
to −48 translates to $3(-14 - 2) = -48.$

71. The quotient of 100 and twice 50 is equal to 1 translates to $\dfrac{100}{2(50)} = 1$.

73. From the height of the bar, approximately 97 million returns are expected to be filed electronically in 2010.

75. Subtract the number of returns in 2006 from the number in 2009.
95 million − 81 million = 14 million
The increase from 2006 to 2009 was approximately 14 million returns.

77. $x^3 - 2xy = 3^3 - 2(3)(-1)$
$\qquad\qquad = 27 - 2(3)(-1)$
$\qquad\qquad = 27 - (-6)$
$\qquad\qquad = 27 + 6$
$\qquad\qquad = 33$

79. $y^5 - 4x^2 = (-1)^5 - 4(3)^2$
$\qquad\qquad = -1 - 4(9)$
$\qquad\qquad = -1 - 36$
$\qquad\qquad = -37$

81. The first step in solving $2x - 5 = -7$ is to add 5 to both sides, which is choice b.

83. The first step in solving $-3x = -12$ is to divide both sides by −3, which is choice a.

85. The error is in the second line.
$2(3x - 5) = 5x - 7$
$6x - 10 = 5x - 7$
$6x - 10 + 10 = 5x - 7 + 10$
$6x = 5x + 3$
$6x - 5x = 5x + 3 - 5x$
$x = 3$

87. $(-8)^2 + 3x = 5x + 4^3$
$64 + 3x = 5x + 64$
$64 + 3x - 3x = 5x - 3x + 64$
$64 = 2x + 64$
$64 - 64 = 2x + 64 - 64$
$0 = 2x$
$\dfrac{0}{2} = \dfrac{2x}{2}$
$0 = x$

89. $2^3(x + 4) = 3^2(x + 4)$
$8(x + 4) = 9(x + 4)$
$8x + 32 = 9x + 36$
$8x - 8x + 32 = 9x - 8x + 36$
$32 = x + 36$
$32 - 36 = x + 36 - 36$
$-4 = x$

91. no; answers may vary

Section 3.4

Practice Problems

1. a. "Four times a number is 20" is $4x = 20$.

   b. "The sum of a number and −5 yields 32" is $x + (-5) = 32$.

   c. "Fifteen subtracted from a number amounts to −23" is $x - 15 = -23$.

   d. "Five times the difference of a number and 7 is equal to −8" is $5(x - 7) = -8$.

   e. "The quotient of triple a number and 5 gives 1" is $\dfrac{3x}{5} = 1$.

2. "The sum of a number and 2 equals 6 added to three times the number" is
$x + 2 = 6 + 3x$
$x - x + 2 = 6 + 3x - x$
$2 = 6 + 2x$
$2 - 6 = 6 - 6 + 2x$
$-4 = 2x$
$\dfrac{-4}{2} = \dfrac{2x}{2}$
$-2 = x$

3. Let x be the distance from Denver to San Francisco. Since the distance from Cincinnati to Denver is 71 miles less than the distance from Denver to San Francisco, the distance from Cincinnati to Denver is $x - 71$. Since the total of the two distances is 2399, the sum of x and $x - 71$ is 2399.

$$x + x - 71 = 2399$$
$$2x - 71 = 2399$$
$$2x - 71 + 71 = 2399 + 71$$
$$2x = 2470$$
$$\frac{2x}{2} = \frac{2470}{2}$$
$$x = 1235$$

The distance from Denver to San Francisco is 1235 miles.

4. Let x be the amount her son receives. Since her husband receives twice as much as her son, her husband receives $2x$. Since the total estate is $57,000, the sum of x and $2x$ is 57,000.
$$x + 2x = 57,000$$
$$3x = 57,000$$
$$\frac{3x}{3} = \frac{57,000}{3}$$
$$x = 19,000$$
$$2x = 2(19,000) = 38,000$$
Her husband will receive $38,000 and her son will receive $19,000.

Exercise Set 3.4

1. "A number added to -5 is -7" is $-5 + x = -7$.

3. "Three times a number yields 27" is $3x = 27$.

5. "A number subtracted from -20 amounts to 104" is $-20 - x = 104$.

7. "Twice a number gives 108" is $2x = 108$.

9. "The product of 5 and the sum of -3 and a number is -20" is $5(-3 + x) = -20$.

11. "Three times a number, added to 9 is 33" is
$$9 + 3x = 33$$
$$9 - 9 + 3x = 33 - 9$$
$$3x = 24$$
$$\frac{3x}{3} = \frac{24}{3}$$
$$x = 8$$

13. "The sum of 3, 4, and a number amounts to 16" is
$$3 + 4 + x = 16$$
$$7 + x = 16$$
$$7 - 7 + x = 16 - 7$$
$$x = 9$$

15. "The difference of a number and 3 is equal to the quotient of 10 and 5" is
$$x - 3 = \frac{10}{5}$$
$$x - 3 = 2$$
$$x - 3 + 3 = 2 + 3$$
$$x = 5$$

17. "Thirty less a number is equal to the product of 3 and the sum of the number and 6" is
$$30 - x = 3(x + 6)$$
$$30 - x = 3x + 18$$
$$30 - 30 - x = 3x + 18 - 30$$
$$-x = 3x - 12$$
$$-x - 3x = 3x - 3x - 12$$
$$-4x = -12$$
$$\frac{-4x}{-4} = \frac{-12}{-4}$$
$$x = 3$$

19. "40 subtracted from five times a number is 8 more than the number" is
$$5x - 40 = x + 8$$
$$5x - x - 40 = x - x + 8$$
$$4x - 40 = 8$$
$$4x - 40 + 40 = 8 + 40$$
$$4x = 48$$
$$\frac{4x}{4} = \frac{48}{4}$$
$$x = 12$$

21. "Three times the difference of some number and 5 amounts to the quotient of 108 and 12" is
$$3(x - 5) = \frac{108}{12}$$
$$3x - 15 = 9$$
$$3x - 15 + 15 = 9 + 15$$
$$3x = 24$$
$$\frac{3x}{3} = \frac{24}{3}$$
$$x = 8$$

23. "The product of 4 and a number is the same as 30 less twice that same number" is
$$4x = 30 - 2x$$
$$4x + 2x = 30 - 2x + 2x$$
$$6x = 30$$
$$\frac{6x}{6} = \frac{30}{6}$$
$$x = 5$$

25. The equation is $x + x - 28 = 82$.
$$x + x - 28 = 82$$
$$2x - 28 = 82$$
$$2x - 28 + 28 = 82 + 28$$
$$2x = 110$$
$$\frac{2x}{2} = \frac{110}{2}$$
$$x = 55$$
California has 55 votes and Florida has
$55 - 28 = 27$ votes.

27. Let x be the fastest speed of the pheasant. Since a falcon's fastest speed is five times as fast as a pheasant, a falcon's fastest speed is $5x$. Since the total speeds for these two birds is 222 miles per hour, the sum of x and $5x$ is 222.
$$x + 5x = 222$$
$$6x = 222$$
$$\frac{6x}{6} = \frac{222}{6}$$
$$x = 37$$
The pheasant's fastest speed is 37 miles per hour and the falcon's fastest speed is
$5(37) = 185$ miles per hour.

29. Let x be the enrollment (in thousands) at the largest university in India. Since the largest university in Pakistan has 306 thousand more students than the one in India, its enrollment is $x + 306$. Since the combined enrollment is 3306 thousand students, the sum of x and $x + 306$ is 3306.
$$x + x + 306 = 3306$$
$$2x + 306 = 3306$$
$$2x + 306 - 306 = 3306 - 306$$
$$2x = 3000$$
$$\frac{2x}{2} = \frac{3000}{2}$$
$$x = 1500$$
The enrollment at the largest university in India is 1500 thousand students, and the enrollment at the largest university in Pakistan is
$1500 + 306 = 1806$ thousand students.

31. Let x be the cost of the games. Since the cost of the Xbox 360 is 3 times as much as the games, the cost of the Xbox 360 is $3x$. Since the total cost is \$560, the sum of x and $3x$ is 560.
$$x + 3x = 560$$
$$4x = 560$$
$$\frac{4x}{4} = \frac{560}{4}$$
$$x = 140$$
The games cost \$140 and the Xbox 360 costs
$3(140) = \$420$.

33. Let x be the distance from Los Angeles to Tokyo. Since the distance from New York to London is 2001 miles less than the distance from Los Angeles to Tokyo, the distance from New York to London is $x - 2001$. Since the total of the two distances is 8939, the sum of x and $x - 2001$ is 8939.
$$x + x - 2001 = 8939$$
$$2x - 2001 = 8939$$
$$2x - 2001 + 2001 = 8939 + 2001$$
$$2x = 10,940$$
$$\frac{2x}{2} = \frac{10,940}{2}$$
$$x = 5470$$
The distance from Los Angeles to Tokyo is 5470 miles.

35. Let x be the capacity of Michigan Stadium. Since the capacity of Beaver Stadium is 1081 more than that of Michigan Stadium, the capacity of Beaver Stadium is $x + 1081$. Since the combined capacity is 213,483, the sum of x and $x + 1081$ is 213,483.
$$x + x + 1081 = 213,483$$
$$2x + 1081 = 213,483$$
$$2x + 1081 - 1081 = 213,483 - 1081$$
$$2x = 212,402$$
$$\frac{2x}{2} = \frac{212,402}{2}$$
$$x = 106,201$$
The capacity of Michigan Stadium is 106,201 and the capacity of Beaver Stadium is
$106,201 + 1081 = 107,282$.

37. Let x be the number of tourists projected to visit Spain in 2020. Since the number of tourists projected to visit China in 2020 is twice the number projected for Spain, the number projected for China is $2x$. Since the total number of tourists projected for the two countries is 210 million, the sum of x and $2x$ is 210 million.
$$x + 2x = 210$$
$$3x = 210$$
$$\frac{3x}{3} = \frac{210}{3}$$
$$x = 70$$
$2x = 2(70) = 140$
70 million tourists are projected to visit Spain in 2020; 140 million are projected to visit China in 2020.

39. Let x be the number of cars manufactured in Spain. Since the number of cars manufactured in Germany is twice as many as those manufactured in Spain, the number of cars manufactured in Germany is $2x$. Since the total number of these cars is 19,827, the sum of x and $2x$ is 19,827.

$$x + 2x = 19,827$$
$$3x = 19,827$$
$$\frac{3x}{3} = \frac{19,827}{3}$$
$$x = 6609$$

The number of cars manufactured in Spain is 6609 per day and the number in Germany is $2(6609) = 13,218$ per day.

41. Let x be the amount the biker received for the accessories. Since he received five times as much for the bike, he received $5x$ for the bike. Since he received a total of \$270 for the bike and accessories, the sum of x and $5x$ is 270.

$$x + 5x = 270$$
$$6x = 270$$
$$\frac{6x}{6} = \frac{270}{6}$$
$$x = 45$$

Thus, the biker received $5 \cdot \$45 = \$225$ for the bike.

43. Let x be the points scored by the Stanford Cardinal. Since the Tennessee Lady Volunteers scored 16 points more than the Stanford Cardinal, the Tennessee Lady Volunteers scored $x + 16$ points. Since both teams scored a total of 132 points, the sum of x and $x + 16$ is 132.

$$x + x + 16 = 132$$
$$2x + 16 = 132$$
$$2x + 16 - 16 = 132 - 16$$
$$2x = 116$$
$$\frac{2x}{2} = \frac{116}{2}$$
$$x = 58$$

The Tennessee Lady Volunteers scored $58 + 16 = 74$ points.

45. Let x be the number of computers in Japan. Since the USA has 162,550 million more computers than Japan, the number of computers in the USA is $x + 162,550$. Since the total number of computers in the two countries is 318,450 million, the sum of x and $x + 162,550$ is 318,450.

$$x + x + 162,550 = 318,450$$
$$2x + 162,550 = 318,450$$
$$2x + 162,550 - 162,550 = 318,450 - 162,550$$
$$2x = 155,900$$
$$\frac{2x}{2} = \frac{155,900}{2}$$
$$x = 77,950$$

Japan has 77,950 million computers, and the USA has $77,950 + 162,550 = 240,500$ million computers.

47. To round 586 to the nearest ten, observe that the digit in the ones place is 6. Since this digit is at least 5, we add 1 to the digit in the tens place. 586 rounded to the nearest ten is 590.

49. To round 1026 to the nearest hundred, observe that the digit in the tens place is 2. Since this digit is less than 5, we do not add 1 to the digit in the hundreds place. 1026 rounded to the nearest hundred is 1000.

51. To round 2986 to the nearest thousand, observe that the digit in the hundreds place is 9. Since this digit is at least 5, we add 1 to the digit in the thousands place. 2986 rounded to the nearest thousand is 3000.

53. Yes; answers may vary

55. Use $P = A + C$, where $P = 230,000$ and $C = 13,800$.
$$P = A + C$$
$$230,000 = A + 13,800$$
$$230,000 - 13,800 = A + 13,800 - 13,800$$
$$216,200 = A$$
The seller received \$216,200.

57. Use $P = C + M$ where $P = 999$ and $M = 450$.
$$P = C + M$$
$$999 = C + 450$$
$$999 - 450 = C + 450 - 450$$
$$549 = C$$
The wholesale cost is \$549.

Chapter 3 Vocabulary Check

1. An algebraic expression is <u>simplified</u> when all like terms have been <u>combined</u>.

2. Terms that are exactly the same, except that they may have different numerical coefficients, are called <u>like</u> terms.

3. A letter used to represent a number is called a <u>variable</u>.

4. A combination of operations on variables and numbers is called an <u>algebraic expression</u>.

5. The addends of an algebraic expression are called the <u>terms</u> of the expression.

6. The number factor of a variable term is called the <u>numerical coefficient</u>.

7. Replacing a variable in an expression by a number and then finding the value of the expression is called <u>evaluating the expression</u> for the variable.

8. A term that is a number only is called a <u>constant</u>.

9. An <u>equation</u> is of the form expression = expression.

10. A <u>solution</u> of an equation is a value for the variable that makes an equation a true statement.

11. To multiply $-3(2x + 1)$, we use the <u>distributive</u> property.

12. By the <u>multiplication</u> property of equality, we may multiply or divide both sides of an equation by any nonzero number without changing the solution of the equation.

13. By the <u>addition</u> property of equality, the same number may be added to or subtracted from both sides of an equation without changing the solution of the equation.

Chapter 3 Review

1. $3y + 7y - 15 = (3 + 7)y - 15 = 10y - 15$

2. $2y - 10 - 8y = 2y - 8y - 10$
$= (2 - 8)y - 10$
$= -6y - 10$

3. $8a + a - 7 - 15a = 8a + a - 15a - 7$
$= (8 + 1 - 15)a - 7$
$= -6a - 7$

4. $y + 3 - 9y - 1 = y - 9y + 3 - 1$
$= (1 - 9)y + 3 - 1$
$= -8y + 2$

5. $2(x + 5) = 2 \cdot x + 2 \cdot 5 = 2x + 10$

6. $-3(y + 8) = -3 \cdot y + (-3) \cdot 8 = -3y - 24$

7. $7x + 3(x - 4) + x = 7x + 3 \cdot x - 3 \cdot 4 + x$
$= 7x + 3x - 12 + x$
$= 7x + 3x + x - 12$
$= (7 + 3 + 1)x - 12$
$= 11x - 12$

8. $-(3m + 2) - m - 10 = -1(3m + 2) - m - 10$
$= -1 \cdot 3m + (-1) \cdot 2 - m - 10$
$= -3m - 2 - m - 10$
$= -3m - m - 2 - 10$
$= (-3 - 1)m - 2 - 10$
$= -4m - 12$

9. $3(5a - 2) - 20a + 10 = 3 \cdot 5a - 3 \cdot 2 - 20a + 10$
$= 15a - 6 - 20a + 10$
$= 15a - 20a - 6 + 10$
$= (15 - 20)a - 6 + 10$
$= -5a + 4$

10. $6y + 3 + 2(3y - 6) = 6y + 3 + 2 \cdot 3y - 2 \cdot 6$
$= 6y + 3 + 6y - 12$
$= 6y + 6y + 3 - 12$
$= (6 + 6)y + 3 - 12$
$= 12y - 9$

11. $6y - 7 + 11y - y + 2 = 6y + 11y - y - 7 + 2$
$= (6 + 11 - 1)y - 7 + 2$
$= 16y - 5$

12. $10 - x + 5x - 12 - 3x = -x + 5x - 3x + 10 - 12$
$= (-1 + 5 - 3)x + 10 - 12$
$= 1x - 2$
$= x - 2$

13. Perimeter $= 2(2x + 3) = 2 \cdot 2x + 2 \cdot 3 = 4x + 6$
The perimeter is $(4x + 6)$ yards.

14. Perimeter $= 4 \cdot 5y = 20y$
The perimeter is $20y$ meters.

15. Area $=$ (length) $\cdot$ (width)
$= 3 \cdot (2x - 1)$
$= 3 \cdot 2x - 3 \cdot 1$
$= 6x - 3$
The area is $(6x - 3)$ square yards.

16. Add the areas of the two rectangles.

$$10(x-2)+7(5x+4) = 10\cdot x-10\cdot 2+7\cdot 5x+7\cdot 4$$
$$= 10x-20+35x+28$$
$$= 10x+35x-20+28$$
$$= (10+35)x-20+28$$
$$= 45x+8$$

The area is $(45x + 8)$ square centimeters.

17.
$$z-5=-7$$
$$z-5+5=-7+5$$
$$z=-2$$

18.
$$3x+10=4x$$
$$3x-3x+10=4x-3x$$
$$10=x$$

19.
$$3y=-21$$
$$\frac{3y}{3}=\frac{-21}{3}$$
$$y=-7$$

20.
$$-3a=-15$$
$$\frac{-3a}{-3}=\frac{-15}{-3}$$
$$a=5$$

21.
$$\frac{x}{-6}=2$$
$$-6\cdot\frac{x}{-6}=-6\cdot 2$$
$$x=-12$$

22.
$$\frac{y}{-15}=-3$$
$$-15\cdot\frac{y}{-15}=-15\cdot(-3)$$
$$y=45$$

23.
$$n+18=10-(-2)$$
$$n+18=10+2$$
$$n+18=12$$
$$n+18-18=12-18$$
$$n=-6$$

24.
$$c-5=-13+7$$
$$c-5=-6$$
$$c-5+5=-6+5$$
$$c=-1$$

25.
$$7x+5-6x=-20$$
$$x+5=-20$$
$$x+5-5=-20-5$$
$$x=-25$$

26.
$$17x=2(8x-4)$$
$$17x=2\cdot 8x-2\cdot 4$$
$$17x=16x-8$$
$$17x-16x=16x-16x-8$$
$$x=-8$$

27.
$$5x+7=-3$$
$$5x+7-7=-3-7$$
$$5x=-10$$
$$\frac{5x}{5}=\frac{-10}{5}$$
$$x=-2$$

28.
$$-14=9y+4$$
$$-14-4=9y+4-4$$
$$-18=9y$$
$$\frac{-18}{9}=\frac{9y}{9}$$
$$-2=y$$

29.
$$\frac{z}{4}=-8-(-6)$$
$$\frac{z}{4}=-8+6$$
$$\frac{z}{4}=-2$$
$$4\cdot\frac{z}{4}=4\cdot(-2)$$
$$z=-8$$

30.
$$-1+(-8)=\frac{x}{5}$$
$$-9=\frac{x}{5}$$
$$5\cdot(-9)=5\cdot\frac{x}{5}$$
$$-45=x$$

31.
$$6y-7y=100-105$$
$$-y=-5$$
$$\frac{-y}{-1}=\frac{-5}{-1}$$
$$y=5$$

32. $19x - 16x = 45 - 60$
$3x = -15$
$\dfrac{3x}{3} = \dfrac{-15}{3}$
$x = -5$

33. $9(2x - 7) = 19x$
$9 \cdot 2x - 9 \cdot 7 = 19x$
$18x - 63 = 19x$
$18x - 18x - 63 = 19x - 18x$
$-63 = x$

34. $-5(3x + 3) = -14x$
$-5 \cdot 3x - 5 \cdot 3 = -14x$
$-15x - 15 = -14x$
$-15x + 15x - 15 = -14x + 15x$
$-15 = x$

35. $3x - 4 = 11$
$3x - 4 + 4 = 11 + 4$
$3x = 15$
$\dfrac{3x}{3} = \dfrac{15}{3}$
$x = 5$

36. $6y + 1 = 73$
$6y + 1 - 1 = 73 - 1$
$6y = 72$
$\dfrac{6y}{6} = \dfrac{72}{6}$
$y = 12$

37. $2(x + 4) - 10 = -2(7)$
$2 \cdot x + 2 \cdot 4 - 10 = -14$
$2x + 8 - 10 = -14$
$2x - 2 = -14$
$2x - 2 + 2 = -14 + 2$
$2x = -12$
$\dfrac{2x}{2} = \dfrac{-12}{2}$
$x = -6$

38. $-3(x - 6) + 13 = 20 - 1$
$-3 \cdot x - (-3) \cdot 6 + 13 = 19$
$-3x + 18 + 13 = 19$
$-3x + 31 = 19$
$-3x + 31 - 31 = 19 - 31$
$-3x = -12$
$\dfrac{-3x}{-3} = \dfrac{-12}{-3}$
$x = 4$

39. The product of -5 and a number is $-5x$.

40. Three subtracted from a number is $x - 3$.

41. The sum of -5 and a number is $-5 + x$.

42. The quotient of -2 and a number is $\dfrac{-2}{x}$ or $-\dfrac{2}{x}$.

43. The product of -5 and a number, decreased by 50 is $-5x - 50$.

44. Eleven added to twice a number is $2x + 11$.

45. The quotient of 70 and the sum of a number and 6 is $\dfrac{70}{x + 6}$.

46. Twice the difference of a number and 13 is $2(x - 13)$.

47. $2x + 5 = 7x - 100$
$2x - 2x + 5 = 7x - 2x - 100$
$5 = 5x - 100$
$5 + 100 = 5x - 100 + 100$
$105 = 5x$
$\dfrac{105}{5} = \dfrac{5x}{5}$
$21 = x$

48. $-6x - 4 = x + 66$
$-6x + 6x - 4 = x + 6x + 66$
$-4 = 7x + 66$
$-4 - 66 = 7x + 66 - 66$
$-70 = 7x$
$\dfrac{-70}{7} = \dfrac{7x}{7}$
$-10 = x$

49. $2x + 7 = 6x - 1$
$2x - 2x + 7 = 6x - 2x - 1$
$7 = 4x - 1$
$7 + 1 = 4x - 1 + 1$
$8 = 4x$
$\dfrac{8}{4} = \dfrac{4x}{4}$
$2 = x$

50.
$$5x - 18 = -4x$$
$$5x - 5x - 18 = -4x - 5x$$
$$-18 = -9x$$
$$\frac{-18}{-9} = \frac{-9x}{-9}$$
$$2 = x$$

51.
$$5(n-3) = 7 + 3n$$
$$5n - 15 = 7 + 3n$$
$$5n - 3n - 15 = 7 + 3n - 3n$$
$$2n - 15 = 7$$
$$2n - 15 + 15 = 7 + 15$$
$$2n = 22$$
$$\frac{2n}{2} = \frac{22}{2}$$
$$n = 11$$

52.
$$7(2 + x) = 4x - 1$$
$$14 + 7x = 4x - 1$$
$$14 + 7x - 4x = 4x - 4x - 1$$
$$14 + 3x = -1$$
$$14 - 14 + 3x = -1 - 14$$
$$3x = -15$$
$$\frac{3x}{3} = \frac{-15}{3}$$
$$x = -5$$

53.
$$6x + 3 - (-x) = -20 + 5x - 7$$
$$6x + 3 + x = -20 + 5x - 7$$
$$7x + 3 = -27 + 5x$$
$$7x - 5x + 3 = -27 + 5x - 5x$$
$$2x + 3 = -27$$
$$2x + 3 - 3 = -27 - 3$$
$$2x = -30$$
$$\frac{2x}{2} = \frac{-30}{2}$$
$$x = -15$$

54.
$$x - 25 + 2x = -5 + 2x - 10$$
$$-25 + 3x = -15 + 2x$$
$$-25 + 3x - 2x = -15 + 2x - 2x$$
$$-25 + x = -15$$
$$-25 + 25 + x = -15 + 25$$
$$x = 10$$

55.
$$3(x - 4) = 5x - 8$$
$$3x - 12 = 5x - 8$$
$$3x - 3x - 12 = 5x - 3x - 8$$
$$-12 = 2x - 8$$
$$-12 + 8 = 2x - 8 + 8$$
$$-4 = 2x$$
$$\frac{-4}{2} = \frac{2x}{2}$$
$$-2 = x$$

56.
$$4(x - 3) = -2x - 48$$
$$4x - 12 = -2x - 48$$
$$4x + 2x - 12 = -2x + 2x - 48$$
$$6x - 12 = -48$$
$$6x - 12 + 12 = -48 + 12$$
$$6x = -36$$
$$\frac{6x}{6} = \frac{-36}{6}$$
$$x = -6$$

57.
$$6(2n - 1) + 18 = 0$$
$$12n - 6 + 18 = 0$$
$$12n + 12 = 0$$
$$12n + 12 - 12 = 0 - 12$$
$$12n = -12$$
$$\frac{12n}{12} = \frac{-12}{12}$$
$$n = -1$$

58.
$$7(3y - 2) - 7 = 0$$
$$21y - 14 - 7 = 0$$
$$21y - 21 = 0$$
$$21y - 21 + 21 = 0 + 21$$
$$21y = 21$$
$$\frac{21y}{21} = \frac{21}{21}$$
$$y = 1$$

59.
$$95x - 14 = 20x - 10 + 10x - 4$$
$$95x - 14 = 30x - 14$$
$$95x - 14 + 14 = 30x - 14 + 14$$
$$95x = 30x$$
$$95x - 30x = 30x - 30x$$
$$65x = 0$$
$$\frac{65x}{65} = \frac{0}{65}$$
$$x = 0$$

60.
$$32z + 11 - 28z = 50 + 2z - (-1)$$
$$4z + 11 = 50 + 2z + 1$$
$$4z + 11 = 51 + 2z$$
$$4z - 2z + 11 = 51 + 2z - 2z$$
$$2z + 11 = 51$$
$$2z + 11 - 11 = 51 - 11$$
$$2z = 40$$
$$\frac{2z}{2} = \frac{40}{2}$$
$$z = 20$$

61. The difference of 20 and -8 is 28 translates to $20 - (-8) = 28$.

62. Nineteen subtracted from -2 amounts to -21 translates to $-2 - 19 = -21$.

63. The quotient of -75 and the sum of 5 and 20 is equal to -3 translates to $\dfrac{-75}{5 + 20} = -3$.

64. Five times the sum of 2 and -6 yields -20 translates to $5[2 + (-6)] = -20$.

65. "Twice a number minus 8 is 40" is $2x - 8 = 40$.

66. "The product of a number and 6 is equal to the sum of the number and $2a$" is $6x = x + 2a$.

67. "Twelve subtracted from the quotient of a number and 2 is 10" is $\dfrac{x}{2} - 12 = 10$.

68. "The difference of a number and 3 is the quotient of 8 and 4" is $x - 3 = \dfrac{8}{4}$.

69. "Five times a number subtracted from 40 is the same as three times the number" is
$$40 - 5x = 3x$$
$$40 - 5x + 5x = 3x + 5x$$
$$40 = 8x$$
$$\frac{40}{8} = \frac{8x}{8}$$
$$5 = x$$
The number is 5.

70. "The product of a number and 3 is twice the difference of that number and 8" is
$$3x = 2(x - 8)$$
$$3x = 2x - 16$$
$$3x - 2x = 2x - 2x - 16$$
$$x = -16$$
The number is -16.

71. Let x be the number of votes for the Independent candidate. Since the Democratic candidate received 272 more votes than the Independent candidate, the Democratic candidate received $x + 272$ votes. The total number of votes is 18,500.
$$x + x + 272 + 14,000 = 18,500$$
$$2x + 14,272 = 18,500$$
$$2x + 14,272 - 14,272 = 18,500 - 14,272$$
$$2x = 4228$$
$$\frac{2x}{2} = \frac{4228}{2}$$
$$x = 2114$$
The Democratic candidate received $2114 + 272 = 2386$ votes.

72. Let x be the number of movies on videotapes. Since the number of movies on DVDs is twice the number on videotapes, the number of movies on DVDs is $2x$. Since the total number of movies is 126, the sum of x and $2x$ is 126.
$$x + 2x = 126$$
$$3x = 126$$
$$\frac{3x}{3} = \frac{126}{3}$$
$$x = 42$$
He has $2(42) = 84$ movies on DVDs.

73. $9x - 20x = (9 - 20)x = -11x$

74. $-5(7x) = (-5 \cdot 7)x = -35x$

75. $12x + 5(2x - 3) - 4 = 12x + 10x - 15 - 4$
$$= 22x - 19$$

76. $-7(x + 6) - 2(x - 5) = -7x - 42 - 2x + 10$
$$= -7x - 2x - 42 + 10$$
$$= -9x - 32$$

77.
$$c - 5 = -13 + 7$$
$$c - 5 = -6$$
$$c - 5 + 5 = -6 + 5$$
$$c = -1$$

78.
$$7x + 5 - 6x = -20$$
$$x + 5 = -20$$
$$x + 5 - 5 = -20 - 5$$
$$x = -25$$

79.
$$-7x + 3x = -50 - 2$$
$$-4x = -52$$
$$\frac{-4x}{-4} = \frac{-52}{-4}$$
$$x = 13$$

80.
$$-x + 8x = -38 - 4$$
$$7x = -42$$
$$\frac{7x}{7} = \frac{-42}{7}$$
$$x = -6$$

81.
$$9x + 12 - 8x = -6 + (-4)$$
$$x + 12 = -10$$
$$x + 12 - 12 = -10 - 12$$
$$x = -22$$

82.
$$-17x + 14 + 20x - 2x = 5 - (-3)$$
$$-17x + 20x - 2x + 14 = 5 + 3$$
$$x + 14 = 8$$
$$x + 14 - 14 = 8 - 14$$
$$x = -6$$

83.
$$5(2x - 3) = 11x$$
$$10x - 15 = 11x$$
$$10x - 10x - 15 = 11x - 10x$$
$$-15 = x$$

84.
$$\frac{y}{-3} = -1 - 5$$
$$\frac{y}{-3} = -6$$
$$-3 \cdot \frac{y}{-3} = -3 \cdot (-6)$$
$$y = 18$$

85.
$$12y - 10 = -70$$
$$12y - 10 + 10 = -70 + 10$$
$$12y = -60$$
$$\frac{12y}{12} = \frac{-60}{12}$$
$$y = -5$$

86.
$$4n - 8 = 2n + 14$$
$$4n - 2n - 8 = 2n - 2n + 14$$
$$2n - 8 = 14$$
$$2n - 8 + 8 = 14 + 8$$
$$2n = 22$$
$$\frac{2n}{2} = \frac{22}{2}$$
$$n = 11$$

87.
$$-6(x - 3) = x + 4$$
$$-6x + 18 = x + 4$$
$$-6x + 6x + 18 = x + 6x + 4$$
$$18 = 7x + 4$$
$$18 - 4 = 7x + 4 - 4$$
$$14 = 7x$$
$$\frac{14}{7} = \frac{7x}{7}$$
$$2 = x$$

88.
$$9(3x - 4) + 63 = 0$$
$$27x - 36 + 63 = 0$$
$$27x + 27 = 0$$
$$27x + 27 - 27 = 0 - 27$$
$$27x = -27$$
$$\frac{27x}{27} = \frac{-27}{27}$$
$$x = -1$$

89.
$$-5z + 3z - 7 = 8z - 1 - 6$$
$$-2z - 7 = 8z - 7$$
$$-2z - 8z - 7 = 8z - 8z - 7$$
$$-10z - 7 = -7$$
$$-10z - 7 + 7 = -7 + 7$$
$$-10z = 0$$
$$\frac{-10z}{-10} = \frac{0}{-10}$$
$$z = 0$$

90.
$$4x - 3 + 6x = 5x - 3 - 30$$
$$10x - 3 = 5x - 33$$
$$10x - 5x - 3 = 5x - 5x - 33$$
$$5x - 3 = -33$$
$$5x - 3 + 3 = -33 + 3$$
$$5x = -30$$
$$\frac{5x}{5} = \frac{-30}{5}$$
$$x = -6$$

91. "Three times a number added to twelve is 27" is
$$12 + 3x = 27$$
$$12 - 12 + 3x = 27 - 12$$
$$3x = 15$$
$$\frac{3x}{3} = \frac{15}{3}$$
$$x = 5$$
The number is 5.

92. "Twice the sum of a number and four is ten" is
$$2(x + 4) = 10$$
$$2x + 8 = 10$$
$$2x + 8 - 8 = 10 - 8$$
$$2x = 2$$
$$\frac{2x}{2} = \frac{2}{2}$$
$$x = 1$$
The number is 1.

93. Let x be the number of roadway miles in Hawaii. Since Delaware has 1585 more roadway miles than Hawaii, Delaware has $x + 1585$ roadway miles. Since the total number of roadway miles is 10,203, the sum of x and $x + 1585$ is 10,203.
$$x + x + 1585 = 10,203$$
$$2x + 1585 = 10,203$$
$$2x + 1585 - 1585 = 10,203 - 1585$$
$$2x = 8618$$
$$\frac{2x}{2} = \frac{8618}{2}$$
$$x = 4309$$
Hawaii has 4309 roadway miles and Delaware has $4309 + 1585 = 5894$ roadway miles.

94. Let x be the number of roadway miles in South Dakota. Since North Dakota has 3094 more roadway miles than South Dakota, North Dakota has $x + 3094$ roadway miles. Since the total number of roadway miles is 170,470, the sum of x and $x + 3094$ is 170,470.
$$x + x + 3094 = 170,470$$
$$2x + 3094 = 170,470$$
$$2x + 3094 - 3094 = 170,470 - 3094$$
$$2x = 167,376$$
$$\frac{2x}{2} = \frac{167,376}{2}$$
$$x = 83,688$$
South Dakota has 83,688 roadway miles and North Dakota has
$83,688 + 3094 = 86,782$ roadway miles.

Chapter 3 Test

1. $7x - 5 - 12x + 10 = 7x - 12x - 5 + 10$
$$= (7 - 12)x - 5 + 10$$
$$= -5x + 5$$

2. $-2(3y + 7) = -2 \cdot 3y + (-2) \cdot 7 = -6y - 14$

3. $-(3z + 2) - 5z - 18 = -1(3z + 2) - 5z - 18$
$$= -1 \cdot 3z + (-1) \cdot 2 - 5z - 18$$
$$= -3z - 2 - 5z - 18$$
$$= -3z - 5z - 2 - 18$$
$$= -8z - 20$$

4. perimeter $= 3(5x + 5) = 3 \cdot 5x + 3 \cdot 5 = 15x + 15$
The perimeter is $(15x + 15)$ inches.

5. Area $= $ (length) $\cdot$ (width)
$$= 4 \cdot (3x - 1)$$
$$= 4 \cdot 3x - 4 \cdot 1$$
$$= 12x - 4$$
The area is $(12x - 4)$ square meters.

6. $12 = y - 3y$
$$12 = -2y$$
$$\frac{12}{-2} = \frac{-2y}{-2}$$
$$-6 = y$$

7. $\dfrac{x}{2} = -5 - (-2)$
$$\frac{x}{2} = -5 + 2$$
$$\frac{x}{2} = -3$$
$$2 \cdot \frac{x}{2} = 2 \cdot (-3)$$
$$x = -6$$

8. $5x + 12 - 4x - 14 = 22$
$$x - 2 = 22$$
$$x - 2 + 2 = 22 + 2$$
$$x = 24$$

9. $-4x + 7 = 15$
$$-4x + 7 - 7 = 15 - 7$$
$$-4x = 8$$
$$\frac{-4x}{-4} = \frac{8}{-4}$$
$$x = -2$$

10.
$$2(x-6) = 0$$
$$2x-12 = 0$$
$$2x-12+12 = 0+12$$
$$2x = 12$$
$$\frac{2x}{2} = \frac{12}{2}$$
$$x = 6$$

11.
$$-4(x-11)-34 = 10-12$$
$$-4x+44-34 = 10-12$$
$$-4x+10 = -2$$
$$-4x+10-10 = -2-10$$
$$-4x = -12$$
$$\frac{-4x}{-4} = \frac{-12}{-4}$$
$$x = 3$$

12.
$$5x-2 = x-10$$
$$5x-x-2 = x-x-10$$
$$4x-2 = -10$$
$$4x-2+2 = -10+2$$
$$4x = -8$$
$$\frac{4x}{4} = \frac{-8}{4}$$
$$x = -2$$

13.
$$4(5x+3) = 2(7x+6)$$
$$20x+12 = 14x+12$$
$$20x+12-14x = 14x+12-14x$$
$$6x+12 = 12$$
$$6x+12-12 = 12-12$$
$$6x = 0$$
$$\frac{6x}{6} = \frac{0}{6}$$
$$x = 0$$

14.
$$6+2(3n-1) = 28$$
$$6+6n-2 = 28$$
$$6n+4 = 28$$
$$6n+4-4 = 28-4$$
$$6n = 24$$
$$\frac{6n}{6} = \frac{24}{6}$$
$$n = 4$$

15. The sum of -23 and a number translates to $-23 + x$.

16. Three times a number, subtracted from -2 translates to $-2 - 3x$.

17. The sum of twice 5 and -15 is -5 translates to $2 \cdot 5 + (-15) = -5$.

18. Six added to three times a number equals -30 translates to $3x + 6 = -30$.

19. The difference of three times a number and five times the same number is 4 translates to
$$3x-5x = 4$$
$$-2x = 4$$
$$\frac{-2x}{-2} = \frac{4}{-2}$$
$$x = -2$$
The number is -2.

20. Let x be the number of free throws Maria made. Since Paula made twice as many free throws as Maria, Paula made $2x$ free throws. Since the total number of free throws was 12, the sum of x and $2x$ is 12.
$$x+2x = 12$$
$$3x = 12$$
$$\frac{3x}{3} = \frac{12}{3}$$
$$x = 4$$
Paula made $2(4) = 8$ free throws.

21. Let x be the number of women runners entered in the race. Since the number of men entered in the race is 112 more than the number of women, the number of men is $x + 112$. Since the total number of runners in the race is 600, the sum of x and $x + 112$ is 600.
$$x+x+112 = 600$$
$$2x+112 = 600$$
$$2x+112-112 = 600-112$$
$$2x = 488$$
$$\frac{2x}{2} = \frac{488}{2}$$
$$x = 244$$
244 women entered the race.

Cumulative Review Chapters 1–3

1. 308,063,557 in words is three hundred eight million, sixty-three thousand, five hundred fifty-seven.

2. 276,004 in words is two hundred seventy-six thousand, four.

3. $2 + 3 + 1 + 3 + 4 = 13$
The perimeter is 13 inches.

4. $6 + 3 + 6 + 3 = 18$
The perimeter is 18 inches.

5.
$$\begin{array}{r} 900 \\ -174 \\ \hline 726 \end{array} \qquad \textit{Check:} \begin{array}{r} 726 \\ +174 \\ \hline 900 \end{array}$$

6.
$$\begin{array}{r} 17{,}801 \\ -\ 8216 \\ \hline 9585 \end{array} \qquad \textit{Check:} \begin{array}{r} 9585 \\ +8216 \\ \hline 17{,}801 \end{array}$$

7. To round 248,982 to the nearest hundred, observe that the digit in the tens place is 8. Since this digit is at least 5, we add 1 to the digit in the hundreds place. The number 248,982 rounded to the nearest hundred is 249,000.

8. To round 844,497 to the nearest thousand, observe that the digit in the hundreds place is 4. Since this digit is less than 5, we do not add 1 to the digit in the thousands place. The number 844,497 rounded to the nearest thousand is 844,000.

9.
$$\begin{array}{r} 25 \\ \times\ 8 \\ \hline 200 \end{array}$$

10.
$$\begin{array}{r} 395 \\ \times\ \ 74 \\ \hline 1\,580 \\ 27\,650 \\ \hline 29{,}230 \end{array}$$

11.
$$\begin{array}{r} 208 \\ 9\overline{)1872} \\ \underline{-18} \\ 07 \\ \underline{-0} \\ 72 \\ \underline{-72} \\ 0 \end{array}$$

Check:
$$\begin{array}{r} 208 \\ \times\ \ 9 \\ \hline 1872 \end{array}$$

12.
$$\begin{array}{r} 86 \\ 46\overline{)3956} \\ \underline{-368} \\ 276 \\ \underline{-276} \\ 0 \end{array}$$

Check:
$$\begin{array}{r} 86 \\ \times\ 46 \\ \hline 516 \\ 3440 \\ \hline 3956 \end{array}$$

13. $2 \cdot 4 - 3 \div 3 = 8 - 3 \div 3 = 8 - 1 = 7$

14. $8 \cdot 4 + 9 \div 3 = 32 + 9 \div 3 = 32 + 3 = 35$

15. $x^2 + z - 3 = 5^2 + 4 - 3$
$ = 25 + 4 - 3$
$ = 29 - 3$
$ = 26$

16. $2a^2 + 5 - c = 2 \cdot 2^2 + 5 - 3$
$ = 2 \cdot 4 + 5 - 3$
$ = 8 + 5 - 3$
$ = 13 - 3$
$ = 10$

17. $2n - 30 = 10$
Let $n = 26$.
$2 \cdot 26 - 30 \stackrel{?}{=} 10$
$52 - 30 \stackrel{?}{=} 10$
$22 = 10$ False
26 is not a solution.
Let $n = 40$.
$2 \cdot 40 - 30 \stackrel{?}{=} 10$
$80 - 30 \stackrel{?}{=} 10$
$50 = 10$ False
40 is not a solution.
Let $n = 20$.
$2 \cdot 20 - 30 \stackrel{?}{=} 10$
$40 - 30 \stackrel{?}{=} 10$
$10 = 10$ True
20 is a solution.

18. a. $-14 < 0$ because -14 is to the left of 0 on the number line.

b. $-(-7) = 7$, so $-(-7) > -8$ because 7 is to the right of -8 on the number line.

19. $5 + (-2) = 3$

20. $-3 + (-4) = -7$

21. $-15 + (-10) = -25$

22. $3 + (-7) = -4$

23. $-2 + 25 = 23$

24. $21 + 15 + (-19) = 36 + (-19) = 17$

25. $-4 - 10 = -4 + (-10) = -14$

26. $-2 - 3 = -2 + (-3) = -5$

27. $6 - (-5) = 6 + 5 = 11$

28. $19 - (-10) = 19 + 10 = 29$

29. $-11 - (-7) = -11 + 7 = -4$

30. $-16 - (-13) = -16 + 13 = -3$

31. $\dfrac{-12}{6} = -2$

32. $\dfrac{-30}{-5} = 6$

33. $-20 \div (-4) = 5$

34. $26 \div (-2) = -13$

35. $\dfrac{48}{-3} = -16$

36. $\dfrac{-120}{12} = -10$

37. $(-3)^2 = (-3)(-3) = 9$

38. $-2^5 = -(2 \cdot 2 \cdot 2 \cdot 2 \cdot 2) = -32$

39. $-3^2 = -(3 \cdot 3) = -9$

40. $(-5)^2 = (-5)(-5) = 25$

41. $2y - 6 + 4y + 8 = 2y + 4y - 6 + 8$
$\qquad\qquad\qquad = (2 + 4)y - 6 + 8$
$\qquad\qquad\qquad = 6y + 2$

42. $6x + 2 - 3x + 7 = 6x - 3x + 2 + 7$
$\qquad\qquad\qquad\quad = (6 - 3)x + 2 + 7$
$\qquad\qquad\qquad\quad = 3x + 9$

43. $\qquad 3y + 1 = 3$
$\qquad 3(-1) + 1 \overset{?}{=} 3$
$\qquad\quad -3 + 1 \overset{?}{=} 3$
$\qquad\qquad\quad -2 = 3 \quad$ False
Since $-2 = 3$ is false, -1 is not a solution of the equation.

44. $\qquad 5x - 3 = 7$
$\qquad 5(2) - 3 \overset{?}{=} 7$
$\qquad\quad 10 - 3 \overset{?}{=} 7$
$\qquad\qquad\quad 7 = 7 \quad$ True
Since $7 = 7$ is true, 2 is a solution of the equation.

45. $\qquad -12x = -36$
$\qquad \dfrac{-12x}{-12} = \dfrac{-36}{-12}$
$\qquad\qquad x = 3$

46. $\qquad -3y = 15$
$\qquad \dfrac{-3y}{-3} = \dfrac{15}{-3}$
$\qquad\qquad y = -5$

47. $\qquad 2x - 6 = 18$
$\qquad 2x - 6 + 6 = 18 + 6$
$\qquad\qquad 2x = 24$
$\qquad\qquad \dfrac{2x}{2} = \dfrac{24}{2}$
$\qquad\qquad x = 12$

48. $\qquad 3a + 5 = -1$
$\qquad 3a + 5 - 5 = -1 - 5$
$\qquad\qquad 3a = -6$
$\qquad\qquad \dfrac{3a}{3} = \dfrac{-6}{3}$
$\qquad\qquad a = -2$

49. Let x be the price of the software. Since the price of the computer system is four times the price of the software, the price of the computer system is $4x$. Since the combined price is \$2100, the sum of x and $4x$ is 2100.
$\qquad x + 4x = 2100$
$\qquad\quad 5x = 2100$
$\qquad\quad \dfrac{5x}{5} = \dfrac{2100}{5}$
$\qquad\qquad x = 420$
The price of the software is \$420 and the price of the computer system is 4(\$420) = \$1680.

50. Let x be the number. "Two times the number plus four is the same amount as three times the number minus seven" translates to

$$2x + 4 = 3x - 7$$
$$2x - 2x + 4 = 3x - 2x - 7$$
$$4 = x - 7$$
$$4 + 7 = x - 7 + 7$$
$$11 = x$$

The number is 11.

Chapter 4

Section 4.1

Practice Problems

1. In the fraction $\dfrac{11}{2}$, the numerator is 11 and the denominator is 2.

2. In the fraction $\dfrac{10y}{17}$, the numerator is $10y$ and the denominator is 17.

3. 3 out of 8 equal parts are shaded: $\dfrac{3}{8}$

4. 1 out of 6 equal parts is shaded: $\dfrac{1}{6}$

5. 7 out of 10 equal parts are shaded: $\dfrac{7}{10}$

6. 9 out of 16 equal parts are shaded: $\dfrac{9}{16}$

7. answers may vary; for example,
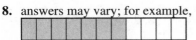

8. answers may vary; for example,

9. $\begin{array}{l}\text{number of planets farther} \to 5 \\ \text{number of planets in our solar system} \to 8\end{array}$

   $\dfrac{5}{8}$ of the planets in our solar system are farther from the Sun than Earth is.

10. Each part is $\dfrac{1}{3}$ of a whole and there are 8 parts shaded, or 2 wholes and 2 more parts.

    $\dfrac{8}{3}; 2\dfrac{2}{3}$

11. Each part is $\dfrac{1}{4}$ of a whole and there are 5 parts shaded, or 1 whole and 1 more part.

    $\dfrac{5}{4}; 1\dfrac{1}{4}$

12. a.

    b.

    c.

13. a.

    b.

    c.

14. $\dfrac{9}{9} = 1$

15. $\dfrac{-6}{-6} = 1$

16. $\dfrac{0}{-1} = 0$

17. $\dfrac{4}{1} = 4$

18. $\dfrac{-13}{0}$ is undefined.

19. $\dfrac{-13}{1} = -13$

20. a. $5\dfrac{2}{7} = \dfrac{7 \cdot 5 + 2}{7} = \dfrac{35 + 2}{7} = \dfrac{37}{7}$

    b. $6\dfrac{2}{3} = \dfrac{3 \cdot 6 + 2}{3} = \dfrac{18 + 2}{3} = \dfrac{20}{3}$

    c. $10\dfrac{9}{10} = \dfrac{10 \cdot 10 + 9}{10} = \dfrac{100 + 9}{10} = \dfrac{109}{10}$

    d. $4\dfrac{1}{5} = \dfrac{5 \cdot 4 + 1}{5} = \dfrac{20 + 1}{5} = \dfrac{21}{5}$

97

Copyright © 2011 Pearson Education, Inc. Publishing as Prentice Hall.

21. a.

$$5\overline{)9}$$
$$\underline{5}$$
$$4$$

$$\frac{9}{5} = 1\frac{4}{5}$$

b.

$$9\overline{)23}$$
$$\underline{18}$$
$$5$$

$$\frac{23}{9} = 2\frac{5}{9}$$

c.

$$4\overline{)48}$$
$$\underline{4}$$
$$8$$
$$\underline{8}$$
$$0$$

$$\frac{48}{4} = 12$$

d.

$$13\overline{)62}$$
$$\underline{52}$$
$$10$$

$$\frac{62}{13} = 4\frac{10}{13}$$

e.

$$7\overline{)51}$$
$$\underline{49}$$
$$2$$

$$\frac{51}{7} = 7\frac{2}{7}$$

f.

$$20\overline{)21}$$
$$\underline{20}$$
$$1$$

$$\frac{21}{20} = 1\frac{1}{20}$$

Vocabulary and Readiness Check

1. The number $\frac{17}{31}$ is called a <u>fraction</u>. The number 31 is called its <u>denominator</u> and 17 is called its <u>numerator</u>.

2. If we simplify each fraction, $\frac{-9}{-9} = 1$, $\frac{0}{-4} = 0$, and we say $\frac{-4}{0}$ is <u>undefined</u>.

3. The fraction $\frac{8}{3}$ is called an <u>improper</u> fraction, the fraction $\frac{3}{8}$ is called a <u>proper</u> fraction, and $10\frac{3}{8}$ is called a <u>mixed number</u>.

4. The value of an improper fraction is always $\underline{\geq 1}$ and the value of a proper fraction is always $\underline{\leq 1}$.

Exercise Set 4.1

1. In the fraction $\frac{1}{2}$, the numerator is 1 and the denominator is 2. Since $1 < 2$, the fraction is proper.

3. In the fraction $\frac{10}{3}$, the numerator is 10 and the denominator is 3. Since $10 > 3$, the fraction is improper.

5. In the fraction $\frac{15}{15}$, the numerator is 15 and the denominator is 15. Since $15 \geq 15$, the fraction is improper.

7. 1 out of 3 equal parts is shaded: $\frac{1}{3}$

9. Each part is $\frac{1}{4}$ of a whole and there are 11 parts shaded, or 2 wholes and 3 more parts.

   a. $\frac{11}{4}$

   b. $2\frac{3}{4}$

11. Each part is $\frac{1}{6}$ of a whole and there are 23 parts shaded, or 3 wholes and 5 more parts.

    a. $\frac{23}{6}$

    b. $3\frac{5}{6}$

13. 7 out of 12 equal parts are shaded: $\frac{7}{12}$

15. 3 out of 7 equal parts are shaded: $\frac{3}{7}$

17. 4 out of 9 equal parts are shaded: $\frac{4}{9}$

19. Each part is $\frac{1}{3}$ of a whole and there are 4 parts shaded, or 1 whole and 1 more part.

    a. $\frac{4}{3}$

    b. $1\frac{1}{3}$

21. Each part is $\frac{1}{2}$ of a whole and there are 11 parts shaded, or 5 wholes and 1 more part.

    a. $\frac{11}{2}$

    b. $5\frac{1}{2}$

23. 1 out of 6 equal parts is shaded: $\frac{1}{6}$

25. 5 of 8 equal parts are shaded: $\frac{5}{8}$

27. answers may vary; for example,

29. answers may vary; for example,

31. answers may vary; for example,

33. freshmen $\rightarrow$ 42
   students $\rightarrow$ $\overline{131}$

   $\frac{42}{131}$ of the students are freshmen.

35. **a.** number of students not freshmen $= 131 - 42$
                            $= 89$

    b. not freshmen $\rightarrow$ 89
       students $\rightarrow \overline{131}$

     $\frac{89}{131}$ of the students are not freshmen.

37. born in Ohio $\rightarrow$ 7
   U.S. presidents $\rightarrow \overline{44}$

   $\frac{7}{44}$ of U.S. presidents were born in Ohio.

39. number turned into hurricanes $\rightarrow 15$
   number of tropical storms $\rightarrow \overline{28}$

   $\frac{15}{28}$ of the tropical storms turned into hurricanes.

41. 11 of 31 days of March is $\frac{11}{31}$ of the month.

43. number of sophomores $\rightarrow 10$
   number of students in class $\rightarrow \overline{31}$

   $\frac{10}{31}$ of the class is sophomores.

45. There are 50 states total. 33 states contain federal Indian reservations.

    a. $\frac{33}{50}$ of the states contain federal Indian reservations.

    b. $50 - 33 = 17$
     17 states do not contain federal Indian reservations.

    c. $\frac{17}{50}$ of the states do not contain federal Indian reservations.

47. a.   blue $\rightarrow 21$
         total $\rightarrow \overline{50}$

   $\dfrac{21}{50}$ of the marbles are blue.

b. $50 - 21 = 29$
      29 of the marbles are red.

c.   red $\rightarrow 29$
      total $\rightarrow \overline{50}$

   $\dfrac{29}{50}$ of the marbles are red.

49.

51.

53.

55.

57. $\dfrac{12}{12} = 1$

59. $\dfrac{-5}{1} = -5$

61. $\dfrac{0}{-2} = 0$

63. $\dfrac{-8}{-8} = 1$

65. $\dfrac{-9}{0}$ is undefined

67. $\dfrac{3}{1} = 3$

69. $2\dfrac{1}{3} = \dfrac{3\cdot2+1}{3} = \dfrac{6+1}{3} = \dfrac{7}{3}$

71. $3\dfrac{3}{5} = \dfrac{5\cdot3+3}{5} = \dfrac{15+3}{5} = \dfrac{18}{5}$

73. $6\dfrac{5}{8} = \dfrac{8\cdot6+5}{8} = \dfrac{48+5}{8} = \dfrac{53}{8}$

75. $11\dfrac{6}{7} = \dfrac{7\cdot11+6}{7} = \dfrac{77+6}{7} = \dfrac{83}{7}$

77. $9\dfrac{7}{20} = \dfrac{20\cdot9+7}{20} = \dfrac{180+7}{20} = \dfrac{187}{20}$

79. $166\dfrac{2}{3} = \dfrac{3\cdot166+2}{3} = \dfrac{498+2}{3} = \dfrac{500}{3}$

81.
$$
\begin{array}{r}
3 \\
5\overline{)17} \\
\underline{15} \\
2
\end{array}
$$
$\dfrac{17}{5} = 3\dfrac{2}{5}$

83.
$$
\begin{array}{r}
4 \\
8\overline{)37} \\
\underline{32} \\
5
\end{array}
$$
$\dfrac{37}{8} = 4\dfrac{5}{8}$

85.
$$
\begin{array}{r}
3 \\
15\overline{)47} \\
\underline{45} \\
2
\end{array}
$$
$\dfrac{47}{15} = 3\dfrac{2}{15}$

87.
$$
\begin{array}{r}
15 \\
15\overline{)225} \\
\underline{15} \\
75 \\
\underline{75} \\
0
\end{array}
$$
$\dfrac{225}{15} = 15$

89.
$$
\begin{array}{r}
1 \\
175\overline{)182} \\
\underline{175} \\
7
\end{array}
$$
$\dfrac{182}{175} = 1\dfrac{7}{175}$

91.
$$
\begin{array}{r}
6 \\
112\overline{)737} \\
\underline{672} \\
65
\end{array}
$$
$\dfrac{737}{112} = 6\dfrac{65}{112}$

93. $3^2 = 3\cdot3 = 9$

95. $5^3 = 5\cdot5\cdot5 = 125$

97. $-\dfrac{11}{2} = \dfrac{-11}{2} = \dfrac{11}{-2}$

99. $\dfrac{-13}{15} = \dfrac{13}{-15} = -\dfrac{13}{15}$

101. answers may vary

103. ●●●●◐○○○○

105. 1 is not close to 8, so $\dfrac{1}{8}$ is closer to 0 than to 1.

$7\dfrac{1}{8}$ rounded to the nearest whole number is 7.

107. $1532 + 576 + 1059 = 3167$
576 of the 3167 stores are named Banana
Republic: $\dfrac{576}{3167}$

109. $1700 + 550 = 2250$
1700 of the 2250 affiliates are located in the
United States: $\dfrac{1700}{2250}$

Section 4.2

Practice Problems

1. a. $30 = 2\cdot15$
$\qquad\quad \downarrow\ \downarrow\searrow$
$\qquad\quad 2\cdot3\ \cdot5$

b. $56 = 2 \cdot 28$
$$\downarrow \quad \downarrow \searrow$$
$$2 \cdot 2 \cdot 14$$
$$\downarrow \quad \downarrow \quad \downarrow \searrow$$
$$2 \cdot 2 \cdot 2 \cdot 7 = 2^3 \cdot 7$$

c. $72 = 2 \cdot 36$
$$\downarrow \quad \downarrow \searrow$$
$$2 \cdot 2 \cdot 18$$
$$\downarrow \quad \downarrow \quad \downarrow \searrow$$
$$2 \cdot 2 \cdot 2 \cdot 9$$
$$\downarrow \quad \downarrow \quad \downarrow \quad \downarrow \searrow$$
$$2 \cdot 2 \cdot 2 \cdot 3 \cdot 3 = 2^3 \cdot 3^2$$

2. $60 = 2 \cdot 30$
$$\downarrow \quad \downarrow \searrow$$
$$2 \cdot 2 \cdot 15$$
$$\downarrow \quad \downarrow \quad \downarrow \searrow$$
$$2 \cdot 2 \cdot 3 \cdot 5 = 2^2 \cdot 3 \cdot 5$$

3.
$$3\overline{)33} = 11$$
$$3\overline{)99}$$
$$3\overline{)297}$$

The prime factorization of 297 is $3^3 \cdot 11$.

4. $\dfrac{30}{45} = \dfrac{15 \cdot 2}{15 \cdot 3} = \dfrac{15}{15} \cdot \dfrac{2}{3} = 1 \cdot \dfrac{2}{3} = \dfrac{2}{3}$

5. $\dfrac{39x}{51} = \dfrac{3 \cdot 13 \cdot x}{3 \cdot 17} = \dfrac{3}{3} \cdot \dfrac{13x}{17} = 1 \cdot \dfrac{13x}{17} = \dfrac{13x}{17}$

6. $-\dfrac{9}{50} = -\dfrac{3 \cdot 3}{2 \cdot 5 \cdot 5}$

Since 9 and 50 have no common factors, $-\dfrac{9}{50}$ is already in simplest form.

7. $\dfrac{49}{112} = \dfrac{7 \cdot 7}{7 \cdot 16} = \dfrac{7}{7} \cdot \dfrac{7}{16} = 1 \cdot \dfrac{7}{16} = \dfrac{7}{16}$

8. $-\dfrac{64}{20} = -\dfrac{4 \cdot 16}{4 \cdot 5} = -\dfrac{\cancel{4} \cdot 16}{\cancel{4} \cdot 5} = -\dfrac{16}{5}$

9. $\dfrac{7a^3}{56a^2} = \dfrac{7 \cdot a \cdot a \cdot a}{7 \cdot 8 \cdot a \cdot a} = \dfrac{\cancel{7} \cdot a \cdot \cancel{a} \cdot \cancel{a}}{\cancel{7} \cdot 8 \cdot \cancel{a} \cdot \cancel{a}} = \dfrac{a}{8}$

10. $\dfrac{7}{9}$ is in simplest form.

$$\dfrac{21}{27} = \dfrac{3 \cdot 7}{3 \cdot 9} = \dfrac{\cancel{3} \cdot 7}{\cancel{3} \cdot 9} = \dfrac{7}{9}$$

Since $\dfrac{7}{9}$ and $\dfrac{21}{27}$ both simplify to $\dfrac{7}{9}$, they are equivalent.

11. Not equivalent, since the cross products are not equal: $13 \cdot 5 = 65$ and $4 \cdot 18 = 72$

12. $\dfrac{6 \text{ parks in Washington}}{58 \text{ national parks}} = \dfrac{2 \cdot 3}{2 \cdot 29} = \dfrac{\cancel{2} \cdot 3}{\cancel{2} \cdot 29} = \dfrac{3}{29}$

$\dfrac{3}{29}$ of the national parks are in Washington state.

Calculator Explorations

1. $\dfrac{128}{224} = \dfrac{4}{7}$

2. $\dfrac{231}{396} = \dfrac{7}{12}$

3. $\dfrac{340}{459} = \dfrac{20}{27}$

4. $\dfrac{999}{1350} = \dfrac{37}{50}$

5. $\dfrac{432}{810} = \dfrac{8}{15}$

6. $\dfrac{225}{315} = \dfrac{5}{7}$

7. $\dfrac{54}{243} = \dfrac{2}{9}$

8. $\dfrac{455}{689} = \dfrac{35}{53}$

Vocabulary and Readiness Check

1. The number 40 equals $2 \cdot 2 \cdot 2 \cdot 5$. Since each factor is prime, we call $2 \cdot 2 \cdot 2 \cdot 5$ the <u>prime factorization</u> of 40.

2. A natural number, other than 1, that is not prime is called a <u>composite</u> number.

3. A natural number that has exactly two different factors, 1 and itself, is called a <u>prime</u> number.

4. In $\dfrac{11}{48}$, since 11 and 48 have no common factors other than 1, $\dfrac{11}{48}$ is in <u>simplest form</u>.

5. Fractions that represent the same portion of a whole are called <u>equivalent</u> fractions.

6. In the statement $\dfrac{5}{12} = \dfrac{15}{36}$, $5 \cdot 36$ and $12 \cdot 15$ are called <u>cross products</u>.

Exercise Set 4.2

1. $20 = 2 \cdot 10$

$2 \cdot 2 \quad \cdot \quad 5 = 2^2 \cdot 5$

3. $48 = 2 \cdot 24$

$2 \cdot 2 \cdot 12$

$2 \cdot 2 \cdot 2 \cdot 6$

$2 \cdot 2 \cdot 2 \cdot 2 \cdot 3 = 2^4 \cdot 3$

5. $81 = 9 \quad \cdot \quad 9$

$3 \cdot 3 \cdot 3 \cdot 3 = 3^4$

7. $162 = 2 \quad \cdot \quad 81$

$2 \cdot 9 \cdot 9$

$2 \cdot 3 \cdot 3 \cdot 3 \cdot 3 = 2 \cdot 3^4$

9. $110 = 2 \cdot 55$

$2 \cdot 5 \cdot 11 = 2 \cdot 5 \cdot 11$

11. $85 = 5 \cdot 17$

13. $240 = 2 \cdot 120$

$2 \cdot 2 \cdot 60$

$2 \cdot 2 \cdot 2 \cdot 30$

$2 \cdot 2 \cdot 2 \cdot 2 \cdot 15$

$2 \cdot 2 \cdot 2 \cdot 2 \cdot 3 \cdot 5 = 2^4 \cdot 3 \cdot 5$

15. $828 = 2 \cdot 414$

$2 \cdot 2 \cdot 207$

$2 \cdot 2 \cdot 3 \cdot 69$

$2 \cdot 2 \cdot 3 \cdot 3 \cdot 23 = 2^2 \cdot 3^2 \cdot 23$

17. $\dfrac{3}{12} = \dfrac{3 \cdot 1}{3 \cdot 4} = \dfrac{1}{4}$

19. $\dfrac{4x}{42} = \dfrac{2 \cdot 2 \cdot x}{2 \cdot 3 \cdot 7} = \dfrac{2 \cdot x}{3 \cdot 7} = \dfrac{2x}{21}$

21. $\dfrac{14}{16} = \dfrac{2 \cdot 7}{2 \cdot 8} = \dfrac{7}{8}$

23. $\dfrac{20}{30} = \dfrac{2 \cdot 10}{3 \cdot 10} = \dfrac{2}{3}$

25. $\dfrac{35a}{50a} = \dfrac{5 \cdot 7 \cdot a}{5 \cdot 10 \cdot a} = \dfrac{7}{10}$

27. $-\dfrac{63}{81} = -\dfrac{9 \cdot 7}{9 \cdot 9} = -\dfrac{7}{9}$

29. $\dfrac{30x^2}{36x} = \dfrac{5 \cdot 6 \cdot x \cdot x}{6 \cdot 6 \cdot x} = \dfrac{5 \cdot x}{6} = \dfrac{5x}{6}$

31. $\dfrac{27}{64} = \dfrac{3 \cdot 3 \cdot 3}{4 \cdot 4 \cdot 4}$

Since 27 and 64 have no common factors, $\dfrac{27}{64}$ is already in simplest form.

33. $\dfrac{25xy}{40y} = \dfrac{5 \cdot 5 \cdot x \cdot y}{5 \cdot 8 \cdot y} = \dfrac{5 \cdot x}{8} = \dfrac{5x}{8}$

35. $-\dfrac{40}{64} = -\dfrac{8 \cdot 5}{8 \cdot 8} = -\dfrac{5}{8}$

37. $\dfrac{36x^3y^2}{24xy} = \dfrac{3 \cdot 12 \cdot x \cdot x \cdot x \cdot y \cdot y}{2 \cdot 12 \cdot x \cdot y} = \dfrac{3 \cdot x \cdot x \cdot y}{2} = \dfrac{3x^2y}{2}$

39. $\dfrac{90}{120} = \dfrac{30 \cdot 3}{30 \cdot 4} = \dfrac{3}{4}$

41. $\dfrac{40xy}{64xyz} = \dfrac{5 \cdot 8 \cdot x \cdot y}{8 \cdot 8 \cdot x \cdot y \cdot z} = \dfrac{5}{8 \cdot z} = \dfrac{5}{8z}$

43. $\dfrac{66}{308} = \dfrac{22 \cdot 3}{22 \cdot 14} = \dfrac{3}{14}$

45. $-\dfrac{55}{85y} = -\dfrac{5 \cdot 11}{5 \cdot 17 \cdot y} = -\dfrac{11}{17 \cdot y} = -\dfrac{11}{17y}$

47. $\dfrac{189z}{216z} = \dfrac{7 \cdot 27 \cdot z}{8 \cdot 27 \cdot z} = \dfrac{7}{8}$

49. $\dfrac{224a^3b^4c^2}{16ab^4c^2} = \dfrac{14 \cdot 16 \cdot a \cdot a \cdot a \cdot b \cdot b \cdot b \cdot b \cdot c \cdot c}{1 \cdot 16 \cdot a \cdot b \cdot b \cdot b \cdot b \cdot c \cdot c}$

$= \dfrac{14 \cdot a \cdot a}{1}$

$= 14a^2$

51. Equivalent, since the cross products are equal:
$2 \cdot 12 = 24$ and $6 \cdot 4 = 24$

53. Not equivalent, since the cross products are not equal: $7 \cdot 8 = 56$ and $5 \cdot 11 = 55$

55. Equivalent, since the cross products are equal:
$10 \cdot 9 = 90$ and $15 \cdot 6 = 90$

57. Equivalent, since the cross products are equal:
$3 \cdot 18 = 54$ and $9 \cdot 6 = 54$

59. Not equivalent, since the cross products are not equal: $10 \cdot 15 = 150$ and $13 \cdot 13 = 169$

61. Not equivalent, since the cross products are not equal: $8 \cdot 24 = 192$ and $12 \cdot 18 = 216$

63. $\dfrac{2 \text{ hours}}{8 \text{ hours}} = \dfrac{1 \cdot 2}{4 \cdot 2} = \dfrac{1}{4}$

2 hours represents $\dfrac{1}{4}$ of a work shift.

65. $\dfrac{2640 \text{ feet}}{5280 \text{ feet}} = \dfrac{2640 \cdot 1}{2640 \cdot 2} = \dfrac{1}{2}$

2640 feet represents $\dfrac{1}{2}$ of a mile.

67. a. $\dfrac{16}{50} = \dfrac{8 \cdot 2}{25 \cdot 2} = \dfrac{8}{25}$

$\dfrac{8}{25}$ of the states can claim at least one Ritz-Carlton hotel.

b. $50 - 16 = 34$
34 states do not have a Ritz-Carlton hotel.

c. $\dfrac{34}{50} = \dfrac{17 \cdot 2}{25 \cdot 2} = \dfrac{17}{25}$

$\dfrac{17}{25}$ of the states do not have a Ritz-Carlton hotel.

69. $\dfrac{10 \text{ inches}}{24 \text{ inches}} = \dfrac{2 \cdot 5}{2 \cdot 12} = \dfrac{5}{12}$

$\dfrac{5}{12}$ of the wall is concrete.

71. a. $50 - 22 = 28$
28 states do not have this type of Web site.

b. $\dfrac{28}{50} = \dfrac{2 \cdot 14}{2 \cdot 25} = \dfrac{14}{25}$

$\dfrac{14}{25}$ of the states do not have this type of Web site.

73. $\dfrac{22 \text{ individuals}}{320 \text{ individuals}} = \dfrac{22}{320} = \dfrac{2 \cdot 11}{2 \cdot 160} = \dfrac{11}{160}$

$\dfrac{11}{160}$ of the U.S. astronauts who had flown in space were born in Texas.

75. $\dfrac{x^3}{9} = \dfrac{(-3)^3}{9} = \dfrac{-27}{9} = -3$

77. $2y = 2(-7) = -14$

79. answers may vary

81. $\dfrac{3975}{6625} = \dfrac{3 \cdot 1325}{5 \cdot 1325} = \dfrac{3}{5}$

83. 36 blood donors have blood type A Rh-positive.

$\dfrac{36 \text{ donors}}{100 \text{ donors}} = \dfrac{4 \cdot 9}{4 \cdot 25} = \dfrac{9}{25}$

$\dfrac{9}{25}$ of blood donors have type A Rh-positive blood type.

85. $3 + 1 = 4$ blood donors have an AB blood type.

$\dfrac{4 \text{ donors}}{100 \text{ donors}} = \dfrac{4 \cdot 1}{4 \cdot 25} = \dfrac{1}{25}$

$\dfrac{1}{25}$ of blood donors have an AB blood type.

87. $34{,}020 = 2 \cdot 17{,}010$

$\phantom{34{,}020 =} 2 \cdot 2 \cdot 8505$

$\phantom{34{,}020 =} 2 \cdot 2 \cdot 3 \cdot 2835$

$\phantom{34{,}020 =} 2 \cdot 2 \cdot 3 \cdot 3 \cdot 945$

$\phantom{34{,}020 =} 2 \cdot 2 \cdot 3 \cdot 3 \cdot 3 \cdot 315$

$\phantom{34{,}020 =} 2 \cdot 2 \cdot 3 \cdot 3 \cdot 3 \cdot 3 \cdot 105$

$\phantom{34{,}020 =} 2 \cdot 2 \cdot 3 \cdot 3 \cdot 3 \cdot 3 \cdot 3 \cdot 35$

$\phantom{34{,}020 =} 2 \cdot 2 \cdot 3 \cdot 3 \cdot 3 \cdot 3 \cdot 3 \cdot 5 \cdot 7$

$34{,}020 = 2^2 \cdot 3^5 \cdot 5 \cdot 7$

89. answers may vary

91. no; answers may vary

93. The piece representing education is labeled $\dfrac{1}{10}$, so $\dfrac{1}{10}$ of entering college freshmen plan to major in education.

95. answers may vary

97. The piece representing National Memorials is labeled $\dfrac{2}{25}$, so $\dfrac{2}{25}$ of National Park Service areas are National Memorials.

99. answers may vary

101. 8691, 786, 2235, 105, 222, 900, and 1470 are divisible by 3 because the sum of each number's digits is divisible by 3. 786, 22, 222, 900, and 1470 are divisible by 2 because they are even numbers. 786, 222, 900, and 1470 are divisible by both 2 and 3.

103. 6; answers may vary

Section 4.3

Practice Problems

1. $\dfrac{3}{7} \cdot \dfrac{5}{11} = \dfrac{3 \cdot 5}{7 \cdot 11} = \dfrac{15}{77}$

2. $\dfrac{1}{3} \cdot \dfrac{1}{9} = \dfrac{1 \cdot 1}{3 \cdot 9} = \dfrac{1}{27}$

3. $\dfrac{6}{77} \cdot \dfrac{7}{8} = \dfrac{6 \cdot 7}{77 \cdot 8} = \dfrac{2 \cdot 3 \cdot 7}{7 \cdot 11 \cdot 2 \cdot 4} = \dfrac{3}{11 \cdot 4} = \dfrac{3}{44}$

4. $\dfrac{4}{27} \cdot \dfrac{3}{8} = \dfrac{4 \cdot 3}{27 \cdot 8} = \dfrac{1 \cdot 4 \cdot 3}{3 \cdot 9 \cdot 4 \cdot 2} = \dfrac{1}{9 \cdot 2} = \dfrac{1}{18}$

5. $\dfrac{1}{2} \cdot \left(-\dfrac{11}{28}\right) = -\dfrac{1 \cdot 11}{2 \cdot 28} = -\dfrac{11}{56}$

6. $\left(-\dfrac{4}{11}\right)\left(-\dfrac{33}{16}\right) = \dfrac{4 \cdot 33}{11 \cdot 16} = \dfrac{4 \cdot 3 \cdot 11}{11 \cdot 4 \cdot 4} = \dfrac{3}{4}$

7. $\dfrac{1}{6} \cdot \dfrac{3}{10} \cdot \dfrac{25}{16} = \dfrac{1 \cdot 3 \cdot 25}{6 \cdot 10 \cdot 16}$

$\phantom{\dfrac{1}{6} \cdot \dfrac{3}{10} \cdot \dfrac{25}{16}} = \dfrac{1 \cdot 3 \cdot 5 \cdot 5}{2 \cdot 3 \cdot 2 \cdot 5 \cdot 16}$

$\phantom{\dfrac{1}{6} \cdot \dfrac{3}{10} \cdot \dfrac{25}{16}} = \dfrac{1 \cdot 5}{2 \cdot 2 \cdot 16}$

$\phantom{\dfrac{1}{6} \cdot \dfrac{3}{10} \cdot \dfrac{25}{16}} = \dfrac{5}{64}$

8. $\dfrac{2}{3} \cdot \dfrac{3y}{2} = \dfrac{2 \cdot 3 \cdot y}{3 \cdot 2 \cdot 1} = \dfrac{y}{1} = y$

9. $\dfrac{a^3}{b^2} \cdot \dfrac{b}{a^2} = \dfrac{a^3 \cdot b}{b^2 \cdot a^2} = \dfrac{a \cdot a \cdot a \cdot b}{b \cdot b \cdot a \cdot a} = \dfrac{a}{b}$

10. a. $\left(\dfrac{3}{4}\right)^3 = \dfrac{3}{4} \cdot \dfrac{3}{4} \cdot \dfrac{3}{4} = \dfrac{3 \cdot 3 \cdot 3}{4 \cdot 4 \cdot 4} = \dfrac{27}{64}$

    b. $\left(-\dfrac{4}{5}\right)^2 = \left(-\dfrac{4}{5}\right)\left(-\dfrac{4}{5}\right) = \dfrac{4 \cdot 4}{5 \cdot 5} = \dfrac{16}{25}$

11. $\dfrac{8}{7} \div \dfrac{2}{9} = \dfrac{8}{7} \cdot \dfrac{9}{2} = \dfrac{8 \cdot 9}{7 \cdot 2} = \dfrac{2 \cdot 4 \cdot 9}{7 \cdot 2} = \dfrac{4 \cdot 9}{7} = \dfrac{36}{7}$

12. $\dfrac{4}{9} \div \dfrac{1}{2} = \dfrac{4}{9} \cdot \dfrac{2}{1} = \dfrac{4 \cdot 2}{9 \cdot 1} = \dfrac{8}{9}$

13. $-\dfrac{10}{4} \div \dfrac{2}{9} = -\dfrac{10}{4} \cdot \dfrac{9}{2}$
$= -\dfrac{10 \cdot 9}{4 \cdot 2}$
$= -\dfrac{2 \cdot 5 \cdot 9}{4 \cdot 2}$
$= -\dfrac{5 \cdot 9}{4}$
$= -\dfrac{45}{4}$

14. $\dfrac{3y}{4} \div 5y^3 = \dfrac{3y}{4} \div \dfrac{5y^3}{1}$
$= \dfrac{3y}{4} \cdot \dfrac{1}{5y^3}$
$= \dfrac{3y \cdot 1}{4 \cdot 5y^3}$
$= \dfrac{3 \cdot y \cdot 1}{4 \cdot 5 \cdot y \cdot y \cdot y}$
$= \dfrac{3 \cdot 1}{4 \cdot 5 \cdot y \cdot y}$
$= \dfrac{3}{20y^2}$

15. $\left(-\dfrac{2}{3} \cdot \dfrac{9}{14}\right) \div \dfrac{7}{15} = \left(-\dfrac{2 \cdot 9}{3 \cdot 14}\right) \div \dfrac{7}{15}$
$= \left(-\dfrac{2 \cdot 3 \cdot 3}{3 \cdot 7 \cdot 2}\right) \div \dfrac{7}{15}$
$= \left(-\dfrac{3}{7}\right) \div \dfrac{7}{15}$
$= \left(-\dfrac{3}{7}\right) \cdot \dfrac{15}{7}$
$= -\dfrac{3 \cdot 15}{7 \cdot 7}$
$= -\dfrac{45}{49}$

16. a. $xy = -\dfrac{3}{4} \cdot \dfrac{9}{2} = -\dfrac{3 \cdot 9}{4 \cdot 2} = -\dfrac{27}{8}$

    b. $x \div y = -\dfrac{3}{4} \div \dfrac{9}{2}$
$= -\dfrac{3}{4} \cdot \dfrac{2}{9}$
$= -\dfrac{3 \cdot 2}{4 \cdot 9}$
$= -\dfrac{1 \cdot 3 \cdot 2}{2 \cdot 2 \cdot 3 \cdot 3}$
$= -\dfrac{1}{2 \cdot 3}$
$= -\dfrac{1}{6}$

17. $2x = -\dfrac{9}{4}$
$2\left(-\dfrac{9}{8}\right) \overset{?}{=} -\dfrac{9}{4}$
$\dfrac{2}{1} \cdot \left(-\dfrac{9}{8}\right) \overset{?}{=} -\dfrac{9}{4}$
$-\dfrac{2 \cdot 9}{1 \cdot 8} \overset{?}{=} -\dfrac{9}{4}$
$-\dfrac{2 \cdot 9}{1 \cdot 2 \cdot 4} \overset{?}{=} -\dfrac{9}{4}$
$-\dfrac{9}{4} = -\dfrac{9}{4}$ True

Yes, $-\dfrac{9}{8}$ is a solution of the equation.

18. $\dfrac{1}{6} \cdot 60 = \dfrac{1}{6} \cdot \dfrac{60}{1} = \dfrac{1 \cdot 60}{6 \cdot 1} = \dfrac{1 \cdot 6 \cdot 10}{6 \cdot 1} = 10$

Thus, there are 10 roller coasters in Hershey Park.

Vocabulary and Readiness Check

1. To multiply two fractions, we write $\dfrac{a}{b} \cdot \dfrac{c}{d} = \dfrac{a \cdot c}{\underline{b \cdot d}}$.

2. Two numbers are <u>reciprocals</u> of each other if their product is 1.

3. The expression $\dfrac{2^3}{7} = \dfrac{2 \cdot 2 \cdot 2}{7}$ while

$$\left(\dfrac{2}{7}\right)^3 = \dfrac{2}{7} \cdot \dfrac{2}{7} \cdot \dfrac{2}{7}.$$

4. Every number has a reciprocal expect <u>0</u>.

5. To divide two fractions, we write $\dfrac{a}{b} \div \dfrac{c}{d} = \dfrac{a \cdot d}{\underline{b \cdot c}}$.

6. The word "of" indicates <u>multiplication</u>.

Exercise Set 4.3

1. $\dfrac{6}{11} \cdot \dfrac{3}{7} = \dfrac{6 \cdot 3}{11 \cdot 7} = \dfrac{18}{77}$

3. $-\dfrac{2}{7} \cdot \dfrac{5}{8} = -\dfrac{2 \cdot 5}{7 \cdot 8} = -\dfrac{2 \cdot 5}{7 \cdot 2 \cdot 4} = -\dfrac{5}{7 \cdot 4} = -\dfrac{5}{28}$

5. $-\dfrac{1}{2} \cdot -\dfrac{2}{15} = \dfrac{1 \cdot 2}{2 \cdot 15} = \dfrac{1}{15}$

7. $\dfrac{18x}{20} \cdot \dfrac{36}{99} = \dfrac{18x \cdot 36}{20 \cdot 99}$
$= \dfrac{2 \cdot 9 \cdot x \cdot 2 \cdot 18}{2 \cdot 2 \cdot 5 \cdot 9 \cdot 11}$
$= \dfrac{18 \cdot x}{5 \cdot 11}$
$= \dfrac{18x}{55}$

9. $3a^2 \cdot \dfrac{1}{4} = \dfrac{3a^2}{1} \cdot \dfrac{1}{4} = \dfrac{3a^2 \cdot 1}{1 \cdot 4} = \dfrac{3a^2}{4}$

11. $\dfrac{x^3}{y^3} \cdot \dfrac{y^2}{x} = \dfrac{x^3 \cdot y^2}{y^3 \cdot x} = \dfrac{x \cdot x \cdot x \cdot y \cdot y}{y \cdot y \cdot y \cdot x} = \dfrac{x \cdot x}{y} = \dfrac{x^2}{y}$

13. $0 \cdot \dfrac{8}{9} = 0$

15. $-\dfrac{17y}{20} \cdot \dfrac{4}{5y} = -\dfrac{17y \cdot 4}{20 \cdot 5y}$
$= -\dfrac{17 \cdot y \cdot 4}{5 \cdot 4 \cdot 5 \cdot y}$
$= -\dfrac{17}{5 \cdot 5}$
$= -\dfrac{17}{25}$

17. $\dfrac{11}{20} \cdot \dfrac{1}{7} \cdot \dfrac{5}{22} = \dfrac{11 \cdot 1 \cdot 5}{20 \cdot 7 \cdot 22}$
$= \dfrac{11 \cdot 1 \cdot 5}{5 \cdot 2 \cdot 2 \cdot 7 \cdot 11 \cdot 2}$
$= \dfrac{1}{2 \cdot 2 \cdot 7 \cdot 2}$
$= \dfrac{1}{56}$

19. $\left(\dfrac{1}{5}\right)^3 = \left(\dfrac{1}{5}\right)\left(\dfrac{1}{5}\right)\left(\dfrac{1}{5}\right) = \dfrac{1 \cdot 1 \cdot 1}{5 \cdot 5 \cdot 5} = \dfrac{1}{125}$

21. $\left(-\dfrac{2}{3}\right)^2 = -\dfrac{2}{3} \cdot -\dfrac{2}{3} = \dfrac{2 \cdot 2}{3 \cdot 3} = \dfrac{4}{9}$

23. $\left(-\dfrac{2}{3}\right)^3 \cdot \dfrac{1}{2} = \left(-\dfrac{2}{3}\right)\left(-\dfrac{2}{3}\right)\left(-\dfrac{2}{3}\right) \cdot \dfrac{1}{2}$
$= -\dfrac{2 \cdot 2 \cdot 2 \cdot 1}{3 \cdot 3 \cdot 3 \cdot 2}$
$= -\dfrac{2 \cdot 2 \cdot 1}{3 \cdot 3 \cdot 3}$
$= -\dfrac{4}{27}$

25. $\dfrac{2}{3} \div \dfrac{5}{6} = \dfrac{2}{3} \cdot \dfrac{6}{5} = \dfrac{2 \cdot 6}{3 \cdot 5} = \dfrac{2 \cdot 2 \cdot 3}{3 \cdot 5} = \dfrac{2 \cdot 2}{5} = \dfrac{4}{5}$

27. $-\dfrac{6}{15} \div \dfrac{12}{5} = -\dfrac{6}{15} \cdot \dfrac{5}{12}$
$= -\dfrac{6 \cdot 5}{15 \cdot 12}$
$= -\dfrac{6 \cdot 5 \cdot 1}{5 \cdot 3 \cdot 6 \cdot 2}$
$= -\dfrac{1}{3 \cdot 2}$
$= -\dfrac{1}{6}$

29. $-\dfrac{8}{9} \div \dfrac{x}{2} = -\dfrac{8}{9} \cdot \dfrac{2}{x} = -\dfrac{8 \cdot 2}{9 \cdot x} = -\dfrac{16}{9x}$

31. $\dfrac{11y}{20} \div \dfrac{3}{11} = \dfrac{11y}{20} \cdot \dfrac{11}{3} = \dfrac{11y \cdot 11}{20 \cdot 3} = \dfrac{121y}{60}$

33. $-\dfrac{2}{3} \div 4 = -\dfrac{2}{3} \div \dfrac{4}{1}$

$\qquad = -\dfrac{2}{3} \cdot \dfrac{1}{4}$

$\qquad = -\dfrac{2 \cdot 1}{3 \cdot 4}$

$\qquad = -\dfrac{2 \cdot 1}{3 \cdot 2 \cdot 2}$

$\qquad = -\dfrac{1}{3 \cdot 2}$

$\qquad = -\dfrac{1}{6}$

35. $\dfrac{1}{5x} \div \dfrac{5}{x^2} = \dfrac{1}{5x} \cdot \dfrac{x^2}{5}$

$\qquad = \dfrac{1 \cdot x^2}{5x \cdot 5}$

$\qquad = \dfrac{1 \cdot x \cdot x}{5 \cdot x \cdot 5}$

$\qquad = \dfrac{1 \cdot x}{5 \cdot 5}$

$\qquad = \dfrac{x}{25}$

37. $\dfrac{2}{3} \cdot \dfrac{5}{9} = \dfrac{2 \cdot 5}{3 \cdot 9} = \dfrac{10}{27}$

39. $\dfrac{3x}{7} \div \dfrac{5}{6x} = \dfrac{3x}{7} \cdot \dfrac{6x}{5} = \dfrac{3x \cdot 6x}{7 \cdot 5} = \dfrac{18x^2}{35}$

41. $\dfrac{16}{27y} \div \dfrac{8}{15y} = \dfrac{16}{27y} \cdot \dfrac{15y}{8}$

$\qquad = \dfrac{16 \cdot 15y}{27y \cdot 8}$

$\qquad = \dfrac{8 \cdot 2 \cdot 3 \cdot 5 \cdot y}{3 \cdot 9 \cdot y \cdot 8}$

$\qquad = \dfrac{2 \cdot 5}{9}$

$\qquad = \dfrac{10}{9}$

43. $-\dfrac{5}{28} \cdot \dfrac{35}{25} = -\dfrac{5 \cdot 35}{28 \cdot 25} = -\dfrac{5 \cdot 7 \cdot 5 \cdot 1}{7 \cdot 4 \cdot 5 \cdot 5} = -\dfrac{1}{4}$

45. $\left(-\dfrac{3}{4}\right)^2 = -\dfrac{3}{4} \cdot -\dfrac{3}{4} = \dfrac{3 \cdot 3}{4 \cdot 4} = \dfrac{9}{16}$

47. $\dfrac{x^2}{y} \cdot \dfrac{y^3}{x} = \dfrac{x^2 \cdot y^3}{y \cdot x} = \dfrac{x \cdot x \cdot y \cdot y \cdot y}{y \cdot x \cdot 1} = \dfrac{x \cdot y \cdot y}{1} = xy^2$

49. $7 \div \dfrac{2}{11} = \dfrac{7}{1} \div \dfrac{2}{11} = \dfrac{7}{1} \cdot \dfrac{11}{2} = \dfrac{7 \cdot 11}{1 \cdot 2} = \dfrac{77}{2}$

51. $-3x \div \dfrac{x^2}{12} = -\dfrac{3x}{1} \div \dfrac{x^2}{12}$

$\qquad = -\dfrac{3x}{1} \cdot \dfrac{12}{x^2}$

$\qquad = -\dfrac{3x \cdot 12}{1 \cdot x^2}$

$\qquad = -\dfrac{3 \cdot x \cdot 12}{1 \cdot x \cdot x}$

$\qquad = -\dfrac{3 \cdot 12}{1 \cdot x}$

$\qquad = -\dfrac{36}{x}$

53. $\left(\dfrac{2}{7} \div \dfrac{7}{2}\right) \cdot \dfrac{3}{4} = \left(\dfrac{2}{7} \cdot \dfrac{2}{7}\right) \cdot \dfrac{3}{4}$

$\qquad = \dfrac{4}{49} \cdot \dfrac{3}{4}$

$\qquad = \dfrac{4 \cdot 3}{49 \cdot 4}$

$\qquad = \dfrac{3}{49}$

55. $-\dfrac{19}{63y} \cdot 9y^2 = -\dfrac{19}{63y} \cdot \dfrac{9y^2}{1}$

$\qquad = -\dfrac{19 \cdot 9y^2}{63y \cdot 1}$

$\qquad = -\dfrac{19 \cdot 9 \cdot y \cdot y}{9 \cdot 7 \cdot y \cdot 1}$

$\qquad = -\dfrac{19 \cdot y}{7 \cdot 1}$

$\qquad = -\dfrac{19y}{7}$

57. $-\dfrac{2}{3} \cdot -\dfrac{6}{11} = \dfrac{2 \cdot 6}{3 \cdot 11} = \dfrac{2 \cdot 2 \cdot 3}{3 \cdot 11} = \dfrac{2 \cdot 2}{11} = \dfrac{4}{11}$

59. $\dfrac{4}{8} \div \dfrac{3}{16} = \dfrac{4}{8} \cdot \dfrac{16}{3} = \dfrac{4 \cdot 16}{8 \cdot 3} = \dfrac{4 \cdot 8 \cdot 2}{8 \cdot 3} = \dfrac{4 \cdot 2}{3} = \dfrac{8}{3}$

61.
$$\frac{21x^2}{10y} \div \frac{14x}{25y} = \frac{21x^2}{10y} \cdot \frac{25y}{14x}$$
$$= \frac{21x^2 \cdot 25y}{10y \cdot 14x}$$
$$= \frac{3 \cdot 7 \cdot x \cdot x \cdot 5 \cdot 5 \cdot y}{2 \cdot 5 \cdot y \cdot 2 \cdot 7 \cdot x}$$
$$= \frac{3 \cdot x \cdot 5}{2 \cdot 2}$$
$$= \frac{15x}{4}$$

63.
$$\left(1 \div \frac{3}{4}\right) \cdot \frac{2}{3} = \left(\frac{1}{1} \div \frac{3}{4}\right) \cdot \frac{2}{3}$$
$$= \left(\frac{1}{1} \cdot \frac{4}{3}\right) \cdot \frac{2}{3}$$
$$= \frac{1 \cdot 4}{1 \cdot 3} \cdot \frac{2}{3}$$
$$= \frac{1 \cdot 4 \cdot 2}{1 \cdot 3 \cdot 3}$$
$$= \frac{8}{9}$$

65.
$$\frac{a^3}{2} \div 30a^3 = \frac{a^3}{2} \div \frac{30a^3}{1}$$
$$= \frac{a^3}{2} \cdot \frac{1}{30a^3}$$
$$= \frac{a^3 \cdot 1}{2 \cdot 30a^3}$$
$$= \frac{a \cdot a \cdot a \cdot 1}{2 \cdot 30 \cdot a \cdot a \cdot a}$$
$$= \frac{1}{2 \cdot 30}$$
$$= \frac{1}{60}$$

67.
$$\frac{ab^2}{c} \cdot \frac{c}{ab} = \frac{ab^2 \cdot c}{c \cdot ab} = \frac{a \cdot b \cdot b \cdot c}{c \cdot a \cdot b} = b$$

69.
$$\left(\frac{1}{2} \cdot \frac{2}{3}\right) \div \frac{5}{6} = \left(\frac{1 \cdot 2}{2 \cdot 3}\right) \div \frac{5}{6}$$
$$= \frac{1}{3} \div \frac{5}{6}$$
$$= \frac{1}{3} \cdot \frac{6}{5}$$
$$= \frac{1 \cdot 6}{3 \cdot 5}$$
$$= \frac{1 \cdot 2 \cdot 3}{3 \cdot 5}$$
$$= \frac{1 \cdot 2}{5}$$
$$= \frac{2}{5}$$

71.
$$-\frac{4}{7} \div \left(\frac{4}{5} \cdot \frac{3}{7}\right) = -\frac{4}{7} \div \left(\frac{4 \cdot 3}{5 \cdot 7}\right)$$
$$= -\frac{4}{7} \div \frac{12}{35}$$
$$= -\frac{4}{7} \cdot \frac{35}{12}$$
$$= -\frac{4 \cdot 35}{7 \cdot 12}$$
$$= -\frac{4 \cdot 7 \cdot 5}{7 \cdot 4 \cdot 3}$$
$$= -\frac{5}{3}$$

73. a.
$$xy = \frac{2}{5} \cdot \frac{5}{6} = \frac{2 \cdot 5}{5 \cdot 6} = \frac{2 \cdot 5}{5 \cdot 2 \cdot 3} = \frac{1}{3}$$

b.
$$x \div y = \frac{2}{5} \div \frac{5}{6} = \frac{2}{5} \cdot \frac{6}{5} = \frac{2 \cdot 6}{5 \cdot 5} = \frac{12}{25}$$

75. a.
$$xy = -\frac{4}{5} \cdot \frac{9}{11} = -\frac{4 \cdot 9}{5 \cdot 11} = -\frac{36}{55}$$

b.
$$x \div y = -\frac{4}{5} \div \frac{9}{11} = -\frac{4}{5} \cdot \frac{11}{9} = -\frac{4 \cdot 11}{5 \cdot 9} = -\frac{44}{45}$$

77.
$$3x = -\frac{5}{6}$$
$$3\left(-\frac{5}{18}\right) \overset{?}{=} -\frac{5}{6}$$
$$\frac{3}{1} \cdot -\frac{5}{18} \overset{?}{=} -\frac{5}{6}$$
$$-\frac{3 \cdot 5}{1 \cdot 18} \overset{?}{=} -\frac{5}{6}$$
$$-\frac{3 \cdot 5}{3 \cdot 6} \overset{?}{=} -\frac{5}{6}$$
$$-\frac{5}{6} = -\frac{5}{6} \quad \text{True}$$

Yes, $-\frac{5}{18}$ is a solution of the equation.

79.
$$-\frac{1}{2}z = \frac{1}{10}$$
$$-\frac{1}{2} \cdot \frac{2}{5} \overset{?}{=} \frac{1}{10}$$
$$-\frac{1 \cdot 2}{2 \cdot 5} \overset{?}{=} \frac{1}{10}$$
$$-\frac{1}{5} = \frac{1}{10} \quad \text{False}$$

No, $\frac{2}{5}$ is not a solution of the equation.

81.
$$\frac{1}{4} \text{ of } 200 = \frac{1}{4} \cdot 200$$
$$= \frac{1}{4} \cdot \frac{200}{1}$$
$$= \frac{1 \cdot 200}{4 \cdot 1}$$
$$= \frac{1 \cdot 4 \cdot 50}{4 \cdot 1}$$
$$= \frac{50}{1}$$
$$= 50$$

83.
$$\frac{5}{6} \text{ of } 24 = \frac{5}{6} \cdot 24$$
$$= \frac{5}{6} \cdot \frac{24}{1}$$
$$= \frac{5 \cdot 24}{6 \cdot 1}$$
$$= \frac{5 \cdot 6 \cdot 4}{6 \cdot 1}$$
$$= \frac{5 \cdot 4}{1}$$
$$= \frac{20}{1}$$
$$= 20$$

85.
$$\frac{4}{25} \text{ of } 800 = \frac{4}{25} \cdot 800$$
$$= \frac{4}{25} \cdot \frac{800}{1}$$
$$= \frac{4 \cdot 800}{25 \cdot 1}$$
$$= \frac{4 \cdot 25 \cdot 32}{25 \cdot 1}$$
$$= \frac{4 \cdot 32}{1}$$
$$= 128$$

128 of the students would be expected to major in business.

87.
$$\frac{7}{25} \text{ of } 175 \text{ million} = \frac{7}{25} \cdot 175,000,000$$
$$= \frac{7}{25} \cdot \frac{175,000,000}{1}$$
$$= \frac{7 \cdot 175,000,000}{25 \cdot 1}$$
$$= \frac{7 \cdot 25 \cdot 7,000,000}{25 \cdot 1}$$
$$= 49,000,000$$

Approximately 49 million people ages 16–24 attended the movies.

89. $\frac{2}{5}$ of $2170 = \frac{2}{5} \cdot 2170$

$= \frac{2}{5} \cdot \frac{2170}{1}$

$= \frac{2 \cdot 2170}{5 \cdot 1}$

$= \frac{2 \cdot 5 \cdot 434}{5 \cdot 1}$

$= \frac{2 \cdot 434}{1}$

$= 868$

He hiked 868 miles.

91. $\frac{1}{2}$ of $\frac{3}{8} = \frac{1}{2} \cdot \frac{3}{8} = \frac{1 \cdot 3}{2 \cdot 8} = \frac{3}{16}$

The radius of the circle is $\frac{3}{16}$ inch.

93. $\frac{2}{3}$ of $2757 = \frac{2}{3} \cdot 2757$

$= \frac{2}{3} \cdot \frac{2757}{1}$

$= \frac{2 \cdot 2757}{3 \cdot 1}$

$= \frac{2 \cdot 3 \cdot 919}{3 \cdot 1}$

$= \frac{2 \cdot 919}{1}$

$= 1838$

The sale price is $1838.

95. $\frac{1}{184}$ of $9200 = \frac{1}{184} \cdot 9200$

$= \frac{1}{184} \cdot \frac{9200}{1}$

$= \frac{1 \cdot 9200}{184 \cdot 1}$

$= \frac{1 \cdot 184 \cdot 50}{184 \cdot 1}$

$= 50$

There are 50 libraries in Mississippi.

97. area = length $\cdot$ width $= \frac{5}{14} \cdot \frac{1}{5} = \frac{5 \cdot 1}{14 \cdot 5} = \frac{1}{14}$

The area is $\frac{1}{14}$ square foot.

99. $\frac{8}{25} \cdot 12,000 = \frac{8}{25} \cdot \frac{12,000}{1}$

$= \frac{8 \cdot 25 \cdot 480}{25 \cdot 1}$

$= \frac{8 \cdot 480}{1}$

$= 3840$

The family drove 3840 miles for work.

101. $\frac{1}{5}$ of $12,000 = \frac{1}{5} \cdot 12,000$

$= \frac{1}{5} \cdot \frac{12,000}{1}$

$= \frac{1 \cdot 5 \cdot 2400}{5 \cdot 1}$

$= 2400$

The family drove 2400 miles for family business.

103. $\begin{array}{r} 27 \\ 76 \\ + 98 \\ \hline 201 \end{array}$

105. $\begin{array}{r} 968 \\ - 772 \\ \hline 196 \end{array}$

107. answers may vary

109. $\frac{42}{25} \cdot \frac{125}{36} \div \frac{7}{6} = \frac{42}{25} \cdot \frac{125}{36} \cdot \frac{6}{7}$

$= \frac{42 \cdot 125 \cdot 6}{25 \cdot 36 \cdot 7}$

$= \frac{6 \cdot 7 \cdot 5 \cdot 25 \cdot 6}{25 \cdot 6 \cdot 6 \cdot 7}$

$= 5$

111. $\frac{1}{8}$ of $305,400,000 = \frac{1}{8} \cdot 305,400,000$

$= \frac{1}{8} \cdot \frac{305,400,000}{1}$

$= \frac{1 \cdot 305,400,000}{8 \cdot 1}$

$= \frac{1 \cdot 8 \cdot 38,175,000}{8 \cdot 1}$

$= \frac{38,175,000}{1}$

$= 38,175,000$

The population of California is approximately 38,175,000.

113. $\dfrac{63}{200}$ of $27{,}000 = \dfrac{63}{200} \cdot 27{,}000$

$$= \dfrac{63}{200} \cdot \dfrac{27{,}000}{1}$$

$$= \dfrac{63 \cdot 27{,}000}{200 \cdot 1}$$

$$= \dfrac{63 \cdot 200 \cdot 135}{200 \cdot 1}$$

$$= \dfrac{63 \cdot 135}{1}$$

$$= 8505$$

The National Park Service is charged with maintaining 8505 monuments and statues.

Section 4.4

Practice Problems

1. $\dfrac{6}{13} + \dfrac{2}{13} = \dfrac{6+2}{13} = \dfrac{8}{13}$

2. $\dfrac{5}{8x} + \dfrac{1}{8x} = \dfrac{5+1}{8x} = \dfrac{6}{8x} = \dfrac{2 \cdot 3}{2 \cdot 4x} = \dfrac{3}{4x}$

3. $\dfrac{20}{11} + \dfrac{6}{11} + \dfrac{7}{11} = \dfrac{20+6+7}{11} = \dfrac{33}{11}$ or 3

4. $\dfrac{11}{12} - \dfrac{6}{12} = \dfrac{11-6}{12} = \dfrac{5}{12}$

5. $\dfrac{7}{15} - \dfrac{2}{15} = \dfrac{7-2}{15} = \dfrac{5}{15} = \dfrac{1 \cdot 5}{3 \cdot 5} = \dfrac{1}{3}$

6. $-\dfrac{8}{17} + \dfrac{4}{17} = \dfrac{-8+4}{17} = \dfrac{-4}{17}$ or $-\dfrac{4}{17}$

7. $\dfrac{2}{5} - \dfrac{7y}{5} = \dfrac{2-7y}{5}$

8. $\dfrac{4}{11} - \dfrac{6}{11} - \dfrac{3}{11} = \dfrac{4-6-3}{11} = \dfrac{-5}{11}$ or $-\dfrac{5}{11}$

9. $x + y = -\dfrac{10}{12} + \dfrac{5}{12} = \dfrac{-10+5}{12} = \dfrac{-5}{12}$ or $-\dfrac{5}{12}$

10. perimeter $= \dfrac{3}{20} + \dfrac{3}{20} + \dfrac{3}{20} + \dfrac{3}{20}$

$$= \dfrac{3+3+3+3}{20}$$

$$= \dfrac{12}{20}$$

$$= \dfrac{3 \cdot 4}{5 \cdot 4}$$

$$= \dfrac{3}{5}$$

The perimeter is $\dfrac{3}{5}$ mile.

11. $\dfrac{13}{4} - \dfrac{11}{4} = \dfrac{13-11}{4} = \dfrac{2}{4} = \dfrac{1 \cdot 2}{2 \cdot 2} = \dfrac{1}{2}$

He ran $\dfrac{1}{2}$ mile farther on Monday.

12. 16 is a multiple of 8, so the LCD of $\dfrac{7}{8}$ and $\dfrac{11}{16}$ is 16.

13.

$30 \cdot 1 = 30$	Not a multiple of 25.
$30 \cdot 2 = 60$	Not a multiple of 25.
$30 \cdot 3 = 90$	Not a multiple of 25.
$30 \cdot 4 = 120$	Not a multiple of 25.
$30 \cdot 5 = 150$	A multiple of 25.

The LCD of $\dfrac{23}{25}$ and $\dfrac{1}{30}$ is 150.

14. $40 = \boxed{2 \cdot 2 \cdot 2 \cdot 5}$
$108 = 2 \cdot 2 \cdot \boxed{3 \cdot 3 \cdot 3}$
LCD $= 2 \cdot 2 \cdot 2 \cdot 3 \cdot 3 \cdot 3 \cdot 5 = 1080$
The LCD of $-\dfrac{3}{40}$ and $\dfrac{11}{108}$ is 1080.

15. $20 = 2 \cdot 2 \cdot \boxed{5}$
$24 = \boxed{2 \cdot 2 \cdot 2} \cdot 3$
$45 = \boxed{3 \cdot 3} \cdot 5$
LCD $= 2 \cdot 2 \cdot 2 \cdot 3 \cdot 3 \cdot 5 = 360$
The LCD of $\dfrac{7}{20}, \dfrac{1}{24}$, and $\dfrac{13}{45}$ is 360.

16. $y = \boxed{y}$
$11 = \boxed{11}$
The LCD of $\dfrac{7}{y}$ and $\dfrac{6}{11}$ is $11y$.

17. $\dfrac{7}{8} = \dfrac{7}{8} \cdot \dfrac{7}{7} = \dfrac{7 \cdot 7}{8 \cdot 7} = \dfrac{49}{56}$

18. $\dfrac{1}{4} = \dfrac{1}{4} \cdot \dfrac{5}{5} = \dfrac{1 \cdot 5}{4 \cdot 5} = \dfrac{5}{20}$

19. $\dfrac{3x}{7} = \dfrac{3x}{7} \cdot \dfrac{6}{6} = \dfrac{3x \cdot 6}{7 \cdot 6} = \dfrac{18x}{42}$

20. $4 = \dfrac{4}{1} \cdot \dfrac{6}{6} = \dfrac{4 \cdot 6}{1 \cdot 6} = \dfrac{24}{6}$

21. $\dfrac{9}{4x} = \dfrac{9}{4x} \cdot \dfrac{9}{9} = \dfrac{9 \cdot 9}{4x \cdot 9} = \dfrac{81}{36x}$

Vocabulary and Readiness Check

1. The fractions $\dfrac{9}{11}$ and $\dfrac{13}{11}$ are called <u>like</u> fractions while $\dfrac{3}{4}$ and $\dfrac{1}{3}$ are called <u>unlike</u> fractions.

2. $\dfrac{a}{b} + \dfrac{c}{b} = \dfrac{a+c}{\underline{b}}$ and $\dfrac{a}{b} - \dfrac{c}{b} = \dfrac{a-c}{\underline{b}}$.

3. As long as b is not 0, $\dfrac{-a}{b} = \dfrac{a}{-b} = -\dfrac{a}{\underline{b}}$.

4. The distance around a figure is called its <u>perimeter</u>.

5. The smallest positive number divisible by all the denominators of a list of fractions is called the <u>least common denominator (LCD)</u>.

6. Fractions that represent the same portion of a whole are called <u>equivalent</u> fractions.

Exercise Set 4.4

1. $\dfrac{5}{11} + \dfrac{2}{11} = \dfrac{5+2}{11} = \dfrac{7}{11}$

3. $\dfrac{2}{9} + \dfrac{4}{9} = \dfrac{2+4}{9} = \dfrac{6}{9} = \dfrac{3 \cdot 2}{3 \cdot 3} = \dfrac{2}{3}$

5. $-\dfrac{6}{20} + \dfrac{1}{20} = \dfrac{-6+1}{20} = \dfrac{-5}{20} = -\dfrac{1 \cdot 5}{4 \cdot 5} = -\dfrac{1}{4}$

7. $-\dfrac{3}{14} + \left(-\dfrac{4}{14}\right) = \dfrac{-3+(-4)}{14} = \dfrac{-7}{14} = -\dfrac{1 \cdot 7}{2 \cdot 7} = -\dfrac{1}{2}$

9. $\dfrac{2}{9x} + \dfrac{4}{9x} = \dfrac{2+4}{9x} = \dfrac{6}{9x} = \dfrac{2 \cdot 3}{3 \cdot 3 \cdot x} = \dfrac{2}{3x}$

11. $-\dfrac{7x}{18} + \dfrac{3x}{18} + \dfrac{2x}{18} = \dfrac{-7x+3x+2x}{18}$

$= \dfrac{-2x}{18}$

$= -\dfrac{2 \cdot x}{2 \cdot 9}$

$= -\dfrac{x}{9}$

13. $\dfrac{10}{11} - \dfrac{4}{11} = \dfrac{10-4}{11} = \dfrac{6}{11}$

15. $\dfrac{7}{8} - \dfrac{1}{8} = \dfrac{7-1}{8} = \dfrac{6}{8} = \dfrac{3 \cdot 2}{4 \cdot 2} = \dfrac{3}{4}$

17. $\dfrac{1}{y} - \dfrac{4}{y} = \dfrac{1-4}{y} = \dfrac{-3}{y} = -\dfrac{3}{y}$

19. $-\dfrac{27}{33} - \left(-\dfrac{8}{33}\right) = -\dfrac{27}{33} + \dfrac{8}{33}$

$= \dfrac{-27+8}{33}$

$= \dfrac{-19}{33}$

$= -\dfrac{19}{33}$

21. $\dfrac{20}{21} - \dfrac{10}{21} - \dfrac{17}{21} = \dfrac{20-10-17}{21}$

$= \dfrac{-7}{21}$

$= -\dfrac{1 \cdot 7}{3 \cdot 7}$

$= -\dfrac{1}{3}$

23. $\dfrac{7a}{4} - \dfrac{3}{4} = \dfrac{7a-3}{4}$

25. $-\dfrac{9}{100} + \dfrac{99}{100} = \dfrac{-9+99}{100} = \dfrac{90}{100} = \dfrac{9 \cdot 10}{10 \cdot 10} = \dfrac{9}{10}$

27. $-\dfrac{13x}{28} - \dfrac{13x}{28} = \dfrac{-13x - 13x}{28}$

$\qquad\qquad\qquad = \dfrac{-26x}{28}$

$\qquad\qquad\qquad = -\dfrac{2 \cdot 13 \cdot x}{2 \cdot 14}$

$\qquad\qquad\qquad = -\dfrac{13x}{14}$

29. $\dfrac{9x}{15} + \dfrac{1}{15} = \dfrac{9x + 1}{15}$

31. $\dfrac{7x}{16} - \dfrac{15x}{16} = \dfrac{7x - 15x}{16} = \dfrac{-8x}{16} = -\dfrac{8 \cdot x}{8 \cdot 2} = -\dfrac{x}{2}$

33. $\dfrac{9}{12} - \dfrac{7}{12} - \dfrac{10}{12} = \dfrac{9 - 7 - 10}{12} = \dfrac{-8}{12} = -\dfrac{2 \cdot 4}{3 \cdot 4} = -\dfrac{2}{3}$

35. $\dfrac{x}{4} + \dfrac{3x}{4} - \dfrac{2x}{4} + \dfrac{x}{4} = \dfrac{x + 3x - 2x + x}{4} = \dfrac{3x}{4}$

37. $x + y = \dfrac{3}{4} + \dfrac{2}{4} = \dfrac{3 + 2}{4} = \dfrac{5}{4}$

39. $x - y = -\dfrac{1}{5} - \left(-\dfrac{3}{5}\right) = -\dfrac{1}{5} + \dfrac{3}{5} = \dfrac{-1 + 3}{5} = \dfrac{2}{5}$

41. $\dfrac{4}{20} + \dfrac{7}{20} + \dfrac{9}{20} = \dfrac{4 + 7 + 9}{20} = \dfrac{20}{20} = 1$

The perimeter is 1 inch.

43. $\dfrac{5}{12} + \dfrac{7}{12} + \dfrac{5}{12} + \dfrac{7}{12} = \dfrac{5 + 7 + 5 + 7}{12} = \dfrac{24}{12} = 2$

The perimeter is 2 meters.

45. To find the remaining amount of track to be inspected, subtract the $\dfrac{5}{20}$ mile that has already been inspected from the $\dfrac{19}{20}$ mile total that must be inspected.

$\dfrac{19}{20} - \dfrac{5}{20} = \dfrac{19 - 5}{20} = \dfrac{14}{20} = \dfrac{2 \cdot 7}{2 \cdot 10} = \dfrac{7}{10}$

$\dfrac{7}{10}$ of a mile of track remains to be inspected.

47. To find the fraction that had speed limits less than 70 mph, subtract the $\dfrac{17}{50}$ that have 70 mph speed limits from the $\dfrac{37}{50}$ that have speed limits up to and including 70.

$\dfrac{37}{50} - \dfrac{17}{50} = \dfrac{37 - 17}{50} = \dfrac{20}{50} = \dfrac{2 \cdot 10}{5 \cdot 10} = \dfrac{2}{5}$

$\dfrac{2}{5}$ of the states have speed limits that were less than 70 mph.

49. North America makes up $\dfrac{16}{100}$ of the world's land area, while South America makes up $\dfrac{12}{100}$ of the land area.

$\dfrac{16}{100} + \dfrac{12}{100} = \dfrac{16 + 12}{100} = \dfrac{28}{100} = \dfrac{4 \cdot 7}{4 \cdot 25} = \dfrac{7}{25}$

$\dfrac{7}{25}$ of the world's land area is within North America and South America.

51. Antarctica makes up $\dfrac{9}{100}$ of the world's land area, while Europe makes up $\dfrac{7}{100}$ of the world's land area.

$\dfrac{9}{100} - \dfrac{7}{100} = \dfrac{9 - 7}{100} = \dfrac{2}{100} = \dfrac{1 \cdot 2}{50 \cdot 2} = \dfrac{1}{50}$

Antarctica's land area is $\dfrac{1}{50}$ greater than that of Europe.

53. Multiples of 15:
$15 \cdot 1 = 15$, not a multiple of 9
$15 \cdot 2 = 30$, not a multiple of 9
$15 \cdot 3 = 45$, a multiple of 9
LCD: 45

55. Multiples of 36:
$36 \cdot 1 = 36$, not a multiple of 24
$36 \cdot 2 = 72$, a multiple of 24
LCD: 72

57. $6 = \boxed{2} \cdot 3$
$15 = \boxed{3} \cdot 5$
$25 = \boxed{5 \cdot 5}$
LCD $= 2 \cdot 3 \cdot 5 \cdot 5 = 150$

59. $24 = \boxed{2 \cdot 2 \cdot 2 \cdot 3}$
$x = \boxed{x}$
$LCD = 2 \cdot 2 \cdot 2 \cdot 3 \cdot x = 24x$

61. $18 = \boxed{2 \cdot 3 \cdot 3}$
$21 = 3 \cdot \boxed{7}$
$LCD = 2 \cdot 3 \cdot 3 \cdot 7 = 126$

63. $3 = \boxed{3}$
$21 = 3 \cdot \boxed{7}$
$56 = \boxed{2 \cdot 2 \cdot 2} \cdot 7$
$LCD = 2 \cdot 2 \cdot 2 \cdot 3 \cdot 7 = 168$

65. $\dfrac{2}{3} = \dfrac{2}{3} \cdot \dfrac{7}{7} = \dfrac{2 \cdot 7}{3 \cdot 7} = \dfrac{14}{21}$

67. $\dfrac{4}{7} = \dfrac{4}{7} \cdot \dfrac{5}{5} = \dfrac{4 \cdot 5}{7 \cdot 5} = \dfrac{20}{35}$

69. $\dfrac{1}{2} = \dfrac{1}{2} \cdot \dfrac{25}{25} = \dfrac{1 \cdot 25}{2 \cdot 25} = \dfrac{25}{50}$

71. $\dfrac{14x}{17} = \dfrac{14x}{17} \cdot \dfrac{4}{4} = \dfrac{14x \cdot 4}{17 \cdot 4} = \dfrac{56x}{68}$

73. $\dfrac{2y}{3} = \dfrac{2y}{3} \cdot \dfrac{4}{4} = \dfrac{2y \cdot 4}{3 \cdot 4} = \dfrac{8y}{12}$

75. $\dfrac{5}{9} = \dfrac{5}{9} \cdot \dfrac{4a}{4a} = \dfrac{5 \cdot 4a}{9 \cdot 4a} = \dfrac{20a}{36a}$

77. books & magazines: $\dfrac{27}{50} = \dfrac{27 \cdot 2}{50 \cdot 2} = \dfrac{54}{100}$

clothing & accessories: $\dfrac{1}{2} = \dfrac{1 \cdot 50}{2 \cdot 50} = \dfrac{50}{100}$

computer hardware: $\dfrac{23}{50} = \dfrac{23 \cdot 2}{50 \cdot 2} = \dfrac{46}{100}$

computer software: $\dfrac{1}{2} = \dfrac{1 \cdot 50}{2 \cdot 50} = \dfrac{50}{100}$

drugs, health & beauty aids: $\dfrac{3}{20} = \dfrac{3 \cdot 5}{20 \cdot 5} = \dfrac{15}{100}$

electronics and appliances: $\dfrac{13}{20} = \dfrac{13 \cdot 5}{20 \cdot 5} = \dfrac{65}{100}$

food, beer, wine: $\dfrac{9}{20} = \dfrac{9 \cdot 5}{20 \cdot 5} = \dfrac{45}{100}$

home furnishings: $\dfrac{13}{25} = \dfrac{13 \cdot 4}{25 \cdot 4} = \dfrac{52}{100}$

music and videos: $\dfrac{3}{5} = \dfrac{3 \cdot 20}{5 \cdot 20} = \dfrac{60}{100}$

office equipment & supplies: $\dfrac{61}{100}$

sporting goods: $\dfrac{12}{25} = \dfrac{12 \cdot 4}{25 \cdot 4} = \dfrac{48}{100}$

toys and hobbies and games: $\dfrac{1}{2} = \dfrac{1 \cdot 50}{2 \cdot 50} = \dfrac{50}{100}$

79. $\dfrac{15}{100}$ is the smallest fraction, so drugs, health and beauty aids has the smallest fraction sold online.

81. $3^2 = 3 \cdot 3 = 9$

83. $5^3 = 5 \cdot 5 \cdot 5 = 125$

85. $7^2 = 7 \cdot 7 = 49$

87. $2^3 \cdot 3 = 2 \cdot 2 \cdot 2 \cdot 3 = 24$

89. $\dfrac{2}{7} + \dfrac{9}{7} = \dfrac{2 + 9}{7} = \dfrac{11}{7}$

91. answers may vary

93. $\dfrac{16}{100} + \dfrac{12}{100} + \dfrac{7}{100} + \dfrac{20}{100} + \dfrac{30}{100} + \dfrac{6}{100} + \dfrac{9}{100}$
$= \dfrac{16 + 12 + 7 + 20 + 30 + 6 + 9}{100}$
$= \dfrac{100}{100}$
$= 1$
answers may vary

95. $\dfrac{37x}{165} = \dfrac{37x}{165} \cdot \dfrac{22}{22} = \dfrac{37x \cdot 22}{165 \cdot 22} = \dfrac{814x}{3630}$

97. answers may vary

99. $\dfrac{2}{3} = \dfrac{2 \cdot 5}{3 \cdot 5} = \dfrac{10}{15}$
$\dfrac{2}{3} = \dfrac{2 \cdot 20}{3 \cdot 20} = \dfrac{40}{60}$
$\dfrac{2}{3} = \dfrac{2 \cdot 100}{3 \cdot 100} = \dfrac{200}{300}$

a, b, and d are equivalent to $\dfrac{2}{3}$.

Section 4.5

Practice Problems

1. The LCD is 21.

$$\frac{2}{7}+\frac{8}{21}=\frac{2\cdot3}{7\cdot3}+\frac{8}{21}=\frac{6}{21}+\frac{8}{21}=\frac{14}{21}=\frac{2\cdot7}{3\cdot7}=\frac{2}{3}$$

2. The LCD is 18.

$$\frac{5y}{6}+\frac{2y}{9}=\frac{5y\cdot3}{6\cdot3}+\frac{2y\cdot2}{9\cdot2}=\frac{15y}{18}+\frac{4y}{18}=\frac{19y}{18}$$

3. The LCD is 20.

$$-\frac{1}{5}+\frac{9}{20}=-\frac{1\cdot4}{5\cdot4}+\frac{9}{20}$$
$$=-\frac{4}{20}+\frac{9}{20}$$
$$=\frac{5}{20}$$
$$=\frac{1\cdot5}{4\cdot5}$$
$$=\frac{1}{4}$$

4. The LCD is 70.

$$\frac{5}{7}-\frac{9}{10}=\frac{5\cdot10}{7\cdot10}-\frac{9\cdot7}{10\cdot7}=\frac{50}{70}-\frac{63}{70}=-\frac{13}{70}$$

5. The LCD is 24.

$$\frac{5}{8}-\frac{1}{3}-\frac{1}{12}=\frac{5\cdot3}{8\cdot3}-\frac{1\cdot8}{3\cdot8}-\frac{1\cdot2}{12\cdot2}$$
$$=\frac{15}{24}-\frac{8}{24}-\frac{2}{24}$$
$$=\frac{5}{24}$$

6. Recall that $5=\frac{5}{1}$. The LCD is 4.

$$\frac{5}{1}-\frac{y}{4}=\frac{5\cdot4}{1\cdot4}-\frac{y}{4}=\frac{20}{4}-\frac{y}{4}=\frac{20-y}{4}$$

7. The LCD is 40. Write each fraction as an equivalent fraction with a denominator of 40.

$$\frac{5}{8}=\frac{5\cdot5}{8\cdot5}=\frac{25}{40}$$
$$\frac{11}{20}=\frac{11\cdot2}{20\cdot2}=\frac{22}{40}$$

Since $25>22$, $\frac{25}{40}>\frac{22}{40}$, so $\frac{5}{8}>\frac{11}{20}$.

8. The LCD is 20. Write each fraction as an equivalent fraction with a denominator of 20.

$$-\frac{17}{20}$$
$$-\frac{4}{5}=-\frac{4\cdot4}{5\cdot4}=-\frac{16}{20}$$

Since $-17<-16$, $-\frac{17}{20}<-\frac{16}{20}$, so $-\frac{17}{20}<-\frac{4}{5}$.

9. The LCD is 99.

$$x-y=\frac{5}{11}-\frac{4}{9}=\frac{5\cdot9}{11\cdot9}-\frac{4\cdot11}{9\cdot11}=\frac{45}{99}-\frac{44}{99}=\frac{1}{99}$$

10. The LCD is 30.

$$\frac{3}{5}+\frac{3}{10}+\frac{1}{15}=\frac{3\cdot6}{5\cdot6}+\frac{3\cdot3}{10\cdot3}+\frac{1\cdot2}{15\cdot2}$$
$$=\frac{18}{30}+\frac{9}{30}+\frac{2}{30}$$
$$=\frac{29}{30}$$

The homeowner needs $\frac{29}{30}$ cubic yard of cement.

11. The LCD is 12.

$$\frac{3}{4}-\frac{2}{3}=\frac{3\cdot3}{4\cdot3}-\frac{2\cdot4}{3\cdot4}=\frac{9}{12}-\frac{8}{12}=\frac{1}{12}$$

The difference in length is $\frac{1}{12}$ foot.

Calculator Explorations

1. $\dfrac{1}{16}+\dfrac{2}{5}=\dfrac{37}{80}$

2. $\dfrac{3}{20}+\dfrac{2}{25}=\dfrac{23}{100}$

3. $\dfrac{4}{9}+\dfrac{7}{8}=\dfrac{95}{72}$

4. $\dfrac{9}{11}+\dfrac{5}{12}=\dfrac{163}{132}$

5. $\dfrac{10}{17}+\dfrac{12}{19}=\dfrac{394}{323}$

6. $\dfrac{14}{31}+\dfrac{15}{21}=\dfrac{253}{217}$

Vocabulary and Readiness Check

1. To add or subtract unlike fractions, we first write the fractions as <u>equivalent</u> fractions with a common denominator. The common denominator we use is called the <u>least common denominator</u>.

2. The LCD for $\dfrac{1}{6}$ and $\dfrac{5}{8}$ is <u>24</u>.

3. $\dfrac{1}{6} + \dfrac{5}{8} = \dfrac{1}{6} \cdot \dfrac{4}{4} + \dfrac{5}{8} \cdot \dfrac{3}{3} = \dfrac{4}{\underline{24}} + \dfrac{15}{\underline{24}} = \dfrac{19}{\underline{24}}$.

4. $\dfrac{1}{6} - \dfrac{5}{8} = \dfrac{1}{6} \cdot \dfrac{4}{4} - \dfrac{5}{8} \cdot \dfrac{3}{3} = \dfrac{4}{\underline{24}} - \dfrac{15}{\underline{24}} = -\dfrac{11}{\underline{24}}$.

5. $x - y$ is an <u>expression</u> while $3x = \dfrac{1}{5}$ is an <u>equation</u>.

6. Since $-10 < -1$, we know that $-\dfrac{10}{13} \underline{\ \ <\ \ } -\dfrac{1}{13}$.

Exercise Set 4.5

1. The LCD is 6.
$$\frac{2}{3} + \frac{1}{6} = \frac{2 \cdot 2}{3 \cdot 2} + \frac{1}{6} = \frac{4}{6} + \frac{1}{6} = \frac{5}{6}$$

3. The LCD is 6.
$$\frac{1}{2} - \frac{1}{3} = \frac{1 \cdot 3}{2 \cdot 3} - \frac{1 \cdot 2}{3 \cdot 2} = \frac{3}{6} - \frac{2}{6} = \frac{1}{6}$$

5. The LCD is 33.
$$-\frac{2}{11} + \frac{2}{33} = -\frac{2 \cdot 3}{11 \cdot 3} + \frac{2}{33} = -\frac{6}{33} + \frac{2}{33} = -\frac{4}{33}$$

7. The LCD is 14.
$$\frac{3}{14} - \frac{3}{7} = \frac{3}{14} - \frac{3 \cdot 2}{7 \cdot 2} = \frac{3}{14} - \frac{6}{14} = -\frac{3}{14}$$

9. The LCD is 35.
$$\begin{aligned}
\frac{11x}{35} + \frac{2x}{7} &= \frac{11x}{35} + \frac{2x \cdot 5}{7 \cdot 5} \\
&= \frac{11x}{35} + \frac{10x}{35} \\
&= \frac{21x}{35} \\
&= \frac{3 \cdot 7 \cdot x}{5 \cdot 7} \\
&= \frac{3x}{5}
\end{aligned}$$

11. The LCD is 12.
$$2 - \frac{y}{12} = \frac{2}{1} - \frac{y}{12} = \frac{2 \cdot 12}{1 \cdot 12} - \frac{y}{12} = \frac{24}{12} - \frac{y}{12} = \frac{24 - y}{12}$$

13. The LCD is 36.
$$\frac{5}{12} - \frac{1}{9} = \frac{5 \cdot 3}{12 \cdot 3} - \frac{1 \cdot 4}{9 \cdot 4} = \frac{15}{36} - \frac{4}{36} = \frac{11}{36}$$

15. The LCD is 7.
$$-7 + \frac{5}{7} = -\frac{7}{1} + \frac{5}{7} = -\frac{7 \cdot 7}{1 \cdot 7} + \frac{5}{7} = -\frac{49}{7} + \frac{5}{7} = -\frac{44}{7}$$

17. The LCD is 99.
$$\begin{aligned}
\frac{5a}{11} + \frac{4a}{9} &= \frac{5a \cdot 9}{11 \cdot 9} + \frac{4a \cdot 11}{9 \cdot 11} \\
&= \frac{45a}{99} + \frac{44a}{99} \\
&= \frac{89a}{99}
\end{aligned}$$

19. The LCD is 6.
$$\frac{2y}{3} - \frac{1}{6} = \frac{2y \cdot 2}{3 \cdot 2} - \frac{1}{6} = \frac{4y}{6} - \frac{1}{6} = \frac{4y - 1}{6}$$

21. The LCD is $2x$.
$$\frac{1}{2} + \frac{3}{x} = \frac{1 \cdot x}{2 \cdot x} + \frac{3 \cdot 2}{x \cdot 2} = \frac{x}{2x} + \frac{6}{2x} = \frac{x + 6}{2x}$$

23. The LCD is 33.
$$-\frac{2}{11} - \frac{2}{33} = -\frac{2 \cdot 3}{11 \cdot 3} - \frac{2}{33} = -\frac{6}{33} - \frac{2}{33} = -\frac{8}{33}$$

25. The LCD is 14.
$$\frac{9}{14} - \frac{3}{7} = \frac{9}{14} - \frac{3 \cdot 2}{7 \cdot 2} = \frac{9}{14} - \frac{6}{14} = \frac{3}{14}$$

27. The LCD is 35.

$$\frac{11y}{35} - \frac{2}{7} = \frac{11y}{35} - \frac{2 \cdot 5}{7 \cdot 5} = \frac{11y}{35} - \frac{10}{35} = \frac{11y - 10}{35}$$

29. The LCD is 36.

$$\frac{1}{9} - \frac{5}{12} = \frac{1 \cdot 4}{9 \cdot 4} - \frac{5 \cdot 3}{12 \cdot 3} = \frac{4}{36} - \frac{15}{36} = -\frac{11}{36}$$

31. The LCD is 60.

$$\frac{7}{15} - \frac{5}{12} = \frac{7 \cdot 4}{15 \cdot 4} - \frac{5 \cdot 5}{12 \cdot 5}$$
$$= \frac{28}{60} - \frac{25}{60}$$
$$= \frac{3}{60}$$
$$= \frac{1 \cdot 3}{20 \cdot 3}$$
$$= \frac{1}{20}$$

33. The LCD is 56.

$$\frac{5}{7} - \frac{1}{8} = \frac{5 \cdot 8}{7 \cdot 8} - \frac{1 \cdot 7}{8 \cdot 7} = \frac{40}{56} - \frac{7}{56} = \frac{33}{56}$$

35. The LCD is 16.

$$\frac{7}{8} + \frac{3}{16} = \frac{7 \cdot 2}{8 \cdot 2} + \frac{3}{16} = \frac{14}{16} + \frac{3}{16} = \frac{17}{16}$$

37. $\dfrac{3}{9} - \dfrac{5}{9} = \dfrac{3-5}{9} = -\dfrac{2}{9}$

39. The LCD is 30.

$$-\frac{2}{5} + \frac{1}{3} - \frac{3}{10} = -\frac{2 \cdot 6}{5 \cdot 6} + \frac{1 \cdot 10}{3 \cdot 10} - \frac{3 \cdot 3}{10 \cdot 3}$$
$$= -\frac{12}{30} + \frac{10}{30} - \frac{9}{30}$$
$$= -\frac{11}{30}$$

41. The LCD is 33.

$$\frac{5}{11} + \frac{y}{3} = \frac{5 \cdot 3}{11 \cdot 3} + \frac{y \cdot 11}{3 \cdot 11}$$
$$= \frac{15}{33} + \frac{11y}{33}$$
$$= \frac{15 + 11y}{33}$$

43. The LCD is 42.

$$-\frac{5}{6} - \frac{3}{7} = -\frac{5 \cdot 7}{6 \cdot 7} - \frac{3 \cdot 6}{7 \cdot 6} = -\frac{35}{42} - \frac{18}{42} = -\frac{53}{42}$$

45. The LCD is 16.

$$\frac{x}{2} + \frac{x}{4} + \frac{2x}{16} = \frac{x \cdot 8}{2 \cdot 8} + \frac{x \cdot 4}{4 \cdot 4} + \frac{2x}{16}$$
$$= \frac{8x}{16} + \frac{4x}{16} + \frac{2x}{16}$$
$$= \frac{14x}{16}$$
$$= \frac{2 \cdot 7x}{2 \cdot 8}$$
$$= \frac{7x}{8}$$

47. The LCD is 18.

$$\frac{7}{9} - \frac{1}{6} = \frac{7 \cdot 2}{9 \cdot 2} - \frac{1 \cdot 3}{6 \cdot 3} = \frac{14}{18} - \frac{3}{18} = \frac{11}{18}$$

49. The LCD is 39.

$$\frac{2a}{3} + \frac{6a}{13} = \frac{2a \cdot 13}{3 \cdot 13} + \frac{6a \cdot 3}{13 \cdot 3}$$
$$= \frac{26a}{39} + \frac{18a}{39}$$
$$= \frac{44a}{39}$$

51. The LCD is 60.

$$\frac{7}{30} - \frac{5}{12} = \frac{7 \cdot 2}{30 \cdot 2} - \frac{5 \cdot 5}{12 \cdot 5} = \frac{14}{60} - \frac{25}{60} = -\frac{11}{60}$$

53. The LCD is 9y.

$$\frac{5}{9} + \frac{1}{y} = \frac{5 \cdot y}{9 \cdot y} + \frac{1 \cdot 9}{y \cdot 9} = \frac{5y}{9y} + \frac{9}{9y} = \frac{5y + 9}{9y}$$

55. The LCD is 20.

$$\frac{6}{5} - \frac{3}{4} + \frac{1}{2} = \frac{6 \cdot 4}{5 \cdot 4} - \frac{3 \cdot 5}{4 \cdot 5} + \frac{1 \cdot 10}{2 \cdot 10}$$
$$= \frac{24}{20} - \frac{15}{20} + \frac{10}{20}$$
$$= \frac{19}{20}$$

57. The LCD is 45.

$$\frac{4}{5} + \frac{4}{9} = \frac{4 \cdot 9}{5 \cdot 9} + \frac{4 \cdot 5}{9 \cdot 5} = \frac{36}{45} + \frac{20}{45} = \frac{56}{45}$$

59. The LCD is $72x$.

$$\frac{5}{9x}+\frac{1}{8}=\frac{5\cdot 8}{9x\cdot 8}+\frac{1\cdot 9x}{8\cdot 9x}$$
$$=\frac{40}{72x}+\frac{9x}{72x}$$
$$=\frac{40+9x}{72x}$$

61. The LCD is 24.

$$-\frac{9}{12}+\frac{17}{24}-\frac{1}{6}=-\frac{9\cdot 2}{12\cdot 2}+\frac{17}{24}-\frac{1\cdot 4}{6\cdot 4}$$
$$=-\frac{18}{24}+\frac{17}{24}-\frac{4}{24}$$
$$=-\frac{5}{24}$$

63. The LCD is 56.

$$\frac{3x}{8}+\frac{2x}{7}-\frac{5}{14}=\frac{3x\cdot 7}{8\cdot 7}+\frac{2x\cdot 8}{7\cdot 8}-\frac{5\cdot 4}{14\cdot 4}$$
$$=\frac{21x}{56}+\frac{16x}{56}-\frac{20}{56}$$
$$=\frac{37x-20}{56}$$

65. The LCD is 70. Write each fraction as an equivalent fraction with a denominator of 70.

$$\frac{2}{7}=\frac{2\cdot 10}{7\cdot 10}=\frac{20}{70}$$

$$\frac{3}{10}=\frac{3\cdot 7}{10\cdot 7}=\frac{21}{70}$$

Since $20<21$, $\frac{20}{70}<\frac{21}{70}$, so $\frac{2}{7}<\frac{3}{10}$.

67. A positive fraction is greater than a negative fraction.

$$\frac{5}{6}>-\frac{13}{15}$$

69. The LCD is 28. Write each fraction as an equivalent fraction with a denominator of 28.

$$-\frac{3}{4}=-\frac{3\cdot 7}{4\cdot 7}=-\frac{21}{28}$$

$$-\frac{11}{14}=-\frac{11\cdot 2}{14\cdot 2}=-\frac{22}{28}$$

Since $-21>-22$, $-\frac{21}{28}>-\frac{22}{28}$, so $-\frac{3}{4}>-\frac{11}{14}$.

71. The LCD is 12.

$$x+y=\frac{1}{3}+\frac{3}{4}=\frac{1\cdot 4}{3\cdot 4}+\frac{3\cdot 3}{4\cdot 3}=\frac{4}{12}+\frac{9}{12}=\frac{13}{12}$$

73. $xy=\dfrac{1}{3}\cdot\dfrac{3}{4}=\dfrac{1\cdot 3}{3\cdot 4}=\dfrac{1}{4}$

75.
$$2y+x=2\left(\frac{3}{4}\right)+\frac{1}{3}$$
$$=\frac{6}{4}+\frac{1}{3}$$
$$=\frac{2\cdot 3}{2\cdot 2}+\frac{1}{3}$$
$$=\frac{3}{2}+\frac{1}{3}$$
$$=\frac{3\cdot 3}{2\cdot 3}+\frac{1\cdot 2}{3\cdot 2}$$
$$=\frac{9}{6}+\frac{2}{6}$$
$$=\frac{11}{6}$$

77. The LCD is 15.

$$\frac{4}{5}+\frac{1}{3}+\frac{4}{5}+\frac{1}{3}=\frac{4}{5}\cdot\frac{3}{3}+\frac{1}{3}\cdot\frac{5}{5}+\frac{4}{5}\cdot\frac{3}{3}+\frac{1}{3}\cdot\frac{5}{5}$$
$$=\frac{12}{15}+\frac{5}{15}+\frac{12}{15}+\frac{5}{15}$$
$$=\frac{34}{15}$$

The perimeter is $\dfrac{34}{15}$ or $2\dfrac{4}{15}$ centimeters.

79. The LCD is 20.

$$\frac{1}{4}+\frac{1}{5}+\frac{1}{2}+\frac{3}{4}=\frac{1\cdot 5}{4\cdot 5}+\frac{1\cdot 4}{5\cdot 4}+\frac{1\cdot 10}{2\cdot 10}+\frac{3\cdot 5}{4\cdot 5}$$
$$=\frac{5}{20}+\frac{4}{20}+\frac{10}{20}+\frac{15}{20}$$
$$=\frac{34}{20}$$
$$=\frac{17\cdot 2}{10\cdot 2}$$
$$=\frac{17}{10}\text{ or }1\frac{7}{10}$$

The perimeter is $\dfrac{17}{10}$ meters or $1\dfrac{7}{10}$ meters.

81. The sum of a number and $\dfrac{1}{2}$ translates as $x+\dfrac{1}{2}$.

83. A number subtracted from $-\dfrac{3}{8}$ translates as

$-\dfrac{3}{8} - x$.

85. The LCD is 100.

$$\frac{17}{100} - \frac{1}{10} = \frac{17}{100} - \frac{1 \cdot 10}{10 \cdot 10} = \frac{17}{100} - \frac{10}{100} = \frac{7}{100}$$

The sloth can travel $\dfrac{7}{100}$ mph faster in trees.

87. $1 - \dfrac{3}{16} - \dfrac{3}{16} = \dfrac{16}{16} - \dfrac{3}{16} - \dfrac{3}{16} = \dfrac{10}{16} = \dfrac{5}{8}$

The inner diameter is $\dfrac{5}{8}$ inch.

89. The LCD is 100.

$$\frac{13}{20} - \frac{4}{25} = \frac{13 \cdot 5}{20 \cdot 5} - \frac{4 \cdot 4}{25 \cdot 4} = \frac{65}{100} - \frac{16}{100} = \frac{49}{100}$$

$\dfrac{49}{100}$ of the American students ages 10 to 17 name math or science as their favorite subject in school.

91. The LCD is 32.

$$\frac{1}{2} + \frac{11}{16} + \frac{9}{32} = \frac{1}{2} \cdot \frac{16}{16} + \frac{11}{16} \cdot \frac{2}{2} + \frac{9}{32}$$

$$= \frac{16}{32} + \frac{22}{32} + \frac{9}{32}$$

$$= \frac{47}{32}$$

The total length is $\dfrac{47}{32}$ inches.

93. The LCD is 50.

$$\frac{13}{50} + \frac{1}{2} = \frac{13}{50} + \frac{1}{2} \cdot \frac{25}{25}$$

$$= \frac{13}{50} + \frac{25}{50}$$

$$= \frac{38}{50}$$

$$= \frac{2 \cdot 19}{2 \cdot 25}$$

$$= \frac{19}{25}$$

The Pacific and Atlantic Oceans account for $\dfrac{19}{25}$ of the world's water surfaces.

95. The piece representing Lakes/Seashores is labeled $\dfrac{1}{25}$, so $\dfrac{1}{25}$ of the areas maintained by the National Park Service are National Lakes or National Seashores.

97. $1 - \dfrac{21}{100} = \dfrac{100}{100} - \dfrac{21}{100} = \dfrac{79}{100}$

$\dfrac{79}{100}$ of areas maintained by the National Park Service are NOT National Monuments.

99. $-50 \div 5 \cdot 2 = -10 \cdot 2 = -20$

101. $(8 - 6) \cdot (4 - 7) = 2 \cdot (-3) = -6$

103. a.

b. There seems to be an error.

c. $\dfrac{3}{5} + \dfrac{4}{5} = \dfrac{3+4}{5} = \dfrac{7}{5} \left(\text{or } \dfrac{14}{10} \text{ not } \dfrac{7}{10} \right)$

105. The LCD is 540.

$$\frac{2}{3} - \frac{1}{4} - \frac{2}{540} = \frac{2}{3} \cdot \frac{180}{180} - \frac{1}{4} \cdot \frac{135}{135} - \frac{2}{540}$$

$$= \frac{360}{540} - \frac{135}{540} - \frac{2}{540}$$

$$= \frac{225}{540} - \frac{2}{540}$$

$$= \frac{223}{540}$$

107. The LCD is 1760.

$$\frac{30}{55} + \frac{1000}{1760} = \frac{30 \cdot 32}{55 \cdot 32} + \frac{1000}{1760}$$

$$= \frac{960}{1760} + \frac{1000}{1760}$$

$$= \frac{1960}{1760}$$

$$= \frac{49 \cdot 40}{44 \cdot 40}$$

$$= \frac{49}{44}$$

109. answers may vary

111. The LCD is 106. Write each fraction as an equivalent fraction with a denominator of 106.

$$\frac{24}{53} = \frac{24 \cdot 2}{53 \cdot 2} = \frac{48}{106}$$

$$\frac{51}{106}$$

Since $51 > 48$, $\frac{51}{106} > \frac{48}{106}$, so $\frac{51}{106} > \frac{24}{53}$.

Standard mail accounted for the greater portion of the mail handled by volume.

Integrated Review

1. 3 out of 7 equal parts are shaded: $\frac{3}{7}$

2. Each part is $\frac{1}{4}$ of a whole and there are 5 parts shaded, or 1 whole and 1 more part: $\frac{5}{4}$ or $1\frac{1}{4}$

3. number that get fewer than $8 \rightarrow 73$
total number of people $\quad\;\; \rightarrow \overline{85}$

$\frac{73}{85}$ of people get fewer than 8 hours of sleep each night.

4.

5. $\frac{11}{-11} = -1$

6. $\frac{17}{1} = 17$

7. $\frac{0}{-3} = 0$

8. $\frac{7}{0}$ is undefined

9. $65 = 5 \cdot 13$

10. $70 = 2 \cdot 35$
$\qquad\quad \downarrow \;\; \downarrow \searrow$
$\qquad\quad 2 \cdot 5 \cdot 7$
$\quad 70 = 2 \cdot 5 \cdot 7$

11. $315 = 3 \cdot 105$
$\qquad\quad \downarrow \;\; \downarrow \searrow$
$\qquad\quad 3 \cdot 3 \cdot 35$
$\qquad\quad \downarrow \; \downarrow \; \downarrow \searrow$
$\qquad\quad 3 \cdot 3 \cdot 5 \cdot 7$
$\quad 315 = 3^2 \cdot 5 \cdot 7$

12. $441 = 3 \cdot 147$
$\qquad\quad \downarrow \;\; \downarrow \searrow$
$\qquad\quad 3 \cdot 3 \cdot 49$
$\qquad\quad \downarrow \; \downarrow \; \downarrow \searrow$
$\qquad\quad 3 \cdot 3 \cdot 7 \cdot 7$
$\quad 441 = 3^2 \cdot 7^2$

13. $\frac{2}{14} = \frac{2 \cdot 1}{2 \cdot 7} = \frac{1}{7}$

14. $\frac{24}{20} = \frac{6 \cdot 4}{5 \cdot 4} = \frac{6}{5}$

15. $-\frac{56}{60} = -\frac{14 \cdot 4}{15 \cdot 4} = -\frac{14}{15}$

16. $-\frac{72}{80} = -\frac{8 \cdot 9}{8 \cdot 10} = -\frac{9}{10}$

17. $\frac{54x}{135} = \frac{27 \cdot 2 \cdot x}{27 \cdot 5} = \frac{2x}{5}$

18. $\frac{90}{240y} = \frac{30 \cdot 3}{30 \cdot 8 \cdot y} = \frac{3}{8y}$

19. $\frac{165z^3}{210z} = \frac{15 \cdot 11 \cdot z \cdot z \cdot z}{15 \cdot 14 \cdot z} = \frac{11 \cdot z \cdot z}{14} = \frac{11z^2}{14}$

20. $\frac{245ab}{385a^2b^3} = \frac{35 \cdot 7 \cdot a \cdot b}{35 \cdot 11 \cdot a \cdot a \cdot b \cdot b \cdot b}$
$\qquad\qquad = \frac{7}{11 \cdot a \cdot b \cdot b}$
$\qquad\qquad = \frac{7}{11ab^2}$

21. Not equivalent, since the cross products are not equal: $7 \cdot 10 = 70$, $8 \cdot 9 = 72$

22. Equivalent, since the cross products are equal: $10 \cdot 18 = 180$, $12 \cdot 15 = 180$

23. a. number not adjacent $\rightarrow 2$
total number $\qquad \rightarrow \overline{50}$

$\dfrac{2}{50} = \dfrac{1 \cdot 2}{25 \cdot 2} = \dfrac{1}{25}$ of the states are not adjacent to any other states.

b. $50 - 2 = 48$; 48 states are adjacent to other states.

c. $\dfrac{48}{50} = \dfrac{2 \cdot 24}{2 \cdot 25} = \dfrac{24}{25}$ of the states are adjacent to other states.

24. a. number not rated $\rightarrow 255$
total number $\qquad \rightarrow \overline{725}$

$\dfrac{255}{725} = \dfrac{5 \cdot 51}{5 \cdot 145} = \dfrac{51}{145}$ of the new films were not rated.

b. $725 - 255 = 470$; 470 of the new films were rated.

c. $\dfrac{470}{725} = \dfrac{5 \cdot 94}{5 \cdot 145} = \dfrac{94}{145}$ of the new films were rated.

25. $5 = \boxed{5}$
$6 = \boxed{2 \cdot 3}$
LCM $= 2 \cdot 3 \cdot 5 = 30$

26. $2 = \boxed{2}$
$14 = 2 \cdot \boxed{7}$
LCM $= 2 \cdot 7 = 14$

27. $6 = \boxed{2} \cdot 3$
$18 = 2 \cdot \boxed{3 \cdot 3}$
$30 = 2 \cdot 3 \cdot \boxed{5}$
LCM $= 2 \cdot 3 \cdot 3 \cdot 5 = 90$

28. $\dfrac{7}{9} = \dfrac{7}{9} \cdot \dfrac{4}{4} = \dfrac{7 \cdot 4}{9 \cdot 4} = \dfrac{28}{36}$

29. $\dfrac{11}{15} = \dfrac{11}{15} \cdot \dfrac{5}{5} = \dfrac{11 \cdot 5}{15 \cdot 5} = \dfrac{55}{75}$

30. $\dfrac{5}{6} = \dfrac{5}{6} \cdot \dfrac{8}{8} = \dfrac{5 \cdot 8}{6 \cdot 8} = \dfrac{40}{48}$

31. $\dfrac{1}{5} + \dfrac{3}{5} = \dfrac{1+3}{5} = \dfrac{4}{5}$

32. $\dfrac{1}{5} - \dfrac{3}{5} = \dfrac{1-3}{5} = \dfrac{-2}{5} = -\dfrac{2}{5}$

33. $\dfrac{1}{5} \cdot \dfrac{3}{5} = \dfrac{1 \cdot 3}{5 \cdot 5} = \dfrac{3}{25}$

34. $\dfrac{1}{5} \div \dfrac{3}{5} = \dfrac{1}{5} \cdot \dfrac{5}{3} = \dfrac{1 \cdot 5}{5 \cdot 3} = \dfrac{1}{3}$

35. $\dfrac{2}{3} \div \dfrac{5}{6} = \dfrac{2}{3} \cdot \dfrac{6}{5} = \dfrac{2 \cdot 6}{3 \cdot 5} = \dfrac{2 \cdot 2 \cdot 3}{3 \cdot 5} = \dfrac{2 \cdot 2}{5} = \dfrac{4}{5}$

36. $\dfrac{2a}{3} \cdot \dfrac{5}{6a} = \dfrac{2a \cdot 5}{3 \cdot 6a} = \dfrac{2 \cdot a \cdot 5}{3 \cdot 2 \cdot 3 \cdot a} = \dfrac{5}{3 \cdot 3} = \dfrac{5}{9}$

37. The LCD is $6y$.
$$\dfrac{2}{3y} - \dfrac{5}{6y} = \dfrac{2}{3y} \cdot \dfrac{2}{2} - \dfrac{5}{6y}$$
$$= \dfrac{2 \cdot 2}{3y \cdot 2} - \dfrac{5}{6y}$$
$$= \dfrac{4}{6y} - \dfrac{5}{6y}$$
$$= -\dfrac{1}{6y}$$

38. The LCD is 6.
$$\dfrac{2x}{3} + \dfrac{5x}{6} = \dfrac{2x}{3} \cdot \dfrac{2}{2} + \dfrac{5x}{6}$$
$$= \dfrac{2x \cdot 2}{3 \cdot 2} + \dfrac{5x}{6}$$
$$= \dfrac{4x}{6} + \dfrac{5x}{6}$$
$$= \dfrac{9x}{6}$$
$$= \dfrac{3 \cdot 3 \cdot x}{3 \cdot 2}$$
$$= \dfrac{3x}{2}$$

39. $-\dfrac{1}{7} \cdot -\dfrac{7}{18} = \dfrac{1 \cdot 7}{7 \cdot 18} = \dfrac{1}{18}$

40. $-\dfrac{4}{9} \cdot -\dfrac{3}{7} = \dfrac{4 \cdot 3}{9 \cdot 7} = \dfrac{4 \cdot 3}{3 \cdot 3 \cdot 7} = \dfrac{4}{3 \cdot 7} = \dfrac{4}{21}$

41.
$$-\frac{7z}{8} \div 6z^2 = -\frac{7z}{8} \div \frac{6z^2}{1}$$
$$= -\frac{7z}{8} \cdot \frac{1}{6z^2}$$
$$= -\frac{7z \cdot 1}{8 \cdot 6z^2}$$
$$= -\frac{7 \cdot z \cdot 1}{8 \cdot 6 \cdot z \cdot z}$$
$$= -\frac{7}{48z}$$

42.
$$-\frac{9}{10} \div 5 = -\frac{9}{10} \div \frac{5}{1} = -\frac{9}{10} \cdot \frac{1}{5} = -\frac{9 \cdot 1}{10 \cdot 5} = -\frac{9}{50}$$

43. The LCD is 40.
$$\frac{7}{8} + \frac{1}{20} = \frac{7 \cdot 5}{8 \cdot 5} + \frac{1 \cdot 2}{20 \cdot 2} = \frac{35}{40} + \frac{2}{40} = \frac{37}{40}$$

44. The LCD is 36.
$$\frac{5}{12} - \frac{1}{9} = \frac{5 \cdot 3}{12 \cdot 3} - \frac{1 \cdot 4}{9 \cdot 4} = \frac{15}{36} - \frac{4}{36} = \frac{11}{36}$$

45. The LCD is 18.
$$\frac{2}{9} + \frac{1}{18} + \frac{1}{3} = \frac{2 \cdot 2}{9 \cdot 2} + \frac{1}{18} + \frac{1 \cdot 6}{3 \cdot 6}$$
$$= \frac{4}{18} + \frac{1}{18} + \frac{6}{18}$$
$$= \frac{11}{18}$$

46. The LCD is 50.
$$\frac{3y}{10} + \frac{y}{5} + \frac{6}{25} = \frac{3y \cdot 5}{10 \cdot 5} + \frac{y \cdot 10}{5 \cdot 10} + \frac{6 \cdot 2}{25 \cdot 2}$$
$$= \frac{15y}{50} + \frac{10y}{50} + \frac{12}{50}$$
$$= \frac{25y}{50} + \frac{12}{50}$$
$$= \frac{25y + 12}{50}$$

47. $\frac{2}{3}$ of a number translates as $\frac{2}{3} \cdot x$ or $\frac{2}{3}x$.

48. The quotient of a number and $-\frac{1}{5}$ translates as
$$x \div \left(-\frac{1}{5}\right).$$

49. A number subtracted from $-\frac{8}{9}$ translates as
$$-\frac{8}{9} - x.$$

50. $\frac{6}{11}$ increased by a number translates as $\frac{6}{11} + x$.

51.
$$\frac{2}{3} \cdot 1530 = \frac{2}{3} \cdot \frac{1530}{1}$$
$$= \frac{2 \cdot 1530}{3 \cdot 1}$$
$$= \frac{2 \cdot 3 \cdot 510}{3 \cdot 1}$$
$$= \frac{2 \cdot 510}{1}$$
$$= 1020$$

$\frac{2}{3}$ of 1530 is 1020.

52.
$$18 \div \frac{3}{4} = \frac{18}{1} \div \frac{3}{4}$$
$$= \frac{18}{1} \cdot \frac{4}{3}$$
$$= \frac{18 \cdot 4}{1 \cdot 3}$$
$$= \frac{3 \cdot 6 \cdot 4}{1 \cdot 3}$$
$$= \frac{6 \cdot 4}{1}$$
$$= 24$$

He can sell 24 lots.

53. The LCD is 16.
$$\frac{7}{8} - \frac{1}{16} - \frac{1}{16} = \frac{7 \cdot 2}{8 \cdot 2} - \frac{1}{16} - \frac{1}{16}$$
$$= \frac{14}{16} - \frac{1}{16} - \frac{1}{16}$$
$$= \frac{12}{16}$$
$$= \frac{4 \cdot 3}{4 \cdot 4}$$
$$= \frac{3}{4}$$

The inner diameter is $\frac{3}{4}$ foot.

Section 4.6

Practice Problems

1. $\dfrac{\frac{7y}{10}}{\frac{1}{5}} = \dfrac{7y}{10} \div \dfrac{1}{5} = \dfrac{7y}{10} \cdot \dfrac{5}{1} = \dfrac{7y \cdot 5}{10 \cdot 1} = \dfrac{7 \cdot y \cdot 5}{2 \cdot 5 \cdot 1} = \dfrac{7y}{2}$

2. $\dfrac{\frac{1}{2}+\frac{1}{6}}{\frac{3}{4}-\frac{2}{3}} = \dfrac{\frac{1 \cdot 3}{2 \cdot 3}+\frac{1}{6}}{\frac{3 \cdot 3}{4 \cdot 3}-\frac{2 \cdot 4}{3 \cdot 4}}$

$= \dfrac{\frac{3}{6}+\frac{1}{6}}{\frac{9}{12}-\frac{8}{12}}$

$= \dfrac{\frac{4}{6}}{\frac{1}{12}}$

$= \dfrac{4}{6} \div \dfrac{1}{12}$

$= \dfrac{4}{6} \cdot \dfrac{12}{1}$

$= \dfrac{4 \cdot 2 \cdot 6}{6 \cdot 1}$

$= \dfrac{8}{1}$ or 8

3. The LCD is 12.

$\dfrac{\frac{1}{2}+\frac{1}{6}}{\frac{3}{4}-\frac{2}{3}} = \dfrac{12\left(\frac{1}{2}+\frac{1}{6}\right)}{12\left(\frac{3}{4}-\frac{2}{3}\right)}$

$= \dfrac{12 \cdot \frac{1}{2}+12 \cdot \frac{1}{6}}{12 \cdot \frac{3}{4}-12 \cdot \frac{2}{3}}$

$= \dfrac{6+2}{9-8}$

$= \dfrac{8}{1}$ or 8

4. The LCD is 20.

$\dfrac{\frac{3}{4}}{\frac{x}{5}-1} = \dfrac{20\left(\frac{3}{4}\right)}{20\left(\frac{x}{5}-1\right)} = \dfrac{20 \cdot \frac{3}{4}}{20 \cdot \frac{x}{5}-20 \cdot 1} = \dfrac{15}{4x-20}$

5. $\left(\dfrac{2}{3}\right)^3 - 2 = \dfrac{8}{27} - 2 = \dfrac{8}{27} - \dfrac{54}{27} = -\dfrac{46}{27}$

6. $\left(-\dfrac{1}{2}+\dfrac{1}{5}\right)\left(\dfrac{7}{8}+\dfrac{1}{8}\right) = \left(-\dfrac{1 \cdot 5}{2 \cdot 5}+\dfrac{1 \cdot 2}{5 \cdot 2}\right)\left(\dfrac{7}{8}+\dfrac{1}{8}\right)$

$= \left(-\dfrac{5}{10}+\dfrac{2}{10}\right)\left(\dfrac{7}{8}+\dfrac{1}{8}\right)$

$= \left(-\dfrac{3}{10}\right)\left(\dfrac{8}{8}\right)$

$= \left(-\dfrac{3}{10}\right)(1)$

$= -\dfrac{3}{10}$

7. $-\dfrac{3}{5} - xy = -\dfrac{3}{5} - \dfrac{3}{10} \cdot \dfrac{2}{3}$

$= -\dfrac{3}{5} - \dfrac{3 \cdot 2}{5 \cdot 2 \cdot 3}$

$= -\dfrac{3}{5} - \dfrac{1}{5}$

$= -\dfrac{4}{5}$

Vocabulary and Readiness Check

1. A fraction whose numerator or denominator or both numerator and denominator contain fractions is called a <u>complex</u> fraction.

2. To simplify $-\dfrac{1}{2}+\dfrac{2}{3} \cdot \dfrac{7}{8}$, which operation do we perform first? <u>multiplication</u>

3. To simplify $-\dfrac{1}{2} \div \dfrac{2}{3} \cdot \dfrac{7}{8}$, which operation do we perform first? <u>division</u>

4. To simplify $\dfrac{7}{8} \cdot \left(\dfrac{1}{2}-\dfrac{2}{3}\right)$, which operation do we perform first? <u>subtraction</u>

5. To simplify $\dfrac{1}{3} \div \dfrac{1}{4} \cdot \left(\dfrac{9}{11}+\dfrac{3}{8}\right)^3$, which operation do we perform first? <u>addition</u>

6. To simplify $9-\left(-\dfrac{3}{4}\right)^2$, which operation do we perform first? <u>evaluate the exponential expression</u>

Exercise Set 4.6

1. $\dfrac{\frac{1}{8}}{\frac{3}{4}} = \dfrac{1}{8} \div \dfrac{3}{4} = \dfrac{1}{8} \cdot \dfrac{4}{3} = \dfrac{1 \cdot 4}{8 \cdot 3} = \dfrac{1 \cdot 4}{2 \cdot 4 \cdot 3} = \dfrac{1}{6}$

3. $\dfrac{\frac{2}{3}}{\frac{2}{7}} = \dfrac{2}{3} \div \dfrac{2}{7} = \dfrac{2}{3} \cdot \dfrac{7}{2} = \dfrac{2 \cdot 7}{3 \cdot 2} = \dfrac{7}{3}$

5. $\dfrac{\frac{2x}{27}}{\frac{4}{9}} = \dfrac{2x}{27} \div \dfrac{4}{9} = \dfrac{2x}{27} \cdot \dfrac{9}{4} = \dfrac{2x \cdot 9}{27 \cdot 4} = \dfrac{2 \cdot x \cdot 9}{3 \cdot 9 \cdot 2 \cdot 2} = \dfrac{x}{6}$

7. The LCD of 4, 5, and 2 is 20.

$$\dfrac{\frac{3}{4} + \frac{2}{5}}{\frac{1}{2} + \frac{3}{5}} = \dfrac{20 \cdot \left(\frac{3}{4} + \frac{2}{5}\right)}{20 \cdot \left(\frac{1}{2} + \frac{3}{5}\right)}$$

$$= \dfrac{20 \cdot \frac{3}{4} + 20 \cdot \frac{2}{5}}{20 \cdot \frac{1}{2} + 20 \cdot \frac{3}{5}}$$

$$= \dfrac{15 + 8}{10 + 12}$$

$$= \dfrac{23}{22}$$

9. The LCD is 8.

$$\dfrac{\frac{3x}{4}}{5 - \frac{1}{8}} = \dfrac{8 \cdot \left(\frac{3x}{4}\right)}{8 \cdot \left(5 - \frac{1}{8}\right)}$$

$$= \dfrac{\frac{8}{1} \cdot \frac{3x}{4}}{8 \cdot 5 - 8 \cdot \frac{1}{8}}$$

$$= \dfrac{\frac{2 \cdot 4 \cdot 3x}{1 \cdot 4}}{40 - 1}$$

$$= \dfrac{6x}{39}$$

$$= \dfrac{2 \cdot 3 \cdot x}{3 \cdot 13}$$

$$= \dfrac{2x}{13}$$

11. $\dfrac{1}{5} + \dfrac{1}{3} \cdot \dfrac{1}{4} = \dfrac{1}{5} + \dfrac{1 \cdot 1}{3 \cdot 4}$

$$= \dfrac{1}{5} + \dfrac{1}{12}$$

$$= \dfrac{1 \cdot 12}{5 \cdot 12} + \dfrac{1 \cdot 5}{12 \cdot 5}$$

$$= \dfrac{12}{60} + \dfrac{5}{60}$$

$$= \dfrac{17}{60}$$

13. $\dfrac{5}{6} \div \dfrac{1}{3} \cdot \dfrac{1}{4} = \dfrac{5}{6} \cdot \dfrac{3}{1} \cdot \dfrac{1}{4} = \dfrac{5 \cdot 3 \cdot 1}{2 \cdot 3 \cdot 1 \cdot 2 \cdot 2} = \dfrac{5}{2 \cdot 2 \cdot 2} = \dfrac{5}{8}$

15. $2^2 - \left(\dfrac{1}{3}\right)^2 = 4 - \dfrac{1}{9}$

$$= \dfrac{4}{1} - \dfrac{1}{9}$$

$$= \dfrac{4 \cdot 9}{1 \cdot 9} - \dfrac{1}{9}$$

$$= \dfrac{36}{9} - \dfrac{1}{9}$$

$$= \dfrac{35}{9}$$

17. $\left(\dfrac{2}{9} + \dfrac{4}{9}\right)\left(\dfrac{1}{3} - \dfrac{9}{10}\right) = \left(\dfrac{6}{9}\right)\left(\dfrac{1}{3} \cdot \dfrac{10}{10} - \dfrac{9}{10} \cdot \dfrac{3}{3}\right)$

$$= \left(\dfrac{6}{9}\right)\left(\dfrac{10}{30} - \dfrac{27}{30}\right)$$

$$= \left(\dfrac{6}{9}\right)\left(\dfrac{-17}{30}\right)$$

$$= -\dfrac{6 \cdot 17}{9 \cdot 30}$$

$$= -\dfrac{2 \cdot 3 \cdot 17}{3 \cdot 3 \cdot 2 \cdot 15}$$

$$= -\dfrac{17}{3 \cdot 15}$$

$$= -\dfrac{17}{45}$$

19.
$$\left(\frac{7}{8}-\frac{1}{2}\right)\div\frac{3}{11}=\left(\frac{7}{8}-\frac{1}{2}\cdot\frac{4}{4}\right)\div\frac{3}{11}$$
$$=\left(\frac{7}{8}-\frac{4}{8}\right)\div\frac{3}{11}$$
$$=\frac{3}{8}\div\frac{3}{11}$$
$$=\frac{3}{8}\cdot\frac{11}{3}$$
$$=\frac{3\cdot11}{8\cdot3}$$
$$=\frac{11}{8}$$

21.
$$2\cdot\left(\frac{1}{4}+\frac{1}{5}\right)+2=2\cdot\left(\frac{1\cdot5}{4\cdot5}+\frac{1\cdot4}{5\cdot4}\right)+2$$
$$=2\left(\frac{5}{20}+\frac{4}{20}\right)+2$$
$$=2\left(\frac{9}{20}\right)+2$$
$$=\frac{2}{1}\cdot\frac{9}{20}+2$$
$$=\frac{2\cdot9}{1\cdot2\cdot10}+2$$
$$=\frac{9}{10}+2$$
$$=\frac{9}{10}+\frac{2\cdot10}{1\cdot10}$$
$$=\frac{9}{10}+\frac{20}{10}$$
$$=\frac{29}{10}$$

23.
$$\left(\frac{3}{4}\right)^2\div\left(\frac{3}{4}-\frac{1}{12}\right)=\left(\frac{3}{4}\right)^2\div\left(\frac{3\cdot3}{4\cdot3}-\frac{1}{12}\right)$$
$$=\left(\frac{3}{4}\right)^2\div\left(\frac{9}{12}-\frac{1}{12}\right)$$
$$=\left(\frac{3}{4}\right)^2\div\frac{8}{12}$$
$$=\frac{9}{16}\div\frac{8}{12}$$
$$=\frac{9}{16}\cdot\frac{12}{8}$$
$$=\frac{9\cdot3\cdot4}{4\cdot4\cdot8}$$
$$=\frac{27}{32}$$

25.
$$\left(\frac{2}{5}-\frac{3}{10}\right)^2=\left(\frac{2}{5}\cdot\frac{2}{2}-\frac{3}{10}\right)^2$$
$$=\left(\frac{4}{10}-\frac{3}{10}\right)^2$$
$$=\left(\frac{1}{10}\right)^2$$
$$=\frac{1}{10}\cdot\frac{1}{10}$$
$$=\frac{1}{100}$$

27.
$$\left(\frac{3}{4}+\frac{1}{8}\right)^2-\left(\frac{1}{2}+\frac{1}{8}\right)=\left(\frac{3\cdot2}{4\cdot2}+\frac{1}{8}\right)^2-\left(\frac{1\cdot4}{2\cdot4}+\frac{1}{8}\right)$$
$$=\left(\frac{6}{8}+\frac{1}{8}\right)^2-\left(\frac{4}{8}+\frac{1}{8}\right)$$
$$=\left(\frac{7}{8}\right)^2-\frac{5}{8}$$
$$=\frac{49}{64}-\frac{5}{8}$$
$$=\frac{49}{64}-\frac{5\cdot8}{8\cdot8}$$
$$=\frac{49}{64}-\frac{40}{64}$$
$$=\frac{9}{64}$$

29.
$$5y-z=5\left(\frac{2}{5}\right)-\frac{5}{6}$$
$$=2-\frac{5}{6}$$
$$=\frac{2}{1}\cdot\frac{6}{6}-\frac{5}{6}$$
$$=\frac{12}{6}-\frac{5}{6}$$
$$=\frac{7}{6}$$

31.
$$\frac{x}{z}=\frac{-\frac{1}{3}}{\frac{5}{6}}=-\frac{1}{3}\div\frac{5}{6}=-\frac{1}{3}\cdot\frac{6}{5}=-\frac{1\cdot3\cdot2}{3\cdot5}=-\frac{2}{5}$$

33. $x^2 - yz = \left(-\dfrac{1}{3}\right)^2 - \left(\dfrac{2}{5}\right)\left(\dfrac{5}{6}\right)$

$\quad = \left(-\dfrac{1}{3}\right)\left(-\dfrac{1}{3}\right) - \left(\dfrac{2}{5}\right)\left(\dfrac{5}{6}\right)$

$\quad = \dfrac{1 \cdot 1}{3 \cdot 3} - \dfrac{2 \cdot 5}{5 \cdot 2 \cdot 3}$

$\quad = \dfrac{1}{9} - \dfrac{1}{3}$

$\quad = \dfrac{1}{9} - \dfrac{1}{3} \cdot \dfrac{3}{3}$

$\quad = \dfrac{1}{9} - \dfrac{3}{9}$

$\quad = -\dfrac{2}{9}$

35. $(1+x)(1+z) = \left[1 + \left(-\dfrac{1}{3}\right)\right]\left[1 + \dfrac{5}{6}\right]$

$\quad = \left(\dfrac{3}{3} - \dfrac{1}{3}\right)\left(\dfrac{6}{6} + \dfrac{5}{6}\right)$

$\quad = \left(\dfrac{2}{3}\right)\left(\dfrac{11}{6}\right)$

$\quad = \dfrac{2 \cdot 11}{3 \cdot 2 \cdot 3}$

$\quad = \dfrac{11}{9}$

37. $\dfrac{\frac{5a}{24}}{\frac{1}{12}} = \dfrac{5a}{24} \div \dfrac{1}{12} = \dfrac{5a}{24} \cdot \dfrac{12}{1} = \dfrac{5 \cdot a \cdot 12}{12 \cdot 2 \cdot 1} = \dfrac{5a}{2}$

39. $\left(\dfrac{3}{2}\right)^3 + \left(\dfrac{1}{2}\right)^3 = \dfrac{27}{8} + \dfrac{1}{8} = \dfrac{28}{8} = \dfrac{4 \cdot 7}{4 \cdot 2} = \dfrac{7}{2}$

41. $\left(-\dfrac{1}{2}\right)^2 + \dfrac{1}{5} = \dfrac{1}{4} + \dfrac{1}{5} = \dfrac{1 \cdot 5}{4 \cdot 5} + \dfrac{1 \cdot 4}{5 \cdot 4} = \dfrac{5}{20} + \dfrac{4}{20} = \dfrac{9}{20}$

43. $\dfrac{2 + \frac{1}{6}}{1 - \frac{4}{3}} = \dfrac{6\left(2 + \frac{1}{6}\right)}{6\left(1 - \frac{4}{3}\right)}$

$\quad = \dfrac{6 \cdot 2 + 6 \cdot \frac{1}{6}}{6 \cdot 1 - 6 \cdot \frac{4}{3}}$

$\quad = \dfrac{12 + 1}{6 - 8}$

$\quad = \dfrac{13}{-2}$

$\quad = -\dfrac{13}{2}$

45. $\left(1 - \dfrac{2}{5}\right)^2 = \left(\dfrac{5}{5} - \dfrac{2}{5}\right)^2 = \left(\dfrac{3}{5}\right)^2 = \dfrac{3}{5} \cdot \dfrac{3}{5} = \dfrac{9}{25}$

47. $\left(\dfrac{3}{4} - 1\right)\left(\dfrac{1}{8} + \dfrac{1}{2}\right) = \left(\dfrac{3}{4} - \dfrac{4}{4}\right)\left(\dfrac{1}{8} + \dfrac{4}{8}\right)$

$\quad = \left(-\dfrac{1}{4}\right)\left(\dfrac{5}{8}\right)$

$\quad = -\dfrac{1 \cdot 5}{4 \cdot 8}$

$\quad = -\dfrac{5}{32}$

49. $\left(-\dfrac{2}{9} - \dfrac{7}{9}\right)^4 = \left(-\dfrac{9}{9}\right)^4$

$\quad = (-1)^4$

$\quad = (-1)(-1)(-1)(-1)$

$\quad = 1$

51. $\dfrac{\frac{1}{3} - \frac{5}{6}}{\frac{3}{4} + \frac{1}{2}} = \dfrac{12\left(\frac{1}{3} - \frac{5}{6}\right)}{12\left(\frac{3}{4} + \frac{1}{2}\right)}$

$\quad = \dfrac{12 \cdot \frac{1}{3} - 12 \cdot \frac{5}{6}}{12 \cdot \frac{3}{4} + 12 \cdot \frac{1}{2}}$

$\quad = \dfrac{4 - 10}{9 + 6}$

$\quad = \dfrac{-6}{15}$

$\quad = -\dfrac{2 \cdot 3}{3 \cdot 5}$

$\quad = -\dfrac{2}{5}$

53. $\left(\dfrac{3}{4} \div \dfrac{6}{5}\right) - \left(\dfrac{3}{4} \cdot \dfrac{6}{5}\right) = \left(\dfrac{3}{4} \cdot \dfrac{5}{6}\right) - \left(\dfrac{3}{4} \cdot \dfrac{6}{5}\right)$

$\quad = \dfrac{3 \cdot 5}{4 \cdot 2 \cdot 3} - \dfrac{3 \cdot 2 \cdot 3}{2 \cdot 2 \cdot 5}$

$\quad = \dfrac{5}{4 \cdot 2} - \dfrac{3 \cdot 3}{2 \cdot 5}$

$\quad = \dfrac{5}{8} - \dfrac{9}{10}$

$\quad = \dfrac{5 \cdot 5}{8 \cdot 5} - \dfrac{9 \cdot 4}{10 \cdot 4}$

$\quad = \dfrac{25}{40} - \dfrac{36}{40}$

$\quad = -\dfrac{11}{40}$

55. $\dfrac{\frac{x}{3}+2}{5+\frac{1}{3}} = \dfrac{3\left(\frac{x}{3}+2\right)}{3\left(5+\frac{1}{3}\right)}$

$= \dfrac{3\cdot\frac{x}{3}+3\cdot 2}{3\cdot 5 + 3\cdot\frac{1}{3}}$

$= \dfrac{x+6}{15+1}$

$= \dfrac{x+6}{16}$

57. $3+\dfrac{1}{2} = \dfrac{3}{1}\cdot\dfrac{2}{2}+\dfrac{1}{2} = \dfrac{6}{2}+\dfrac{1}{2} = \dfrac{7}{2}$ or $3\dfrac{1}{2}$

59. $9-\dfrac{5}{6} = \dfrac{9}{1}\cdot\dfrac{6}{6}-\dfrac{5}{6} = \dfrac{54}{6}-\dfrac{5}{6} = \dfrac{49}{6}$ or $8\dfrac{1}{6}$

61. no; answers may vary

63. $\dfrac{\frac{1}{2}+\frac{3}{4}}{2} = \dfrac{4\left(\frac{1}{2}+\frac{3}{4}\right)}{4(2)} = \dfrac{4\cdot\frac{1}{2}+4\cdot\frac{3}{4}}{4\cdot 2} = \dfrac{2+3}{8} = \dfrac{5}{8}$

65. $\dfrac{\frac{1}{4}+\frac{2}{14}}{2} = \dfrac{28\left(\frac{1}{4}+\frac{2}{14}\right)}{28(2)}$

$= \dfrac{28\cdot\frac{1}{4}+28\cdot\frac{2}{14}}{28\cdot 2}$

$= \dfrac{7+4}{56}$

$= \dfrac{11}{56}$

67. The average of a and b should be halfway between a and b.

69. False; the average cannot be greater than the greatest number.

71. True

73. True

75. addition; answers may vary

77. Subtraction, multiplication, addition, division

79. Division, multiplication, subtraction, addition

81. $\dfrac{2+x}{y} = \dfrac{2+\frac{3}{4}}{-\frac{4}{7}}$

$= \dfrac{28\left(2+\frac{3}{4}\right)}{28\left(-\frac{4}{7}\right)}$

$= \dfrac{28\cdot 2+28\cdot\frac{3}{4}}{28\cdot\left(-\frac{4}{7}\right)}$

$= \dfrac{56+21}{-16}$

$= -\dfrac{77}{16}$

83. $x^2+7y = \left(\dfrac{3}{4}\right)^2 + 7\left(-\dfrac{4}{7}\right)$

$= \dfrac{9}{16}-\dfrac{4}{1}$

$= \dfrac{9}{16}-\dfrac{4\cdot 16}{1\cdot 16}$

$= \dfrac{9}{16}-\dfrac{64}{16}$

$= -\dfrac{55}{16}$

Section 4.7

Practice Problems

1.

2. $1\dfrac{2}{3}\cdot\dfrac{11}{15} = \dfrac{5}{3}\cdot\dfrac{11}{15} = \dfrac{5\cdot 11}{3\cdot 5\cdot 3} = \dfrac{11}{9}$ or $1\dfrac{2}{9}$

3. $\dfrac{5}{6}\cdot 18 = \dfrac{5}{6}\cdot\dfrac{18}{1} = \dfrac{5\cdot 18}{6\cdot 1} = \dfrac{5\cdot 6\cdot 3}{6\cdot 1} = \dfrac{15}{1}$ or 15

4. $3\dfrac{1}{5}\cdot 2\dfrac{3}{4} = \dfrac{16}{5}\cdot\dfrac{11}{4} = \dfrac{16\cdot 11}{5\cdot 4} = \dfrac{4\cdot 4\cdot 11}{5\cdot 4} = \dfrac{44}{5}$ or $8\dfrac{4}{5}$

Estimate: $3\dfrac{1}{5}$ rounds to 3, $2\dfrac{3}{4}$ rounds to 3. $3\cdot 3 = 9$, so the answer is reasonable.

5. $3\cdot 6\dfrac{7}{15} = \dfrac{3}{1}\cdot\dfrac{97}{15} = \dfrac{3\cdot 97}{1\cdot 5\cdot 3} = \dfrac{97}{5}$ or $19\dfrac{2}{5}$

Estimate: $6\dfrac{7}{15}$ rounds to 6 and $3\cdot 6 = 18$, so the answer is reasonable.

6. $\dfrac{4}{9} \div 7 = \dfrac{4}{9} \div \dfrac{7}{1} = \dfrac{4}{9} \cdot \dfrac{1}{7} = \dfrac{4 \cdot 1}{9 \cdot 7} = \dfrac{4}{63}$

7. $\dfrac{8}{15} \div 3\dfrac{4}{5} = \dfrac{8}{15} \div \dfrac{19}{5}$

$= \dfrac{8}{15} \cdot \dfrac{5}{19}$

$= \dfrac{8 \cdot 5}{15 \cdot 19}$

$= \dfrac{8 \cdot 5}{5 \cdot 3 \cdot 19}$

$= \dfrac{8}{57}$

8. $3\dfrac{2}{7} \div 2\dfrac{3}{14} = \dfrac{23}{7} \div \dfrac{31}{14}$

$= \dfrac{23}{7} \cdot \dfrac{14}{31}$

$= \dfrac{23 \cdot 7 \cdot 2}{7 \cdot 31}$

$= \dfrac{46}{31}$ or $1\dfrac{15}{31}$

9. $\begin{array}{r} 2\frac{1}{6} \\ + 4\frac{2}{5} \\ \hline \end{array}$ $\begin{array}{r} 2\frac{5}{30} \\ + 4\frac{12}{30} \\ \hline 6\frac{17}{30} \end{array}$

Estimate: $2\dfrac{1}{6}$ rounds to 2, $4\dfrac{2}{5}$ rounds to 4, and $2 + 4 = 6$, so the answer is reasonable.

10. $\begin{array}{r} 3\frac{5}{14} \\ + 2\frac{6}{7} \\ \hline \end{array}$ $\begin{array}{r} 3\frac{5}{14} \\ + 2\frac{12}{14} \\ \hline 5\frac{17}{14} \end{array} = 5+1\frac{3}{14} = 6\frac{3}{14}$

11. $\begin{array}{r} 12 \\ 3\frac{6}{7} \\ + 2\frac{1}{5} \\ \hline \end{array}$ $\begin{array}{r} 12 \\ 3\frac{30}{35} \\ + 2\frac{7}{35} \\ \hline 17\frac{37}{35} \end{array} = 17+1\frac{2}{35} = 18\frac{2}{35}$

12. $\begin{array}{r} 32\frac{7}{9} \\ - 16\frac{5}{18} \\ \hline \end{array}$ $\begin{array}{r} 32\frac{14}{18} \\ - 16\frac{5}{18} \\ \hline 16\frac{9}{18} \end{array} = 16\frac{1}{2}$

13. $\begin{array}{r} 9\frac{7}{15} \\ - 4\frac{3}{5} \\ \hline \end{array}$ $\begin{array}{r} 9\frac{7}{15} \\ - 4\frac{9}{15} \\ \hline \end{array}$ $\begin{array}{r} 8\frac{22}{15} \\ - 4\frac{9}{15} \\ \hline 4\frac{13}{15} \end{array}$

14. $\begin{array}{r} 25 \\ - 10\frac{2}{9} \\ \hline \end{array}$ $\begin{array}{r} 24\frac{9}{9} \\ - 10\frac{2}{9} \\ \hline 14\frac{7}{9} \end{array}$

15. $\begin{array}{r} 23\frac{1}{4} \\ - 19\frac{5}{12} \\ \hline \end{array}$ $\begin{array}{r} 23\frac{3}{12} \\ - 19\frac{5}{12} \\ \hline \end{array}$ $\begin{array}{r} 22\frac{15}{12} \\ - 19\frac{5}{12} \\ \hline 3\frac{10}{12} \end{array} = 3\frac{5}{6}$

The girth of the largest known American beech tree is $3\dfrac{5}{6}$ feet larger than the girth of the largest known sugar maple tree.

16. $44 \div 3\dfrac{1}{7} = 44 \div \dfrac{22}{7}$

$= \dfrac{44}{1} \cdot \dfrac{7}{22}$

$= \dfrac{2 \cdot 22 \cdot 7}{1 \cdot 22}$

$= \dfrac{14}{1}$ or 14

Therefore, 14 dresses can be made from 44 yards.

17. $-9\dfrac{3}{7} = -\dfrac{7 \cdot 9 + 3}{7} = -\dfrac{66}{7}$

18. $-5\dfrac{10}{11} = -\dfrac{11 \cdot 5 + 10}{11} = -\dfrac{65}{11}$

19. $-\dfrac{37}{8} = -4\dfrac{5}{8}$

$$8\overline{)37} \\ \underline{32} \\ 5$$

with quotient 4 above.

20. $-\dfrac{46}{5} = -9\dfrac{1}{5}$

$$5\overline{)46} \\ \underline{45} \\ 1$$

with quotient 9 above.

21. $2\dfrac{3}{4} \cdot \left(-3\dfrac{3}{5}\right) = \dfrac{11}{4} \cdot \left(-\dfrac{18}{5}\right)$

$$= -\dfrac{11 \cdot 18}{4 \cdot 5}$$

$$= -\dfrac{11 \cdot 2 \cdot 9}{2 \cdot 2 \cdot 5}$$

$$= -\dfrac{99}{10} \text{ or } -9\dfrac{9}{10}$$

22. $-4\dfrac{2}{7} \div 1\dfrac{1}{4} = -\dfrac{30}{7} \div \dfrac{5}{4}$

$$= -\dfrac{30}{7} \cdot \dfrac{4}{5}$$

$$= -\dfrac{30 \cdot 4}{7 \cdot 5}$$

$$= -\dfrac{5 \cdot 6 \cdot 4}{7 \cdot 5}$$

$$= -\dfrac{24}{7} \text{ or } -3\dfrac{3}{7}$$

23.

$$\begin{array}{r} 12\dfrac{3}{4} \\ -\ 6\dfrac{2}{3} \\ \hline \end{array} \qquad \begin{array}{r} 12\dfrac{9}{12} \\ -\ 6\dfrac{8}{12} \\ \hline 6\dfrac{1}{12} \end{array}$$

$$6\dfrac{2}{3} - 12\dfrac{3}{4} = -6\dfrac{1}{12}$$

24.

$$\begin{array}{r} 9\dfrac{2}{7} \\ +\ 30\dfrac{11}{14} \\ \hline \end{array} \qquad \begin{array}{r} 9\dfrac{4}{14} \\ +\ 30\dfrac{11}{14} \\ \hline 39\dfrac{15}{14} = 40\dfrac{1}{14} \end{array}$$

$$-9\dfrac{2}{7} - 30\dfrac{11}{14} = -40\dfrac{1}{14}$$

Calculator Explorations

1. $25\dfrac{5}{11} = \dfrac{280}{11}$

2. $67\dfrac{14}{15} = \dfrac{1019}{15}$

3. $107\dfrac{31}{35} = \dfrac{3776}{35}$

4. $186\dfrac{17}{21} = \dfrac{3923}{21}$

5. $\dfrac{365}{14} = 26\dfrac{1}{14}$

6. $\dfrac{290}{13} = 22\dfrac{4}{13}$

7. $\dfrac{2769}{30} = 92\dfrac{3}{10}$

8. $\dfrac{3941}{17} = 231\dfrac{14}{17}$

Vocabulary and Readiness Check

1. The number $5\dfrac{3}{4}$ is called a <u>mixed number</u>.

2. For $5\dfrac{3}{4}$, the 5 is called the <u>whole number</u> part and $\dfrac{3}{4}$ is called the <u>fraction</u> part.

3. To estimate operations on mixed numbers, we <u>round</u> mixed numbers to the nearest whole number.

4. The mixed number $2\dfrac{5}{8}$ written as an <u>improper</u> fraction is $\dfrac{21}{8}$.

Exercise Set 4.7

1.

3.

5. $2\dfrac{11}{12}$ rounds to 3.

$1\dfrac{1}{4}$ rounds to 1.

$3 \cdot 1 = 3$

The best estimate is b.

7. $12\dfrac{2}{11}$ rounds to 12.

$3\dfrac{9}{10}$ rounds to 4.

$12 \div 4 = 3$

The best estimate is a.

9. $2\dfrac{2}{3} \cdot \dfrac{1}{7} = \dfrac{8}{3} \cdot \dfrac{1}{7} = \dfrac{8}{21}$

11. $7 \div 1\dfrac{3}{5} = \dfrac{7}{1} \div \dfrac{8}{5} = \dfrac{7}{1} \cdot \dfrac{5}{8} = \dfrac{7 \cdot 5}{1 \cdot 8} = \dfrac{35}{8}$ or $4\dfrac{3}{8}$

13. Exact: $2\dfrac{1}{5} \cdot 3\dfrac{1}{2} = \dfrac{11}{5} \cdot \dfrac{7}{2} = \dfrac{77}{10}$ or $7\dfrac{7}{10}$

Estimate: $2\dfrac{1}{5}$ rounds to 2, $3\dfrac{1}{2}$ rounds to 4.

$2 \cdot 4 = 8$ so the answer is reasonable.

15. Exact: $3\dfrac{4}{5} \cdot 6\dfrac{2}{7} = \dfrac{19}{5} \cdot \dfrac{44}{7} = \dfrac{836}{35}$ or $23\dfrac{31}{35}$

Estimate: $3\dfrac{4}{5}$ rounds to 4, $6\dfrac{2}{7}$ rounds to 6.

$4 \cdot 6 = 24$

17. $5 \cdot 2\dfrac{1}{2} = \dfrac{5}{1} \cdot \dfrac{5}{2} = \dfrac{25}{2}$ or $12\dfrac{1}{2}$

19. $3\dfrac{2}{3} \cdot 1\dfrac{1}{2} = \dfrac{11}{3} \cdot \dfrac{3}{2} = \dfrac{11 \cdot 3}{3 \cdot 2} = \dfrac{11}{2}$ or $5\dfrac{1}{2}$

21. $2\dfrac{2}{3} \div \dfrac{1}{7} = \dfrac{8}{3} \cdot \dfrac{7}{1} = \dfrac{56}{3}$ or $18\dfrac{2}{3}$

23. $3\dfrac{7}{8}$ rounds to 4.

$2\dfrac{1}{5}$ rounds to 2.

$4 + 2 = 6$

The best estimate is a.

25. $8\dfrac{1}{3}$ rounds to 8.

$1\dfrac{1}{2}$ rounds to 2.

$8 + 2 = 10$

The best estimate is b.

27. Exact: $\begin{aligned}4\dfrac{7}{12} \\ + 2\dfrac{1}{12} \\ \hline 6\dfrac{8}{12} = 6\dfrac{2}{3}\end{aligned}$

Estimate: $4\dfrac{7}{12}$ rounds to 5, $2\dfrac{1}{12}$ rounds to 2.

$5 + 2 = 7$ so the answer is reasonable.

29. Exact: $\begin{aligned}10\dfrac{3}{14} \\ + 3\dfrac{4}{7}\end{aligned}$ $\begin{aligned}10\dfrac{3}{14} \\ + 3\dfrac{8}{14} \\ \hline 13\dfrac{11}{14}\end{aligned}$

Estimate: $10\dfrac{3}{14}$ rounds to 10, $3\dfrac{4}{7}$ rounds to 4.

$10 + 4 = 14$ so the answer is reasonable.

31. $\begin{aligned}9\dfrac{1}{5} \\ + 8\dfrac{2}{25}\end{aligned}$ $\begin{aligned}9\dfrac{5}{25} \\ + 8\dfrac{2}{25} \\ \hline 17\dfrac{7}{25}\end{aligned}$

33. $\begin{aligned}12\dfrac{3}{14} \\ 10 \\ + 25\dfrac{5}{12}\end{aligned}$ $\begin{aligned}12\dfrac{18}{84} \\ 10 \\ + 25\dfrac{35}{84} \\ \hline 47\dfrac{53}{84}\end{aligned}$

35. $15\dfrac{4}{7}$ $\qquad$ $15\dfrac{8}{14}$

$\quad+\ 9\dfrac{11}{14}$ $\qquad$ $+\ 9\dfrac{11}{14}$

$\qquad\qquad\qquad 24\dfrac{19}{14}=24+1\dfrac{5}{14}=25\dfrac{5}{14}$

37. $3\dfrac{5}{8}$ $\qquad$ $3\dfrac{15}{24}$

$\quad 2\dfrac{1}{6}$ $\qquad$ $2\dfrac{4}{24}$

$\quad+\ 7\dfrac{3}{4}$ $\qquad$ $+\ 7\dfrac{18}{24}$

$\qquad\qquad\qquad 12\dfrac{37}{24}=12+1\dfrac{13}{24}=13\dfrac{13}{24}$

39. Exact: $\quad 4\dfrac{7}{10}$

$\qquad\qquad -\ 2\dfrac{1}{10}$

$\qquad\qquad\quad 2\dfrac{6}{10}=2\dfrac{3}{5}$

Estimate: $4\dfrac{7}{10}$ rounds to 5, $2\dfrac{1}{10}$ rounds to 2.

$5-2=3$ so the answer is reasonable.

41. Exact: $\ 10\dfrac{13}{14}$ $\qquad$ $10\dfrac{13}{14}$

$\qquad\qquad -\ 3\dfrac{4}{7}$ $\qquad$ $-\ 3\dfrac{8}{14}$

$\qquad\qquad\qquad\qquad\qquad 7\dfrac{5}{14}$

Estimate: $10\dfrac{13}{14}$ rounds to 11, $3\dfrac{4}{7}$ rounds to 4.

$11-4=7$ so the answer is reasonable.

43. $9\dfrac{1}{5}$ $\qquad$ $9\dfrac{5}{25}$ $\qquad$ $8\dfrac{30}{25}$

$\quad-\ 8\dfrac{6}{25}$ $\qquad$ $-\ 8\dfrac{6}{25}$ $\qquad$ $-\ 8\dfrac{6}{25}$

$\qquad\qquad\qquad\qquad\qquad\qquad\qquad\ \dfrac{24}{25}$

45. 6 $\qquad\qquad$ $5\dfrac{9}{9}$

$\quad-\ 2\dfrac{4}{9}$ $\qquad$ $-\ 2\dfrac{4}{9}$

$\qquad\qquad\qquad\qquad\ \ 3\dfrac{5}{9}$

47. $63\dfrac{1}{6}$ $\qquad$ $63\dfrac{2}{12}$ $\qquad$ $62\dfrac{14}{12}$

$\quad-\ 47\dfrac{5}{12}$ $\qquad$ $-\ 47\dfrac{5}{12}$ $\qquad$ $-\ 47\dfrac{5}{12}$

$\qquad\qquad\qquad\qquad\qquad\qquad\quad 15\dfrac{9}{12}=15\dfrac{3}{4}$

49. $2\dfrac{3}{4}$

$\quad+\ 1\dfrac{1}{4}$

$\quad\ 3\dfrac{4}{4}=3+1=4$

51. $15\dfrac{4}{7}$ $\qquad$ $15\dfrac{8}{14}$ $\qquad$ $14\dfrac{22}{14}$

$\quad-\ 9\dfrac{11}{14}$ $\qquad$ $-\ 9\dfrac{11}{14}$ $\qquad$ $-\ 9\dfrac{11}{14}$

$\qquad\qquad\qquad\qquad\qquad\qquad\qquad\ 5\dfrac{11}{14}$

53. $3\dfrac{1}{9}\cdot 2=\dfrac{28}{9}\cdot\dfrac{2}{1}=\dfrac{56}{9}$ or $6\dfrac{2}{9}$

55. $1\dfrac{2}{3}\div 2\dfrac{1}{5}=\dfrac{5}{3}\div\dfrac{11}{5}=\dfrac{5}{3}\cdot\dfrac{5}{11}=\dfrac{25}{33}$

57. $22\dfrac{4}{9}+13\dfrac{5}{18}=22\dfrac{8}{18}+13\dfrac{5}{18}=35\dfrac{13}{18}$

59. $5\dfrac{2}{3}-3\dfrac{1}{6}=5\dfrac{4}{6}-3\dfrac{1}{6}=2\dfrac{3}{6}=2\dfrac{1}{2}$

61. $15\dfrac{1}{5}$ $\qquad$ $15\dfrac{6}{30}$

$\quad 20\dfrac{3}{10}$ $\qquad$ $20\dfrac{9}{30}$

$\quad+\ 37\dfrac{2}{15}$ $\qquad$ $+\ 37\dfrac{4}{30}$

$\qquad\qquad\qquad\qquad\ 72\dfrac{19}{30}$

63. $6\dfrac{4}{7}$ $6\dfrac{8}{14}$ $5\dfrac{22}{14}$

$-5\dfrac{11}{14}$ $-5\dfrac{11}{14}$ $-5\dfrac{11}{14}$

$\dfrac{11}{14}$

65. $4\dfrac{2}{7}\cdot 1\dfrac{3}{10}=\dfrac{30}{7}\cdot\dfrac{13}{10}$

$=\dfrac{30\cdot 13}{7\cdot 10}$

$=\dfrac{3\cdot 10\cdot 13}{7\cdot 10}$

$=\dfrac{39}{7}$ or $5\dfrac{4}{7}$

67. $6\dfrac{2}{11}$ $6\dfrac{6}{33}$

$+4\dfrac{10}{33}$ $+4\dfrac{10}{33}$

$13\dfrac{16}{33}$

69. $-5\dfrac{2}{7}$ decreased by a number translates as

$-5\dfrac{2}{7}-x.$

71. Multiply $1\dfrac{9}{10}$ by a number translates as $1\dfrac{9}{10}\cdot x.$

73. $12\dfrac{3}{4}\div 4=\dfrac{51}{4}\div\dfrac{4}{1}=\dfrac{51}{4}\cdot\dfrac{1}{4}=\dfrac{51}{16}$ or $3\dfrac{3}{16}$

The patient walked $3\dfrac{3}{16}$ miles per day.

75. Subtract the standard gauge in the U.S. from the standard gauge in Spain.

$65\dfrac{9}{10}$ $65\dfrac{9}{10}$

$-56\dfrac{1}{2}$ $-56\dfrac{5}{10}$

$9\dfrac{4}{10}=9\dfrac{2}{5}$

Spain's standard gauge is $9\dfrac{2}{5}$ inches wider than the U.S. standard gauge.

77. $11\dfrac{1}{4}$ $11\dfrac{5}{20}$ $10\dfrac{25}{20}$

$-3\dfrac{3}{5}$ $-3\dfrac{12}{20}$ $-3\dfrac{12}{20}$

$7\dfrac{13}{20}$

Tucson gets an average of $7\dfrac{13}{20}$ inches more rain than Yuma.

79. $2\cdot 1\dfrac{3}{4}=\dfrac{2}{1}\cdot\dfrac{7}{4}=\dfrac{2\cdot 7}{1\cdot 4}=\dfrac{2\cdot 7}{1\cdot 2\cdot 2}=\dfrac{7}{2}$ or $3\dfrac{1}{2}$

The area is $\dfrac{7}{2}$ or $3\dfrac{1}{2}$ square yards.

81. $\dfrac{3}{4}\cdot 1\dfrac{1}{4}=\dfrac{3}{4}\cdot\dfrac{5}{4}=\dfrac{3\cdot 5}{4\cdot 4}=\dfrac{15}{16}$

The area is $\dfrac{15}{16}$ square inch.

83. $5\dfrac{1}{3}$ $5\dfrac{8}{24}$

5 5

$7\dfrac{7}{8}$ $7\dfrac{21}{24}$

$+3$ $+3$

$20\dfrac{29}{24}=20+1\dfrac{5}{24}=21\dfrac{5}{24}$

The perimeter is $21\dfrac{5}{24}$ meters.

85. $15\dfrac{2}{3}-\left(3\dfrac{1}{4}+2\dfrac{1}{2}\right)=15\dfrac{2}{3}-\left(3\dfrac{1}{4}+2\dfrac{2}{4}\right)$

$=15\dfrac{2}{3}-5\dfrac{3}{4}$

$15\dfrac{2}{3}$ $15\dfrac{8}{12}$ $14\dfrac{20}{12}$

$-5\dfrac{3}{4}$ $-5\dfrac{9}{12}$ $-5\dfrac{9}{12}$

$9\dfrac{11}{12}$

No; the remaining board is $9\dfrac{11}{12}$ feet which is $\dfrac{1}{12}$ foot short.

87. $12 \div 2\frac{4}{7} = \frac{12}{1} \div \frac{18}{7} = \frac{12}{1} \cdot \frac{7}{18} = \frac{6 \cdot 2 \cdot 7}{1 \cdot 6 \cdot 3} = \frac{14}{3} = 4\frac{2}{3}$

The length is $4\frac{2}{3}$ meters.

89.

$$
\begin{array}{ll}
2\frac{2}{3} & 2\frac{40}{60} \\[2mm]
4\frac{7}{15} & 4\frac{28}{60} \\[2mm]
+2\frac{37}{60} & +2\frac{37}{60} \\[1mm]
\hline
& 8\frac{105}{60} = 8\frac{7}{4} = 8 + 1\frac{3}{4} = 9\frac{3}{4}
\end{array}
$$

The total duration of the eclipses is $9\frac{3}{4}$ minutes.

91.

$$
\begin{array}{lll}
4\frac{7}{15} & 4\frac{7}{15} & 3\frac{22}{15} \\[2mm]
-2\frac{2}{3} & -2\frac{10}{15} & -2\frac{10}{15} \\[1mm]
\hline
& & 1\frac{12}{15} = 1\frac{4}{5}
\end{array}
$$

It will be $1\frac{4}{5}$ minutes longer.

93. $-4\frac{2}{5} \cdot 2\frac{3}{10} = -\frac{22}{5} \cdot \frac{23}{10}$

$= -\frac{2 \cdot 11 \cdot 23}{5 \cdot 2 \cdot 5}$

$= -\frac{253}{25}$ or $-10\frac{3}{25}$

95. $-5\frac{1}{8} - 19\frac{3}{4} = -\left(5\frac{1}{8} + 19\frac{3}{4}\right)$

$= -\left(5\frac{1}{8} + 19\frac{6}{8}\right)$

$= -\left(24\frac{7}{8}\right)$

$= -24\frac{7}{8}$

97. $-31\frac{2}{15} + 17\frac{3}{20} = -31\frac{8}{60} + 17\frac{9}{60}$

$= -30\frac{68}{60} + 17\frac{9}{60}$

$= -13\frac{59}{60}$

99. $-1\frac{5}{7} \cdot \left(-2\frac{1}{2}\right) = \frac{12}{7} \cdot \frac{5}{2} = \frac{6 \cdot 2 \cdot 5}{7 \cdot 2} = \frac{30}{7} = 4\frac{2}{7}$

101. $11\frac{7}{8} - 13\frac{5}{6} = 11\frac{21}{24} - 13\frac{20}{24}$

$= -\left(13\frac{20}{24} - 11\frac{21}{24}\right)$

$= -\left(12\frac{44}{24} - 11\frac{21}{24}\right)$

$= -1\frac{23}{24}$

103. $-7\frac{3}{10} \div (-100) = -\frac{73}{10} \div \left(-\frac{100}{1}\right)$

$= -\frac{73}{10} \cdot \left(-\frac{1}{100}\right)$

$= \frac{73 \cdot 1}{10 \cdot 100}$

$= \frac{73}{1000}$

105. $\frac{1}{3}(3x) = \left(\frac{1}{3} \cdot 3\right)x = 1 \cdot x = x$

107. $\frac{2}{3}\left(\frac{3}{2}a\right) = \left(\frac{2}{3} \cdot \frac{3}{2}\right)a = 1 \cdot a = a$

109. a. $9\frac{5}{5} = 9 + 1 = 10$

b. $9\frac{100}{100} = 9 + 1 = 10$

c. $6\frac{44}{11} = 6 + 4 = 10$

d. $8\frac{13}{13} = 8 + 1 = 9$

a, b, and c are equivalent to 10.

111. Incorrect, to divide mixed numbers, first write each mixed number as an improper fraction.

113. answers may vary

115. answers may vary

117. answers may vary

Section 4.8

Practice Problems

1. $$y - \frac{2}{3} = \frac{5}{12}$$

$$y - \frac{2}{3} + \frac{2}{3} = \frac{5}{12} + \frac{2}{3}$$

$$y = \frac{5}{12} + \frac{2 \cdot 4}{3 \cdot 4}$$

$$y = \frac{5}{12} + \frac{8}{12}$$

$$y = \frac{13}{12}$$

Check: $$y - \frac{2}{3} = \frac{5}{12}$$

$$\frac{13}{12} - \frac{2}{3} \stackrel{?}{=} \frac{5}{12}$$

$$\frac{13}{12} - \frac{2 \cdot 4}{3 \cdot 4} \stackrel{?}{=} \frac{5}{12}$$

$$\frac{13}{12} - \frac{8}{12} \stackrel{?}{=} \frac{5}{12}$$

$$\frac{5}{12} = \frac{5}{12} \quad \text{True}$$

The solution is $\dfrac{13}{12}$.

2. $$\frac{1}{5}y = 2$$

$$5 \cdot \frac{1}{5}y = 5 \cdot 2$$

$$y = 10$$

Check: $$\frac{1}{5}y = 2$$

$$\frac{1}{5} \cdot 10 \stackrel{?}{=} 2$$

$$2 = 2 \quad \text{True}$$

The solution is 10.

3. $$\frac{5}{7}b = 25$$

$$\frac{7}{5} \cdot \frac{5}{7}b = \frac{7}{5} \cdot 25$$

$$1b = \frac{7 \cdot 25}{5}$$

$$b = 35$$

Check: $$\frac{5}{7}b = 25$$

$$\frac{5}{7} \cdot 35 \stackrel{?}{=} 25$$

$$25 = 25 \quad \text{True}$$

The solution is 35.

4. $$-\frac{7}{10}x = \frac{2}{5}$$

$$-\frac{10}{7} \cdot -\frac{7}{10}x = -\frac{10}{7} \cdot \frac{2}{5}$$

$$x = -\frac{10 \cdot 2}{7 \cdot 5}$$

$$x = -\frac{4}{7}$$

Check: $$-\frac{7}{10}x = \frac{2}{5}$$

$$-\frac{7}{10} \cdot -\frac{4}{7} \stackrel{?}{=} \frac{2}{5}$$

$$\frac{28}{70} \stackrel{?}{=} \frac{2}{5}$$

$$\frac{2}{5} = \frac{2}{5} \quad \text{True}$$

The solution is $-\dfrac{4}{7}$.

5. $$5x = -\frac{3}{4}$$

$$\frac{1}{5} \cdot 5x = \frac{1}{5} \cdot -\frac{3}{4}$$

$$x = -\frac{1 \cdot 3}{5 \cdot 4}$$

$$x = -\frac{3}{20}$$

Check: $$5x = -\frac{3}{4}$$

$$5 \cdot -\frac{3}{20} \stackrel{?}{=} -\frac{3}{4}$$

$$-\frac{15}{20} \stackrel{?}{=} -\frac{3}{4}$$

$$-\frac{3}{4} = -\frac{3}{4} \quad \text{True}$$

The solution is $-\dfrac{3}{20}$.

6. The LCD is 15.

$$\frac{11}{15}x = -\frac{3}{5}$$

$$15 \cdot \frac{11}{15}x = 15 \cdot -\frac{3}{5}$$

$$11x = -9$$

$$\frac{11x}{11} = \frac{-9}{11}$$

$$x = -\frac{9}{11}$$

The solution is $-\frac{9}{11}$.

7. The LCD is 8.

$$\frac{y}{8} + \frac{3}{4} = 2$$

$$8\left(\frac{y}{8} + \frac{3}{4}\right) = 8(2)$$

$$8 \cdot \frac{y}{8} + 8 \cdot \frac{3}{4} = 8(2)$$

$$y + 6 = 16$$

$$y + 6 - 6 = 16 - 6$$

$$y = 10$$

Check: $\frac{y}{8} + \frac{3}{4} = 2$

$$\frac{10}{8} + \frac{3}{4} \stackrel{?}{=} 2$$

$$\frac{10}{8} + \frac{6}{8} \stackrel{?}{=} 2$$

$$\frac{16}{8} \stackrel{?}{=} 2$$

$$2 = 2 \quad \text{True}$$

The solution is 10.

8.
$$\frac{x}{5} - x = \frac{1}{5}$$

$$5\left(\frac{x}{5} - x\right) = 5\left(\frac{1}{5}\right)$$

$$5\left(\frac{x}{5}\right) - 5(x) = 5\left(\frac{1}{5}\right)$$

$$x - 5x = 1$$

$$-4x = 1$$

$$\frac{-4x}{-4} = \frac{1}{-4}$$

$$x = -\frac{1}{4}$$

To check, replace x with $-\frac{1}{4}$ in the original equation to see that a true statement results. The solution is $-\frac{1}{4}$.

9. The LCD is 10.

$$\frac{y}{2} = \frac{y}{5} + \frac{3}{2}$$

$$10\left(\frac{y}{2}\right) = 10\left(\frac{y}{5} + \frac{3}{2}\right)$$

$$10\left(\frac{y}{2}\right) = 10\left(\frac{y}{5}\right) + 10\left(\frac{3}{2}\right)$$

$$5y = 2y + 15$$

$$5y - 2y = 2y - 2y + 15$$

$$3y = 15$$

$$\frac{3y}{3} = \frac{15}{3}$$

$$y = 5$$

Check: $\frac{y}{2} = \frac{y}{5} + \frac{3}{2}$

$$\frac{5}{2} \stackrel{?}{=} \frac{5}{5} + \frac{3}{2}$$

$$2\frac{1}{2} \stackrel{?}{=} 1 + 1\frac{1}{2}$$

$$2\frac{1}{2} = 2\frac{1}{2} \quad \text{True}$$

The solution is 5.

10.
$$\frac{9}{10} - \frac{y}{3} = \frac{9}{10} \cdot \frac{3}{3} - \frac{y}{3} \cdot \frac{10}{10}$$

$$= \frac{9 \cdot 3}{10 \cdot 3} + \frac{y \cdot 10}{3 \cdot 10}$$

$$= \frac{27}{30} - \frac{10y}{30}$$

$$= \frac{27 - 10y}{30}$$

Exercise Set 4.8

1. $x + \dfrac{1}{3} = -\dfrac{1}{3}$

$x + \dfrac{1}{3} - \dfrac{1}{3} = -\dfrac{1}{3} - \dfrac{1}{3}$

$x = -\dfrac{2}{3}$

Check: $x + \dfrac{1}{3} = -\dfrac{1}{3}$

$-\dfrac{2}{3} + \dfrac{1}{3} \overset{?}{=} -\dfrac{1}{3}$

$-\dfrac{1}{3} = -\dfrac{1}{3}$ True

The solution is $-\dfrac{2}{3}$.

3. $y - \dfrac{3}{13} = -\dfrac{2}{13}$

$y - \dfrac{3}{13} + \dfrac{3}{13} = -\dfrac{2}{13} + \dfrac{3}{13}$

$y = \dfrac{-2+3}{13}$

$y = \dfrac{1}{13}$

Check: $y - \dfrac{3}{13} = -\dfrac{2}{13}$

$\dfrac{1}{13} - \dfrac{3}{13} \overset{?}{=} -\dfrac{2}{13}$

$\dfrac{1-3}{13} \overset{?}{=} -\dfrac{2}{13}$

$-\dfrac{2}{13} = -\dfrac{2}{13}$ True

The solution is $\dfrac{1}{13}$.

5. $3x - \dfrac{1}{5} - 2x = \dfrac{1}{5} + \dfrac{2}{5}$

$x - \dfrac{1}{5} = \dfrac{3}{5}$

$x - \dfrac{1}{5} + \dfrac{1}{5} = \dfrac{3}{5} + \dfrac{1}{5}$

$x = \dfrac{4}{5}$

Check: $3x - \dfrac{1}{5} - 2x = \dfrac{1}{5} + \dfrac{2}{5}$

$3 \cdot \dfrac{4}{5} - \dfrac{1}{5} - 2 \cdot \dfrac{4}{5} \overset{?}{=} \dfrac{1}{5} + \dfrac{2}{5}$

$\dfrac{12}{5} - \dfrac{1}{5} - \dfrac{8}{5} \overset{?}{=} \dfrac{1}{5} + \dfrac{2}{5}$

$\dfrac{3}{5} = \dfrac{3}{5}$ True

The solution is $\dfrac{4}{5}$.

7. $x - \dfrac{1}{12} = \dfrac{5}{6}$

$x - \dfrac{1}{12} + \dfrac{1}{12} = \dfrac{5}{6} + \dfrac{1}{12}$

$x = \dfrac{5 \cdot 2}{6 \cdot 2} + \dfrac{1}{12}$

$x = \dfrac{10}{12} + \dfrac{1}{12}$

$x = \dfrac{11}{12}$

Check: $x - \dfrac{1}{12} = \dfrac{5}{6}$

$\dfrac{11}{12} - \dfrac{1}{12} \overset{?}{=} \dfrac{5}{6}$

$\dfrac{10}{12} \overset{?}{=} \dfrac{5}{6}$

$\dfrac{5}{6} = \dfrac{5}{6}$ True

The solution is $\dfrac{11}{12}$.

9. $\dfrac{2}{5} + y = -\dfrac{3}{10}$

$\dfrac{2}{5} + y - \dfrac{2}{5} = -\dfrac{3}{10} - \dfrac{2}{5}$

$y = -\dfrac{3}{10} - \dfrac{2 \cdot 2}{5 \cdot 2}$

$y = -\dfrac{3}{10} - \dfrac{4}{10}$

$y = -\dfrac{7}{10}$

Check:
$$\frac{2}{5} + y = -\frac{3}{10}$$
$$\frac{2}{5} + \left(-\frac{7}{10}\right) \stackrel{?}{=} -\frac{3}{10}$$
$$\frac{2}{5} \cdot \frac{2}{2} + \left(-\frac{7}{10}\right) \stackrel{?}{=} -\frac{3}{10}$$
$$\frac{4}{10} + \left(-\frac{7}{10}\right) \stackrel{?}{=} -\frac{3}{10}$$
$$-\frac{3}{10} = -\frac{3}{10} \quad \text{True}$$

The solution is $-\dfrac{7}{10}$.

11. $7z + \dfrac{1}{16} - 6z = \dfrac{3}{4}$
$$z + \frac{1}{16} = \frac{3}{4}$$
$$z + \frac{1}{16} - \frac{1}{16} = \frac{3}{4} - \frac{1}{16}$$
$$z = \frac{3 \cdot 4}{4 \cdot 4} - \frac{1}{16}$$
$$z = \frac{12}{16} - \frac{1}{16}$$
$$z = \frac{11}{16}$$

Check:
$$7z + \frac{1}{16} - 6z = \frac{3}{4}$$
$$7\left(\frac{11}{16}\right) + \frac{1}{16} - 6\left(\frac{11}{16}\right) \stackrel{?}{=} \frac{3}{4}$$
$$\frac{77}{16} + \frac{1}{16} - \frac{66}{16} \stackrel{?}{=} \frac{3}{4}$$
$$\frac{12}{16} \stackrel{?}{=} \frac{3}{4}$$
$$\frac{3}{4} = \frac{3}{4} \quad \text{True}$$

The solution is $\dfrac{11}{16}$.

13.
$$-\frac{2}{9} = x - \frac{5}{6}$$
$$-\frac{2}{9} + \frac{5}{6} = x - \frac{5}{6} + \frac{5}{6}$$
$$-\frac{2}{9} \cdot \frac{2}{2} + \frac{5}{6} \cdot \frac{3}{3} = x$$
$$-\frac{4}{18} + \frac{15}{18} = x$$
$$\frac{11}{18} = x$$

Check:
$$-\frac{2}{9} = x - \frac{5}{6}$$
$$-\frac{2}{9} \stackrel{?}{=} \frac{11}{18} - \frac{5}{6}$$
$$-\frac{2}{9} \cdot \frac{2}{2} \stackrel{?}{=} \frac{11}{18} - \frac{5}{6} \cdot \frac{3}{3}$$
$$-\frac{4}{18} \stackrel{?}{=} \frac{11}{18} - \frac{15}{18}$$
$$-\frac{4}{18} = -\frac{4}{18} \quad \text{True}$$

The solution is $\dfrac{11}{18}$.

15. $7x = 2$
$$\frac{1}{7} \cdot 7x = \frac{1}{7} \cdot 2$$
$$x = \frac{2}{7}$$

17. $\dfrac{1}{4} x = 3$
$$4 \cdot \frac{1}{4} x = 4 \cdot 3$$
$$x = 12$$

19. $\dfrac{2}{9} y = -6$
$$\frac{9}{2} \cdot \frac{2}{9} y = \frac{9}{2} \cdot -6$$
$$y = -\frac{9 \cdot 6}{2}$$
$$y = -\frac{9 \cdot 2 \cdot 3}{2}$$
$$y = -27$$

21. $-\dfrac{4}{9} z = -\dfrac{3}{2}$
$$-\frac{9}{4} \cdot -\frac{4}{9} z = -\frac{9}{4} \cdot -\frac{3}{2}$$
$$z = \frac{27}{8}$$

23. $7a = \dfrac{1}{3}$
$$\frac{1}{7} \cdot 7a = \frac{1}{7} \cdot \frac{1}{3}$$
$$a = \frac{1}{21}$$

25.
$$-3x = -\frac{6}{11}$$
$$-\frac{1}{3} \cdot -3x = -\frac{1}{3} \cdot -\frac{6}{11}$$
$$x = \frac{6}{3 \cdot 11}$$
$$x = \frac{2 \cdot 3}{3 \cdot 11}$$
$$x = \frac{2}{11}$$

27.
$$\frac{5}{9}x = -\frac{3}{18}$$
$$18\left(\frac{5}{9}x\right) = 18\left(-\frac{3}{18}\right)$$
$$10x = -3$$
$$\frac{10x}{10} = \frac{-3}{10}$$
$$x = -\frac{3}{10}$$

29.
$$\frac{x}{3} + 2 = \frac{7}{3}$$
$$3\left(\frac{x}{3} + 2\right) = 3 \cdot \frac{7}{3}$$
$$3 \cdot \frac{x}{3} + 3 \cdot 2 = 7$$
$$x + 6 = 7$$
$$x + 6 - 6 = 7 - 6$$
$$x = 1$$

31.
$$\frac{x}{5} - x = -8$$
$$5\left(\frac{x}{5} - x\right) = 5(-8)$$
$$5\left(\frac{x}{5}\right) - 5(x) = -40$$
$$x - 5x = -40$$
$$-4x = -40$$
$$\frac{-4x}{-4} = \frac{-40}{-4}$$
$$x = 10$$

33.
$$\frac{1}{2} - \frac{3}{5} = \frac{x}{10}$$
$$10\left(\frac{1}{2} - \frac{3}{5}\right) = 10 \cdot \frac{x}{10}$$
$$10 \cdot \frac{1}{2} - 10 \cdot \frac{3}{5} = x$$
$$5 - 6 = x$$
$$-1 = x$$

35.
$$\frac{x}{3} = \frac{x}{5} - 2$$
$$15\left(\frac{x}{3}\right) = 15\left(\frac{x}{5} - 2\right)$$
$$5x = 15 \cdot \frac{x}{5} - 15 \cdot 2$$
$$5x = 3x - 30$$
$$5x - 3x = 3x - 3x - 30$$
$$2x = -30$$
$$\frac{2x}{2} = \frac{-30}{2}$$
$$x = -15$$

37.
$$\frac{x}{7} - \frac{4}{3} = \frac{x}{7} \cdot \frac{3}{3} - \frac{4}{3} \cdot \frac{7}{7}$$
$$= \frac{3x}{21} - \frac{28}{21}$$
$$= \frac{3x - 28}{21}$$

39. $\dfrac{y}{2} + 5 = \dfrac{y}{2} + \dfrac{5}{1} \cdot \dfrac{2}{2} = \dfrac{y}{2} + \dfrac{10}{2} = \dfrac{y + 10}{2}$

41.
$$\frac{3x}{10} + \frac{x}{6} = \frac{3x}{10} \cdot \frac{3}{3} + \frac{x}{6} \cdot \frac{5}{5}$$
$$= \frac{9x}{30} + \frac{5x}{30}$$
$$= \frac{14x}{30}$$
$$= \frac{2 \cdot 7 \cdot x}{2 \cdot 15}$$
$$= \frac{7x}{15}$$

43.
$$\frac{3}{8}x = \frac{1}{2}$$
$$\frac{8}{3} \cdot \frac{3}{8}x = \frac{8}{3} \cdot \frac{1}{2}$$
$$x = \frac{8}{6}$$
$$x = \frac{4}{3}$$

45.
$$\frac{2}{3} - \frac{x}{5} = \frac{4}{15}$$
$$15\left(\frac{2}{3} - \frac{x}{5}\right) = 15 \cdot \frac{4}{15}$$
$$15 \cdot \frac{2}{3} - 15 \cdot \frac{x}{5} = 4$$
$$10 - 3x = 4$$
$$10 - 3x - 10 = 4 - 10$$
$$-3x = -6$$
$$\frac{-3x}{-3} = \frac{-6}{-3}$$
$$x = 2$$

47.
$$\frac{9}{14}z = \frac{27}{20}$$
$$\frac{14}{9} \cdot \frac{9}{14}z = \frac{14}{9} \cdot \frac{27}{20}$$
$$z = \frac{2 \cdot 7 \cdot 9 \cdot 3}{9 \cdot 2 \cdot 10}$$
$$z = \frac{21}{10}$$

49.
$$-3m - 5m = \frac{4}{7}$$
$$-8m = \frac{4}{7}$$
$$-\frac{1}{8} \cdot -8m = -\frac{1}{8} \cdot \frac{4}{7}$$
$$m = -\frac{1 \cdot 4}{2 \cdot 4 \cdot 7}$$
$$m = -\frac{1}{14}$$

51.
$$\frac{x}{4} + 1 = \frac{1}{4}$$
$$4\left(\frac{x}{4} + 1\right) = 4\left(\frac{1}{4}\right)$$
$$4 \cdot \frac{x}{4} + 4 \cdot 1 = 1$$
$$x + 4 = 1$$
$$x + 4 - 4 = 1 - 4$$
$$x = -3$$

53. $\dfrac{5}{9} - \dfrac{2}{3} = \dfrac{5}{9} - \dfrac{2}{3} \cdot \dfrac{3}{3} = \dfrac{5}{9} - \dfrac{6}{9} = -\dfrac{1}{9}$

55.
$$\frac{1}{5}y = 10$$
$$5 \cdot \frac{1}{5}y = 5 \cdot 10$$
$$y = 50$$

57.
$$\frac{5}{7}y = -\frac{15}{49}$$
$$\frac{7}{5} \cdot \frac{5}{7}y = \frac{7}{5} \cdot -\frac{15}{49}$$
$$y = -\frac{7 \cdot 15}{5 \cdot 49}$$
$$y = -\frac{7 \cdot 3 \cdot 5}{5 \cdot 7 \cdot 7}$$
$$y = -\frac{3}{7}$$

59.
$$\frac{x}{2} - x = -2$$
$$2\left(\frac{x}{2} - x\right) = 2(-2)$$
$$2 \cdot \frac{x}{2} - 2 \cdot x = -4$$
$$x - 2x = -4$$
$$-x = -4$$
$$\frac{-x}{-1} = \frac{-4}{-1}$$
$$x = 4$$

61.
$$-\frac{5}{8}y = \frac{3}{16} - \frac{9}{16}$$
$$-\frac{5}{8}y = -\frac{6}{16}$$
$$-\frac{5}{8}y = -\frac{3}{8}$$
$$-\frac{8}{5} \cdot -\frac{5}{8}y = -\frac{8}{5} \cdot -\frac{3}{8}$$
$$y = \frac{8 \cdot 3}{5 \cdot 8}$$
$$y = \frac{3}{5}$$

63.
$$17x - 25x = \frac{1}{3}$$
$$-8x = \frac{1}{3}$$
$$-\frac{1}{8} \cdot -8x = -\frac{1}{8} \cdot \frac{1}{3}$$
$$x = -\frac{1}{24}$$

65.
$$\frac{7}{6}x = \frac{1}{4} - \frac{2}{3}$$
$$12 \cdot \frac{7}{6}x = 12\left(\frac{1}{4} - \frac{2}{3}\right)$$
$$14x = 12 \cdot \frac{1}{4} - 12 \cdot \frac{2}{3}$$
$$14x = 3 - 8$$
$$14x = -5$$
$$\frac{14x}{14} = \frac{-5}{14}$$
$$x = -\frac{5}{14}$$

67.
$$\frac{b}{4} = \frac{b}{12} + \frac{2}{3}$$
$$12 \cdot \frac{b}{4} = 12\left(\frac{b}{12} + \frac{2}{3}\right)$$
$$3b = 12 \cdot \frac{b}{12} + 12 \cdot \frac{2}{3}$$
$$3b = b + 8$$
$$3b - b = b + 8 - b$$
$$2b = 8$$
$$\frac{2b}{2} = \frac{8}{2}$$
$$b = 4$$

69.
$$\frac{x}{3} + 2 = \frac{x}{2} + 8$$
$$6\left(\frac{x}{3} + 2\right) = 6\left(\frac{x}{2} + 8\right)$$
$$6 \cdot \frac{x}{3} + 6 \cdot 2 = 6 \cdot \frac{x}{2} + 6 \cdot 8$$
$$2x + 12 = 3x + 48$$
$$2x + 12 - 2x = 3x + 48 - 2x$$
$$12 = x + 48$$
$$12 - 48 = x + 48 - 48$$
$$-36 = x$$

71. To round 57,236 to the nearest hundred, observe that the digit in the tens place is 3. Since this digit is less than 5, we do not add 1 to the digit in the hundreds place. 57,236 rounded to the nearest hundred is 57,200.

73. To round 327 to the nearest ten, observe that the digit in the ones place is 7. Since this digit is at least 5, we add 1 to the digit in the tens place. 327 rounded to the nearest ten is 330.

75. answers may vary

77.
$$\frac{14}{11} + \frac{3x}{8} = \frac{x}{2}$$
$$88\left(\frac{14}{11} + \frac{3x}{8}\right) = 88 \cdot \frac{x}{2}$$
$$88 \cdot \frac{14}{11} + 88 \cdot \frac{3x}{8} = 44x$$
$$112 + 33x = 44x$$
$$112 + 33x - 33x = 44x - 33x$$
$$112 = 11x$$
$$\frac{112}{11} = \frac{11x}{11}$$
$$\frac{112}{11} = x$$

79. $A = l \cdot w = \frac{3}{4} \cdot \frac{1}{4} = \frac{3}{16}$

The area is $\frac{3}{16}$ square inch.

$P = 2l + 2w = 2 \cdot \frac{3}{4} + 2 \cdot \frac{1}{4} = \frac{3}{2} + \frac{1}{2} = \frac{4}{2} = 2$

The perimeter is 2 inches.

Chapter 4 Vocabulary Check

1. Two numbers are <u>reciprocals</u> of each other if their product is 1.

2. A <u>composite number</u> is a natural number greater than 1 that is not prime.

3. Fractions that represent the same portion of a whole are called <u>equivalent</u> fractions.

4. An <u>improper fraction</u> is a fraction whose numerator is greater than or equal to its denominator.

5. A <u>prime number</u> is a natural number greater than 1 whose only factors are 1 and itself.

6. A fraction is in <u>simplest form</u> when the numerator and the denominator have no factors in common other than 1.

7. A <u>proper fraction</u> is one whose numerator is less than its denominator.

8. A <u>mixed number</u> contains a whole number part and a fraction part.

9. In the fraction $\frac{7}{9}$, the 7 is called the <u>numerator</u> and the 9 is called the <u>denominator</u>.

10. The <u>prime factorization</u> of a number is the factorization in which all the factors are prime numbers.

11. The fraction $\dfrac{3}{0}$ is <u>undefined</u>.

12. The fraction $\dfrac{0}{5} = \underline{0}$.

13. Fractions that have the same denominator are called <u>like</u> fractions.

14. The LCM of the denominators in a list of fractions is called the <u>least common denominator</u>.

15. A fraction whose numerator or denominator or both numerator and denominator contain fractions is called a <u>complex fraction</u>.

16. In $\dfrac{a}{b} = \dfrac{c}{d}$, $a \cdot d$ and $b \cdot c$ are called <u>cross products</u>.

Chapter 4 Review

1. 2 out of 6 equal parts are shaded: $\dfrac{2}{6}$

2. 4 out of 7 equal parts are shaded: $\dfrac{4}{7}$

3. Each part is $\dfrac{1}{3}$ of a whole and there are 7 parts shaded, or 2 wholes and 1 more part: $\dfrac{7}{3}$ or $2\dfrac{1}{3}$

4. Each part is $\dfrac{1}{4}$ of a whole and there are 13 parts shaded, or 3 wholes and 1 more part: $\dfrac{13}{4}$ or $3\dfrac{1}{4}$

5. successful free throws $\rightarrow 11$
total free throws $\quad\rightarrow \overline{12}$

$\dfrac{11}{12}$ of the free throws were made.

6. a. $131 - 23 = 108$
108 cars are not blue.

    b. not blue $\rightarrow 108$
total $\quad\rightarrow \overline{131}$

$\dfrac{108}{131}$ of the cars on the lot are not blue.

7. $\dfrac{3}{-3} = -1$

8. $\dfrac{-20}{-20} = 1$

9. $\dfrac{0}{-1} = 0$

10. $\dfrac{4}{0}$ is undefined

11.

12.

13.

14.

15. $4\overline{\smash{)}15}$ with quotient 3

$\begin{array}{r} 3 \\ 4\overline{)15} \\ \underline{12} \\ 3 \end{array}$

$\dfrac{15}{4} = 3\dfrac{3}{4}$

16.

$\begin{array}{r} 3 \\ 13\overline{)39} \\ \underline{39} \\ 0 \end{array}$

$\dfrac{39}{13} = 3$

17. $2\dfrac{1}{5} = \dfrac{5 \cdot 2 + 1}{5} = \dfrac{10 + 1}{5} = \dfrac{11}{5}$

18. $3\dfrac{8}{9} = \dfrac{9 \cdot 3 + 8}{9} = \dfrac{27 + 8}{9} = \dfrac{35}{9}$

19. $\dfrac{12}{28} = \dfrac{4 \cdot 3}{7 \cdot 4} = \dfrac{3}{7}$

20. $\dfrac{15}{27} = \dfrac{3 \cdot 5}{3 \cdot 9} = \dfrac{5}{9}$

21. $-\dfrac{25x}{75x^2} = -\dfrac{1 \cdot 25 \cdot x}{3 \cdot 25 \cdot x \cdot x} = -\dfrac{1}{3x}$

22. $-\dfrac{36y^3}{72y} = -\dfrac{1 \cdot 36 \cdot y \cdot y \cdot y}{2 \cdot 36 \cdot y} = -\dfrac{y^2}{2}$

23. $\dfrac{29ab}{32abc} = \dfrac{29 \cdot a \cdot b}{32 \cdot a \cdot b \cdot c} = \dfrac{29}{32c}$

24. $\dfrac{18xyz}{23xy} = \dfrac{18 \cdot x \cdot y \cdot z}{23 \cdot x \cdot y} = \dfrac{18z}{23}$

25. $\dfrac{45x^2y}{27xy^3} = \dfrac{9 \cdot 5 \cdot x \cdot x \cdot y}{9 \cdot 3 \cdot x \cdot y \cdot y \cdot y} = \dfrac{5x}{3y^2}$

26. $\dfrac{42ab^2c}{30abc^3} = \dfrac{6 \cdot 7 \cdot a \cdot b \cdot b \cdot c}{6 \cdot 5 \cdot a \cdot b \cdot c \cdot c \cdot c} = \dfrac{7b}{5c^2}$

27. $\dfrac{8 \text{ inches}}{12 \text{ inches}} = \dfrac{8}{12} = \dfrac{4 \cdot 2}{4 \cdot 3} = \dfrac{2}{3}$

8 inches represents $\dfrac{2}{3}$ of a foot.

28. $15 - 6 = 9$ cars are not white.

$\dfrac{9 \text{ non-white cars}}{15 \text{ total cars}} = \dfrac{9}{15} = \dfrac{3 \cdot 3}{3 \cdot 5} = \dfrac{3}{5}$

$\dfrac{3}{5}$ of the cars are not white.

29. Not equivalent, since the cross products are not equal: $34 \cdot 4 = 136$ and $10 \cdot 14 = 140$

30. Equivalent, since the cross products are equal: $30 \cdot 15 = 450$ and $50 \cdot 9 = 450$

31. $\dfrac{3}{5} \cdot \dfrac{1}{2} = \dfrac{3 \cdot 1}{5 \cdot 2} = \dfrac{3}{10}$

32. $-\dfrac{6}{7} \cdot \dfrac{5}{12} = -\dfrac{6 \cdot 5}{7 \cdot 12} = -\dfrac{6 \cdot 5}{7 \cdot 6 \cdot 2} = -\dfrac{5}{7 \cdot 2} = -\dfrac{5}{14}$

33. $-\dfrac{24x}{5} \cdot \left(-\dfrac{15}{8x^3}\right) = \dfrac{24x \cdot 15}{5 \cdot 8x^3}$

$= \dfrac{8 \cdot 3 \cdot x \cdot 5 \cdot 3}{5 \cdot 8 \cdot x \cdot x \cdot x}$

$= \dfrac{3 \cdot 3}{x \cdot x}$

$= \dfrac{9}{x^2}$

34. $\dfrac{27y^3}{21} \cdot \dfrac{7}{18y^2} = \dfrac{27y^3 \cdot 7}{21 \cdot 18y^2} = \dfrac{3 \cdot 9 \cdot y \cdot y \cdot y \cdot 7}{3 \cdot 7 \cdot 9 \cdot 2 \cdot y \cdot y} = \dfrac{y}{2}$

35. $\left(-\dfrac{1}{3}\right)^3 = \left(-\dfrac{1}{3}\right)\left(-\dfrac{1}{3}\right)\left(-\dfrac{1}{3}\right) = -\dfrac{1 \cdot 1 \cdot 1}{3 \cdot 3 \cdot 3} = -\dfrac{1}{27}$

36. $\left(-\dfrac{5}{12}\right)^2 = \left(-\dfrac{5}{12}\right)\left(-\dfrac{5}{12}\right) = \dfrac{5 \cdot 5}{12 \cdot 12} = \dfrac{25}{144}$

37. $-\dfrac{3}{4} \div \dfrac{3}{8} = -\dfrac{3}{4} \cdot \dfrac{8}{3} = -\dfrac{3 \cdot 8}{4 \cdot 3} = -\dfrac{3 \cdot 4 \cdot 2}{1 \cdot 4 \cdot 3} = -\dfrac{2}{1} = -2$

38. $\dfrac{21a}{4} \div \dfrac{7a}{5} = \dfrac{21a}{4} \cdot \dfrac{5}{7a}$

$= \dfrac{21a \cdot 5}{4 \cdot 7a}$

$= \dfrac{7 \cdot 3 \cdot a \cdot 5}{4 \cdot 7 \cdot a}$

$= \dfrac{3 \cdot 5}{4}$

$= \dfrac{15}{4}$

39. $-\dfrac{9}{2} \div -\dfrac{1}{3} = -\dfrac{9}{2} \cdot \left(-\dfrac{3}{1}\right) = \dfrac{9 \cdot 3}{2 \cdot 1} = \dfrac{27}{2}$

40. $-\dfrac{5}{3} \div 2y = -\dfrac{5}{3} \div \dfrac{2y}{1} = -\dfrac{5}{3} \cdot \dfrac{1}{2y} = -\dfrac{5 \cdot 1}{3 \cdot 2y} = -\dfrac{5}{6y}$

41. $x \div y = \dfrac{9}{7} \div \dfrac{3}{4}$

$= \dfrac{9}{7} \cdot \dfrac{4}{3}$

$= \dfrac{9 \cdot 4}{7 \cdot 3}$

$= \dfrac{3 \cdot 3 \cdot 4}{7 \cdot 3}$

$= \dfrac{3 \cdot 4}{7}$

$= \dfrac{12}{7}$

42. $ab = -7 \cdot \dfrac{9}{10} = -\dfrac{7}{1} \cdot \dfrac{9}{10} = -\dfrac{7 \cdot 9}{1 \cdot 10} = -\dfrac{63}{10}$

43. $\text{area} = \text{length} \cdot \text{width} = \dfrac{11}{6} \cdot \dfrac{7}{8} = \dfrac{11 \cdot 7}{6 \cdot 8} = \dfrac{77}{48}$

The area is $\dfrac{77}{48}$ square feet.

44. $\text{area} = \text{side} \cdot \text{side} = \dfrac{2}{3} \cdot \dfrac{2}{3} = \dfrac{2 \cdot 2}{3 \cdot 3} = \dfrac{4}{9}$

The area is $\dfrac{4}{9}$ square meter.

45. $\dfrac{7}{11} + \dfrac{3}{11} = \dfrac{7+3}{11} = \dfrac{10}{11}$

46. $\dfrac{4}{9} + \dfrac{2}{9} = \dfrac{4+2}{9} = \dfrac{6}{9} = \dfrac{2 \cdot 3}{3 \cdot 3} = \dfrac{2}{3}$

47. $\dfrac{1}{12} - \dfrac{5}{12} = \dfrac{1-5}{12} = \dfrac{-4}{12} = -\dfrac{1 \cdot 4}{3 \cdot 4} = -\dfrac{1}{3}$

48. $\dfrac{11x}{15} + \dfrac{x}{15} = \dfrac{11x+x}{15} = \dfrac{12x}{15} = \dfrac{3 \cdot 4 \cdot x}{3 \cdot 5} = \dfrac{4x}{5}$

49. $\dfrac{4y}{21} - \dfrac{3}{21} = \dfrac{4y-3}{21}$

50. $\dfrac{4}{15} - \dfrac{3}{15} - \dfrac{2}{15} = \dfrac{4-3-2}{15} = \dfrac{-1}{15} = -\dfrac{1}{15}$

51. $3 = 3$
$x = x$
$\text{LCD} = 3 \cdot x = 3x$

52. $4 = 2 \cdot 2$
$8 = \boxed{2 \cdot 2 \cdot 2}$
$12 = 2 \cdot 2 \cdot \boxed{3}$
$\text{LCD} = 2 \cdot 2 \cdot 2 \cdot 3 = 24$

53. $\dfrac{2}{3} = \dfrac{2}{3} \cdot \dfrac{10}{10} = \dfrac{2 \cdot 10}{3 \cdot 10} = \dfrac{20}{30}$

54. $\dfrac{5}{8} = \dfrac{5}{8} \cdot \dfrac{7}{7} = \dfrac{5 \cdot 7}{8 \cdot 7} = \dfrac{35}{56}$

55. $\dfrac{7a}{6} = \dfrac{7a}{6} \cdot \dfrac{7}{7} = \dfrac{7a \cdot 7}{6 \cdot 7} = \dfrac{49a}{42}$

56. $\dfrac{9b}{4} = \dfrac{9b}{4} \cdot \dfrac{5}{5} = \dfrac{9b \cdot 5}{4 \cdot 5} = \dfrac{45b}{20}$

57. $\dfrac{4}{5x} = \dfrac{4}{5x} \cdot \dfrac{10}{10} = \dfrac{4 \cdot 10}{5x \cdot 10} = \dfrac{40}{50x}$

58. $\dfrac{5}{9y} = \dfrac{5}{9y} \cdot \dfrac{2}{2} = \dfrac{5 \cdot 2}{9y \cdot 2} = \dfrac{10}{18y}$

59. $\dfrac{3}{8} + \dfrac{2}{8} + \dfrac{1}{8} = \dfrac{3+2+1}{8} = \dfrac{6}{8} = \dfrac{2 \cdot 3}{2 \cdot 4} = \dfrac{3}{4}$

He did $\dfrac{3}{4}$ of his homework that evening.

60. $\dfrac{9}{16} + \dfrac{3}{16} + \dfrac{9}{16} + \dfrac{3}{16} = \dfrac{9+3+9+3}{16}$

$= \dfrac{24}{16}$

$= \dfrac{3 \cdot 8}{2 \cdot 8}$

$= \dfrac{3}{2}$

The perimeter is $\dfrac{3}{2}$ miles.

61. The LCD is 18.
$\dfrac{7}{18} + \dfrac{2}{9} = \dfrac{7}{18} + \dfrac{2 \cdot 2}{9 \cdot 2} = \dfrac{7}{18} + \dfrac{4}{18} = \dfrac{11}{18}$

62. The LCD is 26.
$\dfrac{4}{13} - \dfrac{1}{26} = \dfrac{4 \cdot 2}{13 \cdot 2} - \dfrac{1}{26} = \dfrac{8}{26} - \dfrac{1}{26} = \dfrac{7}{26}$

63. The LCD is 12.
$-\dfrac{1}{3} + \dfrac{1}{4} = -\dfrac{1 \cdot 4}{3 \cdot 4} + \dfrac{1 \cdot 3}{4 \cdot 3} = -\dfrac{4}{12} + \dfrac{3}{12} = -\dfrac{1}{12}$

64. The LCD is 12.
$-\dfrac{2}{3} + \dfrac{1}{4} = -\dfrac{2 \cdot 4}{3 \cdot 4} + \dfrac{1 \cdot 3}{4 \cdot 3} = -\dfrac{8}{12} + \dfrac{3}{12} = -\dfrac{5}{12}$

65. The LCD is 55.
$\dfrac{5x}{11} + \dfrac{2}{55} = \dfrac{5x \cdot 5}{11 \cdot 5} + \dfrac{2}{55} = \dfrac{25x}{55} + \dfrac{2}{55} = \dfrac{25x+2}{55}$

66. The LCD is 15.
$\dfrac{4}{15} + \dfrac{b}{5} = \dfrac{4}{15} + \dfrac{b \cdot 3}{5 \cdot 3} = \dfrac{4}{15} + \dfrac{3b}{15} = \dfrac{4+3b}{15}$

67. The LCD is 36.
$\dfrac{5y}{12} - \dfrac{2y}{9} = \dfrac{5y \cdot 3}{12 \cdot 3} - \dfrac{2y \cdot 4}{9 \cdot 4} = \dfrac{15y}{36} - \dfrac{8y}{36} = \dfrac{7y}{36}$

68. The LCD is 18.

$$\frac{7x}{18}+\frac{2x}{9}=\frac{7x}{18}+\frac{2x\cdot 2}{9\cdot 2}=\frac{7x}{18}+\frac{4x}{18}=\frac{11x}{18}$$

69. The LCD is $9y$.

$$\frac{4}{9}+\frac{5}{y}=\frac{4\cdot y}{9\cdot y}+\frac{5\cdot 9}{y\cdot 9}=\frac{4y}{9y}+\frac{45}{9y}=\frac{4y+45}{9y}$$

70. The LCD is 14.

$$-\frac{9}{14}-\frac{3}{7}=-\frac{9}{14}-\frac{3\cdot 2}{7\cdot 2}=-\frac{9}{14}-\frac{6}{14}=-\frac{15}{14}$$

71. The LCD is 150.

$$\begin{aligned}\frac{4}{25}+\frac{23}{75}+\frac{7}{50}&=\frac{4\cdot 6}{25\cdot 6}+\frac{23\cdot 2}{75\cdot 2}+\frac{7\cdot 3}{50\cdot 3}\\&=\frac{24}{150}+\frac{46}{150}+\frac{21}{150}\\&=\frac{91}{150}\end{aligned}$$

72. The LCD is 18.

$$\begin{aligned}\frac{2}{3}-\frac{2}{9}-\frac{1}{6}&=\frac{2\cdot 6}{3\cdot 6}-\frac{2\cdot 2}{9\cdot 2}-\frac{1\cdot 3}{6\cdot 3}\\&=\frac{12}{18}-\frac{4}{18}-\frac{3}{18}\\&=\frac{5}{18}\end{aligned}$$

73. The LCD is 18.

$$\begin{aligned}\frac{2}{9}+\frac{5}{6}+\frac{2}{9}+\frac{5}{6}&=\frac{2\cdot 2}{9\cdot 2}+\frac{5\cdot 3}{6\cdot 3}+\frac{2\cdot 2}{9\cdot 2}+\frac{5\cdot 3}{6\cdot 3}\\&=\frac{4}{18}+\frac{15}{18}+\frac{4}{18}+\frac{15}{18}\\&=\frac{38}{18}\\&=\frac{2\cdot 19}{2\cdot 9}\\&=\frac{19}{9}\end{aligned}$$

The perimeter is $\frac{19}{9}$ meters.

74. The LCD is 10.

$$\begin{aligned}\frac{1}{5}+\frac{3}{5}+\frac{7}{10}&=\frac{1\cdot 2}{5\cdot 2}+\frac{3\cdot 2}{5\cdot 2}+\frac{7}{10}\\&=\frac{2}{10}+\frac{6}{10}+\frac{7}{10}\\&=\frac{15}{10}\\&=\frac{3\cdot 5}{2\cdot 5}\\&=\frac{3}{2}\end{aligned}$$

The perimeter is $\frac{3}{2}$ feet.

75. The LCD is 50.

$$\frac{9}{25}+\frac{3}{50}=\frac{9\cdot 2}{25\cdot 2}+\frac{3}{50}=\frac{18}{50}+\frac{3}{50}=\frac{21}{50}$$

$\frac{21}{50}$ of the donors have type A blood.

76. The LCD is 12.

$$\frac{2}{3}-\frac{5}{12}=\frac{2\cdot 4}{3\cdot 4}-\frac{5}{12}=\frac{8}{12}-\frac{5}{12}=\frac{3}{12}=\frac{1\cdot 3}{4\cdot 3}=\frac{1}{4}$$

The difference in length is $\frac{1}{4}$ yard.

77.

$$\begin{aligned}\frac{\frac{2x}{5}}{\frac{7}{10}}&=\frac{2x}{5}\div\frac{7}{10}\\&=\frac{2x}{5}\cdot\frac{10}{7}\\&=\frac{2x\cdot 10}{5\cdot 7}\\&=\frac{2\cdot x\cdot 5\cdot 2}{5\cdot 7}\\&=\frac{4x}{7}\end{aligned}$$

78.

$$\frac{\frac{3y}{7}}{\frac{11}{7}}=\frac{3y}{7}\div\frac{11}{7}=\frac{3y}{7}\cdot\frac{7}{11}=\frac{3y\cdot 7}{7\cdot 11}=\frac{3y}{11}$$

79.
$$\frac{\frac{2}{5}-\frac{1}{2}}{\frac{3}{4}-\frac{7}{10}} = \frac{20\left(\frac{2}{5}-\frac{1}{2}\right)}{20\left(\frac{3}{4}-\frac{7}{10}\right)}$$
$$= \frac{20\cdot\frac{2}{5}-20\cdot\frac{1}{2}}{20\cdot\frac{3}{4}-20\cdot\frac{7}{10}}$$
$$= \frac{8-10}{15-14}$$
$$= \frac{-2}{1}$$
$$= -2$$

80.
$$\frac{\frac{5}{6}-\frac{1}{4}}{\frac{-1}{12y}} = \frac{12y\left(\frac{5}{6}-\frac{1}{4}\right)}{12y\left(\frac{-1}{12y}\right)}$$
$$= \frac{12y\cdot\frac{5}{6}-12y\cdot\frac{1}{4}}{-1}$$
$$= \frac{10y-3y}{-1}$$
$$= \frac{7y}{-1}$$
$$= -7y$$

81.
$$\frac{x}{y+z} = \frac{\frac{1}{2}}{-\frac{2}{3}+\frac{4}{5}}$$
$$= \frac{30\cdot\frac{1}{2}}{30\left(-\frac{2}{3}+\frac{4}{5}\right)}$$
$$= \frac{15}{30\left(-\frac{2}{3}\right)+30\cdot\frac{4}{5}}$$
$$= \frac{15}{-20+24}$$
$$= \frac{15}{4}$$

82.
$$\frac{x+y}{z} = \frac{\frac{1}{2}+\left(-\frac{2}{3}\right)}{\frac{4}{5}}$$
$$= \frac{30\left(\frac{1}{2}-\frac{2}{3}\right)}{30\cdot\frac{4}{5}}$$
$$= \frac{30\cdot\frac{1}{2}-30\cdot\frac{2}{3}}{6\cdot4}$$
$$= \frac{15-20}{24}$$
$$= -\frac{5}{24}$$

83.
$$\frac{5}{13}\div\frac{1}{2}\cdot\frac{4}{5} = \frac{5}{13}\cdot\frac{2}{1}\cdot\frac{4}{5} = \frac{5\cdot2\cdot4}{13\cdot1\cdot5} = \frac{8}{13}$$

84.
$$\frac{2}{27}-\left(\frac{1}{3}\right)^2 = \frac{2}{27}-\frac{1}{9}$$
$$= \frac{2}{27}-\frac{1\cdot3}{9\cdot3}$$
$$= \frac{2}{27}-\frac{3}{27}$$
$$= -\frac{1}{27}$$

85.
$$\frac{9}{10}\cdot\frac{1}{3}-\frac{2}{5}\cdot\frac{1}{11} = \frac{9\cdot1}{10\cdot3}-\frac{2\cdot1}{5\cdot11}$$
$$= \frac{3}{10}-\frac{2}{55}$$
$$= \frac{3\cdot11}{10\cdot11}-\frac{2\cdot2}{55\cdot2}$$
$$= \frac{33}{110}-\frac{4}{110}$$
$$= \frac{29}{110}$$

86.
$$-\frac{2}{7}\cdot\left(\frac{1}{5}+\frac{3}{10}\right) = -\frac{2}{7}\cdot\left(\frac{1\cdot2}{5\cdot2}+\frac{3}{10}\right)$$
$$= -\frac{2}{7}\cdot\left(\frac{2}{10}+\frac{3}{10}\right)$$
$$= -\frac{2}{7}\cdot\frac{5}{10}$$
$$= -\frac{2\cdot5}{7\cdot2\cdot5}$$
$$= -\frac{1}{7}$$

87.

$$
\begin{array}{ll}
7\frac{3}{8} & 7\frac{9}{24} \\
9\frac{5}{6} & 9\frac{20}{24} \\
+\,3\frac{1}{12} & +\,3\frac{2}{24} \\
\hline
& 19\frac{31}{24}=19+1\frac{7}{24}=20\frac{7}{24}
\end{array}
$$

88. $8\frac{1}{5}$ rounds to 8.

$5\frac{3}{11}$ rounds to 5.

An estimate is $8 - 5 = 3$.

$$
\begin{array}{ccc}
8\frac{1}{5} & 8\frac{11}{55} & 7\frac{66}{55} \\
-5\frac{3}{11} & -5\frac{15}{55} & -5\frac{15}{55} \\
\hline
& & 2\frac{51}{55}
\end{array}
$$

89. $1\frac{5}{8}$ rounds to 2.

$3\frac{1}{5}$ rounds to 3.

An estimate is $2 \cdot 3 = 6$.

$1\frac{5}{8} \cdot 3\frac{1}{5} = \frac{13}{8} \cdot \frac{16}{5} = \frac{13 \cdot 16}{8 \cdot 5} = \frac{13 \cdot 8 \cdot 2}{8 \cdot 5} = \frac{26}{5} = 5\frac{1}{5}$

90. $6\frac{3}{4} \div 1\frac{2}{7} = \frac{27}{4} \div \frac{9}{7} = \frac{27}{4} \cdot \frac{7}{9} = \frac{9 \cdot 3 \cdot 7}{4 \cdot 9} = \frac{21}{4} = 5\frac{1}{4}$

91. $341 \div 15\frac{1}{2} = \frac{341}{1} \div \frac{31}{2} = \frac{341}{1} \cdot \frac{2}{31} = \frac{11 \cdot 31 \cdot 2}{1 \cdot 31} = 22$

We would expect 22 miles on one gallon.

92. $7\frac{1}{3} \cdot 5 = \frac{22}{3} \cdot \frac{5}{1} = \frac{22 \cdot 5}{3 \cdot 1} = \frac{110}{3} = 36\frac{2}{3}$

There are $\frac{110}{3}$ or $36\frac{2}{3}$ grams of fat in a 5-ounce hamburger patty.

93. $18\frac{7}{8} - 10\frac{3}{8} = 8\frac{4}{8} = 8\frac{1}{2}$

$8\frac{1}{2} \div 2 = \frac{17}{2} \div \frac{2}{1} = \frac{17}{2} \cdot \frac{1}{2} = \frac{17}{4} = 4\frac{1}{4}$

Each measurement is $4\frac{1}{4}$ inches.

94. $1\frac{3}{10} - \frac{3}{5} = \frac{13}{10} - \frac{3}{5} = \frac{13}{10} - \frac{3 \cdot 2}{5 \cdot 2} = \frac{13}{10} - \frac{6}{10} = \frac{7}{10}$

The unknown measurement is $\frac{7}{10}$ yard.

95. $-12\frac{1}{7} + \left(-15\frac{3}{14}\right) = -12\frac{2}{14} + \left(-15\frac{3}{14}\right) = -27\frac{5}{14}$

96. $23\frac{7}{8} - 24\frac{7}{10} = -\left(24\frac{7}{10} - 23\frac{7}{8}\right)$

$$
\begin{array}{ccc}
24\frac{7}{10} & 24\frac{28}{40} & 23\frac{68}{40} \\
-23\frac{7}{8} & -23\frac{35}{40} & -23\frac{35}{40} \\
\hline
& & \frac{33}{40}
\end{array}
$$

$23\frac{7}{8} - 24\frac{7}{10} = -\frac{33}{40}$

97. $-3\frac{1}{5} \div \left(-2\frac{7}{10}\right) = -\frac{16}{5} \div \left(-\frac{27}{10}\right)$

$= -\frac{16}{5} \cdot \left(-\frac{10}{27}\right)$

$= \frac{16 \cdot 5 \cdot 2}{5 \cdot 27}$

$= \frac{32}{27}$

$= 1\frac{5}{27}$

98. $-2\frac{1}{4} \cdot 1\frac{3}{4} = -\frac{9}{4} \cdot \frac{7}{4} = -\frac{63}{16} = -3\frac{15}{16}$

99. $a - \frac{2}{3} = \frac{1}{6}$

$a - \frac{2}{3} + \frac{2}{3} = \frac{1}{6} + \frac{2}{3}$

$a = \frac{1}{6} + \frac{2 \cdot 2}{3 \cdot 2}$

$a = \frac{1}{6} + \frac{4}{6}$

$a = \frac{5}{6}$

100. $9x + \frac{1}{5} - 8x = -\frac{7}{10}$

$x + \frac{1}{5} = -\frac{7}{10}$

$x + \frac{1}{5} - \frac{1}{5} = -\frac{7}{10} - \frac{1}{5}$

$x = -\frac{7}{10} - \frac{2}{10}$

$x = -\frac{9}{10}$

101.
$$-\frac{3}{5}x = 6$$
$$-\frac{5}{3} \cdot -\frac{3}{5}x = -\frac{5}{3} \cdot 6$$
$$x = -10$$

102.
$$\frac{2}{9}y = -\frac{4}{3}$$
$$\frac{9}{2} \cdot \frac{2}{9}y = \frac{9}{2} \cdot -\frac{4}{3}$$
$$y = -\frac{9 \cdot 4}{2 \cdot 3}$$
$$y = -\frac{3 \cdot 3 \cdot 2 \cdot 2}{2 \cdot 3}$$
$$y = -\frac{6}{1}$$
$$y = -6$$

103.
$$\frac{x}{7} - 3 = -\frac{6}{7}$$
$$7\left(\frac{x}{7} - 3\right) = 7\left(-\frac{6}{7}\right)$$
$$7 \cdot \frac{x}{7} - 7 \cdot 3 = -6$$
$$x - 21 = -6$$
$$x - 21 + 21 = -6 + 21$$
$$x = 15$$

104.
$$\frac{y}{5} + 2 = \frac{11}{5}$$
$$5\left(\frac{y}{5} + 2\right) = 5\left(\frac{11}{5}\right)$$
$$5 \cdot \frac{y}{5} + 5 \cdot 2 = 11$$
$$y + 10 = 11$$
$$y + 10 - 10 = 11 - 10$$
$$y = 1$$

105.
$$\frac{1}{6} + \frac{x}{4} = \frac{17}{12}$$
$$12\left(\frac{1}{6} + \frac{x}{4}\right) = 12 \cdot \frac{17}{12}$$
$$12 \cdot \frac{1}{6} + 12 \cdot \frac{x}{4} = 17$$
$$2 + 3x = 17$$
$$2 + 3x - 2 = 17 - 2$$
$$3x = 15$$
$$\frac{3x}{3} = \frac{15}{3}$$
$$x = 5$$

106.
$$\frac{x}{5} - \frac{5}{4} = \frac{x}{2} - \frac{1}{20}$$
$$20\left(\frac{x}{5} - \frac{5}{4}\right) = 20\left(\frac{x}{2} - \frac{1}{20}\right)$$
$$20 \cdot \frac{x}{5} - 20 \cdot \frac{5}{4} = 20 \cdot \frac{x}{2} - 20 \cdot \frac{1}{20}$$
$$4x - 25 = 10x - 1$$
$$4x - 25 - 10x = 10x - 1 - 10x$$
$$-25 - 6x = -1$$
$$-25 - 6x + 25 = -1 + 25$$
$$-6x = 24$$
$$\frac{-6x}{-6} = \frac{24}{-6}$$
$$x = -4$$

107.
$$\frac{6}{15} \cdot \frac{5}{8} = \frac{6 \cdot 5}{15 \cdot 8} = \frac{3 \cdot 2 \cdot 5}{5 \cdot 3 \cdot 2 \cdot 4} = \frac{1}{4}$$

108.
$$\frac{5x^2}{y} \div \frac{10x^3}{y^3} = \frac{5x^2}{y} \cdot \frac{y^3}{10x^3}$$
$$= \frac{5x^2 \cdot y^3}{y \cdot 10x^3}$$
$$= \frac{5 \cdot x \cdot x \cdot y \cdot y \cdot y}{y \cdot 5 \cdot 2 \cdot x \cdot x \cdot x}$$
$$= \frac{y^2}{2x}$$

109.
$$\frac{3}{10} - \frac{1}{10} = \frac{3-1}{10} = \frac{2}{10} = \frac{1 \cdot 2}{5 \cdot 2} = \frac{1}{5}$$

110.
$$\frac{7}{8x} \cdot -\frac{2}{3} = -\frac{7 \cdot 2}{8x \cdot 3} = -\frac{7 \cdot 2}{2 \cdot 4 \cdot x \cdot 3} = -\frac{7}{12x}$$

111.
$$\frac{2x}{3} + \frac{x}{4} = \frac{2x}{3} \cdot \frac{4}{4} + \frac{x}{4} \cdot \frac{3}{3}$$
$$= \frac{8x}{12} + \frac{3x}{12}$$
$$= \frac{8x + 3x}{12}$$
$$= \frac{11x}{12}$$

112.
$$-\frac{5}{11} + \frac{2}{55} = -\frac{5}{11} \cdot \frac{5}{5} + \frac{2}{55} = -\frac{25}{55} + \frac{2}{55} = -\frac{23}{55}$$

113. $-1\dfrac{3}{5} \div \dfrac{1}{4} = -\dfrac{8}{5} \div \dfrac{1}{4}$

$\qquad = -\dfrac{8}{5} \cdot \dfrac{4}{1}$

$\qquad = -\dfrac{8 \cdot 4}{5 \cdot 1}$

$\qquad = -\dfrac{32}{5}$ or $-6\dfrac{2}{5}$

114. $2\dfrac{7}{8}$ rounds to 3.

$9\dfrac{1}{2}$ rounds to 10.

An estimate is $3 + 10 = 13$.

$$\begin{array}{r} 2\dfrac{7}{8} \\ +\,9\dfrac{1}{2} \\ \hline \end{array} \qquad \begin{array}{r} 2\dfrac{7}{8} \\ +\,9\dfrac{4}{8} \\ \hline 11\dfrac{11}{8} = 11 + 1\dfrac{3}{8} = 12\dfrac{3}{8} \end{array}$$

115. $12\dfrac{1}{7}$ rounds to 12.

$9\dfrac{3}{5}$ rounds to 10.

An estimate is $12 - 10 = 2$.

$$\begin{array}{r} 12\dfrac{1}{7} \\ -\,9\dfrac{3}{5} \\ \hline \end{array} \qquad \begin{array}{r} 12\dfrac{5}{35} \\ -\,9\dfrac{21}{35} \\ \hline \end{array} \qquad \begin{array}{r} 11\dfrac{40}{35} \\ -\,9\dfrac{21}{35} \\ \hline 2\dfrac{19}{35} \end{array}$$

116. $\dfrac{2 + \frac{3}{4}}{1 - \frac{1}{8}} = \dfrac{8\left(2 + \frac{3}{4}\right)}{8\left(1 - \frac{1}{8}\right)}$

$\qquad = \dfrac{8 \cdot 2 + 8 \cdot \frac{3}{4}}{8 \cdot 1 - 8 \cdot \frac{1}{8}}$

$\qquad = \dfrac{16 + 6}{8 - 1}$

$\qquad = \dfrac{22}{7}$ or $3\dfrac{1}{7}$

117. $-\dfrac{3}{8} \cdot \left(\dfrac{2}{3} - \dfrac{4}{9}\right) = -\dfrac{3}{8}\left(\dfrac{2 \cdot 3}{3 \cdot 3} - \dfrac{4}{9}\right)$

$\qquad = -\dfrac{3}{8}\left(\dfrac{6}{9} - \dfrac{4}{9}\right)$

$\qquad = -\dfrac{3}{8}\left(\dfrac{2}{9}\right)$

$\qquad = -\dfrac{3 \cdot 2}{8 \cdot 9}$

$\qquad = -\dfrac{3 \cdot 2}{2 \cdot 4 \cdot 3 \cdot 3}$

$\qquad = -\dfrac{1}{12}$

118. $11x - \dfrac{2}{7} - 10x = -\dfrac{13}{14}$

$\qquad x - \dfrac{2}{7} = -\dfrac{13}{14}$

$\qquad x - \dfrac{2}{7} + \dfrac{2}{7} = -\dfrac{13}{14} + \dfrac{2}{7}$

$\qquad x = -\dfrac{13}{14} + \dfrac{2 \cdot 2}{7 \cdot 2}$

$\qquad x = -\dfrac{13}{14} + \dfrac{4}{14}$

$\qquad x = -\dfrac{9}{14}$

119. $-\dfrac{3}{5}x = \dfrac{4}{15}$

$\qquad -\dfrac{5}{3} \cdot -\dfrac{3}{5}x = -\dfrac{5}{3} \cdot \dfrac{4}{15}$

$\qquad x = -\dfrac{5 \cdot 4}{3 \cdot 15}$

$\qquad x = -\dfrac{5 \cdot 4}{3 \cdot 5 \cdot 3}$

$\qquad x = -\dfrac{4}{9}$

120. $\dfrac{x}{12} + \dfrac{5}{6} = -\dfrac{3}{4}$

$\qquad 12\left(\dfrac{x}{12} + \dfrac{5}{6}\right) = 12\left(-\dfrac{3}{4}\right)$

$\qquad 12 \cdot \dfrac{x}{12} + 12 \cdot \dfrac{5}{6} = -9$

$\qquad x + 10 = -9$

$\qquad x + 10 - 10 = -9 - 10$

$\qquad x = -19$

121.
$$50 - 5\frac{1}{2} = \frac{50}{1} - \frac{11}{2}$$
$$= \frac{50 \cdot 2}{1 \cdot 2} - \frac{11}{2}$$
$$= \frac{100}{2} - \frac{11}{2}$$
$$= \frac{89}{2}$$
$$= 44\frac{1}{2}$$

The length of the remaining piece is $44\frac{1}{2}$ yards.

122. $5\frac{1}{2} \cdot 7\frac{4}{11} = \frac{11}{2} \cdot \frac{81}{11} = \frac{11 \cdot 81}{2 \cdot 11} = \frac{81}{2}$ or $40\frac{1}{2}$

The area is $\frac{81}{2}$ or $40\frac{1}{2}$ square feet.

Chapter 4 Test

1. 7 of the 16 equal parts are shaded: $\frac{7}{16}$.

2. $7\frac{2}{3} = \frac{3 \cdot 7 + 2}{3} = \frac{21 + 2}{3} = \frac{23}{3}$

3.
$$\begin{array}{r} 18 \\ 4\overline{)75} \\ \underline{4} \\ 35 \\ \underline{32} \\ 3 \end{array}$$
$$\frac{75}{4} = 18\frac{3}{4}$$

4. $\frac{24}{210} = \frac{6 \cdot 4}{6 \cdot 7 \cdot 5} = \frac{4}{35}$

5. $-\frac{42x}{70} = -\frac{3 \cdot 14 \cdot x}{5 \cdot 14} = -\frac{3x}{5}$

6. Check the cross-products.
$5 \cdot 11 = 55$
$7 \cdot 8 = 56$
Since $55 \neq 56$, the fractions are not equivalent.

7. Check the cross-products.
$6 \cdot 63 = 378$
$27 \cdot 14 = 378$
Since $378 = 378$, the fractions are equivalent.

8. $84 = 2 \cdot 42 = 2 \cdot 2 \cdot 21 = 2 \cdot 2 \cdot 3 \cdot 7 = 2^2 \cdot 3 \cdot 7$

9. $495 = 3 \cdot 165 = 3 \cdot 3 \cdot 55 = 3 \cdot 3 \cdot 5 \cdot 11 = 3^2 \cdot 5 \cdot 11$

10. $\frac{4}{4} \div \frac{3}{4} = \frac{4}{4} \cdot \frac{4}{3} = \frac{4 \cdot 4}{4 \cdot 3} = \frac{4}{3}$

11. $-\frac{4}{3} \cdot \frac{4}{4} = -\frac{4 \cdot 4}{3 \cdot 4} = -\frac{4}{3}$

12. $\frac{7x}{9} + \frac{x}{9} = \frac{7x + x}{9} = \frac{8x}{9}$

13. The LCD is $7x$.
$$\frac{1}{7} - \frac{3}{x} = \frac{1}{7} \cdot \frac{x}{x} - \frac{3}{x} \cdot \frac{7}{7} = \frac{x}{7x} - \frac{21}{7x} = \frac{x - 21}{7x}$$

14. $\frac{xy^3}{z} \cdot \frac{z}{xy} = \frac{xy^3 \cdot z}{z \cdot xy} = \frac{x \cdot y \cdot y \cdot y \cdot z}{x \cdot y \cdot z} = \frac{y \cdot y}{1} = y^2$

15. $-\frac{2}{3} \cdot -\frac{8}{15} = \frac{2 \cdot 8}{3 \cdot 15} = \frac{16}{45}$

16. $\frac{9a}{10} + \frac{2}{5} = \frac{9a}{10} + \frac{2 \cdot 2}{5 \cdot 2} = \frac{9a}{10} + \frac{4}{10} = \frac{9a + 4}{10}$

17. $-\frac{8}{15y} - \frac{2}{15y} = \frac{-8 - 2}{15y} = \frac{-10}{15y} = -\frac{2 \cdot 5}{3 \cdot 5 \cdot y} = -\frac{2}{3y}$

18. $\frac{3a}{8} \cdot \frac{16}{6a^3} = \frac{3a \cdot 16}{8 \cdot 6a^3} = \frac{3 \cdot a \cdot 8 \cdot 2}{8 \cdot 2 \cdot 3 \cdot a \cdot a \cdot a} = \frac{1}{a \cdot a} = \frac{1}{a^2}$

19.
$$\frac{11}{12} - \frac{3}{8} + \frac{5}{24} = \frac{11 \cdot 2}{12 \cdot 2} - \frac{3 \cdot 3}{8 \cdot 3} + \frac{5}{24}$$
$$= \frac{22}{24} - \frac{9}{24} + \frac{5}{24}$$
$$= \frac{22 - 9 + 5}{24}$$
$$= \frac{18}{24}$$
$$= \frac{3 \cdot 6}{4 \cdot 6}$$
$$= \frac{3}{4}$$

20.

$$3\frac{7}{8} \qquad 3\frac{35}{40}$$
$$7\frac{2}{5} \qquad 7\frac{16}{40}$$
$$+\ 2\frac{3}{4} \qquad +\ 2\frac{30}{40}$$
$$\overline{\qquad} \qquad \overline{12\frac{81}{40} = 12 + 2\frac{1}{40} = 14\frac{1}{40}}$$

21.

$$19 \qquad\qquad 18\frac{11}{11}$$
$$-\ 2\frac{3}{11} \qquad\qquad -\ 2\frac{3}{11}$$
$$\overline{\qquad} \qquad\qquad \overline{16\frac{8}{11}}$$

22.

$$-\frac{16}{3} \div -\frac{3}{12} = -\frac{16}{3} \cdot -\frac{12}{3}$$
$$= \frac{16 \cdot 12}{3 \cdot 3}$$
$$= \frac{16 \cdot 3 \cdot 4}{3 \cdot 3}$$
$$= \frac{64}{3} \text{ or } 21\frac{1}{3}$$

23.

$$3\frac{1}{3} \cdot 6\frac{3}{4} = \frac{10}{3} \cdot \frac{27}{4}$$
$$= \frac{10 \cdot 27}{3 \cdot 4}$$
$$= \frac{2 \cdot 5 \cdot 3 \cdot 9}{3 \cdot 2 \cdot 2}$$
$$= \frac{5 \cdot 9}{2}$$
$$= \frac{45}{2} \text{ or } 22\frac{1}{2}$$

24.

$$-\frac{2}{7} \cdot \left(6 - \frac{1}{6}\right) = -\frac{2}{7} \cdot \left(\frac{6}{1} - \frac{1}{6}\right)$$
$$= -\frac{2}{7} \cdot \left(\frac{6 \cdot 6}{1 \cdot 6} - \frac{1}{6}\right)$$
$$= -\frac{2}{7} \cdot \left(\frac{36}{6} - \frac{1}{6}\right)$$
$$= -\frac{2}{7} \cdot \frac{35}{6}$$
$$= -\frac{2 \cdot 35}{7 \cdot 6}$$
$$= -\frac{2 \cdot 7 \cdot 5}{7 \cdot 2 \cdot 3}$$
$$= -\frac{5}{3} \text{ or } -1\frac{2}{3}$$

25. $\dfrac{1}{2} \div \dfrac{2}{3} \cdot \dfrac{3}{4} = \dfrac{1}{2} \cdot \dfrac{3}{2} \cdot \dfrac{3}{4} = \dfrac{1 \cdot 3 \cdot 3}{2 \cdot 2 \cdot 4} = \dfrac{9}{16}$

26.

$$\left(-\frac{3}{4}\right)^2 \div \left(\frac{2}{3} + \frac{5}{6}\right) = \left(-\frac{3}{4}\right)^2 \div \left(\frac{2}{3} \cdot \frac{2}{2} + \frac{5}{6}\right)$$
$$= \left(-\frac{3}{4}\right)^2 \div \left(\frac{4}{6} + \frac{5}{6}\right)$$
$$= \left(-\frac{3}{4}\right)^2 \div \frac{9}{6}$$
$$= \frac{9}{16} \div \frac{9}{6}$$
$$= \frac{9}{16} \cdot \frac{6}{9}$$
$$= \frac{9 \cdot 2 \cdot 3}{2 \cdot 8 \cdot 9}$$
$$= \frac{3}{8}$$

27.

$$\left(\frac{5}{6} + \frac{4}{3} + \frac{7}{12}\right) \div 3 = \left(\frac{5 \cdot 2}{6 \cdot 2} + \frac{4 \cdot 4}{3 \cdot 4} + \frac{7}{12}\right) \div 3$$
$$= \left(\frac{10}{12} + \frac{16}{12} + \frac{7}{12}\right) \div 3$$
$$= \frac{33}{12} \div \frac{3}{1}$$
$$= \frac{33}{12} \cdot \frac{1}{3}$$
$$= \frac{33 \cdot 1}{12 \cdot 3}$$
$$= \frac{11 \cdot 3 \cdot 1}{12 \cdot 3}$$
$$= \frac{11}{12}$$

28.

$$\frac{\frac{5x}{7}}{\frac{20x^2}{21}} = \frac{5x}{7} \div \frac{20x^2}{21}$$
$$= \frac{5x}{7} \cdot \frac{21}{20x^2}$$
$$= \frac{5 \cdot x \cdot 3 \cdot 7}{7 \cdot 4 \cdot 5 \cdot x \cdot x}$$
$$= \frac{3}{4x}$$

29. $\dfrac{5 + \frac{3}{7}}{2 - \frac{1}{2}} = \dfrac{14\left(5 + \frac{3}{7}\right)}{14\left(2 - \frac{1}{2}\right)} = \dfrac{14 \cdot 5 + 14 \cdot \frac{3}{7}}{14 \cdot 2 - 14 \cdot \frac{1}{2}} = \dfrac{70 + 6}{28 - 7} = \dfrac{76}{21}$

30.
$$-\frac{3}{8}x = \frac{3}{4}$$
$$-\frac{8}{3} \cdot -\frac{3}{8}x = -\frac{8}{3} \cdot \frac{3}{4}$$
$$x = -\frac{8 \cdot 3}{3 \cdot 4}$$
$$x = -\frac{4 \cdot 2 \cdot 3}{3 \cdot 4}$$
$$x = -2$$

31.
$$\frac{x}{5} + x = -\frac{24}{5}$$
$$5\left(\frac{x}{5} + x\right) = 5\left(-\frac{24}{5}\right)$$
$$5 \cdot \frac{x}{5} + 5 \cdot x = -24$$
$$x + 5x = -24$$
$$6x = -24$$
$$\frac{6x}{6} = \frac{-24}{6}$$
$$x = -4$$

32.
$$\frac{2}{3} + \frac{x}{4} = \frac{5}{12} + \frac{x}{2}$$
$$12\left(\frac{2}{3} + \frac{x}{4}\right) = 12\left(\frac{5}{12} + \frac{x}{2}\right)$$
$$12 \cdot \frac{2}{3} + 12 \cdot \frac{x}{4} = 12 \cdot \frac{5}{12} + 12 \cdot \frac{x}{2}$$
$$8 + 3x = 5 + 6x$$
$$8 + 3x - 6x = 5 + 6x - 6x$$
$$8 - 3x = 5$$
$$8 - 8 - 3x = 5 - 8$$
$$-3x = -3$$
$$\frac{-3x}{-3} = \frac{-3}{-3}$$
$$x = 1$$

33. $-5x = -5\left(-\dfrac{1}{2}\right) = \dfrac{5}{1} \cdot \dfrac{1}{2} = \dfrac{5 \cdot 1}{1 \cdot 2} = \dfrac{5}{2}$

34.
$$x \div y = \frac{1}{2} \div 3\frac{7}{8}$$
$$= \frac{1}{2} \div \frac{31}{8}$$
$$= \frac{1}{2} \cdot \frac{8}{31}$$
$$= \frac{1 \cdot 8}{2 \cdot 31}$$
$$= \frac{1 \cdot 2 \cdot 4}{2 \cdot 31}$$
$$= \frac{4}{31}$$

35.
$$
\begin{array}{ccc}
6\frac{1}{2} & 6\frac{2}{4} & 5\frac{6}{4} \\
-2\frac{3}{4} & -2\frac{3}{4} & -2\frac{3}{4} \\
\hline
 & & 3\frac{3}{4}
\end{array}
$$

The remaining piece is $3\dfrac{3}{4}$ feet.

36. Housing: $\dfrac{8}{25}$

Food: $\dfrac{7}{50}$

$$\frac{8}{25} + \frac{7}{50} = \frac{8 \cdot 2}{25 \cdot 2} + \frac{7}{50} = \frac{16}{50} + \frac{7}{50} = \frac{16 + 7}{50} = \frac{23}{50}$$

$\dfrac{23}{50}$ of spending goes for housing and food combined.

37. Education: $\dfrac{1}{50}$

Transportation: $\dfrac{1}{5}$

Clothing: $\dfrac{1}{25}$

$$\frac{1}{50} + \frac{1}{5} + \frac{1}{25} = \frac{1}{50} + \frac{1}{5} \cdot \frac{10}{10} + \frac{1}{25} \cdot \frac{2}{2}$$
$$= \frac{1}{50} + \frac{10}{50} + \frac{2}{50}$$
$$= \frac{13}{50}$$

$\dfrac{13}{50}$ of spending goes for education, transportation, and clothing.

38. $\dfrac{3}{50} \cdot 47,000 = \dfrac{3}{50} \cdot \dfrac{47,000}{1} = \dfrac{3 \cdot 50 \cdot 940}{50 \cdot 1} = 2820$

Expect to spend \$2820 on health care.

39. perimeter $= 1 + \dfrac{2}{3} + 1 + \dfrac{2}{3}$

$= \dfrac{3}{3} + \dfrac{2}{3} + \dfrac{3}{3} + \dfrac{2}{3}$

$= \dfrac{10}{3}$

$= 3\dfrac{1}{3}$

area $=$ length $\cdot$ width $= 1 \cdot \dfrac{2}{3} = \dfrac{2}{3}$

The perimeter is $3\dfrac{1}{3}$ feet and the area is

$\dfrac{2}{3}$ square foot.

40. $258 \div 10\dfrac{3}{4} = \dfrac{258}{1} \div \dfrac{43}{4} = \dfrac{258}{1} \cdot \dfrac{4}{43} = \dfrac{43 \cdot 6 \cdot 4}{1 \cdot 43} = 24$

Expect to travel 24 miles on 1 gallon of gas.

Cumulative Review Chapters 1–4

1. 546 in words is five hundred forty-six.

2. 115 in words is one hundred fifteen.

3. 27,034 in words is twenty-seven thousand, thirty-four.

4. 6573 in words is six thousand, five hundred seventy-three.

5.   46
     $+\ 713$
     $\overline{759}$

6.   587
     $+\ 44$
     $\overline{631}$

7.   543
     $-\ 29$
     $\overline{514}$
Check: 514
       $+\ 29$
       $\overline{543}$

8.   995
     $-\ 62$
     $\overline{933}$
Check: 933
       $+\ 62$
       $\overline{995}$

9. To round 278,362 to the nearest thousand, observe that the digit in the hundreds place is 3. Since this digit is less than 5, we do not add 1 to the digit in the thousands place. 278,362 rounded to the nearest thousand is 278,000.

10. To round 1436 to the nearest ten, observe that the digit in the ones place is 6. Since this digit is at least 5, we add 1 to the digit in the tens place. 1436 rounded to the nearest ten is 1440.

11.   4800
     $\times\ \ 12$
     $\overline{9\,600}$
     48,000
     $\overline{57,600}$

Therefore, 12 DVDs can hold 57,600 megabytes of information.

12.   435
     $\times\ \ 3$
     $\overline{1305}$

He travels 1305 miles in 3 days.

13. 7089
     $8\overline{)56,717}$
     $\underline{56}$
     $0\ 7$
     $\underline{0}$
     71
     $\underline{64}$
     77
     $\underline{72}$
     5

$56,717 \div 8 = 7089\ \text{R}\ 5$

Check: $7089 \times 8 + 5 = 56,712 + 5 = 56,717$

14.
$$12\overline{)4558} \quad \frac{379}{}$$
$$\frac{36}{95}$$
$$\frac{84}{118}$$
$$\frac{108}{10}$$

$4558 \div 12 = 379$ R 10

Check: $379 \times 12 + 10 = 4548 + 10 = 4558$

15. $7 \cdot 7 \cdot 7 = 7^3$

16. $7 \cdot 7 = 7^2$

17. $3 \cdot 3 \cdot 3 \cdot 3 \cdot 9 \cdot 9 \cdot 9 = 3^4 \cdot 9^3$

18. $9 \cdot 9 \cdot 9 \cdot 9 \cdot 5 \cdot 5 = 9^4 \cdot 5^2$

19. $2(x - y) = 2(6 - 3) = 2(3) = 6$

20. $8a + 3(b - 5) = 8 \cdot 5 + 3(9 - 5)$
$$= 8 \cdot 5 + 3 \cdot 4$$
$$= 40 + 12$$
$$= 52$$

21. Let 0 represent the surface of the earth. Then 6824 feet *below* the surface is represented as −6824.

22. Let 0 represent a temperature of 0°F. Then 21°F *below* zero is represented as −21.

23. $-7 + 3 = -4$

24. $-3 + 8 = 5$

25. $7 - 8 - (-5) - 1 = 7 - 8 + 5 - 1$
$$= 7 + (-8) + 5 + (-1)$$
$$= -1 + 5 + (-1)$$
$$= 4 + (-1)$$
$$= 3$$

26. $6 + (-8) - (-9) + 3 = 6 + (-8) + 9 + 3$
$$= -2 + 9 + 3$$
$$= 7 + 3$$
$$= 10$$

27. $(-5)^2 = (-5)(-5) = 25$

28. $-2^4 = -2 \cdot 2 \cdot 2 \cdot 2 = -16$

29. $3(4 - 7) + (-2) - 5 = 3(-3) + (-2) - 5$
$$= -9 + (-2) + (-5)$$
$$= -11 + (-5)$$
$$= -16$$

30. $(20 - 5^2)^2 = (20 - 25)^2 = (-5)^2 = 25$

31. $2y - 6 + 4y + 8 = (2y + 4y) + (-6 + 8) = 6y + 2$

32. $5x - 1 + x + 10 = (5x + x) + (-1 + 10) = 6x + 9$

33. $5x + 2 - 4x = 7 - 19$
$$x + 2 = -12$$
$$x + 2 - 2 = -12 - 2$$
$$x = -14$$

34. $9y + 1 - 8y = 3 - 20$
$$y + 1 = -17$$
$$y + 1 - 1 = -17 - 1$$
$$y = -18$$

35. $17 - 7x + 3 = -3x + 21 - 3x$
$$20 - 7x = 21 - 6x$$
$$20 - 7x + 7x = 21 - 6x + 7x$$
$$20 = 21 + x$$
$$20 - 21 = 21 - 21 + x$$
$$-1 = x \text{ or } x = -1$$

36. $9x - 2 = 7x - 24$
$$9x - 7x - 2 = 7x - 7x - 24$$
$$2x - 2 = -24$$
$$2x - 2 + 2 = -24 + 2$$
$$2x = -22$$
$$\frac{2x}{2} = \frac{-22}{2}$$
$$x = -11$$

37. Two of five equal parts are shaded: $\dfrac{2}{5}$

38. $156 = 2 \cdot 78$
$$\downarrow \ \downarrow\searrow$$
$$2 \cdot 2 \cdot 39$$
$$\downarrow \ \downarrow \ \downarrow\searrow$$
$$2 \cdot 2 \cdot 3 \cdot 13$$
$$156 = 2^2 \cdot 3 \cdot 13$$

39. a. $4\dfrac{2}{9} = \dfrac{9 \cdot 4 + 2}{9} = \dfrac{36 + 2}{9} = \dfrac{38}{9}$

b. $1\dfrac{8}{11} = \dfrac{11 \cdot 1 + 8}{11} = \dfrac{11 + 8}{11} = \dfrac{19}{11}$

40.
$$\begin{array}{r} 7 \\ 5\overline{)\,39} \\ \underline{-35} \\ 4 \end{array}$$

$\dfrac{39}{5} = 7\dfrac{4}{5}$

41. $\dfrac{42x}{66} = \dfrac{6 \cdot 7 \cdot x}{6 \cdot 11} = \dfrac{7x}{11}$

42. $\dfrac{70}{105y} = \dfrac{35 \cdot 2}{35 \cdot 3 \cdot y} = \dfrac{2}{3y}$

43. $3\dfrac{1}{3} \cdot \dfrac{7}{8} = \dfrac{10}{3} \cdot \dfrac{7}{8}$

$= \dfrac{10 \cdot 7}{3 \cdot 8}$

$= \dfrac{2 \cdot 5 \cdot 7}{3 \cdot 2 \cdot 4}$

$= \dfrac{5 \cdot 7}{3 \cdot 4}$

$= \dfrac{35}{12} \text{ or } 2\dfrac{11}{12}$

44. $\dfrac{2}{3} \cdot 4 = \dfrac{2}{3} \cdot \dfrac{4}{1} = \dfrac{2 \cdot 4}{3 \cdot 1} = \dfrac{8}{3} \text{ or } 2\dfrac{2}{3}$

45. $\dfrac{5}{16} \div \dfrac{3}{4} = \dfrac{5}{16} \cdot \dfrac{4}{3} = \dfrac{5 \cdot 4}{16 \cdot 3} = \dfrac{5 \cdot 4}{4 \cdot 4 \cdot 3} = \dfrac{5}{4 \cdot 3} = \dfrac{5}{12}$

46. $1\dfrac{1}{10} \div 5\dfrac{3}{5} = \dfrac{11}{10} \div \dfrac{28}{5} = \dfrac{11}{10} \cdot \dfrac{5}{28} = \dfrac{11 \cdot 5}{5 \cdot 2 \cdot 28} = \dfrac{11}{56}$

Chapter 5

Section 5.1

Practice Problems

1. **a.** 0.06 in words is six hundredths.

   b. −200.073 in words is negative two hundred and seventy-three thousandths.

   c. 0.0829 in words in eight hundred twenty-nine ten-thousandths.

2. 87.31 in words is eighty-seven and thirty-one hundredths.

3. 52.1085 in words is fifty-two and one thousand eighty-five ten-thousandths.

4. The check should be paid to "CLECO," for the amount of "207.40," which is written in words as "Two hundred seven and $\dfrac{40}{100}$."

5. Five hundred and ninety-six hundredths is 500.96.

6. Thirty-nine and forty-two thousandths is 39.042.

7. $0.051 = \dfrac{51}{1000}$

8. $29.97 = 29\dfrac{97}{100}$

9. $0.12 = \dfrac{12}{100} = \dfrac{3 \cdot 4}{25 \cdot 4} = \dfrac{3}{25}$

10. $64.8 = 64\dfrac{8}{10} = 64\dfrac{2 \cdot 4}{2 \cdot 5} = 64\dfrac{4}{5}$

11. $-209.986 = -209\dfrac{986}{1000}$
    $= -209\dfrac{2 \cdot 493}{2 \cdot 500}$
    $= -209\dfrac{493}{500}$

12. $\begin{array}{cc} 29.208 & 26.28 \\ \uparrow & \uparrow \\ 0 & 8 \end{array}$
    $0 < 8$
    so $26.208 < 26.28$

13. $\begin{array}{cc} 0.12 & 0.026 \\ \uparrow & \uparrow \\ 1 & 0 \end{array}$
    $1 > 0$
    so $0.12 > 0.026$

14. $\begin{array}{cc} 0.039 & 0.0309 \\ \uparrow & \uparrow \\ 9 & 0 \end{array}$
    $9 > 0$
    so $0.039 > 0.0309$
    Thus, $-0.039 < -0.0309$.

15. To round 482.7817 to the nearest thousandth, observe that the digit in the ten-thousandths place is 7. Since this digit is at least 5, we add 1 to the digit in the thousandths place. The number 482.7817 rounded to the nearest thousandth is 482.782.

16. To round −0.032 to the nearest hundredth, observe that the digit in the thousandths place is 2. Since this digit is less than 5, we do not add 1 to the digit in the hundredths place. The number −0.032 rounded to the nearest hundredth is −0.03.

17. To round 3.14159265 to the nearest ten-thousandth, observe that the digit in the hundred-thousandths place is 9. Since this digit is at least 5, we add 1 to the digit in the ten-thousandths place. The number 3.14159265 rounded to the nearest the ten-thousandth is 3.1416, or $\pi \approx 3.1416$.

18. $24.62 rounded to the nearest dollar is $25, since $6 \geq 5$.

Vocabulary and Readiness Check

1. The number "twenty and eight hundredths" is written in <u>words</u> and "20.08" is written in <u>standard form</u>.

2. Another name for the distance around a circle is its <u>circumference</u>.

3. Like fractions, <u>decimals</u> are used to denote part of a whole.

4. When writing a decimal number in words, the decimal point is written as <u>and</u>.

5. The place value <u>tenths</u> is to the right of the decimal point while <u>tens</u> is to the left of the decimal point.

6. The decimal point in a whole number is <u>after</u> the last digit.

Exercise Set 5.1

1. 5.62 in words is five and sixty-two hundredths.

3. 16.23 in words is sixteen and twenty-three hundredths.

5. −0.205 in words is negative two hundred five thousandths.

7. 167.009 in words is one hundred sixty-seven and nine thousandths.

9. 3000.04 in words is three thousand and four hundredths.

11. 105.6 in words is one hundred five and six tenths.

13. 2.43 in words is two and forty-three hundredths.

15. The check should be paid to "R.W. Financial," for the amount "321.42," which is written in words as "Three hundred twenty-one and $\frac{42}{100}$."

17. The check should be paid to "Bell South," for the amount of "59.68," which is written in words as "Fifty-nine and $\frac{68}{100}$."

19. Two and eight tenths is 2.8.

21. Nine and eight hundredths is 9.08.

23. Negative seven hundred five and six hundred twenty-five thousandths is −705.625.

25. Forty-six ten-thousandths is 0.0046.

27. $0.7 = \dfrac{7}{10}$

29. $0.27 = \dfrac{27}{100}$

31. $0.4 = \dfrac{4}{10} = \dfrac{2 \cdot 2}{2 \cdot 5} = \dfrac{2}{5}$

33. $5.4 = 5\dfrac{4}{10} = 5\dfrac{2 \cdot 2}{2 \cdot 5} = 5\dfrac{2}{5}$

35. $-0.058 = -\dfrac{58}{1000} = -\dfrac{2 \cdot 29}{2 \cdot 500} = \dfrac{29}{500}$

37. $7.008 = 7\dfrac{8}{1000} = 7\dfrac{1 \cdot 8}{125 \cdot 8} = 7\dfrac{1}{125}$

39. $15.802 = 15\dfrac{802}{1000} = 15\dfrac{2 \cdot 401}{2 \cdot 500} = 15\dfrac{401}{500}$

41. $0.3005 = \dfrac{3005}{10,000} = \dfrac{601 \cdot 5}{2000 \cdot 5} = \dfrac{601}{2000}$

43. Eight tenths is 0.8 and as a fraction is $\dfrac{8}{10} = \dfrac{4}{5}$.

45. In words, 0.077 is seventy-seven thousandths. As a fraction, $0.077 = \dfrac{77}{1000}$.

47. 0.15   0.16
    ↑   ↑
    5 < 6
so 0.15 < 0.16

49. 0.57   0.54
    ↑   ↑
    7 > 4
so 0.57 > 0.54
Thus −0.57 < −0.54.

51. 0.098   0.1
    ↑   ↑
    0   <   1
so 0.098 < 0.1

53. 0.54900   0.549
    ↑   ↑
    9   =   9
so 0.54900 = 0.549

55. 167.908   167.980
    ↑   ↑
    0   <   8
so 167.908 < 167.980

57. 1.062   1.07
    ↑   ↑
    6   <   7
so 1.062 < 1.07
Thus, −1.062 > −1.07.

59. −7.052   7.0052
    ↑   ↑
    −   <   +
so −7.052 < 7.0052

61. 0.023   0.024
    ↑   ↑
    3   <   4
so 0.023 < 0.024
Thus, −0.023 > −0.024.

63. To round 0.57 to the nearest tenth, observe that the digit in the hundredths place is 7. Since this digit is at least 5, we add 1 to the digit in the tenths place. The number 0.57 rounded to the nearest tenth is 0.6.

65. To round 98,207.23 to the nearest ten, observe that the digit in the ones place is 7. Since this digit is at least 5, we add 1 to the digit in the tens place. The number 98,207.23 rounded to the nearest ten is 98,210.

67. To round −0.234 to the nearest hundredth, observe that the digit in the thousandths place is 4. Since this digit is less than 5, we do not add 1 to the digit in the hundredths place. The number −0.234 rounded to the nearest hundredth is −0.23.

69. To round 0.5942 to the nearest thousandth, observe that the digit in the ten-thousandths place is 2. Since this digit is less than 5, we do not add 1 to the digit in the thousandths place. The number 0.5942 rounded to the nearest thousandth is 0.594.

71. To round $\pi \approx 3.14159265$ to the nearest tenth, observe that the digit in the hundredths place is 4. Since this digit is less than 5, we do not add 1 to the digit in the tenths place. The number $\pi \approx 3.14159265$ rounded to the nearest tenth is 3.1.

73. To round $\pi \approx 3.14159265$ to the nearest thousandth, observe that the digit in the ten-thousandth place is 5. Since this digit is at least 5, we add 1 to the digit in the thousandths place. The number $\pi \approx 3.14159265$ rounded to the nearest thousandth is 3.142.

75. To round 26.95 to the nearest one, observe that the digit in the tenths place is 9. Since this digit is at least 5, we add 1 to the digit in the ones place. The number 26.95 rounded to the nearest one is 27. The amount is $27.

77. To round 0.1992 to the nearest hundredth, observe that the digit in the thousandths place is 9. Since this digit is at least 5, we add 1 to the digit in the hundredths place. The number 0.1992 rounded to the nearest hundredth is 0.2. The amount is $0.20.

79. To round 0.4064 to the nearest tenth, observe that the digit in the hundredths place is 0. Since this digit is less than 5, we do not add 1 to the digit in the tenths place. The number 0.4064 rounded to the nearest tenth is 0.4. The thickness is 0.4 centimeter.

81. To round 1.8672 to the nearest hundredth, observe that the digit in the thousandths place is 7. Since this digit is at least 5, we add 1 to the digit in the hundredths place. The number 1.8672 rounded to the nearest hundredth is 1.87. The time is 1.87 minutes.

83. To round 67.89 to the nearest one, observe that the digit in the tenths place is 8. Since this digit is at least 5, we add 1 to the digit in the ones place. The number 67.89 rounded to the nearest one is 68. The price is $68.

85. To round 224.695 to the nearest one, observe that the digit in the tenths place is 6. Since this digit is at least 5, we add 1 to the digit in the ones place. The number 224.695 rounded to the nearest one is 225. This is 225 days.

87.
$$\begin{array}{r} 3452 \\ + 2314 \\ \hline 5766 \end{array}$$

89.
$$\begin{array}{r} 82 \\ - 47 \\ \hline 35 \end{array}$$

91. To round 2849.1738 to the nearest hundred, observe that the digit in the tens place is 4. Since this digit is less than 5, we do not add 1 to the digit in the hundreds place. The number 2849.1738 rounded to the nearest hundred is 2800, which is choice b.

93. To round 2849.1738 to the nearest hundredth, observe that the digit in the thousandths place is 3. Since this digit is less than 5, we do not add 1 to the digit in the hundredths place. 2849.1738 rounded to the nearest hundredth is 2849.17, which is choice a.

95. answers may vary

97. $7\dfrac{12}{100} = 7.12$

99. $0.00026849577 = \dfrac{26,849,577}{100,000,000,000}$

101. answers may vary

103. answers may vary

105. 0.26499 and 0.25786 rounded to the nearest hundredth are 0.26. 0.26559 rounds to 0.27 and 0.25186 rounds to 0.25.

107. From smallest to largest, 0.10299, 0.1037, 0.1038, 0.9

109. Round to the nearest hundred million, then add.
$$\begin{array}{r} 600 \\ 500 \\ 500 \\ 400 \\ 400 \\ + 400 \\ \hline 2800 \end{array}$$
The total amount of money is estimated as $2800 million.

Section 5.2

Practice Problems

1. a.   19.520
        + 5.371
        ———
           24.891

    b.   40.080
        + 17.612
        ———
           57.692

    c.   0.125
        + 422.800
        ———
           422.925

2. a.   34.5670
           129.4300
        +   2.8903
        ———
           166.8873

    b.   11.210
           46.013
        + 362.526
        ———
           419.749

3.   19.000
    + 26.072
    ———
       45.072

4. $7.12 + (-9.92)$
    Subtract the absolute values.
        9.92
    − 7.12
    ———
        2.80
    Attach the sign of the larger absolute value.
    $7.12 + (-9.92) = -2.8$

5. a.   6.70   *Check*:   2.78
        − 3.92   + 3.92
        ———   ———
           2.78   6.70

    b.   9.720   *Check*:   5.652
        − 4.068   + 4.068
        ———   ———
           5.652   9.720

6. a.   73.00   *Check*:   43.69
        − 29.31   + 29.31
        ———   ———
           43.69   73.00

    b.   210.00   *Check*:   141.78
        − 68.22   + 68.22
        ———   ———
           141.78   210.00

7.   25.91
    − 19.00
    ———
        6.91

8. $-5.4 - 9.6 = -5.4 + (-9.6)$
    Add the absolute values.
        5.4
    + 9.6
    ———
       15.0
    Attach the common sign.
    $-5.4 - 9.6 = -15$

9. $-1.05 - (-7.23) = -1.05 + 7.23$
    Subtract the absolute values.
        7.23
    − 1.05
    ———
        6.18
    Attach the sign of the larger absolute value.
    $-1.05 - (-7.23) = 6.18$

10. a.   Exact   Estimate 1   Estimate 2
          58.10   60   60
        + 326.97   + 300   + 330
        ———   ———   ———
          385.07   360   390

    b.   Exact   Estimate 1   Estimate 2
          16.080   16   20
        − 0.925   − 1   − 1
        ———   ———   ———
          15.155   15   19

11. $y - z = 11.6 - 10.8 = 0.8$

12. $y - 4.3 = 7.8$
        $12.1 - 4.3 \stackrel{?}{=} 7.8$
            $7.8 = 7.8$ True
        Yes, 12.1 is a solution.

13. $-4.3y + 7.8 - 20.1y + 14.6$
    $= -4.3y - 20.1y + 7.8 + 14.6$
    $= (-4.3 - 20.1)y + (7.8 + 14.6)$
    $= -24.4y + 22.4$

14.   563.52
         52.68
    + 127.50
    ———
       743.70
    The total cost is $743.70.

15.   72.6
     − 70.8
       1.8
    The average height in the Netherlands is 1.8 inches greater than the average height in Czechoslovakia.

Calculator Explorations

1. $315.782 + 12.96 = 328.742$

2. $29.68 + 85.902 = 115.582$

3. $6.249 − 1.0076 = 5.2414$

4. $5.238 − 0.682 = 4.556$

5.   12.555
    224.987
      5.2
    + 622.65
    865.392

6.   47.006
      0.17
    313.259
    + 139.088
    499.523

Vocabulary and Readiness Check

1. The decimal point in a whole number is positioned after the <u>last</u> digit.

2. In $89.2 − 14.9 = 74.3$, the number 74.3 is called the <u>difference</u>, 89.2 is the <u>minuend</u>, and 14.9 is the <u>subtrahend</u>.

3. To simplify an expression, we combine any <u>like</u> terms.

4. True or false: If we replace x with 11.2 and y with −8.6 in the expression $x − y$, we have $11.2 − 8.6$. <u>false</u>

5. To add or subtract decimals, we line up the decimal points <u>vertically</u>.

Exercise Set 5.2

1.   5.6
    + 2.1
     7.7

3.   8.20
    + 2.15
    10.35

5.   24.6000
      2.3900
    + 0.0678
    27.0578

7. $−2.6 + (−5.97)$
Add the absolute values.
    2.60
   + 5.97
    8.57
Attach the common sign.
$−2.6 + (−5.97) = −8.57$

9. $18.56 + (−8.23)$
Subtract the absolute values.
    18.56
   − 8.23
   10.33
Attach the sign of the larger absolute value.
$18.56 + (−8.23) = 10.33$

11. Exact: 234.89
        + 230.67
        465.56
Estimate: 230
        + 230
       460

13. Exact: 100.009
          6.080
       + 9.034
      115.123
Estimate: 100
          6
       + 9
      115

15.   39.000
      3.006
    + 8.403
    50.409

17.   12.6   *Check:*   4.4
    − 8.2   + 8.2
     4.4   12.6

19.

18.0	*Check:*	15.3
− 2.7		+ 2.7
15.3		18.0

21.

654.90	*Check:*	598.23
− 56.67		+ 56.67
598.23		654.90

23. Exact: $5.9 - 4.07 = 1.83$
Estimate: $6 - 4 = 2$
Check: $1.83 + 4.07 = 5.90$

25. Exact:

1000.0	*Check:*	876.6
− 123.4		+ 123.4
876.6		1000.0

Estimate:

1000
− 100
900

27.

200.0	*Check:*	194.4
− 5.6		+ 5.6
194.4		200.0

29. $-1.12 - 5.2 = -1.12 + (-5.2)$
Add the absolute values.

1.12	*Check:*	6.32
+ 5.20		− 5.20
6.32		1.12

Attach the common sign.
$-1.12 - 5.2 = -6.32$

31. $5.21 - 11.36 = 5.21 + (-11.36)$
Subtract the absolute values.

11.36	*Check:*	6.15
− 5.21		+ 5.21
6.15		11.36

Attach the sign of the larger absolute value.
$5.21 - 11.36 = -6.15$

33. $-2.6 - (-5.7) = -2.6 + 5.7$
Subtract the absolute values.

5.7	*Check:*	3.1
− 2.6		+ 2.6
3.1		5.7

Attach the sign of the larger absolute value.
$-2.6 - (-5.7) = 3.1$

35.

3.0000	*Check:*	2.9988
− 0.0012		+ 0.0012
2.9988		3.0000

37.

23.0	*Check:*	16.3
− 6.7		+ 6.7
16.3		23.0

39.

0.9
+ 2.2
3.1

41. $-6.06 + 0.44$
Subtract the absolute values.

6.06
− 0.44
5.62

Attach the sign of the larger absolute value.
$-6.06 + 0.44 = -5.62$

43.

500.21
− 136.85
363.36

45. $50.2 - 600 = 50.2 + (-600)$
Subtract the absolute values.

600.0
− 50.2
549.8

Attach the sign of the larger absolute value.
$50.2 - 600 = -549.8$

47.

923.5
− 61.9
861.6

49.

100.009
6.080
+ 9.034
115.123

51. $-0.003 + 0.091$
Subtract the absolute values.

0.091
− 0.003
0.088

Attach the sign of the larger absolute value.
$-0.003 + 0.091 = 0.088$

53. $-102.4 - 78.04 = -102.4 + (-78.04)$
Add the absolute values.

102.40
+ 78.04
180.44

Attach the common sign.
$-102.4 - 78.04 = -180.44$

55. $-2.9 - (-1.8) = -2.9 + 1.8$
Subtract the absolute values.

$$\begin{array}{r} 2.9 \\ -1.8 \\ \hline 1.1 \end{array}$$

Attach the sign of the larger absolute value.
$-2.9 - (-1.8) = -1.1$

57. $x + z = 3.6 + 0.21 = 3.81$

59. $x - z = 3.6 - 0.21 = 3.39$

61. $\begin{aligned} y - x + z &= 5 - 3.6 + 0.21 \\ &= 5.00 - 3.60 + 0.21 \\ &= 1.40 + 0.21 \\ &= 1.61 \end{aligned}$

63. $x + 2.7 = 9.3$
$7 + 2.7 \stackrel{?}{=} 9.3$
$\quad\quad 9.7 = 9.3$ False
No, 7 is not a solution.

65. $\quad\quad 27.4 + y = 16$
$27.4 + (-11.4) \stackrel{?}{=} 16$
$\quad\quad\quad\quad\quad 16 = 16$ True
Yes, -11.4 is a solution.

67. $2.3 + x = 5.3 - x$
$2.3 + 1 \stackrel{?}{=} 5.3 - 1$
$\quad\quad 3.3 = 4.3$ False
No, 1 is not a solution.

69. $\begin{aligned} 30.7x &+ 17.6 - 23.8x - 10.7 \\ &= 30.7x - 23.8x + 17.6 - 10.7 \\ &= (30.7 - 23.8)x + (17.6 - 10.7) \\ &= 6.9x + 6.9 \end{aligned}$

71. $\begin{aligned} -8.61 &+ 4.23y - 2.36 - 0.76y \\ &= 4.23y - 0.76y - 8.61 - 2.36 \\ &= (4.23 - 0.76)y + (-8.61 - 2.36) \\ &= 3.47y - 10.97 \end{aligned}$

73. Change $= 40 - \underline{32.48}$

$$\begin{array}{r} 40.00 \\ -32.48 \\ \hline 7.52 \end{array}$$

If Ann-Margaret paid with two \$20 bills, her change was \$7.52.

75. Subtract the opening price from the closing price.

$$\begin{array}{r} 22.07 \\ -21.90 \\ \hline 0.17 \end{array}$$

The price of each share increased by \$0.17.

77. Perimeter $= 7.14 + 7.14 + 7.14 + 7.14$
$\quad\quad\quad\quad\quad = 28.56$ meters

79. Perimeter $= 4.5 + 2.4 + 4.5 + 2.4 = 13.8$ inches

81. The phrase "How much faster" indicates that we should subtract the average wind speed from the record speed.

$$\begin{array}{r} 321.0 \\ -35.2 \\ \hline 285.8 \end{array}$$

The highest wind speed is 285.8 miles per hour faster than the average wind speed.

83. To find the increase, subtract.

$$\begin{array}{r} 75.3 \\ -62.9 \\ \hline 12.4 \end{array}$$

The increase was 12.4 million or 12,400,000 users.

85. To find the total, we add.

$$\begin{array}{r} 600.78 \\ 533.32 \\ +460.99 \\ \hline 1595.09 \end{array}$$

The total ticket sales were \$1595.09 million.

87. To find the amount of snow in Blue Canyon, add 111.6 to the amount in Marquette.

$$\begin{array}{r} 129.2 \\ +111.6 \\ \hline 240.8 \end{array}$$

Blue Canyon receives on average 240.8 inches each year.

89. Add the lengths of the sides to get the perimeter.

$$\begin{array}{r} 12.40 \\ 29.34 \\ +25.70 \\ \hline 67.44 \end{array}$$

67.44 feet of border material is needed.

91.
$$
\begin{array}{r}
172.712 \\
- 152.672 \\
\hline
20.040
\end{array}
$$
The difference is 20.04 miles per hour.

93. The tallest bar indicates the greatest chocolate consumption per person, so Switzerland has the greatest chocolate consumption per person.

95.
$$
\begin{array}{r}
22.36 \\
- 17.93 \\
\hline
4.43
\end{array}
$$
The difference in consumption is 4.43 pounds per year.

97.

Country	Pounds of Chocolate per Person
Switzerland	22.36
Austria	20.13
Ireland	19.47
Germany	18.04
Norway	17.93

99. $46 \cdot 3 = 138$

101. $\left(\dfrac{2}{3}\right)^2 = \dfrac{2}{3} \cdot \dfrac{2}{3} = \dfrac{2 \cdot 2}{3 \cdot 3} = \dfrac{4}{9}$

103. It is incorrect. Align the decimals.
$$
\begin{array}{r}
9.200 \\
8.630 \\
+ 4.005 \\
\hline
21.835
\end{array}
$$

105. $10.68 - (2.3 + 2.3) = 10.68 - 4.60 = 6.08$
The unknown length is 6.08 inches.

107. 3 nickels, 3 dimes, and 3 quarters:
$0.05 + 0.05 + 0.05 + 0.10 + 0.10 + 0.10 + 0.25$
$\quad + 0.25 + 0.25 = 1.2$
The value of the coins shown is $1.20.

109. 1 nickel, 1 dime, and 2 pennies:
$0.05 + 0.10 + 0.01 + 0.01 = 0.17$
3 nickels and 2 pennies:
$0.05 + 0.05 + 0.05 + 0.01 + 0.01 = 0.17$
1 dime and 7 pennies:
$0.10 + 0.01 + 0.01 + 0.01 + 0.01 + 0.01 + 0.01$
$\quad + 0.01 = 0.17$
2 nickels and 7 pennies:
$0.05 + 0.05 + 0.01 + 0.01 + 0.01 + 0.01 + 0.01$
$\quad + 0.01 + 0.01 = 0.17$

111. answers may vary

113. answers may vary

115. $-8.689 + 4.286x - 14.295 - 12.966x + 30.861x$
$= 4.286x - 12.966x + 30.861x - 8.689 - 14.295$
$= (4.286 - 12.966 + 30.861)x$
$\qquad + (-8.689 - 14.295)$
$= 22.181x - 22.984$

Section 5.3

Practice Problems

1.
$$
\begin{array}{r}
34.8 \\
\times\ 0.62 \\
\hline
696 \\
20\ 880 \\
\hline
21.576
\end{array}
$$
34.8   1 decimal place
× 0.62   2 decimal places
$1 + 2 = 3$ decimal places

2.
$$
\begin{array}{r}
0.0641 \\
\times\ 27 \\
\hline
4487 \\
1\ 2820 \\
\hline
1.7307
\end{array}
$$
0.0641   4 decimal places
× 27   0 decimal places
$4 + 0 = 4$ decimal places

3. $(7.3)(-0.9) = -6.57$ (Be sure to include the negative sign.)

4. Exact:
$$
\begin{array}{r}
30.26 \\
\times\ 2.89 \\
\hline
2\ 7234 \\
24\ 2080 \\
60\ 5200 \\
\hline
87.4514
\end{array}
$$
Estimate:
$$
\begin{array}{r}
30 \\
\times\ 3 \\
\hline
90
\end{array}
$$

5. $46.8 \times 10 = 468$

6. $203.004 \times 100 = 20{,}300.4$

7. $(-2.33)(1000) = -2330$

8. $6.94 \times 0.1 = 0.694$

9. $3.9 \times 0.01 = 0.039$

10. $(-7682)(-0.001) = 7.682$

11. 60.7 million $= 60.7 \times 1$ million
$\qquad = 60.7 \times 1{,}000{,}000$
$\qquad = 60{,}700{,}000$

12. $7y = 7(-0.028) = -0.196$

13. $-6x = 33$
$-6(-5.5) \overset{?}{=} 33$
$33 = 33$ True
Yes, -5.5 is a solution.

14. $C = 2\pi r = 2\pi \cdot 11 = 22\pi \approx 22(3.14) = 69.08$
The circumference is 22π meters ≈ 69.08 meters.

15. $\begin{array}{r} 60.5 \\ \times\ \ 5.6 \\ \hline 36\ 30 \\ 302\ 50 \\ \hline 338.80 \end{array}$
She needs 338.8 ounces of fertilizer.

Vocabulary and Readiness Check

1. When multiplying decimals, the number of decimal places in the product is equal to the <u>sum</u> of the number of decimal place in the factors.

2. In $8.6 \times 5 = 43$, the number 43 is called the <u>product</u> while 8.6 and 5 are each called a <u>factor</u>.

3. When multiplying a decimal number by powers of 10 such as 10, 100, 1000, and so on, we move the decimal point in the number to the <u>right</u> the same number of places as there are <u>zeros</u> in the power of 10.

4. When multiplying a decimal number by powers of 10 such as 0.1, 0.01, and so on, we move the decimal point in the number to the <u>left</u> the same number of places as there are <u>decimal places</u> in the power of 10.

5. The distance around a circle is called its <u>circumference</u>.

Exercise Set 5.3

1. $\begin{array}{r} 0.17 \\ \times\ \ \ 8 \\ \hline 1.36 \end{array}$ $\begin{array}{l} \text{2 decimal places} \\ \text{0 decimal places} \\ 2+0 = 2 \text{ decimal places} \end{array}$

3. $\begin{array}{r} 1.2 \\ \times 0.5 \\ \hline 0.60 \end{array}$ $\begin{array}{l} \text{1 decimal place} \\ \text{1 decimal place} \\ 1+1 = 2 \text{ decimal places} \end{array}$

5. The product $(-2.3)(7.65)$ is negative.
$\begin{array}{r} 7.65 \\ \times\ \ 2.3 \\ \hline 2\ 295 \\ 15\ 300 \\ \hline -17.595 \end{array}$ $\begin{array}{l} \text{2 decimal places} \\ \text{1 decimal place} \\ \\ \\ 2+1 = 3 \text{ decimal places and} \\ \quad \text{include the negative sign} \end{array}$

7. The product $(-5.73)(-9.6)$ is positive.
$\begin{array}{r} 5.73 \\ \times\ \ 9.6 \\ \hline 3\ 438 \\ 51\ 570 \\ \hline 55.008 \end{array}$ $\begin{array}{l} \text{2 decimal places} \\ \text{1 decimal place} \\ \\ \\ 2+1 = 3 \text{ decimal places} \end{array}$

9. Exact: $\begin{array}{r} 6.8 \\ \times 4.2 \\ \hline 1\ 36 \\ 27\ 20 \\ \hline 28.56 \end{array}$ Estimate: $\begin{array}{r} 7 \\ \times 4 \\ \hline 28 \end{array}$

11. $\begin{array}{r} 0.347 \\ \times\ \ \ 0.3 \\ \hline 0.1041 \end{array}$ $\begin{array}{l} \text{3 decimal places} \\ \text{1 decimal place} \\ 3+1 = 4 \text{ decimal places} \end{array}$

13. Exact: $\begin{array}{r} 1.0047 \\ \times\ \ \ 8.2 \\ \hline 20094 \\ 8\ 03760 \\ \hline 8.23854 \end{array}$ Estimate: $\begin{array}{r} 1 \\ \times 8 \\ \hline 8 \end{array}$

15. $\begin{array}{r} 490.2 \\ \times 0.023 \\ \hline 1\ 4706 \\ 9\ 8040 \\ \hline 11.2746 \end{array}$ $\begin{array}{l} \text{1 decimal place} \\ \text{3 decimal places} \\ \\ \\ 1+3 = 4 \text{ decimal places} \end{array}$

17. $6.5 \times 10 = 65$

19. $8.3 \times 0.1 = 0.83$

21. $(-7.093)(1000) = -7093$

23. $0.7 \times 100 = 70$

25. $(-9.83)(-0.01) = 0.0983$

27. $25.23 \times 0.001 = 0.02523$

29.
$$\begin{array}{r} 0.123 \\ \times\ \ 0.4 \\ \hline 0.0492 \end{array}$$

31. $(147.9)(100) = 14{,}790$

33.
$$\begin{array}{r} 8.6 \\ \times 0.15 \\ \hline 430 \\ 860 \\ \hline 1.290 \end{array}$$ or 1.29

35. $(937.62)(-0.01) = -9.3762$

37. $562.3 \times 0.001 = 0.5623$

39.
$$\begin{array}{r} 6.32 \\ \times\ \ 5.7 \\ \hline 4\ 424 \\ 31\ 600 \\ \hline 36.024 \end{array}$$

41. 1.5 billion $= 1.5 \times 1$ billion
$$= 1.5 \times 1{,}000{,}000{,}000$$
$$= 1{,}500{,}000{,}000$$
The cost at launch was $\$1{,}500{,}000{,}000$.

43. 49.8 million $= 49.8 \times 1$ million
$$= 49.8 \times 1{,}000{,}000$$
$$= 49{,}800{,}000$$
The roller coaster has given more than 49,800,000 rides.

45. $xy = 3(-0.2) = -0.6$

47. $xz - y = 3(5.7) - (-0.2)$
$$= 17.1 - (-0.2)$$
$$= 17.1 + 0.2$$
$$= 17.3$$

49. $\quad 0.6x = 4.92$
$$0.6(14.2) \stackrel{?}{=} 4.92$$
$$8.52 = 4.92 \quad \text{False}$$
No, 14.2 is not a solution.

51. $\quad 3.5y = -14$
$$3.5(-4) \stackrel{?}{=} -14$$
$$-14 = -14 \quad \text{True}$$
Yes, -4 is a solution.

53. $C = \pi d$ is $\pi(10 \text{ cm}) = 10\pi \text{ cm}$
$C \approx 10(3.14) \text{ cm} = 31.4 \text{ cm}$

55. $C = 2\pi r$ is $2\pi \cdot 9.1$ yards $= 18.2\pi$ yards
$C \approx 18.2(3.14)$ yards $= 57.148$ yards

57. pay before taxes $= \underline{17.88} \times \underline{40}$
$$\begin{array}{r} 17.88 \\ \times\ \ \ 40 \\ \hline 715.20 \end{array}$$
His pay for last week was $\$715.20$.

59. Multiply the number of ounces by the number of grams of saturated fat in 1 ounce.
$$\begin{array}{r} 6.2 \\ \times\ \ 4 \\ \hline 24.8 \end{array}$$
There are 24.8 grams of saturated fat in a 4-ounce serving of cream cheese.

61. Area $=$ length $\cdot$ width
$$\begin{array}{r} 4.5 \\ \times 2.4 \\ \hline 1\ 80 \\ 9\ 00 \\ \hline 10.80 \end{array}$$
The area is 10.8 square inches.

63. Circumference $= \pi \cdot$ diameter
$$C = \pi \cdot 250 = 250\pi$$
$$\begin{array}{r} 250 \\ \times\ \ 3.14 \\ \hline 10\ 00 \\ 25\ 00 \\ 750\ 00 \\ \hline 785.00 \end{array}$$
The circumference is 250π feet, which is approximately 785 feet.

65. $C = \pi \cdot d$
$$C = \pi \cdot 135 = 135\pi$$
$$\begin{array}{r} 135 \\ \times 3.14 \\ \hline 5\ 40 \\ 13\ 50 \\ 405\ 00 \\ \hline 423.90 \end{array}$$
He travels 135π meters or approximately 423.9 meters.

67. Multiply her height in meters by the number of
inches in 1 meter.

$$\begin{array}{r} 39.37 \\ \times\ 1.65 \\ \hline 1\ 9685 \\ 23\ 6220 \\ 39\ 3700 \\ \hline 64.9605 \end{array}$$

She is approximately 64.9605 inches tall.

69. a. Circumference $= 2 \cdot \pi \cdot$ radius
Smaller circle:
$C = 2 \cdot \pi \cdot 10 = 20\pi$
$C \approx 20(3.14) = 62.8$
The circumference of the smaller circle is
approximately 62.8 meters.
Larger circle:
$C = 2 \cdot \pi \cdot 20 = 40\pi$
$C \approx 40(3.14) = 125.6$
The circumference of the larger circle is
approximately 125.6 meters.

b. Yes, the circumference gets doubled when
the radius is doubled.

71. $12.145 \times 100 = 1214.5$
The cost of 100 bushels of wheat was $1214.50.

73.
$$\begin{array}{r} 1.182 \\ \times\ \ 750 \\ \hline 59\ 100 \\ 827\ 400 \\ \hline 886.500 \end{array}$$
$750 U.S. is equivalent to 886.50 Canadian
dollars.

75.
$$\begin{array}{r} 1.6252 \\ \times\ \ \ 800 \\ \hline 1300.1600 \end{array}$$
They can "buy" 1300.16 New Zealand dollars
with 800 U.S. dollars.

77.
$$6\overline{)2916} \quad \begin{array}{r} 486 \\ \hline \end{array}$$
$$\begin{array}{r} -24 \\ \hline 51 \\ -48 \\ \hline 36 \\ -36 \\ \hline 0 \end{array}$$

79. $-\dfrac{24}{7} \div \dfrac{8}{21} = -\dfrac{24}{7} \cdot \dfrac{21}{8} = -\dfrac{8 \cdot 3 \cdot 7 \cdot 3}{7 \cdot 8} = -\dfrac{3 \cdot 3}{1} = -9$

81.
$$\begin{array}{r} 3.60 \\ +\ 0.04 \\ \hline 3.64 \end{array}$$

83.
$$\begin{array}{r} 3.60 \\ -\ 0.04 \\ \hline 3.56 \end{array}$$

85. The product of a negative number and a positive
number is a negative number.
$$\begin{array}{r} 0.221 \\ \times\ \ 0.5 \\ \hline 0.1105 \end{array}$$
The product is -0.1105.

87.
$$\begin{array}{r} 20.6 \\ \times\ 1.86 \\ \hline 1\ 236 \\ 16\ 480 \\ 20\ 600 \\ \hline 38.316 \end{array}$$
$38.316 \times 100,000 = 3,831,600$
The radio wave travels 3,831,600 miles in 20.6
seconds.

89. answers may vary

91. answers may vary

Section 5.4

Practice Problems

1.
$$8\overline{)370.4} \quad \begin{array}{r} 46.3 \\ \hline \end{array}$$
$$\begin{array}{r} -32 \\ \hline 50 \\ -48 \\ \hline 2\ 4 \\ -2\ 4 \\ \hline 0 \end{array}$$
Check:
$$\begin{array}{r} 46.3 \\ \times\ \ 8 \\ \hline 370.4 \end{array}$$

2.
$$48\overline{)34.08} \quad \begin{array}{r} 0.71 \\ \hline \end{array}$$
$$\begin{array}{r} -33\ 6 \\ \hline 48 \\ -48 \\ \hline 0 \end{array}$$
Check:
$$\begin{array}{r} 0.71 \\ \times\ \ 48 \\ \hline 5\ 68 \\ 28\ 40 \\ \hline 34.08 \end{array}$$

3. a.
$$\begin{array}{r} 1.135 \\ 14\overline{)15.890} \\ \underline{-14} \\ 18 \\ \underline{-14} \\ 49 \\ \underline{-42} \\ 70 \\ \underline{-70} \\ 0 \end{array}$$

Check:
$$\begin{array}{r} 1.135 \\ \times\ \ \ 14 \\ \hline 4\,540 \\ 11\,350 \\ \hline 15.890 \end{array}$$

Thus, $-15.89 \div 14 = -1.135$.

b.
$$\begin{array}{r} 0.027 \\ 104\overline{)2.808} \\ \underline{-2\,08} \\ 728 \\ \underline{-728} \\ 0 \end{array}$$

Check:
$$\begin{array}{r} 0.027 \\ \times\ 104 \\ \hline 108 \\ 2\,700 \\ \hline 2.808 \end{array}$$

Thus, $-2.808 \div (-104) = 0.027$

4. $5.6\overline{)166.88}$ becomes
$$\begin{array}{r} 29.8 \\ 56\overline{)1668.8} \\ \underline{-112} \\ 548 \\ \underline{-504} \\ 44\,8 \\ \underline{-44\,8} \\ 0 \end{array}$$

5. $0.16\overline{)1.976}$ becomes
$$\begin{array}{r} 12.35 \\ 16\overline{)197.60} \\ \underline{-16} \\ 37 \\ \underline{-32} \\ 56 \\ \underline{-48} \\ 80 \\ \underline{-80} \\ 0 \end{array}$$

6. $0.57\overline{)23.4}$ becomes
$$\begin{array}{r} 41.052 \approx 41.05 \\ 57\overline{)2340.000} \\ \underline{-228} \\ 60 \\ \underline{-57} \\ 3\,00 \\ \underline{-2\,85} \\ 150 \\ \underline{-114} \\ 36 \end{array}$$

7. $91.5\overline{)713.7}$ becomes
$$\begin{array}{r} 7.8 \\ 915\overline{)7137.0} \\ \underline{-6405} \\ 732\,0 \\ \underline{-732\,0} \\ 0 \end{array}$$

Estimate: $100\overline{)700}^{\,7}$

8. $\dfrac{362.1}{1000} = 0.3621$

9. $-\dfrac{0.49}{10} = -0.049$

10. $x \div y = 0.035 \div 0.02$

$0.02\overline{)0.035}$ becomes
$$\begin{array}{r} 1.75 \\ 2\overline{)3.50} \\ \underline{-2} \\ 1\,5 \\ \underline{-1\,4} \\ 10 \\ \underline{-10} \\ 0 \end{array}$$

11. $\dfrac{x}{100} = 3.9$

$\dfrac{39}{100} \stackrel{?}{=} 3.9$

$0.39 = 3.9$ False

No, 39 is not a solution.

12.
$$
\begin{array}{r}
11.84 \\
1250\overline{)\,14800.00} \\
-1250 \\
\hline
2300 \\
-1250 \\
\hline
10500 \\
-10000 \\
\hline
5000 \\
-5000 \\
\hline
0
\end{array}
$$

He needs 11.84 bags or 12 whole bags.

Calculator Explorations

1. $102.62 \times 41.8 \approx 100 \times 40 = 4000$
   Since 4000 is not close to 428.9516, it is not reasonable.

2. $174.835 \div 47.9 \approx 200 \div 50 = 4$
   Since 4 is close to 3.65, it is reasonable.

3. $1025.68 - 125.42 \approx 1000 - 100 = 900$
   Since 900 is close to 900.26, it is reasonable.

4. $562.781 + 2.96 \approx 563 + 3 = 566$
   Since 566 is not close to 858.781, it is not reasonable.

Vocabulary and Readiness Check

1. In $6.5 \div 5 = 1.3$, the number 1.3 is called the quotient, 5 is the divisor, and 6.5 is the dividend.

2. To check a division exercise, we can perform the following multiplication:
   quotient · divisor = dividend.

3. To divide a decimal number by a power of 10 such as 10, 100, 1000, or so on, we move the decimal point in the number to the left the same number of places as there are zeros in the power of 10.

4. True or false: If we replace x with -12.6 and y with 0.3 in the expression $y \div x$, we have $0.3 \div (-12.6)$ true

Exercise Set 5.4

1.
$$
\begin{array}{r}
4.6 \\
6\overline{)\,27.6} \\
-24 \\
\hline
3\,6 \\
-3\,6 \\
\hline
0
\end{array}
$$

3.
$$
\begin{array}{r}
0.094 \\
5\overline{)\,0.470} \\
-45 \\
\hline
20 \\
-20 \\
\hline
0
\end{array}
$$

5. $0.06\overline{)\,18}$ becomes
$$
\begin{array}{r}
300 \\
6\overline{)\,1800} \\
-18 \\
\hline
000
\end{array}
$$

7. $0.82\overline{)\,4.756}$ becomes
$$
\begin{array}{r}
5.8 \\
82\overline{)\,475.6} \\
-410 \\
\hline
65\,6 \\
-65\,6 \\
\hline
0
\end{array}
$$

9. Exact: $5.5\overline{)\,36.3}$ becomes
$$
\begin{array}{r}
6.6 \\
55\overline{)\,363.0} \\
-330 \\
\hline
33\,0 \\
-33\,0 \\
\hline
0
\end{array}
$$

Estimate:
$$
\begin{array}{r}
6 \\
6\overline{)\,36}
\end{array}
$$

11.
$$
\begin{array}{r}
0.413 \\
18\overline{)\,7.434} \\
-7\,2 \\
\hline
23 \\
-18 \\
\hline
54 \\
-54 \\
\hline
0
\end{array}
$$

13. A positive number divided by a negative number is a negative number.

$$0.06\overline{)36} \text{ becomes } 6\overline{)\begin{array}{r} 600 \\ 3600 \\ -36 \\ \hline 0 \end{array}}$$

$$36 \div (-0.06) = -600$$

15. A negative number divided by a negative number is a positive number.

$$0.6\overline{)4.2} \text{ becomes } 6\overline{)\begin{array}{r} 7 \\ 42 \\ -42 \\ \hline 0 \end{array}}$$

$$(-4.2) \div (-0.6) = 7$$

17.

$$0.27\overline{)1.296} \text{ becomes } 27\overline{)\begin{array}{r} 4.8 \\ 129.6 \\ -108 \\ \hline 21\,6 \\ -21\,6 \\ \hline 0 \end{array}}$$

19.

$$0.02\overline{)42} \text{ becomes } 2\overline{)\begin{array}{r} 2100 \\ 4200 \\ -4 \\ \hline 02 \\ -2 \\ \hline 000 \end{array}}$$

21.

$$0.82\overline{)4.756} \text{ becomes } 82\overline{)\begin{array}{r} 5.8 \\ 475.6 \\ -410 \\ \hline 65\,6 \\ -65\,6 \\ \hline 0 \end{array}}$$

23. A negative number divided by a negative number is a positive number.

$$6.6\overline{)36.3} \text{ becomes } 66\overline{)\begin{array}{r} 5.5 \\ 363.0 \\ -330 \\ \hline 33\,0 \\ -33\,0 \\ \hline 0 \end{array}}$$

$$-36.3 \div (-6.6) = 5.5$$

25. Exact:

$$7.2\overline{)70.56} \text{ becomes } 72\overline{)\begin{array}{r} 9.8 \\ 705.6 \\ -648 \\ \hline 57\,6 \\ -57\,6 \\ \hline 0 \end{array}}$$

Estimate:

$$7\overline{)\begin{array}{r} 10 \\ 70 \end{array}}$$

27.

$$5.4\overline{)51.84} \text{ becomes } 54\overline{)\begin{array}{r} 9.6 \\ 518.4 \\ -486 \\ \hline 32\,4 \\ -32\,4 \\ \hline 0 \end{array}}$$

29.

$$0.027\overline{)1.215} \text{ becomes } 27\overline{)\begin{array}{r} 45 \\ 1215 \\ -108 \\ \hline 135 \\ -135 \\ \hline 0 \end{array}}$$

$$\frac{1.215}{0.027} = 45$$

31.

$$0.25\overline{)13.648} \text{ becomes } 25\overline{)\begin{array}{r} 54.592 \\ 1364.800 \\ -125 \\ \hline 114 \\ -100 \\ \hline 14\,8 \\ -12\,5 \\ \hline 2\,30 \\ -2\,25 \\ \hline 50 \\ -50 \\ \hline 0 \end{array}}$$

33.

$$3.78\overline{)0.02079} \text{ becomes } 378\overline{)\begin{array}{r} 0.0055 \\ 2.0790 \\ -1\,890 \\ \hline 1890 \\ -1890 \\ \hline 0 \end{array}}$$

35. $0.023\overline{)0.549}$ becomes

$$
\begin{array}{r}
23.869 \approx 23.87 \\
23\overline{)549.000} \\
\underline{-46} \\
89 \\
\underline{-69} \\
20\,0 \\
\underline{-18\,4} \\
1\,60 \\
\underline{-1\,38} \\
220 \\
\underline{-207} \\
13
\end{array}
$$

37. $0.6\overline{)68.39}$ becomes

$$
\begin{array}{r}
113.98 \approx 114.0 \\
6\overline{)683.90} \\
\underline{-6} \\
08 \\
\underline{-6} \\
23 \\
\underline{-18} \\
5\,9 \\
\underline{-5\,4} \\
50 \\
\underline{-48} \\
2
\end{array}
$$

39. $\dfrac{83.397}{100} = 0.83397$

41. $\dfrac{26.87}{10} = 2.687$

43. $12.9 \div (-1000) = -0.0129$

45.

$$
\begin{array}{r}
12.6 \\
7\overline{)88.2} \\
\underline{-7} \\
18 \\
\underline{-14} \\
4\,2 \\
\underline{-4\,2} \\
0
\end{array}
$$

47. $\dfrac{13.1}{10} = 1.31$

49. $\dfrac{456.25}{10,000} = 0.045625$

51.

$$
\begin{array}{r}
0.413 \\
3\overline{)1.239} \\
\underline{-1\,2} \\
03 \\
\underline{-3} \\
09 \\
\underline{-9} \\
0
\end{array}
$$

53. $0.6\overline{)4.8}$ becomes

$$
\begin{array}{r}
8 \\
6\overline{)48} \\
\underline{-48} \\
0
\end{array}
$$

$4.8 \div (-0.6) = -8$

55. $0.17\overline{)1.224}$ becomes

$$
\begin{array}{r}
7.2 \\
17\overline{)122.4} \\
\underline{-119} \\
3\,4 \\
\underline{-3\,4} \\
0
\end{array}
$$

$-1.224 \div 0.17 = -7.2$

57. $0.03\overline{)42}$ becomes

$$
\begin{array}{r}
1400 \\
3\overline{)4200} \\
\underline{-3} \\
12 \\
\underline{-12} \\
0
\end{array}
$$

$42 \div 0.03 = 1400$

59. $0.6\overline{)18}$ becomes

$$
\begin{array}{r}
30 \\
6\overline{)180} \\
\underline{-18} \\
00
\end{array}
$$

$-18 \div (-0.6) = 30$

61. $0.0015\overline{)87}$ becomes

$$
\begin{array}{r}
58,000 \\
15\overline{)870,000} \\
\underline{-75} \\
120 \\
\underline{-120} \\
0000
\end{array}
$$

$87 \div (-0.0015) = -58,000$

63. $1.6\overline{)1.104}$ becomes

$$16\overline{)\begin{array}{r} 0.69 \\ 11.04 \end{array}}$$
$$\begin{array}{r} -96 \\ \hline 1\;44 \\ -1\;44 \\ \hline 0 \end{array}$$

$-1.104 \div 1.6 = -0.69$

65. $-2.4 \div (-100) = \dfrac{-2.4}{-100} = 0.024$

67. $0.071\overline{)4.615}$ becomes

$$71\overline{)\begin{array}{r} 65 \\ 4615 \end{array}}$$
$$\begin{array}{r} -426 \\ \hline 355 \\ -355 \\ \hline 0 \end{array}$$

$\dfrac{4.615}{0.071} = 65$

69. $z \div y = 4.52 \div (-0.8)$

$0.8\overline{)4.52}$ becomes

$$8\overline{)\begin{array}{r} 5.65 \\ 45.20 \end{array}}$$
$$\begin{array}{r} -40 \\ \hline 5\;2 \\ -4\;8 \\ \hline 40 \\ -40 \\ \hline 0 \end{array}$$

$z \div y = 4.52 \div (-0.8) = -5.65$

71. $x \div y = 5.65 \div (-0.8)$

$0.8\overline{)5.65}$ becomes

$$8\overline{)\begin{array}{r} 7.0625 \\ 56.5000 \end{array}}$$
$$\begin{array}{r} -56 \\ \hline 0\;5 \\ -0 \\ \hline 50 \\ -48 \\ \hline 20 \\ -16 \\ \hline 40 \\ -40 \\ \hline 0 \end{array}$$

$x \div y = 5.65 \div (-0.8) = -7.0625$

73. $\dfrac{x}{4} = 3.04$

$\dfrac{12.16}{4} \overset{?}{=} 3.04$

$3.04 = 3.04$ True

Yes, 12.16 is a solution.

75. $\dfrac{z}{100} = 0.8$

$\dfrac{8}{100} \overset{?}{=} 0.8$

$0.08 = 0.8$ False

No, 8 is not a solution.

77. Number of quarts = $\underline{546} \div \underline{52}$

$$52\overline{)\begin{array}{r} 10.5 \approx 11 \\ 546.0 \end{array}}$$
$$\begin{array}{r} -52 \\ \hline 26 \\ -0 \\ \hline 26\;0 \\ -26\;0 \\ \hline 0 \end{array}$$

Since he must buy whole quarts, 11 quarts are needed.

79. $39.37\overline{)200}$ becomes

$$3937\overline{)\begin{array}{r} 5.08 \approx 5.1 \\ 20000.00 \end{array}}$$
$$\begin{array}{r} -19685 \\ \hline 315\;0 \\ -\quad 0 \\ \hline 31500 \\ -31496 \\ \hline 4 \end{array}$$

There are approximately 5.1 meters in 200 inches.

81. Divide the number of crayons by 64.

$$64\overline{)\begin{array}{r} 11.40 \approx 11.4 \\ 730.00 \end{array}}$$
$$\begin{array}{r} -64 \\ \hline 90 \\ -64 \\ \hline 26\;0 \\ -25\;6 \\ \hline 40 \end{array}$$

740 crayons is approximately 11.4 boxes.

83. $6 \times 4 = 24$

There are 24 teaspoons in 4 fluid ounces.

85. From Exercise 83, we know that there are 24 teaspoons in 4 fluid ounces. Thus, there are 48 half teaspoons (0.5 tsp) or doses in 4 fluid ounces. To see how long the medicine will last, if a dose is taken every 4 hours, there are $24 \div 4 = 6$ doses taken per day. 48 (doses) ÷ 6 (per day) = 8 days. The medicine will last 8 days.

87. There are 52 weeks in 1 year.

$$
\begin{array}{r}
248.07 \approx 248.1 \\
52)\overline{12,900.00} \\
-10\ 4 \\
\hline
2\ 50 \\
-2\ 08 \\
\hline
420 \\
-416 \\
\hline
4\ 0 \\
-0 \\
\hline
400 \\
-364 \\
\hline
36
\end{array}
$$

Americans aged 18–22 drive, on average, 248.1 miles per week.

89.
$$
\begin{array}{r}
345.5 \\
24)\overline{8292.0} \\
-72 \\
\hline
109 \\
-96 \\
\hline
132 \\
-120 \\
\hline
12\ 0 \\
-12\ 0 \\
\hline
0
\end{array}
$$

There were 345.5 thousand books sold each hour.

91. $\dfrac{3}{5} \cdot \dfrac{7}{10} = \dfrac{3 \cdot 7}{5 \cdot 10} = \dfrac{21}{50}$

93. $\dfrac{3}{5} - \dfrac{7}{10} = \dfrac{3}{5} \cdot \dfrac{2}{2} - \dfrac{7}{10} = \dfrac{3 \cdot 2}{5 \cdot 2} - \dfrac{7}{10} = \dfrac{6}{10} - \dfrac{7}{10} = -\dfrac{1}{10}$

95. $0.3)\overline{1.278}$ becomes
$$
\begin{array}{r}
4.26 \\
3)\overline{12.78} \\
-12 \\
\hline
0\ 7 \\
-6 \\
\hline
18 \\
-18 \\
\hline
0
\end{array}
$$

97.
$$
\begin{array}{r}
1.278 \\
+\ 0.300 \\
\hline
1.578
\end{array}
$$

99.
$$
\begin{array}{r}
8.6 \quad \text{1 decimal place} \\
\times\ 3.1 \quad \text{1 decimal place} \\
\hline
86 \\
25\ 80 \\
\hline
26.66 \quad 1+1 = 2 \text{ decimal places}
\end{array}
$$
$(-8.6)(3.1) = -26.66$

101.
$$
\begin{array}{r}
1000.00 \\
-\ 95.71 \\
\hline
904.29
\end{array}
$$

103. 8.62×41.7 is approximately $9 \times 40 = 360$, which is choice c.

105. $78.6 \div 97$ is approximately $78.6 \div 100 = 0.786$, which is choice b.

107. $\dfrac{86+78+91+87}{4} = \dfrac{342}{4} = 85.5$

109. Area = (length)(width)

$4.5)\overline{38.7}$ becomes
$$
\begin{array}{r}
8.6 \\
45)\overline{387.0} \\
-360 \\
\hline
27\ 0 \\
-27\ 0 \\
\hline
0
\end{array}
$$

The length is 8.6 feet.

111. answers may vary

113. $1.15\overline{)75}$ becomes

$$
\begin{array}{r}
65.21 \approx 65.2 \\
115\overline{)7500.00} \\
-690 \\
\hline
600 \\
-575 \\
\hline
250 \\
-230 \\
\hline
200 \\
-115 \\
\hline
85
\end{array}
$$

$1.15\overline{)95}$ becomes

$$
\begin{array}{r}
82.60 \approx 82.6 \\
115\overline{)9500.00} \\
-920 \\
\hline
300 \\
-230 \\
\hline
700 \\
-690 \\
\hline
100 \\
-0 \\
\hline
100
\end{array}
$$

The range of wind speeds is 65.2–82.6 knots.

115. First find the length for one round of wire. Then multiply by 4.

$$
\begin{array}{r}
24.280 \\
15.675 \\
24.280 \\
+\,15.675 \\
\hline
79.910
\end{array}
\qquad
\begin{array}{r}
79.91 \\
\times \quad\ 4 \\
\hline
319.64
\end{array}
$$

He will need 319.64 meters of wire.

Integrated Review

1.
$$
\begin{array}{r}
1.60 \\
+\,0.97 \\
\hline
2.57
\end{array}
$$

2.
$$
\begin{array}{r}
3.20 \\
+\,0.85 \\
\hline
4.05
\end{array}
$$

3.
$$
\begin{array}{r}
9.8 \\
-\,0.9 \\
\hline
8.9
\end{array}
$$

4.
$$
\begin{array}{r}
10.2 \\
-\,6.7 \\
\hline
3.5
\end{array}
$$

5.
$$
\begin{array}{r}
0.8 \\
\times\,0.2 \\
\hline
0.16
\end{array}
$$

6.
$$
\begin{array}{r}
0.6 \\
\times\,0.4 \\
\hline
0.24
\end{array}
$$

7.
$$
\begin{array}{r}
0.27 \\
8\overline{)2.16} \\
-1\,6 \\
\hline
56 \\
-56 \\
\hline
0
\end{array}
$$

8.
$$
\begin{array}{r}
0.52 \\
6\overline{)3.12} \\
-3\,0 \\
\hline
12 \\
-12 \\
\hline
0
\end{array}
$$

9.
$$
\begin{array}{r}
9.6 \\
\times\,0.5 \\
\hline
4.80
\end{array}
$$
$(9.6)(-0.5) = -4.8$

10.
$$
\begin{array}{r}
8.7 \\
\times\,0.7 \\
\hline
6.09
\end{array}
$$
$(-8.7)(-0.7) = 6.09$

11.
$$
\begin{array}{r}
123.60 \\
-\,48.04 \\
\hline
75.56
\end{array}
$$

12.
$$
\begin{array}{r}
325.20 \\
-\,36.08 \\
\hline
289.12
\end{array}
$$

13. Subtract absolute values.
$$
\begin{array}{r}
25.000 \\
-\,0.026 \\
\hline
24.974
\end{array}
$$
Attach the sign of the larger absolute value.
$-25 + 0.026 = -24.974$

14. Subtract absolute values.

$$\begin{array}{r} 44.000 \\ -0.125 \\ \hline 43.875 \end{array}$$

Attach the sign of the larger absolute value.

$0.125 + (-44) = -43.875$

15. $3.4\overline{)29.24}$ becomes

$$34\overline{)292.4}$$
$$\begin{array}{r} 8.6 \\ \hline -272 \\ \hline 20\ 4 \\ -20\ 4 \\ \hline 0 \end{array}$$

$29.24 \div (-3.4) = -8.6$

16. $1.9\overline{)10.26}$ becomes

$$19\overline{)102.6}$$
$$\begin{array}{r} 5.4 \\ \hline -95 \\ \hline 7\ 6 \\ -7\ 6 \\ \hline 0 \end{array}$$

$-10.26 \div (-1.9) = 5.4$

17. $-2.8 \times 100 = -280$

18. $1.6 \times 1000 = 1600$

19.
$$\begin{array}{r} 96.210 \\ 7.028 \\ +\ 121.700 \\ \hline 224.938 \end{array}$$

20.
$$\begin{array}{r} 0.268 \\ 1.930 \\ +\ 142.881 \\ \hline 145.079 \end{array}$$

21. $46\overline{)25.76}$
$$\begin{array}{r} 0.56 \\ \hline -23\ 0 \\ \hline 2\ 76 \\ -2\ 76 \\ \hline 0 \end{array}$$

$-25.76 \div (-46) = 0.56$

22. $43\overline{)27.09}$
$$\begin{array}{r} 0.63 \\ \hline -25\ 8 \\ \hline 1\ 29 \\ -1\ 29 \\ \hline 0 \end{array}$$

$-27.09 \div 43 = -0.63$

23.
$$\begin{array}{rl} 12.004 & \text{3 decimal places} \\ \times2.3 & \text{1 decimal place} \\ \hline 3\ 6012 \\ 24\ 0080 \\ \hline 27.6092 & 3+1=4 \text{ decimal places} \end{array}$$

24.
$$\begin{array}{rl} 28.006 & \text{3 decimal places} \\ \times5.2 & \text{1 decimal place} \\ \hline 5\ 6012 \\ 140\ 0300 \\ \hline 145.6312 & 3+1=4 \text{ decimal places} \end{array}$$

25.
$$\begin{array}{r} 10.0 \\ -4.6 \\ \hline 5.4 \end{array}$$

26. Subtract absolute values.

$$\begin{array}{r} 18.00 \\ -0.26 \\ \hline 17.74 \end{array}$$

Attach the sign of the greater absolute value.

$0.26 - 18 = -17.74$

27. $-268.19 - 146.25 = -268.19 + (-146.25)$

Add absolute values.

$$\begin{array}{r} 268.19 \\ +\ 146.25 \\ \hline 414.44 \end{array}$$

Attach the common sign.

$-268.19 - 146.25 = -414.44$

28. $-860.18 - 434.85 = -860.18 + (-434.85)$

Add absolute values.

$$\begin{array}{r} 860.18 \\ +\ 434.85 \\ \hline 1295.03 \end{array}$$

Attach the common sign.

$-860.18 - 434.85 = -1295.03$

29. $0.087 \overline{)2.958}$ becomes $87 \overline{)2958}$

$$
\begin{array}{r}
34 \\
87 \overline{)2958} \\
-261 \\
\hline
348 \\
-348 \\
\hline
0
\end{array}
$$

$$\frac{2.958}{-0.087} = -34$$

30. $0.061 \overline{)1.708}$ becomes $61 \overline{)1708}$

$$
\begin{array}{r}
28 \\
61 \overline{)1708} \\
-122 \\
\hline
488 \\
-488 \\
\hline
0
\end{array}
$$

$$\frac{-1.708}{0.061} = -28$$

31.
$$
\begin{array}{r}
160.00 \\
-\ 43.19 \\
\hline
116.81
\end{array}
$$

32.
$$
\begin{array}{r}
120.00 \\
-101.21 \\
\hline
18.79
\end{array}
$$

33. $15.62 \times 10 = 156.2$

34. $15.62 \div 10 = 1.562$

35.
$$
\begin{array}{r}
15.62 \\
+10.00 \\
\hline
25.62
\end{array}
$$

36.
$$
\begin{array}{r}
15.62 \\
-10.00 \\
\hline
5.62
\end{array}
$$

37.
53.7	rounds to	50
79.2	rounds to	80
+ 71.2	rounds to	+ 70
		200

The estimated distance is 200 miles.

38.
$$
\begin{array}{r}
4.80 \\
-\ 4.11 \\
\hline
0.69
\end{array}
$$

It costs $0.69 more to send the package as Priority Mail.

39.
$$
\begin{array}{r}
16.0 \\
+\ 7.5 \\
\hline
23.5
\end{array}
$$

$$
\begin{aligned}
23.5 \text{ billion} &= 23.5 \times 1 \text{ billion} \\
&= 23.5 \times 1,000,000,000 \\
&= 23,500,000,000
\end{aligned}
$$

The total amount spent was $23.5 billion or $23,500,000,000.

Section 5.5

Practice Problems

1. a.
$$
\begin{array}{r}
0.4 \\
5 \overline{)2.0} \\
-2.0 \\
\hline
0
\end{array}
$$
$$\frac{2}{5} = 0.4$$

b.
$$
\begin{array}{r}
0.225 \\
40 \overline{)9.000} \\
-8\ 0 \\
\hline
1\ 00 \\
-80 \\
\hline
200 \\
-200 \\
\hline
0
\end{array}
$$
$$\frac{9}{40} = 0.225$$

2.
$$
\begin{array}{r}
0.375 \\
8 \overline{)3.000} \\
-2\ 4 \\
\hline
60 \\
-56 \\
\hline
40 \\
-40 \\
\hline
0
\end{array}
$$
$$-\frac{3}{8} = -0.375$$

3. a.
$$
\begin{array}{r}
0.833... \\
6 \overline{)5.000} \\
-4\ 8 \\
\hline
20 \\
-18 \\
\hline
20 \\
-18 \\
\hline
2
\end{array}
$$
$$\frac{5}{6} = 0.8\overline{3}$$

b. $9\overline{)\begin{array}{l}0.22...\\2.00\end{array}}$

$\underline{-18}$

20

$\underline{-18}$

2

$\dfrac{2}{9} = 0.\overline{2}$

4. $13\overline{)\begin{array}{l}2.1538 \approx 2.154\\28.0000\end{array}}$

$\underline{-26}$

$2\,0$

$\underline{-1\,3}$

70

$\underline{-65}$

50

$\underline{-39}$

110

$\underline{-104}$

6

5. $3\dfrac{5}{16} = \dfrac{53}{16}$

$16\overline{)\begin{array}{l}3.3125\\53.0000\end{array}}$

$\underline{-48}$

$5\,0$

$\underline{-4\,8}$

20

$\underline{-16}$

40

$\underline{-32}$

80

$\underline{-80}$

0

Thus, $3\dfrac{5}{16} = 3.3125.$

6. $\dfrac{3}{5} = \dfrac{3}{5} \cdot \dfrac{2}{2} = \dfrac{6}{10} = 0.6$

7. $\dfrac{3}{50} = \dfrac{3}{50} \cdot \dfrac{2}{2} = \dfrac{6}{100} = 0.06$

8. $5\overline{)\begin{array}{l}0.2\\1.0\end{array}}$

$\underline{-1\,0}$

0

Since $0.2 < 0.25$, then $\dfrac{1}{5} < 0.25.$

9. a. $\dfrac{1}{2} = 0.5$ and $0.5 < 0.54$, so $\dfrac{1}{2} < 0.54.$

b. $9\overline{)\begin{array}{l}0.55...\\5.00\end{array}}$

$\underline{-4\,5}$

50

$\underline{-45}$

5

$0.\overline{5} = 0.55...,$ so $0.\overline{5} = \dfrac{5}{9}.$

c. $7\overline{)\begin{array}{l}0.714\\5.000\end{array}}$

$\underline{-4\,9}$

10

$\underline{-7}$

30

$\underline{-28}$

2

$0.714 < 0.72$, so $\dfrac{5}{7} < 0.72.$

10. a. $\dfrac{1}{3} = 0.333...$

$0.302 = 0.302$

$\dfrac{3}{8} = 0.375$

$0.302,\ \dfrac{1}{3},\ \dfrac{3}{8}$

b. $1.26 = 1.26$

$1\dfrac{1}{4} = 1.25$

$1\dfrac{2}{5} = 1.40$

$1\dfrac{1}{4},\ 1.26,\ 1\dfrac{2}{5}$

c. $0.4 = 0.40$

$0.41 = 0.41$

$\dfrac{3}{7} \approx 0.43$

$0.4, \; 0.41, \; \dfrac{3}{7}$

11. $897.8 \div 100 \times 10 = 8.978 \times 10 = 89.78$

12. $-8.69(3.2 - 1.8) = -8.69(1.4) = -12.166$

13. $(-0.7)^2 + 2.1 = 0.49 + 2.10 = 2.59$

14. $\dfrac{20.06 - (1.2)^2 \div 10}{0.02} = \dfrac{20.06 - 1.44 \div 10}{0.02}$

$\qquad\qquad\quad = \dfrac{20.06 - 0.144}{0.02}$

$\qquad\qquad\quad = \dfrac{19.916}{0.02}$

$\qquad\qquad\quad = 995.8$

15. Area $= \dfrac{1}{2} \cdot$ base $\cdot$ height

$\qquad = \dfrac{1}{2} \cdot 7 \cdot 2.1$

$\qquad = 0.5 \cdot 7 \cdot 2.1$

$\qquad = 7.35$

The area of the triangle is 7.35 square meters.

16. $1.7y - 2 = 1.7(2.3) - 2 = 3.91 - 2 = 1.91$

Vocabulary and Readiness Check

1. The number $0.\overline{5}$ means 0.555. <u>false</u>

2. To write $\dfrac{9}{19}$ as a decimal, perform the division

$19\overline{)9}$. <u>true</u>

3. $(-1.2)^2$ means $(-1.2)(-1.2)$ or -1.44. <u>false</u>

4. To simplify $8.6(4.8 - 9.6)$, we first subtract. <u>true</u>

Exercise Set 5.5

1.
$$\begin{array}{r} 0.2 \\ 5\overline{)\ 1\ 0} \\ \underline{-1.0} \\ 0 \end{array}$$
$\qquad \dfrac{1}{5} = 0.2$

3.
$$\begin{array}{r} 0.68 \\ 25\overline{)\ 17.00} \\ \underline{-15\ 0} \\ 2\ 00 \\ \underline{-2\ 00} \\ 0 \end{array}$$
$\qquad \dfrac{17}{25} = 0.68$

5.
$$\begin{array}{r} 0.75 \\ 4\overline{)\ 3.00} \\ \underline{-2\ 8} \\ 20 \\ \underline{-20} \\ 0 \end{array}$$
$\qquad \dfrac{3}{4} = 0.75$

7.
$$\begin{array}{r} 0.08 \\ 25\overline{)\ 2.00} \\ \underline{-2\ 00} \\ 0 \end{array}$$
$\qquad -\dfrac{2}{25} = -0.08$

9.
$$\begin{array}{r} 2.25 \\ 4\overline{)\ 9.00} \\ \underline{-8} \\ 1\ 0 \\ \underline{-\ 8} \\ 20 \\ \underline{-20} \\ 0 \end{array}$$
$\qquad \dfrac{9}{4} = 2.25$

11.
$$\begin{array}{r} 0.9166... \\ 12\overline{)\ 11.0000} \\ \underline{-10\ 8} \\ 20 \\ \underline{-12} \\ 80 \\ \underline{-72} \\ 80 \\ \underline{-72} \\ 8 \end{array}$$
$\qquad \dfrac{11}{12} = 0.91\overline{6}$

13.
$$\begin{array}{r} 0.425 \\ 40\overline{)\ 17.000} \\ \underline{-16\ 0} \\ 1\ 00 \\ \underline{-80} \\ 200 \\ \underline{-200} \\ 0 \end{array}$$
$\qquad \dfrac{17}{40} = 0.425$

15.
$$20 \overline{)\begin{array}{l} 0.45 \\ 9.00 \\ \underline{-8\ 0} \\ 1\ 00 \\ \underline{-1\ 00} \\ 0 \end{array}}$$

$$\frac{9}{20} = 0.45$$

17.
$$3 \overline{)\begin{array}{l} 0.333... \\ 1.000 \\ \underline{-9} \\ 10 \\ \underline{-9} \\ 10 \\ \underline{-9} \\ 1 \end{array}}$$

$$-\frac{1}{3} = -0.\overline{3}$$

19.
$$16 \overline{)\begin{array}{l} 0.4375 \\ 7.0000 \\ \underline{-6\ 4} \\ 60 \\ \underline{-48} \\ 120 \\ \underline{-112} \\ 80 \\ \underline{-80} \\ 0 \end{array}}$$

$$\frac{7}{16} = 0.4375$$

21.
$$11 \overline{)\begin{array}{l} 0.636363... \\ 7.000000 \\ \underline{-6\ 6} \\ 40 \\ \underline{-33} \\ 70 \\ \underline{-66} \\ 40 \\ \underline{-33} \\ 70 \\ \underline{-66} \\ 40 \\ \underline{-33} \\ 7 \end{array}}$$

$$\frac{7}{11} = 0.\overline{63}$$

23.
$$20 \overline{)\begin{array}{l} 0.85 \\ 17.00 \\ \underline{-16\ 0} \\ 1\ 00 \\ \underline{-1\ 00} \\ 0 \end{array}}$$

$$5\frac{17}{20} = 5.85$$

25.
$$125 \overline{)\begin{array}{l} 0.624 \\ 78.000 \\ \underline{-75\ 0} \\ 3\ 00 \\ \underline{-2\ 50} \\ 500 \\ \underline{-500} \\ 0 \end{array}}$$

$$\frac{78}{125} = 0.624$$

27. $-\dfrac{1}{3} = -0.33\overline{3} \approx -0.33$

29. $\dfrac{7}{16} = 0.4375 \approx 0.44$

31. $\dfrac{7}{11} = 0.63\overline{63} \approx 0.6$

33.
$$91 \overline{)\begin{array}{l} 0.615 \approx 0.62 \\ 56.000 \\ \underline{-54\ 6} \\ 1\ 40 \\ \underline{-91} \\ 490 \\ \underline{-455} \\ 35 \end{array}}$$

35.
$$97 \overline{)\begin{array}{l} 0.731 \approx 0.73 \\ 71.000 \\ \underline{-67\ 9} \\ 3\ 10 \\ \underline{-2\ 91} \\ 190 \\ \underline{-97} \\ 93 \end{array}}$$

37.
$$50 \overline{)\begin{array}{l} 0.02 \\ 1.00 \\ \underline{-1\ 00} \\ 0 \end{array}}$$

39. 0.562　0.569
　　　　↑　　　↑
　　　　2　<　9
so, 0.562 < 0.569

41.
$$200\overline{)43.000}$$
　　0.215
　　−40 0
　　──
　　　3 00
　　−2 00
　　──
　　　1 000
　　−1 000
　　──
　　　　　0

$$0.215 = \frac{43}{200}$$

43. 0.0932　0.0923
　　　　↑　　　　↑
　　　　3　>　2
so, 0.0932 > 0.0923
Thus, −0.0932 < −0.0923.

45.
$$6\overline{)5.000}$$
　　0.833...
　　−4 8
　　──
　　　20
　　−18
　　──
　　　20
　　−18
　　──
　　　2

$$\frac{5}{6} = 0.8\overline{3} \text{ and } 0.\overline{6} < 0.8\overline{3}, \text{ so } 0.\overline{6} < \frac{5}{6}$$

47.
$$91\overline{)51.0000}$$
　　0.5604 ≈ 0.560
　　−45 5
　　──
　　　550
　　−546
　　──
　　　40
　　　−0
　　──
　　　400
　　−364
　　──
　　　36

$$\frac{51}{91} \approx 0.560 \text{ and } 0.560 < 0.56\overline{4}, \text{ so } \frac{51}{91} < 0.56\overline{4}.$$

49.
$$7\overline{)4.000}$$
　　0.571 ≈ 0.57
　　−3 5
　　──
　　　50
　　−49
　　──
　　　10
　　−7
　　──
　　　3

$$\frac{4}{7} \approx 0.57 \text{ and } 0.57 > 0.14, \text{ so } \frac{4}{7} > 0.14.$$

51.
$$13\overline{)18.0000}$$
　　1.3846 ≈ 1.385
　　−13
　　──
　　　5 0
　　−3 9
　　──
　　　1 10
　　−1 04
　　──
　　　60
　　−52
　　──
　　　80
　　−78
　　──
　　　2

$$\frac{18}{13} \approx 1.385 \text{ and } 1.38 < 1.385, \text{ so } 1.38 < \frac{18}{13}.$$

53.
$$64\overline{)456.000}$$
　　7.125
　　−448
　　──
　　　8 0
　　−6 4
　　──
　　　1 60
　　−1 28
　　──
　　　320
　　−320
　　──
　　　0

$$\frac{456}{64} = 7.125 \text{ and } 7.123 < 7.125, \text{ so}$$

$$7.123 < \frac{456}{64}.$$

55. 0.32, 0.34, 0.35

57. 0.49 = 0.490
　　0.49, 0.491, 0.498

59. $\dfrac{42}{8} = 5.25$

$5.23, \ \dfrac{42}{8}, \ 5.34$

61. $\dfrac{5}{8} = 0.625$

$0.612, \ \dfrac{5}{8}, \ 0.649$

63. $(0.3)^2 + 0.5 = 0.09 + 0.5 = 0.59$

65. $\dfrac{1 + 0.8}{-0.6} = \dfrac{1.8}{-0.6} = \dfrac{18}{-6} = -3$

67. $(-2.3)^2(0.3 + 0.7) = (-2.3)^2(1.0)$
$\qquad\qquad\qquad\quad = 5.29(1.0)$
$\qquad\qquad\qquad\quad = 5.29$

69. $(5.6 - 2.3)(2.4 + 0.4) = (3.3)(2.8) = 9.24$

71. $\dfrac{(4.5)^2}{100} = \dfrac{20.25}{100} = 0.2025$

73. $\dfrac{7 + 0.74}{-6} = \dfrac{7.74}{-6} = -1.29$

75. $\dfrac{1}{5} - 2(7.8) = \dfrac{1}{5} - 15.6 = 0.2 - 15.6 = -15.4$

77. $\dfrac{1}{4}(-9.6 - 5.2) = \dfrac{1}{4}(-14.8) = 0.25(-14.8) = -3.7$

79. Area $= \dfrac{1}{2} \cdot b \cdot h$
$\qquad\quad = \dfrac{1}{2}(5.7)(9)$
$\qquad\quad = 0.5(5.7)(9)$
$\qquad\quad = 25.65$ square inches

81. Area $= l \cdot w$
$\qquad\quad = (0.62)\left(\dfrac{2}{5}\right)$
$\qquad\quad = (0.62)(0.4)$
$\qquad\quad = 0.248$ square yard

83. $z^2 = (-2.4)^2 = 5.76$

85. $x - y = 6 - 0.3 = 5.7$

87. $4y - z = 4 \cdot 0.3 - (-2.4) = 1.2 + 2.4 = 3.6$

89. $\dfrac{9}{10} + \dfrac{16}{25} = \dfrac{9}{10} \cdot \dfrac{5}{5} + \dfrac{16}{25} \cdot \dfrac{2}{2} = \dfrac{45}{50} + \dfrac{32}{50} = \dfrac{77}{50}$

91. $\left(\dfrac{2}{5}\right)\left(\dfrac{5}{2}\right)^2 = \left(\dfrac{2}{5}\right)\left(\dfrac{5}{2}\right)\left(\dfrac{5}{2}\right) = \dfrac{2 \cdot 5 \cdot 5}{5 \cdot 2 \cdot 2} = \dfrac{5}{2}$

93. $1.0 = 1$

95. $1.00001 > 1$

97. $99 < 100$, so $\dfrac{99}{100} < 1$

99.
$$
\begin{array}{r}
0.0144 \approx 0.014 \\
14{,}120{\overline{\smash{\big)}\,204.0000}} \\
\underline{-141\ 20} \\
62\ 800 \\
\underline{-56\ 480} \\
6\ 3200 \\
\underline{-\ 5\ 6480} \\
6720
\end{array}
$$

Approximately 0.014 of radio stations had a hip hop music format.

101.

2092	rounds to	2100
1342	rounds to	1300
204	rounds to	200
455	rounds to	500
745	rounds to	700
+ 436	rounds to	+ 400
		5200

The total number of stations with the top six formats was about 5200 stations.

103. answers may vary

Section 5.6

Practice Problems

1. $z + 0.9 = 1.3$
$\quad\ \ z + 0.9 - 0.9 = 1.3 - 0.9$
$\qquad\qquad\quad\ z = 0.4$

2. $0.17x = -0.34$
$\quad \dfrac{0.17x}{0.17} = \dfrac{-0.34}{0.17}$
$\qquad\quad x = -2$

3.
$$2.9 = 1.7 + 0.3x$$
$$2.9 - 1.7 = 1.7 + 0.3x - 1.7$$
$$1.2 = 0.3x$$
$$\frac{1.2}{0.3} = \frac{0.3x}{0.3}$$
$$4 = x$$

4.
$$8x + 4.2 = 10x + 11.6$$
$$8x + 4.2 - 4.2 = 10x + 11.6 - 4.2$$
$$8x = 10x + 7.4$$
$$8x - 10x = 10x - 10x + 7.4$$
$$-2x = 7.4$$
$$\frac{-2x}{-2} = \frac{7.4}{-2}$$
$$x = -3.7$$

5.
$$6.3 - 5x = 3(x + 2.9)$$
$$6.3 - 5x = 3x + 8.7$$
$$6.3 - 5x - 6.3 = 3x + 8.7 - 6.3$$
$$-5x = 3x + 2.4$$
$$-5x - 3x = 3x + 2.4 - 3x$$
$$-8x = 2.4$$
$$\frac{-8x}{-8} = \frac{2.4}{-8}$$
$$x = -0.3$$

6.
$$0.2y + 2.6 = 4$$
$$10(0.2y + 2.6) = 10(4)$$
$$10(0.2y) + 10(2.6) = 10(4)$$
$$2y + 26 = 40$$
$$2y + 26 - 26 = 40 - 26$$
$$2y = 14$$
$$\frac{2y}{2} = \frac{14}{2}$$
$$y = 7$$

Exercise Set 5.6

1.
$$x + 1.2 = 7.1$$
$$x + 1.2 - 1.2 = 7.1 - 1.2$$
$$x = 5.9$$

3.
$$-5y = 2.15$$
$$\frac{-5y}{-5} = \frac{2.15}{-5}$$
$$y = -0.43$$

5.
$$6.2 = y - 4$$
$$6.2 + 4 = y - 4 + 4$$
$$10.2 = y$$

7.
$$3.1x = -13.95$$
$$\frac{3.1x}{3.1} = \frac{-13.95}{3.1}$$
$$x = -4.5$$

9.
$$-3.5x + 2.8 = -11.2$$
$$-3.5x + 2.8 - 2.8 = -11.2 - 2.8$$
$$-3.5x = -14$$
$$\frac{-3.5x}{-3.5} = \frac{-14}{-3.5}$$
$$x = 4$$

11.
$$6x + 8.65 = 3x + 10$$
$$6x + 8.65 - 8.65 = 3x + 10 - 8.65$$
$$6x = 3x + 1.35$$
$$6x - 3x = 3x - 3x + 1.35$$
$$3x = 1.35$$
$$\frac{3x}{3} = \frac{1.35}{3}$$
$$x = 0.45$$

13.
$$2(x - 1.3) = 5.8$$
$$2x - 2.6 = 5.8$$
$$2x - 2.6 + 2.6 = 5.8 + 2.6$$
$$2x = 8.4$$
$$\frac{2x}{2} = \frac{8.4}{2}$$
$$x = 4.2$$

15.
$$0.4x + 0.7 = -0.9$$
$$10(0.4x + 0.7) = 10(-0.9)$$
$$4x + 7 = -9$$
$$4x + 7 - 7 = -9 - 7$$
$$4x = -16$$
$$\frac{4x}{4} = \frac{-16}{4}$$
$$x = -4$$

17.
$$7x - 10.8 = x$$
$$10(7x - 10.8) = 10 \cdot x$$
$$70x - 108 = 10x$$
$$70x - 70x - 108 = 10x - 70x$$
$$-108 = -60x$$
$$\frac{-108}{-60} = \frac{-60x}{-60}$$
$$1.8 = x$$

19.
$$2.1x + 5 - 1.6x = 10$$
$$10(2.1x + 5 - 1.6x) = 10 \cdot 10$$
$$21x + 50 - 16x = 100$$
$$5x + 50 = 100$$
$$5x + 50 - 50 = 100 - 50$$
$$5x = 50$$
$$\frac{5x}{5} = \frac{50}{5}$$
$$x = 10$$

21.
$$y - 3.6 = 4$$
$$y - 3.6 + 3.6 = 4 + 3.6$$
$$y = 7.6$$

23.
$$-0.02x = -1.2$$
$$\frac{-0.02x}{-0.02} = \frac{-1.2}{-0.02}$$
$$x = 60$$

25.
$$6.5 = 10x + 7.2$$
$$6.5 - 7.2 = 10x + 7.2 - 7.2$$
$$-0.7 = 10x$$
$$\frac{-0.7}{10} = \frac{10x}{10}$$
$$-0.07 = x$$

27.
$$2.7x - 25 = 1.2x + 5$$
$$2.7x - 25 + 25 = 1.2x + 5 + 25$$
$$2.7x = 1.2x + 30$$
$$2.7x - 1.2x = 1.2x - 1.2x + 30$$
$$1.5x = 30$$
$$\frac{1.5x}{1.5} = \frac{30}{1.5}$$
$$x = 20$$

29.
$$200x - 0.67 = 100x + 0.81$$
$$200x - 0.67 + 0.67 = 100x + 0.81 + 0.67$$
$$200x = 100x + 1.48$$
$$200x - 100x = 100x - 100x + 1.48$$
$$100x = 1.48$$
$$\frac{100x}{100} = \frac{1.48}{100}$$
$$x = 0.0148$$

31.
$$3(x + 2.71) = 2x$$
$$3x + 8.13 = 2x$$
$$3x - 3x + 8.13 = 2x - 3x$$
$$8.13 = -x$$
$$\frac{8.13}{-1} = \frac{-x}{-1}$$
$$-8.13 = x$$

33.
$$8x - 5 = 10x - 8$$
$$8x - 5 + 8 = 10x - 8 + 8$$
$$8x + 3 = 10x$$
$$8x + 3 - 8x = 10x - 8x$$
$$3 = 2x$$
$$\frac{3}{2} = \frac{2x}{2}$$
$$1.5 = x$$

35.
$$1.2 + 0.3x = 0.9$$
$$1.2 + 0.3x - 1.2 = 0.9 - 1.2$$
$$0.3x = -0.3$$
$$\frac{0.3x}{0.3} = \frac{-0.3}{0.3}$$
$$x = -1$$

37.
$$-0.9x + 2.65 = -0.5x + 5.45$$
$$100(-0.9x + 2.65) = 100(-0.5x + 5.45)$$
$$-90x + 265 = -50x + 545$$
$$-90x + 265 + 90x = -50x + 545 + 90x$$
$$265 = 40x + 545$$
$$265 - 545 = 40x + 545 - 545$$
$$-280 = 40x$$
$$\frac{-280}{40} = \frac{40x}{40}$$
$$-7 = x$$

39.
$$4x + 7.6 = 2(3x - 3.2)$$
$$4x + 7.6 = 6x - 6.4$$
$$10(4x + 7.6) = 10(6x - 6.4)$$
$$40x + 76 = 60x - 64$$
$$40x + 76 + 64 = 60x - 64 + 64$$
$$40x + 140 = 60x$$
$$40x - 40x + 140 = 60x - 40x$$
$$140 = 20x$$
$$\frac{140}{20} = \frac{20x}{20}$$
$$7 = x$$

41.
$$0.7x + 13.8 = x - 2.16$$
$$100(0.7x + 13.8) = 100(x - 2.16)$$
$$70x + 1380 = 100x - 216$$
$$70x + 1380 + 216 = 100x - 216 + 216$$
$$70x + 1596 = 100x$$
$$70x + 1596 - 70x = 100x - 70x$$
$$1596 = 30x$$
$$\frac{1596}{30} = \frac{30x}{30}$$
$$53.2 = x$$

43. $2x - 7 + x - 9 = (2x + x) + (-7 - 9) = 3x - 16$

45. $\dfrac{6x}{5} \cdot \dfrac{1}{2x^2} = \dfrac{6x \cdot 1}{5 \cdot 2x^2} = \dfrac{2 \cdot 3 \cdot x}{5 \cdot 2 \cdot x \cdot x} = \dfrac{3}{5x}$

47. $\dfrac{x}{3} + \dfrac{2x}{7} = \dfrac{x}{3} \cdot \dfrac{7}{7} + \dfrac{2x}{7} \cdot \dfrac{3}{3}$

$\qquad = \dfrac{7x}{21} + \dfrac{6x}{21}$

$\qquad = \dfrac{7x + 6x}{21}$

$\qquad = \dfrac{13x}{21}$

49. $b + 4.6 = 8.3$

$b + 4.6 - 4.6 = 8.3 - 4.6$

$b = 3.7$

51. $2x - 0.6 + 4x - 0.01 = 2x + 4x - 0.6 - 0.01$

$\qquad = 6x - 0.61$

53. $5y - 1.2 - 7y + 8 = 5y - 7y - 1.2 + 8$

$\qquad = -2y + 6.8$

55. $2.8 = z - 6.3$

$2.8 + 6.3 = z - 6.3 + 6.3$

$9.1 = z$

57. $4.7x + 8.3 = -5.8$

$4.7x + 8.3 - 8.3 = -5.8 - 8.3$

$4.7x = -14.1$

$\dfrac{4.7x}{4.7} = \dfrac{-14.1}{4.7}$

$x = -3$

59. $7.76 + 8z - 12z + 8.91 = 8z - 12z + 7.76 + 8.91$

$\qquad = -4z + 16.67$

61. $5(x - 3.14) = 4x$

$5 \cdot x - 5 \cdot 3.14 = 4x$

$5x - 15.7 = 4x$

$5x - 5x - 15.7 = 4x - 5x$

$-15.7 = -x$

$15.7 = x$

63. $2.6y + 8.3 = 4.6y - 3.4$

$10(2.6y + 8.3) = 10(4.6y - 3.4)$

$26y + 83 = 46y - 34$

$26y + 83 - 83 = 46y - 34 - 83$

$26y = 46y - 117$

$26y - 46y = 46y - 46y - 117$

$-20y = -117$

$\dfrac{-20y}{-20} = \dfrac{-117}{-20}$

$y = 5.85$

65. $9.6z - 3.2 - 11.7z - 6.9 = 9.6z - 11.7z - 3.2 - 6.9$

$\qquad = -2.1z - 10.1$

67. answers may vary

69. answers may vary

71. $-5.25x = -40.33575$

$\dfrac{-5.25x}{-5.25} = \dfrac{-40.33575}{-5.25}$

$x = 7.683$

73. $1.95y + 6.834 = 7.65y - 19.8591$

$1.95y + 6.834 - 6.834 = 7.65y - 19.8591 - 6.834$

$1.95y = 7.65y - 26.6931$

$1.95y - 7.65y = 7.65y - 7.65y - 26.6931$

$-5.7y = -26.6931$

$\dfrac{-5.7y}{-5.7} = \dfrac{-26.6931}{-5.7}$

$y = 4.683$

Section 5.7

Practice Problems

1. Mean $= \dfrac{87 + 75 + 96 + 91 + 78}{5} = \dfrac{427}{5} = 85.4$

2. gpa $= \dfrac{4 \cdot 2 + 3 \cdot 4 + 2 \cdot 5 + 1 \cdot 2 + 4 \cdot 2}{2 + 4 + 5 + 2 + 2} = \dfrac{40}{15} \approx 2.67$

3. Because the numbers are in numerical order, and there are an odd number of items, the median is the middle number, 24.

4. Write the numbers in numerical order:
36, 65, 71, 78, 88, 91, 95, 95
Since there are an even number of scores, the median is the mean of the two middle numbers.

median $= \dfrac{78 + 88}{2} = 83$

5. Mode: 15 because it occurs most often, 3 times.

6. Median: Write the numbers in order.
   15, 15, 15, 16, 18, 26, 26, 30, 31, 35
   Median is mean of middle two numbers,
   $\frac{18+26}{2} = 22$.
   Mode: 15 because it occurs most often, 3 times.

Vocabulary and Readiness Check

1. Another word for "mean" is <u>average</u>.

2. The number that occurs most often in a set of numbers is called the <u>mode</u>.

3. The <u>mean (or average)</u> of a set of number items is $\frac{\text{sum of items}}{\text{number of items}}$.

4. The <u>median</u> of a set of numbers is the middle number. If the number of numbers is even, it is the <u>mean (or average)</u> of the two middle numbers.

5. An example of weighted mean is a calculation of <u>grade point average</u>.

Exercise Set 5.7

1. Mean: $\frac{15+23+24+18+25}{5} = \frac{105}{5} = 21$
   Median: Write the numbers in order:
   15, 18, 23, 24, 25
   The middle number is 23.
   Mode: There is no mode, since each number occurs once.

3. Mean:
   $\frac{7.6+8.2+8.2+9.6+5.7+9.1}{6} = \frac{48.4}{6} \approx 8.1$
   Median: Write the numbers in order:
   5.7, 7.6, 8.2, 8.2, 9.1, 9.6
   Median is mean of middle two: $\frac{8.2+8.2}{2} = 8.2$
   Mode: 8.2 since this number appears twice.

5. Mean:
   $\frac{0.5+0.2+0.2+0.6+0.3+1.3+0.8+0.1+0.5}{9}$
   $= \frac{4.5}{9}$
   $= 0.5$
   Median: Write the numbers in order:

0.1, 0.2, 0.2, 0.3, 0.5, 0.5, 0.6, 0.8, 1.3
The middle number is 0.5.
Mode: Since 0.2 and 0.5 occur twice, there are two modes, 0.2 and 0.5.

7. Mean:
   $\frac{231+543+601+293+588+109+334+268}{8}$
   $= \frac{2967}{8}$
   ≈ 370.9
   Median: Write the numbers in order:
   109, 231, 268, 293, 334, 543, 588, 601
   The mean of the middle two: $\frac{293+334}{2} = 313.5$
   Mode: There is no mode, since each number occurs once.

9. Mean:
   $\frac{1670+1614+1483+1483+1451}{5} = \frac{7701}{5}$
   $= 1540.2$ feet

11. Because the numbers are in numerical order, the median is mean of the middle two (of the top 8),
    $\frac{1483+1451}{2} = 1467$ feet.

13. answers may vary

15. $\text{gpa} = \frac{3 \cdot 3 + 2 \cdot 3 + 4 \cdot 4 + 2 \cdot 4}{3+3+4+4} = \frac{39}{14} \approx 2.79$

17. $\text{gpa} = \frac{4 \cdot 3 + 4 \cdot 3 + 4 \cdot 4 + 3 \cdot 3 + 2 \cdot 1}{3+3+4+3+1}$
    $= \frac{51}{14}$
    ≈ 3.64

19. Mean:
    $\frac{7.8+6.9+7.5+4.7+6.9+7.0}{6} = \frac{40.8}{6} = 6.8$

21. Mode: 6.9, since this number appears twice.

23. Median: Write the numbers in order.
    79, 85, 88, 89, 91, 93
    The mean of the middle two: $\frac{88+89}{2} = 88.5$

25. Mean: $\frac{\text{sum of 15 pulse rates}}{15} = \frac{1095}{15} = 73$

27. Mode: Since 70 and 71 occur twice, there are two modes, 70 and 71.

29. There were 9 rates lower than the mean. They are 66, 68, 71, 64, 71, 70, 65, 70, and 72.

31. $\dfrac{6}{18} = \dfrac{1 \cdot 6}{3 \cdot 6} = \dfrac{1}{3}$

33. $\dfrac{18}{30y} = \dfrac{3 \cdot 6}{5 \cdot 6 \cdot y} = \dfrac{3}{5y}$

35. $\dfrac{55y^2}{75y^2} = \dfrac{5 \cdot 11 \cdot y \cdot y}{5 \cdot 15 \cdot y \cdot y} = \dfrac{11}{15}$

37. Since the mode is 35, 35 must occur at least twice in the set.
Since there is an odd number of numbers in the set, the median, 37 is in the set.
Let n be the remaining unknown number.

Mean: $\dfrac{35 + 35 + 37 + 40 + n}{5} = 38$

$\dfrac{147 + n}{5} = 38$

$5 \cdot \dfrac{147 + n}{5} = 5 \cdot 38$

$147 + n = 190$

$147 - 147 + n = 190 - 147$

$n = 43$

The missing numbers are 35, 35, 37, and 43.

39. yes; answers may vary

Chapter 5 Vocabulary Check

1. Like fractional notation, decimal notation is used to denote a part of a whole.

2. To write fractions as decimals, divide the numerator by the denominator.

3. To add or subtract decimals, write the decimals so that the decimal points line up vertically.

4. When writing decimals in words, write "and" for the decimal point.

5. When multiplying decimals, the decimal point in the product is placed so that the number of decimal places in the product is equal to the sum of the number of decimal places in the factors.

6. The mode of a set of numbers is the number that occurs most often.

7. The distance around a circle is called the circumference.

8. The median of a set of numbers in numerical order is the middle number. If there are an even number of numbers, the mode is the mean of the two middle numbers.

9. The mean of a list of numbers of items is $\dfrac{\text{sum of items}}{\text{number of items}}$.

10. When 2 million is written as 2,000,000, we say it is written in standard form.

Chapter 5 Review

1. In 23.45, the 4 is in the tenths place.

2. In 0.000345, the 4 is in the hundred-thousandths place.

3. −23.45 in words is negative twenty-three and forty-five hundredths.

4. 0.00345 in words is three hundred forty-five hundred-thousandths.

5. 109.23 in words is one hundred nine and twenty-three hundredths.

6. 200.000032 in words is two hundred and thirty-two millionths.

7. Eight and six hundredths is 8.06.

8. Negative five hundred three and one hundred two thousandths is −503.102.

9. Sixteen thousand twenty-five and fourteen ten-thousandths is 16,025.0014.

10. Fourteen and eleven thousandths is 14.011.

11. $0.16 = \dfrac{16}{100} = \dfrac{4 \cdot 4}{25 \cdot 4} = \dfrac{4}{25}$

12. $-12.023 = -12\dfrac{23}{1000}$

13. $\dfrac{231}{100,000} = 0.00231$

14. $25\dfrac{1}{4} = 25\dfrac{25}{100} = 25.25$

15. 0.49   0.43
    ↑   ↑
    9 > 3
so 0.49 > 0.43

16. 0.973 = 0.9730

17. 38.0027   38.00056
    ↑   ↑
    2 > 0
so 38.0027 > 38.00056
Thus, −38.0027 < −38.00056.

18. 0.230505   0.23505
    ↑   ↑
    0 < 5
so 0.230505 < 0.23505
Thus, −0.230505 > −0.23505.

19. To round 0.623 to the nearest tenth, observe that the digit in the hundredths place is 2. Since this digit is less than 5, we do not add 1 to the digit in the tenths place. The number 0.623 rounded to the nearest tenth is 0.6.

20. To round 0.9384 to the nearest hundredth, observe that the digit in the thousandths place is 8. Since this digit is at least 5, we add 1 to the digit in the hundredths place. The number 0.9384 rounded to the nearest hundredth is 0.94.

21. To round −42.895 to the nearest hundredth, observe that the digit in the thousandths place is 5. Since this digit is at least 5, we add 1 to the digit in the hundredths place. The number −42.895 rounded to the nearest hundredth is −42.90.

22. To round 16.34925 to the nearest thousandth, observe that the digit in the ten-thousandths place is 2. Since this digit is less than 5, we do not add 1 to the digit in the thousandths place. The number 16.34925 rounded to the nearest thousandth is 16.349.

23. 887 million = 887 × 1 million
              = 887 × 1,000,000
              = 887,000,000

24. 600 thousand = 600 × 1 thousand
               = 600 × 1000
               = 600,000

25.
$$\begin{array}{r} 8.6 \\ + 9.5 \\ \hline 18.1 \end{array}$$

26.
$$\begin{array}{r} 3.9 \\ + 1.2 \\ \hline 5.1 \end{array}$$

27. Add the absolute values.
$$\begin{array}{r} 6.40 \\ + 0.88 \\ \hline 7.28 \end{array}$$
Attach the common sign.
−6.4 + (−0.88) = −7.28

28. Subtract the absolute values.
$$\begin{array}{r} 19.02 \\ - \ 6.98 \\ \hline 12.04 \end{array}$$
Attach the sign of the larger absolute value.
−19.02 + 6.98 = −12.04

29.
$$\begin{array}{r} 200.490 \\ 16.820 \\ + 103.002 \\ \hline 320.312 \end{array}$$

30.
$$\begin{array}{r} 0.00236 \\ 100.45000 \\ + \ 48.29000 \\ \hline 148.74236 \end{array}$$

31.
$$\begin{array}{r} 4.9 \\ - 3.2 \\ \hline 1.7 \end{array}$$

32.
$$\begin{array}{r} 5.23 \\ - 2.74 \\ \hline 2.49 \end{array}$$

33. −892.1 − 432.4 = −892.1 + (−432.4)
Add the absolute values.
$$\begin{array}{r} 892.1 \\ + \ 432.4 \\ \hline 1324.5 \end{array}$$
Attach the common sign.
−892.1 − 432.4 = −1324.5

34. $0.064 - 10.2 = 0.064 + (-10.2)$
Subtract the absolute values.

$$\begin{array}{r} 10.200 \\ -\ 0.064 \\ \hline 10.136 \end{array}$$

Attach the sign of the larger absolute value.
$0.064 - 10.2 = -10.136$

35.
$$\begin{array}{r} 100.00 \\ -\ 34.98 \\ \hline 65.02 \end{array}$$

36.
$$\begin{array}{r} 200.00000 \\ -\ \ \ 0.00198 \\ \hline 199.99802 \end{array}$$

37.
$$\begin{array}{r} 19.9 \\ 15.1 \\ 10.9 \\ +\ 6.7 \\ \hline 52.6 \end{array}$$

The total distance is 52.6 miles.

38. $x - y = 1.2 - 6.9 = -5.7$

39. Perimeter $= 6.2 + 4.9 + 6.2 + 4.9 = 22.2$
The perimeter is 22.2 inches.

40. Perimeter $= 11.8 + 12.9 + 14.2 = 38.9$
The perimeter is 38.9 feet.

41. $7.2 \times 10 = 72$

42. $9.345 \times 1000 = 9345$

43. A negative number multiplied by a positive number is a negative number.

$$\begin{array}{r} 34.02 \quad \text{2 decimal places} \\ \times\ \ 2.3 \quad \text{1 decimal place} \\ \hline 10\ 206 \\ 68\ 040 \\ \hline 78.246 \quad 2+1 = 3 \text{ decimal places} \end{array}$$

$-34.02 \times 2.3 = -78.246$

44. A negative number multiplied by a negative number is a positive number.

$$\begin{array}{r} 839.02 \quad \text{2 decimal places} \\ \times\ \ \ 87.3 \quad \text{1 decimal place} \\ \hline 251\ 706 \\ 5873\ 140 \\ 67121\ 600 \\ \hline 73246.446 \quad 2+1 = 3 \text{ decimal places} \end{array}$$

$-839.02 \times (-87.3) = 73{,}246.446$

45. $C = 2\pi r = 2\pi \cdot 7 = 14\pi$ meters
$C \approx 14 \cdot 3.14 = 43.96$ meters

46. $C = \pi d = \pi \cdot 20 = 20\pi$ inches
$C \approx 20 \cdot 3.14 = 62.8$ inches

47.
$$\begin{array}{r} 0.0877 \\ 3\overline{)0.2631} \\ \underline{-24} \\ 23 \\ \underline{-21} \\ 21 \\ \underline{-21} \\ 0 \end{array}$$

48.
$$\begin{array}{r} 15.825 \\ 20\overline{)\ 316.500} \\ \underline{-20} \\ 116 \\ \underline{-100} \\ 16\ 5 \\ \underline{-16\ 0} \\ 50 \\ \underline{-40} \\ 100 \\ \underline{-100} \\ 0 \end{array}$$

49. A negative number divided by a negative number is a positive number.

$$0.3\overline{)21} \text{ becomes } 3\overline{)\ 210} \begin{array}{c} 70 \\ \underline{-21} \\ 00 \end{array}$$

$-21 \div (-0.3) = 70$

50. A negative number divided by a positive number is a negative number.

$$0.03\overline{)0.0063} \text{ becomes } 3\overline{)0.63}$$

$$
\begin{array}{r}
0.21 \\
3\overline{)0.63} \\
\underline{-6} \\
03 \\
\underline{-3} \\
0
\end{array}
$$

$$-0.0063 \div 0.03 = -0.21$$

51. $0.34\overline{)2.74}$ becomes $34\overline{)274.0000}$

$$
\begin{array}{r}
8.0588 \approx 8.059 \\
34\overline{)274.0000} \\
\underline{-272} \\
2\ 0 \\
\underline{-0} \\
200 \\
\underline{-1\ 70} \\
300 \\
\underline{-272} \\
280 \\
\underline{-272} \\
8
\end{array}
$$

52. $19.8\overline{)601.92}$ becomes $198\overline{)6019.2}$

$$
\begin{array}{r}
30.4 \\
198\overline{)6019.2} \\
\underline{-594} \\
79 \\
\underline{-0} \\
79\ 2 \\
\underline{-79\ 2} \\
0
\end{array}
$$

53. $\dfrac{23.65}{1000} = 0.02365$

54. $\dfrac{93}{-10} = -9.3$

55. $3.28\overline{)24}$ becomes $328\overline{)2400.00}$

$$
\begin{array}{r}
7.31 \approx 7.3 \\
328\overline{)2400.00} \\
\underline{-2296} \\
104\ 0 \\
\underline{-98\ 4} \\
5\ 60 \\
\underline{-3\ 28} \\
2\ 32
\end{array}
$$

There are approximately 7.3 meters in 24 feet.

56. $69.71\overline{)3136.95}$ becomes $6971\overline{)313695}$

$$
\begin{array}{r}
45 \\
6971\overline{)313695} \\
\underline{-27884} \\
34855 \\
\underline{-34855} \\
0
\end{array}
$$

It will take him 45 months to pay off the loan.

57.
$$
\begin{array}{r}
0.8 \\
5\overline{)4.0} \\
\underline{-4\ 0} \\
0
\end{array}
$$
$\qquad \dfrac{4}{5} = 0.8$

58.
$$
\begin{array}{r}
0.9230 \approx 0.923 \\
13\overline{)12.0000} \\
\underline{-11\ 7} \\
30 \\
\underline{-26} \\
40 \\
\underline{-39} \\
10 \\
\underline{-0} \\
10
\end{array}
$$

$$-\dfrac{12}{13} \approx -0.923$$

59.
$$
\begin{array}{r}
0.3333... \\
3\overline{)1.0000} \\
\underline{-9} \\
10 \\
\underline{-9} \\
10 \\
\underline{-9} \\
10 \\
\underline{-9} \\
1
\end{array}
$$

$$2\dfrac{1}{3} = 2.\overline{3} \text{ or } 2.333$$

60.

$$
\begin{array}{r}
0.2166...\\
60{\overline{\smash{\big)}\,13.0000}}\\
\underline{-12\ 0}\\
1\ 00\\
\underline{-60}\\
400\\
\underline{-360}\\
400\\
\underline{-360}\\
40
\end{array}
$$

$\dfrac{13}{16} = 0.21\overline{6}$ or 0.217

61. $0.392 = 0.39200$

62. $\begin{array}{ccc} 0.0231 & & 0.0221 \\ \uparrow & & \uparrow \\ 3 & > & 2 \end{array}$

so $0.0231 > 0.0221$, thus $-0.0231 < -0.0221$.

63.

$$
\begin{array}{r}
0.571 \approx 0.57\\
7{\overline{\smash{\big)}\,4.000}}\\
\underline{-3\ 5}\\
50\\
\underline{-49}\\
10\\
\underline{-7}\\
3
\end{array}
$$

$\dfrac{4}{7} \approx 0.57$ and $0.57 < 0.625$, so $\dfrac{4}{7} < 0.625$.

64.

$$
\begin{array}{r}
0.2941 \approx 0.294\\
17{\overline{\smash{\big)}\,5.0000}}\\
\underline{-3\ 4}\\
1\ 60\\
\underline{-1\ 53}\\
70\\
\underline{-68}\\
20\\
\underline{-17}\\
3
\end{array}
$$

$\dfrac{5}{17} \approx 0.294$ and $0.293 < 0.294$, so $0.293 < \dfrac{5}{17}$.

65. $0.832, 0.837, 0.839$

66. $\dfrac{5}{8} = 0.625$

$\dfrac{5}{8}, 0.626, 0.685$

67. $\dfrac{3}{7} \approx 0.428$

$0.42, \dfrac{3}{7}, 0.43$

68. $\dfrac{18}{11} = 1.6\overline{36}3$

$1.63 = 1.63$

$\dfrac{19}{12} = 1.58\overline{3}$

$\dfrac{19}{12}, 1.63, \dfrac{18}{11}$

69. $-7.6 \times 1.9 + 2.5 = -14.44 + 2.5 = -11.94$

70. $(-2.3)^2 - 1.4 = 5.29 - 1.4 = 3.89$

71. $0.0726 \div 10 \times 1000 = 0.00726 \times 1000 = 7.26$

72. $0.9(6.5 - 5.6) = 0.9(0.9) = 0.81$

73. $\dfrac{(1.5)^2 + 0.5}{0.05} = \dfrac{2.25 + 0.5}{0.05} = \dfrac{2.75}{0.05} = 55$

74. $\dfrac{7 + 0.74}{-0.06} = \dfrac{7.74}{-0.06} = -129$

75. Area $= \dfrac{1}{2} \cdot b \cdot h$

$= \dfrac{1}{2}(4.6)(3)$

$= 0.5(4.6)(3)$

$= 6.9$ square feet

76. Area $= \dfrac{1}{2} \cdot b \cdot h$

$= \dfrac{1}{2}(5.2)(2.1)$

$= 0.5(5.2)(2.1)$

$= 5.46$ square inches

77. $\begin{aligned} x + 3.9 &= 4.2 \\ x + 3.9 - 3.9 &= 4.2 - 3.9 \\ x &= 0.3 \end{aligned}$

78.
$$70 = y - 22.81$$
$$70 + 22.81 = y - 22.81 + 22.81$$
$$92.81 = y$$

79. $2x = 17.2$
$$\frac{2x}{2} = \frac{17.2}{2}$$
$$x = 8.6$$

80. $-1.1y = 88$
$$\frac{-1.1y}{-1.1} = \frac{88}{-1.1}$$
$$y = -80$$

81.
$$3x - 0.78 = 1.2 + 2x$$
$$3x - 0.78 + 0.78 = 1.2 + 2x + 0.78$$
$$3x = 1.98 + 2x$$
$$3x - 2x = 1.98 + 2x - 2x$$
$$x = 1.98$$

82.
$$-x + 0.6 - 2x = -4x - 0.9$$
$$-3x + 0.6 = -4x - 0.9$$
$$-3x + 0.6 - 0.6 = -4x - 0.9 - 0.6$$
$$-3x = -4x - 1.5$$
$$-3x + 4x = -4x + 4x - 1.5$$
$$x = -1.5$$

83.
$$-1.3x - 9.4 = -0.4x + 8.6$$
$$10(-1.3x - 9.4) = 10(-0.4x + 8.6)$$
$$-13x - 94 = -4x + 86$$
$$-13x - 94 + 94 = -4x + 86 + 94$$
$$-13x = -4x + 180$$
$$-13x + 4x = -4x + 4x + 180$$
$$-9x = 180$$
$$\frac{-9x}{-9} = \frac{180}{-9}$$
$$x = -20$$

84.
$$3(x - 1.1) = 5x - 5.3$$
$$3x - 3.3 = 5x - 5.3$$
$$3x - 3.3 + 3.3 = 5x - 5.3 + 3.3$$
$$3x = 5x - 2$$
$$3x - 5x = 5x - 5x - 2$$
$$-2x = -2$$
$$\frac{-2x}{-2} = \frac{-2}{-2}$$
$$x = 1$$

85. Mean: $\dfrac{13+23+33+14+6}{5} = \dfrac{89}{5} = 17.8$

Median: Write the numbers in order.
6, 13, 14, 23, 33
The middle number is 14.
Mode: There is no mode, since each number occurs once.

86. Mean $= \dfrac{45+86+21+60+86+64+45}{7}$

$\quad = \dfrac{407}{7}$

$\quad \approx 58.1$

Median: Write the numbers in order.
21, 45, 45, 60, 64, 86, 86
The middle number is 60.
Mode: There are 2 numbers that occur twice, so there are two modes, 45 and 86.

87. Mean $= \dfrac{14,000+20,000+12,000+20,000+36,000+45,000}{6} = \dfrac{147,000}{6} = 24,500$

Median: Write the numbers in order.
12,000, 14,000, 20,000, 20,000, 36,000, 45,000

The mean of the middle two: $\dfrac{20,000+20,000}{2} = 20,000$

Mode: 20,000 is the mode because it occurs twice.

88. Mean $= \dfrac{560+620+123+400+410+300+400+780+430+450}{10} = \dfrac{4473}{10} = 447.3$

Median: Write the numbers in order.
123, 300, 400, 400, 410, 430, 450, 560, 620, 780

The mean of the two middle numbers: $\dfrac{410+430}{2} = 420$

Mode: 400 is the mode because it occurs twice.

89. gpa $= \dfrac{4\cdot3+4\cdot3+2\cdot2+3\cdot3+2\cdot1}{3+3+2+3+1} = \dfrac{39}{12} = 3.25$

90. gpa $= \dfrac{3\cdot3+3\cdot4+2\cdot2+1\cdot2+3\cdot3}{3+4+2+2+3} = \dfrac{36}{14} \approx 2.57$

91. 200.0032 in words is two hundred and thirty-two ten-thousandths.

92. Negative sixteen and nine hundredths is -16.09 in standard form.

93. $0.0847 = \dfrac{847}{10,000}$

94. $\dfrac{6}{7} \approx 0.857$

$\dfrac{8}{9} \approx 0.889$

$0.75 = 0.750$

$0.75, \dfrac{6}{7}, \dfrac{8}{9}$

95. $-\dfrac{7}{100} = -0.07$

96.

$$\begin{array}{r} 0.1125 \\ 80\overline{)9.0000} \\ \underline{-8\ 0} \\ 1\ 00 \\ \underline{-80} \\ 200 \\ \underline{-160} \\ 400 \\ \underline{-400} \\ 0 \end{array}$$

$\dfrac{9}{80} = 0.1125$

97.

$$\begin{array}{r} 51.0571 \approx 51.057 \\ 175\overline{)8935.0000} \\ \underline{-875} \\ 185 \\ \underline{-175} \\ 100 \\ \underline{-0} \\ 1000 \\ \underline{-875} \\ 1\ 250 \\ \underline{-1\ 225} \\ 250 \\ \underline{-175} \\ 75 \end{array}$$

$\dfrac{8935}{175} \approx 51.057$

98. $402.000032 \quad 402.00032$

$\uparrow \ \ \uparrow$

$0 < 3$

so $402.000032 < 402.00032$

Thus, $-402.000032 > -402.00032$.

99. $\dfrac{6}{11} = 0.\overline{54}$

$0.\overline{54} < 0.55$, so $\dfrac{6}{11} < 0.55$

100. To round 86.905 to the nearest hundredth, observe that the digit in the thousandths place is 5. Since this digit is at least 5, we add 1 to the digit in the hundredths place. The number 86.905 rounded to the nearest hundredth is 86.91.

101. To round 3.11526 to the nearest thousandth, observe that the digit in the ten-thousandths place is 2. Since this digit is less than 5, we do not add 1 to the digit in the thousandths place. The number 3.11526 rounded to the nearest thousandth is 3.115.

102. To round 123.46 to the nearest one, observe that the digit in the tenths place is 4. Since this digit is less than 5, we do not add 1 to the digit in the ones place. The number $123.46 rounded to the nearest dollar (or one) is $123.00.

103. To round 3645.52 to the nearest one, observe that the digit in the tenths place is 5. Since this digit is at least 5, we add 1 to the digit in the ones place. The number $3645.52 rounded to the nearest dollar (or one) is $3646.00.

104. Subtract absolute values.

$$\begin{array}{r} 4.9 \\ \underline{-\ 3.2} \\ 1.7 \end{array}$$

Attach the sign of the larger absolute value.

$3.2 - 4.9 = -1.7$

105.

$$\begin{array}{r} 9.12 \\ \underline{-\ 3.86} \\ 5.26 \end{array}$$

106. Subtract absolute values.

$$\begin{array}{r} 102.06 \\ \underline{-\ 89.30} \\ 12.76 \end{array}$$

Attach the sign of the larger absolute value.

$-102.06 + 89.3 = -12.76$

107.

$$\begin{array}{r} -4.021 \\ -10.830 \\ \underline{(+)\ -0.056} \\ -14.907 \end{array}$$

108.

$$
\begin{array}{r}
2.54 \\
\times\ 3.2 \\
\hline
508 \\
7\ 620 \\
\hline
8.128
\end{array}
$$

2 decimal places
1 decimal place

$2 + 1 = 3$ decimal places

109. The product of a negative number and a positive number is a negative number.

$$
\begin{array}{r}
3.45 \\
\times\ 2.1 \\
\hline
345 \\
6\ 900 \\
\hline
7.245
\end{array}
$$

2 decimal places
1 decimal place

$2 + 1 = 3$ decimal places

The product is -7.245.

110. $0.005\overline{)24.5}$ becomes

$$
\begin{array}{r}
4900 \\
5\overline{)24500} \\
-20 \\
\hline
45 \\
-45 \\
\hline
000
\end{array}
$$

111. $2.3\overline{)54.98}$ becomes $23.9043 \approx 23.904$

$$
\begin{array}{r}
23.9043 \\
23\overline{)549.8000} \\
-46 \\
\hline
89 \\
-69 \\
\hline
20\ 8 \\
-20\ 7 \\
\hline
10 \\
-0 \\
\hline
100 \\
-92 \\
\hline
80 \\
-69 \\
\hline
11
\end{array}
$$

112. length $= 115.9 \approx 120$
width $= 77.3 \approx 80$
Area $=$ length $\cdot$ width
     $= 120 \cdot 80$
     $= 9600$ square feet

113.

$1.89	rounds to	$2
$1.07	rounds to	$1
$0.99	rounds to	$1
		$4

Yes, the items can be purchased with a $5 bill.

114. $\dfrac{(3.2)^2}{100} = \dfrac{10.24}{100} = 0.1024$

115. $(2.6 + 1.4)(4.5 - 3.6) = (4)(0.9) = 3.6$

116. Mean: $\dfrac{73 + 82 + 95 + 68 + 54}{5} = \dfrac{372}{5} = 74.4$
Median: Write the numbers in order.
54, 68, 73, 82, 95
The median is the middle value: 73.
Mode: There is no mode, since each number occurs once.

117. Mean:
$$
\dfrac{952 + 327 + 566 + 814 + 327 + 729}{6} = \dfrac{3715}{6} \approx 619.17
$$
Median: Write the numbers in order.
327, 327, 566, 729, 814, 952
The mean of the two middle values:
$$
\dfrac{566 + 729}{2} = 647.5
$$
Mode: 327, since this number appears twice.

Chapter 5 Test

1. 45.092 in words is forty-five and ninety-two thousandths.

2. Three thousand and fifty-nine thousandths in standard form is 3000.059.

3.

$$
\begin{array}{r}
2.893 \\
4.210 \\
+\ 10.492 \\
\hline
17.595
\end{array}
$$

4. Add the absolute values.

$$
\begin{array}{r}
47.92 \\
+\ 3.28 \\
\hline
51.20
\end{array}
$$

Attach the common sign.
$-47.92 - 3.28 = -51.20$

5. Subtract the absolute values.

$$
\begin{array}{r}
30.25 \\
-\ 9.83 \\
\hline
20.42
\end{array}
$$

Attach the sign of the larger absolute value.
$9.83 - 30.25 = -20.42$

6.
$$\begin{array}{r} 10.2 \\ \times\ 4.01 \\ \hline 102 \\ 40\ 800 \\ \hline 40.902 \end{array}$$

1 decimal place
2 decimal places

$1+2=3$ decimal places

7. $0.23\overline{)0.00843}$ becomes $23\overline{)0.8430}$

$$\begin{array}{r} 0.0366 \approx 0.037 \\ 23\overline{)0.8430} \\ \underline{-69} \\ 153 \\ \underline{-138} \\ 150 \\ \underline{-138} \\ 12 \end{array}$$

$-0.00843 \div (-0.23) \approx 0.037$

8. To round 34.8923 to the nearest tenth, observe that the digit in the hundredths place is 9. Since this digit is at least 5, we add 1 to the digit in the tenths place. 34.8923 rounded to the nearest tenth is 34.9.

9. To round 0.8623 to the nearest thousandth, observe that the digit in the ten-thousandths place is 3. Since this digit is less than 5, we do not add 1 to the digit in the thousandths place. 0.8623 rounded to the nearest thousandth is 0.862.

10. 25.0909   25.9090
       ↑   ↑
       0   <   9
    so 25.0909 < 25.9090

11.
$$\begin{array}{r} 0.444... \\ 9\overline{)4.000} \\ \underline{-3\ 6} \\ 40 \\ \underline{-36} \\ 40 \\ \underline{-36} \\ 4 \end{array}$$

$0.44\overline{4} < 0.445$, so $\dfrac{4}{9} < 0.445$.

12. $0.345 = \dfrac{345}{1000} = \dfrac{5 \cdot 69}{5 \cdot 200} = \dfrac{69}{200}$

13. $-24.73 = -24\dfrac{73}{100}$

14. $-\dfrac{13}{26} = -\dfrac{1 \cdot 13}{2 \cdot 13} = -\dfrac{1}{2} = -\dfrac{1 \cdot 5}{2 \cdot 5} = -\dfrac{5}{10} = -0.5$

15.
$$\begin{array}{r} 0.9411 \approx 0.941 \\ 17\overline{)16.0000} \\ \underline{-15\ 3} \\ 70 \\ \underline{-68} \\ 20 \\ \underline{-17} \\ 30 \\ \underline{-17} \\ 13 \end{array}$$

$\dfrac{16}{17} \approx 0.941$

16. $(-0.6)^2 + 1.57 = 0.36 + 1.57 = 1.93$

17. $\dfrac{0.23+1.63}{-0.3} = \dfrac{1.86}{-0.3} = -6.2$

18. $2.4x - 3.6 - 1.9x - 9.8$
$= (2.4x - 1.9x) + (-3.6 - 9.8)$
$= 0.5x - 13.4$

19.
$$\begin{aligned} 0.2x + 1.3 &= 0.7 \\ 0.2x + 1.3 - 1.3 &= 0.7 - 1.3 \\ 0.2x &= -0.6 \\ \dfrac{0.2x}{0.2} &= \dfrac{-0.6}{0.2} \\ x &= -3 \end{aligned}$$

20.
$$\begin{aligned} 2(x+5.7) &= 6x - 3.4 \\ 2x + 11.4 &= 6x - 3.4 \\ 2x + 11.4 - 11.4 &= 6x - 3.4 - 11.4 \\ 2x &= 6x - 14.8 \\ 2x - 6x &= 6x - 6x - 14.8 \\ -4x &= -14.8 \\ \dfrac{-4x}{-4} &= \dfrac{-14.8}{-4} \\ x &= 3.7 \end{aligned}$$

21. Mean: $\dfrac{26+32+42+43+49}{5} = \dfrac{192}{5} = 38.4$

Median: The numbers are listed in order. The middle number is 42.
Mode: There is no mode since each number occurs once.

22. Mean:

$$\frac{8+10+16+16+14+12+12+13}{8} = \frac{101}{8} = 12.625$$

Median: List the numbers in order.

8, 10, 12, 12, 13, 14, 16, 16

The mean of the middle two: $\frac{12+13}{2} = 12.5$

Mode: 12 and 16 each occur twice, so the modes are 12 and 16.

23. $\text{gpa} = \dfrac{4 \cdot 3 + 3 \cdot 3 + 2 \cdot 3 + 3 \cdot 4 + 4 \cdot 1}{3 + 3 + 3 + 4 + 1} = \dfrac{43}{14} \approx 3.07$

24. 4,583 million = 4583×1 million

$= 4583 \times 1{,}000{,}000$

$= 4{,}583{,}000{,}000$

25. Area $= \dfrac{1}{2}(4.2 \text{ miles})(1.1 \text{ miles})$

$= 0.5(4.2)(1.1)$ square miles

$= 2.31$ square miles

26. $C = 2\pi r = 2\pi \cdot 9 = 18\pi$ miles

$C \approx 18 \cdot 3.14 = 56.52$ miles

27. a. Area = length · width

$= (123.8) \times (80)$

$= 9904$

The area is 9904 square feet.

b. $9904 \times 0.02 = 198.08$

Vivian needs to purchase 198.08 ounces.

28.
```
   14.2
   16.1
 + 23.7
 ──────
   54.0
```
The total distance is 54 miles.

Cumulative Review Chapters 1–5

1. 72 in words is seventy-two.

2. 107 in words is one hundred seven.

3. 546 in words is five hundred forty-six.

4. 5026 in words is five thousand twenty-six.

5.
```
    46
 + 713
 ─────
   759
```

6. $3 + 7 + 9 = 19$

The perimeter is 19 inches.

7.
```
   543            Check:   514
 −  29                   +  29
 ─────                   ─────
   514                     543
```

8.
```
        121 R 1
  27) 3268
     −27
     ───
      56
     −54
     ───
       28
      −27
      ───
        1
```

9. To round 278,362 to the nearest thousand, observe that the digit in the hundreds place is 3. Since this digit is less than 5, we do not add 1 to the digit in the thousands place. The number 278,362 rounded to the nearest thousand is 278,000.

10. $30 = 2 \cdot 15 = 2 \cdot 3 \cdot 5$

11.
```
     236
  ×   86
  ──────
   1 416
  18 880
  ──────
  20,296
```

12. $236 \times 86 \times 0 = 0$

13. a. $1\overline{)7}$ with quotient 7 *Check:* $7 \times 1 = 7$

b. $12 \div 1 = 12$ *Check:* $12 \times 1 = 12$

c. $\dfrac{6}{6} = 1$ *Check:* $1 \times 6 = 6$

d. $9 \div 9 = 1$ *Check:* $1 \times 9 = 9$

e. $\dfrac{20}{1} = 20$ *Check:* $20 \times 1 = 20$

f. $18\overline{)18}$ with quotient 1 *Check:* $1 \times 18 = 18$

14. $\dfrac{25+17+19+39}{4} = \dfrac{100}{4} = 5$

The average is 25.

15. $2 \cdot 4 - 3 \div 3 = 8 - 3 \div 3 = 8 - 1 = 7$

16. $77 \div 11 \cdot 7 = 7 \cdot 7 = 49$

17. $9^2 = 9 \cdot 9 = 81$

18. $5^3 = 5 \cdot 5 \cdot 5 = 125$

19. $3^4 = 3 \cdot 3 \cdot 3 \cdot 3 = 81$

20. $10^3 = 10 \cdot 10 \cdot 10 = 1000$

21. $\dfrac{x-5y}{y} = \dfrac{35-5 \cdot 5}{5} = \dfrac{35-25}{5} = \dfrac{10}{5} = 2$

22. $\dfrac{2a+4}{c} = \dfrac{2 \cdot 7 + 4}{3} = \dfrac{14+4}{3} = \dfrac{18}{3} = 6$

23. **a.** The opposite of 13 is -13.

    b. The opposite of -2 is $-(-2) = 2$.

    c. The opposite of 0 is 0.

24. **a.** The opposite of -7 is $-(-7) = 7$.

    b. The opposite of 4 is -4.

    c. The opposite of -1 is $-(-1) = 1$.

25. $-2 + (-21) = -23$

26. $-7 + (-15) = -22$

27. $5 \cdot 6^2 = 5 \cdot 36 = 180$

28. $4 \cdot 2^3 = 4 \cdot 8 = 32$

29. $-7^2 = -(7 \cdot 7) = -49$

30. $(-2)^5 = (-2)(-2)(-2)(-2)(-2) = -32$

31. $(-5)^2 = (-5)(-5) = 25$

32. $-3^2 = -(3 \cdot 3) = -9$

33. Each part represents $\dfrac{1}{3}$ of a whole. Four parts are shaded, or 1 whole and 1 part.

$\dfrac{4}{3}$ or $1\dfrac{1}{3}$

34. Each part represents $\dfrac{1}{4}$ of a whole. Seven parts are shaded or 1 whole and 3 parts.

$\dfrac{7}{4}$ or $1\dfrac{3}{4}$

35. Each part represents $\dfrac{1}{4}$ of a whole. Eleven parts are shaded or 2 wholes and 3 parts.

$\dfrac{11}{4}$ or $2\dfrac{3}{4}$

36. Each part represents $\dfrac{1}{3}$ of a whole. Fourteen parts are shaded, or 4 wholes and 2 parts.

$\dfrac{14}{3}$ or $4\dfrac{2}{3}$

37. $252 = 2 \cdot 126$

$\qquad\quad \downarrow\ \downarrow\searrow$

$\qquad\quad 2 \cdot 2 \cdot 63$

$\qquad\quad \downarrow\ \ \downarrow\downarrow\searrow$

$\qquad\quad 2 \cdot 2 \cdot 3 \cdot 21$

$\qquad\quad \downarrow\ \downarrow\ \downarrow\ \downarrow\searrow$

$\qquad\quad 2 \cdot 2 \cdot 3 \cdot 3 \cdot 7$

$252 = 2^2 \cdot 3^2 \cdot 7$

38. $\begin{array}{r} 87 \\ -\ 25 \\ \hline 62 \end{array}$

39. $-\dfrac{72}{26} = -\dfrac{36 \cdot 2}{13 \cdot 2} = -\dfrac{36}{13}$

40. $9\dfrac{7}{8} = \dfrac{8 \cdot 9 + 7}{8} = \dfrac{72+7}{8} = \dfrac{79}{8}$

41. $\dfrac{16}{40} = \dfrac{2 \cdot 8}{5 \cdot 8} = \dfrac{2}{5}$

$\dfrac{10}{25} = \dfrac{2 \cdot 5}{5 \cdot 5} = \dfrac{2}{5}$

The fractions are equivalent.

42. $\dfrac{4}{7} \approx 0.571$

$\dfrac{5}{9} \approx 0.556$

Since $0.571 > 0.556$, then $\dfrac{4}{7} > \dfrac{5}{9}$.

or

$\dfrac{4}{7} \cdot \dfrac{9}{9} = \dfrac{36}{63}$ and $\dfrac{5}{9} \cdot \dfrac{7}{7} = \dfrac{35}{63}$

Since $36 > 35$, then $\dfrac{36}{63} > \dfrac{35}{63}$ and $\dfrac{4}{7} > \dfrac{5}{9}$.

43. $\dfrac{2}{3} \cdot \dfrac{5}{11} = \dfrac{2 \cdot 5}{3 \cdot 11} = \dfrac{10}{33}$

44. $2\dfrac{5}{8} \cdot \dfrac{4}{7} = \dfrac{21}{8} \cdot \dfrac{4}{7} = \dfrac{21 \cdot 4}{8 \cdot 7} = \dfrac{7 \cdot 3 \cdot 4}{4 \cdot 2 \cdot 7} = \dfrac{3}{2}$ or $1\dfrac{1}{2}$

45. $\dfrac{1}{4} \cdot \dfrac{1}{2} = \dfrac{1 \cdot 1}{4 \cdot 2} = \dfrac{1}{8}$

46. $7 \cdot 5\dfrac{2}{7} = \dfrac{7}{1} \cdot \dfrac{37}{7} = \dfrac{7 \cdot 37}{1 \cdot 7} = \dfrac{37}{1} = 37$

47. $\dfrac{z}{-4} = 11 - 5$

$\dfrac{z}{-4} = 6$

$-4 \cdot \dfrac{z}{-4} = -4 \cdot 6$

$z = -24$

48. $6x - 12 - 5x = -20$

$x - 12 = -20$

$x - 12 + 12 = -20 + 12$

$x = -8$

49.
$$
\begin{array}{r}
763.7651 \\
22.0010 \\
+\ 43.8900 \\
\hline
829.6561
\end{array}
$$

50.
$$
\begin{array}{r}
89.2700 \\
14.3610 \\
+\ 127.2318 \\
\hline
230.8628
\end{array}
$$

51.
$$
\begin{array}{r}
23.6 \\
\times\quad 0.78 \\
\hline
1\,888 \\
16\,520 \\
\hline
18.408
\end{array}
$$
  1 decimal place
  2 decimal places

  $1 + 2 = 3$ decimal places

52.
$$
\begin{array}{r}
43.8 \\
\times\quad 0.645 \\
\hline
2190 \\
1\,7520 \\
26\,2800 \\
\hline
28.2510
\end{array}
$$
  1 decimal place
  3 decimal places

  $1 + 3 = 4$ decimal places

Chapter 6

Section 6.1

Practice Problems

1. **a.** The ratio of 3 parts oil to 7 parts gasoline is
$\dfrac{3}{7}$.

   b. Convert 3 hours to minutes.
3 hours = 3 · 60 minutes = 180 minutes
The ratio of 40 minutes to 3 hours is
$\dfrac{40}{180} = \dfrac{2}{9}$.

2. $\dfrac{1.68}{4.8} = \dfrac{1.68 \cdot 100}{4.8 \cdot 100} = \dfrac{168}{480} = \dfrac{7}{20}$

3. **a.** The ratio of the length of the shortest side to the length of the longest side is
$\dfrac{6 \text{ meters}}{10 \text{ meters}} = \dfrac{6}{10} = \dfrac{3}{5}$.

   b. Perimeter = 6 + 8 + 10 = 24 meters
The ratio of the length of the longest side to the perimeter is $\dfrac{10 \text{ meters}}{24 \text{ meters}} = \dfrac{10}{24} = \dfrac{5}{12}$.

4. $\dfrac{3}{8} = \dfrac{63}{x}$
$3 \cdot x = 8 \cdot 63$
$3x = 504$
$\dfrac{3x}{3} = \dfrac{504}{3}$
$x = 168$

5. $\dfrac{2x+1}{7} = \dfrac{x-3}{5}$
$5(2x+1) = 7(x-3)$
$10x + 5 = 7x - 21$
$10x = 7x - 26$
$3x = -26$
$\dfrac{3x}{3} = \dfrac{-26}{3}$
$x = -\dfrac{26}{3}$

6. Let x be the length of the wall.
$\begin{array}{l}\text{feet} \rightarrow \\ \text{inches} \rightarrow\end{array} \dfrac{4}{1} = \dfrac{x}{4\frac{1}{4}} \begin{array}{l}\leftarrow \text{feet} \\ \leftarrow \text{inches}\end{array}$
$4 \cdot 4\dfrac{1}{4} = 1 \cdot x$
$\dfrac{4}{1} \cdot \dfrac{17}{4} = x$
$17 = x$
The wall is 17 feet long.

7. $\begin{array}{l}\text{ounces} \rightarrow \\ \text{gallons} \rightarrow\end{array} \dfrac{5}{16} = \dfrac{8}{x} \begin{array}{l}\leftarrow \text{ounces} \\ \leftarrow \text{gallons}\end{array}$
$5 \cdot x = 16 \cdot 8$
$5x = 128$
$\dfrac{5x}{5} = \dfrac{128}{5}$
$x = 25.6 \text{ or } 25\dfrac{3}{5}$

Therefore, 25.6 or $25\dfrac{3}{5}$ gallons of gas can be treated with 8 ounces of alcohol.

Vocabulary and Readiness Check

1. $\dfrac{4.2}{8.4} = \dfrac{1}{2}$ is called a <u>proportion</u>, while $\dfrac{7}{8}$ is called a <u>ratio</u>.

2. In $\dfrac{a}{b} = \dfrac{c}{d}$, $a \cdot d$ and $b \cdot c$ are called <u>cross products</u>.

Exercise Set 6.1

1. The ratio of 2 megabytes to 15 megabytes is $\dfrac{2}{15}$.

3. The ratio of 10 inches to 12 inches is $\dfrac{10}{12} = \dfrac{5}{6}$.

5. 3 gallons = 3 · 4 quarts = 12 quarts
The ratio of 5 quarts to 3 gallons is $\dfrac{5}{12}$.

7. 2 dollars = 2 · 20 nickels = 40 nickels
The ratio of 4 nickels to 2 dollars is $\dfrac{4}{40} = \dfrac{1}{10}$.

9. 5 meters = 5 · 100 centimeters = 500 centimeters
The ratio of 175 centimeters to 5 meters is
$$\frac{175}{500} = \frac{7}{20}.$$

11. 3 hours = 3 · 60 minutes = 180 minutes
The ratio of 190 minutes to hours is $\frac{190}{180} = \frac{19}{18}.$

13. The ratio of the length to the width is
$$\frac{94 \text{ feet}}{50 \text{ feet}} = \frac{94}{50} = \frac{47}{25}.$$

15. Perimeter = 8 + 15 + 17 = 40 feet
The ratio of the longest side to the perimeter is
$$\frac{17 \text{ feet}}{40 \text{ feet}} = \frac{17}{40}.$$

17. The ratio of calories from fat to total calories in a large order of McDonald's french fries is
$$\frac{220}{500} = \frac{11}{25}.$$

19. The ratio of red blood cells to platelet cells is
$$\frac{600}{40} = \frac{15}{1}.$$

21. answers may vary

23.
$$\frac{2}{3} = \frac{x}{6}$$
$$2 \cdot 6 = 3 \cdot x$$
$$12 = 3x$$
$$\frac{12}{3} = \frac{3x}{3}$$
$$4 = x$$

25.
$$\frac{x}{10} = \frac{5}{9}$$
$$x \cdot 9 = 10 \cdot 5$$
$$9x = 50$$
$$\frac{9x}{9} = \frac{50}{9}$$
$$x = \frac{50}{9}$$

27.
$$\frac{4x}{6} = \frac{7}{2}$$
$$4x \cdot 2 = 6 \cdot 7$$
$$8x = 42$$
$$\frac{8x}{8} = \frac{42}{8}$$
$$x = \frac{21}{4}$$

29.
$$\frac{x-3}{x} = \frac{4}{7}$$
$$7(x-3) = 4x$$
$$7x - 21 = 4x$$
$$-21 = -3x$$
$$\frac{-21}{-3} = \frac{-3x}{-3}$$
$$7 = x$$

31.
$$\frac{x+1}{2x+3} = \frac{2}{3}$$
$$3(x+1) = 2(2x+3)$$
$$3x + 3 = 4x + 6$$
$$3 = x + 6$$
$$-3 = x$$

33.
$$\frac{9}{5} = \frac{12}{3x+2}$$
$$9(3x+2) = 5 \cdot 12$$
$$27x + 18 = 60$$
$$27x = 42$$
$$\frac{27x}{27} = \frac{42}{27}$$
$$x = \frac{14}{9}$$

35.
$$\frac{3}{x+1} = \frac{5}{2x}$$
$$3 \cdot 2x = 5(x+1)$$
$$6x = 5x + 5$$
$$x = 5$$

37.
$$\frac{15}{3x-4} = \frac{5}{x}$$
$$15 \cdot x = 5(3x-4)$$
$$15x = 15x - 20$$
$$0 = -20$$
Since 0 = −20 is a false statement, the proportion has no solution.

39. Let x be the elephant's weight on Pluto.

weight on Earth $\rightarrow \dfrac{100}{3} = \dfrac{4100}{x} \leftarrow$ weight on Earth
weight on Pluto $\rightarrow$ ... $\leftarrow$ weight on Pluto

$$100 \cdot x = 3 \cdot 4100$$
$$100x = 12,300$$
$$\frac{100x}{100} = \frac{12,300}{100}$$
$$x = 123$$

The elephant weight 123 pounds on Pluto.

41. Let x be the number of calories in 42.6 grams of the cereal.

calories $\rightarrow \dfrac{110}{28.4} = \dfrac{x}{42.6} \leftarrow$ calories
grams $\rightarrow$ ... $\leftarrow$ grams

$$110 \cdot 42.6 = 28.4 \cdot x$$
$$4686 = 28.4x$$
$$\frac{4686}{28.4} = \frac{28.4x}{28.4}$$
$$165 = x$$

There are 165 calories in 42.6 grams of the cereal.

43. Let x be the number of calories.

ounces $\rightarrow \dfrac{16}{80} = \dfrac{24}{x} \leftarrow$ ounces
calories $\rightarrow$ ... $\leftarrow$ calories

$$16 \cdot x = 80 \cdot 24$$
$$16x = 1920$$
$$\frac{16x}{16} = \frac{1920}{16}$$
$$x = 120$$

There are 120 calories in 24 ounces.

45. a. Let x be the number of teaspoons of granules needed.

water $\rightarrow \dfrac{25}{1} = \dfrac{450}{x} \leftarrow$ water
granules $\rightarrow$ ... $\leftarrow$ granules

$$25 \cdot x = 1 \cdot 450$$
$$25x = 450$$
$$\frac{25x}{25} = \frac{450}{25}$$
$$x = 18$$

18 teaspoons of granules are needed.

b. Let x be the number of tablespoons of granules needed.

tsp $\rightarrow \dfrac{3}{1} = \dfrac{18}{x} \leftarrow$ tsp
tbsp $\rightarrow$ ... $\leftarrow$ tbsp

$$3 \cdot x = 1 \cdot 18$$
$$3x = 18$$
$$\frac{3x}{3} = \frac{18}{3}$$
$$x = 6$$

6 tablespoons of granules are needed.

47. Let x be the number of people.

$$\text{square feet} \rightarrow \frac{625}{1} = \frac{3750}{x} \leftarrow \text{square feet}$$
$$\text{people} \quad \rightarrow \quad \leftarrow \quad \text{people}$$

$$625 \cdot x = 1 \cdot 3750$$
$$\frac{625x}{625} = \frac{3750}{625}$$
$$x = 6$$

It will provide enough oxygen for 6 people.

49. Let x be the estimated head-to-toe height of the Statue of Liberty.

$$\text{height} \quad \rightarrow \frac{x}{42} = \frac{5\frac{1}{3}}{2} \leftarrow \text{height}$$
$$\text{arm length} \rightarrow \quad\quad \leftarrow \text{arm length}$$

$$x \cdot 2 = 42 \cdot 5\frac{1}{3}$$
$$2x = 42 \cdot \frac{16}{3}$$
$$2x = 224$$
$$\frac{2x}{2} = \frac{224}{2}$$
$$x = 112$$

The estimated height is 112 feet.

$$112 - 111\frac{1}{12} = \frac{11}{12}$$

The difference is $\dfrac{11}{12}$ foot or 11 inches.

51. Let x be the number of milligrams.

$$\text{milligrams} \rightarrow \frac{72}{3.5} = \frac{x}{5} \leftarrow \text{milligrams}$$
$$\text{ounces} \quad \rightarrow \quad\quad \leftarrow \quad \text{ounces}$$

$$72 \cdot 5 = 3.5 \cdot x$$
$$360 = 3.5x$$
$$\frac{360}{3.5} = \frac{3.5x}{3.5}$$
$$102.9 \approx x$$

There are about 102.9 milligrams of cholesterol in 5 ounces of lobster.

53. Let x be the estimated height of the Empire State Building.

$$\text{height} \rightarrow \frac{x}{102} = \frac{881}{72} \leftarrow \text{height}$$
$$\text{stories} \rightarrow \quad\quad \leftarrow \text{stories}$$

$$x \cdot 72 = 102 \cdot 881$$
$$72x = 89,862$$
$$\frac{72x}{72} = \frac{89,862}{72}$$
$$x \approx 1248$$

The height of the Empire State Building is approximately 1248 feet.

55. Let x be the number of visits needing a prescription for medication.

$$\text{medication} \rightarrow \frac{7}{10} = \frac{x}{620} \leftarrow \text{medication}$$
$$\text{total} \quad\quad \rightarrow \quad\quad \leftarrow \quad \text{total}$$

$$7 \cdot 620 = 10 \cdot x$$
$$4340 = 10x$$
$$\frac{4340}{10} = \frac{10x}{10}$$
$$434 = x$$

Expect 434 emergency room visits to need a prescription for medication.

57. Let x be the number expected to have worked in the restaurant industry.

$$\text{restaurant} \rightarrow \frac{x}{84} = \frac{1}{3} \leftarrow \text{restaurant}$$
$$\text{workers} \quad \rightarrow \quad\quad \leftarrow \quad \text{workers}$$

$$x \cdot 3 = 84 \cdot 1$$
$$3x = 84$$
$$\frac{3x}{3} = \frac{84}{3}$$
$$x = 28$$

You would expect 28 of the workers to have worked in the restaurant industry.

59. Let x be the cups of salt.

$$\text{ice} \rightarrow \frac{5}{1} = \frac{12}{x} \leftarrow \text{ice}$$
$$\text{salt} \rightarrow \quad\quad \leftarrow \text{salt}$$

$$5 \cdot x = 1 \cdot 12$$
$$\frac{5x}{5} = \frac{12}{5}$$
$$x = 2.4$$

Mix 2.4 cups of salt with the ice.

61. a. Let x be the number of gallons of oil needed.

$$\text{oil} \rightarrow \frac{x}{5} = \frac{1}{50} \leftarrow \text{oil}$$
$$\text{gas} \rightarrow \quad\quad \leftarrow \text{gas}$$

$$x \cdot 50 = 5 \cdot 1$$
$$50x = 5$$
$$\frac{50x}{50} = \frac{5}{50}$$
$$x = \frac{1}{10} = 0.1$$

0.1 gallon of oil is needed.

b. Let x be the number of fluid ounces.

$$\text{gallons} \quad \rightarrow \frac{1}{128} = \frac{0.1}{x} \leftarrow \quad \text{gallons}$$
$$\text{fluid ounces} \rightarrow \quad\quad \leftarrow \text{fluid ounces}$$

$$1 \cdot x = 128 \cdot 0.1$$
$$x = 12.8$$

0.1 gallon is approximately 13 fluid ounces

63. a. Let x be the milligrams of medicine.

milligrams $\rightarrow$ $\dfrac{x}{275} = \dfrac{150}{20}$ $\leftarrow$ milligrams
pounds $\rightarrow$ $\leftarrow$ pounds

$$x \cdot 20 = 275 \cdot 150$$
$$20x = 41,250$$
$$\frac{20x}{20} = \frac{41,250}{20}$$
$$x = 2062.5$$

The daily dose is 2062.5 milligrams.

b. $500 \times \dfrac{24}{8} = 500 \times 3 = 1500$

No, he is not receiving the proper dosage.

65. $200 = 2 \;\cdot\; 100$
$$\downarrow \quad \downarrow \quad \searrow$$
$$= 2 \;\cdot\; 4 \;\cdot\; 25$$
$$\downarrow \quad \swarrow\searrow \quad \swarrow\searrow$$
$$= 2 \cdot 2 \;\cdot\; 2 \cdot 5 \;\cdot\; 5$$
$$= 2^3 \cdot 5^2$$

67. $32 = 2 \cdot 16$
$$\downarrow \downarrow \searrow$$
$$= 2 \cdot 2 \;\cdot\; 8$$
$$\downarrow \downarrow \quad \downarrow \searrow$$
$$= 2 \cdot 2 \;\cdot\; 2 \;\cdot\; 4$$
$$\downarrow \downarrow \quad \downarrow \quad \downarrow \searrow$$
$$= 2 \cdot 2 \;\cdot\; 2 \;\cdot\; 2 \;\cdot\; 2$$
$$= 2^5$$

69. Let x be the number of ml.

mg $\rightarrow$ $\dfrac{15}{1} = \dfrac{12}{x}$ $\leftarrow$ mg
ml $\rightarrow$ $\leftarrow$ ml

$$15 \cdot x = 1 \cdot 12$$
$$15x = 12$$
$$\frac{15x}{15} = \frac{12}{15}$$
$$x = \frac{4}{5} = 0.8$$

0.8 ml of the medicine should be administered.

71. Let x be the number of ml.

mg $\rightarrow$ $\dfrac{8}{1} = \dfrac{10}{x}$ $\leftarrow$ mg
ml $\rightarrow$ $\leftarrow$ ml

$$8 \cdot x = 1 \cdot 10$$
$$8x = 10$$
$$\frac{8x}{8} = \frac{10}{8}$$
$$x = 1.25$$

1.25 ml of the medicine should be administered.

Section 6.2

Practice Problems

1. Since 27 students out of 100 students in a club are freshman, the fraction is $\dfrac{27}{100}$. Then $\dfrac{27}{100} = 27\%$.

2. $\dfrac{31}{100} = 31\%$

3. $49\% = 49(0.01) = 0.49$

4. $3.1\% = 3.1(0.01) = 0.031$

5. $175\% \; 175(0.01) = 1.75$

6. $0.46\% = 0.46(0.01) = 0.0046$

7. $600\% = 600(0.01) = 6.00$ or 6

8. $50\% = 50 \cdot \dfrac{1}{100} = \dfrac{50}{100} = \dfrac{1 \cdot 50}{2 \cdot 50} = \dfrac{1}{2}$

9. $2.3\% = 2.3 \cdot \dfrac{1}{100} = \dfrac{2.3}{100} = \dfrac{2.3 \cdot 10}{100 \cdot 10} = \dfrac{23}{1000}$

10. $150\% = 150 \cdot \dfrac{1}{100} = \dfrac{150}{100} = \dfrac{3 \cdot 50}{2 \cdot 50} = \dfrac{3}{2}$ or $1\dfrac{1}{2}$

11. $66\dfrac{2}{3}\% = 66\dfrac{2}{3} \cdot \dfrac{1}{100}$
$$= \frac{200}{3} \cdot \frac{1}{100}$$
$$= \frac{2 \cdot 100 \cdot 1}{3 \cdot 100}$$
$$= \frac{2}{3}$$

12. $12\% = 12 \cdot \dfrac{1}{100} = \dfrac{12}{100} = \dfrac{3 \cdot 4}{25 \cdot 4} = \dfrac{3}{25}$

13. $0.14 = 0.14(100\%) = 14.\%$ or 14%

14. $1.75 = 1.75(100\%) = 175.\%$ or 175%

15. $0.057 = 0.057(100\%) = 05.7\%$ or 5.7%

16. $0.5 = 0.5(100\%) = 050.\%$ or 50%

17. $\dfrac{3}{25} = \dfrac{3}{25} \cdot 100\% = \dfrac{3}{25} \cdot \dfrac{100}{1}\% = \dfrac{300}{25}\% = 12\%$

18. $\dfrac{9}{40} = \dfrac{9}{40} \cdot 100\%$

$\qquad = \dfrac{9}{40} \cdot \dfrac{100}{1}\%$

$\qquad = \dfrac{900}{40}\%$

$\qquad = 22\dfrac{20}{40}\%$

$\qquad = 22\dfrac{1}{2}\%$

19. $5\dfrac{1}{2} = \dfrac{11}{2}$

$\qquad = \dfrac{11}{2} \cdot 100\%$

$\qquad = \dfrac{11}{2} \cdot \dfrac{100}{1}\%$

$\qquad = \dfrac{1100}{2}\%$

$\qquad = 550\%$

20. $\dfrac{3}{17} = \dfrac{3}{17} \cdot 100\% = \dfrac{3}{17} \cdot \dfrac{100\%}{1} = \dfrac{300}{17}\% \approx 17.65\%$

$$
\begin{array}{r}
17.647 \approx 17.65 \\
17 \overline{)\,300.000} \\
\underline{-17} \\
130 \\
\underline{-119} \\
11\,0 \\
\underline{-10\,2} \\
80 \\
\underline{-68} \\
120 \\
\underline{-119} \\
1
\end{array}
$$

Thus, $\dfrac{3}{17}$ is approximately 17.65%.

21. As a decimal $27.5\% = 27.5(0.01) = 0.275$.

As a fraction $27.5\% = 27.5 \cdot \dfrac{1}{100}$

$\qquad = \dfrac{27.5}{100}$

$\qquad = \dfrac{27.5}{100} \cdot \dfrac{10}{10}$

$\qquad = \dfrac{275}{1000}$

$\qquad = \dfrac{11 \cdot 25}{40 \cdot 25}$

$\qquad = \dfrac{11}{40}.$

Thus, 27.5% written as a decimal is 0.275, and written as a fraction is $\dfrac{11}{40}$.

22. $1\dfrac{3}{4} = \dfrac{7}{4} = \dfrac{7}{4} \cdot 100\% = \dfrac{7}{4} \cdot \dfrac{100\%}{1} = \dfrac{700}{4}\% = 175\%$

Thus, a "$1\dfrac{3}{4}$ times" increase is the same as a "175% increase."

Vocabulary and Readiness Check

1. Percent means "per hundred."

2. $100\% = 1$.

3. The % symbol is read as percent.

4. To write a decimal or a fraction as a percent, multiply by 1 in the form of 100%.

5. To write a percent as a *decimal*, drop the % symbol and multiply by 0.01.

6. To write a percent as a *fraction*, drop the % symbol and multiply by $\dfrac{1}{100}$.

Exercise Set 6.2

1. $\dfrac{96}{100} = 96\%$

96% of these college students use the Internet.

3. 37 out of 100 adults preferred football.

$\dfrac{37}{100} = 37\%$

5. 37 of the adults preferred football, while 13 preferred soccer. Thus, 37 + 13 = 50 preferred football or soccer.

$$\frac{50}{100} = 50\%$$

7. $41\% = 41(0.01) = 0.41$

9. $6\% = 6(0.01) = 0.06$

11. $100\% = 100(0.01) = 1.00$ or 1

13. $73.6\% = 73.6(0.01) = 0.736$

15. $2.8\% = 2.8(0.01) = 0.028$

17. $0.6\% = 0.6(0.01) = 0.006$

19. $300\% = 300(0.01) = 3.00$ or 3

21. $32.58\% = 32.58(0.01) = 0.3258$

23. $8\% = 8 \cdot \frac{1}{100} = \frac{8}{100} = \frac{4 \cdot 2}{4 \cdot 25} = \frac{2}{25}$

25. $4\% = 4 \cdot \frac{1}{100} = \frac{4}{100} = \frac{1 \cdot 4}{4 \cdot 25} = \frac{1}{25}$

27. $4.5\% = 4.5 \cdot \frac{1}{100}$

$$= \frac{4.5}{100}$$
$$= \frac{4.5 \cdot 10}{100 \cdot 10}$$
$$= \frac{45}{1000}$$
$$= \frac{5 \cdot 9}{5 \cdot 200}$$
$$= \frac{9}{200}$$

29. $175\% = 175 \cdot \frac{1}{100} = \frac{175}{100} = \frac{7 \cdot 25}{4 \cdot 25} = \frac{7}{4}$ or $1\frac{3}{4}$

31. $6.25\% = 6.25 \cdot \frac{1}{100}$

$$= \frac{6.25}{100}$$
$$= \frac{6.25 \cdot 100}{100 \cdot 100}$$
$$= \frac{625}{10,000}$$
$$= \frac{1 \cdot 625}{16 \cdot 625}$$
$$= \frac{1}{16}$$

33. $10\frac{1}{3}\% = 10\frac{1}{3} \cdot \frac{1}{100} = \frac{31}{3} \cdot \frac{1}{100} = \frac{31}{300}$

35. $22\frac{3}{8}\% = 22\frac{3}{8} \cdot \frac{1}{100} = \frac{179}{8} \cdot \frac{1}{100} = \frac{179}{800}$

37. $0.22 = 0.22(100\%) = 22\%$

39. $0.006 = 0.006(100\%) = 0.6\%$

41. $5.3 = 5.3(100\%) = 530\%$

43. $0.056 = 0.056(100\%) = 5.6\%$

45. $0.2228 = 0.2228(100\%) = 22.28\%$

47. $3.00 = 3.00(100\%) = 300\%$

49. $0.7 = 0.7(100\%) = 70\%$

51. $\frac{7}{10} = \frac{7}{10} \cdot 100\% = \frac{700}{10}\% = 70\%$

53. $\frac{4}{5} = \frac{4}{5} \cdot 100\% = \frac{400}{5}\% = 80\%$

55. $\frac{34}{50} = \frac{34}{50} \cdot 100\% = \frac{3400}{50}\% = 68\%$

57. $\frac{3}{8} = \frac{3}{8} \cdot 100\% = \frac{300}{8}\% = \frac{75}{2}\% = 37\frac{1}{2}\%$

59. $\frac{1}{3} = \frac{1}{3} \cdot 100\% = \frac{100}{3}\% = 33\frac{1}{3}\%$

61. $4\frac{1}{2} = 4\frac{1}{2} \cdot 100\% = \frac{9}{2} \cdot 100\% = \frac{900}{2}\% = 450\%$

63. $1\dfrac{9}{10} = 1\dfrac{9}{10} \cdot 100\% = \dfrac{19}{10} \cdot 100\% = \dfrac{1900}{10}\% = 190\%$

65. $\dfrac{9}{11} = \dfrac{9}{11} \cdot 100\% = \dfrac{900}{11}\%$

$$
\begin{array}{r}
81.818 \approx 81.82 \\
11\overline{)\ 900.000} \\
\underline{-88} \\
20 \\
\underline{-11} \\
9\ 0 \\
\underline{-8\ 8} \\
20 \\
\underline{-11} \\
90 \\
\underline{-88} \\
2
\end{array}
$$

$\dfrac{9}{11}$ is approximately 81.82%.

67. $\dfrac{4}{15} = \dfrac{4}{15} \cdot 100\% = \dfrac{400}{15}\%$

$$
\begin{array}{r}
26.666 \approx 26.67 \\
15\overline{)\ 400.000} \\
\underline{-30} \\
100 \\
\underline{-90} \\
10\ 0 \\
\underline{-9\ 0} \\
1\ 00 \\
\underline{-90} \\
100 \\
\underline{-90} \\
10
\end{array}
$$

$\dfrac{4}{15}$ is approximately 26.67%.

69.

Percent	Decimal	Fraction
60%	0.6	$\dfrac{3}{5}$
$23\dfrac{1}{2}\%$	0.235	$\dfrac{47}{200}$
80%	0.8	$\dfrac{4}{5}$
$33\dfrac{1}{3}\%$	$0.333\overline{3}$	$\dfrac{1}{3}$
87.5%	0.875	$\dfrac{7}{8}$
7.5%	0.075	$\dfrac{3}{40}$

71.

Percent	Decimal	Fraction
200%	2	2
280%	2.8	$2\dfrac{4}{5}$
705%	7.05	$7\dfrac{1}{20}$
454%	4.54	$4\dfrac{27}{50}$

73. $38\% = 38(0.01) = 0.38$

$38\% = 38 \cdot \dfrac{1}{100} = \dfrac{38}{100} = \dfrac{19}{50}$

75. $15.8\% = 15.8(0.01) = 0.158$

$$15.8\% = 15.8 \cdot \dfrac{1}{100}$$
$$= \dfrac{15.8}{100}$$
$$= \dfrac{15.8 \cdot 10}{100 \cdot 10}$$
$$= \dfrac{158}{1000}$$
$$= \dfrac{79}{500}$$

77. $91\% = 91(0.01) = 0.91$

$91\% = 91 \cdot \dfrac{1}{100} = \dfrac{91}{100}$

79. $0.5\% = 0.5(0.01) = 0.005$

$$0.5\% = 0.5 \cdot \frac{1}{100}$$
$$= \frac{0.5}{100}$$
$$= \frac{0.5}{100} \cdot \frac{10}{10}$$
$$= \frac{5}{1000}$$
$$= \frac{1}{200}$$

81. $14.2\% = 14.2(0.01) = 0.142$

$$14.2\% = 14.2 \cdot \frac{1}{100}$$
$$= \frac{14.2}{100}$$
$$= \frac{14.2 \cdot 10}{100 \cdot 10}$$
$$= \frac{142}{1000}$$
$$= \frac{71}{500}$$

83. $0.781 = 0.781(100\%) = 78.1\%$

85. $\dfrac{7}{1000} = \dfrac{7}{1000}(100\%) = \dfrac{700}{1000}\% = \dfrac{7}{10}\% = 0.7\%$

87. $46\% = 46(0.01) = 0.46$

89.
$$\frac{3}{4} - \frac{1}{2} \cdot \frac{8}{9} = \frac{3}{4} - \frac{1 \cdot 8}{2 \cdot 9}$$
$$= \frac{3}{4} - \frac{1 \cdot 2 \cdot 4}{2 \cdot 9}$$
$$= \frac{3}{4} - \frac{4}{9}$$
$$= \frac{3}{4} \cdot \frac{9}{9} - \frac{4}{9} \cdot \frac{4}{4}$$
$$= \frac{27}{36} - \frac{16}{36}$$
$$= \frac{27 - 16}{36}$$
$$= \frac{11}{36}$$

91.
$$6\frac{2}{3} - 4\frac{5}{6} = \frac{20}{3} - \frac{29}{6}$$
$$= \frac{20}{3} \cdot \frac{2}{2} - \frac{29}{6}$$
$$= \frac{40}{6} - \frac{29}{6}$$
$$= \frac{11}{6}$$
$$= 1\frac{5}{6}$$

93. **a.** 52.8647% rounded to the nearest tenth percent is 52.9%.

  b. 52.8647% rounded to the nearest hundredth percent is 52.86%.

95. **a.** $6.5\% = 6.5(0.01) = 0.065$ INCORRECT

  b. $7.8\% = 7.8(0.01) = 0.078$ CORRECT

  c. $120\% = 120(0.01) = 1.20$ INCORRECT

  d. $0.35\% = 0.35(0.01) = 0.0035$ CORRECT

  b and d are correct.

97. $45\% + 40\% + 11\% = 96\%$
$100\% - 96\% = 4\%$
4% of the U.S. population have AB blood type.

99. 3 of 4 equal parts are shaded, so
$$\frac{3}{4} = \frac{3}{4} \cdot 100\% = \frac{300}{4}\% = 75\%$$

101. A fraction written as a percent is greater than 100% when the numerator is <u>greater</u> than the denominator.

103. $\dfrac{21}{79} \approx 0.2658 \approx 0.266$

$0.2658(100\%) = 26.58\% \approx 26.6\%$

105. The longest bar corresponds to network systems and data communication analysts, so that is predicted to be the fastest growing occupation.

107. The percent change for Veterinarians is 35%, so $35\% = 35(0.01) = 0.35$.

109. answers may vary

Section 6.3

Practice Problems

1. 8 is what percent of 48?

   $\downarrow\downarrow$ $\downarrow$ $\downarrow\downarrow$
   $8 =$ x $\cdot 48$

2. 2.6 is 40% of what number?

   $\downarrow\downarrow\downarrow$ $\downarrow$ $\downarrow$
   $2.6 = 40\% \cdot$ x

3. What number is 90% of 0.045?

   $\downarrow$ $\downarrow\downarrow$ $\downarrow$ $\downarrow$
   x $= 90\% \cdot 0.045$

4. 56% of 180 is what number?

   $\downarrow$ $\downarrow\downarrow$ $\downarrow$
   $56\% \cdot 180 =$ x

5. 12% of what number is 21?

   $\downarrow\downarrow$ $\downarrow$ $\downarrow\downarrow$
   $12\% \cdot$ x $= 21$

6. What percent of 95 is 76?

   $\downarrow$ $\downarrow\downarrow\downarrow$
   x $\cdot 95 = 76$

7. What number is 25% of 90?

   $\downarrow$ $\downarrow\downarrow$ $\downarrow\downarrow$
   x $= 25\% \cdot 90$

   $x = 25\% \cdot 90$
   $x = 0.25 \cdot 90$
   $x = 22.5$
   Then 22.5 is 25% of 90.
   Is this reasonable? To see, round 25% to 30%.
   Then 30% or 0.30(90) is 27. Our result is
   reasonable since 22.5 is close to 27.

8. 95% of 400 is what number?

   $\downarrow$ $\downarrow$ $\downarrow$ $\downarrow$ $\downarrow$
   $95\% \cdot 400 =$ x
   $0.95 \cdot 400 = x$
   $380 = x$
   Then 95% of 400 is 380. Is this result
   reasonable? To see, round 95% to 100%. Then
   100% of 400 or 1.0(400) = 400, which is close to
   380.

9. 15% of what number is 2.4?

   $\downarrow$ $\downarrow$ $\downarrow$ $\downarrow\downarrow$
   $15\% \cdot$ x $= 2.4$
   $0.15 \cdot x = 2.4$
   $\dfrac{0.15x}{0.15} = \dfrac{2.4}{0.15}$
   $x = 16$
   Then 15% of 16 is 2.4. Is this result reasonable?
   To see, round 15% to 20%. Then 20% of 16 or
   0.20(16) = 3.2, which is close to 2.4.

10. 18 is $4\frac{1}{2}$% of what number?

    $\downarrow\downarrow$ $\downarrow$ $\downarrow$ $\downarrow$
    $18 = 4\dfrac{1}{2}\% \cdot$ x
    $18 = 0.045x$
    $\dfrac{18}{0.045} = \dfrac{0.045x}{0.045}$
    $400 = x$

    Then 18 is $4\dfrac{1}{2}$% of 400.

11. What percent of 90 is 27?

    $\downarrow$ $\downarrow$ $\downarrow$ $\downarrow\downarrow$
    x $\cdot 90 = 27$
    $90x = 27$
    $\dfrac{90x}{90} = \dfrac{27}{90}$
    $x = \dfrac{3}{10}$
    or $x = 0.30$
    Since we are looking for percent, we can write
    $\dfrac{3}{10}$ or 0.30 as a percent. $x = 30\%$

    Then 30% of 90 is 27. To check, see that
    $30\% \cdot 90 = 27$.

12. 63 is what percent of 45?

$$\downarrow\downarrow \quad\quad \downarrow \quad\quad\quad \downarrow\downarrow$$
$$63 = \quad\quad x \quad\quad\quad \cdot\; 45$$

$$63 = 45x$$
$$\frac{63}{45} = \frac{45x}{45}$$
$$\frac{7}{5} = x$$
$$1.4 = x$$
$$140\% = x$$

Then 63 is 140% of 45.

Vocabulary and Readiness Check

1. The word is translates to "=."

2. The word of usually translates to "multiplication."

3. In the statement "10% of 90 is 9," the number 9 is called the amount, 90 is called the base, and 10 is called the percent.

4. 100% of a number = the number

5. Any "percent greater than 100%" of "a number" = "a number greater than the original number."

6. Any "percent less than 100%" of "a number" = "a number less than the original number."

Exercise Set 6.3

1. 18% of 81 is what number?

$$\downarrow \quad\quad \downarrow\downarrow\downarrow \quad\quad \downarrow$$
$$18\% \;\cdot\; 81 = \quad\quad x$$

3. 20% of what number is 105?

$$\downarrow \quad \downarrow \quad\quad \downarrow \quad\quad \downarrow\downarrow$$
$$20\% \;\cdot \quad\quad x \quad\quad = 105$$

5. 0.6 is 40% of what number?

$$\downarrow \downarrow \quad \downarrow\downarrow \quad \downarrow \quad\quad \downarrow$$
$$0.6 = \quad 40\% \;\cdot \quad\quad x$$

7. What percent of 80 is 3.8?

$$\downarrow \quad\quad\quad \downarrow\downarrow\downarrow\downarrow$$
$$x \quad\quad\quad \cdot\; 80 = 3.8$$

9. What number is 9% of 43?

$$\downarrow \quad\quad\quad \downarrow\downarrow\downarrow\downarrow$$
$$x \quad\quad = 9\% \;\cdot\; 43$$

11. What percent of 250 is 150?

$$\downarrow \quad\quad\quad \downarrow\downarrow\downarrow\downarrow$$
$$x \quad\quad\quad \cdot\; 250 = 150$$

13. $10\% \cdot 35 = x$
$$0.10 \cdot 35 = x$$
$$3.5 = x$$
10% of 35 is 3.5.

15. $x = 14\% \cdot 205$
$$x = 0.14 \cdot 205$$
$$x = 28.7$$
28.7 is 14% of 205.

17. $1.2 = 12\% \cdot x$
$$1.2 = 0.12x$$
$$\frac{1.2}{0.12} = \frac{0.12x}{0.12}$$
$$10 = x$$
1.2 is 12% of 10.

19. $8\frac{1}{2}\% \cdot x = 51$
$$0.085x = 51$$
$$\frac{0.085x}{0.085} = \frac{51}{0.085}$$
$$x = 600$$
$8\frac{1}{2}\%$ of 600 is 51.

21. $x \cdot 80 = 88$
$$\frac{x \cdot 80}{80} = \frac{88}{80}$$
$$x = 1.1$$
$$x = 110\%$$
88 is 110% of 80.

23. $17 = x \cdot 50$
$$\frac{17}{50} = \frac{x \cdot 50}{50}$$
$$0.34 = x$$
$$34\% = x$$
17 is 34% of 50.

25. $0.1 = 10\% \cdot x$
$0.1 = 0.10x$
$\dfrac{0.1}{0.1} = \dfrac{0.1x}{0.1}$
$1 = x$
0.1 is 10% of 1.

27. $150\% \cdot 430 = x$
$1.5 \cdot 430 = x$
$645 = x$
150% of 430 is 645.

29. $82.5 = 16\dfrac{1}{2}\% \cdot x$
$82.5 = 0.165x$
$\dfrac{82.5}{0.165} = \dfrac{0.165x}{0.165}$
$500 = x$
82.5 is $16\dfrac{1}{2}\%$ of 500.

31. $2.58 = x \cdot 50$
$\dfrac{2.58}{50} = \dfrac{x \cdot 50}{50}$
$0.0516 = x$
$5.16\% = x$
2.58 is 5.16% of 50.

33. $x = 42\% \cdot 60$
$x = 0.42 \cdot 60$
$x = 25.2$
25.2 is 42% of 60.

35. $x \cdot 184 = 64.4$
$\dfrac{x \cdot 184}{184} = \dfrac{64.4}{184}$
$x = 0.35$
$x = 35\%$
35% of 184 is 64.4.

37. $120\% \cdot x = 42$
$1.20 \cdot x = 42$
$\dfrac{1.2x}{1.2} = \dfrac{42}{1.2}$
$x = 35$
120% of 35 is 42.

39. $2.4\% \cdot 26 = x$
$0.024 \cdot 26 = x$
$0.624 = x$
2.4% of 26 is 0.624.

41. $x \cdot 600 = 3$
$\dfrac{x \cdot 600}{600} = \dfrac{3}{600}$
$x = 0.005$
$x = 0.5\%$
0.5% of 600 is 3.

43. $6.67 = 4.6\% \cdot x$
$6.67 = 0.046x$
$\dfrac{6.67}{0.046} = \dfrac{0.046x}{0.046}$
$145 = x$
6.67 is 4.6% of 145.

45. $1575 = x \cdot 2500$
$\dfrac{1575}{2500} = \dfrac{x \cdot 2500}{2500}$
$0.63 = x$
$63\% = x$
1575 is 63% of 2500.

47. $2 = x \cdot 50$
$\dfrac{2}{50} = \dfrac{x \cdot 50}{50}$
$0.04 = x$
$4\% = x$
2 is 4% of 50.

49. $\dfrac{27}{x} = \dfrac{9}{10}$
$27 \cdot 10 = x \cdot 9$
$270 = 9x$
$\dfrac{270}{9} = \dfrac{9x}{9}$
$30 = x$

51. $\dfrac{x}{5} = \dfrac{8}{11}$
$x \cdot 11 = 5 \cdot 8$
$11x = 40$
$\dfrac{11x}{11} = \dfrac{40}{11}$
$x = 3\dfrac{7}{11}$

53. $\dfrac{17}{12} = \dfrac{x}{20}$

55. $\dfrac{8}{9} = \dfrac{14}{x}$

57. $5 \cdot n = 32$

$$\frac{5 \cdot n}{5} = \frac{32}{5}$$

$$n = \frac{32}{5}$$

Choice c is correct.

59. $0.06 = n \cdot 7$

$$\frac{0.06}{7} = \frac{n \cdot 7}{7}$$

$$\frac{0.06}{7} = n$$

Choice b is correct.

61.   answers may vary

63.   Since 100% of 20 is 20, and 30 is greater than 20, x must be greater than 100%; b.

65.   Since 85 is less than 120, the percent is less than 100%; c.

67.   Since 55% is less than 100%, which is 1, 55% of 45 is less than 45; c.

69.   Since 100% is 1, 100% of 45 is equal to 45; a.

71.   Since 100% is 1, 100% of 45 is equal to 45; a.

73.   answers may vary

75. $1.5\% \cdot 45,775 = x$

$0.015 \cdot 45,775 = x$

$\qquad 686.625 = x$

1.5% of 45,775 is 686.625.

77. $22,113 = 180\% \cdot x$

$22,113 = 1.80 \cdot x$

$$\frac{22,113}{1.8} = \frac{1.8 \cdot x}{1.8}$$

$12,285 = x$

22,113 is 180% of 12,285.

Section 6.4

Practice Problems

1.   27%   of   <u>what number</u>   is   54?

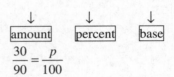

$$\frac{54}{b} = \frac{27}{100}$$

2.   30 is <u>what percent</u> of 90?

$$\frac{30}{90} = \frac{p}{100}$$

3.   <u>What number</u> is 25% of 116?

$$\frac{a}{116} = \frac{25}{100}$$

4.   680 is   65% of <u>what number</u>?

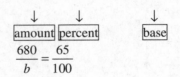

$$\frac{680}{b} = \frac{65}{100}$$

5.   <u>What percent</u> of 40   is   75?

$$\frac{75}{40} = \frac{p}{100}$$

6.   46% of 80 is <u>what number</u>?

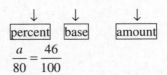

$$\frac{a}{80} = \frac{46}{100}$$

7. What number is 8% of 120?

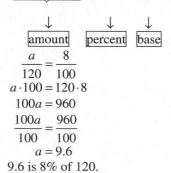

$$\frac{a}{120} = \frac{8}{100}$$
$$a \cdot 100 = 120 \cdot 8$$
$$100a = 960$$
$$\frac{100a}{100} = \frac{960}{100}$$
$$a = 9.6$$

9.6 is 8% of 120.

8. 65% of what number is 52?

↓ percent   ↓ base   ↓ amount

$$\frac{52}{b} = \frac{65}{100}$$
$$52 \cdot 100 = b \cdot 65$$
$$5200 = 65b$$
$$\frac{5200}{65} = \frac{65b}{65}$$
$$80 = b$$

Thus, 65% of 80 is 52.

9. 15.4 is 5% of what number?

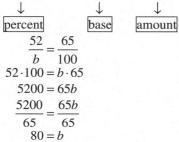

$$\frac{15.4}{b} = \frac{5}{100} \text{ or } \frac{15.4}{b} = \frac{1}{20}$$
$$15.4 \cdot 20 = 1 \cdot b$$
$$308 = b$$

So, 154 is 5% of 308.

10. What percent of 40 is 8?

↓ percent   ↓ base   ↓ amount

$$\frac{8}{40} = \frac{p}{100} \text{ or } \frac{1}{5} = \frac{p}{100}$$
$$1 \cdot 100 = 5 \cdot p$$
$$100 = 5p$$
$$\frac{100}{5} = \frac{5p}{5}$$
$$20 = p$$

So, 20% of 40 is 8.

11. 414 is what percent of 180?

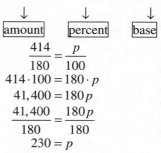

$$\frac{414}{180} = \frac{p}{100}$$
$$414 \cdot 100 = 180 \cdot p$$
$$41,400 = 180p$$
$$\frac{41,400}{180} = \frac{180p}{180}$$
$$230 = p$$

Then 414 is 230% of 180.

Vocabulary and Readiness Check

1. When translating the statement "20% of 15 is 3" to a proportion, the number 3 is called the amount, 15 is the base, and 20 is the percent.

2. In the question "50% of what number is 28?", which part of the percent proportion is unknown? base

3. In the question "What number is 25% of 200?", which part of the percent proportion is unknown? amount

4. In the question "38 is what percent of 380?", which part of the percent proportion is unknown? percent

Exercise Set 6.4

1. 98% of 45 is what number?

↓ percent   ↓ base   ↓ amount = a

$$\frac{a}{45} = \frac{98}{100}$$

3. What number is 4% of 150?

↓ amount = a ↓ percent   ↓ base

$$\frac{a}{150} = \frac{4}{100}$$

5. 14.3 is 26% of what number?

↓ amount   ↓ percent   ↓ base = b

$$\frac{14.3}{b} = \frac{26}{100}$$

7. 35% of <u>what number</u> is 84?

$$\downarrow \qquad\qquad \downarrow \qquad \downarrow$$

percent $\qquad$ base = b $\qquad$ amount

$$\frac{84}{b} = \frac{35}{100}$$

9. <u>What percent</u> of 400 is 70?

$$\downarrow \qquad\qquad \downarrow \qquad \downarrow$$

percent = p $\qquad$ base $\;$ amount

$$\frac{70}{400} = \frac{p}{100}$$

11. 8.2 is <u>what percent</u> of 82?

$$\downarrow \qquad\quad \downarrow \qquad\quad \downarrow$$

amount $\quad$ percent = p $\quad$ base

$$\frac{8.2}{82} = \frac{p}{100}$$

13. $\dfrac{a}{65} = \dfrac{40}{100}$ or $\dfrac{a}{65} = \dfrac{2}{5}$

$$a \cdot 5 = 65 \cdot 2$$
$$5a = 130$$
$$\frac{5a}{5} = \frac{130}{5}$$
$$a = 26$$

40% of 65 is 26.

15. $\dfrac{a}{105} = \dfrac{18}{100}$

$$a \cdot 100 = 105 \cdot 18$$
$$a \cdot 100 = 1890$$
$$\frac{a \cdot 100}{100} = \frac{1890}{100}$$
$$a = 18.9$$

18.9 is 18% of 105.

17. $\dfrac{90}{b} = \dfrac{15}{100}$ or $\dfrac{90}{b} = \dfrac{3}{20}$

$$90 \cdot 20 = b \cdot 3$$
$$1800 = 3b$$
$$\frac{1800}{3} = \frac{3b}{3}$$
$$600 = b$$

15% of 600 is 90.

19. $\dfrac{7.8}{b} = \dfrac{78}{100}$

$$7.8 \cdot 100 = b \cdot 78$$
$$780 = 78 \cdot b$$
$$\frac{780}{78} = \frac{78 \cdot b}{78}$$
$$10 = b$$

7.8 is 78% of 10.

21. $\dfrac{42}{35} = \dfrac{p}{100}$ or $\dfrac{6}{5} = \dfrac{p}{100}$

$$6 \cdot 100 = 5 \cdot p$$
$$600 = 5p$$
$$\frac{600}{5} = \frac{5p}{5}$$
$$120 = p$$

42 is 120% of 35.

23. $\dfrac{14}{50} = \dfrac{p}{100}$ or $\dfrac{7}{25} = \dfrac{p}{100}$

$$7 \cdot 100 = 25 \cdot p$$
$$700 = 25p$$
$$\frac{700}{25} = \frac{25p}{25}$$
$$28 = p$$

14 is 28% of 50.

25. $\dfrac{3.7}{b} = \dfrac{10}{100}$ or $\dfrac{3.7}{b} = \dfrac{1}{10}$

$$3.7 \cdot 10 = b \cdot 1$$
$$37 = b$$

3.7 is 10% of 37.

27. $\dfrac{a}{70} = \dfrac{2.4}{100}$

$$a \cdot 100 = 70 \cdot 2.4$$
$$100a = 168$$
$$\frac{100a}{100} = \frac{168}{100}$$
$$a = 1.68$$

1.68 is 2.4% of 70.

29. $\dfrac{160}{b} = \dfrac{16}{100}$ or $\dfrac{160}{b} = \dfrac{4}{25}$

$$160 \cdot 25 = b \cdot 4$$
$$4000 = 4b$$
$$\frac{4000}{4} = \frac{4b}{4}$$
$$1000 = b$$

160 is 16% of 1000.

31. $\dfrac{394.8}{188} = \dfrac{p}{100}$

$394.8 \cdot 100 = 188 \cdot p$

$39{,}480 = 188p$

$\dfrac{39{,}480}{188} = \dfrac{188p}{188}$

$210 = p$

394.8 is 210% of 188.

33. $\dfrac{a}{62} = \dfrac{89}{100}$

$a \cdot 100 = 62 \cdot 89$

$100a = 5518$

$\dfrac{100a}{100} = \dfrac{5518}{100}$

$a = 55.18$

55.18 is 89% of 62.

35. $\dfrac{2.7}{6} = \dfrac{p}{100}$

$2.7 \cdot 100 = 6 \cdot p$

$270 = 6p$

$\dfrac{270}{6} = \dfrac{6p}{6}$

$45 = p$

45% of 6 is 2.7.

37. $\dfrac{105}{b} = \dfrac{140}{100}$ or $\dfrac{105}{b} = \dfrac{7}{5}$

$105 \cdot 5 = b \cdot 7$

$525 = 7b$

$\dfrac{525}{7} = \dfrac{7b}{7}$

$75 = b$

140% of 75 is 105.

39. $\dfrac{a}{48} = \dfrac{1.8}{100}$

$a \cdot 100 = 48 \cdot 1.8$

$100a = 86.4$

$\dfrac{100a}{100} = \dfrac{86.4}{100}$

$a = 0.864$

1.8% of 48 is 0.864.

41. $\dfrac{4}{800} = \dfrac{p}{100}$ or $\dfrac{1}{200} = \dfrac{p}{100}$

$1 \cdot 100 = 200 \cdot p$

$100 = 200p$

$\dfrac{100}{200} = \dfrac{200p}{200}$

$0.5 = p$

0.5% of 800 is 4.

43. $\dfrac{3.5}{b} = \dfrac{2.5}{100}$

$3.5 \cdot 100 = b \cdot 2.5$

$350 = 2.5b$

$\dfrac{350}{2.5} = \dfrac{2.5b}{2.5}$

$140 = b$

3.5 is 2.5% of 140.

45. $\dfrac{a}{48} = \dfrac{20}{100}$ or $\dfrac{a}{48} = \dfrac{1}{5}$

$a \cdot 5 = 48 \cdot 1$

$5a = 48$

$\dfrac{5a}{5} = \dfrac{48}{5}$

$a = 9.6$

20% of 48 is 9.6.

47. $\dfrac{2486}{2200} = \dfrac{p}{100}$

$2486 \cdot 100 = 2200 \cdot p$

$248{,}600 = 2200p$

$\dfrac{248{,}600}{2200} = \dfrac{2200p}{2200}$

$113 = p$

2486 is 113% of 2200.

49. $-\dfrac{11}{16} + \left(-\dfrac{3}{16}\right) = \dfrac{-11-3}{16} = \dfrac{-14}{16} = -\dfrac{2 \cdot 7}{2 \cdot 8} = -\dfrac{7}{8}$

51. $3\dfrac{1}{2} - \dfrac{11}{30} = \dfrac{7}{2} - \dfrac{11}{30}$

$\qquad = \dfrac{7 \cdot 15}{2 \cdot 15} - \dfrac{11}{30}$

$\qquad = \dfrac{105}{30} - \dfrac{11}{30}$

$\qquad = \dfrac{105 - 11}{30}$

$\qquad = \dfrac{94}{30}$

$\qquad = 3\dfrac{4}{30}$

$\qquad = 3\dfrac{2}{15}$

53. $\begin{array}{r} 1 \\ 0.41 \\ + \, 0.29 \\ \hline 0.70 \end{array}$

55. $\begin{array}{r} 2.38 \\ - \, 0.19 \\ \hline 2.19 \end{array}$

57. answers may vary

59. $\dfrac{a}{64} = \dfrac{25}{100}$

$\dfrac{17}{64} \overset{?}{=} \dfrac{25}{100}$

$17 \cdot 100 \overset{?}{=} 64 \cdot 25$

$\quad 1700 = 1600 \quad$ False

The amount is not 17.

$\dfrac{a}{64} = \dfrac{25}{100}$

$a \cdot 100 = 64 \cdot 25$

$100a = 1600$

$\dfrac{100a}{100} = \dfrac{1600}{100}$

$\qquad a = 16$

25% of 64 is 16.

61. $\dfrac{p}{100} = \dfrac{13}{52}$

$\dfrac{25}{100} \overset{?}{=} \dfrac{13}{52}$

$\dfrac{1}{4} = \dfrac{1}{4} \quad$ True

Yes, the percent is equal to 25 (25%).

63. answers may vary

65. $\dfrac{a}{53,862} = \dfrac{22.3}{100}$

$a \cdot 100 = 53,862 \cdot 22.3$

$100a = 1,201,122.6$

$\dfrac{100a}{100} = \dfrac{1,201,122.6}{100}$

$\qquad a \approx 12,011.2$

22.3% of 53,862 is 12,011.2.

67. $\dfrac{8652}{b} = \dfrac{119}{100}$

$8652 \cdot 100 = b \cdot 119$

$865,200 = 119b$

$\dfrac{865,200}{119} = \dfrac{119b}{119}$

$7270.6 \approx b$

8652 is 119% of 7270.6.

Integrated Review

1. The ratio of 18 to 20 is $\dfrac{18}{20} = \dfrac{9}{10}$.

2. The ratio of 36 to 100 is $\dfrac{36}{100} = \dfrac{9}{25}$.

3. The ratio of 8.6 to 10 is

$\dfrac{8.6}{10} = \dfrac{8.6 \cdot 10}{10 \cdot 10} = \dfrac{86}{100} = \dfrac{43}{50}$.

4. The ratio of 1.6 to 4.6 is

$\dfrac{1.6}{4.6} = \dfrac{1.6 \cdot 10}{4.6 \cdot 10} = \dfrac{16}{46} = \dfrac{8}{23}$.

5. The ratio of the width to the length is

$\dfrac{12 \text{ inches}}{18 \text{ inches}} = \dfrac{12}{18} = \dfrac{2}{3}$.

6. The ratio of assets to debt was

$\dfrac{\$28 \text{ hundred million}}{\$14 \text{ hundred million}} = \dfrac{28}{14} = \dfrac{2}{1}$.

7. $\dfrac{3.5}{12.5} = \dfrac{7}{z}$

$3.5 \cdot z = 12.5 \cdot 7$

$3.5z = 87.5$

$\dfrac{3.5z}{3.5} = \dfrac{87.5}{3.5}$

$\quad z = 25$

216

8. $\dfrac{x+7}{3} = \dfrac{2x}{5}$

$5(x+7) = 3 \cdot 2x$

$5x + 35 = 6x$

$35 = x$

9. Let x be the number of weeks that a gross of boxes is likely to last.

$\begin{array}{c} \text{boxes} \to \\ \text{weeks} \to \end{array} \dfrac{5}{3} = \dfrac{144}{x} \begin{array}{c} \leftarrow \text{boxes} \\ \leftarrow \text{weeks} \end{array}$

$5 \cdot x = 3 \cdot 144$

$5x = 432$

$\dfrac{5x}{5} = \dfrac{432}{5}$

$x = 86.4$

A gross of boxes of envelopes is likely to last about 86 weeks.

10. Use 4.3 for the number of weeks in a month. Let x be the number of boxes that will be needed in a month.

$\begin{array}{c} \text{boxes} \to \\ \text{weeks} \to \end{array} \dfrac{5}{3} = \dfrac{x}{4.3} \begin{array}{c} \leftarrow \text{boxes} \\ \leftarrow \text{weeks} \end{array}$

$5 \cdot 4.3 = 3 \cdot x$

$21.5 = 3x$

$\dfrac{21.5}{3} = \dfrac{3x}{3}$

$7.2 \approx x$

Seven boxes should be purchased to last a month.

11. $0.94 = 0.94(100\%) = 94\%$

12. $0.17 = 0.17(100\%) = 17\%$

13. $\dfrac{3}{8} = \dfrac{3}{8} \cdot 100\% = \dfrac{300}{8}\% = 37.5\%$

14. $\dfrac{7}{2} = \dfrac{7}{2} \cdot 100\% = \dfrac{700\%}{2} = 350\%$

15. $4.7 = 4.7(100\%) = 470\%$

16. $8 = 8(100\%) = 800\%$

17. $\dfrac{9}{20} = \dfrac{9}{20} \cdot 100\% = \dfrac{900}{20}\% = 45\%$

18. $\dfrac{53}{50} = \dfrac{53}{50} \cdot 100\% = \dfrac{5300}{50}\% = 106\%$

19. $6\dfrac{3}{4} = \dfrac{27}{4} = \dfrac{27}{4} \cdot 100\% = \dfrac{2700}{4}\% = 675\%$

20. $3\dfrac{1}{4} = \dfrac{13}{4} = \dfrac{13}{4} \cdot 100\% = \dfrac{1300}{4}\% = 325\%$

21. $0.02 = 0.02(100\%) = 2\%$

22. $0.06 = 0.06(100\%) = 6\%$

23. $71\% = 71(0.01) = 0.71$

24. $31\% = 31(0.01) = 0.31$

25. $3\% = 3(0.01) = 0.03$

26. $4\% = 4(0.01) = 0.04$

27. $224\% = 224(0.01) = 2.24$

28. $700\% = 700(0.01) = 7.0$

29. $2.9\% = 2.9(0.01) = 0.029$

30. $6.6\% = 6.6(0.01) = 0.066$

31. $7\% = 7(0.01) = 0.07$

$7\% = 7 \cdot \dfrac{1}{100} = \dfrac{7}{100}$

32. $5\% = 5(0.01) = 0.05$

$5\% = 5 \cdot \dfrac{1}{100} = \dfrac{5}{100} = \dfrac{1}{20}$

33. $6.8\% = 6.8(0.01) = 0.068$

$6.8\% = 6.8 \cdot \dfrac{1}{100} = \dfrac{6.8}{100} = \dfrac{6.8 \cdot 10}{100 \cdot 10} = \dfrac{68}{1000} = \dfrac{17}{250}$

34. $11.25\% = 11.25(0.01) = 0.1125$

$11.25\% = 11.25 \cdot \dfrac{1}{100}$

$= \dfrac{11.25}{100}$

$= \dfrac{11.25 \cdot 100}{100 \cdot 100}$

$= \dfrac{1125}{10,000}$

$= \dfrac{9}{80}$

35. $74\% = 74(0.01) = 0.74$

$74\% = 74 \cdot \dfrac{1}{100} = \dfrac{74}{100} = \dfrac{37}{50}$

36. $45\% = 45(0.01) = 0.45$

$$45\% = 45 \cdot \frac{1}{100} = \frac{45}{100} = \frac{9}{20}$$

37. $16\frac{1}{3}\% = 16.3\overline{3}(0.01) \approx 0.163$

$$16\frac{1}{3}\% = \frac{49}{3}\% = \frac{49}{3} \cdot \frac{1}{100} = \frac{49}{300}$$

38. $12\frac{2}{3}\% = 12.6\overline{6}(0.01) \approx 0.127$

$$12\frac{2}{3}\% = \frac{38}{3}\% = \frac{38}{3} \cdot \frac{1}{100} = \frac{38}{300} = \frac{19}{150}$$

39.
$$\frac{a}{90} = \frac{15}{100}$$
$$a \cdot 100 = 15 \cdot 90$$
$$100a = 1350$$
$$\frac{100a}{100} = \frac{1350}{100}$$
$$a = 13.5$$
15% of 90 is 13.5.

40.
$$\frac{78}{b} = \frac{78}{100}$$
$$78 \cdot 100 = 78 \cdot b$$
$$7800 = 78b$$
$$\frac{7800}{78} = \frac{78b}{78}$$
$$100 = b$$
78% of 100 is 78.

41.
$$\frac{297.5}{b} = \frac{85}{100}$$
$$297.5 \cdot 100 = 85 \cdot b$$
$$29,750 = 85b$$
$$\frac{29,750}{85} = \frac{85b}{85}$$
$$350 = b$$
297.5 is 85% of 350.

42.
$$\frac{78}{65} = \frac{p}{100}$$
$$78 \cdot 100 = 65 \cdot p$$
$$7800 = 65p$$
$$\frac{7800}{65} = \frac{65p}{65}$$
$$120 = p$$
78 is 120% of 65.

43.
$$\frac{23.8}{85} = \frac{p}{100}$$
$$23.8 \cdot 100 = 85 \cdot p$$
$$2380 = 85p$$
$$\frac{2380}{85} = \frac{85p}{85}$$
$$28 = p$$
23.8 is 28% of 85.

44.
$$\frac{a}{200} = \frac{38}{100}$$
$$a \cdot 100 = 38 \cdot 200$$
$$100a = 7600$$
$$\frac{100a}{100} = \frac{7600}{100}$$
$$a = 76$$
38% of 200 is 76.

45.
$$\frac{a}{85} = \frac{40}{100}$$
$$a \cdot 100 = 40 \cdot 85$$
$$100a = 3400$$
$$\frac{100a}{100} = \frac{3400}{100}$$
$$a = 34$$
34 is 40% of 85.

46.
$$\frac{128.7}{99} = \frac{p}{100}$$
$$128.7 \cdot 100 = p \cdot 99$$
$$12,870 = 99p$$
$$\frac{12,870}{99} = \frac{99p}{99}$$
$$130 = p$$
130% of 99 is 128.7.

47.
$$\frac{115}{250} = \frac{p}{100}$$
$$115 \cdot 100 = p \cdot 250$$
$$11,500 = 250p$$
$$\frac{11,500}{250} = \frac{250p}{250}$$
$$46 = p$$
46% of 250 is 115.

48. $\dfrac{a}{84} = \dfrac{45}{100}$

$a \cdot 100 = 45 \cdot 84$

$100a = 3780$

$\dfrac{100a}{100} = \dfrac{3780}{100}$

$a = 37.8$

37.8 is 45% of 84.

49. $\dfrac{63}{b} = \dfrac{42}{100}$

$63 \cdot 100 = 42 \cdot b$

$6300 = 42b$

$\dfrac{6300}{42} = \dfrac{42b}{42}$

$150 = b$

42% of 150 is 63.

50. $\dfrac{58.9}{b} = \dfrac{95}{100}$

$58.9 \cdot 100 = 95 \cdot b$

$5890 = 95b$

$\dfrac{5890}{95} = \dfrac{95b}{95}$

$62 = b$

95% of 62 is 58.9.

Section 6.5

Practice Problems

1. *Method 1:*

   What number   is 25% of 2174?

$$x = 25\% \cdot 2174$$
$$x = 0.25 \cdot 2174$$
$$x = 543.5$$

We predict 543.5 miles of the trail resides in the state of Virginia.

Method 2:

   What number   is 25% of 2174?

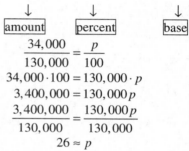

$$\dfrac{a}{2174} = \dfrac{25}{100}$$
$$a \cdot 100 = 2174 \cdot 25$$
$$100a = 54{,}350$$
$$\dfrac{100a}{100} = \dfrac{54{,}350}{100}$$
$$a = 543.5$$

We predict 543.5 miles of the trail resides in the state of Virginia.

2. *Method 1:*

34,000 is what percent of 130,000?

$$34{,}000 = x \cdot 130{,}000$$
$$34{,}000 = 130{,}000x$$
$$\dfrac{34{,}000}{130{,}000} = \dfrac{130{,}000x}{130{,}000}$$
$$0.26 \approx x$$
$$26\% = x$$

In Florida, 34,000 or 26% more new nurses were needed in 2006.

Method 2:

34,000 is what percent of 130,000?

amount   percent   base

$$\dfrac{34{,}000}{130{,}000} = \dfrac{p}{100}$$
$$34{,}000 \cdot 100 = 130{,}000 \cdot p$$
$$3{,}400{,}000 = 130{,}000\,p$$
$$\dfrac{3{,}400{,}000}{130{,}000} = \dfrac{130{,}000\,p}{130{,}000}$$
$$26 \approx p$$

In Florida, 34,000 or 26% more new nurses were needed in 2006.

3. *Method 1:*

864 is 32% of what number?

$$864 = 32\% \cdot x$$
$$864 = 0.32 \cdot x$$
$$\dfrac{864}{0.32} = \dfrac{0.32x}{0.32}$$
$$2700 = x$$

There are 2700 students at Euclid University.

Method 2:

864 is 32% of what number?

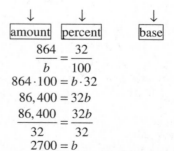

$$\dfrac{864}{b} = \dfrac{32}{100}$$
$$864 \cdot 100 = b \cdot 32$$
$$86{,}400 = 32b$$
$$\dfrac{86{,}400}{32} = \dfrac{32b}{32}$$
$$2700 = b$$

There are 2700 students at Euclid University.

4. *Method 1*:
$\underbrace{\text{What number}}$ is 3% of 240 million?

$$\begin{array}{ccccc} \downarrow & & \downarrow\downarrow\downarrow & & \downarrow \\ x & = & 3\% \cdot & & 240 \end{array}$$

$x = 0.03 \cdot 240$
$x = 7.2$ million

a. The increase in the number of vehicles on the road in 2007 is 7.2 million.

b. The total number of registered vehicles on the road in 2007 was
240 million + 7.2 million = 247.2 million

Method 2:
$\underbrace{\text{What number}}$ is 3% of 240 million?

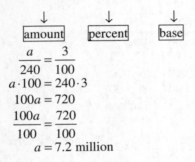

$$\frac{a}{240} = \frac{3}{100}$$
$a \cdot 100 = 240 \cdot 3$
$100a = 720$
$$\frac{100a}{100} = \frac{720}{100}$$
$a = 7.2$ million

a. The increase in the number of vehicles on the road in 2007 is 7.2 million.

b. The total number of registered vehicles on the road in 2007 was
240 million + 7.2 million = 247.2 million

5. Find the amount of increase by subtracting the original number of attendants from the new number of attendants.
amount of increase = 333 − 285 = 48
The amount of increase is 48 attendants.

$$\text{percent of increase} = \frac{\text{amount of increase}}{\text{original amount}}$$
$$= \frac{48}{285}$$
$$\approx 0.168$$
$$= 16.8\%$$

The number of attendants to the local play, *Peter Pan*, increased by about 16.8%.

6. Find the amount of decrease by subtracting 18,483 from 20,200.
Amount of decrease = 20,200 − 18,483 = 1717
The amount of decrease is 1717.

$$\text{percent of decrease} = \frac{\text{amount of decrease}}{\text{original amount}}$$
$$= \frac{1717}{20,200}$$
$$= 0.085$$
$$= 8.5\%$$

The population decreased by 8.5%.

Exercise Set 6.5

1. 24 is 1.5% of what number?
Method 1:
$24 = 1.5\% \cdot x$
$24 = 0.015x$
$$\frac{24}{0.015} = \frac{0.015x}{0.015}$$
$1600 = x$
1600 bolts were inspected.
Method 2:
$$\frac{24}{b} = \frac{1.5}{100}$$
$24 \cdot 100 = b \cdot 1.5$
$2400 = 1.5b$
$$\frac{2400}{1.5} = \frac{1.5b}{1.5}$$
$1600 = b$
1600 bolts were inspected.

3. 4% of 220 is what number?
Method 1:
$4\% \cdot 220 = x$
$0.04 \cdot 220 = x$
$8.8 = x$
The minimum weight resistance is 8.8 pounds.
Method 2:
$$\frac{a}{220} = \frac{4}{100}$$
$a \cdot 100 = 220 \cdot 4$
$100a = 880$
$$\frac{100a}{100} = \frac{880}{100}$$
$a = 8.8$
The minimum weight resistance is 8.8 pounds.

5. 378 is what percent of 2700?
Method 1:
$378 = x \cdot 2700$
$$\frac{378}{2700} = \frac{x \cdot 2700}{2700}$$
$0.14 = x$
$14\% = x$
The student spent 14% of last semester's college

cost on books.
Method 2:

$$\frac{378}{2700} = \frac{p}{100}$$

$$378 \cdot 100 = 2700 \cdot p$$

$$37,800 = 2700p$$

$$\frac{37,800}{2700} = \frac{2700p}{2700}$$

$$14 = p$$

The student spent 14% of last semester's college cost on books.

7. 32% of 725 is what number?
Method 1:

$$32\% \cdot 725 = x$$

$$0.32 \cdot 725 = x$$

$$232 = x$$

232 films were rated R.
Method 2:

$$\frac{a}{725} = \frac{32}{100}$$

$$a \cdot 100 = 725 \cdot 32$$

$$100a = 23,200$$

$$\frac{100a}{100} = \frac{23,200}{100}$$

$$a = 232$$

232 films were rated R.

9. 160,650 is what percent of 945,000?
Method 1:

$$160,650 = x \cdot 945,000$$

$$\frac{160,650}{945,000} = \frac{x \cdot 945,000}{945,000}$$

$$0.17 = x$$

$$17\% = x$$

17% of America's restaurants are pizza restaurants.
Method 2:

$$\frac{160,650}{945,000} = \frac{p}{100}$$

$$160,650 \cdot 100 = 945,000 \cdot p$$

$$16,065,000 = 945,000p$$

$$\frac{16,065,000}{945,000} = \frac{945,000p}{945,000}$$

$$17 = p$$

17% of America's restaurants are pizza restaurants.

11. 8% of 6200 is what number?
Method 1:

$$8\% \cdot 6200 = x$$

$$0.08 \cdot 6200 = x$$

$$496 = x$$

The decrease in the number of chairs produced is 496. The new number of chairs produced each month is $6200 - 496 = 5704$ chairs.
Method 2:

$$\frac{a}{6200} = \frac{8}{100}$$

$$100 \cdot a = 6200 \cdot 8$$

$$100a = 49,600$$

$$\frac{100a}{100} = \frac{49,600}{100}$$

$$a = 496$$

The decrease in the number of chairs produced is 496. The new number of chairs produced each month is $6200 - 496 = 5704$ chairs.

13. What number is 27% of 66,000?
Method 1:

$$x = 27\% \cdot 66,000$$

$$x = 0.27 \cdot 66,000$$

$$x = 17,820$$

The number of people employed as physician assistants is expected to be $66,000 + 17,820 = 83,820$.
Method 2:

$$\frac{a}{66,000} = \frac{27}{100}$$

$$a \cdot 100 = 66,000 \cdot 27$$

$$100a = 1,782,000$$

$$\frac{100a}{100} = \frac{1,782,000}{100}$$

$$a = 17,820$$

The number of people employed as physician assistants is expected to be $66,000 + 17,820 = 83,820$.

15. 0.4% of 642,000 is what number?
Method 1:

$$0.4\% \cdot 642,000 = x$$

$$0.004 \cdot 642,000 = x$$

$$2568 = x$$

The population of North Dakota in 2007 was $642,000 - 2568 = 639,432$.

Method 2:

$$\frac{a}{642,000} = \frac{0.4}{100}$$
$$100 \cdot a = 642,000 \cdot 0.4$$
$$100a = 256,800$$
$$\frac{100a}{100} = \frac{256,800}{100}$$
$$a = 2568$$

The population of North Dakota in 2007 was
$642,000 - 2568 = 639,432.$

17. 41 is what percent of 135?
Method 1:

$$41 = x \cdot 135$$
$$\frac{41}{135} = \frac{x \cdot 135}{135}$$
$$0.30 \approx x$$
$$30\% \approx x$$

30% of the runs are intermediate.
Method 2:

$$\frac{41}{135} = \frac{p}{100}$$
$$41 \cdot 100 = 135 \cdot p$$
$$4100 = 135p$$
$$\frac{4100}{135} = \frac{135p}{135}$$
$$30 \approx p$$

30% of the runs are intermediate.

19. 20 is what percent of 40?
Method 1:

$$20 = x \cdot 40$$
$$\frac{20}{40} = \frac{40x}{40}$$
$$0.5 = x$$
$$50\% = x$$

50% of the total calories come from fat.
Method 2:

$$\frac{20}{40} = \frac{p}{100}$$
$$20 \cdot 100 = 40 \cdot p$$
$$2000 = 40p$$
$$\frac{2000}{40} = \frac{40p}{40}$$
$$50 = p$$

50% of the total calories come from fat.

21. 10 is what percent of 80?
Method 1:

$$10 = x \cdot 80$$
$$\frac{10}{80} = \frac{x \cdot 80}{80}$$
$$0.125 = x$$
$$12.5\% = x$$

12.5% of the total calories come from fat.
Method 2:

$$\frac{10}{80} = \frac{p}{100}$$
$$10 \cdot 100 = 80 \cdot p$$
$$1000 = 80p$$
$$\frac{1000}{80} = \frac{80p}{80}$$
$$12.5 = p$$

12.5% of the total calories come from fat.

23. 35 is what percent of 120?
Method 1:

$$35 = x \cdot 120$$
$$\frac{35}{120} = \frac{120x}{120}$$
$$0.292 \approx x$$
$$29.2\% \approx x$$

29.2% of the total calories come from fat.
Method 2:

$$\frac{35}{120} = \frac{p}{100}$$
$$35 \cdot 100 = 120 \cdot p$$
$$3500 = 120p$$
$$\frac{3500}{120} = \frac{120p}{120}$$
$$29.2 \approx p$$

29.2% of the total calories come from fat.

25. 26,250 is 15% of what number?
Method 1:

$$26,250 = 15\% \cdot x$$
$$26,250 = 0.15 \cdot x$$
$$\frac{26,250}{0.15} = \frac{0.15 \cdot x}{0.15}$$
$$175,000 = x$$

The price of the home was $175,000.

Method 2:

$$\frac{26,250}{b} = \frac{15}{100}$$
$$26,250 \cdot 100 = b \cdot 15$$
$$2,625,000 = 15b$$
$$\frac{2,625,000}{15} = \frac{15b}{15}$$
$$175,000 = b$$

The price of the home was $175,000.

27. What number is 78% of 40?
Method 1:
$$x = 78\% \cdot 40$$
$$x = 0.78 \cdot 40$$
$$x = 31.2$$
The owner can bill 31.2 hours each week for a repairman.
Method 2:
$$\frac{a}{40} = \frac{78}{100}$$
$$a \cdot 100 = 40 \cdot 78$$
$$100a = 3120$$
$$\frac{100a}{100} = \frac{3120}{100}$$
$$a = 31.2$$
The owner can bill 31.2 hours each week for a repairman.

29. What number is 4.5% of 19,286?
Method 1:
$$x = 4.5\% \cdot 19,286$$
$$x = 0.045 \cdot 19,286$$
$$x = 867.87$$
The price of the car will increase by $867.87. The new price of that model will be $19,286 + $867.87 = $20,153.87.
Method 2:
$$\frac{a}{19,286} = \frac{4.5}{100}$$
$$a \cdot 100 = 19,286 \cdot 4.5$$
$$100a = 86,787$$
$$\frac{100a}{100} = \frac{86,787}{100}$$
$$a = 867.87$$
The price of the car will increase by $867.87. The new price of that model will be $19,286 + $867.87 = $20,153.87.

31. 21 is 60% of what number?
Method 1:
$$21 = 60\% \cdot x$$
$$21 = 0.60x$$
$$\frac{21}{0.60} = \frac{0.60x}{0.60}$$
$$35 = x$$
60% of the tower's total height is 35 feet.
Method 2:
$$\frac{21}{b} = \frac{60}{100}$$
$$21 \cdot 100 = b \cdot 60$$
$$2100 = 60b$$
$$\frac{2100}{60} = \frac{60b}{60}$$
$$35 = b$$
60% of the tower's total height is 35 feet.

33. 82.3% of 4761 is what number?
Method 1:
$$82.3\% \cdot 4761 = x$$
$$0.823 \cdot 4761 = x$$
$$3918 \approx x$$
$$4761 + 3918 = 8679$$
The increase is $3918 and the tuition in 2007–2008 was $8679.
Method 2:
$$\frac{a}{4761} = \frac{82.3}{100}$$
$$a \cdot 100 = 4761 \cdot 82.3$$
$$100a = 391,830.3$$
$$\frac{100a}{100} = \frac{391,830.3}{100}$$
$$a \approx 3918$$
$$4761 + 3918 = 8679$$
The increase is $3918 and the tuition in 2007–2008 was $8679.

35. What number is 5.7% of 731,000?
Method 1:
$$x = 5.7\% \cdot 731,000$$
$$x = 0.057 \cdot 731,000$$
$$x = 41,667$$
The increase is projected to be 41,667. The number of associate degrees awarded in 2017–2018 is projected to be 731,000 + 41,667 = 772,667.

Method 2:

$$\frac{a}{731,000} = \frac{5.7}{100}$$

$$a \cdot 100 = 731,000 \cdot 5.7$$

$$100a = 4,166,700$$

$$\frac{100a}{100} = \frac{4,166,700}{100}$$

$$a = 41,667$$

The increase is projected to be 41,667. The number of associate degrees awarded in 2017–2018 is projected to be 731,000 + 41,667 = 772,667.

	Original Amount	New Amount	Amount of Increase	Percent Increase
37.	50	80	80 − 50 = 30	$\frac{30}{50} = 0.6 = 60\%$
39.	65	117	117 − 65 = 52	$\frac{52}{65} = 0.8 = 80\%$

	Original Amount	New Amount	Amount of Decrease	Percent Decrease
41.	8	6	8 − 6 = 2	$\frac{2}{8} = 0.25 = 25\%$
43.	160	40	160 − 40 = 120	$\frac{120}{160} = 0.75 = 75\%$

45. percent decrease $= \dfrac{\text{amount of decrease}}{\text{original amount}}$

$$= \frac{150-84}{150}$$

$$= \frac{66}{150}$$

$$= 0.44$$

The decrease in calories is 44%.

47. percent decrease $= \dfrac{\text{amount of decrease}}{\text{original amount}}$

$$= \frac{10,845-10,700}{10,845}$$

$$= \frac{145}{10,845}$$

$$\approx 0.013$$

The decrease in cable TV systems was 1.3%.

49. $\text{percent increase} = \dfrac{\text{amount of increase}}{\text{original amount}}$

$= \dfrac{449 - 174}{174}$

$= \dfrac{275}{174}$

≈ 1.580

The increase in acres was 158%

51. $\text{percent decrease} = \dfrac{\text{amount of decrease}}{\text{original amount}}$

$= \dfrac{21.50 - 14.88}{21.50}$

$= \dfrac{6.62}{21.50}$

≈ 0.308

The decrease in the list price is 30.8%.

53. $\text{percent increase} = \dfrac{\text{amount of increase}}{\text{original amount}}$

$= \dfrac{3769 - 3570}{3570}$

$= \dfrac{199}{3570}$

≈ 0.056

The increase in elementary and secondary teachers is expected to be 5.6%.

55. $\text{percent decrease} = \dfrac{\text{amount of decrease}}{\text{original amount}}$

$= \dfrac{6903 - 5545}{6903}$

$= \dfrac{1358}{6903}$

≈ 0.197

The decrease in cinema sites was 19.7%

57. $\text{percent increase} = \dfrac{\text{amount of increase}}{\text{original amount}}$

$= \dfrac{19.9 - 13.1}{13.1}$

$= \dfrac{6.8}{13.1}$

≈ 0.519

The increase in soft drink size was 51.9%.

59. $\text{percent increase} = \dfrac{\text{amount of increase}}{\text{original amount}}$

$= \dfrac{220,472 - 178,025}{178,025}$

$= \dfrac{42,447}{178,025}$

≈ 0.24

The increase in cell sites was 24%.

61.
$$\begin{array}{r} 0.12 \\ \times\ \ 38 \\ \hline 96 \\ 360 \\ \hline 4.56 \end{array}$$

63.
$$\begin{array}{r} {}^{1\ 1}\ \ \\ 9.20 \\ +\ 1.98 \\ \hline 11.18 \end{array}$$

65. $-\dfrac{3}{8} + \dfrac{5}{12} = -\dfrac{3}{8} \cdot \dfrac{3}{3} + \dfrac{5}{12} \cdot \dfrac{2}{2}$

$= -\dfrac{9}{24} + \dfrac{10}{24}$

$= \dfrac{1}{24}$

67. $2\dfrac{4}{5} \div 3\dfrac{9}{10} = \dfrac{14}{5} \div \dfrac{39}{10}$

$= \dfrac{14}{5} \cdot \dfrac{10}{39}$

$= \dfrac{14 \cdot 10}{5 \cdot 39}$

$= \dfrac{14 \cdot 2 \cdot 5}{5 \cdot 39}$

$= \dfrac{28}{39}$

69. The increased number is double the original number.

71. To find the percent increase, she should have divided by the original amount, which is 150.

$\text{percent increase} = \dfrac{30}{150} = 0.2 = 20\%$

73. False; the percents are different.

percent increase from 1980 to 1990 = 20%

percent decrease from 1990 to 2000 = $16\dfrac{2}{3}\%$

Section 6.6

Practice Problems

1. sales tax = tax rate · purchase price
   $$= 8.5\% \cdot \$59.90$$
   $$= 0.085 \cdot \$59.90$$
   $$\approx \$5.09$$
   The sales tax is $5.09.
   Total Price = purchase price + sales tax
   $$= \$59.90 + \$5.09$$
   $$= \$64.99$$
   The sales tax on $59.90 is $5.09, and the total price is $64.99.

2. sales tax = tax rate · purchase price
   $$\$1665 = r \cdot \$18,500$$
   $$\frac{1665}{18,500} = \frac{r \cdot 18,500}{18,500}$$
   $$0.09 = r$$
   The sales tax rate is 9%.

3. commission = commission rate · sales
   $$= 6.6\% \cdot \$47,632$$
   $$= 0.066 \cdot \$47,632$$
   $$\approx \$3143.712$$
   The sales representative's commission for the month is $3143.71.

4. commission = commission rate · sales
   $$\$645 = r \cdot \$4300$$
   $$\frac{645}{4300} = r$$
   $$0.15 = r$$
   $$15\% = r$$
   The commission rate is 15%.

5. amount of discount
   = discount rate · original price
   $$= 35\% \cdot \$700$$
   $$= 0.35 \cdot \$700$$
   $$= \$245$$
   The discount is $245.

sale price = original price – discount
$$= \$700 - \$245$$
$$= \$455$$
The sale price is $455.

Vocabulary and Readiness Check

1. sales tax = tax rate · purchase price.

2. total price = purchase price + sales tax.

3. commission = commission rate · sales.

4. amount of discount
   = discount rate · original price.

5. sale price = original price – amount of discount.

Exercise Set 6.6

1. sales tax = 5% · $150 = 0.05 · $150 = $7.50
   The sales tax is $7.50.

3. sales tax = 7.5% · $799 = 0.075 · $799 ≈ $59.93
   total price = $799 + $59.93 = $858.93
   The total price of the camcorder is $858.93.

5. $335.30 = r · $4790
   $$\frac{335.30}{4790} = r$$
   $$0.07 = r$$
   The sales tax rate is 7%.

7. a. $10.20 = 8.5\% \cdot p$
       $10.2 = 0.085p$
       $$\frac{\$10.2}{0.085} = p$$
       $120 = p
       The purchase price of the table saw is $120.

   b. total price = $120 + $10.20 = $130.20
       The total price of the table saw is $130.20.

9. sales tax = 6.5% · $1800
   $$= 0.065 \cdot \$1800$$
   $$= \$117$$
   total price = $1800 + $117 = $1917
   The sales tax was $117 and the total price of the bracelet is $1917.

11. $\$24.25 = 5\% \cdot p$
$\$24.25 = 0.05p$
$\dfrac{\$24.25}{0.05} = p$
$\$485 = p$
The purchase price of the futon is $485.

13. $\$98.70 = r \cdot \$1645$
$\dfrac{98.70}{1645} = r$
$0.06 = r$
The sales tax rate is 6%.

15. Purchase price = $210 + $15 + $5 = $230
Sales tax = 7% · $230 = 0.07 · $230 = $16.10
Total price = $230 + $16.10 = $246.10
The sales tax is $16.10 and the total price of the items is $246.10.

17. commission $= 4\% \cdot \$1,329,401$
$= 0.04 \cdot \$1,329,401$
$= \$53,176.04$
Her commission was $53,176.04.

19. $\$1380.40 = r \cdot \$9860$
$\dfrac{\$1380.40}{\$9860} = r$
$0.14 = r$
The commission rate is 14%.

21. commission $= 1.5\% \cdot \$325,900$
$= 0.015 \cdot \$325,900$
$= \$4888.50$
His commission will be $4888.50.

23. $\$5565 = 3\% \cdot \text{sales}$
$\$5565 = 0.03 \cdot s$
$\dfrac{\$5565}{0.03} = s$
$\$185,500 = s$
The selling price of the house was $185,500.

	Original Price	Discount Rate	Amount of Discount	Sale Price
25.	$89	10%	10% · $89 = $8.90	$89 − $8.90 = $80.10
27.	$196.50	50%	50% · $196.50 = $98.25	$196.50 − $98.25 = $98.25
29.	$410	35%	35% · $410 = $143.50	$410 − $143.50 = $266.50
31.	$21,700	15%	15% · $21,700 = $3255	$21,700 − $3255 = $18,445

33. discount = 15% · $300 = 0.15 · $300 = $45
sale price = $300 − $45 = $255
The discount is $45 and the sale price is $255.

	Purchase Price	Tax Rate	Sales Tax	Total Price
35.	$305	9%	9% · $305 = $27.45	$305 + $27.45 = $332.45
37.	$56	5.5%	5.5% · $56 = $3.08	$56 + $3.08 = $59.08

	Sale	Commission Rate	Commission
39.	$235,800	3%	$235,800 · 3% = $7074
41.	$17,900	$\dfrac{\$1432}{\$17,900} = 0.08 = 8\%$	$1432

43. $2000 \cdot \dfrac{3}{10} \cdot 2 = 600 \cdot 2 = 1200$

45. $400 \cdot \dfrac{3}{100} \cdot 11 = 12 \cdot 11 = 132$

47. $600 \cdot 0.04 \cdot \dfrac{2}{3} = 24 \cdot \dfrac{2}{3} = 16$

49. Round $68 to $70 and 9.5% to 10%.
$10\% \cdot \$70 = 0.10 \cdot \$70 = \$7$
$\$70 + \$7 = \$77$
The best estimate of the total price is $77; d.

	Bill Amount	10%	15%	20%
51.	$40.21 ≈ $40	$4.00	$4 + \dfrac{1}{2}(\$4) = \$4 + \$2 = \$6.00$	$2(\$4) = \$8.00$
53.	$72.17 ≈ $72.00	$7.20	$\$7.20 + \dfrac{1}{2}(\$7.20) = \$7.20 + \$3.60$ $= \$10.80$	$2(\$7.20) = \$14.40$

55. A discount of 60% is better; answers may vary.

57. $7.5\% \cdot \$24,966 = 0.075 \cdot \$24,966 = \$1872.45$
$\$24,966 + \$1872.45 = \$26,838.45$
The total price of the necklace is $26,838.45.

Section 6.7

Practice Problems

1. $I = P \cdot R \cdot T$
$I = \$875 \cdot 7\% \cdot 5$
$= \$875 \cdot (0.07) \cdot 5$
$= \$306.25$
The simple interest is $306.25.

2. $I = P \cdot R \cdot T$

$$I = \$1500 \cdot 20\% \cdot \frac{9}{12}$$

$$= \$1500 \cdot (0.20) \cdot \frac{9}{12}$$

$$= \$225$$

She paid $225 in interest.

3. $I = P \cdot R \cdot T$

$$= \$2100 \cdot 13\% \cdot \frac{6}{12}$$

$$= \$2100 \cdot (0.13) \cdot \frac{6}{12}$$

$$= \$136.50$$

The interest is $136.50.

$$\begin{aligned} \text{total amount} &= \text{principal} + \text{interest} \\ &= \$2100 + \$136.50 \\ &= \$2236.50 \end{aligned}$$

After 6 months, the total amount paid will be $2236.50.

4. $P = \$3000$, $r = 4\% = 0.04$, $n = 1$, $t = 6$ years

$$A = P\left(1 + \frac{r}{n}\right)^{n \cdot t}$$

$$= \$3000\left(1 + \frac{0.04}{1}\right)^{1 \cdot 6}$$

$$= \$3000(1.04)^6$$

$$\approx \$3795.96$$

The total amount after 6 years is $3795.96.

5. $P = \$5500$, $r = 6\frac{1}{4}\% = 0.0625$, $n = 365$, $t = 5$

$$A = P\left(1 + \frac{r}{n}\right)^{n \cdot t}$$

$$= \$5500\left(1 + \frac{0.0625}{365}\right)^{365 \cdot 5}$$

$$\approx \$7517.41$$

The total amount after 5 years is $7517.41.

Calculator Explorations

1. $A = \$600\left(1 + \dfrac{0.09}{4}\right)^{4 \cdot 5} \approx \$936.31$

2. $A = \$10,000\left(1 + \dfrac{0.04}{365}\right)^{365 \cdot 15} \approx \$18,220.59$

3. $A = \$1200\left(1 + \dfrac{0.11}{1}\right)^{1 \cdot 20} \approx \$9674.77$

4. $A = \$5800\left(1 + \dfrac{0.07}{2}\right)^{2 \cdot 1} \approx \$6213.11$

5. $A = \$500\left(1 + \dfrac{0.06}{4}\right)^{4 \cdot 4} \approx \$634.49$

6. $A = \$2500\left(1 + \dfrac{0.05}{365}\right)^{365 \cdot 19} \approx \$6463.85$

Vocabulary and Readiness Check

1. To calculate <u>simple</u> interest, use $I = P \cdot R \cdot T$.

2. To calculate <u>compound</u> interest, use

$$A = P\left(1 + \frac{r}{n}\right)^{n \cdot t}.$$

3. <u>Compound</u> interest is computed on not only the original principal, but on interest already earned in previous compounding periods.

4. When interest is computed on the original principal only, it is called <u>simple</u> interest.

5. <u>Total amount</u> (paid or received) = principal + interest.

6. The <u>principal amount</u> is the money borrowed, loaned, or invested.

Exercise Set 6.7

1. $\begin{aligned} \text{simple interest} &= \text{principal} \cdot \text{rate} \cdot \text{time} \\ &= \$200 \cdot 8\% \cdot 2 \\ &= \$200 \cdot 0.08 \cdot 2 \\ &= \$32 \end{aligned}$

3. $\begin{aligned} \text{simple interest} &= \text{principal} \cdot \text{rate} \cdot \text{time} \\ &= \$160 \cdot 11.5\% \cdot 4 \\ &= \$160 \cdot 0.115 \cdot 4 \\ &= \$73.60 \end{aligned}$

5. $\begin{aligned} \text{simple interest} &= \text{principal} \cdot \text{rate} \cdot \text{time} \\ &= \$5000 \cdot 10\% \cdot 1\frac{1}{2} \\ &= \$5000 \cdot 0.10 \cdot 1.5 \\ &= \$750 \end{aligned}$

7. simple interest = principal · rate · time

$$= \$375 \cdot 18\% \cdot \frac{6}{12}$$
$$= \$375 \cdot 0.18 \cdot 0.5$$
$$= \$33.75$$

9. simple interest = principal · rate · time

$$= \$2500 \cdot 16\% \cdot \frac{21}{12}$$
$$= \$2500 \cdot 0.16 \cdot 1.75$$
$$= \$700$$

11. simple interest = principal · rate · time

$$= \$162,500 \cdot 12.5\% \cdot 5$$
$$= \$162,500 \cdot 0.125 \cdot 5$$
$$= \$101,562.50$$

$\$162,500 + \$101,562.50 = \$264,062.50$
The amount of interest is $101,562.50.
The total amount paid back is $264,062.50.

13. simple interest = principal · rate · time

$$= \$5000 \cdot 9\% \cdot \frac{15}{12}$$
$$= \$5000 \cdot 0.09 \cdot 1.25$$
$$= \$562.50$$

Total = $5000 + $562.50 = $5562.50

15. Simple interest = principal · rate · time

$$= \$8500 \cdot 17\% \cdot 4$$
$$= \$8500 \cdot 0.17 \cdot 4$$
$$= \$5780$$

Total amount = $8500 + $5780 = $14,280

17. $A = P\left(1 + \dfrac{r}{n}\right)^{n \cdot t}$

$$= 6150\left(1 + \frac{0.14}{2}\right)^{2 \cdot 15}$$
$$= 6150(1.07)^{30}$$
$$\approx 46,815.37$$

The total amount is $46,815.37.

19. $A = P\left(1 + \dfrac{r}{n}\right)^{n \cdot t}$

$$= 1560\left(1 + \frac{0.08}{365}\right)^{365 \cdot 5}$$
$$= 1560\left(1 + \frac{0.08}{365}\right)^{1825}$$
$$\approx 2327.14$$

The total amount is $2327.14.

21. $A = P\left(1 + \dfrac{r}{n}\right)^{n \cdot t}$

$$= 10,000\left(1 + \frac{0.09}{2}\right)^{2 \cdot 20}$$
$$= 10,000(1.045)^{40}$$
$$\approx 58,163.65$$

The total amount is $58,163.65.

23. $A = P\left(1 + \dfrac{r}{n}\right)^{n \cdot t}$

$$= 2675\left(1 + \frac{0.09}{1}\right)^{1 \cdot 1}$$
$$= 2675(1.09)$$
$$= 2915.75$$

The total amount is $2915.75.

25. $A = P\left(1 + \dfrac{r}{n}\right)^{n \cdot t}$

$$= 2000\left(1 + \frac{0.08}{1}\right)^{1 \cdot 5}$$
$$= 2000(1.08)^{5}$$
$$\approx 2938.66$$

The total amount is $2938.66.

27. $A = P\left(1 + \dfrac{r}{n}\right)^{n \cdot t}$

$$= 2000\left(1 + \frac{0.08}{4}\right)^{4 \cdot 5}$$
$$= 2000(1.02)^{20}$$
$$\approx 2971.89$$

The total amount is $2971.89.

29. perimeter = 10 + 6 + 10 + 6 = 32
The perimeter is 32 yards.

31. Perimeter = 7 + 7 + 7 + 7 + 7 = 35
The perimeter is 35 meters.

33. $\dfrac{x}{4} + \dfrac{x}{5} = \dfrac{x}{4} \cdot \dfrac{5}{5} + \dfrac{x}{5} \cdot \dfrac{4}{4} = \dfrac{5x}{20} + \dfrac{4x}{20} = \dfrac{9x}{20}$

35. $\left(\dfrac{2}{3}\right)\left(-\dfrac{1}{3}\right)-\left(\dfrac{9}{10}\right)\left(\dfrac{2}{5}\right)=-\dfrac{2}{9}-\dfrac{18}{50}$

$$=-\dfrac{2}{9}\cdot\dfrac{50}{50}-\dfrac{18}{50}\cdot\dfrac{9}{9}$$

$$=-\dfrac{100}{450}-\dfrac{162}{450}$$

$$=-\dfrac{262}{450}$$

$$=-\dfrac{131}{225}$$

37. answers may vary

39. answers may vary

Chapter 6 Vocabulary Check

1. In a mathematical statement, <u>of</u> usually means "multiplication."

2. In a mathematical statement, <u>is</u> means "equals."

3. <u>Percent</u> means "per hundred."

4. <u>Compound interest</u> is computed not only on the principal, but also on interest already earned in previous compounding periods.

5. In the percent proportion $\dfrac{\text{amount}}{\text{base}}=\dfrac{\text{percent}}{100}$.

6. To write a decimal or fraction as a percent, multiply by <u>100%</u>.

7. The decimal equivalent of the % symbol is <u>0.01</u>.

8. The fraction equivalent of the % symbol is $\dfrac{1}{100}$.

9. The percent equation is <u>base</u> · percent = <u>amount</u>.

10. <u>Percent of decrease</u> $=\dfrac{\text{amount of decrease}}{\text{original amount}}$.

11. <u>Percent of increase</u> $=\dfrac{\text{amount of increase}}{\text{original amount}}$.

12. <u>Sales tax</u> = tax rate · purchase price.

13. <u>Total price</u> = purchase price + sales tax.

14. <u>Commission</u> = commission rate · sales.

15. <u>Amount of discount</u> = discount rate · original price.

16. <u>Sale price</u> = original price − amount of discount.

17. A <u>proportion</u> is a mathematical statement that two ratios are equal.

18. A <u>ratio</u> is the quotient of two numbers or two quantities.

Chapter 6 Review

1. 1 dollar = 1 · 100 cents = 100 cents
The ratio of 20 cents to 1 dollar is
$$\dfrac{20\text{ cents}}{100\text{ cents}}=\dfrac{20}{100}=\dfrac{1}{5}.$$

2. The ratio of four parts red to six parts white is
$$\dfrac{4}{6}=\dfrac{2}{3}.$$

3. $\dfrac{x}{2}=\dfrac{12}{4}$
$$x\cdot4=2\cdot12$$
$$4x=24$$
$$\dfrac{4x}{4}=\dfrac{24}{4}$$
$$x=6$$

4. $\dfrac{20}{1}=\dfrac{x}{25}$
$$20\cdot25=1\cdot x$$
$$500=x$$

5. $\dfrac{32}{100}=\dfrac{100}{x}$
$$32\cdot x=100\cdot100$$
$$32x=10{,}000$$
$$\dfrac{32x}{32}=\dfrac{10{,}000}{32}$$
$$x=312.5$$

6. $\dfrac{20}{2}=\dfrac{c}{5}$
$$20\cdot5=2\cdot c$$
$$100=2c$$
$$\dfrac{100}{2}=\dfrac{2c}{2}$$
$$50=c$$

7. $\dfrac{2}{x-1} = \dfrac{3}{x+3}$

$2(x+3) = 3(x-1)$

$2x+6 = 3x-3$

$6 = x-3$

$9 = x$

8. $\dfrac{4}{y-3} = \dfrac{3}{y+2}$

$4(y+2) = 3(y-3)$

$4y+8 = 3y-9$

$y+8 = -9$

$y = -17$

9. $\dfrac{y+2}{y} = \dfrac{5}{3}$

$3(y+2) = 5y$

$3y+6 = 5y$

$6 = 2y$

$\dfrac{6}{2} = \dfrac{2y}{2}$

$3 = y$

10. $\dfrac{x-3}{3x+2} = \dfrac{2}{5}$

$5(x-3) = 2(3x+2)$

$5x-15 = 6x+4$

$-15 = x+4$

$-19 = x$

11. Let x be the number of parts that can be processed in 45 minutes.

parts $\rightarrow \dfrac{300}{20} = \dfrac{x}{45} \leftarrow$ parts

minutes $\rightarrow \phantom{\dfrac{300}{20}} \phantom{\dfrac{x}{45}} \leftarrow$ minutes

$300 \cdot 45 = 20 \cdot x$

$13,500 = 20x$

$\dfrac{13,500}{20} = \dfrac{20x}{20}$

$675 = x$

The machine can process 675 parts in 45 minutes.

12. Let x be the amount charged for 3 hours of consulting.

dollars $\rightarrow \dfrac{90}{8} = \dfrac{x}{3} \leftarrow$ dollars

hours $\rightarrow \phantom{\dfrac{90}{8}} \phantom{\dfrac{x}{3}} \leftarrow$ hours

$90 \cdot 3 = 8 \cdot x$

$270 = 8x$

$\dfrac{270}{8} = \dfrac{8x}{8}$

$33.75 = x$

He charges \$33.75 for 3 hours of consulting.

13. $\dfrac{37}{100} = 37\%$

37% of adults preferred pepperoni.

14. $\dfrac{77}{100} = 77\%$

77% of free throws were made.

15. $26\% = 26(0.01) = 0.26$

16. $75\% = 75(0.01) = 0.75$

17. $3.5\% = 3.5(0.01) = 0.035$

18. $1.5\% = 1.5(0.01) = 0.015$

19. $275\% = 275(0.01) = 2.75$

20. $400\% = 400(0.01) = 4.00$ or 4

21. $47.85\% = 47.85(0.01) = 0.4785$

22. $85.34\% = 85.34(0.01) = 0.8534$

23. $1.6 = 1.6(100\%) = 160\%$

24. $0.055 = 0.055(100\%) = 5.5\%$

25. $0.076 = 0.076(100\%) = 7.6\%$

26. $0.085 = 0.085(100\%) = 8.5\%$

27. $0.71 = 0.71(100\%) = 71\%$

28. $0.65 = 0.65(100\%) = 65\%$

29. $6 = 6(100)\% = 600\%$

30. $9 = 9(100)\% = 900\%$

31. $7\% = 7\left(\dfrac{1}{100}\right) = \dfrac{7}{100}$

32. $15\% = 15\left(\dfrac{1}{100}\right) = \dfrac{15}{100} = \dfrac{3}{20}$

33. $25\% = 25\left(\dfrac{1}{100}\right) = \dfrac{25}{100} = \dfrac{1}{4}$

34. $8.5\% = 8.5\left(\dfrac{1}{100}\right)$

$= \dfrac{8.5}{100}$

$= \dfrac{8.5 \cdot 10}{100 \cdot 10}$

$= \dfrac{85}{1000}$

$= \dfrac{17}{200}$

35. $10.2\% = 10.2\left(\dfrac{1}{100}\right)$

$= \dfrac{10.2}{100}$

$= \dfrac{10.2 \cdot 10}{100 \cdot 10}$

$= \dfrac{102}{1000}$

$= \dfrac{51}{500}$

36. $16\dfrac{2}{3}\% = \dfrac{50}{3}\% = \dfrac{50}{3}\left(\dfrac{1}{100}\right) = \dfrac{50}{300} = \dfrac{1}{6}$

37. $33\dfrac{1}{3}\% = \dfrac{100}{3}\% = \dfrac{100}{3}\left(\dfrac{1}{100}\right) = \dfrac{100}{300} = \dfrac{1}{3}$

38. $110\% = 110\left(\dfrac{1}{100}\right) = \dfrac{110}{100} = 1\dfrac{10}{100} = 1\dfrac{1}{10}$

39. $\dfrac{2}{5} = \dfrac{2}{5} \cdot \dfrac{100}{1}\% = \dfrac{200}{5}\% = 40\%$

40. $\dfrac{7}{10} = \dfrac{7}{10} \cdot \dfrac{100}{1}\% = \dfrac{700}{10}\% = 70\%$

41. $\dfrac{7}{12} = \dfrac{7}{12} \cdot \dfrac{100}{1}\% = \dfrac{700}{12}\% = \dfrac{175}{3}\% = 58\dfrac{1}{3}\%$

42. $1\dfrac{2}{3} = \dfrac{5}{3} \cdot \dfrac{100}{1}\% = \dfrac{500}{3}\% = 166\dfrac{2}{3}\%$

43. $1\dfrac{1}{4} = \dfrac{5}{4} \cdot \dfrac{100}{1}\% = \dfrac{500}{4}\% = 125\%$

44. $\dfrac{3}{5} = \dfrac{3}{5} \cdot \dfrac{100}{1}\% = \dfrac{300}{5}\% = 60\%$

45. $\dfrac{1}{16} = \dfrac{1}{16} \cdot \dfrac{100}{1}\% = \dfrac{100}{16}\% = 6.25\%$

46. $\dfrac{5}{8} = \dfrac{5}{8} \cdot \dfrac{100}{1}\% = \dfrac{500}{8}\% = 62.5\%$

47. $\quad 1250 = 1.25\% \cdot x$

$1250 = 0.0125x$

$\dfrac{1250}{0.0125} = \dfrac{0.0125x}{0.0125}$

$100{,}000 = x$

1250 is 1.25% of 100,000.

48. $x = 33\dfrac{1}{3}\% \cdot 24{,}000$

$x = \dfrac{100}{3} \cdot \dfrac{1}{100} \cdot 24{,}000$

$x = \dfrac{1}{3} \cdot 24{,}000$

$x = 8000$

8000 is $33\dfrac{1}{3}\%$ of 24,000.

49. $\quad 124.2 = x \cdot 540$

$\dfrac{124.2}{540} = \dfrac{540x}{540}$

$0.23 = x$

$23\% = x$

124.2 is 23% of 540.

50. $\quad 22.9 = 20\% \cdot x$

$22.9 = 0.20 \cdot x$

$\dfrac{22.9}{0.20} = \dfrac{0.20x}{0.20}$

$114.50 = x$

22.9 is 20% of 114.50.

51. $x = 17\% \cdot 640$

$x = 0.17 \cdot 640$

$x = 108.8$

108.8 is 17% of 640.

52. $693 = x \cdot 462$

$$\frac{693}{462} = \frac{462x}{462}$$

$$1.5 = x$$

$$150\% = x$$

693 is 150% of 462.

53. $$\frac{104.5}{b} = \frac{25}{100}$$

$$104.5 \cdot 100 = 25 \cdot b$$

$$10,450 = 25b$$

$$\frac{10,450}{25} = \frac{25b}{25}$$

$$418 = b$$

104.5 is 25% of 418.

54. $$\frac{16.5}{b} = \frac{5.5}{100}$$

$$16.5 \cdot 100 = 5.5 \cdot b$$

$$1650 = 5.5b$$

$$\frac{1650}{5.5} = \frac{5.5b}{5.5}$$

$$300 = b$$

16.5 is 5.5% of 300.

55. $$\frac{a}{532} = \frac{30}{100}$$

$$a \cdot 100 = 30 \cdot 532$$

$$100a = 15,960$$

$$\frac{100a}{100} = \frac{15,960}{100}$$

$$a = 159.6$$

159.6 is 30% of 532.

56. $$\frac{63}{35} = \frac{p}{100}$$

$$63 \cdot 100 = p \cdot 35$$

$$6300 = 35p$$

$$\frac{6300}{35} = \frac{35p}{35}$$

$$180 = p$$

63 is 180% of 35.

57. $$\frac{93.5}{85} = \frac{p}{100}$$

$$93.5 \cdot 100 = p \cdot 85$$

$$9350 = 85p$$

$$\frac{9350}{85} = \frac{85p}{85}$$

$$110 = p$$

93.5 is 110% of 85.

58. $$\frac{a}{500} = \frac{33}{100}$$

$$a \cdot 100 = 33 \cdot 500$$

$$100a = 16,500$$

$$\frac{100a}{100} = \frac{16,500}{100}$$

$$a = 165$$

165 is 33% of 500.

59. 1320 is what percent of 2000?

Method 1:

$$1320 = x \cdot 2000$$

$$\frac{1320}{2000} = \frac{2000x}{2000}$$

$$0.66 = x$$

$$66\% = x$$

66% of people own microwaves.

Method 2:

$$\frac{1320}{2000} = \frac{p}{100}$$

$$1320 \cdot 100 = p \cdot 2000$$

$$132,000 = 2000p$$

$$\frac{132,000}{2000} = \frac{2000p}{2000}$$

$$66 = p$$

66% of people own microwaves.

60. 2000 is what percent of 12,360?

Method 1:

$$2000 = x \cdot 12,360$$

$$\frac{2000}{12,360} = \frac{12,360x}{12,360}$$

$$0.16 \approx x$$

$$16\% \approx x$$

16% of freshmen are enrolled in prealgebra.

Method 2:

$$\frac{200}{12,360} = \frac{p}{100}$$

$$2000 \cdot 100 = 12,360 \cdot p$$

$$200,000 = 12,360p$$

$$\frac{200,000}{12,360} = \frac{12,360p}{12,360}$$

$$16 \approx p$$

16% of freshman are enrolled in prealgebra.

61. percent decrease $= \dfrac{\text{amount of decrease}}{\text{original amount}}$

$$= \dfrac{675 - 534}{675}$$

$$= \dfrac{141}{675}$$

$$\approx 0.209$$

$$\approx 20.9\%$$

Violent crime decreased 20.9%.

62. percent increase $= \dfrac{\text{amount of increase}}{\text{original amount}}$

$$= \dfrac{33 - 16}{16}$$

$$= \dfrac{17}{16}$$

$$= 1.0625$$

$$= 106.25\%$$

The charge will increase 106.25%.

63. Amount of decrease
$=$ percent decrease $\cdot$ original amount
$= 4\% \cdot \$215,000$
$= 0.04 \cdot \$215,000$
$= \$8600$
Total amount $= \$215,000 - \$8600 = \$206,400$
$\$206,400$ is expected to be collected next year.

64. Amount of increase
$=$ percent increase $\cdot$ original amount
$= 15\% \cdot \$11.50$
$= 0.15 \cdot \$11.50$
$\approx \$1.73$
Total amount $= \$11.50 + \$1.73 = \$13.23$
The new hourly rate is $13.23.

65. sales tax $=$ tax rate $\cdot$ purchase price
$= 5.5\% \cdot \$250$
$= 0.055 \cdot \$250$
$= \$13.75$
Total amount $= \$250 + \$13.75 = \$263.75$
The total price for the coat is $263.75.

66. sales tax $=$ tax rate $\cdot$ purchase price
$= 4.5\% \cdot \$25.50$
$= 0.045 \cdot \$25.50$
$\approx \$1.15$
The sales tax is $1.15.

67. commission $=$ commission rate $\cdot$ sales
$= 5\% \cdot \$100,000$
$= 0.05 \cdot \$100,000$
$= \$5000$
His commission is $5000.

68. commission $=$ commission rate $\cdot$ sales
$= 7.5\% \cdot \$4005$
$= 0.075 \cdot \$4005$
$\approx \$300.38$
Her commission is $300.38.

69. Amount of discount $=$ discount $\cdot$ original price
$= 30\% \cdot \$3000$
$= 0.30 \cdot \$3000$
$= \$900$
Sale price $= \$3000 - \$900 = \$2100$
The amount of discount is $900; the sale price is $2100.

70. Amount of discount $=$ discount $\cdot$ original price
$= 10\% \cdot \$90$
$= 0.10 \cdot \$90$
$= \$9.00$
Sale price $= \$90 - \$9 = \$81$
The amount of discount is $9; the sale price is $81.

71. $I = P \cdot R \cdot T$

$$= \$4000 \cdot 12\% \cdot \dfrac{4}{12}$$

$$= \$4000 \cdot 0.12 \cdot \dfrac{1}{3}$$

$$= \$160$$

The simple interest is $160.

72. $I = P \cdot R \cdot T$

$$= \$650 \cdot 20\% \cdot \dfrac{3}{12}$$

$$= \$6500 \cdot 0.20 \cdot 0.25$$

$$= \$325$$

The simple interest is $325.

73. $A = P\left(1 + \dfrac{r}{n}\right)^{n \cdot t}$

$$= 5500\left(1 + \dfrac{0.12}{1}\right)^{1 \cdot 15}$$

$$= 5500(1.12)^{15}$$

$$\approx 30,104.61$$

The total amount is $30,104.61.

74. $A = P\left(1 + \dfrac{r}{n}\right)^{n \cdot t}$

$\quad = 6000\left(1 + \dfrac{0.11}{2}\right)^{2 \cdot 10}$

$\quad = 6000(1.055)^{20}$

$\quad \approx 17,506.54$

The total amount is \$17,506.54.

75. $A = P\left(1 + \dfrac{r}{n}\right)^{n \cdot t}$

$\quad = 100\left(1 + \dfrac{0.12}{4}\right)^{4 \cdot 5}$

$\quad = 100(1.03)^{20}$

$\quad \approx 180.61$

The total amount is \$180.61.

76. $A = P\left(1 + \dfrac{r}{n}\right)^{n \cdot t}$

$\quad = 1000\left(1 + \dfrac{0.18}{4}\right)^{4 \cdot 20}$

$\quad = 1000(1.045)^{80}$

$\quad \approx 33,830.10$

The total amount is \$33,830.10.

77. $3.8\% = 3.8(0.01) = 0.038$

78. $124.5\% = 124.5(0.01) = 1.245$

79. $0.54 = 0.54(100\%) = 54\%$

80. $95.2 = 95.2(100\%) = 9520\%$

81. $47\% = 47\left(\dfrac{1}{100}\right) = \dfrac{47}{100}$

82. $5.6\% = 5.6\left(\dfrac{1}{100}\right)$

$\quad = \dfrac{5.6}{100}$

$\quad = \dfrac{5.6 \cdot 10}{100 \cdot 10}$

$\quad = \dfrac{56}{1000}$

$\quad = \dfrac{7}{125}$

83. $\dfrac{3}{8} = \dfrac{3}{8} \cdot \dfrac{100}{1}\% = \dfrac{300}{8}\% = 37\dfrac{1}{2}\%$

84. $\dfrac{6}{5} = \dfrac{6}{5} \cdot \dfrac{100}{1}\% = \dfrac{600}{5}\% = 120\%$

85. $\quad 43 = 16\% \cdot x$

$\quad 43 = 0.16x$

$\quad \dfrac{43}{0.16} = \dfrac{0.16x}{0.16}$

$\quad 268.75 = x$

43 is 16% of 268.75.

86. $\quad 27.5 = x \cdot 25$

$\quad \dfrac{27.5}{25} = \dfrac{25x}{25}$

$\quad 1.1 = x$

$\quad 110\% = x$

27.5 is 110% of 25.

87. $x = 36\% \cdot 1968$

$x = 0.36 \cdot 1968$

$x = 708.48$

708.48 is 36% of 1968.

88. $\quad 67 = x \cdot 50$

$\quad \dfrac{67}{50} = \dfrac{50x}{50}$

$\quad 1.34 = x$

$\quad 134\% = x$

67 is 134% of 50.

89. $\quad \dfrac{75}{25} = \dfrac{p}{100}$

$\quad 75 \cdot 100 = p \cdot 25$

$\quad 7500 = 25p$

$\quad \dfrac{7500}{25} = \dfrac{25p}{25}$

$\quad 300 = p$

75 is 300% of 25.

90. $\quad \dfrac{a}{240} = \dfrac{16}{100}$

$\quad a \cdot 100 = 16 \cdot 240$

$\quad 100a = 3840$

$\quad \dfrac{100a}{100} = \dfrac{3840}{100}$

$\quad a = 38.4$

38.4 is 16% of 240.

91. $\dfrac{28}{b} = \dfrac{5}{100}$

$28 \cdot 100 = 5 \cdot b$

$2800 = 5b$

$\dfrac{2800}{5} = \dfrac{5b}{5}$

$560 = b$

28 is 5% of 560.

92. $\dfrac{52}{16} = \dfrac{p}{100}$

$52 \cdot 100 = p \cdot 16$

$5200 = 16p$

$\dfrac{5200}{16} = \dfrac{16p}{16}$

$325 = p$

52 is 325% of 16.

93. $\dfrac{78}{300} = 0.26 = 26\%$

26% of the soft drinks have been sold.

94. $\$96,950 \cdot 7\% = \$96,950 \cdot 0.07 = \$6786.50$

The house has lost \$6786.50 in value.

95. Sales tax $= 8.75\% \cdot \$568$

$= 0.0875 \cdot \$568$

$= \$49.70$

Total price $= \$568 + \$49.70 = \$617.70$

The total price is \$617.70.

96. Amount of discount $= 15\% \cdot \$23.00$

$= 0.15 \cdot \$23.00$

$= \$3.45$

97. commission $=$ commission rate $\cdot$ sales

$\$1.60 = r \cdot \$12.80$

$\dfrac{\$1.60}{\$12.80} = r$

$0.125 = r$

$12.5\% = r$

His rate of commission is 12.5%.

98. Simple interest $=$ principal $\cdot$ rate $\cdot$ time

$= \$1400 \cdot 13\% \cdot \dfrac{6}{12}$

$= \$1400 \cdot 0.13 \cdot 0.5$

$= \$91$

Total amount $= \$1400 + \$91 = \$1491$

The total amount is \$1491.

99. Simple interest $=$ principal $\cdot$ rate $\cdot$ time

$= \$5500 \cdot 12.5\% \cdot 9$

$= \$5500 \cdot 0.125 \cdot 9$

$= \$6187.50$

Total amount $= \$5500 + \$6187.50 = \$11,687.50$

The total amount is \$11,687.50.

Chapter 6 Test

1. $85\% = 85(0.01) = 0.85$

2. $500\% = 500(0.01) = 5$

3. $0.6\% = 0.6(0.01) = 0.006$

4. $0.056 = 0.056(100\%) = 5.6\%$

5. $6.1 = 6.1(100\%) = 610\%$

6. $0.35 = 0.35(100\%) = 35\%$

7. $120\% = 120\left(\dfrac{1}{100}\right) = \dfrac{120}{100} = 1\dfrac{1}{5}$

8. $38.5\% = 38.5\left(\dfrac{1}{100}\right) = \dfrac{38.5}{100} = \dfrac{385}{1000} = \dfrac{77}{200}$

9. $0.2\% = 0.2\left(\dfrac{1}{100}\right) = \dfrac{0.2}{100} = \dfrac{2}{1000} = \dfrac{1}{500}$

10. $\dfrac{11}{20} = \dfrac{11}{20} \cdot \dfrac{100}{1}\% = \dfrac{1100}{20}\% = 55\%$

11. $\dfrac{3}{8} = \dfrac{3}{8} \cdot \dfrac{100}{1}\% = \dfrac{300}{8}\% = 37.5\%$

12. $1\dfrac{3}{4} = \dfrac{7}{4} \cdot \dfrac{100}{1}\% = \dfrac{700}{4}\% = 175\%$

13. $\dfrac{1}{50} = \dfrac{1}{50} \cdot \dfrac{100}{1}\% = \dfrac{100}{50}\% = 2\%$

14. $43\% = 43\left(\dfrac{1}{100}\right) = \dfrac{43}{100}$

15. *Method 1:*

$x = 42\% \cdot 80$

$x = 0.42 \cdot 80$

$x = 33.6$

33.6 is 42% of 80.

Method 2:

$$\frac{a}{80} = \frac{42}{100}$$
$$a \cdot 100 = 42 \cdot 80$$
$$100a = 3360$$
$$\frac{100a}{100} = \frac{3360}{100}$$
$$a = 33.6$$

33.6 is 42% of 80.

16. *Method 1:*
$$0.6\% \cdot x = 7.5$$
$$0.006x = 7.5$$
$$\frac{0.006x}{0.006} = \frac{7.5}{0.006}$$
$$x = 1250$$
0.6% of 1250 is 7.5.

Method 2:
$$\frac{7.5}{b} = \frac{0.6}{100}$$
$$7.5 \cdot 100 = b \cdot 0.6$$
$$750 = 0.6b$$
$$\frac{750}{0.6} = \frac{0.6b}{0.6}$$
$$1250 = b$$
0.6% of 1250 is 7.5.

17. *Method 1:*
$$567 = x \cdot 756$$
$$\frac{567}{756} = \frac{x \cdot 756}{756}$$
$$0.75 = x$$
$$75\% = x$$
567 is 75% of 756.

Method 2:
$$\frac{567}{756} = \frac{p}{100}$$
$$567 \cdot 100 = 756 \cdot p$$
$$56,700 = 756p$$
$$\frac{56,700}{756} = \frac{756p}{756}$$
$$75 = p$$
567 is 75% of 756.

18. 12% of 320 is what number?
$$12\% \cdot 320 = x$$
$$0.12 \cdot 320 = x$$
$$38.4 = x$$
There are 38.4 pounds of copper.

19. 20% of what number is $11,350?
$$20\% \cdot x = \$11,350$$
$$0.20x = \$11,350$$
$$\frac{0.2x}{0.2} = \frac{\$11,350}{0.2}$$
$$x = \$56,750$$
The value of the potential crop is $56,750.

20. tax = 1.25% · $354 = 0.0125 · $354 ≈ $4.43
total amount = $354 + $4.43 = $358.43
The total amount of the stereo is $358.43.

21. percent increase = $\dfrac{\text{amount of increase}}{\text{original amount}}$

$$= \frac{26,460 - 25,200}{25,200}$$
$$= \frac{1260}{25,200}$$
$$= 0.05$$
The increase in population was 5%.

22. Amount of discount = 15% · $120
$$= 0.15 \cdot \$120$$
$$= \$18$$
Sale price = $120 − $18 = $102
The amount of the discount is $18; the sale price is $102.

23. commission = 4% · $9875
$$= 0.04 \cdot \$9875$$
$$= \$395$$
His commission was $395.

24. $1.53 = rate · $152.99
$$\frac{\$1.53}{\$152.99} = r$$
$$0.01 \approx r$$
$$1\% \approx r$$
The sales tax rate is 1%.

25. simple interest = principal · rate · time
$$= \$2000 \cdot 9.25\% \cdot 3\frac{1}{2}$$
$$= \$2000 \cdot 0.0925 \cdot 3.5$$
$$= \$647.5$$

26. $A = P\left(1+\dfrac{r}{n}\right)^{n\cdot t}$

$= 1365\left(1+\dfrac{0.08}{1}\right)^{1.5}$

$= 1365(1.08)^5$

≈ 2005.63

The total amount of $2005.63.

27. Simple interest $=$ principal $\cdot$ rate $\cdot$ time

$= \$400 \cdot 13.5\% \cdot \dfrac{6}{12}$

$= \$400 \cdot 0.135 \cdot 0.5$

$= \$27$

Total amount $= \$400 + \$27 = \$427$

28. percent decrease $= \dfrac{\text{amount of decrease}}{\text{original amount}}$

$= \dfrac{162,064 - 120,982}{162,064}$

$= \dfrac{41,082}{162,064}$

≈ 0.25349

$\approx 25.3\%$

The number of crimes has decreased 25.3%.

29. The ratio of $75 to $10 is $\dfrac{\$75}{\$10} = \dfrac{75}{10} = \dfrac{15}{2}$.

30. $\dfrac{5}{y+1} = \dfrac{4}{y+2}$

$5(y+2) = 4(y+1)$

$5y + 10 = 4y + 4$

$y + 10 = 4$

$y = -6$

31. Let x be the number of defective bulbs out of 510 bulbs.

defective $\rightarrow \dfrac{3}{85} = \dfrac{x}{510} \leftarrow$ defective
bulbs $\rightarrow$ $\leftarrow$ bulbs

$3 \cdot 510 = 85 \cdot x$

$1530 = 85x$

$\dfrac{1530}{85} = \dfrac{85x}{85}$

$18 = x$

There should be 18 defective bulbs in 510.

Cumulative Review Chapters 1–6

1.
$$\begin{array}{r} 236 \\ \times\ \ 86 \\ \hline 1\ 416 \\ 18\ 880 \\ \hline 20,296 \end{array}$$

2.
$$\begin{array}{r} 409 \\ \times\ \ 76 \\ \hline 2\ 454 \\ 28\ 630 \\ \hline 31,084 \end{array}$$

3. $-3 - 7 = -3 + (-7) = -10$

4. $8 - (-2) = 8 + 2 = 10$

5. $x - 2 = -1$
$x - 2 + 2 = -1 + 2$
$x = 1$

6. $x + 4 = 3$
$x + 4 - 4 = 3 - 4$
$x = -1$

7. $3(2x - 6) + 6 = 0$
$3 \cdot 2x - 3 \cdot 6 + 6 = 0$
$6x - 18 + 6 = 0$
$6x - 12 = 0$
$6x - 12 + 12 = 0 + 12$
$6x = 12$
$\dfrac{6x}{6} = \dfrac{12}{6}$
$x = 2$

8. $5(x - 2) = 3x$
$5 \cdot x - 5 \cdot 2 = 3x$
$5x - 10 = 3x$
$5x - 5x - 10 = 3x - 5x$
$-10 = -2x$
$\dfrac{-10}{-2} = \dfrac{-2x}{-2}$
$5 = x$

9. $3 = \dfrac{3}{1} \cdot \dfrac{7}{7} = \dfrac{3 \cdot 7}{1 \cdot 7} = \dfrac{21}{7}$

10. $8 = \dfrac{8}{1} \cdot \dfrac{5}{5} = \dfrac{8 \cdot 5}{1 \cdot 5} = \dfrac{40}{5}$

11. $-\dfrac{10}{27} = -\dfrac{2 \cdot 5}{3 \cdot 3 \cdot 3}$

Since 10 and 27 have no common factors, $-\dfrac{10}{27}$

is already in simplest form.

12. $\dfrac{10y}{32} = \dfrac{5 \cdot 2 \cdot y}{16 \cdot 2} = \dfrac{5y}{16}$

13. $-\dfrac{7}{12} \div -\dfrac{5}{6} = -\dfrac{7}{12} \cdot -\dfrac{6}{5} = \dfrac{7 \cdot 6}{2 \cdot 6 \cdot 5} = \dfrac{7}{10}$

14. $\dfrac{-2}{5} \div \dfrac{7}{10} = -\dfrac{2}{5} \cdot \dfrac{10}{7} = -\dfrac{2 \cdot 2 \cdot 5}{5 \cdot 7} = -\dfrac{4}{7}$

15. $y - x = -\dfrac{8}{10} - \left(-\dfrac{3}{10}\right) = -\dfrac{8}{10} + \dfrac{3}{10} = -\dfrac{5}{10} = -\dfrac{1}{2}$

16. $2x + 3y = 2\left(\dfrac{2}{5}\right) + 3\left(\dfrac{-1}{5}\right) = \dfrac{4}{5} + \dfrac{-3}{5} = \dfrac{1}{5}$

17. $-\dfrac{3}{4} - \dfrac{1}{14} + \dfrac{6}{7} = -\dfrac{3}{4} \cdot \dfrac{7}{7} - \dfrac{1}{14} \cdot \dfrac{2}{2} + \dfrac{6}{7} \cdot \dfrac{4}{4}$

$= -\dfrac{21}{28} - \dfrac{2}{28} + \dfrac{24}{28}$

$= \dfrac{1}{28}$

18. $\dfrac{2}{9} + \dfrac{7}{15} - \dfrac{1}{3} = \dfrac{2}{9} \cdot \dfrac{5}{5} + \dfrac{7}{15} \cdot \dfrac{3}{3} - \dfrac{1}{3} \cdot \dfrac{15}{15}$

$= \dfrac{10}{45} + \dfrac{21}{45} - \dfrac{15}{45}$

$= \dfrac{16}{45}$

19. $\dfrac{\frac{1}{2} + \frac{3}{8}}{\frac{3}{4} - \frac{1}{6}} = \dfrac{\frac{1}{2} \cdot \frac{4}{4} + \frac{3}{8}}{\frac{3}{4} \cdot \frac{3}{3} - \frac{1}{6} \cdot \frac{2}{2}}$

$= \dfrac{\frac{4}{8} + \frac{3}{8}}{\frac{9}{12} - \frac{2}{12}}$

$= \dfrac{\frac{7}{8}}{\frac{7}{12}}$

$= \dfrac{7}{8} \div \dfrac{7}{12}$

$= \dfrac{7}{8} \cdot \dfrac{12}{7}$

$= \dfrac{7 \cdot 4 \cdot 3}{4 \cdot 2 \cdot 7}$

$= \dfrac{3}{2}$

20. $\dfrac{\frac{2}{3} + \frac{1}{6}}{\frac{3}{4} - \frac{3}{5}} = \dfrac{\frac{2}{3} \cdot \frac{2}{2} + \frac{1}{6}}{\frac{3}{4} \cdot \frac{5}{5} - \frac{3}{5} \cdot \frac{4}{4}}$

$= \dfrac{\frac{4}{6} + \frac{1}{6}}{\frac{15}{20} - \frac{12}{20}}$

$= \dfrac{\frac{5}{6}}{\frac{3}{20}}$

$= \dfrac{5}{6} \div \dfrac{3}{20}$

$= \dfrac{5}{6} \cdot \dfrac{20}{3}$

$= \dfrac{5 \cdot 2 \cdot 10}{2 \cdot 3 \cdot 3}$

$= \dfrac{50}{9}$

21. $\dfrac{x}{2} = \dfrac{x}{3} + \dfrac{1}{2}$

$6\left(\dfrac{x}{2}\right) = 6\left(\dfrac{x}{3} + \dfrac{1}{2}\right)$

$3x = 6 \cdot \dfrac{x}{3} + 6 \cdot \dfrac{1}{2}$

$3x = 2x + 3$

$3x - 2x = 2x + 3 - 2x$

$x = 3$

22.

$$\frac{x}{2} + \frac{1}{5} = 3 - \frac{x}{5}$$

$$10\left(\frac{x}{2} + \frac{1}{5}\right) = 10\left(3 - \frac{x}{5}\right)$$

$$10\cdot\frac{x}{2} + 10\cdot\frac{1}{5} = 10\cdot 3 - 10\cdot\frac{x}{5}$$

$$5x + 2 = 30 - 2x$$

$$5x + 2 + 2x = 30 - 2x + 2x$$

$$7x + 2 = 30$$

$$7x + 2 - 2 = 30 - 2$$

$$7x = 28$$

$$\frac{7x}{7} = \frac{28}{7}$$

$$x = 4$$

23. a. $4\frac{2}{9} = \frac{9\cdot 4 + 2}{9} = \frac{36 + 2}{9} = \frac{38}{9}$

    b. $1\frac{8}{11} = \frac{11\cdot 1 + 8}{11} = \frac{11 + 8}{11} = \frac{19}{11}$

24. a. $3\frac{2}{5} = \frac{5\cdot 3 + 2}{5} = \frac{15 + 2}{5} = \frac{17}{5}$

    b. $6\frac{2}{7} = \frac{7\cdot 6 + 2}{7} = \frac{42 + 2}{7} = \frac{44}{7}$

25. $0.125 = \frac{125}{1000} = \frac{1}{8}$

26. $0.85 = \frac{85}{100} = \frac{17}{20}$

27. $-105.083 = -105\frac{83}{1000}$

28. $17.015 = 17\frac{15}{1000} = 17\frac{3}{200}$

29.
$$\begin{array}{r} 85.00 \\ -\,17.31 \\ \hline 67.69 \end{array}$$

30.
$$\begin{array}{r} 38.00 \\ -\,10.06 \\ \hline 27.94 \end{array}$$

31. $7.68 \times 10 = 76.8$

32. $12.483 \times 100 = 1248.3$

33. $(-76.3)(1000) = -76,300$

34. $-853.75 \times 10 = -8537.5$

35. $x \div y = 2.5 \div 0.05$

    $0.05\overline{)2.5}$ becomes $5\overline{)250}$

$$\begin{array}{r} 50 \\ 5\overline{)250} \\ -25 \\ \hline 00 \end{array}$$

36. $\dfrac{x}{100} = 4.75$

    $\dfrac{470}{100} \overset{?}{=} 4.75$

    $4.7 = 4.75$ False

    No, 470 is not a solution.

37.   55, 67, 75, 86, 91, 91

    median $= \dfrac{75 + 86}{2} = \dfrac{161}{2} = 80.5$

38.   mean $= \dfrac{36 + 40 + 86 + 30}{4} = \dfrac{192}{4} = 48$

39. $\dfrac{2.5}{3.15} = \dfrac{2500}{3150} = \dfrac{50}{63}$

40. $\dfrac{5.8}{7.6} = \dfrac{58}{76} = \dfrac{29}{38}$

41.

$$\frac{45}{x} = \frac{5}{7}$$

$$45\cdot 7 = 5\cdot x$$

$$315 = 5x$$

$$\frac{315}{5} = \frac{5x}{5}$$

$$63 = x$$

42.

$$\frac{x - 1}{3x + 1} = \frac{3}{8}$$

$$8(x - 1) = 3(3x + 1)$$

$$8x - 8 = 9x + 3$$

$$-8 = x + 3$$

$$-11 = x$$

43. $\dfrac{5 \text{ miles}}{2 \text{ inches}} = \dfrac{x \text{ miles}}{7 \text{ inches}}$

$5 \cdot 7 = 2 \cdot x$

$35 = 2x$

$\dfrac{35}{2} = \dfrac{2x}{2}$

$17.5 = x$

17.5 miles corresponds to 7 inches.

44. $\dfrac{7 \text{ problems}}{6 \text{ minutes}} = \dfrac{x \text{ problems}}{30 \text{ minutes}}$

$7 \cdot 30 = 6 \cdot x$

$210 = 6x$

$\dfrac{210}{6} = \dfrac{6x}{6}$

$35 = x$

The student can complete 35 problems in 30 minutes.

45. $1.9\% = 1.9\left(\dfrac{1}{100}\right) = \dfrac{1.9}{100} = \dfrac{19}{1000}$

46. $2.3\% = 2.3\left(\dfrac{1}{100}\right) = \dfrac{2.3}{100} = \dfrac{23}{1000}$

47. $33\dfrac{1}{3}\% = \dfrac{100}{3}\left(\dfrac{1}{100}\right) = \dfrac{100}{300} = \dfrac{1}{3}$

48. $108\% = 108\left(\dfrac{1}{100}\right) = \dfrac{108}{100} = 1\dfrac{2}{25}$

49. $\underline{\text{What number}}$ is 35% of 60?

$\downarrow \qquad \downarrow\downarrow \quad \downarrow\downarrow$

$x \qquad\quad = 35\% \ \cdot \ 60$

$x \qquad\quad = 0.35 \ \cdot \ 60$

$x \qquad\quad = 21$

21 is 35% of 60.

50. $\underline{\text{What number}}$ is 42% of 85?

$\downarrow \qquad \downarrow\downarrow \quad \downarrow\downarrow$

$x \qquad\quad = 42\% \ \cdot \ 85$

$x \qquad\quad = 0.42 \ \cdot \ 85$

$x \qquad\quad = 35.7$

35.7 is 42% of 85.

Chapter 7

Section 7.1

Practice Problems

1. **a.** English has 6 symbols and each symbol represents 50 million speakers, so English is spoken by 6(50) = 300 million people.

   b. Portuguese has 3.5 symbols, or 3.5(50) = 175 million speakers. So, 300 million − 175 million = 125 million more people speak English than Portuguese.

2. **a.** The height of the bar for birds is 75, so approximately 75 endangered species are birds.

   b. The shortest bar corresponds to arachnids, so arachnids have the fewest endangered species.

3.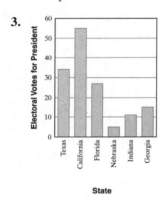

4. The height of the bar for 80–89 is 12, so 12 students scored 80–89 on the test.

5. The height of the bar for 40–49 is 1, for 50–59 is 3, for 60–69 is 2, for 70–79 is 10. So, 1 + 3 + 2 + 10 = 16 students scored less than 80 on the test.

6.

Class Interval (Credit Card Balances)	Tally	Class Frequency (Number of Months)
$0–$49	|||	3
$50–$99	||||	4
$100–$149	||	2
$150–$199	|	1
$200–$249	|	1
$250–$299	|	1

7.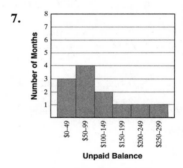

8. **a.** The lowest point on the graph corresponds to January, so the average daily temperature is the lowest during January.

   b. The point on the graph that corresponds to 25 is December, so the average daily temperature is 25°F in December.

   c. The points on the graph that are greater than 70 are June, July, and August. So, the average daily temperature is greater than 70°F in June, July, and August.

Vocabulary and Readiness Check

1. A <u>bar</u> graph presents data using vertical or horizontal bars.

2. A <u>pictograph</u> is a graph in which pictures or symbols are used to visually present data.

3. A <u>line</u> graph displays information with a line that connects data points.

4. A <u>histogram</u> is a special bar graph in which the width of each bar represents a <u>class interval</u> and the height of each bar represents the <u>class frequency</u>.

Exercise Set 7.1

1. Kansas has the greatest number of wheat symbols, so the greatest quantity of acreage in wheat was planted by the state of Kansas.

3. Oklahoma is represented by 3.5 wheat symbols, and each symbol represents 1 million acres, so there were approximately 3.5(1 million) = 3.5 million or 3,500,000 acres of wheat planted.

5. Each wheat symbol represents 1 million acres, so find the state that has $\dfrac{5 \text{ million}}{1 \text{ million}} = 5$ wheat symbols. Montana has 5 wheat symbols, so it plants about 5,000,000 acres of wheat.

7. North Dakota is represented by 8 wheat symbols. From the pictograph, Montana, with 5 symbols, and South Dakota, with 3 symbols, together plant about the same acreage of wheat as North Dakota.

9. The year 2008 has 6.5 flames and each flame represents 12,000 wildfires, so there were approximately 6.5(12,000) = 78,000 wildfires in 2008.

11. The year with the most flames is 2006, so the most wildfires occurred in 2006.

13. 2004 has 5.5 flames and 2006 has 8 flames, which is 2.5 more. Thus, the increase in the number of wildfires from 2004 to 2006 was 2.5(12,000) or 30,000.

15. 2006 has 8 flames, 2007 has 7 flames, and 2008 has 6.5 flames. The average is $\dfrac{8+7+6.5}{3} = 7\dfrac{1}{6}$. Each flame represents 12,000 wildfires, so the average annual number of wildfires from 2006 to 2008 is $7\dfrac{1}{6}(12,000) = 86,000$.

17. The longest bar corresponds to September, so the month in which most hurricanes made landfall is September.

19. The length of the bar for August is 75, so approximately 75 hurricanes made landfall in August.

21. Two of the 76 hurricanes that made landfall in August did so in 2008. The fraction is $\dfrac{2}{76} = \dfrac{1}{38}$.

23. The longest bar corresponds to Tokyo, Japan, and the length of the bar is 33.8 million. So, the city with the largest population is Tokyo, Japan and its population is about 33.8 million or 33,800,000.

25. The longest bar corresponding to a city in the United States is the bar for New York. The population is approximately 21.9 million or 21,900,000.

27. The bar corresponding to Seoul, South Korea has length 23.8 and the bar corresponding to São Paolo, Brazil has length 20.9. Thus, Seoul, South Korea is about 23.8 − 20.9 = 2.9 ≈ 3 million larger than São Paolo, Brazil.

29.

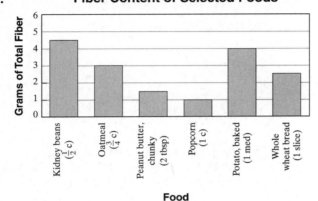

Fiber Content of Selected Foods

31.

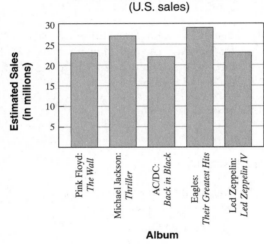

Best-selling Albums of All Time
(U.S. sales)

33. The height of the bar for 100–149 miles per week is 15, so 15 of the adults drive 100–149 miles per week.

35. 29 of the adults drive 0–49 miles per week, 17 of the adults drive 50–99 miles per week, and 15 of the adults drive 100–149 miles per week, so 29 + 17 + 15 = 61 of the adults drive fewer than 150 miles per week.

37. 15 of the adults drive 100–149 miles per week and 9 of the adults drive 150–199 miles per week, so 15 + 9 = 24 of the adults drive 100–199 miles per week.

39. 21 of the adults drive 250–299 miles per week and 9 of the adults drive 200–249 miles per week, so 21 − 9 = 12 more adults drive 250–299 miles per week than 200–249 miles per week.

41. 9 of the 100 adults surveyed drive 150–199 miles per week, so the ratio is $\dfrac{9}{100}$.

43. The tallest bar corresponds to 45–54, so the most householders are in the 45–54 age range.

45. According to the bar graph, approximately 21 million householders will be 55–64 years old.

47. The sum of the first three bars is 21 + 17 + 6 = 44, so approximately 44 million householders will be 44 years old or younger.

49. The height of the bar for 45–54 is 25 and the height of the bar for 55–64 is 21. So approximately $25 - 21 = 4$ million more householders will be 45–54 years old than 55–64 years old.

Class Interval (Scores)	Tally	Class Frequency (Number of Games)
51. 70–79			1
53. 90–99	⧸⧵⧸⧵ |||	8

Class Interval (Account Balances)	Tally	Class Frequency (Number of People)
55. $0–$99	⧸⧵⧸⧵		6
57. $200–$299	⧸⧵⧸⧵		6
59. $400–$499	||	2

61.

63. The point on the graph corresponding to 2004 is 7.8, so the average number of goals per game in 2004 was 7.8.

65. The highest point on the graph corresponds to 2003, so the average number of goals per game was the greatest in 2003.

67. The graph increases between 2004 and 2006, so the average number of goals per game increased from 2004 to 2006.

69. The dots for 2001, 2004, and 2007 are below the 8-level, so the average number of goals per game was less than 8 in 2001, 2004, and 2007.

71. 30% of 12 is $0.30 \cdot 12 = 3.6$.

73. 10% of 62 is $0.10 \cdot 62 = 6.2$

75. $\dfrac{1}{4} = \dfrac{1}{4} \cdot 100\% = \dfrac{25 \cdot 4}{4}\% = 25\%$

77. $\dfrac{17}{50} = \dfrac{17}{50} \cdot 100\% = \dfrac{17 \cdot 2 \cdot 50}{50}\% = 34\%$

79. The point on the high temperature graph corresponding to Thursday is 83, so the high temperature reading on Thursday was 83°F.

81. The lowest point on the graph of low temperatures corresponds to Sunday. The low temperature on Sunday was 68°F.

83. The difference between the graphs is the greatest for Tuesday. The high temperature was 86°F and the low temperature was 73°F, so the difference is $86 - 73 = 13$°F.

85. answers may vary

Section 7.2

Practice Problems

1. Eight of the 100 adults prefer golf. The ratio is
$$\dfrac{\text{adults preferring golf}}{\text{total adults}} = \dfrac{8}{100} = \dfrac{2}{25}$$

2. Add the percents corresponding to Europe, Asia, and South America.
$$20\% + 11\% + 4\% = 35\%$$

3. amount = percent · base
$$= 0.25 \cdot 61,000,000$$
$$= 15,250,000$$
Thus, 15,250,000 tourists might come from Mexico in 2011.

4.

Year	Percent	Degrees in Sector
Freshmen	30%	30% of 360° = 0.30(360°) = 108°
Sophomores	27%	27% of 360° = 0.27(360°) = 97.2°
Juniors	25%	25% of 360° = 0.25(360°) = 90°
Seniors	18%	18% of 360° = 0.18(360°) = 64.8°

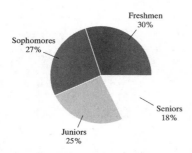

Freshmen 30%

Sophomores 27%

Seniors 18%

Juniors 25%

Vocabulary and Readiness Check

1. In a <u>circle</u> graph, each section (shaped like a piece of pie) shows a category and the relative size of the category.

2. A circle graph contains pie-shaped sections, each called a <u>sector</u>.

3. The number of degrees in a whole circle is <u>360</u>.

4. If a circle graph has percent labels, the percents should add up to <u>100</u>.

Exercise Set 7.2

1. The largest sector corresponds to the category "parent or guardian's home," thus most of the students live in a parent or guardian's home.

3. 180 of the 700 total students live in campus housing.
$$\frac{180}{700} = \frac{9}{35}$$
The ratio is $\frac{9}{35}$.

5. 180 of the students live in campus housing while 320 live in a parent or guardian's home.
$$\frac{180}{320} = \frac{9}{16}$$
The ratio is $\frac{9}{16}$.

7. The largest sector corresponds to Asia. Thus, the largest continent is Asia.

9. 30% + 7% = 37%
37% of the land on Earth is accounted for by Europe and Asia.

11. Asia accounts for 30% of the land on Earth.
30% of 57,000,000 = 0.30 · 57,000,000
= 17,100,000
Asia is 17,100,000 square miles.

13. Australia accounts for 5% of the land on Earth.
5% of 57,000,000 = 0.05 · 57,000,000
= 2,850,000
Australia is 2,850,000 square miles.

15. Add the percent for adult's fiction (33%) to the percent for children's fiction (22%).
33% + 22% = 55%
Thus, 55% of books are classified as some type of fiction.

17. The second-largest sector corresponds to nonfiction, so the second-largest category of books is nonfiction.

19. Nonfiction accounts for 25% of the books.
25% of 125,600 = 0.25 · 125,600 = 31,400
The library has 31,400 nonfiction books.

21. Children's fiction accounts for 22% of the books.
22% of 125,600 = 0.22 · 125,600 = 27,632
The library has 27,632 children's fiction books.

23. Reference or other accounts for 17% + 3% = 20% of the books.
20% of 125,600 = 0.20 · 125,600 = 25,120
The library has 25,120 reference or other books.

25.

Type of Apple	Percent	Degrees in Sector
Red Delicious	37%	37% of 360° = 0.37(360°) ≈ 133°
Golden Delicious	13%	13% of 360° = 0.13(360°) ≈ 47°
Fuji	14%	14% of 360° = 0.14(360°) ≈ 50°
Gala	15%	15% of 360° = 0.15(360°) ≈ 54°
Granny Smith	12%	12% of 360° = 0.12(360°) ≈ 43°
Other varieties	6%	6% of 360° = 0.06(360°) ≈ 22°
Braeburn	3%	3% of 360° = 0.03(360°) ≈ 11°

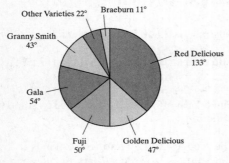

27.

Distribution of Large Dams by Continent		
Continent	Percent	Degrees in Sector
Europe	19%	19% of 360° = 0.19(360°) ≈ 68°
North America	32%	32% of 360° = 0.32(360°) ≈ 115°
South America	3%	3% of 360° = 0.03(360°) ≈ 11°
Asia	39%	39% of 360° = 0.39(360°) ≈ 140°
Africa	5%	5% of 360° = 0.05(360°) = 18°
Australia	2%	2% of 360° = 0.02(360°) ≈ 7°

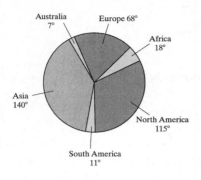

Australia 7°
Europe 68°
Africa 18°
Asia 140°
North America 115°
South America 11°

29. $20 = 2 \cdot 10 = 2 \cdot 2 \cdot 5 = 2^2 \cdot 5$

31. $40 = 2 \cdot 20 = 2 \cdot 2 \cdot 10 = 2 \cdot 2 \cdot 2 \cdot 5 = 2^3 \cdot 5$

33. $85 = 5 \cdot 17$

35. answers may vary

37. Pacific Ocean:
$$49\% \cdot 264,489,800 = 0.49 \cdot 264,489,800$$
$$= 129,600,002 \text{ square}$$
$$\text{kilometers}$$

39. Indian Ocean:
$$21\% \cdot 264,489,800 = 0.21 \cdot 264,489,800$$
$$= 55,542,858 \text{ square}$$
$$\text{kilometers}$$

41. $21.5\% \cdot 2800 = 0.215 \cdot 2800 = 602$ respondents

43. $21.5\% + 59.8\% = 81.3\%$
$0.813 \cdot 2800 \approx 2276$ respondents

45.
$$\frac{\text{number of respondents who spend } \$0 - \$15}{\text{number of respondents who spend } \$15 - \$175}$$
$$= \frac{602}{1674}$$
$$= \frac{2 \cdot 301}{2 \cdot 837}$$
$$= \frac{301}{837}$$

47. no; answers may vary

Integrated Review

1. Customer service representatives has 10 figures and each figure represents 50,000 workers. Thus, the increase in the number of customer service representatives is approximately
$10 \cdot 50,000 = 500,000$.

2. Post-secondary teachers has 11 figures and each figure represents 50,000 workers. Thus, the increase in the number of post-secondary teachers is approximately
$11 \cdot 50,000 = 550,000$.

3. Retail salespeople has the greatest number of figures, so the greatest increase is expected for retail salespeople.

4. Waitstaff has the least number of figures, so the least increase is expected for waitstaff.

5. The tallest bar corresponds to Oroville, CA. Thus, the U.S. dam with the greatest height is the Oroville Dam, which is approximately 755 feet.

6. The bar whose height is between 625 and 650 feet corresponds to New Bullards Bar, CA. Thus, the U.S. dam with a height between 625 and 650 feet is the New Bullards Bar Dam, which is approximately 635 feet.

7. From the graph, the Hoover Dam is approximately 725 feet and the Glen Canyon Dam is approximately 710 feet. The Hoover Dam is $725 - 710 = 15$ feet higher than the Glen Canyon Dam.

8. There are 4 bars that are taller than the 700-feet level, so there are 4 dams with heights over 700 feet.

9. The highest points on the graph correspond to Thursday and Saturday. Thus, the highest temperature occurs on Thursday and Saturday and is 100°F.

10. The lowest point on the graph corresponds to Monday. Thus, the lowest temperature occurs on Monday, and is 82°F.

11. The points on the graph that are lower than the 90 level correspond to Sunday, Monday, and Tuesday. Thus, the temperature was less than 90°F on Sunday, Monday, and Tuesday.

12. The points on the graph that are higher than the 90 level correspond to Wednesday, Thursday, Friday, and Saturday. Thus, the temperature was greater than 90°F on Wednesday, Thursday, Friday, and Saturday.

13. The sector corresponding to whole milk is 35%.
35% of $200 = 0.35 \cdot 200 = 70$
Thus, 70 quart containers of whole milk are sold.

14. The sector corresponding to skim milk is 26%.
26% of 200 = 0.26 · 200 = 52
Thus, 52 quart containers of skim milk are sold.

15. The sector corresponding to buttermilk is 1%.
1% of 200 = 0.01 · 200 = 2
Thus, 2 quart containers of buttermilk are sold.

16. The sector corresponding to Flavored reduced fat
and skim milk is 3%.
3% of 200 = 0.03 · 200 = 6
Thus, 6 quart containers of flavored reduced fat
and skim milk are sold.

	Class Intervals (Scores)	Tally	Class Frequency (Number of Quizzes)
17.	50–59	‖	2
18.	60–69	∣	1
19.	70–79	‖‖	3
20.	80–89	⫴‖∣	6
21.	90–99	⫴‖	5

22.

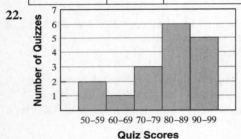

Section 7.3

Practice Problems

1. $\sqrt{100} = 10$ because $10^2 = 100$.

2. $\sqrt{64} = 8$ because $8^2 = 64$.

3. $\sqrt{169} = 13$ because $13^2 = 169$.

4. $\sqrt{0} = 0$ because $0^2 = 0$.

5. $\sqrt{\dfrac{1}{4}} = \dfrac{1}{2}$ because $\left(\dfrac{1}{2}\right)^2 = \dfrac{1}{4}$.

6. $\sqrt{\dfrac{9}{16}} = \dfrac{3}{4}$ because $\left(\dfrac{3}{4}\right)^2 = \dfrac{9}{16}$.

7. a. $\sqrt{10} \approx 3.162$

   b. $\sqrt{62} \approx 7.874$

8. Recall that $\sqrt{49} = 7$ and $\sqrt{64} = 8$. Since 62 is
between 49 and 64, then $\sqrt{62}$ is between $\sqrt{49}$
and $\sqrt{64}$. Thus, $\sqrt{62}$ is between 7 and 8. Since
62 is closer to 64, then $\sqrt{62}$ is closer to $\sqrt{64}$, or
8.

9. Let $a = 12$ and $b = 16$.
$$a^2 + b^2 = c^2$$
$$12^2 + 16^2 = c^2$$
$$144 + 256 = c^2$$
$$400 = c^2$$
$$\sqrt{400} = c$$
$$20 = c$$
The hypotenuse is 20 feet.

10. Let $a = 9$ and $b = 7$.
$$a^2 + b^2 = c^2$$
$$9^2 + 7^2 = c^2$$
$$81 + 49 = c^2$$
$$130 = c^2$$
$$\sqrt{130} = c$$
$$11 \approx c$$
The hypotenuse is approximately 11 kilometers.

11. Let $a = 7$ and $c = 13$.
$$a^2 + b^2 = c^2$$
$$7^2 + b^2 = 13^2$$
$$49 + b^2 = 169$$
$$b^2 = 120$$
$$b = \sqrt{120}$$
$$b \approx 10.95$$
The length of the hypotenuse is exactly
$\sqrt{120}$ feet or approximately 10.95 feet.

12.

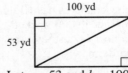

Let $a = 53$ and $b = 100$.

$$a^2 + b^2 = c^2$$
$$53^2 + 100^2 = c^2$$
$$2809 + 10,000 = c^2$$
$$12,809 = c^2$$
$$\sqrt{12,809} = c$$
$$113 \approx c$$

The diagonal is approximately 113 yards.

Calculator Explorations

1. $\sqrt{1024} = 32$

2. $\sqrt{676} = 26$

3. $\sqrt{15} \approx 3.873$

4. $\sqrt{19} \approx 4.359$

5. $\sqrt{97} \approx 9.849$

6. $\sqrt{56} \approx 7.483$

Vocabulary and Readiness Check

1. The square roots of 100 are <u>10</u> and <u>−10</u> because $10 \cdot 10 = 100$ and $(-10)(-10) = 100$.

2. $\sqrt{100} = \underline{10}$ only because $10 \cdot 10 = 100$ and 10 is positive.

3. The <u>radical</u> sign is used to denote the positive square root of a nonnegative number.

4. The reverse process of <u>squaring</u> a number is finding a square root of a number.

5. The numbers 9, 1, and $\frac{1}{25}$ are called <u>perfect squares</u>.

6. Label the parts of the right triangle.

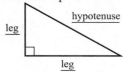

7. In the given triangle, $a^2 + \underline{c^2} = \underline{b^2}$.

8. The <u>Pythagorean Theorem</u> can be used for right triangles.

Exercise Set 7.3

1. $\sqrt{4} = 2$ because $2^2 = 4$.

3. $\sqrt{121} = 11$ because $11^2 = 121$.

5. $\sqrt{\frac{1}{81}} = \frac{1}{9}$ because $\left(\frac{1}{9}\right)^2 = \frac{1}{9} \cdot \frac{1}{9} = \frac{1}{81}$.

7. $\sqrt{\frac{16}{64}} = \frac{4}{8} = \frac{1}{2}$ because $\left(\frac{4}{8}\right)^2 = \frac{4}{8} \cdot \frac{4}{8} = \frac{16}{64}$.

9. $\sqrt{3} \approx 1.732$

11. $\sqrt{15} \approx 3.873$

13. $\sqrt{31} \approx 5.568$

15. $\sqrt{26} \approx 5.099$

17. Since 38 is between $36 = 6 \cdot 6$ and $49 = 7 \cdot 7$, $\sqrt{38}$ is between 6 and 7; $\sqrt{38} \approx 6.16$.

19. Since 101 is between $100 = 10 \cdot 10$ and $121 = 11 \cdot 11$, $\sqrt{101}$ is between 10 and 11; $\sqrt{101} \approx 10.05$.

21. $\sqrt{256} = 16$ because $16^2 = 256$.

23. $\sqrt{92} \approx 9.592$

25. $\sqrt{\frac{49}{144}} = \frac{7}{12}$ because $\left(\frac{7}{12}\right)^2 = \frac{7}{12} \cdot \frac{7}{12} = \frac{49}{144}$.

27. $\sqrt{71} \approx 8.426$

29. Let $a = 5$ and $b = 12$.
$$a^2 + b^2 = c^2$$
$$5^2 + 12^2 = c^2$$
$$25 + 144 = c^2$$
$$169 = c^2$$
$$\sqrt{169} = c$$
$$13 = c$$
The missing length is 13 inches.

31. Let $a = 10$ and $c = 12$.

$$a^2 + b^2 = c^2$$
$$10^2 + b^2 = 12^2$$
$$100 + b^2 = 144$$
$$b^2 = 44$$
$$b = \sqrt{44}$$
$$b \approx 6.633$$

The missing length is approximately 6.633 centimeters.

33. Let $a = 22$ and $b = 48$.

$$c^2 = a^2 + b^2$$
$$c^2 = 22^2 + 48^2$$
$$c^2 = 484 + 2304$$
$$c^2 = 2788$$
$$c = \sqrt{2788}$$
$$c \approx 52.802$$

The missing length is approximately 52.802 meters.

35. Let $a = 108$ and $b = 45$.

$$a^2 + b^2 = c^2$$
$$108^2 + 45^2 = c^2$$
$$11,664 + 2025 = c^2$$
$$13,689 = c^2$$
$$\sqrt{13,689} = c$$
$$117 = c$$

The missing length is 117 millimeters.

37.

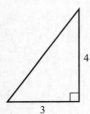

$$\text{hypotenuse} = \sqrt{(\text{leg})^2 + (\text{other leg})^2}$$
$$= \sqrt{(3)^2 + (4)^2}$$
$$= \sqrt{9 + 16}$$
$$= \sqrt{25}$$
$$= 5$$

The hypotenuse has length 5 units.

39.

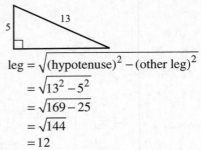

$$\text{leg} = \sqrt{(\text{hypotenuse})^2 - (\text{other leg})^2}$$
$$= \sqrt{13^2 - 5^2}$$
$$= \sqrt{169 - 25}$$
$$= \sqrt{144}$$
$$= 12$$

The leg has length 12 units.

41.

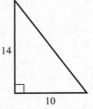

$$\text{hypotenuse} = \sqrt{(\text{leg})^2 + (\text{other leg})^2}$$
$$= \sqrt{(10)^2 + (14)^2}$$
$$= \sqrt{100 + 196}$$
$$= \sqrt{296}$$
$$\approx 17.205$$

The hypotenuse has length of about 17.205 units.

43.

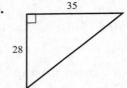

$$\text{hypotenuse} = \sqrt{(\text{leg})^2 + (\text{other leg})^2}$$
$$= \sqrt{35^2 + 28^2}$$
$$= \sqrt{1225 + 784}$$
$$= \sqrt{2009}$$
$$\approx 44.822$$

The hypotenuse has length of about 44.822 units.

45.

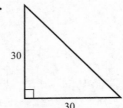

$$\text{hypotenuse} = \sqrt{(\text{leg})^2 + (\text{other leg})^2}$$
$$= \sqrt{(30)^2 + (30)^2}$$
$$= \sqrt{900 + 900}$$
$$= \sqrt{1800}$$
$$\approx 42.426$$

The hypotenuse has length of about 42.426 units.

47.

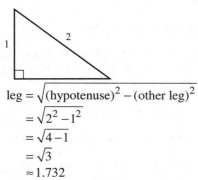

$$\text{leg} = \sqrt{(\text{hypotenuse})^2 - (\text{other leg})^2}$$
$$= \sqrt{2^2 - 1^2}$$
$$= \sqrt{4 - 1}$$
$$= \sqrt{3}$$
$$\approx 1.732$$

The leg has length of about 1.732 units.

49.

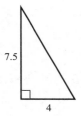

$$\text{hypotenuse} = \sqrt{(\text{leg})^2 + (\text{other leg})^2}$$
$$= \sqrt{(7.5)^2 + (4)^2}$$
$$= \sqrt{56.25 + 16}$$
$$= \sqrt{72.25}$$
$$= 8.5$$

The hypotenuse has length 8.5 units.

51. $\text{hypotenuse} = \sqrt{(\text{leg})^2 + (\text{other leg})^2}$
$$= \sqrt{100^2 + 100^2}$$
$$= \sqrt{10,000 + 10,000}$$
$$= \sqrt{20,000}$$
$$\approx 141.42$$

The length of the diagonal is about 141.42 yards.

53. $\text{leg} = \sqrt{(\text{hypotenuse})^2 - (\text{other leg})^2}$
$$= \sqrt{(32)^2 - (20)^2}$$
$$= \sqrt{1024 - 400}$$
$$= \sqrt{624}$$
$$\approx 25.0$$

The tree is about 25.0 feet tall.

55. $\text{hypotenuse} = \sqrt{(\text{leg})^2 + (\text{other leg})^2}$
$$= \sqrt{160^2 + 300^2}$$
$$= \sqrt{25,600 + 90,000}$$
$$= \sqrt{115,600}$$
$$= 340$$

The length of the run was 340 feet.

57. $\dfrac{10}{12} = \dfrac{5 \cdot 2}{6 \cdot 2} = \dfrac{5}{6}$

59. $\dfrac{2x}{60} = \dfrac{2 \cdot x}{2 \cdot 30} = \dfrac{x}{30}$

61. $\dfrac{9}{13y} + \dfrac{12}{13y} = \dfrac{9 + 12}{13y} = \dfrac{21}{13y}$

63. $\dfrac{9}{8} \cdot \dfrac{x}{8} = \dfrac{9 \cdot x}{8 \cdot 8} = \dfrac{9x}{64}$

65. Recall that $\sqrt{36} = 6$ and $\sqrt{49} = 7$. Since 38 is between 36 and 49, then $\sqrt{38}$ is between $\sqrt{36}$ and $\sqrt{49}$. Thus, $\sqrt{38}$ is between 6 and 7. Since 38 is closer to 36, then $\sqrt{38}$ is closer to $\sqrt{36}$, or 6. Check: $\sqrt{38} \approx 6.16$

67. Recall that $\sqrt{100} = 10$ and $\sqrt{121} = 11$. Since 101 is between 100 and 121, then $\sqrt{101}$ is between $\sqrt{100}$ and $\sqrt{121}$. Thus, $\sqrt{101}$ is between 10 and 11. Since 101 is closer to 100, then $\sqrt{101}$ is closer to $\sqrt{100}$, or 10. Check: $\sqrt{101} \approx 10.05$

69. answers may vary

71.
$$a^2 + b^2 = c^2$$
$$25^2 + 60^2 \stackrel{?}{=} 65^2$$
$$625 + 3600 \stackrel{?}{=} 4225$$
$$4225 = 4225$$
Yes, the set forms the lengths of the sides of a right triangle.

73. Find the missing length in the large right triangle by letting $a = 8$ and $c = 12$.
$$a^2 + b^2 = c^2$$
$$8^2 + b^2 = 12^2$$
$$64 + b^2 = 144$$
$$b^2 = 80$$
$$b = \sqrt{80}$$
Find the unlabeled length by letting $a = 8$ and $c = 10$.
$$a^2 + b^2 = c^2$$
$$8^2 + b^2 = 10^2$$
$$64 + b^2 = 100$$
$$b^2 = 36$$
$$b^2 = \sqrt{36}$$
$$b = 6$$
The unlabeled length is 6 inches. Thus $6 + x = \sqrt{80}$ or $x = \sqrt{80} - 6 \approx 2.94$ inches.

Section 7.4

Practice Problems

1. a. The triangles are congruent by Side-Angle-Side.

b. The triangles are not congruent.

2. $\dfrac{9 \text{ meters}}{13 \text{ meters}} = \dfrac{9}{13}$

The ratio of corresponding sides is $\dfrac{9}{13}$.

3. $\dfrac{x}{5} = \dfrac{6}{9}$
$$x \cdot 9 = 5 \cdot 6$$
$$9x = 30$$
$$\dfrac{9x}{9} = \dfrac{30}{9}$$
$$x = \dfrac{10}{3} \text{ or } 3\dfrac{1}{3}$$

4. $\dfrac{5}{n} = \dfrac{8}{60}$
$$5 \cdot 60 = n \cdot 8$$
$$300 = 8n$$
$$\dfrac{300}{8} = \dfrac{8n}{8}$$
$$37.5 = n$$
The height of the building is approximately 37.5 feet.

Vocabulary and Readiness Check

1. Two triangles that have the same shape, but not necessarily the same size are congruent. <u>false</u>

2. Two triangles are congruent if they have the same shape and size. <u>true</u>

3. Congruent triangles are also similar. <u>true</u>

4. Similar triangles are also congruent. <u>false</u>

5. For the two similar triangles, the ratio of corresponding sides is $\dfrac{5}{6}$. <u>false</u>

Exercise Set 7.4

1. The triangles are congruent by Side-Side-Side.

3. The triangles are not congruent.

5. The triangles are congruent by Angle-Side-Angle.

7. The triangles are congruent by Side-Angle-Side.

9. $\dfrac{22}{11} = \dfrac{14}{7} = \dfrac{12}{6} = \dfrac{2}{1}$

The ratio of corresponding sides is $\dfrac{2}{1}$.

11. $\dfrac{10.5}{7} = \dfrac{9}{6} = \dfrac{12}{8} = \dfrac{3}{2}$

13. $\dfrac{x}{3} = \dfrac{9}{6}$
$$x \cdot 6 = 3 \cdot 9$$
$$6x = 27$$
$$\dfrac{6x}{6} = \dfrac{27}{6}$$
$$x = 4.5$$

15.
$$\frac{n}{18} = \frac{4}{12}$$
$$n \cdot 12 = 18 \cdot 4$$
$$12n = 72$$
$$\frac{12n}{12} = \frac{72}{12}$$
$$n = 6$$

17.
$$\frac{y}{3.75} = \frac{12}{9}$$
$$y \cdot 9 = 12 \cdot 3.75$$
$$9y = 45$$
$$\frac{9y}{9} = \frac{45}{9}$$
$$y = 5$$

19.
$$\frac{z}{18} = \frac{30}{40}$$
$$z \cdot 40 = 18 \cdot 30$$
$$40z = 540$$
$$\frac{40z}{40} = \frac{540}{40}$$
$$z = 13.5$$

21.
$$\frac{x}{3.25} = \frac{17.5}{3.25}$$
$$x \cdot 3.25 = 3.25 \cdot 17.5$$
$$3.25x = 56.875$$
$$\frac{3.25x}{3.25} = \frac{56.875}{3.25}$$
$$x = 17.5$$

23.
$$\frac{y}{2} = \frac{18\frac{1}{3}}{3\frac{2}{3}}$$
$$y \cdot 3\frac{2}{3} = 2 \cdot 18\frac{1}{3}$$
$$y \cdot \frac{11}{3} = 2 \cdot \frac{55}{3}$$
$$\frac{11}{3} \cdot y = \frac{110}{3}$$
$$\frac{3}{11} \cdot \frac{11}{3} y = \frac{3}{11} \cdot \frac{110}{3}$$
$$y = 10$$

25.
$$\frac{z}{60} = \frac{15}{32}$$
$$z \cdot 32 = 60 \cdot 15$$
$$32z = 900$$
$$\frac{32z}{32} = \frac{900}{32}$$
$$z = 28.125$$

27.
$$\frac{x}{7} = \frac{15}{10\frac{1}{2}}$$
$$x \cdot 10\frac{1}{2} = 7 \cdot 15$$
$$10.5x = 105$$
$$\frac{10.5x}{10.5} = \frac{105}{10.5}$$
$$x = 10$$

29.
$$\frac{x}{13} = \frac{80}{2}$$
$$x \cdot 2 = 13 \cdot 80$$
$$2x = 1040$$
$$\frac{2x}{2} = \frac{1040}{2}$$
$$x = 520$$
The observation deck is 520 feet high.

31.
$$\frac{x}{25} = \frac{40}{2}$$
$$x \cdot 2 = 40 \cdot 25$$
$$2x = 1000$$
$$\frac{2x}{2} = \frac{1000}{2}$$
$$x = 500$$
The building is 500 feet tall.

33.
$$\frac{x}{18} = \frac{24}{30}$$
$$x \cdot 30 = 18 \cdot 24$$
$$30x = 432$$
$$\frac{30x}{30} = \frac{432}{30}$$
$$x = 14.4$$
The shadow of the tree is 14.4 feet long.

35. $$\frac{x}{55} = \frac{19}{20}$$
$$x \cdot 20 = 55 \cdot 19$$
$$20x = 1045$$
$$\frac{20x}{20} = \frac{1045}{20}$$
$$x = 52.25$$
$$x \approx 52$$
Pete can place 52 neon tetras in the tank.

37. Let $a = 200$ and $c = 430$.
$$a^2 + b^2 = c^2$$
$$200^2 + b^2 = 430^2$$
$$40,000 + b^2 = 184,900$$
$$b^2 = 144,900$$
$$b = \sqrt{144,900}$$
$$b \approx 381$$
The gantry is approximately 381 feet tall.

39. $$\begin{array}{r} 3.60 \\ + \ 0.41 \\ \hline 4.01 \end{array}$$

41. $(0.41)(-3) = -1.23$

43. Let x be the new width.
$$\frac{x}{7} = \frac{5}{9}$$
$$x \cdot 9 = 7 \cdot 5$$
$$9x = 35$$
$$\frac{9x}{9} = \frac{35}{9}$$
$$x = 3\frac{8}{9}$$

The new width is $3\frac{8}{9}$ inches. No, it will not fit

on a 3-by-5-inch card because $3\frac{8}{9} > 3$.

45. $$\frac{n}{5.2} = \frac{12.6}{7.8}$$
$$n \cdot 7.8 = 5.2 \cdot 12.6$$
$$7.8n = 65.52$$
$$\frac{7.8n}{7.8} = \frac{65.52}{7.8}$$
$$n = 8.4$$

47. answers may vary

49. $$\frac{x}{5} = \frac{10}{\frac{1}{4}}$$
$$x \cdot \frac{1}{4} = 5 \cdot 10$$
$$\frac{1}{4}x = 50$$
$$x = 200$$
$$\frac{y}{7\frac{1}{2}} = \frac{10}{\frac{1}{4}}$$
$$y \cdot \frac{1}{4} = 7\frac{1}{2} \cdot 10$$
$$\frac{1}{4}y = 75$$
$$y = 300$$
$$\frac{z}{10\frac{5}{8}} = \frac{10}{\frac{1}{4}}$$
$$z \cdot \frac{1}{4} = 10\frac{5}{8} \cdot 10$$
$$\frac{1}{4}z = 106.25$$
$$z = 425$$
The actual proposed dimensions are 200 feet by 300 feet by 425 feet.

Section 7.5

Practice Problems

1.

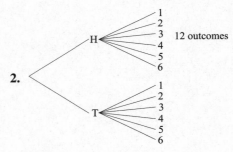

8 outcomes

2.

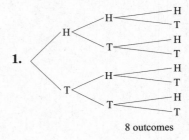

12 outcomes

3. The possibilities are:
H, H, H,   H, H, T,   H, T, H,   H, T, T,
T, H, H,   T, H, T,   T, T, H,   T, T, T
T, H, T is one of the 8 possible outcomes, so the
probability is $\frac{1}{8}$.

4. A 2 or a 5 are two of the six possible outcomes.
The probability is $\frac{2}{6} = \frac{1}{3}$.

5. A blue is 2 out of the 4 possible marbles. The
probability is $\frac{2}{4} = \frac{1}{2}$.

Vocabulary and Readiness Check

1. A possible result of an experiment is called an
<u>outcome</u>.

2. A <u>tree diagram</u> shows each outcome of an
experiment as a separate branch.

3. The <u>probability</u> of an event is a measure of the
likelihood of it occurring.

4. <u>Probability</u> is calculated by number of ways that
the event can occur divided by number of
possible outcomes.

5. A probability of <u>0</u> means that an event won't
occur.

6. A probability of <u>1</u> means that an event is certain
to occur.

Exercise Set 7.5

1.

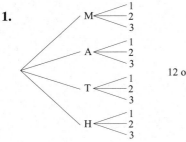

12 outcomes

3.

3 outcomes

5.

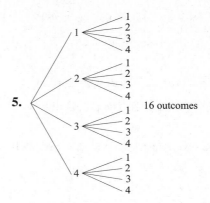

16 outcomes

7.

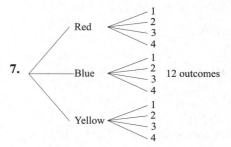

12 outcomes

9.

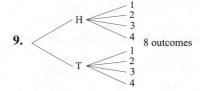

8 outcomes

11. A 5 is one of the six possible outcomes. The
probability is $\frac{1}{6}$.

13. A 1 or a 6 are two of the six possible outcomes.
The probability is $\frac{2}{6} = \frac{1}{3}$.

15. Three of the six possible outcomes are even. The
probability is $\frac{3}{6} = \frac{1}{2}$.

17. Four of the six possible outcomes are numbers
greater than 2. The probability is $\frac{4}{6} = \frac{2}{3}$.

19. A 2 is one of three possible outcomes. The
probability is $\frac{1}{3}$.

21. A 1, a 2, or a 3 are three of three possible outcomes. The probability is $\frac{3}{3} = 1$.

23. An odd number is a 1 or a 3, which are two of three possible outcomes. The probability is $\frac{2}{3}$.

25. One of the seven marbles is red. The probability is $\frac{1}{7}$.

27. Two of the seven marbles are yellow. The probability is $\frac{2}{7}$.

29. Four of the seven marbles are either green or red. The probability is $\frac{4}{7}$.

31. The blood pressure was higher for 38 of the 200 people. The probability is $\frac{38}{200} = \frac{19}{100}$.

33. The blood pressure did not change for 10 of the 200 people. The probability is $\frac{10}{200} = \frac{1}{20}$.

35. $\frac{1}{2} + \frac{1}{3} = \frac{1}{2} \cdot \frac{3}{3} + \frac{1}{3} \cdot \frac{2}{2} = \frac{3}{6} + \frac{2}{6} = \frac{3+2}{6} = \frac{5}{6}$

37. $\frac{1}{2} \cdot \frac{1}{3} = \frac{1 \cdot 1}{2 \cdot 3} = \frac{1}{6}$

39. $5 \div \frac{3}{4} = \frac{5}{1} \div \frac{3}{4} = \frac{5}{1} \cdot \frac{4}{3} = \frac{5 \cdot 4}{1 \cdot 3} = \frac{20}{3}$ or $6\frac{2}{3}$

41. One of the 52 cards is the king of hearts. The probability is $\frac{1}{52}$.

43. Four of the 52 cards are kings. The probability is $\frac{4}{52} = \frac{1}{13}$.

45. Thirteen of the 52 cards are hearts. The probability is $\frac{13}{52} = \frac{1}{4}$.

47. Twenty six of the cards are in black ink. The probability is $\frac{26}{52} = \frac{1}{2}$.

Tree diagram for 49.–51.

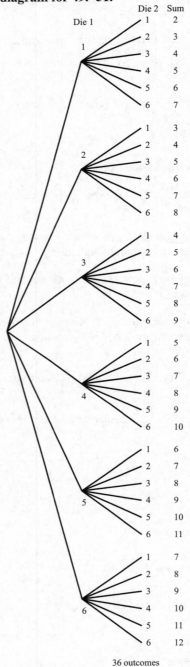

36 outcomes

49. Five of the 36 sums are 6. The probability is $\frac{5}{36}$.

51. None of the 36 sums are 13. The probability is
$\frac{0}{36} = 0$.

53. answers may vary

Chapter 7 Vocabulary Check

1. <u>Congruent</u> triangles have the same shape and the same size.

2. <u>Similar</u> triangles have exactly the same shape but not necessarily the same size.

3–5.

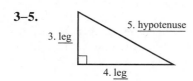

6. A triangle with one right angle is called a <u>right</u> triangle.

7. In the right triangle,

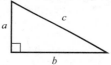

$a^2 + b^2 = c^2$ is called the <u>Pythagorean</u> theorem.

8. A <u>bar</u> graph presents data using vertical or horizontal bars.

9. The possible results of an experiment are the <u>outcomes</u>.

10. A <u>pictograph</u> is a graph in which pictures or symbols are used to visually present data.

11. A <u>tree diagram</u> is one way to picture and count outcomes.

12. An <u>experiment</u> is an activity being considered, such as tossing a coin or rolling a die.

13. In a <u>circle</u> graph, each section (shaped like a piece of pie) shows a category and the relative size of the category.

14. The <u>probability</u> of an event is
$\frac{\text{number of ways that event can occur}}{\text{number of possible outcomes}}$.

15. A <u>histogram</u> is a special bar graph in which the width of each bar represents a <u>class interval</u> and the height of each bar represents the <u>class frequency</u>.

Chapter 7 Review

1. Midwest has 4 houses, and each house represents 500,000 homes, so there were
$4(500,000) = 2,000,000$ new homes constructed in the Midwest.

2. Northeast has 3.5 houses, and each house represents 500,000 homes, so there were
$3.5(500,000) = 1,750,000$ new homes constructed in the Northeast.

3. South has the greatest number of houses, so the most new homes constructed were in the South.

4. Northeast has the least number of houses, so the fewest new homes constructed were in the Northeast.

5. Each house represents 500,000 homes, so look for the regions with $\frac{3,000,000}{500,000} = 6$ or more houses. The South and West had 3,000,000 or more new homes constructed.

6. Each house represents 500,000 homes, so look for the regions with fewer than
$\frac{3,000,000}{500,000} = 8$ houses. The Northeast and Midwest had fewer than 3,000,000 new homes constructed.

7. The height of the bar representing 1970 is 11. Thus, approximately 11% of persons completed four or more years of college in 1970.

8. The tallest bar corresponds to 2006. Thus, the greatest percent of persons completing four or more years of college was in 2006.

9. The bars whose height is at a level of 20 or more are 1990, 2000, and 2006. Thus, 20% or more persons completed four or more years of college in 1990, 2000, and 2006.

10. answers may vary

11. The point on the graph corresponding to 2008 is about 960. Thus, there were approximately 960 medals awarded at the Summer Olympics in 2008.

12. The point on the graph corresponding to 2000 is about 920. Thus, there were approximately 920 medals awarded at the Summer Olympics in 2000.

13. The point on the graph corresponding to 2004 is about 930. Thus, there were approximately 930 medals awarded at the Summer Olympics in 2004.

14. The point on the graph corresponding to 1992 is about 815. Thus, there were approximately 815 medals awarded at the Summer Olympics in 1992.

15. The points on the graph corresponding to 1996 and 1992 are 840 and 815, respectively. Thus, there were 840 − 815 = 25 more medals awarded in 1996 than in 1992.

16. The points on the graph corresponding to 2008 and 1992 are 960 and 815, respectively. Thus, there were 960 − 815 = 145 more medals awarded in 2008 than in 1992.

17. The height of the bar corresponding to 41–45 is 1. Thus, 1 employee works 41–45 hours per week.

18. The height of the bar corresponding to 21–25 is 4. Thus, 4 employees work 21–25 hours per week.

19. Add the heights of the bars corresponding to 16–20, 21–25, and 26–30. Thus, 6 + 4 + 8 = 18 employees work 30 hours or less per week.

20. Add the heights of the bars corresponding to 36–40 and 41–45. Thus, 8 + 1 = 9 employees work 36 or more hours per week.

	Class Interval (Temperatures)	Tally	Class Frequency (Number of Months)
21.	80°–89°	⠀卌	5
22.	90°–99°	|||	3
23.	100°–109°	||||	4

24.

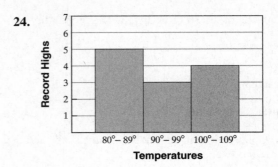

25. The largest sector corresponds to the category "Mortgage payment," thus the largest budget item is mortgage payment.

26. The smallest sector corresponds to the category "Utilities," thus the smallest budget item is utilities.

27. Add the amounts for mortgage payment and utilities. Thus, $975 + $250 = $1225 is budgeted for the mortgage payment and utilities.

28. Add the amounts for savings and contributions. Thus, $400 + $300 = $700 is budgeted for savings and contributions.

29. $\dfrac{\text{mortgage payment}}{\text{total}} = \dfrac{\$975}{\$4000} = \dfrac{39 \cdot 25}{160 \cdot 25} = \dfrac{39}{160}$

The ratio is $\dfrac{39}{160}$.

30. $\dfrac{\text{food}}{\text{total}} = \dfrac{\$700}{\$4000} = \dfrac{7 \cdot 100}{40 \cdot 100} = \dfrac{7}{40}$

The ratio is $\dfrac{7}{40}$.

31. The sector corresponding to Asia is 62%.
62% of 61 = 0.62 · 61 ≈ 38
Thus, 38 tall buildings are located in Asia.

32. The sector corresponding to North America is 29.5%.
29.5% of 61 = 0.295 · 61 ≈ 18
Thus, 18 tall buildings are located in North America.

33. The sector corresponding to Oceania is 1.6%.
1.6% of 61 = 0.016 · 61 ≈ 1
Thus, 1 tall building is located in Oceania.

34. The sector corresponding to Europe is 6.6%.
6.6% of 61 = 0.066 · 61 ≈ 4
Thus, 4 tall buildings are located in Europe.

35. $\sqrt{64} = 8$ because $8^2 = 64$.

36. $\sqrt{144} = 12$ because $12^2 = 144$.

37. $\sqrt{12} \approx 3.464$

38. $\sqrt{15} \approx 3.873$

39. $\sqrt{0} = 0$ because $0^2 = 0$.

40. $\sqrt{1} = 1$ because $1^2 = 1$.

41. $\sqrt{50} \approx 7.071$

42. $\sqrt{65} \approx 8.062$

43. $\sqrt{\dfrac{4}{25}} = \dfrac{2}{5}$ because $\left(\dfrac{2}{5}\right)^2 = \dfrac{2}{5} \cdot \dfrac{2}{5} = \dfrac{4}{25}$.

44. $\sqrt{\dfrac{1}{100}} = \dfrac{1}{10}$ because $\left(\dfrac{1}{10}\right)^2 = \dfrac{1}{10} \cdot \dfrac{1}{10} = \dfrac{1}{100}$.

45. hypotenuse $= \sqrt{(\text{leg})^2 + (\text{other leg})^2}$
$$= \sqrt{12^2 + 5^2}$$
$$= \sqrt{144 + 25}$$
$$= \sqrt{169}$$
$$= 13$$
The leg has length 13 units.

46. hypotenuse $= \sqrt{(\text{leg})^2 + (\text{other leg})^2}$
$$= \sqrt{20^2 + 21^2}$$
$$= \sqrt{400 + 441}$$
$$= \sqrt{841}$$
$$= 29$$
The leg has length 29 units.

47. leg $= \sqrt{(\text{hypotenuse})^2 - (\text{other leg})^2}$
$$= \sqrt{14^2 - 9^2}$$
$$= \sqrt{196 - 81}$$
$$= \sqrt{115}$$
$$\approx 10.7$$
The leg has length of about 10.7 units.

48. leg $= \sqrt{(\text{hypotenuse})^2 - (\text{other leg})^2}$
$$= \sqrt{86^2 - 66^2}$$
$$= \sqrt{7396 - 4356}$$
$$= \sqrt{3040}$$
$$\approx 55.1$$
The leg has length of about 55.1 units.

49. hypotenuse $= \sqrt{(\text{leg})^2 + (\text{other leg})^2}$
$$= \sqrt{20^2 + 20^2}$$
$$= \sqrt{400 + 400}$$
$$= \sqrt{800}$$
$$\approx 28.28$$
The diagonal is about 28.28 centimeters.

50. leg $= \sqrt{(\text{hypotenuse})^2 - (\text{other leg})^2}$
$$= \sqrt{126^2 - 90^2}$$
$$= \sqrt{15,876 - 8100}$$
$$= \sqrt{7776}$$
$$\approx 88.2$$
The height is about 88.2 feet.

51. The triangles are congruent by Angle-Side-Angle.

52. The triangles are not congruent.

53. $\dfrac{x}{20} = \dfrac{20}{30}$
$$x \cdot 30 = 20 \cdot 20$$
$$30x = 400$$
$$\dfrac{30x}{30} = \dfrac{400}{30}$$
$$x = \dfrac{40}{3} \text{ or } 13\dfrac{1}{3}$$

54. $\dfrac{x}{5.8} = \dfrac{24}{8}$
$$x \cdot 8 = 5.8 \cdot 24$$
$$8x = 139.2$$
$$\dfrac{8x}{8} = \dfrac{139.2}{8}$$
$$x = 17.4$$

55. $\dfrac{x}{5.5} = \dfrac{42}{7}$

$x \cdot 7 = 5.5 \cdot 42$

$7x = 231$

$\dfrac{7x}{7} = \dfrac{231}{7}$

$x = 33$

The height of the building is approximately 33 feet.

56. $\dfrac{x}{10} = \dfrac{2}{24}$ $\dfrac{y}{26} = \dfrac{2}{24}$

$x \cdot 24 = 10 \cdot 2$ $y \cdot 24 = 26 \cdot 2$

$24x = 20$ $24y = 52$

$\dfrac{24x}{24} = \dfrac{20}{24}$ $\dfrac{24y}{24} = \dfrac{52}{24}$

$x = \dfrac{5}{6}$ $y = \dfrac{13}{6}$ or $2\dfrac{1}{6}$

The unknown lengths are $x = \dfrac{5}{6}$ inch and

$y = 2\dfrac{1}{6}$ inches.

57. 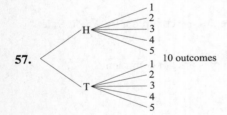 10 outcomes

58. 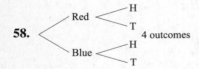 4 outcomes

59. 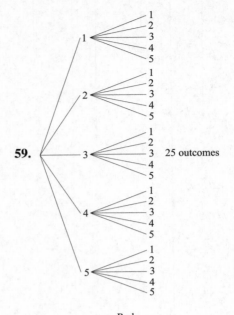 25 outcomes

60. 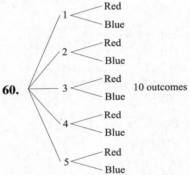 10 outcomes

61. One of the six possible outcomes is 4. The probability is $\dfrac{1}{6}$.

62. One of the six possible outcomes is 3. The probability is $\dfrac{1}{6}$.

63. One of the five possible outcomes is 4. The probability is $\dfrac{1}{5}$.

64. One of the five possible outcomes is 3. The probability is $\dfrac{1}{5}$.

65. Three of the five possible outcomes are a 1, 3, or 5. The probability is $\dfrac{3}{5}$.

66. Two of the five possible outcomes are a 2 or a 4. The probability is $\dfrac{2}{5}$.

67. Two of the eight marbles are blue. The probability is $\dfrac{2}{8} = \dfrac{1}{4}$.

68. Three of the eight marbles are yellow. The probability is $\dfrac{3}{8}$.

69. Two of the eight marbles are red. The probability is $\dfrac{2}{8} = \dfrac{1}{4}$.

70. One of the eight marbles is green. The probability is $\dfrac{1}{8}$.

71. The longest bar corresponds to the Insight 2WD Manual. This model gets about 66 miles per gallons.

72. The shortest bar corresponds to the RX 400h 4WD eCVT. This model gets about 25 miles per gallon.

73. The bar that ends between 50 and 60 corresponds to the Insight 2WD CVT. This model gets about 55 miles per gallon.

74. The bar that ends closest to 40 corresponds to the Camry 2WD ECT-1. This model gets about 37 miles per gallon.

75. $\sqrt{36} = 6$ because $6^2 = 36$.

76. $\sqrt{\dfrac{16}{81}} = \dfrac{4}{9}$ because $\left(\dfrac{4}{9}\right)^2 = \dfrac{4}{9} \cdot \dfrac{4}{9} = \dfrac{16}{81}$.

77. $\sqrt{105} \approx 10.247$

78. $\sqrt{32} \approx 5.657$

79. $\begin{aligned} \text{hypotenuse} &= \sqrt{(\text{leg})^2 + (\text{other leg})^2} \\ &= \sqrt{66^2 + 56^2} \\ &= \sqrt{4356 + 3136} \\ &= \sqrt{7492} \\ &\approx 86.6 \end{aligned}$

80. $\begin{aligned} \text{leg} &= \sqrt{(\text{hypotenuse})^2 - (\text{other leg})^2} \\ &= \sqrt{24^2 - 12^2} \\ &= \sqrt{576 - 144} \\ &= \sqrt{432} \\ &\approx 20.8 \end{aligned}$

81. $\begin{aligned} \dfrac{n}{6} &= \dfrac{10}{5} \\ n \cdot 5 &= 6 \cdot 10 \\ 5n &= 60 \\ \dfrac{5n}{5} &= \dfrac{60}{5} \\ n &= 12 \end{aligned}$

82. $\begin{aligned} \dfrac{n}{8\frac{2}{3}} &= \dfrac{9\frac{3}{8}}{12\frac{1}{2}} \\ n \cdot 12\frac{1}{2} &= 8\frac{2}{3} \cdot 9\frac{3}{8} \\ n \cdot \dfrac{25}{2} &= \dfrac{26}{3} \cdot \dfrac{75}{8} \\ \dfrac{25}{2}n &= \dfrac{325}{4} \\ \dfrac{2}{25} \cdot \dfrac{25}{2}n &= \dfrac{2}{25} \cdot \dfrac{325}{4} \\ n &= \dfrac{13}{2} \text{ or } 6\frac{1}{2} \end{aligned}$

Chapter 7 Test

1. There are $4\frac{1}{2}$ dollar symbols for the second week. Each dollar symbol corresponds to $50.
$4\frac{1}{2} \cdot \$50 = \dfrac{9}{2} \cdot \$50 = \dfrac{\$450}{2} = \$225$
$225 was collected during the second week.

2. Week 3 has the greatest number of dollar symbols. So the most money was collected during the 3rd week. The 3rd week has 7 dollar symbols and each dollar symbol corresponds to $50, so 4 · $50 = $350 was collected during week 3.

3. There are a total of 22 dollar symbols and each dollar symbol corresponds to $50, so a total of 22 · $50 = $1100 was collected.

4. Look for the bars whose height is greater than 9. June, August, and September normally have more than 9 centimeters.

5. The shortest bar corresponds to February. The normal monthly rainfall in February in Chicago is 3 centimeters.

6. The bars corresponding to March and November have a height of 7. Thus, during March and November, 7 centimeters of precipitation normally occurs.

7.

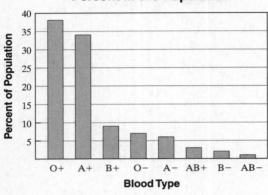

8. The point on the graph corresponding to 2003 is at about 2.25. Thus, the annual inflation rate in 2003 was about 2.25%.

9. The line graph is above the 3 level for 2000, 2005, 2006, and 2008. Thus the inflation rate was greater than 3% in 2000, 2005, 2006, and 2008.

10. Look for the years where the line graph is decreasing. During 1997–1998, 2000–2002, and 2005–2007, the inflation rate was decreasing.

11. $\dfrac{\text{number who prefer rock music}}{\text{total number}} = \dfrac{85}{200} = \dfrac{17}{40}$

    The ratio is $\dfrac{17}{40}$.

12. $\dfrac{\text{number who prefer country}}{\text{number who prefer jazz}} = \dfrac{62}{44} = \dfrac{31}{22}$

    The ratio is $\dfrac{31}{22}$.

13. 14% of 309 million = $0.14 \cdot 309 \approx 43$ million.
    Thus, 43 million people are expected to be in the twenties age group by 2010.

14. The sector corresponding to eighties plus is 4.2%.
    4.2% of 309 million = $0.042 \cdot 309 \approx 13$ million.
    Thus, 13 million people are expected to be in the eighties plus group by 2010.

15. The height of the bar for 5'8"–5'11" is 9. Thus, there are 9 students who are 5'8"–5'11" tall.

16. Add the heights of the bars for 5'0"–5'3" and 5'4"–5'7". There are $5 + 6 = 11$ students who are 5'7" tall or shorter.

17.

Class Interval (Scores)	Tally	Class Frequency (Number of Students)
40–49	|	1
50–59	|||	3
60–69	||||	4
70–79	卌	5
80–89	卌 |||	8
90–99	||||	4

18.

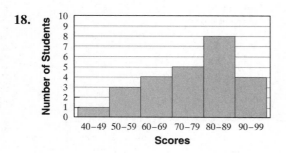

19. $\sqrt{49} = 7$ because $7^2 = 49$.

20. $\sqrt{157} \approx 12.530$

21. $\sqrt{\dfrac{64}{100}} = \dfrac{8}{10} = \dfrac{4}{5}$ because $\left(\dfrac{8}{10}\right)^2 = \dfrac{8}{10} \cdot \dfrac{8}{10} = \dfrac{64}{100}$.

22. $\text{hypotenuse} = \sqrt{(\text{leg})^2 + (\text{other leg})^2}$
$= \sqrt{4^2 + 4^2}$
$= \sqrt{16 + 16}$
$= \sqrt{32}$
≈ 5.66
The hypotenuse is 5.66 centimeters.

23. $\dfrac{n}{12} = \dfrac{5}{8}$
$n \cdot 8 = 12 \cdot 5$
$8n = 60$
$\dfrac{8n}{8} = \dfrac{60}{8}$
$n = 7.5$

24. Let x be the height of the tower.
$\dfrac{x}{5\frac{3}{4}} = \dfrac{48}{4}$
$x \cdot 4 = 5\dfrac{3}{4} \cdot 48$
$4x = \dfrac{23}{4} \cdot 48$
$4x = 276$
$\dfrac{4x}{4} = \dfrac{276}{4}$
$x = 69$
The tower is approximately 69 feet tall.

25.

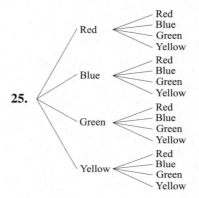

26.

H ⟨ H, T
T ⟨ H, T

27. One of the ten possible outcomes is a 6. The probability is $\dfrac{1}{10}$.

28. Two of the ten possible outcomes are a 3 or a 4. The probability is $\dfrac{2}{10} = \dfrac{1}{5}$.

Cumulative Review Chapters 1–7

1. $4^3 + [3^2 - (10 \div 2)] - 7 \cdot 3$
$= 4^3 + [3^2 - 5] - 7 \cdot 3$
$= 4^3 + (9 - 5) - 7 \cdot 3$
$= 4^3 + 4 - 7 \cdot 3$
$= 64 + 4 - 7 \cdot 3$
$= 64 + 4 - 21$
$= 68 - 21$
$= 47$

2. $7^2 - [5^3 + (6 \div 3)] + 4 \cdot 2$

$= 7^2 - [5^3 + 2] + 4 \cdot 2$

$= 7^2 - (125 + 2) + 4 \cdot 2$

$= 7^2 - 127 + 4 \cdot 2$

$= 49 - 127 + 4 \cdot 2$

$= 49 - 127 + 8$

$= -78 + 8$

$= -70$

3. $x - y = -3 - 9 = -3 + (-9) = -12$

4. $x - y = 7 - (-2) = 7 + 2 = 9$

5. $3y - 7y = 12$

$(3 - 7)y = 12$

$-4y = 12$

$\dfrac{-4y}{-4} = \dfrac{12}{-4}$

$y = -3$

6. $2x - 6x = 24$

$(2 - 6)x = 24$

$-4x = 24$

$\dfrac{-4x}{-4} = \dfrac{24}{-4}$

$x = -6$

7. $\dfrac{x}{6} + 1 = \dfrac{4}{3}$

$6\left(\dfrac{x}{6} + 1\right) = 6\left(\dfrac{4}{3}\right)$

$6 \cdot \dfrac{x}{6} + 6 \cdot 1 = 6 \cdot \dfrac{4}{3}$

$x + 6 = 8$

$x + 6 - 6 = 8 - 6$

$x = 2$

8. $\dfrac{7}{2} + \dfrac{a}{4} = 1$

$4\left(\dfrac{7}{2} + \dfrac{a}{4}\right) = 4(1)$

$4 \cdot \dfrac{7}{2} + 4 \cdot \dfrac{a}{4} = 4 \cdot 1$

$14 + a = 4$

$14 - 14 + a = 4 - 14$

$a = -10$

9.

$$\begin{array}{cc} 2\dfrac{1}{3} & 2\dfrac{8}{24} \\[6pt] +5\dfrac{3}{8} & +5\dfrac{9}{24} \\[4pt] \hline & 7\dfrac{17}{24} \end{array}$$

$2\dfrac{1}{3} + 5\dfrac{3}{8} = 7\dfrac{17}{24}$

10.

$$\begin{array}{cc} 3\dfrac{2}{5} & 3\dfrac{8}{20} \\[6pt] +4\dfrac{3}{4} & +4\dfrac{15}{20} \\[4pt] \hline & 7\dfrac{23}{20} = 7 + 1\dfrac{3}{20} = 8\dfrac{3}{20} \end{array}$$

$3\dfrac{2}{5} + 4\dfrac{3}{4} = 8\dfrac{3}{20}$

11. $5.9 = 5\dfrac{9}{10}$

12. $2.8 = 2\dfrac{8}{10} = 2\dfrac{4}{5}$

13.
$$\begin{array}{r} 3.500 \\ -\ 0.068 \\ \hline 3.432 \end{array}$$

14.
$$\begin{array}{r} 7.400 \\ -\ 0.073 \\ \hline 7.327 \end{array}$$

15.
$$\begin{array}{r} 0.0531 \\ \times\ \ \ 16 \\ \hline 3186 \\ 5310 \\ \hline 0.8496 \end{array}$$
4 decimal places

4 decimal places

16.
$$\begin{array}{r} 0.147 \\ 0.2 \\ \hline 0.0294 \end{array}$$
3 decimal places

1 decimal place

$3 + 1 = 4$ decimal places

17.
$$115\overline{)\,5.980}$$

$$\begin{array}{r} 0.052 \\ 115\overline{)\,5.980} \\ -5\ 75 \\ \hline 230 \\ -230 \\ \hline 0 \end{array}$$

$-5.98 \div 115 = -0.052$

18.

$$205\overline{)27.880} \quad 0.136$$

$$\underline{-20\;5}$$
$$7\;38$$
$$\underline{-6\;15}$$
$$1\;230$$
$$\underline{-1\;230}$$
$$0$$

$$27.88 \div 205 = 0.136$$

19. $(-1.3)^2 + 2.4 = 1.69 + 2.4 = 4.09$

20. $(-2.7)^2 = (-2.7)(-2.7) = 7.29$

21. $\dfrac{1}{4} = \dfrac{1 \cdot 25}{4 \cdot 25} = \dfrac{25}{100} = 0.25$

22. $\dfrac{3}{8} = \dfrac{3 \cdot 125}{8 \cdot 125} = \dfrac{375}{1000} = 0.375$

23.
$$5(x - 0.36) = -x + 2.4$$
$$5 \cdot x - 5 \cdot 0.36 = -x + 2.4$$
$$5x - 1.8 = -x + 2.4$$
$$5x + x - 1.8 = -x + x + 2.4$$
$$6x - 1.8 = 2.4$$
$$6x - 1.8 + 1.8 = 2.4 + 1.8$$
$$6x = 4.2$$
$$\dfrac{6x}{6} = \dfrac{4.2}{6}$$
$$x = 0.7$$

24.
$$4(0.35 - x) = x - 7$$
$$4 \cdot 0.35 - 4 \cdot x = x - 7$$
$$1.4 - 4x = x - 7$$
$$1.4 - 4x - x = x - x - 7$$
$$1.4 - 5x = -7$$
$$1.4 - 1.4 - 5x = -7 - 1.4$$
$$-5x = -8.4$$
$$\dfrac{-5x}{-5} = \dfrac{-8.4}{-5}$$
$$x = 1.68$$

25. $\sqrt{80} \approx 8.944$

26. $\sqrt{60} \approx 7.746$

27. $\sqrt{\dfrac{1}{36}} = \dfrac{1}{6}$ because $\left(\dfrac{1}{6}\right)^2 = \dfrac{1}{6} \cdot \dfrac{1}{6} = \dfrac{1}{36}$.

28. $\sqrt{\dfrac{16}{49}} = \dfrac{4}{7}$ because $\left(\dfrac{4}{7}\right)^2 = \dfrac{4}{7} \cdot \dfrac{4}{7} = \dfrac{16}{49}$.

29.

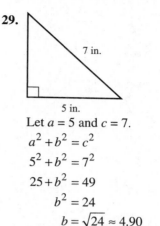

7 in.

5 in.

Let $a = 5$ and $c = 7$.
$$a^2 + b^2 = c^2$$
$$5^2 + b^2 = 7^2$$
$$25 + b^2 = 49$$
$$b^2 = 24$$
$$b = \sqrt{24} \approx 4.90$$

The length of the leg is approximately 4.90 inches.

30.

16

2

Let $a = 2$ and $b = 16$.
$$c^2 = a^2 + b^2$$
$$c^2 = 2^2 + 16^2$$
$$c^2 = 4 + 256$$
$$c^2 = 260$$
$$c = \sqrt{260} \approx 16.12$$

The length of the hypotenuse is approximately 16.12 units.

31. $\dfrac{x - 5}{3} = \dfrac{x + 2}{5}$
$$5(x - 5) = 3(x + 2)$$
$$5x - 25 = 3x + 6$$
$$2x - 25 = 6$$
$$2x = 31$$
$$\dfrac{2x}{2} = \dfrac{31}{2}$$
$$x = \dfrac{31}{2}$$

Check:
$$\frac{x-5}{3}=\frac{x+2}{5}$$
$$\frac{\frac{31}{2}-5}{3}\stackrel{?}{=}\frac{\frac{31}{2}+2}{5}$$
$$\frac{1}{3}\left(\frac{31}{2}-\frac{10}{2}\right)\stackrel{?}{=}\frac{1}{5}\left(\frac{31}{2}+\frac{4}{2}\right)$$
$$\frac{1}{3}\left(\frac{21}{2}\right)\stackrel{?}{=}\frac{1}{5}\left(\frac{35}{2}\right)$$
$$\frac{7}{2}=\frac{7}{2}\quad\text{True}$$

32.
$$\frac{8}{5}=\frac{x}{10}$$
$$8\cdot 10=5\cdot x$$
$$80=5x$$
$$\frac{80}{5}=\frac{5x}{5}$$
$$16=x$$

Check:
$$\frac{8}{5}=\frac{x}{10}$$
$$\frac{8}{5}\stackrel{?}{=}\frac{16}{10}$$
$$8\cdot 10\stackrel{?}{=}5\cdot 16$$
$$80=80\quad\text{True}$$
The solution is 16.

33. $\frac{12\text{ feet}}{19\text{ feet}}=\frac{12}{19}$

34. $\frac{4}{9}$

35. $4.6\%=4.6(0.01)=0.046$

36. $32\%=32(0.01)=0.32$

37. $0.74\%=0.74(0.01)=0.0074$

38. $2.7\%=2.7(0.01)=0.027$

39. 35% of $60=0.35\cdot 60=21$
21 is 35% of 60.

40. 40% of $36=0.40\cdot 36=14.4$
14.4 is 40% of 36.

41. $20.8=40\%\cdot x$
$20.8=0.4x$
$$\frac{20.8}{0.4}=\frac{0.4x}{0.4}$$
$52=x$
20.8 is 40% of 52.

42. $9.5=25\%\cdot x$
$9.5=0.25x$
$$\frac{9.5}{0.25}=\frac{0.25x}{0.25}$$
$38=x$
9.5 is 25% of 38.

43. $\$406\cdot r=\$34.51$
$406r=34.51$
$$\frac{406r}{406}=\frac{34.51}{406}$$
$r=0.085$ or 8.5%
The sales tax rate is 8.5%.

44. $\$2\cdot r=\$0.13$
$2r=0.13$
$$\frac{2r}{2}=\frac{0.13}{2}$$
$r=0.065$ or 6.5%
The sales tax rate is 6.5%.

45.
$$A=P\left(1+\frac{r}{n}\right)^{n\cdot t}$$
$$=\$4000\cdot\left(1+\frac{0.053}{4}\right)^{4\cdot 10}$$
$$=\$4000(1.01325)^{40}$$
$$\approx\$6772.12$$

46.
$$\frac{\text{total}}{12\text{ months}}=\frac{\$1600+\$128.60}{12}$$
$$=\frac{\$1728.60}{12}$$
$$=\$144.05$$
The monthly payment is $\$144.05$.

47. The list is in numerical order and there is an odd number of values, so the median is the middle value, 57.

48. The numbers are listed in order. Since there is an even number of values, the median is
$$\frac{47+50}{2}=\frac{97}{2}=48.5.$$

49. Two of the six possible outcomes are a 3 or a 4. The probability is $\frac{2}{6}=\frac{1}{3}$.

50. Three of the six possible outcomes are even. The probability is $\frac{3}{6}=\frac{1}{2}$.

Chapter 8

Section 8.1

Practice Problems

1. Figure (a) is part of a line with one endpoint, so it is a ray. It is ray AB or $\overrightarrow{AB}$.
   Figure (b) has two endpoints, so it is a line segment. It is line segment RS or $\overline{RS}$.
   Figure (c) extends indefinitely in two directions, so it is a line. It is line EF or $\overleftrightarrow{EF}$.
   Figure (d) has two rays with a common endpoint, so it is an angle. It is $\angle HVT$ or $\angle TVH$ or $\angle V$.

2. Two other ways to name $\angle z$ are $\angle RTS$ and $\angle STR$.

3. a. $\angle R$ is an obtuse angle. It measures between $90°$ and $180°$.

   b. $\angle N$ is a straight angle. It measures $180°$.

   c. $\angle M$ is an acute angle. It measures between $0°$ and $90°$.

   d. $\angle Q$ is a right angle. It measures $90°$.

4. The complement of a $29°$ angle is an angle that measures $90° - 29° = 61°$.

5. The supplement of a $67°$ angle is an angle that measures $180° - 67° = 113°$.

6. a. $m\angle y = m\angle ADC - m\angle BDC$
      $= 141° - 97°$
      $= 44°$

   b. $m\angle x = 79° - 51° = 28°$

   c. Since the measures of both $\angle x$ and $\angle y$ are between $0°$ and $90°$, they are acute angles.

7. Since $\angle a$ and the angle marked $109°$ are vertical angles, they have the same measure; so $m\angle a = 109°$.
   Since $\angle a$ and $\angle b$ are adjacent angles, their measures have a sum of $180°$. So $m\angle b = 180° - 109° = 71°$.
   Since $\angle b$ and $\angle c$ are vertical angles, they have the same measure; so $m\angle c = 71°$.

8. $\angle w$ and $\angle x$ are vertical angles. $\angle w$ and $\angle y$ are corresponding angles, as are $\angle x$ and $\angle d$. So all of these angles have the same measure: $m\angle x = m\angle y = m\angle d = m\angle w = 45°$.
   $\angle w$ and $\angle a$ are adjacent angles, as are $\angle w$ and $\angle b$, so $m\angle a = m\angle b = 180° - 45° = 135°$.
   $\angle a$ and $\angle c$ are corresponding angles so $m\angle c = m\angle a = 135°$. $\angle c$ and $\angle z$ are vertical angles, so $m\angle z = m\angle c = 135°$.

Vocabulary and Readiness Check

1. A <u>plane</u> is a flat surface that extends indefinitely.

2. A <u>point</u> has no length, no width, and no height.

3. <u>Space</u> extends in all directions indefinitely.

4. A <u>line</u> is a set of points extending indefinitely in two directions.

5. A <u>ray</u> is part of a line with one end point.

6. An <u>angle</u> is made up of two rays that share a common end point. The common end point is called the <u>vertex</u>.

7. A <u>straight</u> angle measures $180°$.

8. A <u>right</u> angle measures $90°$.

9. An <u>acute</u> angle measures between $0°$ and $90°$.

10. An <u>obtuse</u> angle measures between $90°$ and $180°$.

11. <u>Parallel</u> lines never meet and <u>intersecting</u> lines meet at a point.

12. Two intersecting lines are <u>perpendicular</u> if they form right angles when they intersect.

13. An angle can be measured in <u>degrees</u>.

14. A line that intersects two or more lines at different points is called a <u>transversal</u>.

15. When two lines intersect, four angles are formed, called <u>vertical</u> angles.

16. Two angles that share a common side are called <u>adjacent</u> angles.

Exercise Set 8.1

1. The figure extends indefinitely in two directions, so it is a line. It is line CD, line l, or $\overleftrightarrow{CD}$

3. The figure has two end points, so it is a line segment. It is line segment MN or $\overline{MN}$.

5. The figure has two rays with a common end point. It is an angle, which can be named $\angle GHI$, $\angle IHG$, or $\angle H$.

7. The figure has one end point and extends indefinitely in one direction, so it is a ray. It is ray UW or $\overrightarrow{UW}$.

9. Two other ways to name $\angle x$ are $\angle CPR$ and $\angle RPC$.

11. Two other ways to name $\angle z$ are $\angle TPM$ and $\angle MPT$.

13. $\angle S$ is a straight angle. It measures $180°$.

15. $\angle R$ is a right angle. It measures $90°$.

17. $\angle Q$ is an obtuse angle. It measures between $90°$ and $180°$.

19. $\angle P$ is an acute angle. It measures between $0°$ and $90°$.

21. The complement of an angle that measures $23°$ is an angle that measures $90° - 23° = 67°$.

23. The supplement of an angle that measures $17°$ is an angle that measures $180° - 17° = 163°$.

25. The complement of an angle that measures $58°$ is an angle that measures $90° - 58° = 32°$.

27. The supplement of an angle that measures $150°$ is an angle that measures $180° - 150° = 30°$.

29. $52° + 38° = 90°$, so $\angle PNQ$ and $\angle QNR$ are complementary. $60° + 30° = 90°$, so $\angle MNP$ and $\angle RNO$ are complementary.

31. $45° + 135° = 180°$, so there are 4 pairs of supplementary angles: $\angle SPT$ and $\angle RPS$, $\angle SPT$ and $\angle QPT$, $\angle QPR$ and $\angle RPS$, $\angle QPR$ and $\angle QPT$.

33. $m\angle x = 74° - 47° = 27°$

35. $m\angle x = 42° + 90° = 132°$

37. $\angle x$ and the angle marked $150°$ are supplementary, so $m\angle x = 180° - 150° = 30°$. $\angle y$ and the angle marked $150°$ are vertical angles, so $m\angle y = 150°$. $\angle z$ and $\angle x$ are vertical angles so $m\angle z = m\angle x = 30°$.

39. $\angle x$ and the angle marked $103°$ are supplementary, so $m\angle x = 180° - 103° = 77°$. $\angle y$ and the angle marked $103°$ are vertical angles, so $m\angle y = 103°$. $\angle x$ and $\angle z$ are vertical angles, so $m\angle z = m\angle x = 77°$.

41. $\angle x$ and the angle marked $80°$ are supplementary, so $m\angle x = 180° - 80° = 100°$. $\angle y$ and the angle marked $80°$ are alternate interior angles, so $m\angle y = 80°$. $\angle x$ and $\angle z$ are corresponding angles, so $m\angle z = m\angle x = 100°$.

43. $\angle x$ and the angle marked $46°$ are supplementary, so $m\angle x = 180° - 46° = 134°$. $\angle y$ and the angle marked $46°$ are corresponding angles, so $m\angle y = 46°$. $\angle x$ and $\angle z$ are corresponding angles, so $m\angle z = m\angle x = 134°$.

45. $\angle x$ can also be named $\angle ABC$ or $\angle CBA$.

47. $\angle z$ can also be named $\angle DBE$ or $\angle EBD$.

49. $m\angle ABC = 15°$

51. $m\angle CBD = 50°$

53. $m\angle DBA = m\angle DBC + m\angle CBA$
$= 50° + 15°$
$= 65°$

55. $m\angle CBE = m\angle CBD + m\angle DBE$
$= 50° + 45°$
$= 95°$

57. $\dfrac{7}{8} + \dfrac{1}{4} = \dfrac{7}{8} + \dfrac{2}{8} = \dfrac{9}{8}$ or $1\dfrac{1}{8}$

59. $\dfrac{7}{8} \cdot \dfrac{1}{4} = \dfrac{7 \cdot 1}{8 \cdot 4} = \dfrac{7}{32}$

61. $3\dfrac{1}{3} - 2\dfrac{1}{2} = \dfrac{10}{3} - \dfrac{5}{2}$

$\qquad = \dfrac{10 \cdot 2}{3 \cdot 2} - \dfrac{5 \cdot 3}{2 \cdot 3}$

$\qquad = \dfrac{20}{6} - \dfrac{15}{6}$

$\qquad = \dfrac{5}{6}$

63. $3\dfrac{1}{3} \div 2\dfrac{1}{2} = \dfrac{10}{3} \div \dfrac{5}{2} = \dfrac{10}{3} \cdot \dfrac{2}{5} = \dfrac{5 \cdot 2 \cdot 2}{3 \cdot 5} = \dfrac{4}{3}$ or $1\dfrac{1}{3}$

65. The supplement of an angle that measures 125.2°
is an angle with measure
$180° - 125.2° = 54.8°$.

67. False; answers may vary

69. True; answers may vary

71. $\angle a$ and the angle marked 60° are alternate
interior angles, so $m\angle a = 60°$. The sum of
$\angle a$, $\angle b$, and the angle marked 70° is a straight
angle, so $m\angle b = 180° - 60° - 70° = 50°$. $\angle d$ and
the angle marked 70° are alternate interior
angles, so $m\angle d = 70°$. $\angle c$ and $\angle d$ are
supplementary, so $m\angle c = 180° - 70° = 110°$. $\angle e$
and the angle marked 60° are supplementary, so
$m\angle e = 180° - 60° = 120°$.

73. no; answers may vary

75. Let *x* be the measure of each of the angles, in
degrees. We are given that $x° + x° = 90°$, so
$2x = 90$ and $x = 45$. The angles both measure
45°.

Section 8.2

Practice Problems

1. a. Perimeter $= 10$ m $+ 10$ m $+ 18$ m $+ 18$ m
$\qquad\qquad = 56$ meters
The perimeter is 56 meters.

b. Perimeter $= 125$ ft $+ 125$ ft $+ 50$ ft $+ 50$ ft
$\qquad\qquad = 350$ ft
The perimeter is 350 feet.

2. $P = 2 \cdot l + 2 \cdot w$
$\quad = 2 \cdot 32$ cm $+ 2 \cdot 15$ cm
$\quad = 64$ cm $+ 30$ cm
$\quad = 94$ centimeters
The perimeter is 94 centimeters.

3. $P = 4 \cdot s = 4 \cdot 4$ ft $= 16$ feet
The perimeter is 16 feet.

4. $P = a + b + c$
$\quad = 6$ cm $+ 10$ cm $+ 8$ cm
$\quad = 24$ centimeters
The perimeter is 24 centimeters.

5. Perimeter $= 6$ km $+ 4$ km $+ 9$ km $+ 4$ km
$\qquad\qquad = 23$ kilometers
The perimeter is 23 kilometers.

6. The unmarked horizontal side has length
20 m $-$ 15 m $=$ 5 m. The unmarked vertical side
has length 31 m $-$ 6 m $=$ 25 m.
$P = 15$ m $+ 31$ m $+ 20$ m $+ 6$ m $+ 5$ m $+ 25$ m
$\quad = 102$ meters
The perimeter is 102 meters.

7. $P = 2 \cdot l + 2 \cdot w$
$\quad = 2 \cdot 120$ feet $+ 2 \cdot 60$ feet
$\quad = 240$ feet $+ 120$ feet
$\quad = 360$ feet
cost $= \$1.90$ per foot $\cdot$ 360 feet $= \$684$
The cost of the fencing is \$684.

8. $C = \pi \cdot d = \pi \cdot 20$ yd $= 20\pi$ yd ≈ 62.8 yd
The exact circumference of the watered region is
20π yards, which is approximately 62.8 yards.

Vocabulary and Readiness Check

1. The <u>perimeter</u> of a polygon is the sum of the
lengths of its sides.

2. The distance around a circle is called the
<u>circumference</u>.

3. The exact ratio of circumference to diameter is
<u>π</u>.

4. The diameter of a circle is double its <u>radius</u>.

5. Both $\dfrac{22}{7}$ (or 3.14) and $3.14 \left(\text{or } \dfrac{22}{7}\right)$ are
approximations for π.

6. The radius of a circle is half its <u>diameter</u>.

Exercise Set 8.2

1. $P = 2 \cdot l + 2 \cdot w$
$= 2 \cdot 17 \text{ ft} + 2 \cdot 15 \text{ ft}$
$= 34 \text{ ft} + 30 \text{ ft}$
$= 64 \text{ ft}$
The perimeter is 64 feet.

3. $P = 35 \text{ cm} + 25 \text{ cm} + 35 \text{ cm} + 25 \text{ cm}$
$= 120 \text{ cm}$
The perimeter is 120 centimeters.

5. $P = a + b + c$
$= 5 \text{ in.} + 7 \text{ in.} + 9 \text{ in.}$
$= 21 \text{ in.}$
The perimeter is 21 inches.

7. Sum the lengths of the sides.
$P = 10 \text{ ft} + 8 \text{ ft} + 8 \text{ ft} + 15 \text{ ft} + 7 \text{ ft}$
$= 48 \text{ ft}$
The perimeter is 48 feet.

9. All sides of a regular polygon have the same length, so the perimeter is the number of sides multiplied by the length of a side.
$P = 3 \cdot 14 \text{ in.} = 42 \text{ in.}$
The perimeter is 42 inches.

11. All sides of a regular polygon have the same length, so the perimeter is the number of sides multiplied by the length of a side.
$P = 5 \cdot 31 \text{ cm} = 155 \text{ cm}$
The perimeter is 155 centimeters.

13. Sum the lengths of the sides.
$P = 5 \text{ ft} + 3 \text{ ft} + 2 \text{ ft} + 7 \text{ ft} + 4 \text{ ft}$
$= 21 \text{ ft}$
The perimeter is 21 feet.

15. total distance $= 2(312) = 624$
624 feet of lime powder will be deposited.

17. $P = 2 \cdot l + 2 \cdot w$
$= 2 \cdot 120 \text{ yd} + 2 \cdot 53 \text{ yd}$
$= 240 \text{ yd} + 106 \text{ yd}$
$= 346 \text{ yd}$
The perimeter of the football field is 346 yards.

19. $P = 2 \cdot l + 2 \cdot w$
$= 2 \cdot 8 \text{ ft} + 2 \cdot 3 \text{ ft}$
$= 16 \text{ ft} + 6 \text{ ft}$
$= 22 \text{ ft}$
22 feet of stripping is needed for this project.

21. The amount of stripping needed is 22 feet.
22 feet · $2.50 per foot = $55
The total cost of the stripping is $55.

23. All sides of a regular polygon have the same length, so the perimeter is the number of sides multiplied by the length of a side.
$P = 8 \cdot 9 \text{ in.} = 72 \text{ in.}$
The perimeter is 72 inches.

25. $P = 4 \cdot s = 4 \cdot 7 \text{ in.} = 28 \text{ in.}$
The perimeter is 28 inches.

27. $P = 2 \cdot l + 2 \cdot w$
$= 2 \cdot 11 \text{ ft} + 2 \cdot 10 \text{ ft}$
$= 22 \text{ ft} + 20 \text{ ft}$
$= 42 \text{ ft}$
42 ft · $0.86 per foot = $36.12
The cost is $36.12.

29. The unmarked vertical side has length
28 m − 20 m = 8 m.
The unmarked horizontal side has length
20 m − 17 m = 3m.
$P = 17 \text{ m} + 8 \text{ m} + 3 \text{ m} + 20 \text{ m} + 20 \text{ m} + 28 \text{ m}$
$= 96 \text{ m}$
The perimeter is 96 meters.

31. The unmarked horizontal side has length
(3 + 6 + 4) ft = 13 ft.
$P = (3 + 5 + 6 + 5 + 4 + 15 + 13 + 15) \text{ ft} = 66 \text{ ft}$
The perimeter is 66 feet.

33. The unmarked vertical side has length
5 cm + 14 cm = 19 cm.
The unmarked horizontal side has length
18 cm − 9 cm = 9 cm.
$P = 18 \text{ cm} + 19 \text{ cm} + 9 \text{ cm} + 14 \text{ cm} + 9 \text{ cm} + 5 \text{ cm}$
$= 74 \text{ cm}$
The perimeter is 74 centimeters.

35. $C = \pi \cdot d = \pi \cdot 17 \text{ cm} = 17\pi \text{ cm} \approx 53.38 \text{ cm}$
The circumference is exactly 17π centimeters or approximately 53.38 centimeters.

37. $C = 2 \cdot \pi \cdot r$
$= 2 \cdot \pi \cdot 8 \text{ mi}$
$= 16\pi \text{ mi}$
$\approx 50.24 \text{ mi}$
The circumference is exactly 16π miles, or approximately 50.24 miles.

39. $C = \pi \cdot d = \pi \cdot 26 \text{ m} = 26\pi \text{ m} \approx 81.64 \text{ m}$
The circumference is exactly 26π meters or approximately 81.64 meters.

41. $\pi \cdot d = \pi \cdot 15 \text{ ft} = 15\pi \text{ ft} \approx 47.1$
He needs 15π feet of netting or 47.1 feet.

43. $C = \pi \cdot d = \pi \cdot 4000 \text{ ft} = 4000\pi \text{ ft} \approx 12,560 \text{ ft}$
The distance around is about 12,560 feet.

45. Sum the lengths of the sides.
$\begin{aligned} P &= 9 \text{ mi} + 6 \text{ mi} + 11 \text{ mi} + 4.7 \text{ mi} \\ &= 30.7 \text{ mi} \end{aligned}$
The perimeter is 30.7 miles.

47. $C = \pi \cdot d = \pi \cdot 14 \text{ cm} = 14\pi \text{ cm} \approx 43.96 \text{ cm}$
The circumference is
14π centimeters ≈ 43.96 centimeters.

49. $P = 5 \cdot 8 \text{ mm} = 40 \text{ mm}$
The perimeter is 40 millimeters.

51. The unmarked vertical side has length
$(22 - 8) \text{ ft} = 14 \text{ ft}$.
The unmarked horizontal side has length
$(20 - 7) \text{ ft} = 13 \text{ ft}$.
$P = (7 + 8 + 13 + 14 + 20 + 22) \text{ ft} = 84 \text{ ft}$
The perimeter is 84 feet.

53. $5 + 6 \cdot 3 = 5 + 18 = 23$

55. $(20 - 16) \div 4 = 4 \div 4 = 1$

57. $72 \div (2 \cdot 6) = 72 \div 12 = 6$

59. $(18 + 8) - (12 + 4) = 26 - 16 = 10$

61. a. The first age category that 8-year-old children fit into is "Under 9," thus the minimum width is 30 yards and the minimum length is 40 yards.

    b. $\begin{aligned} P &= 2 \cdot l + 2 \cdot w \\ &= 2 \cdot 40 \text{ yd} + 2 \cdot 30 \text{ yd} \\ &= 80 \text{ yd} + 60 \text{ yd} \\ &= 140 \text{ yd} \end{aligned}$
       The perimeter of the field is 140 yards.

63. The square's perimeter is $4 \cdot 3 \text{ in.} = 12 \text{ in.}$
The circle's circumference is $\pi \cdot 4 \text{ in.} \approx 12.56 \text{ in.}$
So the circle has the greater distance around; b.

65. a. Smaller circle:
$\begin{aligned} C &= 2 \cdot \pi \cdot r \\ &= 2 \cdot \pi \cdot 10 \text{ m} \\ &= 20\pi \text{ m} \\ &\approx 62.8 \text{ m} \end{aligned}$
Larger circle:
$\begin{aligned} C &= 2 \cdot \pi \cdot r \\ &= 2 \cdot \pi \cdot 20 \text{ m} \\ &= 40\pi \text{ m} \\ &\approx 125.6 \text{ m} \end{aligned}$

    b. Yes, when the radius of a circle is doubled, the circumference is also doubled.

67. answers may vary

69. The length of the curved section at the top is half of the circumference of a circle of diameter 6 meters.
$\frac{1}{2} \cdot C = \frac{1}{2} \cdot \pi \cdot d = \frac{1}{2} \cdot \pi \cdot 6 \text{ m} = 3\pi \text{ m} \approx 9.4 \text{ meters}$
The total length of the straight sides is
$3 \cdot 6 \text{ m} = 18 \text{ m}$.
The perimeter is the sum of these.
$9.4 \text{ m} + 18 \text{ m} = 27.4 \text{ m}$
The perimeter of the figure is 27.4 meters.

71. The total length of the two straight sections is $2 \cdot 22 \text{ m} = 44 \text{ m}$. The total length of the two curved sections is the circumference of a circle of radius 5 m.
$C = 2 \cdot \pi \cdot r = 2 \cdot \pi \cdot 5 \text{ m} = 10\pi \text{ m}$
The perimeter of the track is the sum of these.
$P = 44 \text{ m} + 10\pi \text{ m} = (44 + 10\pi) \text{ m} \approx 75.4 \text{ m}$

Section 8.3

Practice Problems

1. $\begin{aligned} A &= \frac{1}{2} bh \\ &= \frac{1}{2} \cdot 12 \text{ in.} \cdot 8\frac{1}{4} \text{ in.} \\ &= \frac{1}{2} \cdot 12 \text{ in.} \cdot \frac{33}{4} \text{ in.} \\ &= \frac{4 \cdot 3 \cdot 33}{2 \cdot 4} \text{ sq in.} \\ &= 49\frac{1}{2} \text{ sq in.} \end{aligned}$

The area is $49\frac{1}{2}$ square inches.

2. $A = \dfrac{1}{2}(b + B)h$

      $= \dfrac{1}{2}(5 \text{ yd} + 11 \text{ yd})(6.1 \text{ yd})$

      $= 48.8 \text{ sq yd}$

      The area is 48.8 square yards.

3.   Split the rectangle into two pieces, a top rectangle with dimensions 12 m by 24 m, and a bottom rectangle with dimensions 6 m by 18 m. The area of the figure is the sum of the areas of these.

      $A = 12 \text{ m} \cdot 24 \text{ m} + 6 \text{ m} \cdot 18 \text{ m}$

      $= 288 \text{ sq m} + 108 \text{ sq m}$

      $= 396 \text{ sq m}$

      The area is 396 square meters.

4. $A = \pi r^2$

      $= \pi \cdot (7 \text{ cm})^2$

      $= 49\pi \text{ sq cm}$

      $\approx 153.86 \text{ sq cm}$

      The area is 49π square centimeters, which is approximately 153.86 square centimeters.

5. $V = lwh = 7 \text{ ft} \cdot 3 \text{ ft} \cdot 4 \text{ ft} = 84 \text{ cu ft}$
      The volume of the box is 84 cubic feet.

      $SA = 2lh + 2wh + 2lw$

      $= 2(7 \text{ ft})(4 \text{ ft}) + 2(3 \text{ ft})(4 \text{ ft}) + 2(7 \text{ ft})(3 \text{ ft})$

      $= 56 \text{ sq ft} + 24 \text{ sq ft} + 42 \text{ sq ft}$

      $= 122 \text{ sq ft}$

      The surface area of the box is 122 square feet.

6. $V = \dfrac{4}{3}\pi r^3 = \dfrac{4}{3}\pi \cdot \left(\dfrac{1}{2} \text{ cm}\right)^3$

      $= \dfrac{4}{3}\pi \cdot \dfrac{1}{8} \text{ cu cm}$

      $= \dfrac{1}{6}\pi \text{ cu cm}$

      $\approx \dfrac{1}{6} \cdot \dfrac{22}{7} \text{ cu cm}$

      $= \dfrac{11}{21} \text{ cu cm}$

      The volume is $\dfrac{1}{6}\pi$ cubic centimeter, which is

      approximately $\dfrac{11}{21}$ cubic centimeter.

$SA = 4\pi r^2 = 4\pi \cdot \left(\dfrac{1}{2} \text{ cm}\right)^2$

      $= 4\pi \cdot \dfrac{1}{4} \text{ sq cm}$

      $= \pi \text{ sq cm}$

      $\approx \dfrac{22}{7} \text{ sq cm or } 3\dfrac{1}{7} \text{ sq cm}$

The surface area is π square centimeters, which is approximately $3\dfrac{1}{7}$ square centimeters.

7. $V = \pi r^2 h = \pi \cdot (5 \text{ in.})^2 \cdot 9 \text{ in.}$

      $= \pi \cdot 25 \text{ sq in.} \cdot 9 \text{ in.}$

      $= 225\pi \text{ cu in.}$

      $\approx 706.5 \text{ cu in.}$

      The volume is 225π cubic inches, which is approximately 706.5 cubic inches.

8. $V = \dfrac{1}{3}s^2 h = \dfrac{1}{3} \cdot (3 \text{ m})^2 \cdot 5.1 \text{ m}$

      $= \dfrac{1}{3} \cdot 9 \text{ sq m} \cdot 5.1 \text{ m}$

      $= 15.3 \text{ cu m}$

      The volume is 15.3 cubic meters.

Vocabulary and Readiness Check

1.   The <u>surface area</u> of a polyhedron is the sum of the areas of its faces.

2.   The measure of the amount of space inside a solid is its <u>volume</u>.

3.   <u>Area</u> measures the amount of surface enclosed by a region.

4.   Volume is measured in <u>cubic</u> units.

5.   Area is measured in <u>square</u> units.

6.   Surface area is measured in <u>square</u> units.

Exercise Set 8.3

1. $A = l \cdot w = 3.5 \text{ m} \cdot 2 \text{ m} = 7 \text{ sq m}$
      The area is 7 square meters.

3. $A = \dfrac{1}{2} \cdot b \cdot h$

     $= \dfrac{1}{2} \cdot 6\dfrac{1}{2} \text{ yd} \cdot 3 \text{ yd}$

     $= \dfrac{1}{2} \cdot \dfrac{13}{2} \text{ yd} \cdot 3 \text{ yd}$

     $= \dfrac{39}{4} \text{ sq yd}$

     $= 9\dfrac{3}{4} \text{ sq yd}$

     The area is $9\dfrac{3}{4}$ square yards.

5. $A = \dfrac{1}{2} \cdot b \cdot h = \dfrac{1}{2} \cdot 6 \text{ yd} \cdot 5 \text{ yd} = 15 \text{ sq yd}$

     The area is 15 square yards.

7. $r = d \div 2 = (3 \text{ in.}) \div 2 = 1.5 \text{ in.}$

     $A = \pi r^2$

     $= \pi (1.5 \text{ in.})^2$

     $= 2.25\pi \text{ sq in.}$

     $\approx 7.065 \text{ sq in.}$

     The area is 2.25π square inches ≈ 7.065 square inches.

9. $A = b \cdot h = 7 \text{ ft} \cdot 5.25 \text{ ft} = 36.75 \text{ sq ft}$

     The area is 36.75 square feet.

11. $A = \dfrac{1}{2}(b + B) \cdot h$

     $= \dfrac{1}{2}(5 \text{ m} + 9 \text{ m}) \cdot 4 \text{ m}$

     $= \dfrac{1}{2} \cdot 14 \text{ m} \cdot 4 \text{ m}$

     $= 28 \text{ sq m}$

     The area is 28 square meters.

13. $A = \dfrac{1}{2}(b + B) \cdot h$

     $= \dfrac{1}{2}(7 \text{ yd} + 4 \text{ yd}) \cdot 4 \text{ yd}$

     $= \dfrac{1}{2}(11 \text{ yd}) \cdot 4 \text{ yd}$

     $= 22 \text{ sq yd}$

     The area is 22 square yards.

15. $A = b \cdot h$

     $= 7 \text{ ft} \cdot 5\dfrac{1}{4} \text{ ft}$

     $= 7 \text{ ft} \cdot \dfrac{21}{4} \text{ ft}$

     $= \dfrac{147}{4} \text{ sq ft}$

     $= 36\dfrac{3}{4} \text{ sq ft}$

     The area is $36\dfrac{3}{4}$ square feet.

17. $A = b \cdot h$

     $= 5 \text{ in.} \cdot 4\dfrac{1}{2} \text{ in.}$

     $= 5 \text{ in.} \cdot \dfrac{9}{2} \text{ in.}$

     $= \dfrac{45}{2} \text{ sq in.}$

     $= 22\dfrac{1}{2} \text{ sq in.}$

     The area is $22\dfrac{1}{2}$ square inches.

19. The base of the triangle is

     $7 \text{ cm} - 1\dfrac{1}{2} \text{ cm} - 1\dfrac{1}{2} \text{ cm} = 4 \text{ cm},$ so its area is

     $\dfrac{1}{2} \cdot 4 \text{ cm} \cdot 2 \text{ cm} = 4 \text{ sq cm}.$

     The area of the rectangle is
     $7 \text{ cm} \cdot 3 \text{ cm} = 21 \text{ sq cm}.$
     The area of the figure is the sum of these.
     $A = 4 \text{ sq cm} + 21 \text{ sq cm} = 25 \text{ sq cm}$
     The total area is 25 square centimeters.

21. The figure can be divided into two rectangles, one measuring 10 mi by 5 mi and one measuring 12 mi by 3 mi. The area of the figure is the sum of the areas of the two rectangles.

     $A = 10 \text{ mi} \cdot 5 \text{ mi} + 12 \text{ mi} \cdot 3 \text{ mi}$

     $= 50 \text{ sq mi} + 36 \text{ sq mi}$

     $= 86 \text{ sq mi}$

     The total area is 86 square miles.

23. The top of the figure is a square with sides of length 3 cm, so its area is

     $s^2 = (3 \text{ cm})^2 = 9 \text{ sq cm}.$

     The bottom of the figure is a parallelogram with area $b \cdot h = 3 \text{ cm} \cdot 5 \text{ cm} = 15 \text{ sq cm}.$
     The area of the figure is the sum of these.
     $A = 9 \text{ sq cm} + 15 \text{ sq cm} = 24 \text{ sq cm}$
     The total area is 24 square centimeters.

25. $A = \pi r^2$

$\quad = \pi(6 \text{ in.})^2$

$\quad = 36\pi \text{ sq in.}$

$\quad \approx 36 \cdot \dfrac{22}{7} \text{ sq in.}$

$\quad \approx 113\dfrac{1}{7} \text{ sq in.}$

The area is

36π square inches $\approx 113\dfrac{1}{7}$ square inches.

27. $V = l \cdot w \cdot h = 6 \text{ in.} \cdot 4 \text{ in.} \cdot 3 \text{ in.} = 72 \text{ cu in.}$

The volume is 72 cubic inches.

$SA = 2lh + 2wh + 2lw$

$\quad = 2 \cdot 6 \text{ in.} \cdot 3 \text{ in.} + 2 \cdot 4 \text{ in.} \cdot 3 \text{ in.} + 2 \cdot 6 \text{ in.} \cdot 4 \text{ in.}$

$\quad = 36 \text{ sq in.} + 24 \text{ sq in.} + 48 \text{ sq in.}$

$\quad = 108 \text{ sq in.}$

The surface area is 108 square inches.

29. $V = s^3 = (8 \text{ cm})^3 = 512 \text{ cu cm}$

The volume is 512 cubic centimeters.

$SA = 6s^2 = 6(8 \text{ cm})^2 = 6 \cdot 64 \text{ sq cm} = 384 \text{ sq cm}$

The surface area is 384 square centimeters.

31. $V = \dfrac{1}{3} \cdot \pi \cdot r^2 \cdot h$

$\quad = \dfrac{1}{3} \cdot \pi(2 \text{ yd})^2 (3 \text{ yd})$

$\quad = 4\pi \text{ cu yd}$

$\quad \approx 4 \cdot \dfrac{22}{7} \text{ cu yd}$

$\quad = \dfrac{88}{7} \text{ cu yd}$

$\quad = 12\dfrac{4}{7} \text{ cu yd}$

The volume is $12\dfrac{4}{7}$ cubic yards.

$SA = \pi \cdot r\sqrt{r^2 + h^2} + \pi r^2$

$\quad = \pi \cdot 2 \text{ yd}\sqrt{(2 \text{ yd})^2 + (3 \text{ yd})^2} + \pi(2 \text{ yd})^2$

$\quad = 2\pi\sqrt{13} \text{ sq yd} + 4\pi \text{ sq yd}$

$\quad = \left(2\sqrt{13}\pi + 4\pi\right) \text{ sq yd}$

$\quad \approx 35.20 \text{ sq yd}$

The surface area is

$\left(2\sqrt{13}\pi + 4\pi\right)$ square yards ≈ 35.20 square yards.

33. $r = \dfrac{1}{2} \cdot d = \dfrac{1}{2} \cdot 10 \text{ in.} = 5 \text{ in.}$

$V = \dfrac{4}{3}\pi r^3$

$\quad = \dfrac{4}{3}\pi(5 \text{ in.})^3$

$\quad = \dfrac{4}{3}\pi \cdot 125 \text{ cu in.}$

$\quad = \dfrac{500}{3}\pi \text{ cu in.}$

$\quad \approx \dfrac{500}{3} \cdot \dfrac{22}{7} \text{ cu in.} = 523\dfrac{17}{21} \text{ cu in.}$

The volume is

$\dfrac{500}{3}\pi$ cubic inches $\approx 523\dfrac{17}{21}$ cubic inches.

$SA = 4\pi r^2$

$\quad = 4\pi(5 \text{ in.})^2$

$\quad = 4\pi \cdot 25 \text{ sq in.}$

$\quad = 100\pi \text{ sq in.}$

$\quad \approx 100 \cdot \dfrac{22}{7} \text{ sq in.} = 314\dfrac{2}{7} \text{ sq in.}$

The surface area is

100π square inches $\approx 314\dfrac{2}{7}$ square inches.

35. $r = \dfrac{1}{2}d = \dfrac{1}{2} \cdot 2 \text{ in.} = 1 \text{ in.}$

$V = \pi \cdot r^2 \cdot h$

$\quad = \pi(1 \text{ in.})^2 \cdot 9 \text{ in}$

$\quad = 9\pi \text{ cu in.}$

$\quad \approx 9 \cdot \dfrac{22}{7} \text{ cu in.} = 28\dfrac{2}{7} \text{ cu in.}$

The volume is

9π cubic inches $\approx 28\dfrac{2}{7}$ cubic inches.

37. $V = \dfrac{1}{3}s^2 h$

$\quad = \dfrac{1}{3}(5 \text{ cm})^2 (9 \text{ cm})$

$\quad = \dfrac{1}{3} \cdot 25 \text{ sq cm} \cdot 9 \text{ cm}$

$\quad = 75 \text{ cu cm}$

The volume is 75 cubic centimeters.

39. $V = s^3 = \left(1\frac{1}{3} \text{ in.}\right)^3$

$\qquad = \left(\frac{4}{3} \text{ in.}\right)^3$

$\qquad = \frac{64}{27} \text{ cu in.}$

$\qquad = 2\frac{10}{27} \text{ cu in.}$

The volume is $2\frac{10}{27}$ cubic inches.

41. $V = lwh = (2 \text{ ft})(1.4 \text{ ft})(3 \text{ ft}) = 8.4 \text{ cu ft}$
The volume is 8.4 cubic feet.
$SA = 2lh + 2wh + 2lw$
$\qquad = 2(2 \text{ ft})(3 \text{ ft}) + 2(1.4 \text{ ft})(3 \text{ ft}) + 2(2 \text{ ft})(1.4 \text{ ft})$
$\qquad = 12 \text{ sq ft} + 8.4 \text{ sq ft} + 5.6 \text{ sq ft}$
$\qquad = 26 \text{ sq ft}$
The surface area is 26 square feet.

43. $A = l \cdot w = 505 \text{ ft} \cdot 225 \text{ ft} = 113{,}625 \text{ sq ft}$
The area of the flag is 113,625 square feet.

45. $A = l \cdot w = 7 \text{ ft} \cdot 6 \text{ ft} = 42 \text{ sq ft}$
$4 \cdot 42 \text{ sq ft} = 168 \text{ sq ft}$
Four panels require 168 square feet of material.

47. $V = \frac{1}{3} \cdot s^2 \cdot h = \frac{1}{3} \cdot (12 \text{ cm})^2 \cdot 20 \text{ cm} = 960 \text{ cu cm}$
The volume is 960 cubic centimeters.

49. The land is in the shape of a trapezoid.
$A = \frac{1}{2}(b + B) \cdot h$

$\qquad = \frac{1}{2}(90 \text{ ft} + 140 \text{ ft}) \cdot 80 \text{ ft}$

$\qquad = \frac{1}{2} \cdot 230 \text{ ft} \cdot 80 \text{ ft}$

$\qquad = 9200 \text{ sq ft}$

There are 9200 square feet of land in the plot.

51. $V = \frac{4}{3} \cdot \pi \cdot r^3$

$\qquad = \frac{4}{3}\pi(7 \text{ in.})^3$

$\qquad = \frac{1372}{3}\pi \text{ cu in. or } 457\frac{1}{3}\pi \text{ cu in.}$

The volume is $\frac{1372}{3}\pi$ cubic inches or

$457\frac{1}{3}\pi$ cubic inches.

$SA = 4 \cdot \pi \cdot r^2 = 4\pi(7 \text{ in.})^2 = 196\pi \text{ sq in.}$
The surface area is 196π square inches.

53. a. $A = \frac{1}{2}(b + B) \cdot h$

$\qquad = \frac{1}{2}(25 \text{ ft} + 36 \text{ ft}) \cdot 12\frac{1}{2} \text{ ft}$

$\qquad = \frac{1}{2} \cdot 61 \text{ ft} \cdot 12\frac{1}{2} \text{ ft}$

$\qquad = 381\frac{1}{4} \text{ sq ft}$

To the nearest square foot, the area is 381 square feet.

b. Divide the area of the roof by the area covered by one "square."

$\frac{381}{100} = 3.81$

Since you cannot purchase a part of a square, a total of 4 squares needs to be purchased.

55. $r = \frac{1}{2} \cdot d = \frac{1}{2} \cdot 3 \text{ in.} = 1.5 \text{ in.}$

$V = \frac{1}{3}\pi \cdot r^2 \cdot h$

$\qquad = \frac{1}{3}\pi \cdot (1.5 \text{ in.})^2 \cdot 7 \text{ in.}$

$\qquad = 5.25\pi \text{ cu in.}$

The volume is 5.25π cubic inches.

57. $r = \frac{1}{2} \cdot d = \frac{1}{2} \cdot 4 \text{ ft} = 2 \text{ ft}$

$A = \pi r^2 = \pi(2 \text{ ft})^2 = \pi \cdot 4 \text{ sq ft}$

The area of the pizza is 4π square feet, or approximately $4 \cdot 3.14 = 12.56$ square feet.

59. $r = \frac{1}{2} \cdot d = \frac{1}{2} \cdot 3 \text{ m} = 1.5 \text{ m}$

$V = \frac{4}{3} \cdot \pi \cdot r^3$

$\qquad = \frac{4}{3}\pi(1.5 \text{ m})^3$

$\qquad = 4.5\pi \text{ cu m}$

$\qquad \approx 4.5 \cdot 3.14 \text{ cu m} = 14.13 \text{ cu m}$

The volume is
4.5π cubic meters ≈ 14.13 cubic meters.

61. $A = l \cdot w = 16 \text{ ft} \cdot 10\frac{1}{2} \text{ ft}$

$\qquad = 16 \text{ ft} \cdot \frac{21}{2} \text{ ft}$

$\qquad = 168 \text{ sq ft}$

The area of the wall is 168 square feet.

63. $V = \frac{1}{3} \cdot s^2 \cdot h$

$\qquad = \frac{1}{3}(5 \text{ in.})^2 \cdot \frac{13}{10} \text{ in.}$

$\qquad = \frac{1}{3} \cdot 25 \cdot \frac{13}{10} \text{ cu in.}$

$\qquad = 10\frac{5}{6} \text{ cu in.}$

The volume is $10\frac{5}{6}$ cubic inches.

65. $V = lwh = (2 \text{ in.})(2 \text{ in.})(2.2 \text{ in.}) = 8.8 \text{ cu in.}$
The volume is 8.8 cubic inches.

67. $5^2 = 5 \cdot 5 = 25$

69. $3^2 = 3 \cdot 3 = 9$

71. $1^2 + 2^2 = 1 \cdot 1 + 2 \cdot 2 = 1 + 4 = 5$

73. $4^2 + 2^2 = 4 \cdot 4 + 2 \cdot 2 = 16 + 4 = 20$

75. A fence goes around the edge of a yard, thus the situation involves perimeter.

77. Carpet covers the entire floor of a room, so the situation involves area.

79. Paint covers the surface of the wall, thus the situation involves area.

81. A wallpaper border goes around the edge of a room, so the situation involves perimeter.

83. Note that the dimensions given are the diameters of the pizzas.
12-inch pizza:

$r = \frac{1}{2} \cdot d = \frac{1}{2} \cdot 12 \text{ in.} = 6 \text{ in.}$

$A = \pi \cdot r^2 = \pi(6 \text{ in.})^2 = 36\pi \text{ sq in.}$

Price per square inch $= \dfrac{\$10}{36\pi \text{ sq in.}} \approx \$0.0884$

8-inch pizzas:

$r = \frac{1}{2} \cdot d = \frac{1}{2} \cdot 8 \text{ in.} = 4 \text{ in.}$

$A = \pi \cdot r^2 = \pi(4 \text{ in.})^2 = 16\pi \text{ sq in.}$

$2 \cdot A = 2 \cdot 16\pi \text{ sq in.} = 32\pi \text{ sq in.}$

Price per square inch: $\dfrac{\$9}{32\pi \text{ sq in.}} \approx \$0.0895$

Since the price per square inch for the 12-inch pizza is less, the 12-inch pizza is the better deal.

85. $r = \dfrac{d}{2} = \dfrac{20 \text{ m}}{2} = 10 \text{ m}$

The volume is half the volume of a sphere.

$V = \frac{1}{2} \cdot \frac{4}{3}\pi r^3$

$\quad = \frac{1}{2} \cdot \frac{4}{3}(3.14)(10 \text{ m})^3$

$\quad \approx 2093.33 \text{ cu m}$

The volume of the hemisphere is about 2093.33 cu m.

87. no; answers may vary

89. The area of the shaded region is the area of the square minus the area of the circle.
Square:

$A = s^2 = (6 \text{ in.})^2 = 36 \text{ sq in.}$

Circle:

$r = \frac{1}{2} \cdot d = \frac{1}{2}(6 \text{ in.}) = 3 \text{ in.}$

$A = \pi \cdot r^2 = \pi(3 \text{ in.})^2 = 9\pi \text{ sq in.} \approx 28.26 \text{ sq in.}$

$36 \text{ sq in.} - 28.26 \text{ sq in.} = 7.74 \text{ sq in.}$
The shaded region has area of approximately 7.74 square inches.

91. The skating area is a rectangle with a half circle on each end.
Rectangle:
$A = l \cdot w = 22 \text{ m} \cdot 10 \text{ m} = 220 \text{ sq m}$
Half circles:

$A = 2 \cdot \frac{1}{2} \cdot \pi \cdot r^2$

$\quad = \pi(5 \text{ m})^2$

$\quad = 25\pi \text{ sq m} \approx 78.5 \text{ sq m}$

$220 \text{ sq m} + 78.5 \text{ sq m} = 298.5 \text{ sq m}$
The skating surface has area of 298.5 square meters.

93. no; answers may vary

Integrated Review

1. The supplement of a 27° angle measures
   $180° - 27° = 153°$.
   The complement of a 27° angle measures
   $90° - 27° = 63°$.

2. $\angle x$ and the angle marked 105° are
   supplementary angles, so
   $m\angle x = 180° - 105° = 75°$.
   $\angle y$ and the angle marked 105° are vertical
   angles, so $m\angle y = 105°$.
   $\angle z$ and the angle marked 105° are
   supplementary angles, so
   $m\angle z = 180° - 105° = 75°$.

3. $\angle x$ and the angle marked 52° are supplementary
   angles, so $m\angle x = 180° - 52° = 128°$.
   $\angle y$ and the angle marked 52° are corresponding
   angles, so $m\angle y = 52°$.
   $\angle z$ and $\angle y$ are supplementary angles, so
   $m\angle z = 180° - m\angle y = 180° - 52° = 128°$.

4. The sum of the measures of the angles of a
   triangle is 180°.
   $m\angle x = 180° - 90° - 38° = 52°$

5. $d = 2 \cdot r = 2 \cdot 2.3$ in. = 4.6 in.

6. $r = \dfrac{1}{2} \cdot d$
   $= \dfrac{1}{2} \cdot 8\dfrac{1}{2}$ in.
   $= \dfrac{1}{2} \cdot \dfrac{17}{2}$ in.
   $= \dfrac{17}{4}$ in.
   $= 4\dfrac{1}{4}$ in.

7. $P = 4 \cdot s = 4 \cdot 5$ m = 20 m
   The perimeter is 20 meters.
   $A = s^2 = (5 \text{ m})^2 = 25$ sq m
   The area is 25 square meters.

8. $P = a + b + c = 4$ ft + 5 ft + 3 ft = 12 ft
   The perimeter is 12 feet.
   $A = \dfrac{1}{2} \cdot b \cdot h = \dfrac{1}{2} \cdot 3$ ft $\cdot 4$ ft = 6 sq ft
   The area is 6 square feet.

9. $C = 2 \cdot \pi \cdot r = 2 \cdot \pi \cdot 5$ cm $= 10\pi$ cm ≈ 31.4 cm
   The circumference is
   10π centimeters ≈ 31.4 centimeters.
   $A = \pi \cdot r^2 = \pi(5 \text{ cm})^2 = 25\pi$ sq cm ≈ 78.5 sq cm
   The area is 25π square centimeters ≈ 78.5 square
   centimeters.

10. $P = 11$ mi + 5 mi + 11 mi + 5 mi = 32 mi
    The perimeter is 32 miles.
    $A = l \cdot w = 11$ mi $\cdot 4$ mi = 44 sq mi
    The area is 44 square meters.

11. The unmarked horizontal side has length
    17 cm − 8 cm = 9 cm.
    The unmarked vertical side has length
    7 cm + 3 cm = 10 cm.
    $P = (8 + 3 + 9 + 7 + 17 + 10)$ cm = 54 cm
    The perimeter is 54 centimeters.
    The figure is made up of two rectangles, one
    with dimensions 10 cm by 8 cm, the other with
    dimensions 7 cm by 9 cm.
    $A = 10$ cm $\cdot 8$ cm + 7 cm $\cdot 9$ cm = 143 sq cm
    The area is 143 square centimeters.

12. $P = 2 \cdot l + 2 \cdot w$
    $= 2(17 \text{ ft}) + 2(14 \text{ ft})$
    $= 34$ ft + 28 ft
    $= 62$ ft
    The perimeter is 62 feet.
    $A = l \cdot w = 17$ ft $\cdot 14$ ft = 238 sq ft
    The area is 238 square feet.

13. $V = s^3 = (4 \text{ in.})^3 = 64$ cu in.
    The volume is 64 cubic inches.
    $SA = 6 \cdot s^2 = 6(4 \text{ in.})^2 = 6 \cdot 16$ sq in. = 96 sq in.
    The surface area is 96 square inches.

14. $V = l \cdot w \cdot h = 3$ ft $\cdot 2$ ft $\cdot 5.1$ ft = 30.6 cu ft
    The volume is 30.6 cubic feet.
    $SA = 2lh + 2wh + 2lw$
    $= 2(3 \text{ ft})(5.1 \text{ ft}) + 2(2 \text{ ft})(5.1 \text{ ft}) + 2(3 \text{ ft})(2 \text{ ft})$
    $= 30.6$ sq ft + 20.4 sq ft + 12 sq ft
    $= 63$ sq ft
    The surface area is 63 square feet.

15. $V = \dfrac{1}{3} s^2 h = \dfrac{1}{3}(10 \text{ cm})^2(12 \text{ cm}) = 400$ cu cm
    The volume is 400 cubic centimeters.

16. $r = \frac{1}{2} \cdot d = \frac{1}{2} \cdot 3 \text{ mi} = \frac{3}{2} \text{ mi}$

$V = \frac{4}{3}\pi r^3$

$= \frac{4}{3}\pi \left(\frac{3}{2} \text{ mi}\right)^3$

$= \frac{9}{2}\pi \text{ cu mi}$

$= 4\frac{1}{2}\pi \text{ cu mi}$

$\approx \frac{9}{2} \cdot \frac{22}{7} \text{ cu mi} = 14\frac{1}{7} \text{ cu mi}$

The volume is

$4\frac{1}{2}\pi$ cubic miles $\approx 14\frac{1}{7}$ cubic miles.

Section 8.4

Practice Problems

1. $6 \text{ ft} = \frac{6 \text{ ft}}{1} \cdot 1 = \frac{6 \text{ ft}}{1} \cdot \frac{12 \text{ in.}}{1 \text{ ft}} = 6 \cdot 12 \text{ in.} = 72 \text{ in.}$

2. $8 \text{ yd} = \frac{8 \text{ yd}}{1} \cdot 1 = \frac{8 \text{ yd}}{1} \cdot \frac{3 \text{ ft}}{1 \text{ yd}} = 8 \cdot 3 \text{ ft} = 24 \text{ ft}$

3. $18 \text{ in.} = \frac{18 \text{ in.}}{1} \cdot \frac{1 \text{ ft}}{12 \text{ in.}} = \frac{18}{12} \text{ ft} = 1.5 \text{ ft}$

4. $68 \text{ in.} = \frac{68 \text{ in.}}{1} \cdot \frac{1 \text{ ft}}{12 \text{ in.}} = \frac{68}{12} \text{ ft}$

$$
\begin{array}{r}
5 \\
12 \overline{)\ 68} \\
-60 \\
\hline
8
\end{array}
$$

Thus, 68 in. = 5 ft 8 in.

5. $5 \text{ yd} = \frac{5 \text{ yd}}{1} \cdot \frac{3 \text{ ft}}{1 \text{ yd}} = 15 \text{ ft}$

5 yd 2 ft = 15 ft + 2 ft = 17 ft

6.   4 ft 8 in.
  + 8 ft 11 in.
  ————————
  12 ft 19 in.
Since 19 inches is the same as 1 ft 7 in., we have
12 ft 19 in. = 12 ft + 1 ft 7 in. = 13 ft 7 in.

7.   4 ft 7 in.
  ×   4
  ——————————
  16 ft 28 in.
Since 28 in. is the same as 2 ft 4 in., we simplify
as 16 ft 28 in. = 16 ft + 2 ft 4 in. = 18 ft 4 in.

8.   5 ft 8 in. →   4 ft 20 in.
 − 1 ft 9 in.   − 1 ft 9 in.
 ———————   ———————
                 3 ft 11 in.
The remaining board length is 3 ft 11 in.

9. $2.5 \text{ m} = \frac{2.5 \text{ m}}{1} \cdot \frac{1000 \text{ mm}}{1 \text{ m}} = 2500 \text{ mm}$

10. 3500 m = 3.500 km or 3.5 km

11. 640 m = 0.64 km
    2.10 km
  − 0.64 km
  —————————
    1.46 km

  2.1 km = 2100 m
    2100 m
  − 640 m
  —————————
    1460 m

12. 18.3 hm
  ×   5
  —————
  91.5 hm

13. 0.8 m = 80 cm
80 cm + 45 cm = 125 cm
The scarf will be 125 cm or 1.25 m.

Vocabulary and Readiness Check

1. The basic unit of length in the metric system is the <u>meter</u>.

2. The expression $\frac{1 \text{ foot}}{12 \text{ inches}}$ is an example of a <u>unit fraction</u>.

3. A meter is slightly longer than a <u>yard</u>.

4. One foot equals 12 <u>inches</u>.

5. One yard equals 3 <u>feet</u>.

6. One yard equals 36 <u>inches</u>.

7. One mile equals 5280 <u>feet</u>.

Exercise Set 8.4

1. $60 \text{ in.} = \dfrac{60 \text{ in.}}{1} \cdot \dfrac{1 \text{ ft}}{12 \text{ in.}} = \dfrac{60}{12} \text{ ft} = 5 \text{ ft}$

3. $12 \text{ yd} = \dfrac{12 \text{ yd}}{1} \cdot \dfrac{3 \text{ ft}}{1 \text{ yd}} = 12 \cdot 3 \text{ ft} = 36 \text{ ft}$

5. $42,240 \text{ ft} = \dfrac{42,240 \text{ ft}}{1} \cdot \dfrac{1 \text{ mi}}{5280 \text{ ft}}$
$\qquad = \dfrac{42,240}{5280} \text{ mi}$
$\qquad = 8 \text{ mi}$

7. $8\dfrac{1}{2} \text{ ft} = \dfrac{8.5 \text{ ft}}{1} \cdot \dfrac{12 \text{ in.}}{1 \text{ ft}} = 8.5 \cdot 12 \text{ in.} = 102 \text{ in.}$

9. $10 \text{ ft} = \dfrac{10 \text{ ft}}{1} \cdot \dfrac{1 \text{ yd}}{3 \text{ ft}} = \dfrac{10}{3} \text{ yd} = 3\dfrac{1}{3} \text{ yd}$

11. $6.4 \text{ mi} = \dfrac{6.4 \text{ mi}}{1} \cdot \dfrac{5280 \text{ ft}}{1 \text{ mi}}$
$\qquad = 6.4 \cdot 5280 \text{ ft}$
$\qquad = 33,792 \text{ ft}$

13. $162 \text{ in.} = \dfrac{162 \text{ in.}}{1} \cdot \dfrac{1 \text{ ft}}{12 \text{ in.}} \cdot \dfrac{1 \text{ yd}}{3 \text{ ft}}$
$\qquad = \dfrac{162}{36} \text{ yd}$
$\qquad = 4.5 \text{ yd}$

15. $3 \text{ in.} = \dfrac{3 \text{ in.}}{1} \cdot \dfrac{1 \text{ ft}}{12 \text{ in.}} = \dfrac{3}{12} \text{ ft} = 0.25 \text{ ft}$

17. $40 \text{ ft} = \dfrac{40 \text{ ft}}{1} \cdot \dfrac{1 \text{ yd}}{3 \text{ ft}} = \dfrac{40}{3} \text{ yd}$

$$
\begin{array}{r}
13 \text{ yd } 1 \text{ ft} \\
3\overline{)\ 40} \\
\underline{-3} \\
10 \\
\underline{-9} \\
1
\end{array}
$$

19. $85 \text{ in.} = \dfrac{85 \text{ in.}}{1} \cdot \dfrac{1 \text{ ft}}{12 \text{ in.}} = \dfrac{85}{12} \text{ ft}$

$$
\begin{array}{r}
7 \text{ ft } 1 \text{ in.} \\
12\overline{)\ 85} \\
\underline{-84} \\
1
\end{array}
$$

21. $10,000 \text{ ft} = \dfrac{10,000 \text{ ft}}{1} \cdot \dfrac{1 \text{ mi}}{5280 \text{ ft}} = \dfrac{10,000}{5280} \text{ mi}$

$$
\begin{array}{r}
1 \text{ mi } 4720 \text{ ft} \\
5280\overline{)\ 10,000} \\
\underline{-5280} \\
4720
\end{array}
$$

23. $5 \text{ ft } 2 \text{ in.} = \dfrac{5 \text{ ft}}{1} \cdot \dfrac{12 \text{ in.}}{1 \text{ ft}} + 2 \text{ in.}$
$\qquad = 60 \text{ in.} + 2 \text{ in.}$
$\qquad = 62 \text{ in.}$

25. $8 \text{ yd } 2 \text{ ft} = \dfrac{8 \text{ yd}}{1} \cdot \dfrac{3 \text{ ft}}{1 \text{ yd}} + 2 \text{ ft}$
$\qquad = 24 \text{ ft} + 2 \text{ ft}$
$\qquad = 26 \text{ ft}$

27. $2 \text{ yd } 1 \text{ ft} = \dfrac{2 \text{ yd}}{1} \cdot \dfrac{3 \text{ ft}}{1 \text{ yd}} + 1 \text{ ft} = 6 \text{ ft} + 1 \text{ ft} = 7 \text{ ft}$

$\quad\ 7 \text{ ft} = \dfrac{7 \text{ ft}}{1} \cdot \dfrac{12 \text{ in.}}{1 \text{ ft}} = 7 \cdot 12 \text{ in.} = 84 \text{ in.}$

29. $3 \text{ ft } 10 \text{ in.} + 7 \text{ ft } 4 \text{ in.} = 10 \text{ ft } 14 \text{ in.}$
$\qquad\qquad\qquad\qquad\quad = 10 \text{ ft} + 1 \text{ ft } 2 \text{ in.}$
$\qquad\qquad\qquad\qquad\quad = 11 \text{ ft } 2 \text{ in.}$

31. $12 \text{ yd } 2 \text{ ft} + 9 \text{ yd } 2 \text{ ft} = 21 \text{ yd } 4 \text{ ft}$
$\qquad\qquad\qquad\qquad\qquad = 21 \text{ yd} + 1 \text{ yd } 1 \text{ ft}$
$\qquad\qquad\qquad\qquad\qquad = 22 \text{ yd } 1 \text{ ft}$

33.
$$
\begin{array}{r}
22 \text{ ft } 8 \text{ in.} \\
-\ 16 \text{ ft } 3 \text{ in.} \\
\hline
6 \text{ ft } 5 \text{ in.}
\end{array}
$$

35.
$$
\begin{array}{rcr}
18 \text{ ft } 3 \text{ in.} & \rightarrow & 17 \text{ ft } 15 \text{ in.} \\
-\ 10 \text{ ft } 9 \text{ in.} & & -\ 10 \text{ ft }\ \ 9 \text{ in.} \\
\hline
& & 7 \text{ ft }\ \ 6 \text{ in.}
\end{array}
$$

37. $28 \text{ ft } 8 \text{ in.} \div 2 = 14 \text{ ft } 4 \text{ in.}$

39.
$$
\begin{array}{r}
16 \text{ yd }\ \ 2 \text{ ft} \\
\times \qquad\quad 5 \\
\hline
80 \text{ yd } 10 \text{ ft} = 80 \text{ yd} + 3 \text{ yd } 1 \text{ ft} = 83 \text{ yd } 1 \text{ ft}
\end{array}
$$

41. $60 \text{ m} = \dfrac{60 \text{ m}}{1} \cdot \dfrac{100 \text{ cm}}{1 \text{ m}} = 6000 \text{ cm}$

43. $40 \text{ mm} = \dfrac{40 \text{ mm}}{1} \cdot \dfrac{1 \text{ cm}}{10 \text{ mm}} = 4 \text{ cm}$

45. $500 \text{ m} = \dfrac{500 \text{ m}}{1} \cdot \dfrac{1 \text{ km}}{1000 \text{ m}} = \dfrac{500}{1000} \text{ km} = 0.5 \text{ km}$

47. $1700 \text{ mm} = \dfrac{1700 \text{ mm}}{1} \cdot \dfrac{1 \text{ m}}{1000 \text{ mm}} = 1.7 \text{ m}$

49. $1500 \text{ cm} = \dfrac{1500 \text{ cm}}{1} \cdot \dfrac{1 \text{ m}}{100 \text{ cm}} = \dfrac{1500}{100} \text{ m} = 15 \text{ m}$

51. $0.42 \text{ km} = \dfrac{0.42 \text{ km}}{1} \cdot \dfrac{100,000 \text{ cm}}{1 \text{ km}} = 42,000 \text{ cm}$

53. $7 \text{ km} = \dfrac{7 \text{ km}}{1} \cdot \dfrac{1000 \text{ m}}{1 \text{ km}} = 7000 \text{ m}$

55. $8.3 \text{ cm} = \dfrac{8.3 \text{ cm}}{1} \cdot \dfrac{10 \text{ mm}}{1 \text{ cm}} = 83 \text{ mm}$

57. $20.1 \text{ mm} = \dfrac{20.1 \text{ mm}}{1} \cdot \dfrac{1 \text{ dm}}{100 \text{ mm}}$

$\qquad = \dfrac{20.1}{100} \text{ dm}$

$\qquad = 0.201 \text{ dm}$

59. $0.04 \text{ m} = \dfrac{0.04 \text{ m}}{1} \cdot \dfrac{1000 \text{ mm}}{1 \text{ m}} = 40 \text{ mm}$

61.
$$
\begin{array}{r}
8.60 \text{ m} \\
+\ 0.34 \text{ m} \\
\hline
8.94 \text{ m}
\end{array}
$$

63.
$$
\begin{array}{r}
2.9 \text{ m} \\
+\ 40.0 \text{ mm} \\
\hline
\end{array}
\qquad
\begin{array}{r}
2.90 \text{ m} \\
+\ 0.04 \text{ m} \\
\hline
2.94 \text{ m}
\end{array}
\text{ or }
\begin{array}{r}
2900 \text{ mm} \\
+\ 40 \text{ mm} \\
\hline
2940 \text{ mm}
\end{array}
$$

65.
$$
\begin{array}{r}
24.8 \text{ mm} \\
-\ 1.19 \text{ cm} \\
\hline
\end{array}
\qquad
\begin{array}{r}
24.8 \text{ mm} \\
-\ 11.9 \text{ mm} \\
\hline
12.9 \text{ mm}
\end{array}
\text{ or }
\begin{array}{r}
2.48 \text{ cm} \\
-\ 1.19 \text{ cm} \\
\hline
1.29 \text{ cm}
\end{array}
$$

67.
$$
\begin{array}{r}
15 \text{ km} \\
-\ 2360 \text{ m} \\
\hline
\end{array}
\qquad
\begin{array}{r}
15.00 \text{ km} \\
-\ 2.36 \text{ km} \\
\hline
12.64 \text{ km}
\end{array}
\text{ or }
\begin{array}{r}
15,000 \text{ m} \\
-\ 2360 \text{ m} \\
\hline
12,640 \text{ m}
\end{array}
$$

69. $18.3 \text{ m} \times 3 = 54.9 \text{ m}$

71. $6.2 \text{ km} \div 4 = 1.55 \text{ km}$

		Yards	Feet	Inches
73.	Chrysler Building in New York City	$348\frac{2}{3}$	1046	12,552
75.	Python length	$11\frac{2}{3}$	35	420

		Meters	Millimeters	Kilometers	Centimeters
77.	Length of elephant	5	5000	0.005	500
79.	Tennis ball diameter	0.065	65	0.000065	6.5
81.	Distance from London to Paris	342,000	342,000,000	342	34,200,000

83.   6 ft 10 in.
     + 3 ft   8 in.
      9 ft 18 in. = 9 ft + 1 ft 6 in. = 10 ft 6 in.
The bamboo is 10 ft 6 in. now.

85.   6000 ft
     − 900 ft
      5100 ft
The Grand Canyon of the Colorado River is 5100 feet deeper than the Grand Canyon of the Yellowstone River.

87.   8 ft 11 in. ÷ 22.5 in. = 107 in. ÷ 22.5 in. ≈ 4.8
Robert is 4.8 times as tall as Gul.

89.   80 mm   80.0 mm
    − 5.33 cm   − 53.3 mm
                26.7 mm

The ice must be 26.7 mm thicker before skating is allowed.

91.   1 ft 9 in. × 9 = 9 ft 81 in.
                 = 9 ft + 6 ft 9 in.
                 = 15 ft 9 in.
The stacks extend 15 ft 9 in. from the wall.

93.
$$
\begin{array}{r}
3.35 \\
20 \overline{)\ 67.00} \\
\underline{-60} \\
70 \\
\underline{-60} \\
1\,00 \\
\underline{-1\,00} \\
0
\end{array}
$$
Each piece will be 3.35 meters long.

95. $182 \text{ ft} \times 2 = 364 \text{ ft}$
Two trucks are 364 feet long.

$364 \text{ ft} = \dfrac{364 \text{ ft}}{1} \cdot \dfrac{1 \text{ yd}}{3 \text{ ft}} = 121 \dfrac{1}{3} \text{ yd}$

Two trucks are $121 \dfrac{1}{3}$ yards long.

97. $0.21 = \dfrac{21}{100}$

99. $\dfrac{13}{100} = 0.13$

101. $\dfrac{1}{4} = \dfrac{1}{4} \cdot \dfrac{25}{25} = \dfrac{25}{100} = 0.25$

103. No, the width of a twin-size bed being 20 meters is not reasonable.

105. Yes, glass for a drinking glass being 2 millimeters thick is reasonable.

107. No, the distance across the Colorado River being 50 kilometers is not reasonable.

109. 5 yd 2 in. is close to 5 yd. 7 yd 30 in. is close to 7 yd 36 in. = 8 yd.
Estimate: 5 yd + 8 yd = 13 yd.

111. answers may vary; for example,

$4 \text{ ft} = \dfrac{4 \text{ ft}}{1} \cdot \dfrac{1 \text{ yd}}{3 \text{ ft}} = \dfrac{4}{3} \text{ yd} = 1 \dfrac{1}{3} \text{ yd}$

$4 \text{ ft} = \dfrac{4 \text{ ft}}{1} \cdot \dfrac{12 \text{ in.}}{1 \text{ ft}} = 48 \text{ in.}$

113. answers may vary

115. $18.3 \text{ m} \times 18.3 \text{ m} = 334.89 \text{ sq m}$
The area of the sign is 334.89 square meters.

Section 8.5

Practice Problems

1. $6500 \text{ lb} = \dfrac{6500 \text{ lb}}{1} \cdot \dfrac{1 \text{ ton}}{2000 \text{ lb}}$

$= \dfrac{6500}{2000} \text{ tons}$

$= \dfrac{13}{4} \text{ tons or } 3 \dfrac{1}{4} \text{ tons}$

2. $72 \text{ oz} = \dfrac{72 \text{ oz}}{1} \cdot \dfrac{1 \text{ lb}}{16 \text{ oz}} = \dfrac{72}{16} \text{ lb} = \dfrac{9}{2} \text{ lb or } 4 \dfrac{1}{2} \text{ lb}$

3. $47 \text{ oz} = 47 \text{ oz} \cdot \dfrac{1 \text{ lb}}{16 \text{ oz}} = \dfrac{47}{16} \text{ lb}$

$$
\begin{array}{r}
2 \text{ lb } 15 \text{ oz} \\
16\overline{)\,47} \\
\underline{-32} \\
15
\end{array}
$$

Thus, 47 oz = 2 lb 15 oz

4.
$$
\begin{array}{r}
8 \text{ tons} \quad 100 \text{ lb} \\
-\ 5 \text{ tons } 1200 \text{ lb}
\end{array}
\rightarrow
\begin{array}{r}
7 \text{ tons } 2100 \text{ lb} \\
-\ 5 \text{ tons } 1200 \text{ lb} \\
\hline
2 \text{ tons} \quad 900 \text{ lb}
\end{array}
$$

5.
$$
\begin{array}{r}
1 \text{ lb} \quad 6 \text{ oz} \\
4\overline{)\,5 \text{ lb} \quad 8 \text{ oz}} \\
\underline{-\ 4 \text{ lb}} \\
1 \text{ lb} = 16 \text{ oz} \\
\overline{24 \text{ oz}}
\end{array}
$$

6.
$$
\begin{array}{r}
\text{batch weight} \\
+\ \text{container weight} \\
\hline
\text{total weight}
\end{array}
\rightarrow
\begin{array}{r}
5 \text{ lb } 14 \text{ oz} \\
+\quad\quad 6 \text{ oz} \\
\hline
5 \text{ lb } 20 \text{ oz}
\end{array}
$$

5 lb 20 oz = 5 lb + 1 lb 4 oz = 6 lb 4 oz
The total weight is 6 lb 4 oz.

7. $3.41 \text{ g} = \dfrac{3.41 \text{ g}}{1} \cdot \dfrac{1000 \text{ mg}}{1 \text{ g}} = 3410 \text{ mg}$

8. $56.2 \text{ cg} = 56.2 \text{ cg} = 0.562 \text{ g}$

9. 3.1 dg = 0.31 g   or   2.5 g = 25 dg

$$
\begin{array}{r}
2.50 \text{ g} \\
-\ 0.31 \text{ g} \\
\hline
2.19 \text{ g}
\end{array}
\qquad
\begin{array}{r}
25.0 \text{ dg} \\
-\ 3.1 \text{ dg} \\
\hline
21.9 \text{ dg}
\end{array}
$$

10.
$$
\begin{array}{r}
22.9 \quad \approx 23 \\
24\overline{)\,550.0 \text{ kg}} \\
\underline{-48} \\
70 \\
\underline{-48} \\
22\ 0 \\
\underline{-21\ 6} \\
4
\end{array}
$$

Each bag weighs about 23 kg.

Vocabulary and Readiness Check

1. <u>Mass</u> is a measure of the amount of substance in an object. This measure does not change.

2. <u>Weight</u> is the measure of the pull of gravity.

3. The basic unit of mass in the metric system is the <u>gram</u>.

4. One pound equals <u>16</u> ounces.

5. One ton equals <u>2000</u> pounds.

Exercise Set 8.5

1. $2 \text{ lb} = \dfrac{2 \text{ lb}}{1} \cdot \dfrac{16 \text{ oz}}{1 \text{ lb}} = 2 \cdot 16 \text{ oz} = 32 \text{ oz}$

3. $5 \text{ tons} = \dfrac{5 \text{ tons}}{1} \cdot \dfrac{2000 \text{ lb}}{1 \text{ ton}}$
    $= 5 \cdot 2000 \text{ lb}$
    $= 10,000 \text{ lb}$

5. $18,000 \text{ lb} = \dfrac{18,000 \text{ lb}}{1} \cdot \dfrac{1 \text{ ton}}{2000 \text{ lb}}$
    $= \dfrac{18,000}{2000} \text{ tons}$
    $= 9 \text{ tons}$

7. $60 \text{ oz} = \dfrac{60 \text{ oz}}{1} \cdot \dfrac{1 \text{ lb}}{16 \text{ oz}} = \dfrac{60}{16} \text{ lb} = \dfrac{15}{4} \text{ lb} = 3\dfrac{3}{4} \text{ lb}$

9. $3500 \text{ lb} = \dfrac{3500 \text{ lb}}{1} \cdot \dfrac{1 \text{ ton}}{2000 \text{ lb}}$
    $= \dfrac{3500}{2000} \text{ tons}$
    $= \dfrac{7}{4} \text{ tons}$
    $= 1\dfrac{3}{4} \text{ tons}$

11. $12.75 \text{ lb} = \dfrac{12.75 \text{ lb}}{1} \cdot \dfrac{16 \text{ oz}}{1 \text{ lb}}$
    $= 12.75 \cdot 16 \text{ oz}$
    $= 204 \text{ oz}$

13. $4.9 \text{ tons} = \dfrac{4.9 \text{ tons}}{1} \cdot \dfrac{2000 \text{ lb}}{1 \text{ ton}}$
    $= 4.9 \cdot 2000 \text{ lb}$
    $= 9800 \text{ lb}$

15. $4\dfrac{3}{4} \text{ lb} = \dfrac{19}{4} \text{ lb}$
    $= \dfrac{\frac{19}{4} \text{ lb}}{1} \cdot \dfrac{16 \text{ oz}}{1 \text{ lb}}$
    $= \dfrac{19}{4} \cdot 16 \text{ oz}$
    $= 76 \text{ oz}$

17. $2950 \text{ lb} = \dfrac{2950 \text{ lb}}{1} \cdot \dfrac{1 \text{ ton}}{2000 \text{ lb}}$
    $= \dfrac{2950}{2000} \text{ tons}$
    $= \dfrac{59}{40} \text{ tons}$
    $= 1.475 \text{ tons}$
    $\approx 1.5 \text{ tons}$

19. $\dfrac{4}{5} \text{ oz} = \dfrac{\frac{4}{5}}{1} \cdot \dfrac{1 \text{ lb}}{16 \text{ oz}} = \dfrac{4}{5} \cdot \dfrac{1}{16} \text{ lb} = \dfrac{1}{20} \text{ lb}$

21. $5\dfrac{3}{4} \text{ lb} = \dfrac{23}{4} \text{ lb}$
    $= \dfrac{\frac{23}{4} \text{ lb}}{1} \cdot \dfrac{16 \text{ oz}}{1 \text{ lb}}$
    $= \dfrac{23}{4} \cdot 16 \text{ oz}$
    $= 92 \text{ oz}$

23. $10 \text{ lb } 1 \text{ oz} = 10 \cdot 16 \text{ oz} + 1 \text{ oz}$
    $= 160 \text{ oz} + 1 \text{ oz}$
    $= 161 \text{ oz}$

25. $89 \text{ oz} = \dfrac{89 \text{ oz}}{1} \cdot \dfrac{1 \text{ lb}}{16 \text{ oz}} = \dfrac{89}{16} \text{ lb}$

    $\begin{array}{r} 5 \text{ lb } 9 \text{ oz} \\ 16\overline{)\;89} \\ \underline{-80} \\ 9 \end{array}$

    $89 \text{ oz} = 5 \text{ lb } 9 \text{ oz}$

27. $34 \text{ lb } 12 \text{ oz} + 18 \text{ lb } 14 \text{ oz} = 52 \text{ lb } 26 \text{ oz}$
    $= 52 \text{ lb} + 1 \text{ lb } 10 \text{ oz}$
    $= 53 \text{ lb } 10 \text{ oz}$

29. $3 \text{ tons } 1820 \text{ lb} + 4 \text{ tons } 930 \text{ lb}$
    $= 7 \text{ tons } 2750 \text{ lb}$
    $= 7 \text{ tons} + 1 \text{ ton } 750 \text{ lb}$
    $= 8 \text{ tons } 750 \text{ lb}$

31.
$$\begin{array}{r} 5 \text{ tons } 1050 \text{ lb} \\ - 2 \text{ tons } 875 \text{ lb} \\ \hline 3 \text{ tons } 175 \text{ lb} \end{array}$$

33.
$$\begin{array}{rr} 12 \text{ lb } 4 \text{ oz} & 11 \text{ lb } 20 \text{ oz} \\ - 3 \text{ lb } 9 \text{ oz} & - 3 \text{ lb } 9 \text{ oz} \\ \hline & 8 \text{ lb } 11 \text{ oz} \end{array}$$

35. $5 \text{ lb } 3 \text{ oz} \times 6 = 30 \text{ lb } 18 \text{ oz}$
$$= 30 \text{ lb} + 1 \text{ lb } 2 \text{ oz}$$
$$= 31 \text{ lb } 2 \text{ oz}$$

37. $6 \text{ tons } 1500 \text{ lb} \div 5 = \dfrac{6}{5} \text{ tons } 300 \text{ lb}$
$$= 1\frac{1}{5} \text{ tons } 300 \text{ lb}$$
$$= 1 \text{ ton} + \frac{2000 \text{ lb}}{5} + 300 \text{ lb}$$
$$= 1 \text{ ton} + 400 \text{ lb} + 300 \text{ lb}$$
$$= 1 \text{ ton } 700 \text{ lb}$$

39. $500 \text{ g} = \dfrac{500 \text{ g}}{1} \cdot \dfrac{1 \text{ kg}}{1000 \text{ g}} = \dfrac{500}{1000} \text{ kg} = 0.5 \text{ kg}$

41. $4 \text{ g} = \dfrac{4 \text{ g}}{1} \cdot \dfrac{1000 \text{ mg}}{1 \text{ g}} = 4 \cdot 1000 \text{ mg} = 4000 \text{ mg}$

43. $25 \text{ kg} = \dfrac{25 \text{ kg}}{1} \cdot \dfrac{1000 \text{ g}}{1 \text{ kg}} = 25 \cdot 1000 \text{ g} = 25,000 \text{ g}$

45. $48 \text{ mg} = \dfrac{48 \text{ mg}}{1} \cdot \dfrac{1 \text{ g}}{1000 \text{ mg}} = \dfrac{48}{1000} \text{ g} = 0.048 \text{ g}$

47. $6.3 \text{ g} = \dfrac{6.3 \text{ g}}{1} \cdot \dfrac{1 \text{ kg}}{1000 \text{ g}} = \dfrac{6.3}{1000} \text{ kg} = 0.0063 \text{ kg}$

49. $15.14 \text{ g} = \dfrac{15.14 \text{ g}}{1} \cdot \dfrac{1000 \text{ mg}}{1 \text{ g}}$
$$= 15.14 \cdot 1000 \text{ mg}$$
$$= 15,140 \text{ mg}$$

51. $6.25 \text{ kg} = \dfrac{6.25 \text{ kg}}{1} \cdot \dfrac{1000 \text{ g}}{1 \text{ kg}}$
$$= 6.25 \cdot 1000 \text{ g}$$
$$= 6250 \text{ g}$$

53. $35 \text{ hg} = \dfrac{35 \text{ hg}}{1} \cdot \dfrac{10,000 \text{ cg}}{1 \text{ hg}}$
$$= 35 \cdot 10,000 \text{ cg}$$
$$= 350,000 \text{ cg}$$

55.
$$\begin{array}{r} 3.8 \text{ mg} \\ + 9.7 \text{ mg} \\ \hline 13.5 \text{ mg} \end{array}$$

57. $205 \text{ mg} + 5.61 \text{ g} = 0.205 \text{ g} + 5.61 \text{ g} = 5.815 \text{ g}$
or
$$205 \text{ mg} + 5.61 \text{ g} = 205 \text{ mg} + 5610 \text{ mg}$$
$$= 5815 \text{ mg}$$

59. $9 \text{ g} - 7150 \text{ mg}$
$$\begin{array}{rr} 9000 \text{ mg} & 9.000 \text{ g} \\ - 7150 \text{ mg} \quad \text{or} & - 7.150 \text{ g} \\ \hline 1850 \text{ mg} & 1.850 \text{ g} \text{ or } 1.85 \text{ g} \end{array}$$

61. $1.61 \text{ kg} - 250 \text{ g} = 1.61 \text{ kg} - 0.250 \text{ kg} = 1.36 \text{ kg}$
or
$$1.61 \text{ kg} - 250 \text{ g} = 1610 \text{ g} - 250 \text{ g} = 1360 \text{ g}$$

63.
$$\begin{array}{r} 5.2 \text{ kg} \\ \times 2.6 \\ \hline 13.52 \text{ kg} \end{array}$$

65. $17 \text{ kg} \div 8 = \dfrac{17}{8} \text{ kg}$

$$\begin{array}{r} 2.125 \\ 8{\overline{\smash{\big)}\,17.000}} \\ \underline{-16} \\ 1\ 0 \\ \underline{-8} \\ 20 \\ \underline{-16} \\ 40 \\ \underline{-40} \\ 0 \end{array}$$

$17 \text{ kg} \div 8 = 2.125 \text{ kg}$

	Object	Tons	Pounds	Ounces
67.	Statue of Liberty—weight of copper sheeting	100	200,000	3,200,000
69.	A 12-inch cube of osmium (heaviest metal)	$\frac{269}{400}$ or 0.6725	1345	21,520

	Object	Grams	Kilograms	Milligrams	Centigrams
71.	Capsule of Amoxicillin (antibiotic)	0.5	0.0005	500	50
73.	A six-year-old boy	21,000	21	21,000,000	2,100,000

75.
$$\begin{array}{r} 336 \\ \times\ 24 \\ \hline 1344 \\ 6720 \\ \hline 8064 \end{array}$$

$8064 \text{ g} = \dfrac{8064 \text{ g}}{1} \cdot \dfrac{1 \text{ kg}}{1000 \text{ g}} = \dfrac{8064}{1000} \text{ kg} = 8.064 \text{ kg}$

24 cans weigh 8.064 kg.

77. $\quad 0.09 \text{ g} = \dfrac{0.09 \text{ g}}{1} \cdot \dfrac{1000 \text{ mg}}{1 \text{ g}}$
$$= 0.09 \cdot 1000 \text{ mg}$$
$$= 90 \text{ mg}$$

90 mg − 60 mg = 30 mg
The extra-strength tablet contains 30 mg more medication.

79.
$$\begin{array}{r} 1 \text{ lb } 10 \text{ oz} \\ +\ 3 \text{ lb } 14 \text{ oz} \\ \hline 4 \text{ lb } 24 \text{ oz} \end{array} = 4 \text{ lb} + 1 \text{ lb } 8 \text{ oz} = 5 \text{ lb } 8 \text{ oz}$$

The total amount of rice is 5 lb 8 oz.

81.
$$\begin{array}{r} 64 \text{ lb }\ \ 8 \text{ oz} \\ -\ 28 \text{ lb } 10 \text{ oz} \end{array} \qquad \begin{array}{r} 63 \text{ lb } 24 \text{ oz} \\ -\ 28 \text{ lb } 10 \text{ oz} \\ \hline 35 \text{ lb } 14 \text{ oz} \end{array}$$

Carla's zucchini was 35 lb 14 oz lighter than the record weight.

83.
$$\begin{array}{r} 7 \text{ lb }\ \ 8 \text{ oz} \\ -\ \ \ \ \ \ 8.6 \text{ oz} \end{array} \qquad \begin{array}{r} 6 \text{ lb }\ \ 24 \text{ oz} \\ -\ \ \ \ \ \ 8.6 \text{ oz} \\ \hline 6 \text{ lb } 15.4 \text{ oz} \end{array}$$

This is 6 lb 15.4 oz lighter.

85. $3 \times 16 = 48$
3 cartons contain 48 boxes of fruit.
$3 \text{ mg} \times 48 = 144 \text{ mg}$
3 cartons contain 144 mg of preservatives.

87. $26 \text{ g} \times 12 = 312 \text{ g}$

$\dfrac{312 \text{ g}}{1} \cdot \dfrac{1 \text{ kg}}{1000 \text{ g}} = 0.312 \text{ kg of packaging in a carton}$

6.432 kg − 0.312 kg = 6.12 kg
The actual weight of the oatmeal is 6.12 kg.

89. $3 \text{ lb } 4 \text{ oz} \times 10 = 30 \text{ lb } 40 \text{ oz}$
$= 30 \text{ lb} + 2 \text{ lb } 8 \text{ oz}$
$= 32 \text{ lb } 8 \text{ oz}$
Each box weighs 32 lb 8 oz.
$32 \text{ lb } 8 \text{ oz} \times 4 = 128 \text{ lb } 32 \text{ oz}$
$= 128 \text{ lb} + 2 \text{ lb}$
$= 130 \text{ lb}$
4 boxes of meat weigh 130 lb.

91. 55 lb 4 oz   54 lb 20 oz
$-$ 2 lb 8 oz $-$ 2 lb 8 oz
                              52 lb 12 oz

        52 lb 12 oz
$\times$ 4
208 lb 48 oz $= 208 \text{ lb} + 3 \text{ lb} = 211 \text{ lb}$
4 cartons contain 211 lb of pineapple.

93. $\dfrac{4}{25} = \dfrac{4}{25} \cdot \dfrac{4}{4} = \dfrac{16}{100} = 0.16$

95. $\dfrac{7}{8} = \dfrac{7}{8} \cdot \dfrac{125}{125} = \dfrac{875}{1000} = 0.875$

97. No, a pill containing 2 kg of medication is not reasonable.

99. Yes, a bag of flour weighing 4.5 kg is reasonable.

101. No, a professor weighing less than 150 g is not reasonable.

103. answers may vary; for example 250 mg or 0.25 g

105. True, a kilogram is 1000 grams.

107. answers may vary

Section 8.6

Practice Problems

1. $43 \text{ pt} = \dfrac{43 \text{ pt}}{1} \cdot \dfrac{1 \text{ qt}}{2 \text{ pt}} = \dfrac{43}{2} \text{ qt} = 21\dfrac{1}{2} \text{ qt}$

2. $26 \text{ qt} = \dfrac{26 \text{ qt}}{1} \cdot \dfrac{4 \text{ c}}{1 \text{ qt}} = 26 \cdot 4 \text{ c} = 104 \text{ c}$

3. 1 gal 1 qt   5 qt
$-$ 2 qt $\rightarrow$ $-$ 2 qt
                              3 qt

4. 15 gal 3 qt
$+$ 4 gal 3 qt
19 gal 6 qt $= 19 \text{ gal} + 1 \text{ gal } 2 \text{ qt} = 20 \text{ gal } 2 \text{ qt}$
The total amount of oil will be 20 gal 2 qt.

5. $2100 \text{ ml} = \dfrac{2100 \text{ ml}}{1} \cdot \dfrac{1 \text{ L}}{1000 \text{ ml}} = \dfrac{2100}{1000} \text{ L} = 2.1 \text{ L}$

6. $2.13 \text{ dal} = \dfrac{2.13 \text{ dal}}{1} \cdot \dfrac{10 \text{ L}}{1 \text{ dal}} = 2.13 \cdot 10 \text{ L} = 21.3 \text{ L}$

7. $1250 \text{ ml} = 1.250 \text{ L}$ $2.9 \text{ L} = 2900 \text{ ml}$
  1.25 L   1250 ml
$+$ 2.9 L $+$ 2900 ml
  4.15 L   4150 ml
The total is 4.15 L or 4150 ml.

8.   28.6 L
$\times$ 85
  143 0
2288 0
2431.0 L
Thus, 2431 L can be pumped in 85 minutes.

Vocabulary and Readiness Check

1. Units of <u>capacity</u> are generally used to measure liquids.

2. The basic unit of capacity in the metric system is the <u>liter</u>.

3. One cup equals 8 <u>fluid ounces</u>.

4. One quart equals 2 <u>pints</u>.

5. One pint equals 2 <u>cups</u>.

6. One quart equals 4 <u>cups</u>.

7. One gallon equals 4 <u>quarts</u>.

Exercise Set 8.6

1. $32 \text{ fl oz} = \dfrac{32 \text{ fl oz}}{1} \cdot \dfrac{1 \text{ c}}{8 \text{ fl oz}} = \dfrac{32}{8} \text{ c} = 4 \text{ c}$

3. $8 \text{ qt} = \dfrac{8 \text{ qt}}{1} \cdot \dfrac{2 \text{ pt}}{1 \text{ qt}} = 8 \cdot 2 \text{ pt} = 16 \text{ pt}$

5. $14 \text{ qt} = \dfrac{14 \text{ qt}}{1} \cdot \dfrac{1 \text{ gal}}{4 \text{ qt}} = \dfrac{14}{4} \text{ gal} = 3\dfrac{1}{2} \text{ gal}$

7. $80 \text{ fl oz} = \dfrac{80 \text{ fl oz}}{1} \cdot \dfrac{1 \text{ c}}{8 \text{ fl oz}} = \dfrac{80}{8} \text{ c} = 10 \text{ c}$

$10 \text{ c} = \dfrac{10 \text{ c}}{1} \cdot \dfrac{1 \text{ pt}}{2 \text{ c}} = \dfrac{10}{2} \text{ pt} = 5 \text{ pt}$

9. $2 \text{ qt} = \dfrac{2 \text{ qt}}{1} \cdot \dfrac{2 \text{ pt}}{1 \text{ qt}} \cdot \dfrac{2 \text{ c}}{1 \text{ pt}} = 2 \cdot 2 \cdot 2 \text{ c} = 8 \text{ c}$

11. $120 \text{ fl oz} = \dfrac{120 \text{ fl oz}}{1} \cdot \dfrac{1 \text{ c}}{8 \text{ fl oz}} \cdot \dfrac{1 \text{ pt}}{2 \text{ c}} \cdot \dfrac{1 \text{ qt}}{2 \text{ pt}}$

$= \dfrac{120}{8 \cdot 2 \cdot 2} \text{ qt}$

$= \dfrac{15}{4} \text{ qt}$

$= 3\dfrac{3}{4} \text{ qt}$

13. $42 \text{ c} = \dfrac{42 \text{ c}}{1} \cdot \dfrac{1 \text{ qt}}{4 \text{ c}} = \dfrac{42}{4} \text{ qt} = 10\dfrac{1}{2} \text{ qt}$

15. $4\dfrac{1}{2} \text{ pt} = \dfrac{9}{2} \text{ pt} = \dfrac{\frac{9}{2} \text{ pt}}{1} \cdot \dfrac{2 \text{ c}}{1 \text{ pt}} = \dfrac{9}{2} \cdot 2 \text{ c} = 9 \text{ c}$

17. $5 \text{ gal } 3 \text{ qt} = \dfrac{5 \text{ gal}}{1} \cdot \dfrac{4 \text{ qt}}{1 \text{ gal}} + 3 \text{ qt}$

$= 5 \cdot 4 \text{ qt} + 3 \text{ qt}$

$= 20 \text{ qt} + 3 \text{ qt}$

$= 23 \text{ qt}$

19. $\dfrac{1}{2} \text{ c} = \dfrac{\frac{1}{2} \text{ c}}{1} \cdot \dfrac{1 \text{ pt}}{2 \text{ c}} = \dfrac{1}{2} \cdot \dfrac{1}{2} \text{ pt} = \dfrac{1}{4} \text{ pt}$

21. $58 \text{ qt} = 56 \text{ qt} + 2 \text{ qt}$

$= \dfrac{56 \text{ qt}}{1} \cdot \dfrac{1 \text{ gal}}{4 \text{ qt}} + 2 \text{ qt}$

$= \dfrac{56}{4} \text{ gal} + 2 \text{ qt}$

$= 14 \text{ gal } 2 \text{ qt}$

23. $39 \text{ pt} = 38 \text{ pt} + 1 \text{ pt}$

$= \dfrac{38 \text{ pt}}{1} \cdot \dfrac{1 \text{ qt}}{2 \text{ pt}} + 1 \text{ pt}$

$= 19 \text{ qt} + 1 \text{ pt}$

$= 16 \text{ qt} + 3 \text{ qt} + 1 \text{ pt}$

$= \dfrac{16 \text{ qt}}{1} \cdot \dfrac{1 \text{ gal}}{4 \text{ qt}} + 3 \text{ qt} + 1 \text{ pt}$

$= 4 \text{ gal} + 3 \text{ qt} + 1 \text{ pt}$

$= 4 \text{ gal } 3 \text{ qt } 1 \text{ pt}$

25. $2\dfrac{3}{4} \text{ gal} = \dfrac{11}{4} \text{ gal}$

$= \dfrac{\frac{11}{4} \text{ gal}}{1} \cdot \dfrac{4 \text{ qt}}{1 \text{ gal}} \cdot \dfrac{2 \text{ pt}}{1 \text{ qt}}$

$= \dfrac{11}{4} \cdot 4 \cdot 2 \text{ pt}$

$= 22 \text{ pt}$

27. $\begin{array}{r} 5 \text{ gal } 3 \text{ qt} \\ + \ 7 \text{ gal } 3 \text{ qt} \\ \hline 12 \text{ gal } 6 \text{ qt} \end{array}$ $= 12 \text{ gal} + 1 \text{ gal } 2 \text{ qt} = 13 \text{ gal } 2 \text{ qt}$

29. $1 \text{ c } 5 \text{ fl oz} + 2 \text{ c } 7 \text{ fl oz} = 3 \text{ c } 12 \text{ fl oz}$

$= 3 \text{ c} + 1 \text{ c } 4 \text{ fl oz}$

$= 4 \text{ c } 4 \text{ fl oz}$

31. $\begin{array}{r} 3 \text{ gal} \\ - \ 1 \text{ gal } 3 \text{ qt} \end{array}$ $\begin{array}{r} 2 \text{ gal } 4 \text{ qt} \\ - \ 1 \text{ gal } 3 \text{ qt} \\ \hline 1 \text{ gal } 1 \text{ qt} \end{array}$

33. $\begin{array}{r} 3 \text{ gal } 1 \text{ qt} \\ - \ 1 \text{ qt } 1 \text{ pt} \end{array}$ $\begin{array}{r} 2 \text{ gal } 5 \text{ qt} \\ - \ 1 \text{ qt } 1 \text{ pt} \end{array}$ $\begin{array}{r} 2 \text{ gal } 4 \text{ qt } 2 \text{ pt} \\ - \ 1 \text{ qt } 1 \text{ pt} \\ \hline 2 \text{ gal } 3 \text{ qt } 1 \text{ pt} \end{array}$

35. $8 \text{ gal } 2 \text{ qt} \times 2 = 16 \text{ gal } 4 \text{ qt}$

$= 16 \text{ gal} + 1 \text{ gal}$

$= 17 \text{ gal}$

37. $9 \text{ gal } 2 \text{ qt} \div 2 = (8 \text{ gal } 4 \text{ qt} + 2 \text{ qt}) \div 2$

$= 8 \text{ gal } 6 \text{ qt} \div 2$

$= 4 \text{ gal } 3 \text{ qt}$

39. $5 \text{L} = \dfrac{5 \text{L}}{1} \cdot \dfrac{1000 \text{ ml}}{1 \text{ L}} = 5000 \text{ ml}$

41. $0.16 \text{ L} = \dfrac{0.16 \text{ L}}{1} \cdot \dfrac{1 \text{ kl}}{1000 \text{ L}}$

$= \dfrac{0.16}{1000} \text{ kl}$

$= 0.00016 \text{ kl}$

43. $5600 \text{ ml} = \dfrac{5600 \text{ ml}}{1} \cdot \dfrac{1 \text{ L}}{1000 \text{ ml}} = \dfrac{5600}{1000} \text{ L} = 5.6 \text{ L}$

45. $3.2 \text{ L} = \dfrac{3.2 \text{ L}}{1} \cdot \dfrac{100 \text{ cl}}{1 \text{ L}} = 3.2 \cdot 100 \text{ cl} = 320 \text{ cl}$

47. $410 \text{ L} = \dfrac{410 \text{ L}}{1} \cdot \dfrac{1 \text{ kl}}{1000 \text{ L}} = \dfrac{410}{1000} \text{ kl} = 0.41 \text{ kl}$

49. $64 \text{ ml} = \dfrac{64 \text{ ml}}{1} \cdot \dfrac{1 \text{ L}}{1000 \text{ ml}} = \dfrac{64}{1000} \text{ L} = 0.064 \text{ L}$

51. $0.16 \text{ kl} = \dfrac{0.16 \text{ kl}}{1} \cdot \dfrac{1000 \text{ L}}{1 \text{ kl}}$
$= 0.16 \cdot 1000 \text{ L}$
$= 160 \text{ L}$

53. $3.6 \text{ L} = \dfrac{3.6 \text{ L}}{1} \cdot \dfrac{1000 \text{ ml}}{1 \text{ L}}$
$= 3.6 \cdot 1000 \text{ ml}$
$= 3600 \text{ ml}$

55. $3.4 \text{ L} + 15.9 \text{ L} = 19.3 \text{ L}$

57. $2700 \text{ ml} + 1.8 \text{ L} = 2.7 \text{ L} + 1.8 \text{ L} = 4.5 \text{ L}$
or
$2700 \text{ ml} + 1.8 \text{ L} = 2700 \text{ ml} + 1800 \text{ ml} = 4500 \text{ ml}$

59.
$$\begin{array}{r} 8.6 \text{ L} \\ - \ 190 \text{ ml} \\ \hline \end{array} \quad \begin{array}{r} 8600 \text{ ml} \\ - \ 190 \text{ ml} \\ \hline 8410 \text{ ml} \end{array} \quad \text{or} \quad \begin{array}{r} 8.60 \text{ L} \\ - \ 0.19 \text{ L} \\ \hline 8.41 \text{ L} \end{array}$$

61. $17{,}500 \text{ ml} - 0.9 \text{ L} = 17{,}500 \text{ ml} - 900 \text{ ml}$
$= 16{,}600 \text{ ml}$
or
$17{,}500 \text{ ml} - 0.9 \text{ L} = 17.5 \text{ L} - 0.9 \text{ L} = 16.6 \text{ L}$

63. $480 \text{ ml} \times 8 = 3840 \text{ ml}$

65. $81.2 \text{ L} \div 0.5 = 81.2 \text{ L} \div \dfrac{1}{2}$
$= 81.2 \text{ L} \cdot 2$
$= 162.4 \text{ L}$

	Capacity	Cups	Gallons	Quarts	Pints
67.	An average-size bath of water	336	21	84	168
69.	Your kidneys filter about this amount of blood every minute	4	$\frac{1}{4}$	1	2

71.
$$\begin{array}{r} 2 \text{ L} \\ - \ 410 \text{ ml} \\ \hline \end{array} \quad \begin{array}{r} 2.000 \text{ L} \\ - \ 0.410 \text{ L} \\ \hline 1.590 \text{ L} \end{array}$$
There was 1.59 L left in the bottle.

73. $354 \text{ ml} + 18.6 \text{ L} = 0.354 \text{ L} + 18.6 \text{ L} = 18.954 \text{ L}$
There were 18.954 liters of gasoline in her tank.

75. $\dfrac{1}{30}$ gal $= \dfrac{\frac{1}{30}\text{ gal}}{1} \cdot \dfrac{4\text{ qt}}{1\text{ gal}} \cdot \dfrac{2\text{ pt}}{1\text{ qt}} \cdot \dfrac{2\text{ c}}{1\text{ pt}} \cdot \dfrac{8\text{ fl oz}}{1\text{ c}}$

$\qquad\qquad = \dfrac{1}{30} \cdot 128\text{ fl oz}$

$\qquad\qquad \approx 4.3\text{ fl oz}$

$\dfrac{1}{30}$ gal is about 4.3 fluid ounces.

77. 5 pt 1 c $+$ 2 pt 1 c $=$ 7 pt 2 c

$\qquad\qquad\qquad\qquad = 7\text{ pt} + 1\text{ pt}$

$\qquad\qquad\qquad\qquad = 8\text{ pt}$

$\qquad\qquad\qquad\qquad = \dfrac{8\text{ pt}}{1} \cdot \dfrac{1\text{ qt}}{2\text{ pt}}$

$\qquad\qquad\qquad\qquad = \dfrac{8}{2}\text{ qt}$

$\qquad\qquad\qquad\qquad = \dfrac{4\text{ qt}}{1} \cdot \dfrac{1\text{ gal}}{4\text{ qt}}$

$\qquad\qquad\qquad\qquad = \dfrac{4}{4}\text{ gal}$

$\qquad\qquad\qquad\qquad = 1\text{ gal}$

Yes, the liquid can be poured into the container without causing it to overflow.

79. $44.3\overline{)14.0}$ becomes $443\overline{)140.0000}$

$$\begin{array}{r} 0.3160 \approx 0.316 \\ 443\overline{)140.0000} \\ \underline{-132\ 9} \\ 7\ 10 \\ \underline{-4\ 43} \\ 2\ 670 \\ \underline{-2\ 658} \\ 120 \\ \underline{-0} \\ 120 \end{array}$$

$\dfrac{\$14}{44.3\text{ L}} \approx \dfrac{\$0.316}{1\text{ L}}$

The price was \$0.316 per liter.

81. $\dfrac{20}{25} = \dfrac{4 \cdot 5}{5 \cdot 5} = \dfrac{4}{5}$

83. $\dfrac{27}{45} = \dfrac{3 \cdot 9}{5 \cdot 9} = \dfrac{3}{5}$

85. $\dfrac{72}{80} = \dfrac{8 \cdot 9}{8 \cdot 10} = \dfrac{9}{10}$

87. No, a 2 L dose of cough medicine is not reasonable.

89. No, a tub filled with 3000 ml of hot water is not reasonable.

91. less than; answers may vary

93. answers may vary

95. 1 gal $= \dfrac{1\text{ gal}}{1} \cdot \dfrac{4\text{ qt}}{1\text{ gal}} \cdot \dfrac{2\text{ pt}}{1\text{ qt}} \cdot \dfrac{2\text{ c}}{1\text{ pt}} \cdot \dfrac{8\text{ fl oz}}{1\text{ c}}$

$\qquad\quad = 1 \cdot 4 \cdot 2 \cdot 2 \cdot 8\text{ fl oz}$

$\qquad\quad = 128\text{ fl oz}$

There are 128 fl oz in 1 gallon.

97. B indicates 1.5 cc.

99. D indicates 2.7 cc.

101. B indicates 54 u or 0.54 cc.

103. D indicates 86 u or 0.86 cc.

Section 8.7

Practice Problems

1. 1.5 cm $= \dfrac{1.5\text{ cm}}{1} \cdot \dfrac{1\text{ in.}}{2.54\text{ cm}} = \dfrac{1.5}{2.54}\text{ in.} \approx 0.59\text{ in.}$

2. 8 oz $\approx \dfrac{8\text{ oz}}{1} \cdot \dfrac{28.35\text{ g}}{1\text{ oz}} = 8 \cdot 28.35\text{ g} = 226.8\text{ g}$

3. 237 ml $\approx \dfrac{237\text{ ml}}{1} \cdot \dfrac{1\text{ fl oz}}{29.57\text{ ml}}$

$\qquad\qquad = \dfrac{237}{29.57}\text{ fl oz}$

$\qquad\qquad \approx 8\text{ fl oz}$

4. $F = \dfrac{9}{5} \cdot C + 32 = \dfrac{9}{5} \cdot 60 + 32 = 108 + 32 = 140$

Thus, 60°C is equivalent to 140°F.

5. $F = 1.8 \cdot C + 32 = 1.8 \cdot 32 + 32 = 57.6 + 32 = 89.6$

Therefore, 32°C is the same as 89.6°F.

6. $C = \dfrac{5}{9} \cdot (F - 32) = \dfrac{5}{9} \cdot (68 - 32) = \dfrac{5}{9} \cdot (36) = 20$

Therefore, 68°F is the same temperature as 20°C.

7. $C = \dfrac{5}{9} \cdot (F - 32) = \dfrac{5}{9} \cdot (113 - 32) = \dfrac{5}{9} \cdot (81) = 45$

Therefore, 113°F is 45°C.

8. $C = \dfrac{5}{9} \cdot (F - 32)$

    $= \dfrac{5}{9} \cdot (102.8 - 32)$

    $= \dfrac{5}{9} \cdot (70.8)$

    $= 39.3$

    Albert's temperature is 39.3°C.

Exercise Set 8.7

1. $756 \text{ ml} \approx \dfrac{756 \text{ ml}}{1} \cdot \dfrac{1 \text{ fl oz}}{29.57 \text{ ml}}$

    $= \dfrac{756}{29.57} \text{ fl oz}$

    $\approx 25.57 \text{ fl oz}$

3. $86 \text{ in.} = \dfrac{86 \text{ in.}}{1} \cdot \dfrac{2.54 \text{ cm}}{1 \text{ in.}}$

    $= 86 \cdot 2.54 \text{ cm}$

    $= 218.44 \text{ cm}$

5. $1000 \text{ g} \approx \dfrac{1000 \text{ g}}{1} \cdot \dfrac{0.04 \text{ oz}}{1 \text{ g}}$

    $= 1000 \cdot 0.04 \text{ oz}$

    $= 40 \text{ oz}$

7. $93 \text{ km} \approx \dfrac{93 \text{ km}}{1} \cdot \dfrac{0.62 \text{ mi}}{1 \text{ km}}$

    $= 93 \cdot 0.62 \text{ mi}$

    $= 57.66 \text{ mi}$

9. $14.5 \text{ L} \approx \dfrac{14.5 \text{ L}}{1} \cdot \dfrac{0.26 \text{ gal}}{1 \text{ L}} \approx 3.77 \text{ gal}$

11. $30 \text{ lb} \approx \dfrac{30 \text{ lb}}{1} \cdot \dfrac{0.45 \text{ kg}}{1 \text{ lb}} = 30 \cdot 0.45 \text{ kg} = 13.5 \text{ kg}$

		Meters	Yards	Centimeters	Feet	Inches
13.	The Height of a Woman	1.5	$1\frac{2}{3}$	150	5	60
15.	Leaning Tower of Pisa	55	60	5500	180	2160

17. $10 \text{ cm} = \dfrac{10 \text{ cm}}{1} \cdot \dfrac{1 \text{ in.}}{2.54 \text{ cm}} \approx 3.94 \text{ in.}$

    The balance beam is approximately 3.94 inches wide.

19. $50 \text{ mph} \approx \dfrac{50 \text{ mph}}{1} \cdot \dfrac{1.61 \text{ km}}{1 \text{ mi}} = 80.5 \text{ kph}$

The speed limit is approximately 80.5 kilometers per hour.

21. $200 \text{ mg} = 0.2 \text{ g} \approx \dfrac{0.2 \text{ g}}{1} \cdot \dfrac{0.04 \text{ oz}}{1 \text{ g}} = 0.008 \text{ oz}$

23. $100 \text{ kg} \approx \dfrac{100 \text{ kg}}{1} \cdot \dfrac{2.2 \text{ lb}}{1 \text{ kg}} = 100 \cdot 2.2 \text{ lb} = 220 \text{ lb}$

15 stone 10 lb

$= \dfrac{15 \text{ stone}}{1} \cdot \dfrac{14 \text{ lb}}{1 \text{ stone}} + 10 \text{ lb}$

$= 15 \cdot 14 \text{ lb} + 10 \text{ lb}$

$= 210 \text{ lb} + 10 \text{ lb}$

$= 220 \text{ lb}$

Yes; the stamp is approximately correct.

25. $4500 \text{ km} = \dfrac{4500 \text{ km}}{1} \cdot \dfrac{0.62 \text{ mi}}{1 \text{ km}} = 2790 \text{ mi}$

The trip is about 2790 miles.

27. $3\dfrac{1}{2} \text{ in.} = \dfrac{3\frac{1}{2} \text{ in.}}{1} \cdot \dfrac{2.54 \text{ cm}}{1 \text{ in.}} = 8.89 \text{ cm}$

$8.89 \text{ cm} = \dfrac{8.89 \text{ cm}}{1} \cdot \dfrac{10 \text{ mm}}{1 \text{ cm}} = 88.9 \text{ mm} \approx 90 \text{ mm}$

The width is approximately 90 mm.

29. $1.5 \text{ lb} - 1.25 \text{ lb} = 0.25 \text{ lb}$

$0.25 \text{ lb} \approx \dfrac{0.25 \text{ lb}}{1} \cdot \dfrac{0.45 \text{ kg}}{1 \text{ lb}} \cdot \dfrac{1000 \text{ g}}{1 \text{ kg}} \approx 112.5 \text{ g}$

The difference is approximately 112.5 g.

31. $167 \text{ kmh} \approx \dfrac{167 \text{ kmh}}{1} \cdot \dfrac{0.62 \text{ mi}}{1 \text{ km}} \approx 104 \text{ mph}$

The sneeze is approximately 104 miles per hour.

33. $8 \text{ m} \approx \dfrac{8 \text{ m}}{1} \cdot \dfrac{3.28 \text{ ft}}{1 \text{ m}} \approx 26.24 \text{ ft}$

The base diameter is approximately 26.24 ft.

35. $4.5 \text{ km} \approx \dfrac{4.5 \text{ km}}{1} \cdot \dfrac{0.62 \text{ mi}}{1 \text{ km}} \approx 3 \text{ mi}$

The track is approximately 3 mi.

37. One dose every 4 hours results in $\dfrac{24}{4} = 6$ doses per day and $6 \times 7 = 42$ doses per week.

$5 \text{ ml} \times 42 = 210 \text{ ml}$

$210 \text{ ml} \approx \dfrac{210 \text{ ml}}{1} \cdot \dfrac{1 \text{ fl oz}}{29.57 \text{ ml}} \approx 7.1 \text{ fl oz}$

8 fluid ounces of medicine should be purchased.

39. This math book has a height of about 28 cm; b.

41. A liter has greater capacity than a quart; b.

43. A kilogram weighs greater than a pound; c

45. An $8\dfrac{1}{2}$-ounce glass of water has a capacity of about 250 ml $\left(\dfrac{1}{4} \text{ L} \right)$; d.

47. The weight of an average man is about 70 kg $(70 \text{ kg} \approx 2.2 \cdot 70 \text{ lb} = 154 \text{ lb})$; d

49. $C = \dfrac{5}{9}(F - 32) = \dfrac{5}{9}(77 - 32) = \dfrac{5}{9}(45) = 25$

77°F is 25°C.

51. $C = \dfrac{5}{9}(F - 32) = \dfrac{5}{9}(104 - 32) = \dfrac{5}{9}(72) = 40$

104°F is 40°C.

53. $F = \dfrac{9}{5}C + 32 = \dfrac{9}{5}(50) + 32 = 90 + 32 = 122$

50°C is 122°F.

55. $F = \dfrac{9}{5}C + 32 = \dfrac{9}{5}(115) + 32 = 207 + 32 = 239$

115°C is 239°F.

57. $C = \dfrac{5}{9}(F - 32) = \dfrac{5}{9}(20 - 32) = \dfrac{5}{9}(-12) \approx -6.7$

20°F is −6.7°C.

59. $C = \dfrac{5}{9}(F - 32)$

$= \dfrac{5}{9}(142.1 - 32)$

$= \dfrac{5}{9}(110.1)$

≈ 61.2

142.1°F is 61.2°C.

61. $F = 1.8C + 32$
$= 1.8(92) + 32$
$= 165.6 + 32$
$= 197.6$
$92°C$ is $197.6°F$.

63. $F = 1.8C + 32$
$= 1.8(12.4) + 32$
$= 22.32 + 32$
≈ 54.3
$12.4°C$ is $54.3°F$.

65. $C = \dfrac{5}{9}(F - 32)$
$= \dfrac{5}{9}(134 - 32)$
$= \dfrac{5}{9}(102)$
≈ 56.7
$134°F$ is $56.7°C$.

67. $F = 1.8C + 32 = 1.8(27) + 32 = 48.6 + 32 = 80.6$
$27°C$ is $80.6°F$.

69. $C = \dfrac{5}{9}(F - 32) = \dfrac{5}{9}(70 - 32) = \dfrac{5}{9}(38) \approx 21.1$
$70°F$ is $21.1°C$.

71. $F = 1.8C + 32$
$= 1.8(118) + 32$
$= 212.4 + 32$
$= 244.4$
$118°C$ is $244.4°F$.

73. $F = 1.8C + 32$
$= 1.8(4000) + 32$
$= 7200 + 32$
$= 7232$
$4000°C$ is $7232°F$.

75. $6 \cdot 4 + 5 \div 1 = 24 + 5 \div 1 = 24 + 5 = 29$

77. $3[(1 + 5) \cdot (8 - 6)] = 3(6 \cdot 2) = 3(12) = 36$

79. Yes, a $72°F$ room feels comfortable.

81. No, a fever of $40°F$ is not reasonable.

83. No, an overcoat is not needed when the temperature is $30°C$.

85. Yes, a fever of $40°C$ is reasonable.

87. $BSA = \sqrt{\dfrac{90 \times 182}{3600}} \approx 2.13$
The BSA is approximately 2.13 sq m.

89. $40 \text{ in.} = \dfrac{40 \text{ in.}}{1} \cdot \dfrac{2.54 \text{ cm}}{1 \text{ in.}} = 101.6 \text{ cm}$

$BSA = \sqrt{\dfrac{50 \times 101.6}{3600}} \approx 1.19$
The BSA is approximately 1.19 sq m.

91. $60 \text{ in.} = \dfrac{60 \text{ in.}}{1} \cdot \dfrac{2.54 \text{ cm}}{1 \text{ in.}} = 152.4 \text{ cm}$

$150 \text{ lb} \approx \dfrac{150 \text{ lb}}{1} \cdot \dfrac{0.45 \text{ kg}}{1 \text{ lb}} = 67.5 \text{ kg}$

$BSA \approx \sqrt{\dfrac{67.5 \times 152.4}{3600}} \approx 1.69$
The BSA is approximately 1.69 sq m.

93. $C = \dfrac{5}{9}(F - 32)$
$= \dfrac{5}{9}(918,000,000 - 32)$
$= \dfrac{5}{9}(917,999,968)$
$\approx 510,000,000$
$918,000,000°F$ is approximately $510,000,000°C$.

95. answers may vary

Chapter 8 Vocabulary Check

1. <u>Weight</u> is a measure of the pull of gravity.

2. <u>Mass</u> is a measure of the amount of substance in an object. This measure does not change.

3. The basic unit of length in the metric system is the <u>meter</u>.

4. To convert from one unit of length to another, <u>unit fractions</u> may be used.

5. The <u>gram</u> is the basic unit of mass in the metric system.

6. The <u>liter</u> is the basic unit of capacity in the metric system.

7. A <u>line segment</u> is a piece of a line with two endpoints.

8. Two angles that have a sum of 90° are called complementary angles.

9. A line is a set of points extending indefinitely in two directions.

10. The perimeter of a polygon is the distance around the polygon.

11. An angle is made up of two rays that share the same end point. The common end point is called the vertex.

12. Area measures the amount of surface of a region.

13. A ray is a part of a line with one end point. A ray extends indefinitely in one direction.

14. A line that intersects two or more lines at different points is called a transversal.

15. An angle that measures 180° is called a straight angle.

16. The measure of the space of a solid is called its volume.

17. When two lines intersect, four angles are formed. Two of these angles that are opposite each other are called vertical angles.

18. Two of the angles from #17 that share a common side are called adjacent angles.

19. An angle whose measure is between 90° and 180° is called an obtuse angle.

20. An angle that measures 90° is called a right angle.

21. An angle whose measure is between 0° and 90° is called an acute angle.

22. Two angles that have a sum of 180° are called supplementary angles.

23. The surface area of a polyhedron is the sum of the areas of the faces of the polyhedron.

Chapter 8 Review

1. $\angle A$ is a right angle. It measures 90°.

2. $\angle B$ is a straight angle. It measures 180°.

3. $\angle C$ is an acute angle. It measures between 0° and 90°.

4. $\angle D$ is an obtuse angle. It measures between 90° and 180°.

5. The complement of a 25° angle has measure $90° - 25° = 65°$.

6. The supplement of a 105° angle has measure $180° - 105° = 75°$.

7. $m\angle x = 90° - 32° = 58°$

8. $m\angle x = 180° - 82° = 98°$

9. $m\angle x = 105° - 15° = 90°$

10. $m\angle x = 45° - 20° = 25°$

11. $47° + 133° = 180°$, so $\angle a$ and $\angle b$ are supplementary. So are $\angle b$ and $\angle c$, $\angle c$ and $\angle d$, and $\angle d$ and $\angle a$.

12. $47° + 43° = 90°$, so $\angle x$ and $\angle w$ are complementary. Also, $58° + 32° = 90°$, so $\angle y$ and $\angle z$ are complementary.

13. $\angle x$ and the angle marked 100° are vertical angles, so $m\angle x = 100°$.
$\angle x$ and $\angle y$ are adjacent angles, so $m\angle y = 180° - 100° = 80°$.
$\angle y$ and $\angle z$ are vertical angles, so $m\angle z = m\angle y = 80°$.

14. $\angle x$ and the angle marked 25° are adjacent angles, so $m\angle x = 180° - 25° = 155°$.
$\angle x$ and $\angle y$ are vertical angles, so $m\angle y = m\angle x = 155°$.
$\angle z$ and the angle marked 25° are vertical angles, so $m\angle z = 25°$.

15. $\angle x$ and the angle marked 53° are vertical angles, so $m\angle x = 53°$.
$\angle x$ and $\angle y$ are alternate interior angles, so $m\angle y = m\angle x = 53°$.
$\angle y$ and $\angle z$ are adjacent angles, so $m\angle z = 180° - m\angle y = 180° - 53° = 127°$.

16. $\angle x$ and the angle marked 42° are vertical angles, so $m\angle x = 42°$.
$\angle x$ and $\angle y$ are alternate interior angles, so $m\angle y = m\angle x = 42°$.
$\angle y$ and $\angle z$ are adjacent angles, so $m\angle z = 180° - m\angle y = 180° - 42° = 138°$.

17. $P = 23 \text{ m} + 11\frac{1}{2} \text{ m} + 23 \text{ m} + 11\frac{1}{2} \text{ m} = 69 \text{ m}$
    The perimeter is 69 meters.

18. $P = 11 \text{ cm} + 7.6 \text{ cm} + 12 \text{ cm} = 30.6 \text{ cm}$
    The perimeter is 30.6 centimeters.

19. The unmarked vertical side has length
    $8 \text{ m} - 5 \text{ m} = 3 \text{ m}$. The unmarked horizontal side
    has length $10 \text{ m} - 7 \text{ m} = 3 \text{ m}$.
    $P = (7 + 3 + 3 + 5 + 10 + 8) \text{ m} = 36 \text{ m}$
    The perimeter is 36 meters.

20. The unmarked vertical side has length
    $5 \text{ ft} + 4 \text{ ft} + 11 \text{ ft} = 20 \text{ ft}$.
    $P = (22 + 20 + 22 + 11 + 3 + 4 + 3 + 5) \text{ ft} = 90 \text{ ft}$
    The perimeter is 90 feet.

21. $P = 2 \cdot l + 2 \cdot w = 2 \cdot 10 \text{ ft} + 2 \cdot 6 \text{ ft} = 32 \text{ ft}$
    The perimeter is 32 feet.

22. $P = 4 \cdot s = 4 \cdot 110 \text{ ft} = 440 \text{ ft}$
    The perimeter is 440 feet.

23. $C = \pi \cdot d = \pi \cdot 1.7 \text{ in.} \approx 3.14 \cdot 1.7 \text{ in.} = 5.338 \text{ in.}$
    The circumference is 5.338 inches.

24. $C = 2 \cdot \pi \cdot r$
    $= 2 \cdot \pi \cdot 5 \text{ yd}$
    $= \pi \cdot 10 \text{ yd}$
    $\approx 3.14 \cdot 10 \text{ yd}$
    $= 31.4 \text{ yd}$
    The circumference is 31.4 yards.

25. $A = \frac{1}{2} \cdot (b + B) \cdot h$
    $= \frac{1}{2} \cdot (12 \text{ ft} + 36 \text{ ft}) \cdot 10 \text{ ft}$
    $= \frac{1}{2} \cdot 48 \text{ ft} \cdot 10 \text{ ft}$
    $= 240 \text{ sq ft}$
    The area is 240 square feet.

26. $A = b \cdot h = 21 \text{ yd} \cdot 9 \text{ yd} = 189 \text{ sq yd}$
    The area is 189 square yards.

27. $A = l \cdot w = 40 \text{ cm} \cdot 15 \text{ cm} = 600 \text{ sq cm}$
    The area is 600 square centimeters.

28. $A = s^2 = (9.1 \text{ m})^2 = 82.81 \text{ sq m}$
    The area is 82.81 square meters.

29. $A = \pi \cdot r^2 = \pi \cdot (7 \text{ ft})^2 = 49\pi \text{ sq ft} \approx 153.86 \text{ sq ft}$
    The area is 49π square feet ≈ 153.86 square feet.

30. $A = \pi \cdot r^2 = \pi (3 \text{ in.})^2 = 9\pi \text{ sq in.} \approx 28.26 \text{ sq in.}$
    The area is
    9π square inches ≈ 28.26 square inches.

31. $A = \frac{1}{2} \cdot b \cdot h = \frac{1}{2} \cdot 34 \text{ in.} \cdot 7 \text{ in.} = 119 \text{ sq in.}$
    The area is 119 square inches.

32. $A = \frac{1}{2} \cdot b \cdot h = \frac{1}{2} \cdot 20 \text{ m} \cdot 14 \text{ m} = 140 \text{ sq m}$
    The area is 140 square meters.

33. The unmarked horizontal side has length
    $13 \text{ m} - 3 \text{ m} = 10 \text{ m}$. The unmarked vertical side
    has length $12 \text{ m} - 4 \text{ m} = 8 \text{ m}$. The area is the
    sum of the areas of the two rectangles.
    $A = 12 \text{ m} \cdot 10 \text{ m} + 8 \text{ m} \cdot 3 \text{ m}$
    $= 120 \text{ sq m} + 24 \text{ sq m}$
    $= 144 \text{ sq m}$
    The area is 144 square meters.

34. The unmarked vertical side has length
    $30 \text{ cm} - 5 \text{ cm} = 25 \text{ cm}$.
    The unmarked horizontal side has length
    $60 \text{ cm} - 35 \text{ cm} = 25 \text{ cm}$.
    The area is the sum of the areas of the two
    rectangles.
    $A = 30 \text{ cm} \cdot 25 \text{ cm} + 35 \text{ cm} \cdot 25 \text{ cm} = 1625 \text{ sq cm}$
    The area is 1625 square centimeters.

35. $A = l \cdot w = 36 \text{ ft} \cdot 12 \text{ ft} = 432 \text{ sq ft}$
    The area of the driveway is 432 square feet.

36. $A = 10 \text{ ft} \cdot 13 \text{ ft} = 130 \text{ sq ft}$
    130 square feet of carpet are needed.

37. $V = s^3$
    $= \left(2\frac{1}{2} \text{ in.}\right)^3$
    $= \left(\frac{5}{2} \text{ in.}\right)^3$
    $= \frac{125}{8} \text{ cu in.}$
    $= 15\frac{5}{8} \text{ cu in.}$
    The volume is $15\frac{5}{8}$ cubic inches.

$SA = 6s^2$

$$= 6\left(2\frac{1}{2}\ \text{in.}\right)^2$$

$$= 6\left(\frac{5}{2}\ \text{in.}\right)^2$$

$$= 6\left(\frac{25}{4}\right)\ \text{sq in.}$$

$$= \frac{75}{2}\ \text{sq in.}$$

$$= 37\frac{1}{2}\ \text{sq in.}$$

The surface area is $37\frac{1}{2}$ square inches.

38. $V = l \cdot w \cdot h = 2\ \text{ft} \cdot 7\ \text{ft} \cdot 6\ \text{ft} = 84\ \text{cu ft}$
The volume is 84 cubic feet.
$SA = 2lh + 2wh + 2lw$

$$= 2 \cdot 7\ \text{ft} \cdot 6\ \text{ft} + 2 \cdot 2\ \text{ft} \cdot 6\ \text{ft} + 2 \cdot 7\ \text{ft} \cdot 2\ \text{ft}$$

$$= 84\ \text{sq ft} + 24\ \text{sq ft} + 28\ \text{sq ft}$$

$$= 136\ \text{sq ft}$$

The surface area is 136 square feet.

39. $V = \pi \cdot r^2 \cdot h$

$$= \pi \cdot (20\ \text{cm})^2 \cdot 50\ \text{cm}$$

$$= 20,000\pi\ \text{cu cm}$$

$$\approx 62,800\ \text{cu cm}$$

The volume is $20,000\pi$ cubic centimeters
$\approx 62,800$ cubic centimeters.

40. $V = \frac{4}{3} \cdot \pi \cdot r^3$

$$= \frac{4}{3} \cdot \pi \cdot \left(\frac{1}{2}\ \text{km}\right)^3$$

$$= \frac{1}{6}\pi\ \text{cu km}$$

$$\approx \frac{11}{21}\ \text{cu km}$$

The volume is
$\frac{1}{6}\pi$ cubic kilometers $\approx \frac{11}{21}$ cubic kilometers.

41. $V = \frac{1}{3} \cdot s^2 \cdot h$

$$= \frac{1}{3} \cdot (2\ \text{ft})^2 \cdot 2\ \text{ft}$$

$$= \frac{8}{3}\ \text{cu ft}$$

$$= 2\frac{2}{3}\ \text{cu ft}$$

The volume of the pyramid is $2\frac{2}{3}$ cubic feet.

42. $V = \pi \cdot r^2 \cdot h$

$$= \pi \cdot (3.5\ \text{in.})^2 \cdot 8\ \text{in.}$$

$$= 98\pi\ \text{cu in.}$$

$$\approx 307.72\ \text{cu in.}$$

The volume of the can is about 307.72 cubic inches.

43. Find the volume of each drawer.
$V = l \cdot w \cdot h$

$$= \left(2\frac{1}{2}\ \text{ft}\right) \cdot \left(1\frac{1}{2}\ \text{ft}\right) \cdot \left(\frac{2}{3}\ \text{ft}\right)$$

$$= \frac{5}{2} \cdot \frac{3}{2} \cdot \frac{2}{3}\ \text{cu ft}$$

$$= \frac{5}{2}\ \text{cu ft}$$

The three drawers have volume
$3 \cdot \frac{5}{2} = \frac{15}{2} = 7\frac{1}{2}$ cubic feet.

44. $r = d \div 2 = 1\ \text{ft} \div 2 = 0.5\ \text{ft}$
$V = \pi \cdot r^2 \cdot h = \pi \cdot (0.5\ \text{ft})^2 \cdot 2\ \text{ft} = 0.5\pi\ \text{cu ft}$
The volume of the canister is 0.5π cubic feet or
$\frac{1}{2}\pi$ cubic feet.

45. $108\ \text{in.} = \frac{108\ \text{in.}}{1} \cdot \frac{1\ \text{ft}}{12\ \text{in.}} = \frac{108}{12}\ \text{ft} = 9\ \text{ft}$

46. $72\ \text{ft} = \frac{72\ \text{ft}}{1} \cdot \frac{1\ \text{yd}}{3\ \text{ft}} = \frac{72}{3}\ \text{yd} = 24\ \text{yd}$

47. $1.5\ \text{mi} = \frac{1.5\ \text{mi}}{1} \cdot \frac{5280\ \text{ft}}{1\ \text{mi}} = 1.5 \cdot 5280\ \text{ft} = 7920\ \text{ft}$

48. $\frac{1}{2}\ \text{yd} = \frac{\frac{1}{2}\ \text{yd}}{1} \cdot \frac{3\ \text{ft}}{1\ \text{yd}} \cdot \frac{12\ \text{in.}}{1\ \text{ft}} = \frac{1}{2} \cdot 3 \cdot 12\ \text{in.} = 18\ \text{in.}$

49. $52 \text{ ft} = 51 \text{ ft} + 1 \text{ ft}$

$= \dfrac{51 \text{ ft}}{1} \cdot \dfrac{1 \text{ yd}}{3 \text{ ft}} + 1 \text{ ft}$

$= \dfrac{51}{3} \text{ yd} + 1 \text{ ft}$

$= 17 \text{ yd } 1 \text{ ft}$

50. $46 \text{ in.} = 36 \text{ in.} + 10 \text{ in.}$

$= \dfrac{36 \text{ in.}}{1} \cdot \dfrac{1 \text{ ft}}{12 \text{ in.}} + 10 \text{ in.}$

$= \dfrac{36}{12} \text{ ft} + 10 \text{ in.}$

$= 3 \text{ ft } 10 \text{ in.}$

51. $42 \text{ m} = \dfrac{42 \text{ m}}{1} \cdot \dfrac{100 \text{ cm}}{1 \text{ m}} = 42 \cdot 100 \text{ cm} = 4200 \text{ cm}$

52. $82 \text{ cm} = \dfrac{82 \text{ cm}}{1} \cdot \dfrac{10 \text{ mm}}{1 \text{ cm}} = 82 \cdot 10 \text{ mm} = 820 \text{ mm}$

53. $12.18 \text{ mm} = \dfrac{12.18 \text{ mm}}{1} \cdot \dfrac{1 \text{ m}}{1000 \text{ mm}}$

$= \dfrac{12.18}{1000} \text{ m}$

$= 0.01218 \text{ m}$

54. $2.31 \text{ m} = \dfrac{2.31 \text{ m}}{1} \cdot \dfrac{1 \text{ km}}{1000 \text{ m}}$

$= \dfrac{2.31}{1000} \text{ km}$

$= 0.00231 \text{ km}$

55. $\begin{array}{r} 4 \text{ yd } 2 \text{ ft} \\ + 16 \text{ yd } 2 \text{ ft} \\ \hline 20 \text{ yd } 4 \text{ ft} \end{array} = 20 \text{ yd} + 1 \text{ yd } 1 \text{ ft} = 21 \text{ yd } 1 \text{ ft}$

56. $7 \text{ ft } 4 \text{ in.} \div 2 = (6 \text{ ft} + 1 \text{ ft } 4 \text{ in.}) \div 2$

$= (6 \text{ ft} + 16 \text{ in.}) \div 2$

$= \dfrac{6}{2} \text{ ft} + \dfrac{16}{2} \text{ in.}$

$= 3 \text{ ft } 8 \text{ in.}$

57. $8 \text{ cm} = 80 \text{ mm} \qquad 15 \text{ mm} = 1.5 \text{ cm}$

$\begin{array}{r} 80 \text{ mm} \\ + 15 \text{ mm} \\ \hline 95 \text{ mm} \end{array}$ or $\begin{array}{r} 8.0 \text{ cm} \\ + 1.5 \text{ cm} \\ \hline 9.5 \text{ cm} \end{array}$

58. $4 \text{ m} = 400 \text{ cm} \qquad 126 \text{ cm} = 1.26 \text{ m}$

$\begin{array}{r} 400 \text{ cm} \\ - 126 \text{ cm} \\ \hline 274 \text{ cm} \end{array}$ or $\begin{array}{r} 4.00 \text{ m} \\ - 1.26 \text{ m} \\ \hline 2.74 \text{ m} \end{array}$

59. $\begin{array}{r} 333 \text{ yd } 1 \text{ ft} \\ - 163 \text{ yd } 2 \text{ ft} \\ \hline \end{array} \qquad \begin{array}{r} 332 \text{ yd } 4 \text{ ft} \\ - 163 \text{ yd } 2 \text{ ft} \\ \hline 169 \text{ yd } 2 \text{ ft} \end{array}$

The amount of material that remains is 169 yd 2 ft.

60. $\begin{array}{r} 5 \text{ ft} \quad 2 \text{ in.} \\ \times \qquad 50 \\ \hline 250 \text{ ft } 100 \text{ in.} \end{array} = 250 \text{ ft} + 96 \text{ in.} + 4 \text{ in.}$

$= 250 \text{ ft} + 8 \text{ ft } 4 \text{ in.}$

$= 258 \text{ ft } 4 \text{ in.}$

The sashes require 258 ft 4 in. of material.

61. $\begin{array}{r} 217 \text{ km} \\ \times \quad 2 \\ \hline 434 \text{ km} \end{array}$

$434 \text{ km} \div 4 = \dfrac{434}{4} \text{ km} = 108.5 \text{ km}$

Each must drive 108.5 km.

62. $\begin{array}{r} 0.8 \text{ m} \\ \times 30 \text{ cm} \end{array} \qquad \begin{array}{r} 0.8 \text{ m} \\ \times \quad 0.3 \text{ m} \\ \hline 0.24 \text{ sq m} \end{array}$

The area is 0.24 sq m.

63. $66 \text{ oz} = \dfrac{66 \text{ oz}}{1} \cdot \dfrac{1 \text{ lb}}{16 \text{ oz}} = \dfrac{66}{16} \text{ lb} = \dfrac{33}{8} \text{ lb} = 4\dfrac{1}{8} \text{ lb}$

64. $2.3 \text{ tons} = \dfrac{2.3 \text{ tons}}{1} \cdot \dfrac{2000 \text{ lb}}{1 \text{ ton}}$

$= 2.3 \cdot 2000 \text{ lb}$

$= 4600 \text{ lb}$

65. $52 \text{ oz} = 48 \text{ oz} + 4 \text{ oz}$

$= \dfrac{48 \text{ oz}}{1} \cdot \dfrac{1 \text{ lb}}{16 \text{ oz}} + 4 \text{ oz}$

$= \dfrac{48}{16} \text{ lb} + 4 \text{ oz}$

$= 3 \text{ lb } 4 \text{ oz}$

66. $10,300 \text{ lb} = 10,000 \text{ lb} + 300 \text{ lb}$

$= \dfrac{10,000 \text{ lb}}{1} \cdot \dfrac{1 \text{ ton}}{2000 \text{ lb}} + 300 \text{ lb}$

$= \dfrac{10,000}{2000} \text{ tons} + 300 \text{ lb}$

$= 5 \text{ tons } 300 \text{ lb}$

67. $27 \text{ mg} = \dfrac{27 \text{ mg}}{1} \cdot \dfrac{1 \text{ g}}{1000 \text{ mg}} = \dfrac{27}{1000} \text{ g} = 0.027 \text{ g}$

68. $40 \text{ kg} = \dfrac{40 \text{ kg}}{1} \cdot \dfrac{1000 \text{ g}}{1 \text{ kg}} = 40 \cdot 1000 \text{ g} = 40{,}000 \text{ g}$

69. $2.1 \text{ hg} = \dfrac{2.1 \text{ hg}}{1} \cdot \dfrac{10 \text{ dag}}{1 \text{ hg}} = 2.1 \cdot 10 \text{ dag} = 21 \text{ dag}$

70. $0.03 \text{ mg} = \dfrac{0.03 \text{ mg}}{1} \cdot \dfrac{1 \text{ dg}}{100 \text{ mg}}$

$\phantom{0.03 \text{ mg}} = \dfrac{0.03}{100} \text{ dg}$

$\phantom{0.03 \text{ mg}} = 0.0003 \text{ dg}$

71.
$$\begin{array}{r} 6 \text{ lb } 5 \text{ oz} \\ - 2 \text{ lb } 12 \text{ oz} \\ \hline \end{array} \qquad \begin{array}{r} 5 \text{ lb } 21 \text{ oz} \\ - 2 \text{ lb } 12 \text{ oz} \\ \hline 3 \text{ lb } 9 \text{ oz} \end{array}$$

72.
$$\begin{array}{r} 8 \text{ lb } 6 \text{ oz} \\ \times \qquad 4 \\ \hline 32 \text{ lb } 24 \text{ oz} \end{array} = 32 \text{ lb} + 1 \text{ lb } 8 \text{ oz} = 33 \text{ lb } 8 \text{ oz}$$

73.
$$\begin{array}{r} 4.3 \text{ mg} \\ \times \quad 5 \\ \hline 21.5 \text{ mg} \end{array}$$

74. $4.8 \text{ kg} = 4800 \text{ g} \qquad 4200 \text{ g} = 4.2 \text{ kg}$
$$\begin{array}{r} 4800 \text{ g} \\ - 4200 \text{ g} \\ \hline 600 \text{ g} \end{array} \quad \text{or} \quad \begin{array}{r} 4.8 \text{ kg} \\ - 4.2 \text{ kg} \\ \hline 0.6 \text{ kg} \end{array}$$

75.
$$\begin{array}{r} 1 \text{ lb } 12 \text{ oz} \\ + 2 \text{ lb } 8 \text{ oz} \\ \hline 3 \text{ lb } 20 \text{ oz} \end{array} = 3 \text{ lb} + 1 \text{ lb } 4 \text{ oz} = 4 \text{ lb } 4 \text{ oz}$$
The total weight was 4 lb 4 oz.

76. $38 \text{ tons } 300 \text{ lb} \div 4 = \dfrac{38}{4} \text{ tons } \dfrac{300}{4} \text{ lb}$

$\phantom{38 \text{ tons } 300 \text{ lb} \div 4} = 9\dfrac{1}{2} \text{ tons } 75 \text{ lb}$

$\phantom{38 \text{ tons } 300 \text{ lb} \div 4} = 9 \text{ tons} + \dfrac{1}{2} \text{ ton} + 75 \text{ lb}$

$\phantom{38 \text{ tons } 300 \text{ lb} \div 4} = 9 \text{ tons} + 1000 \text{ lb} + 75 \text{ lb}$

$\phantom{38 \text{ tons } 300 \text{ lb} \div 4} = 9 \text{ tons } 1075 \text{ lb}$

They each receive 9 tons 1075 lb.

77. $28 \text{ pt} = \dfrac{28 \text{ pt}}{1} \cdot \dfrac{1 \text{ qt}}{2 \text{ pt}} = \dfrac{28}{2} \text{ qt} = 14 \text{ qt}$

78. $40 \text{ fl oz} = \dfrac{40 \text{ fl oz}}{1} \cdot \dfrac{1 \text{ c}}{8 \text{ fl oz}} = \dfrac{40}{8} \text{ c} = 5 \text{ c}$

79. $3 \text{ qt } 1 \text{ pt} = \dfrac{3 \text{ qt}}{1} \cdot \dfrac{2 \text{ pt}}{1 \text{ qt}} + 1 \text{ pt}$

$\phantom{3 \text{ qt } 1 \text{ pt}} = 3 \cdot 2 \text{ pt} + 1 \text{ pt}$

$\phantom{3 \text{ qt } 1 \text{ pt}} = 6 \text{ pt} + 1 \text{ pt}$

$\phantom{3 \text{ qt } 1 \text{ pt}} = 7 \text{ pt}$

80. $18 \text{ qt} = \dfrac{18 \text{ qt}}{1} \cdot \dfrac{2 \text{ pt}}{1 \text{ qt}} \cdot \dfrac{2 \text{ c}}{1 \text{ pt}} = 18 \cdot 2 \cdot 2 \text{ c} = 72 \text{ c}$

81. $9 \text{ pt} = 8 \text{ pt} + 1 \text{ pt}$

$\phantom{9 \text{ pt}} = \dfrac{8 \text{ pt}}{1} \cdot \dfrac{1 \text{ qt}}{2 \text{ pt}} + 1 \text{ pt}$

$\phantom{9 \text{ pt}} = \dfrac{8}{2} \text{ qt} + 1 \text{ pt}$

$\phantom{9 \text{ pt}} = 4 \text{ qt } 1 \text{ pt}$

82. $15 \text{ qt} = 12 \text{ qt} + 3 \text{ qt}$

$\phantom{15 \text{ qt}} = \dfrac{12 \text{ qt}}{1} \cdot \dfrac{1 \text{ gal}}{4 \text{ qt}} + 3 \text{ qt}$

$\phantom{15 \text{ qt}} = \dfrac{12}{4} \text{ gal} + 3 \text{ qt}$

$\phantom{15 \text{ qt}} = 3 \text{ gal } 3 \text{ qt}$

83. $3.8 \text{ L} = \dfrac{3.8 \text{ L}}{1} \cdot \dfrac{1000 \text{ ml}}{1 \text{ L}}$

$\phantom{3.8 \text{ L}} = 3.8 \cdot 1000 \text{ ml}$

$\phantom{3.8 \text{ L}} = 3800 \text{ ml}$

84. $14 \text{ hl} = \dfrac{14 \text{ hl}}{1} \cdot \dfrac{1 \text{ kl}}{10 \text{ hl}} = \dfrac{14}{10} \text{ kl} = 1.4 \text{ kl}$

85. $30.6 \text{ L} = \dfrac{30.6 \text{ L}}{1} \cdot \dfrac{100 \text{ cl}}{1 \text{ L}} = 30.6 \cdot 100 \text{ cl} = 3060 \text{ cl}$

86. $2.45 \text{ ml} = \dfrac{2.45 \text{ ml}}{1} \cdot \dfrac{1 \text{ L}}{1000 \text{ ml}} = 0.00245 \text{ L}$

87.
$$\begin{array}{r} 1 \text{ qt } 1 \text{ pt} \\ + 3 \text{ qt } 1 \text{ pt} \\ \hline 4 \text{ qt } 2 \text{ pt} \end{array} = 4 \text{ qt} + 1 \text{ qt} = 1 \text{ gal } 1 \text{ qt}$$

88.
$$\begin{array}{r} 3 \text{ gal } 2 \text{ qt} \\ \times \qquad 2 \\ \hline 6 \text{ gal } 4 \text{ qt} \end{array} = 6 \text{ gal} + 1 \text{ gal} = 7 \text{ gal}$$

89. $0.946 \text{ L} = 946 \text{ ml} \qquad 210 \text{ ml} = 0.21 \text{ L}$
$$\begin{array}{r} 946 \text{ ml} \\ - 210 \text{ ml} \\ \hline 736 \text{ ml} \end{array} \quad \text{or} \quad \begin{array}{r} 0.946 \text{ L} \\ - 0.210 \text{ L} \\ \hline 0.736 \text{ L} \end{array}$$

90.

6.1 L = 6100 ml	9400 ml = 9.4 L
6100 ml	6.1 L
+ 9400 ml or	+ 9.4 L
15,500 ml	15.5 L

91.

$$\begin{array}{r} 4 \text{ gal } 2 \text{ qt} \\ - 1 \text{ gal } 3 \text{ qt} \\ \hline \end{array} \qquad \begin{array}{r} 3 \text{ gal } 6 \text{ qt} \\ - 1 \text{ gal } 3 \text{ qt} \\ \hline 2 \text{ gal } 3 \text{ qt} \end{array}$$

There are 2 gal 3 qt of tea remaining.

92. $1 \text{ c } 4 \text{ fl oz} \div 2 = (8 \text{ fl oz} + 4 \text{ fl oz}) \div 2$
$= 12 \text{ fl oz} \div 2$
$= 6 \text{ fl oz}$
Use 6 fl oz of stock for half of a recipe.

93. $85 \text{ ml} \times 8 \times 16 = 10,880 \text{ ml}$
$$\frac{10,880 \text{ ml}}{1} \cdot \frac{1 \text{ L}}{1000 \text{ ml}} = \frac{10,880}{1000} \text{ L} = 10.88 \text{ L}$$
There are 10.88 L of polish in 8 boxes.

94. $6 \text{ L} + 1300 \text{ ml} + 2.6 \text{ L} = 6 \text{ L} + 1.3 \text{ L} + 2.6 \text{ L}$
$= 9.9 \text{ L}$
Since 9.9 L is less than 10 L, yes it will fit.

95. $7 \text{ m} \approx \dfrac{7 \text{ m}}{1} \cdot \dfrac{3.28 \text{ ft}}{1 \text{ m}} = 22.96 \text{ ft}$

96. $11.5 \text{ yd} \approx \dfrac{11.5 \text{ yd}}{1} \cdot \dfrac{1 \text{ m}}{1.09 \text{ yd}} \approx 10.55 \text{ m}$

97. $17.5 \text{ L} \approx \dfrac{17.5 \text{ L}}{1} \cdot \dfrac{0.26 \text{ gal}}{1 \text{ L}} = 4.55 \text{ gal}$

98. $7.8 \text{ L} \approx \dfrac{7.8 \text{ L}}{1} \cdot \dfrac{1.06 \text{ qt}}{1 \text{ L}} = 8.268 \text{ qt}$

99. $15 \text{ oz} \approx \dfrac{15 \text{ oz}}{1} \cdot \dfrac{28.35 \text{ g}}{1 \text{ oz}} = 425.25 \text{ g}$

100. $23 \text{ lb} \approx \dfrac{23 \text{ lb}}{1} \cdot \dfrac{0.45 \text{ kg}}{1 \text{ lb}} = 10.35 \text{ kg}$

101. $1.2 \text{ mm} \times 50 = 60 \text{ mm}$
$$60 \text{ mm} = \frac{60 \text{ mm}}{1} \cdot \frac{1 \text{ cm}}{10 \text{ mm}} = 6 \text{ cm}$$
$$6 \text{ cm} = \frac{6 \text{ cm}}{1} \cdot \frac{1 \text{ in.}}{2.54 \text{ cm}} \approx 2.36 \text{ in.}$$
The height of the stack is approximately 2.36 in.

102. $82 \text{ kg} \approx \dfrac{82 \text{ kg}}{1} \cdot \dfrac{2.20 \text{ lb}}{1 \text{ kg}} = 180.4 \text{ lb}$
The person weighs approximately 180.4 lb.

103. $F = 1.8C + 32$
$= 1.8(42) + 32$
$= 75.6 + 32$
$= 107.6$
42°C is 107.6°F.

104. $F = 1.8C + 32 = 1.8(160) + 32 = 288 + 32 = 320$
160°C is 320°F.

105. $C = \dfrac{5}{9}(F - 32) = \dfrac{5}{9}(41.3 - 32) = \dfrac{5}{9}(9.3) \approx 5.2$
41.3°F is 5.2°C.

106. $C = \dfrac{5}{9}(F - 32) = \dfrac{5}{9}(80 - 32) = \dfrac{5}{9}(48) \approx 26.7$
80°F is 26.7°C.

107. $C = \dfrac{5}{9}(F - 32) = \dfrac{5}{9}(35 - 32) = \dfrac{5}{9}(3) \approx 1.7$
35°F is 1.7°C.

108. $F = 1.8C + 32 = 1.8(165) + 32 = 297 + 32 = 329$
165°C is 329°F.

109. The supplement of a 72° angle is an angle that measures 180° − 72° = 108°.

110. The complement of a 1° angle is an angle that measures 90° − 1° = 89°.

111. $\angle x$ and the angle marked 85° are adjacent angles, so $m\angle x = 180° - 85° = 95°$.

112. Let $\angle y$ be the angle corresponding to $\angle x$ at the bottom intersection. Then $\angle y$ and the angle marked 123° are adjacent angles, so $m\angle x = m\angle y = 180° - 123° = 57°$.

113. $P = 7 \text{ in.} + 11.2 \text{ in.} + 9.1 \text{ in.} = 27.3 \text{ in.}$
The perimeter is 27.3 inches.

114. The unmarked horizontal side has length 40 ft − 22 ft − 11 ft = 7 ft.
$P = (22 + 15 + 7 + 15 + 11 + 42 + 40 + 42) \text{ ft}$
$= 194 \text{ ft}$
The perimeter is 194 feet.

115. The unmarked horizontal side has length
$43 \text{ m} - 13 \text{ m} = 30 \text{ m}$. The unmarked vertical side
has length $42 \text{ m} - 14 \text{ m} = 28 \text{ m}$. The area is the
sum of the areas of the two rectangles.
$A = 28 \text{ m} \cdot 13 \text{ m} + 42 \text{ m} \cdot 30 \text{ m}$
   $= 364 \text{ sq m} + 1260 \text{ sq m}$
   $= 1624 \text{ sq m}$
The area is 1624 square meters.

116. $A = \pi \cdot r^2 = \pi \cdot (3 \text{ m})^2 = 9\pi \text{ sq m} \approx 28.26 \text{ sq m}$
The area is
9π square meters ≈ 28.26 square meters.

117. $V = \dfrac{1}{3} \cdot \pi \cdot r^2 \cdot h$

$= \dfrac{1}{3} \cdot \pi \cdot \left(5\dfrac{1}{4} \text{ in.}\right)^2 \cdot 12 \text{ in.}$

$= \dfrac{1}{3} \cdot \pi \cdot \left(\dfrac{21}{4} \text{ in.}\right)^2 \cdot 12 \text{ cu in.}$

$= \dfrac{441}{4} \pi \text{ cu in.}$

$\approx \dfrac{441}{4} \cdot \dfrac{22}{7} \text{ cu in.} = 346\dfrac{1}{2} \text{ cu in.}$

The volume is $346\dfrac{1}{2}$ cubic inches.

118. $V = l \cdot w \cdot h = 5 \text{ in.} \cdot 4 \text{ in.} \cdot 7 \text{ in.} = 140 \text{ cu in.}$
The volume is 140 cubic inches.
$SA = 2lh + 2wh + 2lw$
   $= 2 \cdot 7 \text{ in.} \cdot 5 \text{ in.} + 2 \cdot 4 \text{ in.} \cdot 5 \text{ in.} + 2 \cdot 7 \text{ in.} \cdot 4 \text{ in.}$
   $= 70 \text{ sq in.} + 40 \text{ sq in.} + 56 \text{ sq in.}$
   $= 166 \text{ sq in.}$
The surface area is 166 square inches.

119. $6.25 \text{ ft} = \dfrac{6.25 \text{ ft}}{1} \cdot \dfrac{12 \text{ in.}}{1 \text{ ft}} = 75 \text{ in.}$

120. $8200 \text{ lb} = 8000 \text{ lb} + 200 \text{ lb}$

$= \dfrac{8000 \text{ lb}}{1} \cdot \dfrac{1 \text{ ton}}{2000 \text{ lb}} + 200 \text{ lb}$

$= 4 \text{ tons } 200 \text{ lb}$

121. $5 \text{ m} = \dfrac{5 \text{ m}}{1} \cdot \dfrac{100 \text{ cm}}{1 \text{ m}} = 500 \text{ cm}$

122. $286 \text{ mm} = \dfrac{286 \text{ mm}}{1} \cdot \dfrac{1 \text{ km}}{1,000,000 \text{ mm}}$

$= 0.000286 \text{ km}$

123. $1400 \text{ mg} = \dfrac{1400 \text{ mg}}{1} \cdot \dfrac{1 \text{ g}}{1000 \text{ mg}} = 1.4 \text{ g}$

124. $6.75 \text{ gal} = \dfrac{6.75 \text{ gal}}{1} \cdot \dfrac{4 \text{ qt}}{1 \text{ gal}} = 27 \text{ qt}$

125. $F = 1.8C + 32 = 1.8(86) + 32 = 154.8 + 32 = 186.8$
$86°C$ is $186.8°F$.

126. $C = \dfrac{5}{9}(F - 32) = \dfrac{5}{9}(51.8 - 32) = \dfrac{5}{9}(19.8) = 11$

$51.8°F$ is $11°C$.

127.
$9.3 \text{ km} = 9300 \text{ m}$		$183 \text{ m} = 0.183 \text{ km}$
9300 m		9.300 km
$\underline{-\ 183 \text{ m}}$	or	$\underline{-\ 0.183 \text{ km}}$
9117 m		9.117 km

128.
$35 \text{ L} = 35,000 \text{ ml}$	$700 \text{ ml} = 0.7 \text{ L}$
$35,000 \text{ ml}$	35.0 L
$\underline{+\ \ \ 700 \text{ ml}}$	$\underline{+\ 0.7 \text{ L}}$
$35,700 \text{ ml}$	35.7 L

129.
   $3 \text{ gal } 3 \text{ qt}$
$\underline{+\ 4 \text{ gal } 2 \text{ qt}}$
   $7 \text{ gal } 5 \text{ qt} = 7 \text{ gal} + 1 \text{ gal } 1 \text{ qt} = 8 \text{ gal } 1 \text{ qt}$

130.
   3.2 kg
$\underline{\times\ \ \ 4}$
12.8 kg

Chapter 8 Test

1. The complement of an angle that measures $78°$ is
an angle that measures $90° - 78° = 12°$.

2. The supplement of a $124°$ angle is an angle that
measures $180° - 124° = 56°$.

3. $m\angle x = 90° - 40° = 50°$

4. $\angle x$ and the angle marked $62°$ are adjacent
angles, so $m\angle x = 180° - 62° = 118°$.
$\angle y$ and the angle marked $62°$ are vertical
angles, so $m\angle y = 62°$.
$\angle x$ and $\angle z$ are vertical angles, so
$m\angle z = m\angle x = 118°$.

5. $\angle x$ and the angle marked $73°$ are vertical angles, so $m\angle x = 73°$.

$\angle x$ and $\angle y$ are alternate interior angles, so $m\angle y = m\angle x = 73°$.

$\angle x$ and $\angle z$ are corresponding angles, so $m\angle z = m\angle x = 73°$.

6. $d = 2 \cdot r = 2 \cdot 3.1 \text{ m} = 6.2 \text{ m}$

7. $r = d \div 2 = 20 \text{ in.} \div 2 = 10 \text{ in.}$

8. Circumference:
$C = 2 \cdot \pi \cdot r$
$= 2 \cdot \pi \cdot 9 \text{ in.}$
$= 18\pi \text{ in.}$
$\approx 56.52 \text{ in.}$
The circumference is 18π inches ≈ 56.52 inches.
Area:
$A = \pi r^2$
$= \pi(9 \text{ in.})^2$
$= 81\pi \text{ sq in.}$
$\approx 254.34 \text{ sq in.}$
The area is
81π square inches ≈ 254.34 square inches.

9. $P = 2 \cdot l + 2 \cdot w$
$= 2(7 \text{ yd}) + 2(5.3 \text{ yd})$
$= 14 \text{ yd} + 10.6 \text{ yd}$
$= 24.6 \text{ yd}$
The perimeter is 24.6 yards.
$A = l \cdot w = 7 \text{ yd} \cdot 5.3 \text{ yd} = 37.1 \text{ sq yd}$
The area is 37.1 square yards.

10. The unmarked vertical side has length $11 \text{ in.} - 7 \text{ in.} = 4 \text{ in.}$ The unmarked horizontal side has length $23 \text{ in.} - 6 \text{ in.} = 17 \text{ in.}$
$P = (6 + 4 + 17 + 7 + 23 + 11) \text{ in.} = 68 \text{ in.}$
The perimeter is 68 inches.
Extending the unmarked vertical side downward divides the region into two rectangles. The region's area is the sum of the areas of these:
$A = 11 \text{ in.} \cdot 6 \text{ in.} + 7 \text{ in.} \cdot 17 \text{ in.}$
$= 66 \text{ sq in.} + 119 \text{ sq in.}$
$= 185 \text{ sq in.}$
The area is 185 square inches.

11. $V = \pi \cdot r^2 \cdot h$
$= \pi \cdot (2 \text{ in.})^2 \cdot 5 \text{ in.}$
$= 20\pi \text{ cu in.}$
$\approx 20 \cdot \dfrac{22}{7} \text{ cu in.} = 62\dfrac{6}{7} \text{ cu in.}$
The volume is $62\dfrac{6}{7}$ cubic inches.

12. $V = l \cdot w \cdot h = 5 \text{ ft} \cdot 3 \text{ ft} \cdot 2 \text{ ft} = 30 \text{ cu ft}$
The volume is 30 cubic feet.

13. $P = 4 \cdot s = 4 \cdot 4 \text{ in.} = 16 \text{ in.}$
The perimeter of the frame is 16 inches.

14. $V = l \cdot w \cdot h = 3 \text{ ft} \cdot 3 \text{ ft} \cdot 2 \text{ ft} = 18 \text{ cu ft}$
18 cubic feet of soil are needed.

15. $P = 2 \cdot l + 2 \cdot w$
$= 2 \cdot 18 \text{ ft} + 2 \cdot 13 \text{ ft}$
$= 36 \text{ ft} + 26 \text{ ft}$
$= 62 \text{ ft}$
$\text{cost} = P \cdot \$1.87 \text{ per ft}$
$= 62 \text{ ft} \cdot \$1.87 \text{ per ft}$
$= \$115.94$
62 feet of baseboard are needed, at a total cost of $115.94.

16.
$$\begin{array}{r} 23 \\ 12\overline{)280} \\ -24 \\ \hline 40 \\ -36 \\ \hline 4 \end{array}$$
280 inches = 23 ft 4 in.

17. $2\dfrac{1}{2} \text{ gal} = \dfrac{2\frac{1}{2} \text{ gal}}{1} \cdot \dfrac{4 \text{ qt}}{1 \text{ gal}} = 2\dfrac{1}{2} \cdot 4 \text{ qt} = 10 \text{ qt}$

18. $30 \text{ oz} = \dfrac{30 \text{ oz}}{1} \cdot \dfrac{1 \text{ lb}}{16 \text{ oz}} = \dfrac{30}{16} \text{ lb} = \dfrac{15}{8} \text{ lb} = 1\dfrac{7}{8} \text{ lb}$

19. $2.8 \text{ tons} = \dfrac{2.8 \text{ tons}}{1} \cdot \dfrac{2000 \text{ lb}}{1 \text{ ton}}$
$= 2.8 \cdot 2000 \text{ lb}$
$= 5600 \text{ lb}$

20. $38 \text{ pt} = \dfrac{38 \text{ pt}}{1} \cdot \dfrac{1 \text{ qt}}{2 \text{ pt}} \cdot \dfrac{1 \text{ gal}}{4 \text{ qt}}$

$\qquad = \dfrac{38}{8} \text{ gal}$

$\qquad = \dfrac{19}{4} \text{ gal}$

$\qquad = 4\dfrac{3}{4} \text{ gal}$

21. $40 \text{ mg} = \dfrac{40 \text{ mg}}{1} \cdot \dfrac{1 \text{ g}}{1000 \text{ mg}} = \dfrac{40}{1000} \text{ g} = 0.04 \text{ g}$

22. $2.4 \text{ kg} = \dfrac{2.4 \text{ kg}}{1} \cdot \dfrac{1000 \text{ g}}{1 \text{ kg}} = 2.4 \cdot 1000 \text{ g} = 2400 \text{ g}$

23. $3.6 \text{ cm} = \dfrac{3.6 \text{ cm}}{1} \cdot \dfrac{10 \text{ mm}}{1 \text{ cm}} = 3.6 \cdot 10 \text{ mm} = 36 \text{ mm}$

24. $4.3 \text{ dg} = \dfrac{4.3 \text{ dg}}{1} \cdot \dfrac{1 \text{ g}}{10 \text{ dg}} = \dfrac{4.3}{10} \text{ g} = 0.43 \text{ g}$

25. $0.83 \text{ L} = \dfrac{0.83 \text{ L}}{1} \cdot \dfrac{1000 \text{ ml}}{1 \text{ L}} = 0.83 \cdot 1000 = 830 \text{ ml}$

26.
$\begin{array}{r} 3 \text{ qt } 1 \text{ pt} \\ + \ 2 \text{ qt } 1 \text{ pt} \\ \hline 5 \text{ qt } 2 \text{ pt} \end{array}$ $= 4 \text{ qt} + 1 \text{ qt} + 2 \text{ pt}$

$\qquad\qquad = 1 \text{ gal} + 1 \text{ qt} + 1 \text{ qt}$

$\qquad\qquad = 1 \text{ gal } 2 \text{ qt}$

27.
$\begin{array}{r} 8 \text{ lb } 6 \text{ oz} \\ - \ 4 \text{ lb } 9 \text{ oz} \end{array} \rightarrow \begin{array}{r} 7 \text{ lb } 22 \text{ oz} \\ - \ 4 \text{ lb } \ \ 9 \text{ oz} \\ \hline 3 \text{ lb } 13 \text{ oz} \end{array}$

28. $2 \text{ ft } 9 \text{ in.} \times 3 = 6 \text{ ft } 27 \text{ in.}$

$\qquad\qquad\qquad\quad = 6 \text{ ft} + 2 \text{ ft } 3 \text{ in.}$

$\qquad\qquad\qquad\quad = 8 \text{ ft } 3 \text{ in.}$

29. $5 \text{ gal } 2 \text{ qt} \div 2 = 4 \text{ gal } 6 \text{ qt} \div 2$

$\qquad\qquad\qquad = \dfrac{4}{2} \text{ gal } \dfrac{6}{2} \text{ qt}$

$\qquad\qquad\qquad = 2 \text{ gal } 3 \text{ qt}$

30. $8 \text{ cm} = 80 \text{ mm} \qquad 14 \text{ mm} = 1.4 \text{ cm}$

$\begin{array}{r} 80 \text{ mm} \\ - \ 14 \text{ mm} \\ \hline 66 \text{ mm} \end{array}$ or $\begin{array}{r} 8.0 \text{ cm} \\ - \ 1.4 \text{ cm} \\ \hline 6.6 \text{ cm} \end{array}$

31. $1.8 \text{ km} = 1800 \text{ m} \qquad 456 \text{ m} = 0.456 \text{ km}$

$\begin{array}{r} 1800 \text{ m} \\ + \ 456 \text{ m} \\ \hline 2256 \text{ m} \end{array}$ or $\begin{array}{r} 1.800 \text{ km} \\ + \ 0.456 \text{ km} \\ \hline 2.256 \text{ km} \end{array}$

32. $C = \dfrac{5}{9}(F - 32)$

$\qquad = \dfrac{5}{9}(84 - 32)$

$\qquad = \dfrac{5}{9}(52)$

$\qquad \approx 28.9$

$84°F$ is $28.9°C.$

33. $F = 1.8C + 32$

$\qquad = 1.8(12.6) + 32$

$\qquad = 22.68 + 32$

$\qquad \approx 54.7$

$12.6°C$ is $54.7°F$

34. $8.4 \text{ m} \cdot \dfrac{2}{3} = \dfrac{8.4}{1} \cdot \dfrac{2}{3} \text{ m} = 5.6 \text{ m}$

The trees will be 5.6 m tall.

35.
$\begin{array}{r} 20 \text{ gal} \\ - \ 15 \text{ gal } 1 \text{ qt} \end{array}$ $\qquad \begin{array}{r} 19 \text{ gal } 4 \text{ qt} \\ - \ 15 \text{ gal } 1 \text{ qt} \\ \hline 4 \text{ gal } 3 \text{ qt} \end{array}$

Thus, 4 gal 3 qt remains in the container.

36. $88 \text{ m} + 340 \text{ cm} = 88 \text{ m} + 3.40 \text{ m} = 91.4 \text{ m}$

The span is 91.4 meters

37.
$\begin{array}{r} 2 \text{ ft } \ 9 \text{ in.} \\ \times \qquad 6 \\ \hline 12 \text{ ft } 54 \text{ in.} \end{array}$ $= 12 \text{ ft} + 4 \text{ ft } 6 \text{ in.} = 16 \text{ ft } 6 \text{ in.}$

Thus, 16 ft 6 in. of material is needed.

Cumulative Review Chapters 1–8

1. $3a - 6 = a + 4$

$\quad 3a - a - 6 = a - a + 4$

$\qquad 2a - 6 = 4$

$\quad 2a - 6 + 6 = 4 + 6$

$\qquad\qquad 2a = 10$

$\qquad\qquad \dfrac{2a}{2} = \dfrac{10}{2}$

$\qquad\qquad\quad a = 5$

2.
$$2x+1 = 3x-5$$
$$2x-2x+1 = 3x-2x-5$$
$$1 = x-5$$
$$1+5 = x-5+5$$
$$6 = x$$

3. a. $\left(\dfrac{2}{5}\right)^4 = \dfrac{2}{5}\cdot\dfrac{2}{5}\cdot\dfrac{2}{5}\cdot\dfrac{2}{5} = \dfrac{2^4}{5^4} = \dfrac{16}{625}$

    b. $\left(-\dfrac{1}{4}\right)^2 = \left(-\dfrac{1}{4}\right)\left(-\dfrac{1}{4}\right) = \dfrac{1}{16}$

4. a. $\left(-\dfrac{1}{3}\right)^3 = \left(-\dfrac{1}{3}\right)\left(-\dfrac{1}{3}\right)\left(-\dfrac{1}{3}\right) = -\dfrac{1}{27}$

    b. $\left(\dfrac{3}{7}\right)^2 = \dfrac{3}{7}\cdot\dfrac{3}{7} = \dfrac{9}{49}$

5.
$$\begin{array}{r} 2\dfrac{4}{5} \\ 5 \\ +1\dfrac{1}{2} \\ \hline \end{array} \qquad \begin{array}{r} 2\dfrac{8}{10} \\ 5 \\ +1\dfrac{5}{10} \\ \hline 8\dfrac{13}{10} = 8+1\dfrac{3}{10} = 9\dfrac{3}{10} \end{array}$$

6.
$$\begin{array}{r} 2\dfrac{1}{3} \\ 4\dfrac{2}{5} \\ +3 \\ \hline \end{array} \qquad \begin{array}{r} 2\dfrac{5}{15} \\ 4\dfrac{6}{15} \\ +3 \\ \hline 9\dfrac{11}{15} \end{array}$$

7. $11.1x-6.3+8.9x-4.6 = 11.1x+8.9x-6.3-4.6$
$$= 20x-10.9$$

8. $2.5y+3.7-1.3y-1.9 = 2.5y-1.3y+3.7-1.9$
$$= 1.2y+1.8$$

9. $\dfrac{5.68+(0.9)^2 \div 100}{0.2} = \dfrac{5.69+0.81\div100}{0.2}$

$$= \dfrac{5.69+0.0081}{0.2}$$

$$= \dfrac{5.6981}{0.2}$$

$$= 28.4905$$

10. $\dfrac{0.12+0.96}{0.5} = \dfrac{1.08}{0.5} = 2.16$

11.
$$\begin{array}{r} 0.77... \\ 9\overline{)\,7.00} \\ -63 \\ \hline 70 \\ -63 \\ \hline 7 \end{array}$$

Thus $0.\overline{7} = \dfrac{7}{9}$.

12.
$$\begin{array}{r} 0.4 \\ 5\overline{)\,2.0} \\ -2\,0 \\ \hline 0 \end{array}$$

Thus $0.43 > \dfrac{2}{5}$.

13.
$$0.5y+2.3 = 1.65$$
$$0.5y+2.3-2.3 = 1.65-2.3$$
$$0.5y = -0.65$$
$$\dfrac{0.5y}{0.5} = \dfrac{-0.65}{0.5}$$
$$y = -1.3$$

14.
$$0.4x-9.3 = 2.7$$
$$0.4x-9.3+9.3 = 2.7+9.3$$
$$0.4x = 12$$
$$\dfrac{0.4x}{0.4} = \dfrac{12}{0.4}$$
$$x = 30$$

15. Use $a^2+b^2 = c^2$ where $a = b = 300$.
$$300^2+300^2 = c^2$$
$$90,000+90,000 = c^2$$
$$180,000 = c^2$$
$$\sqrt{180,000} = c$$
$$424 \approx c$$

The length of the diagonal is approximately 424 feet.

16. Use $a^2 + b^2 = c^2$ where $a = 200$ and $b = 125$.

$$200^2 + 125^2 = c^2$$
$$40,000 + 15,625 = c^2$$
$$55,625 = c^2$$
$$\sqrt{55,625} = c$$
$$236 \approx c$$

The length of the diagonal is approximately 236 feet.

17. a. $\dfrac{\text{width}}{\text{length}} = \dfrac{5 \text{ feet}}{7 \text{ feet}} = \dfrac{5}{7}$

b. $P = 2 \cdot l + 2 \cdot w$
$= 2(7 \text{ feet}) + 2(5 \text{ feet})$
$= 14 \text{ feet} + 10 \text{ feet}$
$= 24 \text{ feet}$

$\dfrac{\text{length}}{\text{perimeter}} = \dfrac{7 \text{ feet}}{24 \text{ feet}} = \dfrac{7}{24}$

18. a. $P = 4s = 4(9 \text{ in.}) = 36 \text{ in.}$

$\dfrac{\text{side}}{\text{perimeter}} = \dfrac{9 \text{ inches}}{36 \text{ inches}} = \dfrac{9}{36} = \dfrac{1}{4}$

b. $A = s^2 = (9 \text{ in.})^2 = 81 \text{ sq in.}$

$\dfrac{\text{perimeter}}{\text{area}} = \dfrac{36 \text{ inches}}{81 \text{ sq inches}} = \dfrac{36}{81} = \dfrac{4}{9}$

19. $3y + 1 = 3$
$3(-1) + 1 \stackrel{?}{=} 3$
$-3 + 1 \stackrel{?}{=} 3$
$-2 = 3$ False

No, -1 is not a solution.

20. $4(x + 7) = 8$
$4(-5 + 7) \stackrel{?}{=} 8$
$4(2) \stackrel{?}{=} 8$
$8 = 8$ True

Yes, -5 is a solution.

21. $\dfrac{x}{3} = -2$

$3 \cdot \dfrac{x}{3} = 3 \cdot -2$

$x = -6$

22. $9x = 8x + 1.02$
$9x - 8x = 8x - 8x + 1.02$
$x = 1.02$

23. Let x be the dose for a 140-lb woman.

$$\frac{4 \text{ cc}}{25 \text{ lb}} = \frac{x \text{ cc}}{140 \text{ lb}}$$
$$\frac{4}{25} = \frac{x}{140}$$
$$4 \cdot 140 = 25 \cdot x$$
$$560 = 25x$$
$$\frac{560}{25} = \frac{25x}{25}$$
$$22.4 = x$$

The dose is 22.4 cc.

24. Let x be the amount for 5 pie crusts.

$$\frac{3 \text{ c}}{2 \text{ crusts}} = \frac{x \text{ c}}{5 \text{ crusts}}$$
$$\frac{3}{2} = \frac{x}{5}$$
$$3 \cdot 5 = 2 \cdot x$$
$$15 = 2x$$
$$\frac{15}{2} = \frac{2x}{2}$$
$$7.5 = x$$

5 pie crusts require 7.5 cups of flour.

25. $\dfrac{17}{100} = 17\%$

17% of the people surveyed drive blue cars.

26. $\dfrac{38}{100} = 38\%$

38% of the shoppers used only cash.

27. $13 = 6\dfrac{1}{2}\% \cdot x$
$13 = 0.065x$
$\dfrac{13}{0.065} = \dfrac{0.065x}{0.065}$
$200 = x$

13 is $6\dfrac{1}{2}\%$ of 200.

28. $54 = 4\dfrac{1}{2}\% \cdot x$
$54 = 0.045x$
$\dfrac{54}{0.045} = \dfrac{0.045x}{0.045}$
$1200 = x$

54 is $4\dfrac{1}{2}\%$ of 1200.

29. $x = 30\% \cdot 9$
$x = 0.3 \cdot 9$
$x = 2.7$
2.7 is 30% of 9.

30. $x = 42\% \cdot 30$
$x = 0.42 \cdot 30$
$x = 12.6$
12.6 is 42% of 30.

31. percent increase $= \dfrac{\text{amount of increase}}{\text{original amount}}$
$= \dfrac{45 - 34}{34}$
$= \dfrac{11}{34}$
≈ 0.32
The scholarship applications increased by 32%.

32. percent increase $= \dfrac{\text{amount of increase}}{\text{original amount}}$
$= \dfrac{19 - 15}{15}$
$= \dfrac{4}{15}$
≈ 0.27
The price of the paint increased by 27%.

33. sales tax $= 85.50 \cdot 0.075 = 6.4125$
The sales tax is $6.41.
$85.50 + 6.41 = 91.91$
The total price is $91.91.

34. sales tax $= 375 \cdot 0.08 = 30$
The sales tax is $30.
$375 + 30 = 405$
The total price is $405.

35. The seven numbers are listed in order. The median is the middle number, 57.

36. The five numbers in order are:
60, 72, 83, 89, 95.
The median is the middle number, 83.

37. There is 1 red marble and $1 + 1 + 2 = 4$ total marbles. The probability is $\dfrac{1}{4}$.

38. There are 2 nickels and $2 + 2 + 3 = 7$ total coins. The probability is $\dfrac{2}{7}$.

39. The complement of a 48° angle is an angle that has measure $90° - 48° = 42°$.

40. The supplement of a 137° angle is an angle that has measure $180° - 137° = 43°$.

41. $8 \text{ ft} = \dfrac{8 \text{ ft}}{1} \cdot \dfrac{12 \text{ in.}}{1 \text{ ft}} = 8 \cdot 12 \text{ in.} = 96 \text{ in.}$

42. $7 \text{ yd} = \dfrac{7 \text{ yd}}{1} \cdot \dfrac{3 \text{ ft}}{1 \text{ yd}} = 7 \cdot 3 \text{ ft} = 21 \text{ ft}$

43.
$$\begin{array}{r} 8 \text{ tons } 1000 \text{ lb} \\ - 3 \text{ tons } 1350 \text{ lb} \\ \hline \end{array} \qquad \begin{array}{r} 7 \text{ tons } 3000 \text{ lb} \\ - 3 \text{ tons } 1350 \text{ lb} \\ \hline 4 \text{ tons } 1650 \text{ lb} \end{array}$$

44.
$$\begin{array}{r} 8 \text{ lb } 15 \text{ oz} \\ + 9 \text{ lb } 3 \text{ oz} \\ \hline 17 \text{ lb } 18 \text{ oz} = 17 \text{ lb} + 1 \text{ lb } 2 \text{ oz} = 18 \text{ lb } 2 \text{ oz} \end{array}$$

45. $C = \dfrac{5}{9}(F - 32) = \dfrac{5}{9}(59 - 32) = \dfrac{5}{9}(27) = 15$
59°F is 15°C.

46. $C = \dfrac{5}{9}(F - 32) = \dfrac{5}{9}(86 - 32) = \dfrac{5}{9}(54) = 30$
86°F is 30°C.

Chapter 9

Practice Problems

1. Since 8 is to the right of 6 on the number line, the statement 8 < 6 is false.

2. Since 100 is to the right of 10 on the number line, the statement 100 > 10 is true.

3. Since 21 = 21, the statement $21 \leq 21$ is true.

4. Since 21 = 21, the statement $21 \geq 21$ is true.

5. Since neither 0 > 5 nor 0 = 5 is true, the statement $0 \geq 5$ is false.

6. Since 25 > 22, the statement $25 \geq 22$ is true.

7. **a.** Fourteen is greater than or equal to fourteen is written as $14 \geq 14$.

   b. Zero is less than five is written as 0 < 5.

   c. Nine is not equal to 10 is written as $9 \neq 10$.

8. The integer −8 represents 8 feet below sea level.

9. $\frac{5}{4} = 1\frac{1}{4}$

10. **a.** −11 < −9 since −11 is to the left of −9 on the number line.

    b. By comparing digits in the same places, we find that 4.511 > 4.151, since 0.5 > 0.1.

    c. By dividing, we find that $\frac{7}{8} = 0.875$ and

    $\frac{2}{3} = 0.66....$ Since 0.875 > 0.66..., then

    $\frac{7}{8} > \frac{2}{3}$.

11. **a.** The natural numbers are 6 and 913.

    b. The whole numbers are 0, 6, and 913.

    c. The integers are −100, 0, 6, and 913.

    d. The rational numbers are −100, $-\frac{2}{5}$, 0, 6, and 913.

    e. The irrational number is π.

    f. All numbers in the given set are real numbers.

Vocabulary and Readiness Check

1. The <u>whole</u> numbers are {0, 1, 2, 3, 4, ...}.

2. The <u>natural</u> numbers are {1, 2, 3, 4, 5, ...}.

3. The symbols $\neq$, $\leq$, and > are called <u>inequality</u> symbols.

4. The <u>integers</u> are {..., −3, −2, −1, 0, 1, 2, 3, ...}.

5. The <u>real</u> numbers are {all numbers that correspond to points on the number line}.

6. The <u>rational</u> numbers are $\left\{ \frac{a}{b} \middle| a \text{ and } b \text{ are integers, } b \neq 0 \right\}$.

7. The integer <u>0</u> is neither positive nor negative.

8. The point on a number line halfway between 0 and $\frac{1}{2}$ can be represented by $\frac{1}{\underline{4}}$.

Exercise Set 9.1

1. Since 4 is to the left of 10 on the number line, 4 < 10.

3. Since 7 is to the right of 3 on the number line, 7 > 3.

5. 6.26 = 6.26

7. Since 0 is to the left of 7 on the number line, 0 < 7.

9. Since 32 is to the left of 212 on the number line, 32 < 212.

11. Since 30 is to the left of 45 on the number line, $30 \leq 45$.

13. Since 11 = 11, the statement 11 ≤ 11 is true.

15. Since −11 is to the left of −10 on the number line, −11 > −10 is false.

17. Comparing digits with the same place value, we have 0.0 < 0.9. Thus the statement 5.092 < 5.902 is true.

19. Rewrite the fractions with a common denominator and compare numerators.
$$\frac{9}{10} = \frac{81}{90}; \frac{8}{9} = \frac{80}{90}$$
Since 81 > 80, then $\frac{9}{10} \le \frac{8}{9}$ is false.

21. 25 ≥ 20 has the same meaning as 20 ≤ 25.

23. 0 < 6 has the same meaning as 6 > 0.

25. −10 > −12 has the same meaning as −12 < −10.

27. Seven is less than eleven is written as 7 < 11.

29. Five is greater than or equal to four is written as 5 ≥ 4.

31. Fifteen is not equal to negative two is written as 15 ≠ −2.

33. The integer 14,494 represents 14,494 feet above sea level. The integer −282 represents 282 feet below sea level.

35. The integer −28,000 represents 28,000 fewer students.

37. The integer 475 represents a $475 deposit. The integer −195 represents a $195 withdrawal.

39.

41.

43.

45. 0 is a whole number, an integer, a rational number, and a real number.

47. −7 is an integer, a rational number, and a real number.

49. 265 is a natural number, a whole number, an integer, a rational number, and a real number.

51. $\frac{2}{3}$ is a rational number and a real number.

53. False; the rational number $\frac{2}{3}$ is not an integer.

55. True; 0 is a real number.

57. False; the negative number $-\sqrt{2}$ is not a rational number.

59. False; the real number $\sqrt{7}$ is not a rational number.

61. $|-5| = 5$
$-4 = -4$
Since 5 is to the right of −4 on the number line, $|-5| > -4$.

63. $\left|-\frac{5}{8}\right| = \frac{5}{8}$
$\left|\frac{5}{8}\right| = \frac{5}{8}$
Since $\frac{5}{8} = \frac{5}{8}$, then $\left|-\frac{5}{8}\right| = \left|\frac{5}{8}\right|$.

65. $|-2| = 2$
$|-2.7| = 2.7$
Since 2 is to the left of 2.7 on the number line, $|-2| < |-2.7|$.

67. $|0| = 0$
$|-8| = 8$
Since 0 is to the left of 8 on the number line, $|0| < |-8|$.

69. The 2008 cranberry production in Oregon was 50 million pounds, while the 2008 cranberry production in Washington was 15 million pounds.
15 million > 15 million or
50,000,000 > 15,000,000

71. The 2008 cranberry production in Washington was 15 million pounds, while the 2008 cranberry production in New Jersey was 49 million pounds.

$49 - 15 = 34$

The production in Washington was 34 million pounds less or −34 million.

73. Since −0.04 is to the right of −26.7 on the number line, $-0.04 > -26.7$.

75. Sun: −26.7

Arcturus: −0.04

Since $-26.7 < -0.04$, the sun is brighter than Arcturus.

77. Since the brightest star corresponds to the smallest apparent magnitude, which is −26.7, the brightest star is the sun.

79. answers may vary

Section 9.2

Practice Problems

1. a. $7 \cdot y = y \cdot 7$

   b. $4 + x = x + 4$

2. a. $5 \cdot (-3 \cdot 6) = (5 \cdot -3) \cdot 6$

   b. $(-2 + 7) + 3 = -2 + (7 + 3)$

   c. $(q + r) + 17 = q + (r + 17)$

   d. $(ab) \cdot 21 = a \cdot (b \cdot 21)$

3. Since the order of two numbers was changed but their grouping was not, the statement is true by the commutative property of multiplication.

4. Since the grouping of the numbers was changed and their order was not, the statement is true by the associative property of addition.

5. $(-3 + x) + 17 = -3 + (x + 17)$
$= -3 + (17 + x)$
$= (-3 + 17) + x$
$= 14 + x$

6. $4(5x) = (4 \cdot 5) \cdot x = 20x$

7. $5(x + y) = 5(x) + 5(y) = 5x + 5y$

8. $-3(2 + 7x) = -3(2) + (-3)(7x) = -6 - 21x$

9. $4(x + 6y - 2z) = 4(x) + 4(6y) - 4(2z)$
$= 4x + 24y - 8z$

10. $-1(3 - a) = (-1)(3) - (-1)(a) = -3 + a$

11. $-(8 + a - b) = -1(8 + a - b)$
$= (-1)(8) + (-1)(a) - (-1)(b)$
$= -8 - a + b$

12. $\frac{1}{2}(2x + 4) + 9 = \frac{1}{2}(2x) + \frac{1}{2}(4) + 9$
$= 1x + 2 + 9$
$= x + 11$

13. $9 \cdot 3 + 9 \cdot y = 9(3 + y)$

14. $4x + 4y = 4(x + y)$

15. $7(a + b) = 7 \cdot a + 7 \cdot b$ illustrates the distributive property.

16. $12 + y = y + 12$ illustrates the commutative property of addition.

17. $-4 \cdot (6 \cdot x) = (-4 \cdot 6) \cdot x$ illustrates the associative property of multiplication.

18. $6 + (z + 2) = 6 + (2 + z)$ illustrates the commutative property of addition.

19. $3\left(\frac{1}{3}\right) = 1$ illustrates the multiplicative inverse property.

20. $(x + 0) + 23 = x + 23$ illustrates the identity element for addition.

21. $(7 \cdot y) \cdot 10 = y \cdot (7 \cdot 10)$ illustrates the commutative and associative properties of multiplication.

Vocabulary and Readiness Check

1. $x + 5 = 5 + x$ is a true statement by the <u>commutative property of addition</u>.

2. $x \cdot 5 = 5 \cdot x$ is a true statement by the <u>commutative property of multiplication</u>.

3. $3(y + 6) = 3 \cdot y + 3 \cdot 6$ is true by the <u>distributive property</u>.

4. $2 \cdot (x \cdot y) = (2 \cdot x) \cdot y$ is a true statement by the <u>associative property of multiplication</u>.

5. $x + (7 + y) = (x + 7) + y$ is a true statement by the <u>associative property of addition</u>.

6. The numbers $-\dfrac{2}{3}$ and $-\dfrac{3}{2}$ are called <u>reciprocals or multiplicative inverses</u>.

7. The numbers $-\dfrac{2}{3}$ and $\dfrac{2}{3}$ are called <u>opposites or additive inverses</u>.

Exercise Set 9.2

1. $x + 16 = 16 + x$ by the commutative property of addition.

3. $-4 \cdot y = y \cdot (-4)$ by the commutative property of multiplication.

5. $xy = yx$ by the commutative property of multiplication.

7. $2x + 13 = 13 + 2x$ by the commutative property of addition.

9. $(xy) \cdot z = x \cdot (yz)$ by the associative property of multiplication.

11. $2 + (a + b) = (2 + a) + b$ by the associative property of addition.

13. $4 \cdot (ab) = 4a \cdot (b)$ by the associative property of multiplication.

15. $(a + b) + c = a + (b + c)$ by the associative property of addition.

17. $8 + (9 + b) = (8 + 9) + b = 17 + b$

19. $4(6y) = (4 \cdot 6)y = 24y$

21. $\dfrac{1}{5}(5y) = \left(\dfrac{1}{5} \cdot 5\right)y = 1y = y$

23. $(13 + a) + 13 = (a + 13) + 13$
$$= a + (13 + 13)$$
$$= a + 26$$

25. $-9(8x) = (-9 \cdot 8)x = -72x$

27. $\dfrac{3}{4}\left(\dfrac{4}{3}s\right) = \left(\dfrac{3}{4} \cdot \dfrac{4}{3}\right)s = 1s = s$

29. $-\dfrac{1}{2}(5x) = \left(-\dfrac{1}{2} \cdot 5\right)x = -\dfrac{5}{2}x$

31. $4(x + y) = 4(x) + 4(y) = 4x + 4y$

33. $9(x - 6) = 9(x) - 9(6) = 9x - 54$

35. $2(3x + 5) = 2(3x) + 2(5) = 6x + 10$

37. $7(4x - 3) = 7(4x) - 7(3) = 28x - 21$

39. $3(6 + x) = 3(6) + 3(x) = 18 + 3x$

41. $-2(y - z) = -2(y) - (-2)z = -2y + 2z$

43. $-\dfrac{1}{3}(3y + 5) = -\dfrac{1}{3}(3y) - \dfrac{1}{3}(5) = -y - \dfrac{5}{3}$

45. $5(x + 4m + 2) = 5(x) + 5(4m) + 5(2)$
$$= 5x + 20m + 10$$

47. $-4(1 - 2m + n) + 4 = -4(1) - 4(-2m) - 4(n) + 4$
$$= -4 + 8m - 4n + 4$$
$$= (-4 + 4) + 8m - 4n$$
$$= 0 + 8m - 4n$$
$$= 8m - 4n$$

49. $-(5x + 2) = -1(5x + 2)$
$$= -1(5x) + (-1)(2)$$
$$= -5x - 2$$

51. $-(r - 3 - 7p) = -1(r - 3 - 7p)$
$$= -1(r) - 1(-3) - 1(-7p)$$
$$= -r + 3 + 7p$$

53. $\dfrac{1}{2}(6x + 7) + \dfrac{1}{2} = \dfrac{1}{2}(6x) + \dfrac{1}{2}(7) + \dfrac{1}{2}$
$$= \left(\dfrac{1}{2} \cdot 6\right)x + \dfrac{7}{2} + \dfrac{1}{2}$$
$$= 3x + \dfrac{8}{2}$$
$$= 3x + 4$$

55. $-\dfrac{1}{3}(3x - 9y) = -\dfrac{1}{3}(3x) - \dfrac{1}{3}(-9y) = -x + 3y$

57. $3(2r + 5) - 7 = 3(2r) + 3(5) - 7$
$$= 6r + 15 - 7$$
$$= 6r + 8$$

59. $-9(4x+8)+2 = -9(4x)-9(8)+2$
$= -36x-72+2$
$= -36x-70$

61. $-0.4(4x+5)-0.5 = -0.4(4x)+(-0.4)(5)-0.5$
$= -1.6x-2-0.5$
$= -1.6x-2.5$

63. $4 \cdot 1 + 4 \cdot y = 4(1+y)$

65. $11x+11y = 11 \cdot x + 11 \cdot y = 11(x+y)$

67. $(-1) \cdot 5 + (-1) \cdot x = -1(5+x) = -(5+x)$

69. $30a+30b = 30 \cdot a + 30 \cdot b = 30(a+b)$

71. $3 \cdot 5 = 5 \cdot 3$ illustrates the commutative property of multiplication.

73. $2+(x+5) = (2+x)+5$ illustrates the associative property of addition.

75. $(x+9)+3 = (9+x)+3$ illustrates the commutative property of addition.

77. $(4 \cdot y) \cdot 9 = 4 \cdot (y \cdot 9)$ illustrates the associative property of multiplication.

79. $0+6 = 6$ illustrates the identity property of addition.

81. $-4(y+7) = -4 \cdot y + (-4) \cdot 7$ illustrates the distributive property.

83. $6 \cdot \dfrac{1}{6} = 1$ illustrates the multiplicative inverse property.

85. $-6 \cdot 1 = -6$ illustrates the identity element for multiplication.

87. $y-x^2 = 3-(-1)^2 = 3-1 = 2$

89. $a-b^2 = 2-(-5)^2 = 2-25 = -23$

91. $yz-y^2 = -5(0)-(-5)^2$
$= -5(0)-25$
$= 0-25$
$= -25$

93. The opposite of 8 is -8.
The reciprocal of 8 is $\dfrac{1}{8}$.

95. The opposite of x is $-x$.
The reciprocal of x is $\dfrac{1}{x}$.

97. The expression is the reciprocal of $\dfrac{1}{2x}$ or $2x$.
The opposite of $2x$ is $-2x$.

99. False; the opposite of $-\dfrac{a}{2}$ is $\dfrac{a}{2}$. $-\dfrac{2}{a}$ is the reciprocal of $-\dfrac{a}{2}$.

101. "Taking a test" and "studying for the test" are not commutative, since the order in which they are performed affects the outcome.

103. "Putting on your left shoe" and "putting on your right shoe" are commutative, since the order in which they are performed does not affect the outcome.

105. "Mowing the lawn" and "trimming the hedges" are commutative, since the order in which they are performed does not affect the outcome.

107. "Feeding the dog" and "feeding the cat" are commutative, since the order in which they are performed does not affect the outcome.

109. a. The property illustrated is the commutative property of addition since the order in which they are added changed.

   b. The property illustrated is the commutative property of addition since the order in which they are added changed.

   c. The property illustrated is the associative property of addition since the grouping of addition changed.

111. answers may vary

113. answers may vary

Section 9.3

Practice Problems

1. $5(3x-1)+2=12x+6$
   $15x-5+2=12x+6$
   $15x-3=12x+6$
   $15x-3-12x=12x+6-12x$
   $3x-3=6$
   $3x-3+3=6+3$
   $3x=9$
   $\dfrac{3x}{3}=\dfrac{9}{3}$
   $x=3$

   Check: $5(3x-1)+2=12x+6$
   $5[3(3)-1]+2\overset{?}{=}12(3)+6$
   $5(9-1)+2\overset{?}{=}36+6$
   $5(8)+2\overset{?}{=}42$
   $40+2\overset{?}{=}42$
   $42=42$ True

   The solution is 3.

2. $9(5-x)=-3x$
   $45-9x=-3x$
   $45-9x+9x=-3x+9x$
   $45=6x$
   $\dfrac{45}{6}=\dfrac{6x}{6}$
   $\dfrac{15}{2}=x$

   Check: $9(5-x)=-3x$
   $9\left(5-\dfrac{15}{2}\right)\overset{?}{=}-3\left(\dfrac{15}{2}\right)$
   $9\left(\dfrac{10}{2}-\dfrac{15}{2}\right)\overset{?}{=}-\dfrac{45}{2}$
   $9\left(-\dfrac{5}{2}\right)\overset{?}{=}-\dfrac{45}{2}$
   $-\dfrac{45}{2}=-\dfrac{45}{2}$ True

   The solution is $\dfrac{15}{2}$.

3. $\dfrac{5}{2}x-1=\dfrac{3}{2}x-4$
   $2\left(\dfrac{5}{2}x-1\right)=2\left(\dfrac{3}{2}x-4\right)$
   $5x-2=3x-8$
   $5x-2-3x=3x-8-3x$
   $2x-2=-8$
   $2x-2+2=-8+2$
   $2x=-6$
   $\dfrac{2x}{2}=\dfrac{-6}{2}$
   $x=-3$

   Check: $\dfrac{5}{2}x-1=\dfrac{3}{2}x-4$
   $\dfrac{5}{2}(-3)-1\overset{?}{=}\dfrac{3}{2}(-3)-4$
   $-\dfrac{15}{2}-1\overset{?}{=}-\dfrac{9}{2}-4$
   $-\dfrac{15}{2}-\dfrac{2}{2}\overset{?}{=}-\dfrac{9}{2}-\dfrac{8}{2}$
   $-\dfrac{17}{2}=-\dfrac{17}{2}$ True

   The solution is -3.

4. $\dfrac{3(x-2)}{5}=3x+6$
   $5\cdot\dfrac{3(x-2)}{5}=5(3x+6)$
   $3(x-2)=5(3x+6)$
   $3x-6=15x+30$
   $3x-6-3x=15x+30-3x$
   $-6=12x+30$
   $-6-30=12x+30-30$
   $-36=12x$
   $\dfrac{-36}{12}=\dfrac{12x}{12}$
   $-3=x$

   Check: $\dfrac{3(x-2)}{5}=3x+6$
   $\dfrac{3(-3-2)}{5}\overset{?}{=}3(-3)+6$
   $\dfrac{3(-5)}{5}\overset{?}{=}-9+6$
   $\dfrac{-15}{5}\overset{?}{=}-3$
   $-3=-3$

   The solution is -3.

5.
$$0.06x - 0.10(x-2) = -0.02(8)$$
$$100[0.06x - 0.10(x-2)] = 100[-0.02(8)]$$
$$6x - 10(x-2) = -2(8)$$
$$6x - 10x + 20 = -16$$
$$-4x + 20 = -16$$
$$-4x + 20 - 20 = -16 - 20$$
$$-4x = -36$$
$$\frac{-4x}{-4} = \frac{-36}{-4}$$
$$x = 9$$

To check, replace x with 9 in the original equation. The solution is 9.

6.
$$5(2-x) + 8x = 3(x-6)$$
$$10 - 5x + 8x = 3x - 18$$
$$10 + 3x = 3x - 18$$
$$10 + 3x - 3x = 3x - 18 - 3x$$
$$10 = -18$$

Since the statement $10 = -18$ is false, the equation has no solution.

7.
$$-6(2x+1) - 14 = -10(x+2) - 2x$$
$$-12x - 6 - 14 = -10x - 20 - 2x$$
$$-12x - 20 = -12x - 20$$
$$12x - 12x - 20 = 12x - 12x - 20$$
$$-20 = -20$$

Since $-20 = -20$ is a true statement, every real number is a solution.

Calculator Explorations

1. $2x = 48 + 6x$

2 ✕ −12 =   Display: −24
48 + 6 ✕ −12 =   Display: −24

Since the left side equals the right side, $x = -12$ is a solution.

2. $-3x - 7 = 3x - 1$

−3 ✕ −1 − 7 =   Display: −4
3 ✕ −1 − 1 =   Display: −4

Since the left side equals the right side, $x = -1$ is a solution.

3. $5x - 2.6 = 2(x + 0.8)$

5 ✕ 4.4 − 2.6 =   Display: 19.4
2 (4.4 + 0.8) =   Display: 10.4

Since the left side does not equal the right side, $x = 4.4$ is not a solution.

4. $-1.6x - 3.9 = -6.9x - 25.6$

−1.6 ✕ 5 − 3.9 =   Display: −11.9
−6.9 ✕ 5 − 25.6 =   Display: −60.1

Since the left side does not equal the right side, $x = 5$ is not a solution.

5. $\dfrac{564x}{4} = 200x - 11(649)$

(564 ✕ 121) ÷ 4 =   Display: 17061
200 ✕ 121 − 11 ✕ 649 =   Display: 17061

Since the left side equals the right side, $x = 121$ is a solution.

6. $20(x - 39) = 5x - 432$

20 (23.2 − 39) =   Display: −316
5 ✕ 23.2 − 432 =   Display: −316

Since the left side equals the right side, $x = 23.2$ is a solution.

Vocabulary and Readiness Check

1. $x = -7$ is an <u>equation</u>.

2. $x - 7$ is an <u>expression</u>.

3. $4y - 6 + 9y + 1$ is an <u>expression</u>.

4. $4y - 6 = 9y + 1$ is an <u>equation</u>.

5. $\dfrac{1}{x} - \dfrac{x-1}{8}$ is an <u>expression</u>.

6. $\dfrac{1}{x} - \dfrac{x-1}{8} = 6$ is an <u>equation</u>.

7. $0.1x + 9 = 0.2x$ is an <u>equation</u>.

8. $0.1x^2 + 9y - 0.2x^2$ is an <u>expression</u>.

Exercise Set 9.3

1.
$$-4y + 10 = -2(3y+1)$$
$$-4y + 10 = -6y - 2$$
$$-4y + 10 - 10 = -6y - 2 - 10$$
$$-4y = -6y - 12$$
$$-4y + 6y = -6y - 12 + 6y$$
$$2y = -12$$
$$\frac{2y}{2} = \frac{-12}{2}$$
$$y = -6$$

3.
$$15x - 8 = 10 + 9x$$
$$15x - 8 - 9x = 10 + 9x - 9x$$
$$6x - 8 = 10$$
$$6x - 8 + 8 = 10 + 8$$
$$6x = 18$$
$$\frac{6x}{6} = \frac{18}{6}$$
$$x = 3$$

5.
$$-2(3x - 4) = 2x$$
$$-6x + 8 = 2x$$
$$-6x + 8 + 6x = 2x + 6x$$
$$8 = 8x$$
$$\frac{8}{8} = \frac{8x}{8}$$
$$1 = x$$

7.
$$5(2x - 1) - 2(3x) = 1$$
$$10x - 5 - 6x = 1$$
$$-5 + 4x = 1$$
$$5 - 5 + 4x = 5 + 1$$
$$4x = 6$$
$$\frac{4x}{4} = \frac{6}{4}$$
$$x = \frac{3}{2}$$

9.
$$-6(x - 3) - 26 = -8$$
$$-6x + 18 - 26 = -8$$
$$-6x - 8 = -8$$
$$-6x - 8 + 8 = -8 + 8$$
$$-6x = 0$$
$$\frac{-6x}{-6} = \frac{0}{-6}$$
$$x = 0$$

11.
$$8 - 2(a + 1) = 9 + a$$
$$8 - 2a - 2 = 9 + a$$
$$-2a + 6 = 9 + a$$
$$-2a + 6 - a = 9 + a - a$$
$$-3a + 6 = 9$$
$$-3a + 6 - 6 = 9 - 6$$
$$-3a = 3$$
$$\frac{-3a}{-3} = \frac{3}{-3}$$
$$a = -1$$

13.
$$4x + 3 = -3 + 2x + 14$$
$$4x + 3 = 11 + 2x$$
$$4x + 3 - 2x = 11 + 2x - 2x$$
$$2x + 3 = 11$$
$$2x + 3 - 3 = 11 - 3$$
$$2x = 8$$
$$\frac{2x}{2} = \frac{8}{2}$$
$$x = 4$$

15.
$$-2y - 10 = 5y + 18$$
$$-2y - 10 + 10 = 5y + 18 + 10$$
$$-2y = 5y + 28$$
$$-2y - 5y = 5y + 28 - 5y$$
$$-7y = 28$$
$$\frac{-7y}{-7} = \frac{28}{-7}$$
$$y = -4$$

17.
$$\frac{2}{3}x + \frac{4}{3} = -\frac{2}{3}$$
$$3\left(\frac{2}{3}x + \frac{4}{3}\right) = 3\left(-\frac{2}{3}\right)$$
$$2x + 4 = -2$$
$$2x + 4 - 4 = -2 - 4$$
$$2x = -6$$
$$\frac{2x}{2} = \frac{-6}{2}$$
$$x = -3$$

19.
$$\frac{3}{4}x - \frac{1}{2} = 1$$
$$4\left(\frac{3}{4}x - \frac{1}{2}\right) = 4(1)$$
$$3x - 2 = 4$$
$$3x - 2 + 2 = 4 + 2$$
$$3x = 6$$
$$\frac{3x}{3} = \frac{6}{3}$$
$$x = 2$$

21.
$$0.50x + 0.15(70) = 35.5$$
$$50x + 15(70) = 3550$$
$$50x + 1050 = 3550$$
$$50x + 1050 - 1050 = 3550 - 1050$$
$$50x = 2500$$
$$\frac{50x}{50} = \frac{2500}{50}$$
$$x = 50$$

23.
$$\frac{2(x+1)}{4} = 3x-2$$
$$4\left[\frac{2(x+1)}{4}\right] = 4(3x-2)$$
$$2(x+1) = 4(3x-2)$$
$$2x+2 = 12x-8$$
$$2x+2+8 = 12x-8+8$$
$$2x+10 = 12x$$
$$2x+10-2x = 12x-2x$$
$$10 = 10x$$
$$\frac{10}{10} = \frac{10x}{10}$$
$$1 = x$$

25.
$$x+\frac{7}{6} = 2x-\frac{7}{6}$$
$$6\left(x+\frac{7}{6}\right) = 6\left(2x-\frac{7}{6}\right)$$
$$6x+7 = 12x-7$$
$$6x+7+7 = 12x-7+7$$
$$6x+14 = 12x$$
$$6x+14-6x = 12x-6x$$
$$14 = 6x$$
$$\frac{14}{6} = \frac{6x}{6}$$
$$\frac{7}{3} = x$$

27.
$$0.12(y-6)+0.06y = 0.08y-0.7$$
$$12(y-6)+6y = 8y-70$$
$$12y-72+6y = 8y-70$$
$$18y-72 = 8y-70$$
$$18y-72-8y = 8y-70-8y$$
$$10y-72 = -70$$
$$10y-72+72 = -70+72$$
$$10y = 2$$
$$\frac{10y}{10} = \frac{2}{10}$$
$$y = 0.2$$

29. $4(3x+2) = 12x+8$
$$12x+8 = 12x+8$$
Since both sides of the equation are identical, the equation is an identity and every real number is a solution.

31.
$$\frac{x}{4}+1 = \frac{x}{4}$$
$$\frac{x}{4}+1-\frac{x}{4} = \frac{x}{4}-\frac{x}{4}$$
$$1 = 0$$
Since the statement $1 = 0$ is false, the equation has no solution.

33.
$$3x-7 = 3(x+1)$$
$$3x-7 = 3x+3$$
$$3x-7-3x = 3x+3-3x$$
$$-7 = 3$$
Since the statement $-7 = 3$ is false, the equation has no solution.

35. $-2(6x-5)+4 = -12x+14$
$$-12x+10+4 = -12x+14$$
$$-12x+14 = -12x+14$$
Since both sides of the equation are identical, the equation is an identity and every real number is a solution.

37.
$$\frac{6(3-z)}{5} = -z$$
$$5 \cdot \frac{6(3-z)}{5} = 5(-z)$$
$$6(3-z) = -5z$$
$$18-6z = -5z$$
$$18-6z+6z = -5z+6z$$
$$18 = z$$

39. $-3(2t-5)+2t = 5t-4$
$$-6t+15+2t = 5t-4$$
$$-4t+15 = 5t-4$$
$$-4t+15+4t = 5t-4+4t$$
$$15 = 9t-4$$
$$15+4 = 9t-4+4$$
$$19 = 9t$$
$$\frac{19}{9} = \frac{9t}{9}$$
$$\frac{19}{9} = t$$

41.
$$5y + 2(y-6) = 4(y+1) - 2$$
$$5y + 2y - 12 = 4y + 4 - 2$$
$$7y - 12 = 4y + 2$$
$$7y - 12 + 12 = 4y + 2 + 12$$
$$7y = 4y + 14$$
$$7y - 4y = 4y + 14 - 4y$$
$$3y = 14$$
$$\frac{3y}{3} = \frac{14}{3}$$
$$y = \frac{14}{3}$$

43.
$$\frac{3(x-5)}{2} = \frac{2(x+5)}{3}$$
$$6\left[\frac{3(x-5)}{2}\right] = 6\left[\frac{2(x+5)}{3}\right]$$
$$9(x-5) = 4(x+5)$$
$$9x - 45 = 4x + 20$$
$$9x - 45 + 45 = 4x + 20 + 45$$
$$9x = 4x + 65$$
$$9x - 4x = 4x + 65 - 4x$$
$$5x = 65$$
$$\frac{5x}{5} = \frac{65}{5}$$
$$x = 13$$

45.
$$0.7x - 2.3 = 0.5$$
$$7x - 23 = 5$$
$$7x - 23 + 23 = 5 + 23$$
$$7x = 28$$
$$\frac{7x}{7} = \frac{28}{7}$$
$$x = 4$$

47.
$$5x - 5 = 2(x+1) + 3x - 7$$
$$5x - 5 = 2x + 2 + 3x - 7$$
$$5x - 5 = 5x - 5$$
Since both sides of the equation are identical, the equation is an identity and every real number is a solution.

49.
$$4(2n+1) = 3(6n+3) + 1$$
$$8n + 4 = 18n + 9 + 1$$
$$8n + 4 = 18n + 10$$
$$8n + 4 - 10 = 18n + 10 - 10$$
$$8n - 6 = 18n$$
$$8n - 6 - 8n = 18n - 8n$$
$$-6 = 10n$$
$$\frac{-6}{10} = \frac{10n}{10}$$
$$-\frac{3}{5} = n$$

51.
$$x + \frac{5}{4} = \frac{3}{4}x$$
$$4\left(x + \frac{5}{4}\right) = 4\left(\frac{3}{4}x\right)$$
$$4x + 5 = 3x$$
$$4x + 5 - 4x = 3x - 4x$$
$$5 = -x$$
$$\frac{5}{-1} = \frac{-x}{-1}$$
$$-5 = x$$

53.
$$\frac{x}{2} - 1 = \frac{x}{5} + 2$$
$$10\left(\frac{x}{2} - 1\right) = 10\left(\frac{x}{5} + 2\right)$$
$$5x - 10 = 2x + 20$$
$$5x - 10 + 10 = 2x + 20 + 10$$
$$5x = 2x + 30$$
$$5x - 2x = 2x + 30 - 2x$$
$$3x = 30$$
$$\frac{3x}{3} = \frac{30}{3}$$
$$x = 10$$

55.
$$2(x+3) - 5 = 5x - 3(1+x)$$
$$2x + 6 - 5 = 5x - 3 - 3x$$
$$2x + 1 = 2x - 3$$
$$2x + 1 - 2x = 2x - 3 - 2x$$
$$1 = -3$$
Since the statement $1 = -3$ is false, the equation has no solution.

57.
$$0.06 - 0.01(x+1) = -0.02(2-x)$$
$$6 - 1(x+1) = -2(2-x)$$
$$6 - x - 1 = -4 + 2x$$
$$5 - x = -4 + 2x$$
$$5 - x + x = -4 + 2x + x$$
$$5 = -4 + 3x$$
$$5 + 4 = -4 + 3x + 4$$
$$9 = 3x$$
$$\frac{9}{3} = \frac{3x}{3}$$
$$3 = x$$

59.
$$\frac{9}{2} + \frac{5}{2}y = 2y - 4$$
$$2\left(\frac{9}{2} + \frac{5}{2}y\right) = 2(2y - 4)$$
$$9 + 5y = 4y - 8$$
$$9 + 5y - 4y = 4y - 8 - 4y$$
$$9 + y = -8$$
$$9 + y - 9 = -8 - 9$$
$$y = -17$$

61. The perimeter is the sum of the lengths of the sides.
$$x + (2x - 3) + (3x - 5) = x + 2x - 3 + 3x - 5$$
$$= 6x - 8$$
The perimeter is $(6x - 8)$ meters.

63. A number subtracted from -8 is $-8 - x$.

65. The sum of -3 and twice a number is $-3 + 2x$.

67. The product of 9 and the sum of a number and 20 is $9(x + 20)$.

69. a. Since both sides of the equation are identical, the equation is an identity and every real number is a solution.

    b. answers may vary

    c. answers may vary

71. $5x + 1 = 5x + 1$
Since both sides of the equation are identical, the equation is an identity and every real number is a solution. The choice is a.

73.
$$2x - 6x - 10 = -4x + 3 - 10$$
$$-4x - 10 = -4x - 7$$
$$-4x - 10 + 4x = -4x - 7 + 4x$$
$$-10 = -7$$
Since the statement $-10 = -7$ is false, the equation has no solution. The choice is b.

75.
$$9x - 20 = 8x - 20$$
$$9x - 20 - 8x = 8x - 20 - 8x$$
$$x - 20 = -20$$
$$x - 20 + 20 = -20 + 20$$
$$x = 0$$
The choice is c.

77. answers may vary

79. a. The perimeter is the sum of the lengths of the sides.
$$x + x + x + 2x + 2x = 28$$

b.
$$x + x + x + 2x + 2x = 28$$
$$7x = 28$$
$$\frac{7x}{7} = \frac{28}{7}$$
$$x = 4$$

c. The sides of length x are 4 cm and the sides of length $2x$ are $2(4) = 8$ cm.

81. answers may vary

83.
$$1000(7x - 10) = 50(412 + 100x)$$
$$7000x - 10,000 = 20,600 + 5000x$$
$$7000x - 10,000 - 5000x = 20,600 + 5000x - 5000x$$
$$2000x - 10,000 = 20,600$$
$$2000x - 10,000 + 10,000 = 20,600 + 10,000$$
$$2000x = 30,600$$
$$\frac{2000x}{2000} = \frac{30,600}{2000}$$
$$x = 15.3$$

85.
$$0.035x + 5.112 = 0.010x + 5.107$$
$$35x + 5112 = 10x + 5107$$
$$35x + 5112 - 10x = 10x + 5107 - 10x$$
$$25x + 5112 = 5107$$
$$25x + 5112 - 5112 = 5107 - 5112$$
$$25x = -5$$
$$\frac{25x}{25} = \frac{-5}{25}$$
$$x = -\frac{1}{5}$$
$$x = -0.2$$

Integrated Review

1. 0 is a whole number, an integer, a rational number, and a real number.

2. 143 is a natural number, a whole number, an integer, a rational number, and a real number.

3. $\frac{3}{8}$ is a rational number and a real number.

4. 1 is a natural number, a whole number, an integer, a rational number, and a real number.

5. -13 is an integer, a rational number, and a real number.

6. $\dfrac{9}{10}$ is a rational number and a real number.

7. $-\dfrac{1}{9}$ is a rational number and a real number.

8. $\sqrt{5}$ is an irrational number and a real number.

9. $\begin{aligned} 7(d-3)+10 &= 7\cdot d - 7\cdot 3 + 10 \\ &= 7d - 21 + 10 \\ &= 7d - 11 \end{aligned}$

10. $\begin{aligned} 9(z+7)-15 &= 9\cdot z + 9\cdot 7 - 15 \\ &= 9z + 63 - 15 \\ &= 9z + 48 \end{aligned}$

11. $\begin{aligned} -4(3y-4)+12y &= -4\cdot 3y - 4(-4) + 12y \\ &= -12y + 16 + 12y \\ &= -12y + 12y + 16 \\ &= 16 \end{aligned}$

12. $\begin{aligned} -3(2x+5)-6x &= -3\cdot 2x - 3\cdot 5 - 6x \\ &= -6x - 15 - 6x \\ &= -6x - 6x - 15 \\ &= -12x - 15 \end{aligned}$

13. $\begin{aligned} 2x - 7 &= 6x - 27 \\ 2x - 7 + 7 &= 6x - 27 + 7 \\ 2x &= 6x - 20 \\ 2x - 6x &= 6x - 20 - 6x \\ -4x &= -20 \\ \frac{-4x}{-4} &= \frac{-20}{-4} \\ x &= 5 \end{aligned}$

14. $\begin{aligned} 3 + 8y &= 3y - 2 \\ 3 + 8y - 3y &= 3y - 2 - 3y \\ 3 + 5y &= -2 \\ -3 + 3 + 5y &= -3 - 2 \\ 5y &= -5 \\ \frac{5y}{5} &= \frac{-5}{5} \\ y &= -1 \end{aligned}$

15. $\begin{aligned} -3a + 6 + 5a &= 7a - 8a \\ 6 + 2a &= -a \\ 6 + 2a - 2a &= -a - 2a \\ 6 &= -3a \\ \frac{6}{-3} &= \frac{-3a}{-3} \\ -2 &= a \end{aligned}$

16. $\begin{aligned} 4b - 8 - b &= 10b - 3b \\ 3b - 8 &= 7b \\ -3b + 3b - 8 &= -3b + 7b \\ -8 &= 4b \\ \frac{-8}{4} &= \frac{4b}{4} \\ -2 &= b \end{aligned}$

17. $\begin{aligned} -\frac{2}{3}x &= \frac{5}{9} \\ -\frac{3}{2}\cdot\left(-\frac{2}{3}x\right) &= -\frac{3}{2}\cdot\frac{5}{9} \\ x &= -\frac{15}{18} \\ x &= -\frac{5}{6} \end{aligned}$

18. $\begin{aligned} -\frac{3}{8}y &= -\frac{1}{16} \\ -\frac{8}{3}\cdot\left(-\frac{3}{8}y\right) &= -\frac{8}{3}\cdot\left(-\frac{1}{16}\right) \\ y &= \frac{1}{6} \end{aligned}$

19. $\begin{aligned} 10 &= -6n + 16 \\ 10 - 16 &= -6n + 16 - 16 \\ -6 &= -6n \\ \frac{-6}{-6} &= \frac{-6n}{-6} \\ 1 &= n \end{aligned}$

20. $\begin{aligned} -5 &= -2m + 7 \\ -5 - 7 &= -2m + 7 - 7 \\ -12 &= -2m \\ \frac{-12}{-2} &= \frac{-2m}{-2} \\ 6 &= m \end{aligned}$

21. $3(5c-1)-2=13c+3$
$$15c-3-2=13c+3$$
$$15c-5=13c+3$$
$$15c-5+5=13c+3+5$$
$$15c=13c+8$$
$$15c-13c=13c+8-13c$$
$$2c=8$$
$$\frac{2c}{2}=\frac{8}{2}$$
$$c=4$$

22. $4(3t+4)-20=3+5t$
$$12t+16-20=3+5t$$
$$12t-4=3+5t$$
$$12t-4-5t=3+5t-5t$$
$$7t-4=3$$
$$7t-4+4=3+4$$
$$7t=7$$
$$\frac{7t}{7}=\frac{7}{7}$$
$$t=1$$

23. $\dfrac{2(z+3)}{3}=5-z$
$$3\left[\frac{2(z+3)}{3}\right]=3(5-z)$$
$$2(z+3)=3(5-z)$$
$$2z+6=15-3z$$
$$2z+6+3z=15-3z+3z$$
$$6+5z=15$$
$$6+5z-6=15-6$$
$$5z=9$$
$$\frac{5z}{5}=\frac{9}{5}$$
$$z=\frac{9}{5}$$

24. $\dfrac{3(w+2)}{4}=2w+3$
$$4\left[\frac{3(w+2)}{4}\right]=4(2w+3)$$
$$3(w+2)=4(2w+3)$$
$$3w+6=8w+12$$
$$3w+6-6=8w+12-6$$
$$3w=8w+6$$
$$3w-8w=8w+6-8w$$
$$-5w=6$$
$$\frac{-5w}{-5}=\frac{6}{-5}$$
$$w=-\frac{6}{5}$$

25. $-2(2x-5)=-3x+7-x+3$
$$-4x+10=-4x+10$$
Since both sides of the equation are identical, the equation is an identity and every real number is a solution.

26. $-4(5x-2)=-12x+4-8x+4$
$$-20x+8=-20x+8$$
Since both sides of the equation are identical, the equation is an identity and every real number is a solution.

27. $0.02(6t-3)=0.04(t-2)+0.02$
$$2(6t-3)=4(t-2)+2$$
$$12t-6=4t-8+2$$
$$12t-6=4t-6$$
$$12t-6-4t=4t-6-4t$$
$$8t-6=-6$$
$$8t-6+6=-6+6$$
$$8t=0$$
$$\frac{8t}{8}=\frac{0}{8}$$
$$t=0$$

28. $0.03(m+7)=0.02(5-m)+0.03$
$$3(m+7)=2(5-m)+3$$
$$3m+21=10-2m+3$$
$$3m+21=13-2m$$
$$3m+21+2m=13-2m+2m$$
$$5m+21=13$$
$$5m+21-21=13-21$$
$$5m=-8$$
$$\frac{5m}{5}=\frac{-8}{5}$$
$$m=-1.6$$

29.
$$-3y = \frac{4(y-1)}{5}$$
$$5(-3y) = 5\left[\frac{4(y-1)}{5}\right]$$
$$-15y = 4(y-1)$$
$$-15y = 4y-4$$
$$-15y-4y = 4y-4-4y$$
$$-19y = -4$$
$$\frac{-19y}{-19} = \frac{-4}{-19}$$
$$y = \frac{4}{19}$$

30.
$$-4x = \frac{5(1-x)}{6}$$
$$6(-4x) = 6 \cdot \frac{5(1-x)}{6}$$
$$-24x = 5(1-x)$$
$$-24x = 5-5x$$
$$-24x+5x = 5-5x+5x$$
$$-19x = 5$$
$$\frac{-19x}{-19} = \frac{5}{-19}$$
$$x = -\frac{5}{19}$$

31.
$$\frac{5}{3}x - \frac{7}{3} = x$$
$$3\left(\frac{5}{3}x - \frac{7}{3}\right) = 3x$$
$$5x-7 = 3x$$
$$-5x+5x-7 = -5x+3x$$
$$-7 = -2x$$
$$\frac{-7}{-2} = \frac{-2x}{-2}$$
$$\frac{7}{2} = x$$

32.
$$\frac{7}{5}n + \frac{3}{5} = -n$$
$$5\left(\frac{7}{5}n + \frac{3}{5}\right) = 5(-n)$$
$$7n+3 = -5n$$
$$-7n+7n+3 = -7n-5n$$
$$3 = -12n$$
$$\frac{3}{-12} = \frac{-12n}{-12}$$
$$-\frac{1}{4} = n$$

Section 9.4

Practice Problems

1. Let x represent the number.
$$3x-6 = 2x+3$$
$$3x-6-2x = 2x+3-2x$$
$$x-6 = 3$$
$$x-6+6 = 3+6$$
$$x = 9$$
The number is 9.

2. Let x represent the number.
$$3(x-5) = 2x-3$$
$$3x-15 = 2x-3$$
$$3x-15-2x = 2x-3-2x$$
$$x-15 = -3$$
$$x-15+15 = -3+15$$
$$x = 12$$
The number is 12.

3. Let x represent the length of the shorter piece. Then $5x$ represents the length of the longer piece. Their sum is 18 feet.
$$x+5x = 18$$
$$6x = 18$$
$$\frac{6x}{6} = \frac{18}{6}$$
$$x = 3$$
The shorter piece is 3 feet and the longer piece is $5(3) = 15$ feet.

4. Let x represent the number of votes for Texas. Then $x + 21$ represents the number of votes for California. Their sum is 89.
$$x+x+21 = 89$$
$$2x+21 = 89$$
$$2x+21-21 = 89-21$$
$$2x = 68$$
$$\frac{2x}{2} = \frac{68}{2}$$
$$x = 34$$
Texas has 34 electoral votes and California has $34 + 21 = 55$ electoral votes.

5. Let x represent the number of miles driven. The cost for x miles is $0.15x$. The daily cost is \$28.

$$0.15x + 28 = 52$$
$$0.15x + 28 - 28 = 52 - 28$$
$$0.15x = 24$$
$$\frac{0.15x}{0.15} = \frac{24}{0.15}$$
$$x = 160$$

You drove 160 miles.

6. Let x represent the measure of the smallest angle. Then $2x$ represents the measure of the second angle and $3x$ represents the measure of the third angle. The sum of the measures of the angles of a triangle equals 180.

$$x + 2x + 3x = 180$$
$$6x = 180$$
$$\frac{6x}{6} = \frac{180}{6}$$
$$x = 30$$

If $x = 30$, then $2x = 2(30) = 60$ and $3x = 3(30) = 90$.

The smallest is 30°, second is 60°, and third is 90°.

7. If x is the first even integer, then $x + 2$ and $x + 4$ are the next two even integers.

$$x + x + 2 + x + 4 = 144$$
$$3x + 6 = 144$$
$$3x + 6 - 6 = 144 - 6$$
$$3x = 138$$
$$\frac{3x}{3} = \frac{138}{3}$$
$$x = 46$$

If $x = 46$, then $x + 2 = 48$ and $x + 4 = 50$. The integers are 46, 48, 50.

Vocabulary and Readiness Check

1. If x is the number, then "double the number" is $2x$, and "double the number, decreased by 31" is $2x - 31$.

2. If x is the number, then "three times the number" is $3x$, and "three times the number, increased by 17" is $3x + 17$.

3. If x is the number, then "the sum of the number and 5" is $x + 5$, and "twice the sum of the number and 5" is $2(x + 5)$.

4. If x is the number, then "the difference of the number and 11" is $x - 11$, and "seven times the difference of the number and 11" is $7(x - 11)$.

5. If y is the number, then "the difference of 20 and the number" is $20 - y$, and "the difference of 20 and the number, divided by 3" is $\dfrac{20 - y}{3}$ or $(20 - y) \div 3$.

6. If y is the number, then "the sum of -10 and the number" is $-10 + y$, and "the sum of -10 and the number, divided by 9" is $\dfrac{(-10 + y)}{9}$ or $(-10 + y) \div 9$.

Exercise Set 9.4

1.
$$2x + 7 = x + 6$$
$$2x + 7 - x = x + 6 - x$$
$$x + 7 = 6$$
$$x + 7 - 7 = 6 - 7$$
$$x = -1$$
The number is -1.

3.
$$3x - 6 = 2x + 8$$
$$3x - 6 - 2x = 2x + 8 - 2x$$
$$x - 6 = 8$$
$$x - 6 + 6 = 8 + 6$$
$$x = 14$$
The number is 14.

5.
$$2(x - 8) = 3(x + 3)$$
$$2x - 16 = 3x + 9$$
$$2x - 16 - 2x = 3x + 9 - 2x$$
$$-16 = x + 9$$
$$-16 - 9 = x + 9 - 9$$
$$-25 = x$$
The number is -25.

7.
$$2x(3) = 5x - \frac{3}{4}$$
$$6x = 5x - \frac{3}{4}$$
$$6x - 5x = 5x - \frac{3}{4} - 5x$$
$$x = -\frac{3}{4}$$
The number is $-\dfrac{3}{4}$.

9. The sum of the three lengths is 25 inches.
$$x + 2x + 1 + 5x = 25$$
$$1 + 8x = 25$$
$$1 + 8x - 1 = 25 - 1$$
$$8x = 24$$
$$\frac{8x}{8} = \frac{24}{8}$$
$$x = 3$$
$2x = 2(3) = 6$
$1 + 5x = 1 + 5(3) = 1 + 15 = 16$
The lengths are 3 inches, 6 inches, and 16 inches.

11. Let x be the length of the first piece. Then the second piece is $2x$ and the third piece is $5x$. The sum of the lengths is 40 inches.
$$x + 2x + 5x = 40$$
$$8x = 40$$
$$\frac{8x}{8} = \frac{40}{8}$$
$$x = 5$$
$2x = 2(5) = 10$
$5x = 5(5) = 25$
The 1st piece is 5 inches, 2nd piece is 10 inches, and 3rd piece is 25 inches.

13. Let x represent the number of millions of pounds of pecans produced in Texas. Then $x + 15$ represents the number of millions of pounds of pecans produced in New Mexico.
$$x + x + 15 = 75$$
$$2x + 15 = 75$$
$$2x + 15 - 15 = 75 - 15$$
$$2x = 60$$
$$\frac{2x}{2} = \frac{60}{2}$$
$$x = 30$$
$x + 15 = 30 + 15 = 45$
Texas produced 30 million pounds of pecans and New Mexico produced 45 million pounds.

15. Let x be the number of miles. Then the cost for x miles is $0.29x$. Each day costs $24.95.
$$0.29x + 2(24.95) = 100$$
$$0.29x + 49.9 = 100$$
$$0.29x + 49.9 - 49.9 = 100 - 49.9$$
$$0.29x = 50.1$$
$$\frac{0.29x}{0.29} = \frac{50.1}{0.29}$$
$$x \approx 172.8$$
You can drive 172 whole miles on a $100 budget.

17. Let x be the number of miles. Then the total fare is $3 + 0.8x + 4.5$.
$$3 + 0.8x + 4.5 = 27.5$$
$$30 + 8x + 45 = 275$$
$$8x + 75 = 275$$
$$8x + 75 - 75 = 275 - 75$$
$$8x = 200$$
$$\frac{8x}{8} = \frac{200}{8}$$
$$x = 25$$
You can travel 25 miles from the airport by taxi for $27.50.

19. Let x be the measure of each of the two equal angles. Then $2x + 30$ is the measure of the third angle. Their sum is $180°$.
$$x + x + 2x + 30 = 180$$
$$4x + 30 = 180$$
$$4x + 30 - 30 = 180 - 30$$
$$4x = 150$$
$$\frac{4x}{4} = \frac{150}{4}$$
$$x = 37.5$$
$2x + 30 = 2(37.5) + 30 = 75 + 30 = 105$
The 1st angle measures $37.5°$, the 2nd angle measures $37.5°$, and the 3rd angle measures $105°$.

21. Angles A and D both measure $x°$, while angles C and B both measure $(2x)°$. The sum of the angle measures is $360°$.
$$x + 2x + x + 2x = 360$$
$$6x = 360$$
$$\frac{6x}{6} = \frac{360}{6}$$
$$x = 60$$
$2x = 2(60) = 120$
Angles A and D measure $60°$; angles B and C measure $120°$.

	First Integer	Next Integers			Indicated Sum
23.	x	$x+1$	$x+2$		$x + (x + 1) + (x + 2) = 3x + 3$
25.	x	$x+2$	$x+4$		$x + (x + 4) = 2x + 4$
27.	x	$x+1$	$x+2$	$x+3$	$x + (x + 1) + (x + 2) + (x + 3) = 4x + 6$
29.	x	$x+2$	$x+4$		$(x + 2) + (x + 4) = 2x + 6$

31. If x is the first integer, the next consecutive integer is $x + 1$.
$$x + x + 1 = 469$$
$$2x + 1 = 469$$
$$2x + 1 - 1 = 469 - 1$$
$$2x = 468$$
$$\frac{2x}{2} = \frac{468}{2}$$
$$x = 234$$
The page numbers are 234 and $234 + 1 = 235$.

33. If x is the first integer, the next two consecutive integers are $x + 1$ and $x + 2$.
$$x + x + 1 + x + 2 = 99$$
$$3x + 3 = 99$$
$$3x + 3 - 3 = 99 - 3$$
$$3x = 96$$
$$\frac{3x}{3} = \frac{96}{3}$$
$$x = 32$$
The code for Belgium is 32, France is $32 + 1 = 33$, and Spain is $32 + 2 = 34$.

35. Let x be the length of the shorter piece. Then $2x + 2$ is the length of the longer piece. The measures sum to 17 feet.
$$x + 2x + 2 = 17$$
$$3x + 2 = 17$$
$$3x + 2 - 2 = 17 - 2$$
$$3x = 5$$
$$\frac{3x}{3} = \frac{15}{3}$$
$$x = 5$$
$2x + 2 = 2(5) + 2 = 10 + 2 = 12$
The pieces measure 5 feet and 12 feet.

37. Let x represent the speed of the TGV. Then the speed of the Maglev is $x + 3.8$.
$$x + x + 3.8 = 718.2$$
$$2x + 3.8 = 718.2$$
$$2x + 3.8 - 3.8 = 718.2 - 3.8$$
$$2x = 714.4$$
$$\frac{2x}{2} = \frac{714.4}{2}$$
$$x = 357.2$$
$x + 3.8 = 357.2 + 3.8 = 361$
The speed of the TGV is 357.2 miles per hour and the speed of the Maglev is 361 miles per hour.

39. Let x be the measure of the smaller angle. Then the larger angle measures $3x + 8$. Their sum is $180°$.

$$x + 3x + 8 = 180$$
$$4x + 8 = 180$$
$$4x + 8 - 8 = 180 - 8$$
$$4x = 172$$
$$\frac{4x}{4} = \frac{172}{4}$$
$$x = 43$$

$3x + 8 = 3(43) + 8 = 129 + 8 = 137$
The angles measure $43°$ and $137°$.

41. Let x be the first even integer. Then the next two consecutive even integers are $x + 2$ and $x + 4$. The sum of the measures of the angles of a triangle is $180°$.

$$x + x + 2 + x + 4 = 180$$
$$3x + 6 = 180$$
$$3x + 6 - 6 = 180 - 6$$
$$3x = 174$$
$$\frac{3x}{3} = \frac{174}{3}$$
$$x = 58$$

$x + 2 = 58 + 2 = 60$
$x + 4 = 58 + 4 = 62$
The angles measure $58°$, $60°$, and $62°$.

43.
$$\frac{1}{5} + 2x = 3x - \frac{4}{5}$$
$$\frac{1}{5} + 2x - 2x = 3x - \frac{4}{5} - 2x$$
$$\frac{1}{5} = x - \frac{4}{5}$$
$$\frac{1}{5} + \frac{4}{5} = x - \frac{4}{5} + \frac{4}{5}$$
$$\frac{5}{5} = x$$
$$1 = x$$

The number is 1.

45. Let x be the number of miles. Then the charge for driving x miles in one day is $39 + 0.2x$.

$$39 + 0.2x = 95$$
$$390 + 2x = 950$$
$$390 + 2x - 390 = 950 - 390$$
$$2x = 560$$
$$\frac{2x}{2} = \frac{560}{2}$$
$$x = 280$$

You drove 280 miles.

47. Let x represent the number of points scored by Penn State. Then USC scored $x + 14$ points. Their combined scores totaled 62 points.

$$x + x + 14 = 62$$
$$2x + 14 = 62$$
$$2x + 14 - 14 = 62 - 14$$
$$2x = 48$$
$$\frac{2x}{2} = \frac{48}{2}$$
$$x = 24$$

$x + 14 = 24 + 14 = 38$
Penn State scored 24 points and USC scored 38 points.

49. Let x represent the number of counties in Montana. Then $x + 2$ represents the number of counties in California.

$$x + x + 2 = 114$$
$$2x + 2 = 114$$
$$2x + 2 - 2 = 114 - 2$$
$$2x = 112$$
$$\frac{2x}{2} = \frac{112}{2}$$
$$x = 56$$

$x + 2 = 56 + 2 = 58$
Montana has 56 counties and California has 58 counties.

51. Let x represent the number of moons for Neptune. Then $x + 13$ represents the number of moons for Uranus and $2x + 2$ represents the number of moons for Saturn. The total is 47.

$$x + x + 13 + 2x + 2 = 47$$
$$4x + 15 = 47$$
$$4x + 15 - 15 = 47 - 15$$
$$4x = 32$$
$$\frac{4x}{4} = \frac{32}{4}$$
$$x = 8$$

$x + 13 = 8 + 13 = 21$
$2x + 2 = 2(8) + 2 = 16 + 2 = 18$
Neptune has 8 moons, Uranus has 21 moons, and Saturn has 18 moons.

53.
$$3(x + 5) = 2x - 1$$
$$3x + 15 = 2x - 1$$
$$3x + 15 - 2x = 2x - 1 - 2x$$
$$x + 15 = -1$$
$$x + 15 - 15 = -1 - 15$$
$$x = -16$$

The number is -16.

55. Let x represent the area of the Gobi Desert, in square miles. Then $7x$ represents the area of the Sahara Desert.
$$x + 7x = 4,000,000$$
$$8x = 4,000,000$$
$$\frac{8x}{8} = \frac{4,000,000}{8}$$
$$x = 500,000$$
$7x = 7(500,000) = 3,500,000$
The Gobi Desert's area is 500,000 square miles and the Sahara Desert's area is 3,500,000 square miles.

57. Let x represent the number of gold medals won by Australia. Then Germany won $x + 1$ gold medals and Korea won $x + 2$ gold medals.
$$x + x + 1 + x + 2 = 21$$
$$3x + 3 = 21$$
$$3x + 3 - 3 = 21 - 3$$
$$3x = 18$$
$$\frac{3x}{3} = \frac{18}{3}$$
$$x = 6$$
$x + 1 = 6 + 1 = 7$
$x + 2 = 6 + 2 = 8$
Australia won 6 gold medals, Germany won 7, and Korea won 8.

59. Let x be the number of votes for Jim Martin. Then $x + 315,217$ is the number of votes for Saxby Chambliss.
$$x + x + 315,217 = 2,126,491$$
$$2x + 315,217 = 2,126,491$$
$$2x + 315,217 - 315,217 = 2,126,491 - 315,217$$
$$2x = 1,811,274$$
$$\frac{2x}{2} = \frac{1,811,274}{2}$$
$$x = 905,637$$
$x + 315,217 = 905,637 + 315,217 = 1,220,854$
Martin received 905,637 votes and Chambliss received 1,220,854 votes.

61. Let x be the measure of the two equal angles. Then $x + 76.5$ is the measure of the third angle.
$$x + x + x + 76.5 = 180$$
$$3x + 76.5 = 180$$
$$3x + 76.5 - 76.5 = 180 - 76.5$$
$$3x = 103.5$$
$$\frac{3x}{3} = \frac{103.5}{3}$$
$$x = 34.5$$
$x + 76.5 = 34.5 + 76.5 = 111$
The three angles measure 34.5°, 34.5°, and 111°.

63. The tallest bar represents the amount spent by Illinois, so Illinois spends the most on tourism.

65. Let x be the amount spent by Florida. Then $x + 2.2$ is the amount spent by Texas.
$$x + x + 2.2 = 56.6$$
$$2x + 2.2 = 56.6$$
$$2x + 2.2 - 2.2 = 56.6 - 2.2$$
$$2x = 54.4$$
$$\frac{2x}{2} = \frac{54.4}{2}$$
$$x = 27.2$$
$x + 2.2 = 27.2 + 2.2 = 29.4$
Florida spent $27.2 million and Texas spent $29.4 million.

67. answers may vary

69. Replace W by 7 and L by 10.
$2W + 2L = 2(7) + 2(10) = 14 + 20 = 34$

71. Replace r by 15.
$\pi r^2 = \pi(15)^2 = \pi(225) = 225\pi$

73. Let x represent the width. Then $1.6x$ represents the length. The perimeter is
$2 \cdot \text{length} + 2 \cdot \text{width}$.
$$2(1.6x) + 2x = 78$$
$$3.2x + 2x = 78$$
$$5.2x = 78$$
$$\frac{5.2x}{5.2} = \frac{78}{5.2}$$
$$x = 15$$
$1.6x = 1.6(15) = 24$
The dimensions of the garden are 15 feet by 24 feet.

75. 90 chirps every minute is $\dfrac{90 \text{ chirps}}{1 \text{ min}}$. There are 60 minutes in one hour.
$\dfrac{90 \text{ chirps}}{1 \text{ min}} \cdot 60 \text{ min} = 5400 \text{ chirps}$
At this rate, there are 5400 chirps each hour.
$24 \cdot 5400 = 129,600$
There are 129,600 chirps in one 24-hour day.
$365 \cdot 129,600 = 47,304,000$
There are 47,304,000 chirps in one year.

77. answers may vary

79. answers may vary

81. Measurements may vary. Rectangle (c) best approximates the shape of the golden rectangle.

326

Section 9.5

Practice Problems

1. Use $d = rt$ when $d = 1180$ and $r = 50$.

$$d = rt$$
$$1180 = 50t$$
$$\frac{1180}{50} = \frac{50t}{50}$$
$$23.6 = t$$

They will spend 23.6 hours driving.

2. Use $A = lw$ when $w = 18$.

$$A = lw$$
$$450 = l \cdot 18$$
$$\frac{450}{18} = \frac{18l}{18}$$
$$25 = l$$

The length of the deck is 25 feet.

3. Use $F = \frac{9}{5}C + 32$ with $C = 5$.

$$F = \frac{9}{5}C + 32$$
$$F = \frac{9}{5} \cdot 5 + 32$$
$$F = 9 + 32$$
$$F = 41$$

Thus, 5°C is equivalent to 41°F.

4. Let x be the width. Then $4x + 1$ is the length. The perimeter is 52 meters.

$$P = 2l + 2w$$
$$52 = 2(4x + 1) + 2x$$
$$52 = 8x + 2 + 2x$$
$$52 = 10x + 2$$
$$52 - 2 = 10x + 2 - 2$$
$$50 = 10x$$
$$\frac{50}{10} = \frac{10x}{10}$$
$$5 = x$$

$4x + 1 = 4(5) + 1 = 20 + 1 = 21$
The width is 5 meters and the length is 21 meters.

5.
$$C = 2\pi r$$
$$\frac{C}{2\pi} = \frac{2\pi r}{2\pi}$$
$$\frac{C}{2\pi} = r \text{ or } r = \frac{C}{2\pi}$$

6.
$$P = 2l + 2w$$
$$P - 2w = 2l + 2w - 2w$$
$$P - 2w = 2l$$
$$\frac{P - 2w}{2} = \frac{2l}{2}$$
$$\frac{P - 2w}{2} = l \text{ or } l = \frac{P - 2w}{2}$$

7.
$$P = 2a + b - c$$
$$P + c = 2a + b - c + c$$
$$P + c = 2a + b$$
$$P + c - b = 2a + b - b$$
$$P + c - b = 2a$$
$$\frac{P + c - b}{2} = a \text{ or } a = \frac{P - b - c}{2}$$

8.
$$A = \frac{a + b}{2}$$
$$2A = 2 \cdot \frac{a + b}{2}$$
$$2A = a + b$$
$$2A - a = a + b - a$$
$$2A - a = b \text{ or } b = 2A - a$$

Exercise Set 9.5

1. Use $A = bh$ when $A = 45$ and $b = 15$.

$$A = bh$$
$$45 = 15 \cdot h$$
$$\frac{45}{15} = \frac{15h}{15}$$
$$3 = h$$

3. Use $S = 4lw + 2wh$ when $S = 102$, $l = 7$, and $w = 3$.

$$S = 4lw + 2wh$$
$$102 = 4 \cdot 7 \cdot 3 + 2 \cdot 3 \cdot h$$
$$102 = 84 + 6h$$
$$102 - 84 = 84 + 6h - 84$$
$$18 = 6h$$
$$\frac{18}{6} = \frac{6h}{6}$$
$$3 = h$$

5. Use $A = \dfrac{1}{2}h(B+b)$ when $A = 180$, $B = 11$, and $b = 7$.

$$A = \dfrac{1}{2}h(B+b)$$
$$180 = \dfrac{1}{2}h(11+7)$$
$$180 = \dfrac{1}{2}h(18)$$
$$180 = 9h$$
$$\dfrac{180}{9} = \dfrac{9h}{9}$$
$$20 = h$$

7. Use $P = a + b + c$ when $P = 30$, $a = 8$, and $b = 10$.
$$P = a + b + c$$
$$30 = 8 + 10 + c$$
$$30 = 18 + c$$
$$30 - 18 = 18 + c - 18$$
$$12 = c$$

9. Use $C = 2\pi r$ when $C = 15.7$ and 3.14 is used as an approximation for π.
$$C = 2\pi r$$
$$15.7 = 2(3.14)r$$
$$15.7 = 6.28r$$
$$\dfrac{15.7}{6.28} = \dfrac{6.28r}{6.28}$$
$$2.5 = r$$

11. $f = 5gh$
$$\dfrac{f}{5g} = \dfrac{5gh}{5g}$$
$$\dfrac{f}{5g} = h$$

13. $V = lwh$
$$\dfrac{V}{lh} = \dfrac{lwh}{lh}$$
$$\dfrac{V}{lh} = w$$

15.
$$3x + y = 7$$
$$3x + y - 3x = 7 - 3x$$
$$y = 7 - 3x$$

17.
$$A = P + PRT$$
$$A - P = P + PRT - P$$
$$A - P = PRT$$
$$\dfrac{A - P}{PT} = \dfrac{PRT}{PT}$$
$$\dfrac{A - P}{PT} = R$$

19. $V = \dfrac{1}{3}Ah$
$$3V = 3 \cdot \dfrac{1}{3}Ah$$
$$3V = Ah$$
$$\dfrac{3V}{h} = \dfrac{Ah}{h}$$
$$\dfrac{3V}{h} = A$$

21.
$$P = a + b + c$$
$$P - b - c = a + b + c - b - c$$
$$P - b - c = a$$

23.
$$S = 2\pi rh + 2\pi r^2$$
$$S - 2\pi r^2 = 2\pi rh + 2\pi r^2 - 2\pi r^2$$
$$S - 2\pi r^2 = 2\pi rh$$
$$\dfrac{S - 2\pi r^2}{2\pi r} = \dfrac{2\pi rh}{2\pi r}$$
$$\dfrac{S - 2\pi r^2}{2\pi r} = h$$

25. **a.** Area $= l \cdot w = (11.5)(9) = 103.5$
Perimeter $= 2l + 2w$
$$= 2(11.5) + 2(9)$$
$$= 23 + 18$$
$$= 41$$
The area is 103.5 square feet and the perimeter is 41 feet.

b. The baseboard goes around the edges of the room, so it involves the perimeter. The carpet covers the floor of the room, so it involves area.

27. **a.** Area $= \dfrac{1}{2}h(B+b)$
$$= \dfrac{1}{2} \cdot 12(56 + 24)$$
$$= 6(80)$$
$$= 480$$
Perimeter $= 24 + 20 + 56 + 20 = 120$
The area is 480 square inches and the perimeter is 120 inches.

b. The frame goes around the edges of the picture, so it involves perimeter. The glass covers the picture, so it involves area.

29. Use $A = lw$ when $A = 10,080$ and $w = 84$.

$$A = lw$$
$$10,080 = l(84)$$
$$\frac{10,080}{84} = \frac{84l}{84}$$
$$120 = l$$

The length (height) of the sign is 120 feet.

31. Use $F = \frac{9}{5}C + 32$ when $F = 14$.

$$F = \frac{9}{5}C + 32$$
$$14 = \frac{9}{5}C + 32$$
$$14 - 32 = \frac{9}{5}C + 32 - 32$$
$$-18 = \frac{9}{5}C$$
$$\frac{5}{9} \cdot (-18) = \frac{5}{9} \cdot \frac{9}{5}C$$
$$-10 = C$$

Thus, 14°F is equivalent to −10°C.

33. Use $d = rt$ when $d = 25,000$ and $r = 4000$.

$$d = rt$$
$$25,000 = 4000t$$
$$\frac{25,000}{4000} = \frac{4000t}{4000}$$
$$6.25 = t$$

It will take the X-30 6.25 hours to travel around the Earth.

35. Let x be the length. Then $\frac{2}{3}x$ is the width. Use $P = 2 \cdot \text{length} + 2 \cdot \text{width}$ when $P = 260$.

$$P = 2 \cdot \text{length} + 2 \cdot \text{width}$$
$$260 = 2x + 2 \cdot \frac{2}{3}x$$
$$260 = 2x + \frac{4}{3}x$$
$$260 = \frac{6}{3}x + \frac{4}{3}x$$
$$260 = \frac{10}{3}x$$
$$\frac{3}{10} \cdot 260 = \frac{3}{10} \cdot \frac{10}{3}x$$
$$78 = x$$

The length is 78 feet and the width is $\frac{2}{3} \cdot 78 = 52$ feet.

37. Let x represent the length of the shortest side. Then the second side has length $2x$ and the third side has length $30 + x$. The perimeter is the sum of the lengths of the sides.

$$x + 2x + 30 + x = 102$$
$$4x + 30 = 102$$
$$4x + 30 - 30 = 102 - 30$$
$$4x = 72$$
$$\frac{4x}{4} = \frac{72}{4}$$
$$x = 18$$

$2x = 2(18) = 36$
$30 + x = 30 + 18 = 48$

The flower bed has sides of length 18 feet, 36 feet, and 48 feet.

39. Use $d = rt$ when $r = 55$ and $t = 2\frac{1}{2}$.

$$d = rt$$
$$d = 55 \cdot 2\frac{1}{2}$$
$$d = 55 \cdot 2.5$$
$$d = 137.5$$

The distance between Bar Harbor and Yarmouth is 137.5 miles.

41. Use $N = 86$.

$$T = 50 + \frac{N - 40}{4}$$
$$T = 50 + \frac{86 - 40}{4}$$
$$T = 50 + \frac{46}{4}$$
$$T = 50 + 11.5$$
$$T = 61.5$$

The temperature is 61.5° Fahrenheit.

43. Use $T = 55$.

$$T = 50 + \frac{N-40}{4}$$

$$55 = 50 + \frac{N-40}{4}$$

$$55 - 50 = 50 + \frac{N-40}{4} - 50$$

$$5 = \frac{N-40}{4}$$

$$4 \cdot 5 = 4 \cdot \frac{N-40}{4}$$

$$20 = N - 40$$

$$20 + 40 = N - 40 + 40$$

$$60 = N$$

There are 60 chirps per minute.

45. As the number of cricket chirps per minute increases, the air temperature of their environment <u>increases</u>.

47. To find the amount of water in the tank, use $V = lwh$ with $l = 8$, $w = 3$, and $h = 6$.
$V = lwh = 8 \cdot 3 \cdot 6 = 144$
The tank holds 144 cubic feet of water. Let x represent the number of piranhas the tank could hold. Then $1.5x = 144$.

$$1.5x = 144$$

$$\frac{1.5x}{1.5} = \frac{144}{1.5}$$

$$x = 96$$

The tank could hold 96 piranhas.

49. Use $A = \frac{1}{2}h(B+b)$ to find the area of the lawn.

$$A = \frac{1}{2}h(B+b)$$

$$A = \frac{1}{2}(60)(130 + 70) = 30(200) = 6000$$

Let x be the number of bags of fertilizer.

$$4000x = 6000$$

$$\frac{4000x}{4000} = \frac{6000}{4000}$$

$$x = 1.5$$

Since $\frac{1}{2}$ bag cannot be purchased, 2 bags must be purchased to cover the lawn.

51. Use $A = \pi r^2$ to find the area of a pizza.

For the 16-inch pizza, $r = \frac{16}{2} = 8$.

$A = \pi r^2 = \pi(8)^2 = 64\pi$

For a 10-inch pizza, $r = \frac{10}{2} = 5$.

$A = \pi r^2 = \pi(5)^2 = 25\pi$

Two 10-inch pizzas have an area of $2 \cdot 25\pi = 50\pi$ square inches. Since $50\pi < 64\pi$, you get more pizza by buying the 16-inch pizza.

53. Use $d = rt$ when $r = 552$ and $d = 42.8$.

$$d = rt$$

$$42.8 = 552t$$

$$\frac{42.8}{552} = \frac{552t}{552}$$

$$0.0775 = t$$

It would last 0.0775 hour or $0.0775(60) \approx 4.65$ minutes.

55. Let s represent the length of one side of the square. Then the perimeter of the square is $4s$. A side of the triangle is $s + 5$ and the triangle's perimeter is $3(s + 5)$.

$$3(s + 5) = 4s + 7$$

$$3s + 15 = 4s + 7$$

$$3s + 15 - 3s = 4s + 7 - 3s$$

$$15 = s + 7$$

$$15 - 7 = s + 7 - 7$$

$$8 = s$$

$$s + 5 = 8 + 5 = 13$$

Each side of the triangle has length 13 inches.

57. Use $d = rt$ when $d = 135$ an $r = 60$.

$$d = rt$$

$$135 = 60t$$

$$\frac{135}{60} = \frac{60t}{60}$$

$$2.25 = t$$

It will take 2.25 hours.

59. Use $A = lw$ when $A = 1,813,500$ and $w = 150$.

$$A = lw$$

$$1,813,500 = l(150)$$

$$\frac{1,813,500}{150} = \frac{150l}{150}$$

$$12,090 = l$$

The length of the runway is 12,090 feet (more than 2 miles!).

61. Use $F = \dfrac{9}{5}C + 32$ when $F = 122$.

$$122 = \frac{9}{5}C + 32$$

$$122 - 32 = \frac{9}{5}C + 32 - 32$$

$$90 = \frac{9}{5}C$$

$$\frac{5}{9} \cdot 90 = \frac{5}{9} \cdot \frac{9}{5}C$$

$$50 = C$$

Thus, 122°F is equivalent to 50°C.

63. Use $V = lwh$ when $l = 199$, $w = 78.5$, and $h = 33$.
$V = lwh = 199(78.5)(33) = 515,509.5$
The smallest possible shipping crate has a volume of 515,509.5 cubic inches.

65. Use $V = \dfrac{4}{3}\pi r^3$ when $r = \dfrac{9.5}{2} = 4.75$ and

$\pi = 3.14$.

$$V = \frac{4}{3}\pi r^3 = \frac{4}{3}(3.14)(4.75)^3 \approx 449$$

The volume of the sphere is 449 cubic inches.

67. Use $F = \dfrac{9}{5}C + 32$ when $C = 167$.

$$F = \frac{9}{5}C + 32$$

$$= \frac{9}{5}(167) + 32$$

$$= 300.6 + 32$$

$$= 332.6$$

$$\approx 333$$

The average temperature on the planet Mercury is 333°F.

69. $32\% = 0.32$

71. $200\% = 2.00$ or 2

73. $0.17 = 0.17(100\%) = 17\%$

75. $7.2 = 7.2(100\%) = 720\%$

77.
$$N = R + \frac{V}{G}$$

$$N - R = R + \frac{V}{G} - R$$

$$N - R = \frac{V}{G}$$

$$G(N - R) = G \cdot \frac{V}{G}$$

$$G(N - R) = V$$

79. Use $V = lwh$. If the length is doubled, the new length is $2l$. If the width and height are doubled, the new width and height are $2w$ and $2h$, respectively.
$V = (2l)(2w)(2h) = 2 \cdot 2 \cdot 2lwh = 8lwh$
The volume of the box is multiplied by 8.

81. Replace T with N and solve for N.

$$T = 50 + \frac{N - 40}{4}$$

$$N = 50 + \frac{N - 40}{4}$$

$$N - 50 = 50 + \frac{N - 40}{4} - 50$$

$$N - 50 = \frac{N - 40}{4}$$

$$4(N - 50) = 4 \cdot \frac{N - 40}{4}$$

$$4N - 200 = N - 40$$

$$4N - 200 - N = N - 40 - N$$

$$3N - 200 = -40$$

$$3N - 200 + 200 = -40 + 200$$

$$3N = 160$$

$$\frac{3N}{3} = \frac{160}{3}$$

$$N = 53\frac{1}{3}$$

They are the same when the number of cricket chirps per minute is $53\dfrac{1}{3}$.

83. ▲ − ● · ■ = ■

     − ● · ■ = ■ − ▲

     ● = $\dfrac{▲ − ■}{■}$

85. $\dfrac{20 \text{ miles}}{1 \text{ hour}} \cdot \dfrac{5280 \text{ feet}}{1 \text{ mile}} \cdot \dfrac{1 \text{ hour}}{60 \text{ minutes}} \cdot \dfrac{1 \text{ minute}}{60 \text{ seconds}}$

$= \dfrac{20 \cdot 5280 \text{ feet}}{60 \cdot 60 \text{ seconds}}$

$\approx 29.3 \text{ feet/second}$

Use $d = rt$ when $d = 1300$ and $r = 29.3$.

$d = rt$

$1300 = 29.3t$

$\dfrac{1300}{29.3} = \dfrac{29.3t}{29.3}$

$44.3 \approx t$

It took 44.3 seconds to travel that distance.

87. Use $I = PRT$ when $I = 1{,}056{,}000$, $R = 0.055$, and $T = 6$.

$I = PRT$

$1{,}056{,}000 = P(0.055)(6)$

$1{,}056{,}000 = 0.33P$

$\dfrac{1{,}056{,}000}{0.33} = \dfrac{0.33P}{0.33}$

$3{,}200{,}000 = P$

89. Use $V = \dfrac{4}{3}\pi r^3$ when $r = 3$.

$V = \dfrac{4}{3}\pi \cdot 3^3$

$V \approx 113.1$

Section 9.6

Practice Problems

1. $x \geq -2$

2. $5 > x$ or $x < 5$

3. $-3 \leq x < 1$

4. $x - 6 \geq -11$

$x - 6 + 6 \geq -11 + 6$

$x \geq -5$

5. $-3x \leq 12$

$\dfrac{-3x}{-3} \geq \dfrac{12}{-3}$

$x \geq -4$

6. $5x > -20$

$\dfrac{5x}{5} > \dfrac{-20}{5}$

$x > -4$

7. $-3x + 11 \leq -13$

$-3x + 11 - 11 \leq -13 - 11$

$-3x \leq -24$

$\dfrac{-3x}{-3} \geq \dfrac{-24}{-3}$

$x \geq 8$

$\{x \mid x \geq 8\}$

8. $2x - 3 > 4(x - 1)$

$2x - 3 > 4x - 4$

$2x - 3 - 4x > 4x - 4 - 4x$

$-2x - 3 > -4$

$-2x - 3 + 3 > -4 + 3$

$-2x > -1$

$\dfrac{-2x}{-2} < \dfrac{-1}{-6}$

$x < \dfrac{1}{2}$

$\left\{ x \mid x < \dfrac{1}{2} \right\}$

9. $3(x + 5) - 1 \geq 5(x - 1) + 7$

$3x + 15 - 1 \geq 5x - 5 + 7$

$3x + 14 \geq 5x + 2$

$3x + 14 - 5x \geq 5x + 2 - 5x$

$-2x + 14 \geq 2$

$-2x + 14 - 14 \geq 2 - 14$

$-2x \geq -12$

$\dfrac{-2x}{-2} \leq \dfrac{-12}{-2}$

$x \leq 6$

$\{x \mid x \leq 6\}$

10. Let x be the unknown number.

$35 - 2x > 15$

$35 - 2x - 35 > 15 - 35$

$-2x > -20$

$\dfrac{-2x}{-2} < \dfrac{-20}{-2}$

$x < 10$

All numbers less than 10 make the statement true.

11. Let x represent the minimum sales.
$$600 + 0.04x \geq 3000$$
$$0.04x \geq 2400$$
$$x \geq 60,000$$
Alex must have minimum sales of $60,000.

Vocabulary and Readiness Check

1. $6x - 7(x + 9)$ is an <u>expression</u>.

2. $6x = 7(x + 9)$ is an <u>equation</u>.

3. $6x < 7(x + 9)$ is an <u>inequality</u>.

4. $5y - 2 \geq -38$ is an <u>inequality</u>.

5. $\dfrac{9}{7} = \dfrac{x+2}{14}$ is an <u>equation</u>.

6. $\dfrac{9}{7} - \dfrac{x+2}{14}$ is an <u>expression</u>.

7. $x \geq -3$
-5 is not a solution.

8. $x < 6$
$|-6| = 6$ is not a solution.

9. $x < 4.01$
4.1 is not a solution.

10. $x \geq -3$
-4 is not a solution.

Exercise Set 9.6

1.

3.

5.

7.

9.

11.

13.
$$x - 2 \geq -7$$
$$x - 2 + 2 \geq -7 + 2$$
$$x \geq -5$$
$$\{x \mid x \geq -5\}$$

15.
$$-9 + y < 0$$
$$9 - 9 + y < 9 + 0$$
$$y < 9$$
$$\{y \mid y < 9\}$$

17.
$$3x - 5 > 2x - 8$$
$$3x - 5 - 2x > 2x - 8 - 2x$$
$$x - 5 > -8$$
$$x - 5 + 5 > -8 + 5$$
$$x > -3$$
$$\{x \mid x > -3\}$$

19.
$$4x - 1 \leq 5x - 2x$$
$$4x - 1 \leq 3x$$
$$4x - 1 - 4x \leq 3x - 4x$$
$$-1 \leq -x$$
$$\frac{-1}{-1} \geq \frac{-x}{-1}$$
$$1 \geq x \text{ or } x \leq 1$$
$$\{x \mid x \leq 1\}$$

21.
$$2x < -6$$
$$\frac{2x}{2} < \frac{-6}{2}$$
$$x < -3$$
$$\{x \mid x < -3\}$$

23.
$$-8x \leq 16$$
$$\frac{-8x}{-8} \geq \frac{16}{-8}$$
$$x \geq -2$$
$$\{x \mid x \geq -2\}$$

25.
$$-x > 0$$
$$(-1)(-x) < (-1)(0)$$
$$x < 0$$
$$\{x | x < 0\}$$

27.
$$\frac{3}{4} y \geq -2$$
$$\frac{4}{3} \cdot \frac{3}{4} y \geq \frac{4}{3} \cdot (-2)$$
$$y \geq -\frac{8}{3}$$
$$\left\{ y \,\middle|\, y \geq -\frac{8}{3} \right\}$$

29.
$$-0.6y < -1.8$$
$$\frac{-0.6y}{-0.6} > \frac{-1.8}{-0.6}$$
$$y > 3$$
$$\{y | y > 3\}$$

31.
$$-8 < x + 7$$
$$-8 - 7 < x + 7 - 7$$
$$-15 < x$$
$$\{x | x > -15\}$$

33.
$$7(x+1) - 6x \geq -4$$
$$7x + 7 - 6x \geq -4$$
$$x + 7 \geq -4$$
$$x + 7 - 7 \geq -4 - 7$$
$$x \geq -11$$
$$\{x | x \geq -11\}$$

35.
$$4x > 1$$
$$\frac{4x}{4} > \frac{1}{4}$$
$$x > \frac{1}{4}$$
$$\left\{ x \,\middle|\, x > \frac{1}{4} \right\}$$

37.
$$-\frac{2}{3} y \leq 8$$
$$-\frac{3}{2}\left(-\frac{2}{3} y\right) \geq -\frac{3}{2}(8)$$
$$y \geq -12$$
$$\{y | y \geq -12\}$$

39.
$$4(2z + 1) < 4$$
$$8z + 4 < 4$$
$$8z + 4 - 4 < 4 - 4$$
$$8z < 0$$
$$\frac{8z}{8} < \frac{0}{8}$$
$$z < 0$$
$$\{z | z < 0\}$$

41.
$$3x - 7 < 6x + 2$$
$$3x - 7 - 3x < 6x + 2 - 3x$$
$$-7 < 3x + 2$$
$$-7 - 2 < 3x + 2 - 2$$
$$-9 < 3x$$
$$\frac{-9}{3} < \frac{3x}{3}$$
$$-3 < x$$
$$\{x | x > -3\}$$

43.
$$5x - 7x \leq x + 2$$
$$-2x \leq x + 2$$
$$-2x - x \leq x + 2 - x$$
$$-3x \leq 2$$
$$\frac{-3x}{-3} \geq \frac{2}{-3}$$
$$x \geq -\frac{2}{3}$$
$$\left\{ x \,\middle|\, x \geq -\frac{2}{3} \right\}$$

45.
$$-6x + 2 \geq 2(5 - x)$$
$$-6x + 2 \geq 10 - 2x$$
$$-6x + 2 + 6x \geq 10 - 2x + 6x$$
$$2 \geq 10 + 4x$$
$$2 - 10 \geq 10 + 4x - 10$$
$$-8 \geq 4x$$
$$\frac{-8}{4} \geq \frac{4x}{4}$$
$$-2 \geq x$$
$$\{x | x \leq -2\}$$

47.
$$3(x-5) < 2(2x-1)$$
$$3x-15 < 4x-2$$
$$3x-15-3x < 4x-2-3x$$
$$-15 < x-2$$
$$-15+2 < x-2+2$$
$$-13 < x$$
$$\{x | x > -13\}$$

49.
$$4(3x-1) \le 5(2x-4)$$
$$12x-4 \le 10x-20$$
$$12x-4-10x \le 10x-20-10x$$
$$2x-4 \le -20$$
$$2x-4+4 \le -20+4$$
$$2x \le -16$$
$$\frac{2x}{2} \le \frac{-16}{2}$$
$$x \le -8$$
$$\{x | x \le -8\}$$

51.
$$3(x+2)-6 > -2(x-3)+14$$
$$3x+6-6 > -2x+6+14$$
$$3x > -2x+20$$
$$3x+2x > -2x+20+2x$$
$$5x > 20$$
$$\frac{5x}{5} > \frac{20}{5}$$
$$x > 4$$
$$\{x | x > 4\}$$

53.
$$-5(1-x)+x \le -(6-2x)+6$$
$$-5+5x+x \le -6+2x+6$$
$$-5+6x \le 2x$$
$$-5+6x-6x \le 2x-6x$$
$$-5 \le -4x$$
$$\frac{-5}{-4} \ge \frac{-4x}{-4}$$
$$\frac{5}{4} \ge x$$
$$\left\{x | x \le \frac{5}{4}\right\}$$

55.
$$\frac{1}{4}(x+4) < \frac{1}{5}(2x+3)$$
$$20 \cdot \frac{1}{4}(x+4) < 20 \cdot \frac{1}{5}(2x+3)$$
$$5(x+4) < 4(2x+3)$$
$$5x+20 < 8x+12$$
$$5x+20-5x < 8x+12-5x$$
$$20 < 3x+12$$
$$20-12 < 3x+12-12$$
$$8 < 3x$$
$$\frac{8}{3} < \frac{3x}{3}$$
$$\frac{8}{3} < x$$
$$\left\{x | x > \frac{8}{3}\right\}$$

57.
$$-5x+4 \le -4(x-1)$$
$$-5x+4 \le -4x+4$$
$$-5x+4+4x \le -4x+4+4x$$
$$-x+4 \le 4$$
$$-x+4-4 \le 4-4$$
$$-x \le 0$$
$$-1(-x) \ge -1(0)$$
$$x \ge 0$$
$$\{x | x \ge 0\}$$

59. Let x be the number.
$$2x+6 > -14$$
$$2x+6-6 > -14-6$$
$$2x > -20$$
$$\frac{2x}{2} > \frac{-20}{2}$$
$$x > -10$$
All numbers greater than -10 make this statement true.

61. Use $P = 2l + 2w$ when $w = 15$ and $P \le 100$.
$$2l+2(15) \le 100$$
$$2l+30 \le 100$$
$$2l+30-30 \le 100-30$$
$$2l \le 70$$
$$\frac{2l}{2} \le \frac{70}{2}$$
$$l \le 35$$
The maximum length of the rectangle is 35 cm.

63. Let x be the score in his third game.
$$\frac{146+201+x}{3} \geq 180$$
$$\frac{347+x}{3} \geq 180$$
$$3 \cdot \frac{347+x}{3} \geq 3 \cdot 180$$
$$347+x \geq 540$$
$$347+x-347 \geq 540-347$$
$$x \geq 193$$
He must bowl at least 193 on the third game.

65. Let x represent the number of people. Then the cost is $50+34x$.
$$50+34x \leq 3000$$
$$50+34x-50 \leq 3000-50$$
$$34x \leq 2950$$
$$\frac{34x}{34} \leq \frac{2950}{34}$$
$$x \leq \frac{2950}{34} \approx 86.76$$
They can invite at most 86 people.

67. Let x represent the number of minutes.
$$5.8x \geq 200$$
$$\frac{5.8x}{5.8} \geq \frac{200}{5.8}$$
$$x \geq \frac{200}{5.8} \approx 35$$
The person must walk at least 35 minutes.

69. $3^4 = 3 \cdot 3 \cdot 3 \cdot 3 = 81$

71. $1^8 = 1 \cdot 1 \cdot 1 \cdot 1 \cdot 1 \cdot 1 \cdot 1 \cdot 1 = 1$

73. $\left(\frac{7}{8}\right)^2 = \left(\frac{7}{8}\right)\left(\frac{7}{8}\right) = \frac{49}{64}$

75. There were about 3200 Starbucks locations in 2002.

77. The greatest increase occurred between 2006 and 2007.

79. The number of Starbucks locations rose above 5000 in 2005.

81. Since $3 < 5$, $3(-4) > 5(-4)$.

83. If $m \leq n$, then $-2m \geq -2n$.

85. Reverse the direction of the inequality symbol when multiplying or dividing by a negative number.

87. Let x be the score on his final exam. Since the final counts as two tests, his final course average is $\frac{75+83+85+2x}{5}$.
$$\frac{75+83+85+2x}{5} \geq 80$$
$$\frac{243+2x}{5} \geq 80$$
$$5\left(\frac{243+2x}{5}\right) \geq 5(80)$$
$$243+2x \geq 400$$
$$243+2x-243 \geq 400-243$$
$$2x \geq 157$$
$$\frac{2x}{2} \geq \frac{157}{2}$$
$$x \geq 78.5$$
His final exam score must be at least 78.5 for him to get a B.

Chapter 9 Vocabulary Check

1. A <u>linear equation in one variable</u> can be written in the form $ax + b = c$.

2. Inequalities that have the same solution are called <u>equivalent inequalities</u>.

3. An equation that describes a known relationship among quantities is called a <u>formula</u>.

4. A <u>linear inequality in one variable</u> can be written in the form $ax + b < c$, (or $>$, $\leq$, $\geq$).

5. The solution(s) to the equation $x + 5 = x + 5$ is/are <u>all real numbers</u>.

6. The solution(s) to the equation $x + 5 = x + 4$ is/are <u>no solution</u>.

7. If both sides of an inequality are multiplied or divided by the same positive number, the direction of the inequality symbol is <u>the same</u>.

8. If both sides of an inequality are multiplied by the same negative number, the direction of the inequality symbol is <u>reversed</u>.

9. Two numbers whose sum is 0 are called <u>opposites</u>.

10. Two numbers whose product is 1 are called <u>reciprocals</u>.

Chapter 9 Review

1. Since 8 is to the left of 10 on the number line, $8 < 10$.

2. Since 7 is to the right of 2 on the number line, $7 > 2$.

3. Since −4 is to the right of −5 on the number line, $-4 > -5$.

4. Since $\frac{12}{2} = 6$ is to the right of −8 on the number line, $\frac{12}{2} > -8$.

5. Since $|-7| = 7$ is to the left of $|-8| = 8$ on the number line, $|-7| < |-8|$.

6. Since $|-9| = 9$ is to the right of −9 on the number line, $|-9| > -9$.

7. $-|-1| = -1$

8. Since $|-14| = 14$ and $-(-14) = 14$, $|-14| = -(-14)$.

9. Since 1.2 is to the right of 1.02 on the number line, $1.2 > 1.02$.

10. Since $-\frac{3}{2} = -\frac{6}{4}$ and $-\frac{6}{4}$ is to the left of $-\frac{3}{4}$ on the number line, $-\frac{3}{2} < -\frac{3}{4}$.

11. Four is greater than or equal to negative three is written as $4 \geq -3$.

12. Six is not equal to five is written as $6 \neq 5$.

13. 0.03 is less than 0.3 is written as $0.03 < 0.3$.

14. Since 155 is to the left of 400 on the number line, $155 < 400$.

15. a. The natural numbers are 1, 3.

    b. The whole numbers are 0, 1, 3.

    c. The integers are −6, 0, 1, 3.

d. The rational numbers are −6, 0, 1, $1\frac{1}{2}$, 3, 9.62.

e. The irrational number is π.

f. The real numbers are all numbers in the set.

16. a. The natural numbers are 2, 5.

    b. The whole numbers are 2, 5.

    c. The integers are −3, 2, 5.

    d. The rational numbers are −3, −1.6, 2, 5, $\frac{11}{2}$, 15.1.

    e. The irrational numbers are $\sqrt{5}$, 2π.

    f. The real numbers are all numbers in the set.

17. Since $-4 < -2$, the most negative number is −4 which corresponds to Friday. Thus, Friday showed the greatest loss.

18. The greatest positive number is +5 which corresponds to Wednesday. Thus, Wednesday showed the greatest gain.

19. $-6 + 5 = 5 + (-6)$ illustrates the commutative property of addition.

20. $6 \cdot 1 = 6$ illustrates the multiplicative identity property.

21. $3(8 - 5) = 3 \cdot 8 + 3 \cdot (-5)$ illustrates the distributive property.

22. $4 + (-4) = 0$ illustrates the additive inverse property.

23. $2 + (3 + 9) = (2 + 3) + 9$ illustrates the associative property of addition.

24. $2 \cdot 8 = 8 \cdot 2$ illustrates the commutative property of multiplication.

25. $6(8 + 5) = 6 \cdot 8 + 6 \cdot 5$ illustrates the distributive property.

26. $(3 \cdot 8) \cdot 4 = 3 \cdot (8 \cdot 4)$ illustrates the associative property of multiplication.

27. $4 \cdot \dfrac{1}{4} = 1$ illustrates the multiplicative inverse property.

28. $8 + 0 = 8$ illustrates the additive identity property.

29.
$$\frac{5}{3}x + 4 = \frac{2}{3}x$$
$$3\left(\frac{5}{3}x + 4\right) = 3\left(\frac{2}{3}x\right)$$
$$5x + 12 = 2x$$
$$5x + 12 - 5x = 2x - 5x$$
$$12 = -3x$$
$$\frac{12}{-3} = \frac{-3x}{-3}$$
$$-4 = x$$

30.
$$\frac{7}{8}x + 1 = \frac{5}{8}x$$
$$8\left(\frac{7}{8}x + 1\right) = 8\left(\frac{5}{8}x\right)$$
$$7x + 8 = 5x$$
$$7x + 8 - 7x = 5x - 7x$$
$$8 = -2x$$
$$\frac{8}{-2} = \frac{-2x}{-2}$$
$$-4 = x$$

31.
$$-(5x + 1) = -7x + 3$$
$$-5x - 1 = -7x + 3$$
$$-5x - 1 + 7x = -7x + 3 + 7x$$
$$2x - 1 = 3$$
$$2x - 1 + 1 = 3 + 1$$
$$2x = 4$$
$$\frac{2x}{2} = \frac{4}{2}$$
$$x = 2$$

32.
$$-4(2x + 1) = -5x + 5$$
$$-8x - 4 = -5x + 5$$
$$-8x - 4 + 8x = -5x + 5 + 8x$$
$$-4 = 3x + 5$$
$$-4 - 5 = 3x + 5 - 5$$
$$-9 = 3x$$
$$\frac{-9}{3} = \frac{3x}{3}$$
$$-3 = x$$

33.
$$-6(2x - 5) = -3(9 + 4x)$$
$$-12x + 30 = -27 - 12x$$
$$12x - 12x + 30 = 12x - 27 - 12x$$
$$30 = -27$$
Since the statement $30 = -27$ is false, the equation has no solution.

34.
$$3(8y - 1) = 6(5 + 4y)$$
$$24y - 3 = 30 + 24y$$
$$24y - 3 - 24y = 30 + 24y - 24y$$
$$-3 = 30$$
Since the statement $-3 = 30$ is false, the equation has no solution.

35.
$$\frac{3(2 - z)}{5} = z$$
$$5\left[\frac{3(2 - z)}{5}\right] = 5 \cdot z$$
$$3(2 - z) = 5z$$
$$6 - 3z = 5z$$
$$6 - 3z + 3z = 5z + 3z$$
$$6 = 8z$$
$$\frac{6}{8} = \frac{8z}{8}$$
$$\frac{3}{4} = z$$

36.
$$\frac{4(n + 2)}{5} = -n$$
$$5\left[\frac{4(n + 2)}{5}\right] = 5(-n)$$
$$4(n + 2) = -5n$$
$$4n + 8 = -5n$$
$$4n + 8 - 4n = -5n - 4n$$
$$8 = -9n$$
$$\frac{8}{-9} = \frac{-9n}{-9}$$
$$-\frac{8}{9} = n$$

37. $0.5(2n-3)-0.1=0.4(6+2n)$
$5(2n-3)-1=4(6+2n)$
$10n-15-1=24+8n$
$10n-16=24+8n$
$10n-16-8n=24+8n-8n$
$2n-16=24$
$2n-16+16=24+16$
$2n=40$
$\dfrac{2n}{2}=\dfrac{40}{2}$
$n=20$

38. $1.72y-0.04y=0.42$
$172y-4y=42$
$168y=42$
$\dfrac{168y}{168}=\dfrac{42}{168}$
$y=0.25$

39. $\dfrac{5(c+1)}{6}=2c-3$
$6\left[\dfrac{5(c+1)}{6}\right]=6(2c-3)$
$5(c+1)=6(2c-3)$
$5c+5=12c-18$
$5c+5-5c=12c-18-5c$
$5=7c-18$
$5+18=7c-18+18$
$23=7c$
$\dfrac{23}{7}=\dfrac{7c}{7}$
$\dfrac{23}{7}=c$

40. $-9-5a=3(6a-1)$
$-9-5a=18a-3$
$9-5a+5a=18a-3+5a$
$-9=23a-3$
$-9+3=23a-3+3$
$-6=23a$
$\dfrac{-6}{23}=\dfrac{23a}{23}$
$-\dfrac{6}{23}=a$

41. Let x be the length of the side of the square base. Then the height is $10x+50.5$. The sum is 7327.
$x+10x+50.5=7327$
$11x+50.5=7327$
$11x+50.5-50.5=7327-50.5$
$11x=7276.5$
$\dfrac{11x}{11}=\dfrac{7276.5}{11}$
$x=661.5$
$10x+50.5=10(661.5)+50.5$
$=6615+50.5$
$=6665.5$
The height is 6665.5 inches.

42. Let x be the length of the short piece. Then $2x$ is the length of the long piece. The lengths sum to 12.
$x+2x=12$
$3x=12$
$\dfrac{3x}{3}=\dfrac{12}{3}$
$x=4$
$2x=2(4)=8$
The short piece is 4 feet and the long piece is 8 feet.

43. Let x be the number of Cornell library sites. Then $2x+2$ is the number of Harvard library sites. The total number of libraries is 119.
$x+2x+2=119$
$3x+2=119$
$3x+2-2=119-2$
$3x=117$
$\dfrac{3x}{3}=\dfrac{117}{3}$
$x=39$
$2x+2=2(39)+2=78+2=80$
Cornell has 39 libraries and Harvard has 80 libraries.

44. Let x be the first integer. Then $x+1$ and $x+2$ are the next two consecutive integers. Their sum is -114.
$x+x+1+x+2=-114$
$3x+3=-114$
$3x+3-3=-114-3$
$3x=-117$
$\dfrac{3x}{3}=\dfrac{-117}{3}$
$x=-39$
$x+1=-39+1=-38$
$x+2=-39+2=-37$
The integers are -39, -38, and -37.

45.
$$\frac{x}{3} = x - 2$$
$$3 \cdot \frac{x}{3} = 3(x - 2)$$
$$x = 3x - 6$$
$$x - 3x = 3x - 6 - 3x$$
$$-2x = -6$$
$$\frac{-2x}{-2} = \frac{-6}{-2}$$
$$x = 3$$
The number is 3.

46.
$$2(x + 6) = -x$$
$$2x + 12 = -x$$
$$-2x + 2x + 12 = -2x - x$$
$$12 = -3x$$
$$\frac{12}{-3} = \frac{-3x}{-3}$$
$$-4 = x$$
The number is -4.

47. Use $P = 2l + 2w$ when $P = 46$ and $l = 14$.
$$P = 2l + 2w$$
$$46 = 2(14) + 2w$$
$$46 = 28 + 2w$$
$$46 - 28 = 28 + 2w - 28$$
$$18 = 2w$$
$$\frac{18}{2} = \frac{2w}{2}$$
$$9 = w$$

48. Use $V = lwh$ when $V = 192$, $l = 8$, and $w = 6$.
$$V = lwh$$
$$192 = 8 \cdot 6 \cdot h$$
$$192 = 48h$$
$$\frac{192}{48} = \frac{48h}{48}$$
$$4 = h$$

49.
$$y = mx + b$$
$$y - b = mx + b - b$$
$$y - b = mx$$
$$\frac{y - b}{x} = \frac{mx}{x}$$
$$\frac{y - b}{x} = m$$

50.
$$r = vst - 5$$
$$r + 5 = vst - 5 + 5$$
$$r + 5 = vst$$
$$\frac{r + 5}{vt} = \frac{vst}{vt}$$
$$\frac{r + 5}{vt} = s$$

51.
$$2y - 5x = 7$$
$$-2y + 2y - 5x = -2y + 7$$
$$-5x = -2y + 7$$
$$\frac{-5x}{-5} = \frac{-2y + 7}{-5}$$
$$x = \frac{2y - 7}{5}$$

52.
$$3x - 6y = -2$$
$$-3x + 3x - 6y = -3x - 2$$
$$-6y = -3x - 2$$
$$\frac{-6y}{-6} = \frac{-3x - 2}{-6}$$
$$y = \frac{3x + 2}{6}$$

53.
$$C = \pi d$$
$$\frac{C}{\pi} = \frac{\pi d}{\pi}$$
$$\frac{C}{\pi} = d$$

54.
$$C = 2\pi r$$
$$\frac{C}{2\pi} = \frac{2\pi r}{2\pi}$$
$$\frac{C}{2\pi} = r$$

55. Use $V = lwh$ when $V = 900$, $l = 20$ and $h = 3$.
$$V = lwh$$
$$900 = 20 \cdot w \cdot 3$$
$$900 = 60w$$
$$\frac{900}{60} = \frac{60w}{60}$$
$$15 = w$$
The width is 15 meters.

56. Let x be the width. Then the length is $x + 6$. Use $P = 2 \cdot \text{length} + 2 \cdot \text{width}$ when $P = 60$.

$$P = 2 \cdot \text{length} + 2 \cdot \text{width}$$
$$60 = 2(x+6) + 2x$$
$$60 = 2x + 12 + 2x$$
$$60 = 4x + 12$$
$$60 - 12 = 4x + 12 - 12$$
$$48 = 4x$$
$$\frac{48}{4} = \frac{4x}{4}$$
$$12 = x$$
$$x + 6 = 12 + 6 = 18$$

The dimensions of the billboard are 12 feet by 18 feet.

57. Use $d = rt$ when $d = 10K$ or $10,000$ m and $r = 125$.

$$d = rt$$
$$10,000 = 125t$$
$$\frac{10,000}{125} = \frac{125t}{125}$$
$$80 = t$$

The time is 80 minutes or $\frac{80}{60} = 1\frac{1}{3}$ hours or 1 hour and 20 minutes.

58. Use $F = \frac{9}{5}C + 32$ when $F = 104$.

$$F = \frac{9}{5}C + 32$$
$$104 = \frac{9}{5}C + 32$$
$$104 - 32 = \frac{9}{5}C + 32 - 32$$
$$72 = \frac{9}{5}C$$
$$\frac{5}{9} \cdot 72 = \frac{5}{9} \cdot \frac{9}{5}C$$
$$40 = C$$

Thus, 104°F is equivalent to 40°C.

59.

60.

61.
$$x - 5 \le -4$$
$$x - 5 + 5 \le -4 + 5$$
$$x \le 1$$
$$\{x \mid x \le 1\}$$

62.
$$x + 7 > 2$$
$$x + 7 - 7 > 2 - 7$$
$$x > -5$$
$$\{x \mid x > -5\}$$

63.
$$-2x \ge -20$$
$$\frac{-2x}{-2} \le \frac{-20}{-2}$$
$$x \le 10$$
$$\{x \mid x \le 10\}$$

64.
$$-3x > 12$$
$$\frac{-3x}{-3} < \frac{12}{-3}$$
$$x < -4$$
$$\{x \mid x < -4\}$$

65.
$$5x - 7 > 8x + 5$$
$$5x - 7 - 8x > 8x + 5 - 8x$$
$$-3x - 7 > 5$$
$$-3x - 7 + 7 > 5 + 7$$
$$-3x > 12$$
$$\frac{-3x}{-3} < \frac{12}{-3}$$
$$x < -4$$
$$\{x \mid x < -4\}$$

66.
$$x + 4 \ge 6x - 16$$
$$x + 4 - 6x \ge 6x - 16 - 6x$$
$$-5x + 4 \ge -16$$
$$-5x + 4 - 4 \ge -16 - 4$$
$$-5x \ge -20$$
$$\frac{-5x}{-5} \le \frac{-20}{-5}$$
$$x \le 4$$
$$\{x \mid x \le 4\}$$

67.
$$\frac{2}{3}y > 6$$
$$\frac{3}{2} \cdot \frac{2}{3}y > \frac{3}{2} \cdot 6$$
$$y > 9$$
$$\{y \mid y > 9\}$$

68.
$$-0.5y \le 7.5$$
$$\frac{-0.5y}{-0.5} \ge \frac{7.5}{-0.5}$$
$$y \ge -15$$
$$\{y \mid y \ge -15\}$$

69.
$$-2(x-5) > 2(3x-2)$$
$$-2x+10 > 6x-4$$
$$-2x+10-6x > 6x-4-6x$$
$$-8x+10 > -4$$
$$-8x+10-10 > -4-10$$
$$-8x > -14$$
$$\frac{-8x}{-8} < \frac{-14}{-8}$$
$$x < \frac{7}{4}$$
$$\left\{ x \middle| x < \frac{7}{4} \right\}$$

70.
$$4(2x-5) \le 5x-1$$
$$8x-20 \le 5x-1$$
$$8x-20-5x \le 5x-1-5x$$
$$3x-20 \le -1$$
$$3x-20+20 \le -1+20$$
$$3x \le 19$$
$$\frac{3x}{3} \le \frac{19}{3}$$
$$x \le \frac{19}{3}$$
$$\left\{ x \middle| x \le \frac{19}{3} \right\}$$

71. Let x be the sales. Her weekly earnings are $175 + 0.05x$.
$$175 + 0.05x \ge 300$$
$$175 + 0.05x - 175 \ge 300 - 175$$
$$0.05x \ge 125$$
$$\frac{0.05x}{0.05} \ge \frac{125}{0.05}$$
$$x \ge 2500$$
She must have weekly sales of at least $2500.

72. Let x be his score on the fourth round.
$$\frac{76+82+79+x}{4} < 80$$
$$\frac{237+x}{4} < 80$$
$$4 \cdot \frac{237+x}{4} < 4 \cdot 80$$
$$237 + x < 320$$
$$237 + x - 237 < 320 - 237$$
$$x < 83$$
His score must be less than 83.

73.
$$6x + 2x - 1 = 5x + 11$$
$$8x - 1 = 5x + 11$$
$$8x - 1 - 5x = 5x + 11 - 5x$$
$$3x - 1 = 11$$
$$3x - 1 + 1 = 11 + 1$$
$$3x = 12$$
$$\frac{3x}{3} = \frac{12}{3}$$
$$x = 4$$

74.
$$2(3y-4) = 6 + 7y$$
$$6y - 8 = 6 + 7y$$
$$6y - 8 - 6y = 6 + 7y - 6y$$
$$-8 = 6 + y$$
$$-8 - 6 = 6 + y - 6$$
$$-14 = y$$

75.
$$4(3-a) - (6a+9) = -12a$$
$$12 - 4a - 6a - 9 = -12a$$
$$3 - 10a = -12a$$
$$3 - 10a + 10a = -12a + 10a$$
$$3 = -2a$$
$$\frac{3}{-2} = \frac{-2a}{-2}$$
$$-\frac{3}{2} = a$$

76.
$$\frac{x}{3} - 2 = 5$$
$$\frac{x}{3} - 2 + 2 = 5 + 2$$
$$\frac{x}{3} = 7$$
$$3 \cdot \frac{x}{3} = 3 \cdot 7$$
$$x = 21$$

77.
$$2(y+5) = 2y + 10$$
$$2y + 10 = 2y + 10$$
Since both sides of the equation are identical, the equation is an identity and every real number is a solution.

78.
$$7x - 3x + 2 = 2(2x-1)$$
$$4x + 2 = 4x - 2$$
$$4x + 2 - 4x = 4x - 2 - 4x$$
$$2 = -2$$
Since the statement $2 = -2$ is false, there is no solution.

79. Let x be the number.
$$6 + 2x = x - 7$$
$$6 + 2x - x = x - 7 - x$$
$$6 + x = -7$$
$$6 + x - 6 = -7 - 6$$
$$x = -13$$
The number is -13.

80. Let x be the length of the shorter piece. Then $4x + 3$ is the length of the longer piece. The lengths sum to 23.
$$x + 4x + 3 = 23$$
$$5x + 3 = 23$$
$$5x + 3 - 3 = 23 - 3$$
$$5x = 20$$
$$\frac{5x}{5} = \frac{20}{5}$$
$$x = 4$$
$4x + 3 = 4(4) + 3 = 16 + 3 = 19$
The shorter piece is 4 inches and the longer piece is 19 inches.

81. $$V = \frac{1}{3}Ah$$
$$3V = 3 \cdot \frac{1}{3}Ah$$
$$3V = Ah$$
$$\frac{3V}{A} = \frac{Ah}{A}$$
$$\frac{3V}{A} = h$$

82. $$4x - 7 > 3x + 2$$
$$4x - 7 - 3x > 3x + 2 - 3x$$
$$x - 7 > 2$$
$$x - 7 + 7 > 2 + 7$$
$$x > 9$$
$$\{x \mid x > 9\}$$

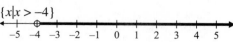

83. $$-5x < 20$$
$$\frac{-5x}{5} > \frac{20}{-5}$$
$$x > -4$$
$$\{x \mid x > -4\}$$

84. $$-3(1 + 2x) + x \geq -(3 - x)$$
$$-3 - 6x + x \geq -3 + x$$
$$-3 - 5x \geq -3 + x$$
$$-3 - 5x - x \geq -3 + x - x$$
$$-3 - 6x \geq -3$$
$$-3 - 6x + 3 \geq -3 + 3$$
$$-6x \geq 0$$
$$\frac{-6x}{-6} \leq \frac{0}{-6}$$
$$x \leq 0$$
$$\{x \mid x \leq 0\}$$

Chapter 9 Test

1. The absolute value of negative seven is greater than five is written as $|-7| > 5$.

2. The sum of nine and five is greater than or equal to four is written as $(9 + 5) \geq 4$.

3. a. The natural numbers are 1, 7.

   b. The whole numbers are 0, 1, 7.

   c. The integers are $-5, -1, 0, 1, 7$.

   d. The rational numbers are $-5, -1, \frac{1}{4}, 0, 1, 7,$ 11.6.

   e. The irrational numbers are $\sqrt{7}, 3\pi$.

   f. The real numbers are $-5, -1, \frac{1}{4}, 0, 1, 7,$ 11.6, $\sqrt{7}, 3\pi$.

4. $8 + (9 + 3) = (8 + 9) + 3$ illustrates the associative property of addition.

5. $6 \cdot 8 = 8 \cdot 6$ illustrates the commutative property of multiplication.

6. $-6(2 + 4) = -6 \cdot 2 + (-6) \cdot 4$ illustrates the distributive property.

7. $\frac{1}{6}(6) = 1$ illustrates the multiplicative inverse property.

8. The opposite of -9 is 9.

9. The reciprocal of $-\dfrac{1}{3}$ of -3.

10. $7+2(5y-3)=7+10y-6$
$=7-6+10y$
$=1+10y$
$=10y+1$

11. $4(x-2)-3(2x-6)=4x-8-6x+18$
$=4x-6x-8+18$
$=-2x+10$

12. $4(n-5)=-(4-2n)$
$4n-20=-4+2n$
$4n-20-2n=-4+2n-2n$
$2n-20=-4$
$2n-20+20=-4+20$
$2n=16$
$\dfrac{2n}{2}=\dfrac{16}{2}$
$n=8$

13. $-2(x-3)=x+5-3x$
$-2x+6=-2x+5$
$2x-2x+6=2x-2x+5$
$6=5$
Since the statement $6=5$ is false, there is no solution.

14. $4z+1-z=1+z$
$3z+1=1+z$
$3z+1-z=1+z-z$
$2z+1=1$
$2z+1-1=1-1$
$2z=0$
$\dfrac{2z}{2}=\dfrac{0}{2}$
$z=0$

15. $\dfrac{2(x+6)}{3}=x-5$
$3\left(\dfrac{2(x+6)}{3}\right)=3(x-5)$
$2(x+6)=3(x-5)$
$2x+12=3x-15$
$2x+12-2x=3x-15-2x$
$12=x-15$
$12+15=x-15+15$
$27=x$

16. $\dfrac{1}{2}-x+\dfrac{3}{2}=x-4$
$-x+\dfrac{4}{2}=x-4$
$-x+2=x-4$
$-x+2+x=x-4+x$
$2=2x-4$
$2+4=2x-4+4$
$6=2x$
$\dfrac{6}{2}=\dfrac{2x}{2}$
$3=x$

17. $-0.3(x-4)+x=0.5(3-x)$
$-0.3(x-4)+1.0x=0.5(3-x)$
$-3(x-4)+10x=5(3-x)$
$-3x+12+10x=15-5x$
$7x+12=15-5x$
$7x+12+5x=15-5x+5x$
$12x+12=15$
$12x+12-12=15-12$
$12x=3$
$\dfrac{12x}{12}=\dfrac{3}{12}$
$x=\dfrac{1}{4}=0.25$

18. $-4(a+1)-3a=-7(2a-3)$
$-4a-4-3a=-14a+21$
$-4-7a=-14a+21$
$-4-7a+14a=-14a+21+14a$
$-4+7a=21$
$-4+7a+4=21+4$
$7a=25$
$\dfrac{7a}{7}=\dfrac{25}{7}$
$a=\dfrac{25}{7}$

19. Let x be the number.
$x+\dfrac{2}{3}x=35$
$\dfrac{3}{3}x+\dfrac{2}{3}x=35$
$\dfrac{5}{3}x=35$
$\dfrac{3}{5}\cdot\dfrac{5}{3}x=\dfrac{3}{5}\cdot 35$
$x=21$
The number is 21.

20. $A = lw = (35)(20) = 700$
The area of the deck is 700 square feet. To paint two coats of water seal means covering $2 \cdot 700 = 1400$ square feet.

$$1400 \text{ sq ft} \cdot \frac{1 \text{ gal}}{200 \text{ sq ft}} = 7 \text{ gal}$$

7 gallons of water seal are needed.

21. Use $y = mx + b$ when $y = -14$, $m = -2$, and $b = -2$.

$$y = mx + b$$
$$-14 = -2x + (-2)$$
$$-14 + 2 = -2x + (-2) + 2$$
$$-12 = -2x$$
$$\frac{-12}{-2} = \frac{-2x}{-2}$$
$$6 = x$$

22. $V = \pi r^2 h$

$$\frac{V}{\pi r^2} = \frac{\pi r^2 h}{\pi r^2}$$
$$\frac{V}{\pi r^2} = h$$

23.
$$3x - 4y = 10$$
$$3x - 4y - 3x = 10 - 3x$$
$$-4y = 10 - 3x$$
$$\frac{-4y}{-4} = \frac{10 - 3x}{-4}$$
$$y = \frac{3x - 10}{4}$$

24.
$$3x - 5 > 7x + 3$$
$$3x - 5 - 3x > 7x + 3 - 3x$$
$$-5 > 4x + 3$$
$$-5 - 3 > 4x + 3 - 3$$
$$-8 > 4x$$
$$\frac{-8}{4} > \frac{4x}{4}$$
$$-2 > x$$

$\{x | x < -2\}$

25. $-0.3x \geq 2.4$

$$\frac{-0.3x}{-0.3} \leq \frac{2.4}{-0.3}$$
$$x \leq -8$$

$\{x | x \leq -8\}$

26.
$$-5(x - 1) + 6 \leq -3(x + 4) + 1$$
$$-5x + 5 + 6 \leq -3x - 12 + 1$$
$$-5x + 11 \leq -3x - 11$$
$$-5x + 11 + 3x \leq -3x - 11 + 3x$$
$$-2x + 11 \leq -11$$
$$-2x + 11 - 11 \leq -11 - 11$$
$$-2x \leq -22$$
$$\frac{-2x}{-2} \geq \frac{-22}{-2}$$
$$x \geq 11$$

$\{x | x \geq 11\}$

27.
$$\frac{2(5x + 1)}{3} > 2$$
$$3 \cdot \frac{2(5x + 1)}{3} > 3(2)$$
$$2(5x + 1) > 6$$
$$10x + 2 > 6$$
$$10x + 2 - 2 > 6 - 2$$
$$10x > 4$$
$$\frac{10x}{10} > \frac{4}{10}$$
$$x > \frac{2}{5}$$

$$\left\{ x \,\middle|\, x > \frac{2}{5} \right\}$$

28. Let x represent the number of public libraries in Indiana. Then there are $x + 650$ public libraries in New York.

$$x + x + 650 = 1504$$
$$2x + 650 = 1504$$
$$2x + 650 - 650 = 1504 - 650$$
$$2x = 854$$
$$\frac{2x}{2} = \frac{854}{2}$$
$$x = 427$$

$x + 650 = 427 + 650 = 1077$
Indiana has 427 public libraries and New York has 1077.

Cumulative Review Chapters 1–9

1. a. $-(-4) = 4$

   b. $-|-5| = -5$

   c. $-|6| = -6$

2. a. $|0| < 2$ since $|0| = 0$ and $0 < 2$.

   b. $|-5| = 5$

c. $|-3| > |-2|$ since $3 > 2$.

d. $|5| < |6|$ since $5 < 6$.

e. $|-7| > |6|$ since $7 > 6$.

3. $-2[-3+2(-1+6)]-5 = -2[-3+2(5)]-5$
$$= -2(-3+10)-5$$
$$= -2(7)-5$$
$$= -14-5$$
$$= -19$$

4. $\dfrac{3+|4-3|+2^2}{6-3} = \dfrac{3+|1|+2^2}{6-3}$
$$= \dfrac{3+1+2^2}{3}$$
$$= \dfrac{3+1+4}{3}$$
$$= \dfrac{8}{3}$$

5. $-18 + 10 = -8$

6. $(-8) + (-11) = -19$

7. $12 + (-8) = 4$

8. $(-2) + 10 = 8$

9. $(-3) + 4 + (-11) = 1 + (-11) = -10$

10. $0.2 + (-0.5) = -0.3$

11. $\dfrac{2}{3} - \dfrac{10}{11} = \dfrac{2}{3} \cdot \dfrac{11}{11} - \dfrac{10}{11} \cdot \dfrac{3}{3}$
$$= \dfrac{22}{33} - \dfrac{30}{33}$$
$$= \dfrac{22-30}{33}$$
$$= \dfrac{-8}{33}$$
$$= -\dfrac{8}{33}$$

12. $\dfrac{2}{5} - \dfrac{39}{40} = \dfrac{2}{5} \cdot \dfrac{8}{8} - \dfrac{39}{40}$
$$= \dfrac{16}{40} - \dfrac{39}{40}$$
$$= \dfrac{16-39}{40}$$
$$= \dfrac{-23}{40}$$
$$= -\dfrac{23}{40}$$

13. $2 - \dfrac{x}{3} = \dfrac{2}{1} - \dfrac{x}{3} = \dfrac{2}{1} \cdot \dfrac{3}{3} - \dfrac{x}{3} = \dfrac{6}{3} - \dfrac{x}{3} = \dfrac{6-x}{3}$

14. $5 + \dfrac{x}{2} = \dfrac{5}{1} + \dfrac{x}{2} = \dfrac{5}{1} \cdot \dfrac{2}{2} + \dfrac{x}{2} = \dfrac{10}{2} + \dfrac{x}{2} = \dfrac{10+x}{2}$

15. $2x + y^2 = 2\left(-\dfrac{1}{2}\right) + \left(\dfrac{1}{3}\right)^2$
$$= 2\left(-\dfrac{1}{2}\right) + \dfrac{1}{9}$$
$$= -1 + \dfrac{1}{9}$$
$$= -\dfrac{9}{9} + \dfrac{1}{9}$$
$$= -\dfrac{8}{9}$$

16. $2y + x^2 = 2\left(\dfrac{1}{3}\right) + \left(-\dfrac{1}{2}\right)^2$
$$= 2\left(\dfrac{1}{3}\right) + \dfrac{1}{4}$$
$$= \dfrac{2}{3} + \dfrac{1}{4}$$
$$= \dfrac{8}{12} + \dfrac{3}{12}$$
$$= \dfrac{11}{12}$$

17. $-4\dfrac{2}{5} \cdot 1\dfrac{3}{11} = -\dfrac{22}{5} \cdot \dfrac{14}{11} = -\dfrac{2 \cdot 11 \cdot 14}{5 \cdot 11} = -\dfrac{28}{5} = -5\dfrac{3}{5}$

18. $-2\dfrac{1}{2} \cdot \left(-2\dfrac{1}{2}\right) = -\dfrac{5}{2} \cdot \left(-\dfrac{5}{2}\right) = \dfrac{25}{4} = 6\dfrac{1}{4}$

19. $-2\dfrac{1}{3} \div \left(-2\dfrac{1}{2}\right) = -\dfrac{7}{3} \div \left(-\dfrac{5}{2}\right) = -\dfrac{7}{3} \cdot \left(-\dfrac{2}{5}\right) = \dfrac{14}{15}$

20.
$$3\frac{3}{5} \div \left(-3\frac{1}{3}\right) = \frac{18}{5} \div \left(-\frac{10}{3}\right)$$
$$= \frac{18}{5} \cdot \left(-\frac{3}{10}\right)$$
$$= -\frac{2 \cdot 9 \cdot 3}{5 \cdot 2 \cdot 5}$$
$$= -\frac{27}{25}$$
$$= -1\frac{2}{25}$$

21. $(-1.3)^2 + 2.4 = 1.69 + 2.4 = 4.09$

22. $1.2(7.3 - 9.3) = 1.2(-2) = -2.4$

23. $\sqrt{49} = 7$ since $7^2 = 7 \cdot 7 = 49$.

24. $\sqrt{64} = 8$ since $8^2 = 8 \cdot 8 = 64$.

25. $\sqrt{\frac{4}{25}} = \frac{2}{5}$ since $\left(\frac{2}{5}\right)^2 = \frac{2}{5} \cdot \frac{2}{5} = \frac{4}{25}$.

26. $\sqrt{\frac{9}{100}} = \frac{3}{10}$ since $\left(\frac{3}{10}\right)^2 = \frac{3}{10} \cdot \frac{3}{10} = \frac{9}{100}$.

27.
$$1.2x + 5.8 = 8.2$$
$$10(1.2x + 5.8) = 10(8.2)$$
$$12x + 58 = 82$$
$$12x + 58 - 58 = 82 - 58$$
$$12x = 24$$
$$\frac{12x}{12} = \frac{24}{12}$$
$$x = 2$$

28.
$$1.3x - 2.6 = -9.1$$
$$10(1.3x - 2.6) = 10(-9.1)$$
$$13x - 26 = -91$$
$$13x - 26 + 26 = -91 + 26$$
$$13x = -65$$
$$\frac{13x}{13} = \frac{-65}{13}$$
$$x = -5$$

29. Since $8 = 8$, the statement $8 \geq 8$ is true.

30. Since $-4 = -4$, the statement $-4 \leq -4$ is true.

31. Since $8 = 8$, the statement $8 \leq 8$ is true.

32. Since $-4 = -4$, the statement $-4 \geq -4$ is true.

33. Since neither $23 < 0$ nor $23 = 0$ is true, the statement $23 \leq 0$ is false.

34. Since $-8 < 0$ is true, the statement $-8 \leq 0$ is true.

35. Since $0 < 23$ is true, the statement $0 \leq 23$ is true.

36. Since neither $0 < -8$ nor $0 = -8$ is true, the statement $0 \leq -8$ is false.

37. $-5(-3 + 2z) = -5(-3) + (-5)(2z) = 15 - 10z$

38. $-4(2x - 1) = -4(2x) - (-4)(1) = -8x + 4$

39.
$$\frac{1}{2}(6x + 14) + 10 = \frac{1}{2}(6x) + \frac{1}{2}(14) + 10$$
$$= 3x + 7 + 10$$
$$= 3x + 17$$

40.
$$9 + 2(5x + 6) = 9 + 2(5x) + 2(6)$$
$$= 9 + 10x + 12$$
$$= 10x + 9 + 12$$
$$= 10x + 21$$

41.
$$\frac{2(a + 3)}{3} = 6a + 2$$
$$3 \cdot \frac{2(a + 3)}{3} = 3(6a + 2)$$
$$2(a + 3) = 3(6a + 2)$$
$$2a + 6 = 18a + 6$$
$$2a + 6 - 18a = 18a + 6 - 18a$$
$$-16a + 6 = 6$$
$$-16a + 6 - 6 = 6 - 6$$
$$-16a = 0$$
$$\frac{-16a}{-16} = \frac{0}{-16}$$
$$a = 0$$

42.
$$\frac{x}{2} + \frac{x}{5} = 3$$
$$10\left(\frac{x}{2} + \frac{x}{5}\right) = 10(3)$$
$$5x + 2x = 30$$
$$7x = 30$$
$$\frac{7x}{7} = \frac{30}{7}$$
$$x = \frac{30}{7}$$

43. Let x be the number of Republicans. Then $x + 78$ is the number of Democrats. The total number is 434.

$$x + x + 78 = 434$$
$$2x + 78 = 434$$
$$2x + 78 - 78 = 434 - 78$$
$$2x = 356$$
$$\frac{2x}{2} = \frac{356}{2}$$
$$x = 178$$

$x + 78 = 178 + 78 = 256$

There are 178 Republicans and 256 Democrats.

44. Let x be the number.

$$3(x + 2) = 9x$$
$$3x + 6 = 9x$$
$$3x - 3x + 6 = 9x - 3x$$
$$6 = 6x$$
$$\frac{6}{6} = \frac{6x}{6}$$
$$1 = x$$

The number is 1.

45. Use $d = rt$ when $d = 31{,}680$ and $r = 400$.

$$d = rt$$
$$31{,}680 = 400t$$
$$\frac{31{,}680}{400} = \frac{400t}{400}$$
$$79.2 = t$$

It will take the ice 79.2 years to reach the lake.

46.
$$V = lwh$$
$$\frac{V}{lh} = \frac{lwh}{lh}$$
$$\frac{V}{lh} = w$$

47. $-1 > x$ or $x < -1$

48. $-3x < -30$
$$\frac{-3x}{-3} > \frac{-30}{-3}$$
$$x > 10$$
$$\{x | x > 10\}$$

49. $2(x - 3) - 5 \le 3(x + 2) - 18$
$$2x - 6 - 5 \le 3x + 6 - 18$$
$$2x - 11 \le 3x - 12$$
$$-x - 11 \le -12$$
$$-x \le -1$$
$$\frac{-x}{-1} \ge \frac{-1}{-1}$$
$$x \ge 1$$
$$\{x | x \ge 1\}$$

50. $10 + x < 6x - 10$
$$10 + x - x < 6x - x - 10$$
$$10 < 5x - 10$$
$$10 + 10 < 5x - 10 + 10$$
$$20 < 5x$$
$$\frac{20}{5} < \frac{5x}{5}$$
$$4 < x$$
$$\{x | x > 4\}$$

Chapter 10

Practice Problems

1. $3^4 = 3 \cdot 3 \cdot 3 \cdot 3 = 81$

2. $7^1 = 7$

3. $(-2)^3 = (-2)(-2)(-2) = -8$

4. $-2^3 = -(2 \cdot 2 \cdot 2) = -8$

5. $\left(\dfrac{2}{3}\right)^2 = \dfrac{2}{3} \cdot \dfrac{2}{3} = \dfrac{4}{9}$

6. $5 \cdot 6^2 = 5 \cdot 36 = 180$

7. a. When x is 4, $3x^2 = 3 \cdot 4^2$
$$= 3 \cdot (4 \cdot 4)$$
$$= 3 \cdot 16$$
$$= 48.$$

b. When x is -2, $\dfrac{x^4}{-8} = \dfrac{(-2)^4}{-8}$
$$= \dfrac{(-2)(-2)(-2)(-2)}{-8}$$
$$= \dfrac{16}{-8}$$
$$= -2.$$

8. $7^3 \cdot 7^2 = 7^{3+2} = 7^5$

9. $x^4 \cdot x^9 = x^{4+9} = x^{13}$

10. $r^5 \cdot r = r^{5+1} = r^6$

11. $s^6 \cdot s^2 \cdot s^3 = s^{6+2+3} = s^{11}$

12. $(-3)^9 \cdot (-3) = (-3)^{9+1} = (-3)^{10}$

13. $(6x^3)(-2x^9) = (6 \cdot x^3) \cdot (-2 \cdot x^9)$
$$= (6 \cdot -2) \cdot (x^3 \cdot x^9)$$
$$= -12x^{12}$$

14. $(m^5 n^{10})(mn^8) = (m^5 \cdot m) \cdot (n^{10} \cdot n^8)$
$$= m^6 \cdot n^{18}$$
$$= m^6 n^{18}$$

15. $(-x^9 y)(4x^2 y^{11}) = (-1 \cdot 4) \cdot (x^9 \cdot x^2) \cdot (y \cdot y^{11})$
$$= -4x^{11} y^{12}$$

16. $(9^4)^{10} = 9^{4 \cdot 10} = 9^{40}$

17. $(z^6)^3 = z^{6 \cdot 3} = z^{18}$

18. $(xy)^7 = x^7 \cdot y^7 = x^7 y^7$

19. $(3y)^4 = 3^4 \cdot y^4 = 81y^4$

20. $(-2p^4 q^2 r)^3 = (-2)^3 \cdot (p^4)^3 \cdot (q^2)^3 \cdot (r^1)^3$
$$= -8p^{12} q^6 r^3$$

21. $(-a^4 b)^7 = (-1a^4 b)^7$
$$= (-1)^7 \cdot (a^4)^7 \cdot (b^1)^7$$
$$= -1a^{28} b^7$$
$$= -a^{28} b^7$$

22. $\left(\dfrac{r}{s}\right)^6 = \dfrac{r^6}{s^6}, \ s \neq 0$

23. $\left(\dfrac{5x^6}{9y^3}\right)^2 = \dfrac{5^2 \cdot (x^6)^2}{9^2 \cdot (y^3)^2} = \dfrac{25x^{12}}{81y^6}, \ y \neq 0$

24. $\dfrac{y^7}{y^3} = y^{7-3} = y^4$

25. $\dfrac{5^9}{5^6} = 5^{9-6} = 5^3 = 125$

26. $\dfrac{(-2)^{14}}{(-2)^{10}} = (-2)^{14-10} = (-2)^4 = 16$

27. $\dfrac{7a^4 b^{11}}{ab} = 7 \cdot \dfrac{a^4}{a^1} \cdot \dfrac{b^{11}}{b^1}$

$\quad = 7 \cdot (a^{4-1}) \cdot (b^{11-1})$

$\quad = 7a^3 b^{10}$

28. $8^0 = 1$

29. $(2r^2 s)^0 = 1$

30. $(-7)^0 = 1$

31. $-7^0 = -1 \cdot 7^0 = -1 \cdot 1 = -1$

32. $7y^0 = 7 \cdot y^0 = 7 \cdot 1 = 7$

33. a. $\dfrac{x^7}{x^4} = x^{7-4} = x^3$

   b. $(3y^4)^4 = 3^4 \cdot (y^4)^4 = 81y^{16}$

   c. $\left(\dfrac{x}{4}\right)^3 = \dfrac{x^3}{4^3} = \dfrac{x^3}{64}$

Vocabulary and Readiness Check

1. Repeated multiplication of the same factor can be written using an <u>exponent</u>.

2. In 5^2, the 2 is called the <u>exponent</u> and the 5 is called the <u>base</u>.

3. To simplify $x^2 \cdot x^7$, keep the base and <u>add</u> the exponents.

4. To simplify $(x^3)^6$, keep the base and <u>multiply</u> the exponents.

5. The understood exponent on the term y is <u>1</u>.

6. If $x^{\square} = 1$, the exponent is <u>0</u>.

7. In 3^2, the base is 3 and the exponent is 2.

8. In $(-3)^6$, the base is -3 and the exponent is 6.

9. In -4^2, the base is 4 and the exponent is 2.

10. In $5 \cdot 3^4 = 5^1 \cdot 3^4$, the base 5 has exponent 1 and the base 3 has exponent 4.

11. In $5x^2 = 5^1 x^2$, the base 5 has exponent 1 and the base x has exponent 2.

12. In $(5x)^2$, the base is $5x$ and the exponent is 2.

Exercise Set 10.1

1. $7^2 = 7 \cdot 7 = 49$

3. $(-5)^1 = -5$

5. $-2^4 = -(2 \cdot 2 \cdot 2 \cdot 2) = -16$

7. $(-2)^4 = (-2)(-2)(-2)(-2) = 16$

9. $\left(\dfrac{1}{3}\right)^3 = \dfrac{1}{3} \cdot \dfrac{1}{3} \cdot \dfrac{1}{3} = \dfrac{1}{27}$

11. $7 \cdot 2^4 = 7(2 \cdot 2 \cdot 2 \cdot 2) = 7 \cdot 16 = 112$

13. When x is -2, $x^2 = (-2)^2 = (-2)(-2) = 4$.

15. When x is 3,

$5x^3 = 5(3)^3 = 5(3)(3)(3) = 5(27) = 135$.

17. When $x = 3$ and $y = -5$,

$2xy^2 = 2(3)(-5)^2$

$\quad = 2(3)(-5)(-5)$

$\quad = 2(3)(25)$

$\quad = 150$.

19. When z is -2,

$\dfrac{2z^4}{5} = \dfrac{2(-2)^4}{5}$

$\quad = \dfrac{2(-2)(-2)(-2)(-2)}{5}$

$\quad = \dfrac{2(16)}{5}$

$\quad = \dfrac{32}{5}$.

21. $x^2 \cdot x^5 = x^{2+5} = x^7$

23. $(-3)^3 \cdot (-3)^9 = (-3)^{3+9} = (-3)^{12}$

25. $(5y^4)(3y) = (5 \cdot 3)(y^4 \cdot y) = 15y^{4+1} = 15y^5$

27. $(x^9 y)(x^{10} y^5) = (x^9 \cdot x^{10})(y \cdot y^5)$
$\qquad = (x^{9+10})(y^{1+5})$
$\qquad = x^{19} y^6$

29. $(-8mn^6)(9m^2 n^2) = (-8 \cdot 9)(m \cdot m^2)(n^6 \cdot n^2)$
$\qquad = -72m^{1+2} n^{6+2}$
$\qquad = -72m^3 n^8$

31. $(4z^{10})(-6z^7)(z^3) = (4 \cdot -6 \cdot 1)(z^{10} \cdot z^7 \cdot z^3)$
$\qquad = -24z^{10+7+3}$
$\qquad = -24z^{20}$

33. Area = (length)(width)
$\qquad = (5x^3 \text{ feet})(4x^2 \text{ feet})$
$\qquad = (5 \cdot 4)(x^3 \cdot x^2) \text{ square feet}$
$\qquad = 20x^{3+2} \text{ square feet}$
$\qquad = 20x^5 \text{ square feet}$

35. $(x^9)^4 = x^{9 \cdot 4} = x^{36}$

37. $(pq)^8 = p^8 \cdot q^8 = p^8 q^8$

39. $(2a^5)^3 = (2)^3 (a^5)^3 = 2^3 a^{15} = 8a^{15}$

41. $(x^2 y^3)^5 = (x^2)^5 (y^3)^5 = x^{10} y^{15}$

43. $(-7a^2 b^5 c)^2 = (-7)^2 (a^2)^2 (b^5)^2 (c)^2$
$\qquad = 49a^4 b^{10} c^2$

45. $\left(\dfrac{r}{s}\right)^9 = \dfrac{r^9}{s^9}$

47. $\left(\dfrac{mp}{n}\right)^9 = \dfrac{m^9 p^9}{n^9}$

49. $\left(\dfrac{-2xz}{y^5}\right)^2 = \dfrac{(-2)^2 (x)^2 (z)^2}{(y^5)^2}$
$\qquad = \dfrac{4x^2 z^2}{y^{5 \cdot 2}}$
$\qquad = \dfrac{4x^2 z^2}{y^{10}}$

51. Area = (length)(length)
$\qquad = (8z^5 \text{ decimeters})(8z^5 \text{ decimeters})$
$\qquad = (8 \cdot 8)(z^5 \cdot z^5) \text{ square decimeters}$
$\qquad = 64z^{5+5} \text{ square decimeters}$
$\qquad = 64z^{10} \text{ square decimeters}$

53. Volume = (length)(width)(height)
$\qquad = (3y^4 \text{ feet})(3y^4 \text{ feet})(3y^4 \text{ feet})$
$\qquad = (3)^3 (y^4)^3 \text{ cubic feet}$
$\qquad = 27y^{4 \cdot 3} \text{ cubic feet}$
$\qquad = 27y^{12} \text{ cubic feet}$

55. $\dfrac{x^3}{x} = x^{3-1} = x^2$

57. $\dfrac{(-4)^6}{(-4)^3} = (-4)^{6-3} = (-4)^3 = -64$

59. $\dfrac{p^7 q^{20}}{pq^{15}} = \dfrac{p^7}{p} \cdot \dfrac{q^{20}}{q^{15}} = p^{7-1} \cdot q^{20-15} = p^6 q^5$

61. $\dfrac{7x^2 y^6}{14x^2 y^3} = \dfrac{7}{14} \cdot \dfrac{x^2}{x^2} \cdot \dfrac{y^6}{y^3}$
$\qquad = \dfrac{1}{2} \cdot x^{2-2} \cdot y^{6-3}$
$\qquad = \dfrac{1}{2} x^0 y^3$
$\qquad = \dfrac{y^3}{2}$

63. $7^0 = 1$

65. $(2x)^0 = 1$

67. $-7x^0 = -7 \cdot x^0 = -7 \cdot 1 = -7$

69. $5^0 + y^0 = 1 + 1 = 2$

71. $-9^2 = -(9)^2 = -(9 \cdot 9) = -81$

73. $\left(\dfrac{1}{4}\right)^3 = \dfrac{1}{4} \cdot \dfrac{1}{4} \cdot \dfrac{1}{4} = \dfrac{1}{64}$

75. $b^4 b^2 = b^{4+2} = b^6$

77. $a^2 a^3 a^4 = a^{2+3+4} = a^9$

79. $(2x^3)(-8x^4) = (2 \cdot -8)(x^3 \cdot x^4)$
$= -16x^{3+4}$
$= -16x^7$

81. $(a^7 b^{12})(a^4 b^8) = a^7 a^4 \cdot b^{12} b^8$
$= a^{7+4} b^{12+8}$
$= a^{11} b^{20}$

83. $(-2mn^6)(-13m^8 n) = (-2)(-13)(m \cdot m^8)(n^6 \cdot n)$
$= 26m^{1+8} n^{6+1}$
$= 26m^9 n^7$

85. $(z^4)^{10} = z^{4 \cdot 10} = z^{40}$

87. $(4ab)^3 = (4)^3 a^3 b^3 = 64a^3 b^3$

89. $(-6xyz^3)^2 = (-6)^2 x^2 y^2 (z^3)^2$
$= 36x^2 y^2 z^{3 \cdot 2}$
$= 36x^2 y^2 z^6$

91. $\dfrac{z^{12}}{z^4} = z^{12-4} = z^8$

93. $\dfrac{3x^5}{x^4} = 3 \cdot \dfrac{x^5}{x^4} = 3x^{5-4} = 3x^1 = 3x$

95. $(6b)^0 = 1$

97. $(9xy)^2 = 9^2 \cdot x^2 y^2 = 81x^2 y^2$

99. $2^3 + 2^5 = (2 \cdot 2 \cdot 2) + (2 \cdot 2 \cdot 2 \cdot 2 \cdot 2)$
$= 8 + 32$
$= 40$

101. $\left(\dfrac{3y^5}{6x^4}\right)^3 = \left(\dfrac{y^5}{2x^4}\right)^3 = \dfrac{(y^5)^3}{2^3 (x^4)^3} = \dfrac{y^{5 \cdot 3}}{8x^{4 \cdot 3}} = \dfrac{y^{15}}{8x^{12}}$

103. $\dfrac{2x^3 y^2 z}{xyz} = 2 \cdot \dfrac{x^3}{x} \cdot \dfrac{y^2}{y} \cdot \dfrac{z}{z}$
$= 2x^{3-1} y^{2-1} z^{1-1}$
$= 2x^2 y^1 z^0$
$= 2x^2 y$

105. $5 - 7 = 5 + (-7) = -2$

107. $3 - (-2) = 3 + 2 = 5$

109. $-11 - (-4) = -11 + 4 = -7$

111. The expression $(x^{14})^{23}$ can be simplified by multiplying the exponents; c.

113. The expression $x^{14} + x^{23}$ cannot be simplified by adding subtracting, multiplying, or dividing the exponents; e.

115. answers may vary

117. answers may vary

119. $V = x^3$
$= (7 \text{ meters})^3$
$= 7^3$ cubic meters
$= 343$ cubic meters

121. The volume of a cube measures the amount of material that the cube can hold, so to find the amount of water that a swimming pool can hold, the formula for volume should be used.

123. answers may vary

125. answers may vary

127. $x^{5a} x^{4a} = x^{5a+4a} = x^{9a}$

129. $(a^b)^5 = a^{b \cdot 5} = a^{5b}$

131. $\dfrac{x^{9a}}{x^{4a}} = x^{9a-4a} = x^{5a}$

Section 10.2

Practice Problems

1. $5^{-3} = \dfrac{1}{5^3} = \dfrac{1}{125}$

2. $7x^{-4} = 7^1 \cdot \dfrac{1}{x^4} = \dfrac{7^1}{x^4}$ or $\dfrac{7}{x^4}$

3. $5^{-1} + 3^{-1} = \dfrac{1}{5} + \dfrac{1}{3} = \dfrac{3}{15} + \dfrac{5}{15} = \dfrac{8}{15}$

4. $(-3)^{-4} = \dfrac{1}{(-3)^4} = \dfrac{1}{(-3)(-3)(-3)(-3)} = \dfrac{1}{81}$

5. $\left(\dfrac{6}{7}\right)^{-2} = \dfrac{6^{-2}}{7^{-2}} = \dfrac{6^{-2}}{1} \cdot \dfrac{1}{7^{-2}} = \dfrac{1}{6^2} \cdot \dfrac{7^2}{1} = \dfrac{7^2}{6^2} = \dfrac{49}{36}$

6. $\dfrac{x}{x^{-4}} = \dfrac{x^1}{x^{-4}} = x^{1-(-4)} = x^5$

7. $\dfrac{y^{-9}}{z^{-5}} = y^{-9} \cdot \dfrac{1}{z^{-5}} = \dfrac{1}{y^9} \cdot z^5 = \dfrac{z^5}{y^9}$

8. $\dfrac{y^{-4}}{y^6} = y^{-4-6} = y^{-10} = \dfrac{1}{y^{10}}$

9. $\dfrac{(x^5)^3 x}{x^4} = \dfrac{x^{15} \cdot x}{x^4}$
$= \dfrac{x^{15+1}}{x^4}$
$= \dfrac{x^{16}}{x^4}$
$= x^{16-4}$
$= x^{12}$

10. $\left(\dfrac{9x^3}{y}\right)^{-2} = \dfrac{9^{-2}(x^3)^{-2}}{y^{-2}}$
$= \dfrac{9^{-2}x^{-6}}{y^{-2}}$
$= \dfrac{y^2}{9^2 x^6}$
$= \dfrac{y^2}{81x^6}$

11. $(a^{-4}b^7)^{-5} = (a^{-4})^{-5}(b^7)^{-5} = a^{20}b^{-35} = \dfrac{a^{20}}{b^{35}}$

12. $\dfrac{(2x)^4}{x^8} = \dfrac{2^4 x^4}{x^8} = 2^4 x^{4-8} = 2^4 x^{-4} = \dfrac{16}{x^4}$

13. $\dfrac{y^{-10}}{(y^5)^4} = \dfrac{y^{-10}}{y^{20}} = y^{-10-20} = y^{-30} = \dfrac{1}{y^{30}}$

14. $(4a^2)^{-3} = 4^{-3}(a^2)^{-3} = 4^{-3}a^{-6} = \dfrac{1}{4^3 a^6} = \dfrac{1}{64a^6}$

15. $-\dfrac{32x^{-3}y^{-6}}{8x^{-5}y^{-2}} = -\dfrac{32}{8} \cdot x^{-3-(-5)}y^{-6-(-2)}$
$= -4x^2 y^{-4}$
$= -\dfrac{4x^2}{y^4}$

16. $\dfrac{(3x^{-2}y)^{-2}}{(2x^7 y)^3} = \dfrac{3^{-2}(x^{-2})^{-2}y^{-2}}{2^3(x^7)^3 y^3}$
$= \dfrac{3^{-2}x^4 y^{-2}}{2^3 x^{21} y^3}$
$= \dfrac{3^{-2}}{2^3} \cdot x^{4-21}y^{-2-3}$
$= \dfrac{3^{-2}}{2^3} x^{-17} y^{-5}$
$= \dfrac{1}{2^3 3^2 x^{17} y^5}$
$= \dfrac{1}{72x^{17} y^5}$

17. a. $420,000 = 4.2 \times 10^5$

b. $0.00017 = 1.7 \times 10^{-4}$

c. $9,060,000,000 = 9.06 \times 10^9$

d. $0.000007 = 7.0 \times 10^{-6}$

18. a. $3.062 \times 10^{-4} = 0.0003062$

b. $5.21 \times 10^4 = 52,100$

c. $9.6 \times 10^{-5} = 0.000096$

d. $6.002 \times 10^6 = 6,002,000$

19. a. $(9 \times 10^7)(4 \times 10^{-9}) = 9 \cdot 4 \cdot 10^7 \cdot 10^{-9}$
$= 36 \times 10^{-2}$
$= 0.36$

b. $\dfrac{8\times10^4}{2\times10^{-3}} = \dfrac{8}{2}\times10^{4-(-3)}$

$\qquad\qquad = 4\times10^7$

$\qquad\qquad = 40,000,000$

Calculator Explorations

1. 5.31×10^3 5.31 EE 3

2. -4.8×10^{14} -4.8 EE 14

3. 6.6×10^{-9} 6.6 EE -9

4. -9.9811×10^{-2} -9.9811 EE -2

5. $3,000,000\times5,000,000 = 1.5\times10^{13}$

6. $230,000\times1,000 = 2.3\times10^8$

7. $(3.26\times10^6)(2.5\times10^{13}) = 8.15\times10^{19}$

8. $(8.76\times10^{-4})(1.237\times10^9) = 1.083612\times10^6$

Vocabulary and Readiness Check

1. The expression x^{-3} equals $\dfrac{1}{x^3}$.

2. The expression 5^{-4} equals $\dfrac{1}{625}$.

3. The number 3.021×10^{-3} is written in <u>scientific notation</u>.

4. The number 0.0261 is written in <u>standard form</u>.

5. $5x^{-2} = 5\cdot\dfrac{1}{x^2} = \dfrac{5}{x^2}$

6. $3x^{-3} = 3\cdot\dfrac{1}{x^3} = \dfrac{3}{x^3}$

7. $\dfrac{1}{y^{-6}} = y^6$

8. $\dfrac{1}{x^{-3}} = x^3$

9. $\dfrac{4}{y^{-3}} = 4\cdot\dfrac{1}{y^{-3}} = 4y^3$

10. $\dfrac{16}{y^{-7}} = 16\cdot\dfrac{1}{y^{-7}} = 16y^7$

Exercise Set 10.2

1. $4^{-3} = \dfrac{1}{4^3} = \dfrac{1}{64}$

3. $7x^{-3} = 7\cdot\dfrac{1}{x^3} = \dfrac{7}{x^3}$

5. $\left(-\dfrac{1}{4}\right)^{-3} = \dfrac{(-1)^{-3}}{4^{-3}}$

$\qquad\qquad = (-1)^{-3}\cdot\dfrac{1}{4^{-3}}$

$\qquad\qquad = \dfrac{1}{(-1)^3}\cdot4^3$

$\qquad\qquad = \dfrac{1}{-1}\cdot64$

$\qquad\qquad = -64$

7. $3^{-1}+2^{-1} = \dfrac{1}{3}+\dfrac{1}{2} = \dfrac{2}{6}+\dfrac{3}{6} = \dfrac{5}{6}$

9. $\dfrac{1}{p^{-3}} = p^3$

11. $\dfrac{p^{-5}}{q^{-4}} = \dfrac{1}{p^5}\cdot\dfrac{q^4}{1} = \dfrac{q^4}{p^5}$

13. $\dfrac{x^{-2}}{x} = \dfrac{x^{-2}}{x^1} = x^{-2-1} = x^{-3} = \dfrac{1}{x^3}$

15. $\dfrac{z^{-4}}{z^{-7}} = z^{-4-(-7)} = z^{-4+7} = z^3$

17. $3^{-2}+3^{-1} = \dfrac{1}{3^2}+\dfrac{1}{3} = \dfrac{1}{9}+\dfrac{1}{3} = \dfrac{4}{9}$

19. $(-3)^{-2} = \dfrac{1}{(-3)^2} = \dfrac{1}{9}$

21. $\dfrac{-1}{p^{-4}} = -1\cdot\dfrac{1}{p^{-4}} = -1\cdot p^4 = -p^4$

23. $-2^0 - 3^0 = -(2^0) - (3^0) = -1 - 1 = -2$

25. $\dfrac{x^2 x^5}{x^3} = \dfrac{x^{2+5}}{x^3} = \dfrac{x^7}{x^3} = x^{7-3} = x^4$

27. $\dfrac{p^2 p}{p^{-1}} = \dfrac{p^{2+1}}{p^{-1}} = \dfrac{p^3}{p^{-1}} = p^{3-(-1)} = p^{3+1} = p^4$

29. $\dfrac{(m^5)^4 m}{m^{10}} = \dfrac{m^{5 \cdot 4} m^1}{m^{10}}$

$\qquad = \dfrac{m^{20} m^1}{m^{10}}$

$\qquad = \dfrac{m^{20+1}}{m^{10}}$

$\qquad = \dfrac{m^{21}}{m^{10}}$

$\qquad = m^{21-10}$

$\qquad = m^{11}$

31. $\dfrac{r}{r^{-3} r^{-2}} = \dfrac{r}{r^{(-3)+(-2)}} = \dfrac{r}{r^{-5}} = r^{1-(-5)} = r^{1+5} = r^6$

33. $(x^5 y^3)^{-3} = (x^5)^{-3}(y^3)^{-3} = x^{-15} y^{-9} = \dfrac{1}{x^{15} y^9}$

35. $\dfrac{(x^2)^3}{x^{10}} = \dfrac{x^6}{x^{10}} = x^{6-10} = x^{-4} = \dfrac{1}{x^4}$

37. $\dfrac{(a^5)^2}{(a^3)^4} = \dfrac{a^{10}}{a^{12}} = a^{10-12} = a^{-2} = \dfrac{1}{a^2}$

39. $\dfrac{8k^4}{2k} = \dfrac{8}{2} \cdot \dfrac{k^4}{k} = 4 \cdot k^{4-1} = 4k^3$

41. $\dfrac{-6m^4}{-2m^3} = \dfrac{-6}{-2} \cdot \dfrac{m^4}{m^3} = 3 \cdot m^{4-3} = 3m^1 = 3m$

43. $\dfrac{-24a^6 b}{6ab^2} = \dfrac{-24}{6} \cdot \dfrac{a^6}{a} \cdot \dfrac{b}{b^2}$

$\qquad = -4a^{6-1} b^{1-2}$

$\qquad = -4a^5 b^{-1}$

$\qquad = -\dfrac{4a^5}{b}$

45. $\dfrac{6x^2 y^3}{-7x^2 y^5} = \dfrac{6}{-7} \cdot \dfrac{x^2}{x^2} \cdot \dfrac{y^3}{y^5}$

$\qquad = -\dfrac{6}{7} \cdot x^{2-2} y^{3-5}$

$\qquad = -\dfrac{6}{7} x^0 y^{-2}$

$\qquad = -\dfrac{6}{7} \cdot 1 \cdot \dfrac{1}{y^2}$

$\qquad = -\dfrac{6}{7y^2}$

47. $(3a^2 b^{-4})^3 = 3^3 a^{2 \cdot 3} b^{-4 \cdot 3} = 27a^6 b^{-12} = \dfrac{27a^6}{b^{12}}$

49. $(a^{-5} b^2)^{-6} = (a^{-5})^{-6} (b^2)^{-6} = a^{30} b^{-12} = \dfrac{a^{30}}{b^{12}}$

51. $\left(\dfrac{x^{-2} y^4}{x^3 y^7}\right)^2 = \dfrac{x^{-2 \cdot 2}}{x^{3 \cdot 2}} \cdot \dfrac{y^{4 \cdot 2}}{y^{7 \cdot 2}}$

$\qquad = \dfrac{x^{-4}}{x^6} \cdot \dfrac{y^8}{y^{14}}$

$\qquad = x^{-4-6} y^{8-14}$

$\qquad = x^{-10} y^{-6}$

$\qquad = \dfrac{1}{x^{10} y^6}$

53. $\dfrac{4^2 z^{-3}}{4^3 z^{-5}} = \dfrac{4^2}{4^3} \cdot \dfrac{z^{-3}}{z^{-5}}$

$\qquad = 4^{2-3} z^{-3-(-5)}$

$\qquad = 4^{-1} z^{-3+5}$

$\qquad = \dfrac{1}{4} \cdot z^2$

$\qquad = \dfrac{z^2}{4}$

55. $\dfrac{3^{-1} x^4}{3^3 x^{-7}} = \dfrac{3^{-1}}{3^3} \cdot \dfrac{x^4}{x^{-7}}$

$\qquad = 3^{-1-3} x^{4-(-7)}$

$\qquad = 3^{-4} x^{4+7}$

$\qquad = 3^{-4} x^{11}$

$\qquad = \dfrac{x^{11}}{3^4}$

$\qquad = \dfrac{x^{11}}{81}$

57. $\dfrac{7ab^{-4}}{7^{-1}a^{-3}b^2} = \dfrac{7}{7^{-1}} \cdot \dfrac{a^1}{a^{-3}} \cdot \dfrac{b^{-4}}{b^2}$

$= 7^{1-(-1)}a^{1-(-3)}b^{-4-2}$

$= 7^{1+1}a^{1+3}b^{-6}$

$= 7^2 a^4 b^{-6}$

$= \dfrac{49a^4}{b^6}$

59. $\dfrac{-12m^5 n^{-7}}{4m^{-2}n^{-3}} = \dfrac{-12}{4} \cdot \dfrac{m^5}{m^{-2}} \cdot \dfrac{n^{-7}}{n^{-3}}$

$= -3m^{5-(-2)}n^{-7-(-3)}$

$= -3m^{5+2}n^{-7+3}$

$= -3m^7 n^{-4}$

$= -\dfrac{3m^7}{n^4}$

61. $\left(\dfrac{a^{-5}b}{ab^3}\right)^{-4} = \dfrac{(a^{-5})^{-4}b^{-4}}{a^{-4}(b^3)^{-4}}$

$= \dfrac{a^{20}b^{-4}}{a^{-4}b^{-12}}$

$= a^{20-(-4)}b^{-4-(-12)}$

$= a^{20+4}b^{-4+12}$

$= a^{24}b^8$

63. $(5^2)(8)(2^0) = (25)(8)(1) = 200$

65. $\dfrac{(xy^3)^5}{(xy)^{-4}} = \dfrac{x^5(y^3)^5}{x^{-4}y^{-4}}$

$= \dfrac{x^5 y^{15}}{x^{-4}y^{-4}}$

$= x^{5-(-4)}y^{15-(-4)}$

$= x^{5+4}y^{15+4}$

$= x^9 y^{19}$

67. $\dfrac{(-2xy^{-3})^{-3}}{(xy^{-1})^{-1}} = \dfrac{-2^{-3}x^{-3}(y^{-3})^{-3}}{x^{-1}(y^{-1})^{-1}}$

$= \dfrac{-2^{-3}x^{-3}y^9}{x^{-1}y}$

$= -2^{-3}x^{-3-(-1)}y^{9-1}$

$= -2^{-3}x^{-3+1}y^8$

$= -2^{-3}x^{-2}y^8$

$= -\dfrac{y^8}{2^3 x^2}$

$= -\dfrac{y^8}{8x^2}$

69. $\dfrac{(a^4 b^{-7})^{-5}}{(5a^2 b^{-1})^{-2}} = \dfrac{(a^4)^{-5}(b^{-7})^{-5}}{5^{-2}(a^2)^{-2}(b^{-1})^{-2}}$

$= \dfrac{a^{-20}b^{35}}{5^{-2}a^{-4}b^2}$

$= 5^2 a^{-20-(-4)}b^{35-2}$

$= 25a^{-20+4}b^{33}$

$= 25a^{-16}b^{33}$

$= \dfrac{25b^{33}}{a^{16}}$

71. $V = s^3$

$= \left(\dfrac{3x^{-2}}{z} \text{ inches}\right)^3$

$= \left(\dfrac{3^3(x^{-2})^3}{z^3}\right) \text{ cubic inches}$

$= \dfrac{27x^{-6}}{z^3} \text{ cubic inches}$

$= \dfrac{27}{z^3 x^6} \text{ cubic inches}$

73. $78,000 = 7.8 \times 10^4$

75. $0.00000167 = 1.67 \times 10^{-6}$

77. $0.00635 = 6.35 \times 10^{-3}$

79. $1,160,000 = 1.16 \times 10^6$

81. $2400 = 2.4 \times 10^3$

83. $8.673 \times 10^{-10} = 0.0000000008673$

85. $3.3 \times 10^{-2} = 0.033$

87. $2.032 \times 10^4 = 20,320$

89. $7.0 \times 10^8 = 700,000,000$

91. $184,000,000,000 = 1.84 \times 10^{11}$

93. $1.55 \times 10^{11} = 155,000,000,000$

95. $3.5 \times 10^4 = 35,000$

97. $(1.2 \times 10^{-3})(3 \times 10^{-2}) = 1.2 \cdot 3 \cdot 10^{-3} \cdot 10^{-2}$
$$= 3.6 \times 10^{-5}$$
$$= 0.000036$$

99. $(4 \times 10^{-10})(7 \times 10^{-9}) = (4 \cdot 7)(10^{-10} \cdot 10^{-9})$
$$= 28 \cdot 10^{-19}$$
$$= 0.0000000000000000028$$

101. $\dfrac{8 \times 10^{-1}}{16 \times 10^5} = \dfrac{8}{16} \times 10^{-1-5}$
$$= 0.5 \times 10^{-6}$$
$$= 5.0 \times 10^{-7}$$
$$= 0.0000005$$

103. $\dfrac{1.4 \times 10^{-2}}{7 \times 10^{-8}} = \dfrac{1.4}{7} \cdot \dfrac{10^{-2}}{10^{-8}}$
$$= 0.2 \cdot 10^{-2-(-8)}$$
$$= 0.2 \cdot 10^{-2+8}$$
$$= 0.2 \cdot 10^6$$
$$= 200,000$$

105. $7.5 \times 10^5 \cdot 3600 = 7.5 \times 10^5 \cdot 3.6 \times 10^3$
$$= 7.5 \cdot 3.6 \cdot 10^5 \cdot 10^3$$
$$= 27 \times 10^8$$
$$= 2.7 \times 10^9$$

107. $3x - 5x + 2 = -2x + 7$

109. $y - 10 + y = y + y - 10 = 2y - 10$

111. $7x + 2 - 8x - 6 = 7x - 8x + 2 - 6 = -x - 4$

113. 90 million $= 90,000,000 = 9 \times 10^7$

115. 1 billion $= 1,000,000,000 = 1 \times 10^9$

117. 0.44 billion $= 440,000,000 = 4.4 \times 10^8$

119. no; answers may vary

121. $(2a^3)^3 a^4 + a^5 a^8 = 2^3 (a^3)^3 a^4 + a^5 a^8$
$$= 8a^9 a^4 + a^5 a^8$$
$$= 8a^{13} + a^{13}$$
$$= 9a^{13}$$

123. If $x^{\square} = \dfrac{1}{x^5}$, the exponent is -5.

125. answers may vary

127. a. 9.7×10^{-2} or $1.3 \times 10^1 \Rightarrow 1.3 \times 10^1$

     b. 8.6×10^5 or $4.4 \times 10^7 \Rightarrow 4.4 \times 10^7$

     c. 6.1×10^{-2} or $5.6 \times 10^{-4} \Rightarrow 6.1 \times 10^{-2}$

129. answers may vary

131. $(x^{-3s})^3 = x^{-9s} = \dfrac{1}{x^{9s}}$

133. $a^{4m+1} \cdot a^4 = a^{4m+1+4} = a^{4m+5}$

Section 10.3

Practice Problems

  1. $-6x^6 + 4x^5 + 7x^3 - 9x^2 - 1$

Term	Coefficient
$7x^3$	7
$-9x^2$	-9
$-6x^6$	-6
$4x^5$	4
-1	-1

2. $-15x^3 + 2x^2 - 5$

The term $-15x^3$ has degree 3.

The term $2x^2$ has degree 2.

The term -5 has degree 0 since -5 is $-5x^0$.

3. a. The degree of the binomial $-6x + 14$ is 1.

    b. The degree of the polynomial
$9x - 3x^6 + 5x^4 + 2$ is 6. The polynomial is neither a monomial, binomial, or trinomial.

    c. The degree of the trinomial $10x^2 - 6x - 6$ is 2.

4. a. When $x = -1$,
$-2x + 10 = -2(-1) + 10 = 2 + 10 = 12.$

    b. When $x = -1$,
$$6x^2 + 11x - 20 = 6(-1)^2 + 11(-1) - 20$$
$$= 6 - 11 - 20$$
$$= -25.$$

5. When $t = 2$ seconds,
$$-16t^2 + 592.1 = -16(2)^2 + 592.1$$
$$= -16(4) + 592.1$$
$$= -64 + 592.1$$
$$= 528.1 \text{ feet.}$$

When $t = 4$ seconds,
$$-16t^2 + 592.1 = -16(4)^2 + 592.1$$
$$= -16(16) + 592.1$$
$$= -256 + 592.1$$
$$= 336.1 \text{ feet.}$$

6. $-6y + 8y = (-6 + 8)y = 2y$

7. $14y^2 + 3 - 10y^2 - 9 = 14y^2 - 10y^2 + 3 - 9$
$$= 4y^2 - 6$$

8. $7x^3 + x^3 = 7x^3 + 1x^3 = 8x^3$

9. $23x^2 - 6x - x - 15 = 23x^2 - 7x - 15$

10. $\dfrac{2}{7}x^3 - \dfrac{1}{4}x + 2 - \dfrac{1}{2}x^3 + \dfrac{3}{8}x$

$= \dfrac{2}{7}x^3 - \dfrac{1}{2}x^3 - \dfrac{1}{4}x + \dfrac{3}{8}x + 2$

$= \dfrac{4}{14}x^3 - \dfrac{7}{14}x^3 - \dfrac{2}{8}x + \dfrac{3}{8}x + 2$

$= -\dfrac{3}{14}x^3 + \dfrac{1}{8}x + 2$

11. Area $= 5 \cdot x + x \cdot x + 4 \cdot 5 + x \cdot x + 8 \cdot x$
$$= 5x + x^2 + 20 + x^2 + 8x$$
$$= x^2 + x^2 + 5x + 8x + 20$$
$$= 2x^2 + 13x + 20$$

12.

Terms of Polynomial	Degree of Term
$-2x^3y^2$	$3 + 2$ or 5
4	0
$-8xy$	$1 + 1$ or 2
$3x^3y$	$3 + 1$ or 4
$5xy^2$	$1 + 2$ or 3

The degree of the polynomial is 5.

13. $11ab - 6a^2 - ba + 8b^2 = (11 - 1)ab - 6a^2 + 8b^2$
$$= 10ab - 6a^2 + 8b^2$$

14. $7x^2y^2 + 2y^2 - 4y^2x^2 + x^2 - y^2 + 5x^2$
$$= 7x^2y^2 - 4x^2y^2 + 2y^2 - y^2 + x^2 + 5x^2$$
$$= 3x^2y^2 + y^2 + 6x^2$$

15. a. $x^2 + 9 = x^2 + 0x^1 + 9$ or $x^2 + 0x + 9$

    b. $9m^3 + m^2 - 5 = 9m^3 + m^2 + 0m^1 - 5$
$$= 9m^3 + m^2 + 0m - 5$$

    c. $-3a^3 + a^4 = a^4 - 3a^3 + 0a^2 + 0a^1 + 0a^0$
$$= a^4 - 3a^3 + 0a^2 + 0a + 0a^0$$

Vocabulary and Readiness Check

1. A <u>binomial</u> is a polynomial with exactly two terms.

2. A <u>monomial</u> is a polynomial with exactly one term.

3. A <u>trinomial</u> is a polynomial with exactly three terms.

4. The numerical factor of a term is called the <u>coefficient</u>.

5. A number term is also called a <u>constant</u>.

6. The degree of a polynomial is the <u>greatest</u> degree of any term of the polynomial.

Exercise Set 10.3

1.

Term	Coefficient
x^2	1
$-3x$	-3
5	5

3.

Term	Coefficient
$-5x^4$	-5
$3.2x^2$	3.2
x	1
-5	-5

5. $x + 2 = x^1 + 2$
This is a binomial of degree 1.

7. $9m^3 - 5m^2 + 4m - 8$
This is a polynomial of degree 3. None of these.

9. $12x^4 - x^6 - 12x^2 = -x^6 + 12x^4 - 12x^2$
This is a trinomial of degree 6.

11. $3z - 5z^4 = -5z^4 + 3z$
This is a binomial of degree 4.

13. a. $5x - 6 = 5(0) - 6 = 0 - 6 = -6$

b. $5x - 6 = 5(-1) - 6 = -5 - 6 = -11$

15. a. $x^2 - 5x - 2 = (0)^2 - 5(0) - 2 = 0 - 0 - 2 = -2$

b. $x^2 - 5x - 2 = (-1)^2 - 5(-1) - 2 = 1 + 5 - 2 = 4$

17. a. $-x^3 + 4x^2 - 15 = -(0)^3 + 4(0)^2 - 15$
$$= 0 + 0 - 15$$
$$= -15$$

b. $-x^3 + 4x^2 - 15 = -(-1)^3 + 4(-1)^2 - 15$
$$= -(-1) + 4(1) - 15$$
$$= 1 + 4 - 15$$
$$= -10$$

19. $-16t^2 + 200t = -16(1)^2 + 200(1)$
$$= -16 + 200$$
$$= 184$$
After 1 second, the height of the rocket is 184 feet.

21. $-16t^2 + 200t = -16(7.6)^2 + 200(7.6)$
$$= -16(57.76) + 1520$$
$$= -924.16 + 1520$$
$$= 595.84$$
After 7.6 seconds, the height of the rocket is 595.84 feet.

23. $-7.5x^2 + 93x - 100 = -7.5(8)^2 + 93(8) - 100$
$$= -7.5(64) + 93(8) - 100$$
$$= -480 + 744 - 100$$
$$= 164$$
There were 164 thousand or 164,000 visitors in 2008.

25. $0.52x^2 + 11.4x + 27.87$
$$= 0.52(17)^2 + 11.4(17) + 27.87$$
$$= 0.52(289) + 11.4(17) + 27.87$$
$$= 150.28 + 193.8 + 27.87$$
$$= 371.95$$
There will be 371.95 million or 371,950,000 subscribers in 2012.

27. $9x - 20x = (9 - 20)x = -11x$

29. $14x^3 + 9x^3 = (14 + 9)x^3 = 23x^3$

31. $7x^2 + 3 + 9x^2 - 10 = 7x^2 + 9x^2 + 3 - 10$
$$= (7 + 9)x^2 + 3 - 10$$
$$= 16x^2 - 7$$

33. $15x^2 - 3x^2 - 13 = (15 - 3)x^2 - 13 = 12x^2 - 13$

35. $8s - 5s + 4s = (8 - 5 + 4)s = 7s$

37. $0.1y^2 - 1.2y^2 + 6.7 - 1.9$

$= (0.1 - 1.2)y^2 + 6.7 - 1.9$

$= -1.1y^2 + 4.8$

39. $\dfrac{2}{3}x^4 + 12x^3 + \dfrac{1}{6}x^4 - 19x^3 - 19$

$= \dfrac{2}{3}x^4 + \dfrac{1}{6}x^4 + 12x^3 - 19x^3 - 19$

$= \left(\dfrac{4}{6} + \dfrac{1}{6}\right)x^4 + (12 - 19)x^3 - 19$

$= \dfrac{5}{6}x^4 - 7x^3 - 19$

41. $\dfrac{3}{20}x^3 + \dfrac{1}{10} - \dfrac{3}{10}x - \dfrac{1}{5} - \dfrac{7}{20}x + 6x^2$

$= \dfrac{3}{20}x^3 + 6x^2 - \dfrac{3}{10}x - \dfrac{7}{20}x + \dfrac{1}{10} - \dfrac{1}{5}$

$= \dfrac{3}{20}x^3 + 6x^2 + \left(-\dfrac{6}{20} - \dfrac{7}{20}\right)x + \dfrac{1}{10} - \dfrac{2}{10}$

$= \dfrac{3}{20}x^3 + 6x^2 - \dfrac{13}{20}x - \dfrac{1}{10}$

43. $4x^2 + 7x + x^2 + 5x = 4x^2 + x^2 + 7x + 5x$

$= (4 + 1)x^2 + (7 + 5)x$

$= 5x^2 + 12x$

45. $5x + 3 + 4x + 3 + 2x + 6 + 3x + 7x$

$= 5x + 4x + 2x + 3x + 7x + 3 + 3 + 6$

$= (5 + 4 + 2 + 3 + 7)x + 12$

$= 21x + 12$

47. $9ab = 9a^1b^1$ has degree $1 + 1 = 2$.

$-6a = -6a^1$ has degree 1.

$5b = 5b^1$ has degree 1.

$-3 = -3a^0b^0$ has degree 0.

$9ab - 6a + 5b - 3$ is a polynomial of degree 2.

49. $x^3y = x^3y^1$ has degree $3 + 1 = 4$.

$-6 = -6x^0y^0$ has degree 0.

$2x^2y^2$ has degree $2 + 2 = 4$.

$5y^3$ has degree 3.

$x^3y - 6 + 2x^2y^2 + 5y^3$ is a polynomial of degree 4.

51. $3ab - 4a + 6ab - 7a = 3ab + 6ab - 4a - 7a$

$= (3 + 6)ab - (4 + 7)a$

$= 9ab - 11a$

53. $4x^2 - 6xy + 3y^2 - xy = 4x^2 - 6xy - xy + 3y^2$

$= 4x^2 + (-6 - 1)xy + 3y^2$

$= 4x^2 - 7xy + 3y^2$

55. $5x^2y + 6xy^2 - 5yx^2 + 4 - 9y^2x$

$= 5x^2y - 5x^2y + 6xy^2 - 9xy^2 + 4$

$= (5 - 5)x^2y + (6 - 9)xy^2 + 4$

$= 0x^2y - 3xy^2 + 4$

$= -3xy^2 + 4$

57. $14y^3 - 9 + 3a^2b^2 - 10 - 19b^2a^2$

$= 14y^3 - 9 - 10 + 3a^2b^2 - 19a^2b^2$

$= 14y^3 + (-9 - 10) + (3 - 19)a^2b^2$

$= 14y^3 - 19 - 16a^2b^2$

59. $7x^2 + 3 = 7x^2 + 0x + 3$

61. $x^3 - 64 = x^3 + 0x^2 + 0x - 64$

63. $5y^3 + 2y - 10 = 5y^3 + 0y^2 + 2y - 10$

65. $8y + 2y^4 = 2y^4 + 0y^3 + 0y^2 + 8y + 0$

67. $6x^5 + x^3 - 3x + 15$

$= 6x^5 + 0x^4 + x^3 + 0x^2 - 3x + 15$

69. $4 + 5(2x + 3) = 4 + 10x + 15 = 10x + 19$

71. $2(x - 5) + 3(5 - x) = 2x - 10 + 15 - 3x$

$= 2x - 3x - 10 + 15$

$= (2 - 3)x + 5$

$= -x + 5$

73. answers may vary

75. answers may vary

77. $x^4 \cdot x^9 = x^{4+9} = x^{13}$

79. $a \cdot b^3 \cdot a^2 \cdot b^7 = a^1 \cdot a^2 \cdot b^3 \cdot b^7$
$$= a^{1+2} b^{3+7}$$
$$= a^3 b^{10}$$

81. $(y^5)^4 + (y^2)^{10} = y^{20} + y^{20} = 2y^{20}$

83. answers may vary

85. answers may vary

87. $1.85x^2 - 3.76x + 9.25x^2 + 10.76 - 4.21x = 1.85x^2 + 9.25x^2 - 3.76x - 4.21x + 10.76$
$$= (1.85 + 9.25)x^2 - (3.76 + 4.21)x + 10.76$$
$$= 11.1x^2 - 7.97x + 10.76$$

Section 10.4

Practice Problems

1. $(3x^5 - 7x^3 + 2x - 1) + (3x^3 - 2x) = 3x^5 - 7x^3 + 2x - 1 + 3x^3 - 2x$
$$= 3x^5 + (-7x^3 + 3x^3) + (2x - 2x) - 1$$
$$= 3x^5 - 4x^3 - 1$$

2. $(5x^2 - 2x + 1) + (-6x^2 + x - 1) = 5x^2 - 2x + 1 - 6x^2 + x - 1$
$$= (5x^2 - 6x^2) + (-2x + x) + (1 - 1)$$
$$= -x^2 - x$$

3. $9y^2 - 6y + 5$
$$\underline{\phantom{9y^2 - 6y + {}}4y + 3}$$
$$9y^2 - 2y + 8$$

4. $(9x + 5) - (4x - 3) = (9x + 5) + [-(4x - 3)]$
$$= (9x + 5) + (-4x + 3)$$
$$= 9x + 5 - 4x + 3$$
$$= 5x + 8$$

5. $(4x^3 - 10x^2 + 1) - (-4x^3 + x^2 - 11) = (4x^3 - 10x^2 + 1) + (4x^3 - x^2 + 11)$
$$= 4x^3 - 10x^2 + 1 + 4x^3 - x^2 + 11$$
$$= 4x^3 + 4x^3 - 10x^2 - x^2 + 1 + 11$$
$$= 8x^3 - 11x^2 + 12$$

6. $2y^2 - 2y + 7 \qquad\qquad 2y^2 - 2y + 7$
$$\underline{-(6y^2 - 3y + 2)} \quad \Rightarrow \quad \underline{-6y^2 + 3y - 2}$$
$$-4y^2 + y + 5$$

7. $[(4x - 3) + (12x - 5)] - (3x + 1) = 4x - 3 + 12x - 5 - 3x - 1$
$$= 4x + 12x - 3x - 3 - 5 - 1$$
$$= 13x - 9$$

8. $(2a^2 - ab + 6b^2) + (-3a^2 + ab - 7b^2) = 2a^2 - ab + 6b^2 - 3a^2 + ab - 7b^2$
$$= -a^2 - b^2$$

9. $(5x^2 y^2 + 3 - 9x^2 y + y^2) - (-x^2 y^2 + 7 - 8xy^2 + 2y^2) = 5x^2 y^2 + 3 - 9x^2 y + y^2 + x^2 y^2 - 7 + 8xy^2 - 2y^2$
$$= 6x^2 y^2 - 4 - 9x^2 y + 8xy^2 - y^2$$

Vocabulary and Readiness Check

1. $-9y - 5y = -14y$

2. $6m^5 + 7m^5 = 13m^5$

3. $x + 6x = 7x$

4. $7z - z = 6z$

5. $5m^2 + 2m = 5m^2 + 2m$

6. $8p^3 + 3p^2 = 8p^3 + 3p^2$

Exercise Set 10.4

1. $(3x + 7) + (9x + 5) = 3x + 7 + 9x + 5$
$$= 3x + 9x + 7 + 5$$
$$= 12x + 12$$

3. $(-7x + 5) + (-3x^2 + 7x + 5) = -7x + 5 - 3x^2 + 7x + 5$
$$= -3x^2 - 7x + 7x + 5 + 5$$
$$= -3x^2 + 10$$

5. $(-5x^2 + 3) + (2x^2 + 1) = -5x^2 + 3 + 2x^2 + 1$
$$= -5x^2 + 2x^2 + 3 + 1$$
$$= -3x^2 + 4$$

7. $(-3y^2 - 4y) + (2y^2 + y - 1) = -3y^2 - 4y + 2y^2 + y - 1$
$$= -3y^2 + 2y^2 - 4y + y - 1$$
$$= -y^2 - 3y - 1$$

9. $(1.2x^3 - 3.4x + 7.9) + (6.7x^3 + 4.4x^2 - 10.9) = 1.2x^3 - 3.4x + 7.9 + 6.7x^3 + 4.4x^2 - 10.9$
$$= 1.2x^3 + 6.7x^3 + 4.4x^2 - 3.4x + 7.9 - 10.9$$
$$= 7.9x^3 + 4.4x^2 - 3.4x - 3$$

11. $\left(\dfrac{3}{4}m^2 - \dfrac{2}{5}m + \dfrac{1}{8}\right) + \left(-\dfrac{1}{4}m^2 - \dfrac{3}{10}m + \dfrac{11}{16}\right)$

$= \dfrac{3}{4}m^2 - \dfrac{2}{5}m + \dfrac{1}{8} - \dfrac{1}{4}m^2 - \dfrac{3}{10}m + \dfrac{11}{16}$

$= \dfrac{3}{4}m^2 - \dfrac{1}{4}m^2 - \dfrac{2}{5}m - \dfrac{3}{10}m + \dfrac{1}{8} + \dfrac{11}{16}$

$= \dfrac{3}{4}m^2 - \dfrac{1}{4}m^2 - \dfrac{4}{10}m - \dfrac{3}{10}m + \dfrac{2}{16} + \dfrac{11}{16}$

$= \dfrac{2}{4}m^2 - \dfrac{7}{10}m + \dfrac{13}{16}$

$= \dfrac{1}{2}m^2 - \dfrac{7}{10}m + \dfrac{13}{16}$

13. $3t^2 + 4$

$\dfrac{5t^2 - 8}{8t^2 - 4}$

15. $10a^3 - 8a^2 + 4a + 9$

$\dfrac{5a^3 + 9a^2 - 7a + 7}{15a^3 + a^2 - 3a + 16}$

17. $(2x+5) - (3x-9) = (2x+5) + (-3x+9)$
$= 2x + 5 - 3x + 9$
$= 2x - 3x + 5 + 9$
$= -x + 14$

19. $(5x^2+4) - (-2y^2+4) = (5x^2+4) + (2y^2-4)$
$= 5x^2 + 4 + 2y^2 - 4$
$= 5x^2 + 2y^2 + 4 - 4$
$= 5x^2 + 2y^2$

21. $3x - (5x-9) = 3x + (-5x+9)$
$= 3x - 5x + 9$
$= -2x + 9$

23. $(2x^2+3x-9) - (-4x+7)$
$= (2x^2+3x-9) + (4x-7)$
$= 2x^2 + 3x - 9 + 4x - 7$
$= 2x^2 + 3x + 4x - 9 - 7$
$= 2x^2 + 7x - 16$

25. $(5x+8) - (-2x^2-6x+8)$
$= (5x+8) + (2x^2+6x-8)$
$= 5x + 8 + 2x^2 + 6x - 8$
$= 2x^2 + 5x + 6x + 8 - 8$
$= 2x^2 + 11x$

27. $(0.7x^2+0.2x-0.8) - (0.9x^2+1.4)$
$= (0.7x^2+0.2x-0.8) + (-0.9x^2-1.4)$
$= 0.7x^2 + 0.2x - 0.8 - 0.9x^2 - 1.4$
$= 0.7x^2 - 0.9x^2 + 0.2x - 0.8 - 1.4$
$= -0.2x^2 + 0.2x - 2.2$

29. $\left(\dfrac{1}{4}z^2 - \dfrac{1}{5}z\right) - \left(-\dfrac{3}{20}z^2 + \dfrac{1}{10}z - \dfrac{7}{20}\right)$

$= \left(\dfrac{1}{4}z^2 - \dfrac{1}{5}z\right) + \left(\dfrac{3}{20}z^2 - \dfrac{1}{10}z + \dfrac{7}{20}\right)$

$= \dfrac{1}{4}z^2 - \dfrac{1}{5}z + \dfrac{3}{20}z^2 - \dfrac{1}{10}z + \dfrac{7}{20}$

$= \dfrac{5}{20}z^2 + \dfrac{3}{20}z^2 - \dfrac{2}{10}z - \dfrac{1}{10}z + \dfrac{7}{20}$

$= \dfrac{8}{20}z^2 - \dfrac{3}{10}z + \dfrac{7}{20}$

$= \dfrac{2}{5}z^2 - \dfrac{3}{10}z + \dfrac{7}{20}$

31. $\begin{array}{l} 4z^2 - 8z + 3 \\ \underline{-\ (6z^2 + 8z - 3)} \end{array} \Rightarrow \begin{array}{l} 4z^2 - 8z + 3 \\ \underline{-6z^2 - 8z + 3} \\ -2z^2 - 16z + 6 \end{array}$

33. $\begin{array}{l} 5u^5 - 4u^2 + 3u - 7 \\ \underline{-(3u^5 + 6u^2 - 8u + 2)} \end{array} \quad \begin{array}{l} 5u^5 - 4u^2 + 3u - 7 \\ \underline{-3u^5 - 6u^2 + 8u - 2} \\ 2u^5 - 10u^2 + 11u - 9 \end{array}$

35. $(3x+5) + (2x-14) = 3x + 5 + 2x - 14$
$= 3x + 2x + 5 - 14$
$= 5x - 9$

37. $(9x-1) - (5x+2) = (9x-1) + (-5x-2)$
$= 9x - 1 - 5x - 2$
$= 4x - 3$

39. $(14y+12) + (-3y-5) = 14y + 12 - 3y - 5$
$= 11y + 7$

41. $(x^2+2x+1) - (3x^2-6x+2)$
$= (x^2+2x+1) + (-3x^2+6x-2)$
$= x^2 + 2x + 1 - 3x^2 + 6x - 2$
$= -2x^2 + 8x - 1$

43. $(3x^2+5x-8) + (5x^2+9x+12) - (8x^2-14)$
$= (3x^2+5x-8) + (5x^2+9x+12) + (-8x^2+14)$
$= 3x^2 + 5x - 8 + 5x^2 + 9x + 12 - 8x^2 + 14$
$= 14x + 18$

45. $(-a^2+1)-(a^2-3)+(5a^2-6a+7)=(-a^2+1)+(-a^2+3)+(5a^2-6a+7)$
$$=-a^2+1-a^2+3+5a^2-6a+7$$
$$=3a^2-6a+11$$

47. $(7x-3)-4x=7x-3-4x=3x-3$

49. $(4x^2-6x+1)+(3x^2+2x+1)=4x^2-6x+1+3x^2+2x+1$
$$=7x^2-4x+2$$

51. $(7x^2+3x+9)-(5x+7)=(7x^2+3x+9)+(-5x-7)$
$$=7x^2+3x+9-5x-7$$
$$=7x^2-2x+2$$

53. $(8y^2+7)+(6y+9)-(4y^2-6y-3)=(8y^2+7)+(6y+9)+(-4y^2+6y+3)$
$$=8y^2+7+6y+9-4y^2+6y+3$$
$$=4y^2+12y+19$$

55. $(x^2-9x+2)+(2x^2-6x+1)-(3x^2-4)=(x^2-9x+2)+(2x^2-6x+1)+(-3x^2+4)$
$$=x^2-9x+2+2x^2-6x+1-3x^2+4$$
$$=-15x+7$$

57. $(9a+6b-5)+(-11a-7b+6)=9a+6b-5-11a-7b+6$
$$=-2a-b+1$$

59. $(4x^2+y^2+3)-(x^2+y^2-2)=4x^2+y^2+3-x^2-y^2+2$
$$=3x^2+5$$

61. $(x^2+2xy-y^2)+(5x^2-4xy+20y^2)=x^2+2xy-y^2+5x^2-4xy+20y^2$
$$=6x^2-2xy+19y^2$$

63. $(11r^2s+16rs-3-2r^2s^2)-(3sr^2+5-9r^2s^2)=11r^2s+16rs-3-2r^2s^2-3r^2s-5+9r^2s^2$
$$=8r^2s+16rs-8+7r^2s^2$$

65. $(2x^2+5)+(4x-1)+(-x^2+3x)=2x^2+5+4x-1-x^2+3x$
$$=x^2+7x+4$$
The perimeter is (x^2+7x+4) feet.

67. $(2x-3)+\left(\dfrac{4}{5}x\right)+\left(\dfrac{7}{10}x-1\right)+(2x-2)+(x+4)+(3x+5)=2x-3+\dfrac{4}{5}x+\dfrac{7}{10}x-1+2x-2+x+4+3x+5$
$$=\dfrac{19}{2}x+3$$

The perimeter is $\left(\dfrac{19}{2}x+3\right)$ units.

69. $(4y^2 + 4y + 1) - (y^2 - 10) = (4y^2 + 4y + 1) + (-y^2 + 10)$
$$= 4y^2 + 4y + 1 - y^2 + 10$$
$$= 3y^2 + 4y + 11$$

The remaining piece is $(3y^2 + 4y + 11)$ meters long.

71. $[(1.2x^2 - 3x + 9.1) - (7.8x^2 - 3.1 + 8)] + (1.2x - 6) = (1.2x^2 - 3x + 9.1) + (-7.8x^2 + 3.1 - 8) + (1.2x - 6)$
$$= 1.2x^2 - 3x + 9.1 - 7.8x^2 + 3.1 - 8 + 1.2x - 6$$
$$= -6.6x^2 - 1.8x - 1.8$$

73. $3x(2x) = (3 \cdot 2)(x \cdot x) = 6x^2$

75. $(12x^3)(-x^5) = (12 \cdot -1)(x^3 \cdot x^5) = -12x^8$

77. $10x^2(20xy^2) = 10 \cdot 20 \cdot (x^2 \cdot x)(y^2) = 200x^3y^2$

79. Since $3 + 4 = 7$, $3x^2 + 4x^2 = 7x^2$ is a true statement.

81. Since $2 + 4 = 6$ and $3 - 5 = -2$, $2x^4 + 3x^3 - 5x^3 + 4x^4 = 6x^4 - 2x^3$ is a true statement.

83. $10y - 6y^2 - y = 9y - 6y^2$; b

85. $(5x - 3) + (5x - 3) = 5x - 3 + 5x - 3 = 10x - 6$; e

87. a. $z + 3z = 1z + 3z = 4z$

    b. $z \cdot 3z = z^1 \cdot 3z^1 = 3z^{1+1} = 3z^2$

    c. $-z - 3z = -1z - 3z = -4z$

    d. $(-z)(-3z) = (-z^1)(-3z^1) = 3z^{1+1} = 3z^2$; answers may vary

89. a. $m \cdot m \cdot m = m^1 \cdot m^1 \cdot m^1 = m^{1+1+1} = m^3$

    b. $m + m + m = 1m + 1m + 1m = (1 + 1 + 1)m = 3m$

    c. $(-m)(-m)(-m) = (-1 \cdot m^1)(-1 \cdot m^1)(-1 \cdot m^1)$
$$= (-1)(-1)(-1)(m \cdot m \cdot m)$$
$$= -1m^3$$
$$= -m^3$$

    d. $-m - m - m = -1m - 1m - 1m$
$$= (-1 - 1 - 1)m$$
$$= -3m;\ \text{answers may vary}$$

91. $(-20x^2 + 156x + 14,437) + (894x^2 - 90x + 10,939)$

$\quad = -20x^2 + 156x + 14,437 + 894x^2 - 90x + 10,939$

$\quad = 874x^2 + 66x + 25,376$

Section 10.5

Practice Problems

1. $10x \cdot 9x = (10 \cdot 9)(x \cdot x) = 90x^2$

2. $8x^3(-11x^7) = (8 \cdot -11)(x^3 \cdot x^7) = -88x^{10}$

3. $(-5x^4)(-x) = (-5 \cdot -1)(x^4 \cdot x) = 5x^5$

4. $4x(x^2 + 4x + 3) = 4x(x^2) + 4x(4x) + 4x(3)$

$\qquad\qquad\qquad\quad = 4x^3 + 16x^2 + 12x$

5. $8x(7x^4 + 1) = 8x(7x^4) + 8x(1) = 56x^5 + 8x$

6. $-2x^3(3x^2 - x + 2) = -2x^3(3x^2) - 2x^3(-x) - 2x^3(2)$

$\qquad\qquad\qquad\qquad\quad = -6x^5 + 2x^4 - 4x^3$

7. **a.** $(x+5)(x+10) = x(x+10) + 5(x+10)$

$\qquad\qquad\qquad\qquad = x \cdot x + x \cdot 10 + 5 \cdot x + 5 \cdot 10$

$\qquad\qquad\qquad\qquad = x^2 + 10x + 5x + 50$

$\qquad\qquad\qquad\qquad = x^2 + 15x + 50$

    b. $(4x+5)(3x-4) = 4x(3x-4) + 5(3x-4)$

$\qquad\qquad\qquad\qquad = 4x(3x) + 4x(-4) + 5(3x) + 5(-4)$

$\qquad\qquad\qquad\qquad = 12x^2 - 16x + 15x - 20$

$\qquad\qquad\qquad\qquad = 12x^2 - x - 20$

8. $(3x - 2y)^2 = (3x - 2y)(3x - 2y)$

$\qquad\qquad\quad = 3x(3x) + 3x(-2y) + (-2y)(3x) + (-2y)(-2y)$

$\qquad\qquad\quad = 9x^2 - 6xy - 6xy + 4y^2$

$\qquad\qquad\quad = 9x^2 - 12xy + 4y^2$

9. $(x+3)(2x^2 - 5x + 4) = x(2x^2) + x(-5x) + x(4) + 3(2x^2) + 3(-5x) + 3(4)$

$\qquad\qquad\qquad\qquad\qquad = 2x^3 - 5x^2 + 4x + 6x^2 - 15x + 12$

$\qquad\qquad\qquad\qquad\qquad = 2x^3 + x^2 - 11x + 12$

10.

$$y^2 - 4y + 5$$
$$3y^2 + 1$$
$$\overline{}$$
$$y^2 - 4y + 5$$
$$3y^4 - 12y^3 + 15y^2$$
$$\overline{3y^4 - 12y^3 + 16y^2 - 4y + 5}$$

11.

$$4x^2 - x - 1$$
$$3x^2 + 6x - 2$$
$$\overline{}$$
$$-8x^2 + 2x + 2$$
$$24x^3 - 6x^2 - 6x$$
$$12x^4 - 3x^3 - 3x^2$$
$$\overline{12x^4 + 21x^3 - 17x^2 - 4x + 2}$$

Vocabulary and Readiness Check

1. The expression $5x(3x + 2)$ equals $5x \cdot 3x + 5x \cdot 2$ by the <u>distributive</u> property.

2. The expression $(x + 4)(7x - 1)$ equals $x(7x - 1) + 4(7x - 1)$ by the <u>distributive</u> property.

3. The expression $(5y - 1)^2$ equals <u>$(5y - 1)(5y - 1)$</u>.

4. The expression $9x \cdot 3x$ equals <u>$27x^2$</u>.

5. $x^3 \cdot x^5 = x^{3+5} = x^8$

6. $x^2 \cdot x^6 = x^{2+6} = x^8$

7. $x^3 + x^5$ cannot be simplified.

8. $x^2 + x^6$ cannot be simplified.

9. $x^7 \cdot x^7 = x^{7+7} = x^{14}$

10. $x^{11} \cdot x^{11} = x^{11+11} = x^{22}$

11. $x^7 + x^7 = 1x^7 + 1x^7 = (1+1)x^7 = 2x^7$

12. $x^{11} + x^{11} = 1x^{11} + 1x^{11} = (1+1)x^{11} = 2x^{11}$

Exercise Set 10.5

1. $8x^2 \cdot 3x = (8 \cdot 3)(x^2 \cdot x) = 24x^3$

3. $(-x^3)(-x) = (-1 \cdot -1)(x^3 \cdot x) = x^4$

5. $-4n^3 \cdot 7n^7 = (-4 \cdot 7)(n^3 \cdot n^7) = -28n^{10}$

7. $(-3.1x^3)(4x^9) = (-3.1 \cdot 4)(x^3 \cdot x^9) = -12.4x^{12}$

9. $\left(-\dfrac{1}{3}y^2\right)\left(\dfrac{2}{5}y\right) = \left(-\dfrac{1}{3}\right)\left(\dfrac{2}{5}\right)(y^2 \cdot y) = -\dfrac{2}{15}y^3$

11. $(2x)(-3x^2)(4x^5) = (2 \cdot -3 \cdot 4)(x \cdot x^2 \cdot x^5)$
$$= -24x^8$$

13. $3x(2x + 5) = 3x(2x) + 3x(5) = 6x^2 + 15x$

15. $7x(x^2 + 2x - 1) = 7x(x^2) + 7x(2x) + 7x(-1)$
$$= 7x^3 + 14x^2 - 7x$$

17. $-2a(a + 4) = -2a(a) + (-2a)(4) = -2a^2 - 8a$

19. $3x(2x^2 - 3x + 4) = 3x(2x^2) + 3x(-3x) + 3x(4)$
$$= 6x^3 - 9x^2 + 12x$$

21. $3a^2(4a^3 + 15) = 3a^2(4a^3) + 3a^2(15)$
$$= 12a^5 + 45a^2$$

23. $-2a^2(3a^2 - 2a + 3)$
$$= -2a^2(3a^2) - 2a^2(-2a) - 2a^2(3)$$
$$= -6a^4 + 4a^3 - 6a^2$$

25. $3x^2y(2x^3 - x^2y^2 + 8y^3)$
$$= 3x^2y(2x^3) + 3x^2y(-x^2y^2) + 3x^2y(8y^3)$$
$$= 6x^5y - 3x^4y^3 + 24x^2y^4$$

27. $-y(4x^3 - 7x^2y + xy^2 + 3y^3)$
$$= -y(4x^3) - y(-7x^2y) - y(xy^2) - y(3y^3)$$
$$= -4x^3y + 7x^2y^2 - xy^3 - 3y^4$$

29. $\dfrac{1}{2}x^2(8x^2 - 6x + 1)$
$$= \dfrac{1}{2}x^2(8x^2) + \dfrac{1}{2}x^2(-6x) + \dfrac{1}{2}x^2(1)$$
$$= 4x^4 - 3x^3 + \dfrac{1}{2}x^2$$

31. $(x + 4)(x + 3) = x(x + 3) + 4(x + 3)$
$$= x(x) + x(3) + 4(x) + 4(3)$$
$$= x^2 + 3x + 4x + 12$$
$$= x^2 + 7x + 12$$

33. $(a+7)(a-2) = a(a-2)+7(a-2)$
$$= a(a)+a(-2)+7(a)+7(-2)$$
$$= a^2-2a+7a-14$$
$$= a^2+5a-14$$

35. $\left(x+\dfrac{2}{3}\right)\left(x-\dfrac{1}{3}\right) = x\left(x-\dfrac{1}{3}\right)+\dfrac{2}{3}\left(x-\dfrac{1}{3}\right)$
$$= x(x)+x\left(-\dfrac{1}{3}\right)+\dfrac{2}{3}(x)+\dfrac{2}{3}\left(-\dfrac{1}{3}\right)$$
$$= x^2-\dfrac{1}{3}x+\dfrac{2}{3}x-\dfrac{2}{9}$$
$$= x^2+\dfrac{1}{3}x-\dfrac{2}{9}$$

37. $(3x^2+1)(4x^2+7) = 3x^2(4x^2+7)+1(4x^2+7)$
$$= 3x^2(4x^2)+3x^2(7)+1(4x^2)+1(7)$$
$$= 12x^4+21x^2+4x^2+7$$
$$= 12x^4+25x^2+7$$

39. $(4x-3)(3x-5) = 4x(3x-5)+(-3)(3x-5)$
$$= 4x(3x)+4x(-5)+(-3)(3x)+(-3)(-5)$$
$$= 12x^2-20x-9x+15$$
$$= 12x^2-29x+15$$

41. $(1-3a)(1-4a) = 1(1-4a)+(-3a)(1-4a)$
$$= 1(1)+1(-4a)+(-3a)(1)+(-3a)(-4a)$$
$$= 1-4a-3a+12a^2$$
$$= 1-7a+12a^2$$

43. $(2y-4)^2 = (2y-4)(2y-4)$
$$= 2y(2y-4)+(-4)(2y-4)$$
$$= 2y(2y)+2y(-4)+(-4)(2y)+(-4)(-4)$$
$$= 4y^2-8y-8y+16$$
$$= 4y^2-16y+16$$

45. $(x-2)(x^2-3x+7) = x(x^2-3x+7)+(-2)(x^2-3x+7)$
$$= x(x^2)+x(-3x)+x(7)+(-2)(x^2)+(-2)(-3x)+(-2)(7)$$
$$= x^3-3x^2+7x-2x^2+6x-14$$
$$= x^3-5x^2+13x-14$$

47. $(x+5)(x^3-3x+4) = x(x^3-3x+4)+5(x^3-3x+4)$
$$= x(x^3)+x(-3x)+x(4)+5(x^3)+5(-3x)+5(4)$$
$$= x^4-3x^2+4x+5x^3-15x+20$$
$$= x^4+5x^3-3x^2-11x+20$$

49. $(2a-3)(5a^2-6a+4) = 2a(5a^2-6a+4)+(-3)(5a^2-6a+4)$
$$= 2a(5a^2)+2a(-6a)+2a(4)+(-3)(5a^2)+(-3)(-6a)+(-3)(4)$$
$$= 10a^3-12a^2+8a-15a^2+18a-12$$
$$= 10a^3-27a^2+26a-12$$

51. $(7xy-y)^2 = (7xy-y)(7xy-y)$
$$= 7xy(7xy-y)+(-y)(7xy-y)$$
$$= 7xy(7xy)+7xy(-y)+(-y)(7xy)+(-y)(-y)$$
$$= 49x^2y^2-7xy^2-7xy^2+y^2$$
$$= 49x^2y^2-14xy^2+y^2$$

53.
$$
\begin{array}{r}
2x-11 \\
6x+\;1 \\
\hline
2x-11 \\
12x^2-66x \\
\hline
12x^2-64x-11
\end{array}
$$

55.
$$
\begin{array}{r}
2x^2+4x-1 \\
x+3 \\
\hline
6x^2+12x-3 \\
2x^3+\;4x^2-\;\;x \\
\hline
2x^3+10x^2+11x-3
\end{array}
$$

57.
$$
\begin{array}{r}
x^2\;+5x\;-7 \\
2x^2\;-7x\;-9 \\
\hline
-9x^2-45x+63 \\
-7x^3-35x^2+49x \\
2x^4+10x^3-14x^2 \\
\hline
2x^4\;+3x^3-58x^2\;+4x+63
\end{array}
$$

59. $-1.2y(-7y^6) = (-1.2\cdot-7)(y\cdot y^6) = 8.4y^7$

61. $-3x(x^2+2x-8) = -3x(x^2)+(-3x)(2x)+(-3x)(-8)$
$$= -3x^3-6x^2+24x$$

63. $(x+19)(2x+1) = x(2x+1)+19(2x+1)$
$$= x(2x)+x(1)+19(2x)+19(1)$$
$$= 2x^2+x+38x+19$$
$$= 2x^2+39x+19$$

65. $\left(x+\dfrac{1}{7}\right)\left(x-\dfrac{3}{7}\right)$

$= x\left(x-\dfrac{3}{7}\right)+\dfrac{1}{7}\left(x-\dfrac{3}{7}\right)$

$= x(x)+x\left(-\dfrac{3}{7}\right)+\dfrac{1}{7}(x)+\dfrac{1}{7}\left(-\dfrac{3}{7}\right)$

$= x^2 -\dfrac{3}{7}x+\dfrac{1}{7}x-\dfrac{3}{49}$

$= x^2 -\dfrac{2}{7}x-\dfrac{3}{49}$

67. $(3y+5)^2 = (3y+5)(3y+5)$

$= 3y(3y+5)+5(3y+5)$

$= 3y(3y)+3y(5)+5(3y)+5(5)$

$= 9y^2 +15y+15y+25$

$= 9y^2 +30y+25$

69. $(a+4)(a^2 -6a+6)$

$= a(a^2 -6a+6)+4(a^2 -6a+6)$

$= a(a^2)+a(-6a)+a(6)+4(a^2)+4(-6a)+4(6)$

$= a^3 -6a^2 +6a+4a^2 -24a+24$

$= a^3 -2a^2 -18a+24$

71. $(2x+5)(2x-5)$

$= 2x(2x-5)+5(2x-5)$

$= 2x(2x)+2x(-5)+5(2x)+5(-5)$

$= 4x^2 -10x+10x-25$

$= 4x^2 -25$

The area is $(4x^2 -25)$ square yards.

73. Area $= \dfrac{1}{2}$(base)(height)

$= \dfrac{1}{2}(3x-2)(4x)$

$= 2x(3x-2)$

$= 2x(3x)+2x(-2)$

$= 6x^2 -4x$

The area is $(6x^2 -4x)$ square inches.

75. $(5x)^2 = 5^2 x^2 = 25x^2$

77. $(-3y^3)^2 = (-3)^2 (y^3)^2 = 9y^6$

79. a. $(3x+5)+(3x+7) = 3x+5+3x+7$
$= 6x+12$

b. $(3x+5)(3x+7)$
$= 3x(3x+7)+5(3x+7)$
$= 3x(3x)+3x(7)+5(3x)+5(7)$
$= 9x^2 +21x+15x+35$
$= 9x^2 +36x+35$
answers may vary

81. $(3x-1)+(10x-6) = 3x-1+10x-6 = 13x-7$

83. $(3x-1)(10x-6)$
$= 3x(10x-6)+(-1)(10x-6)$
$= 3x(10x)+3x(-6)+(-1)(10x)+(-1)(-6)$
$= 30x^2 -18x-10x+6$
$= 30x^2 -28x+6$

85. $(3x-1)-(10x-6) = (3x-1)+(-10x+6)$
$= 3x-1-10x+6$
$= -7x+5$

87. The areas of the smaller rectangles are:
$x \cdot x = x^2$
$x \cdot 3 = 3x$
The area of the figure is $x^2 +3x$.

89. The area of the figure is $x(1+2x)$.
The areas of the smaller rectangles are
$x \cdot 1 = x$
$x \cdot 2x = 2x^2$
The area of the figure is $x+2x^2$.

91. $5a+6a = (5+6)a = 11a$

93. $(5x)^2 +(2y)^2 = 5^2 x^2 +2^2 y^2 = 25x^2 +4y^2$

95. a. $(a+b)(a-b) = a(a-b)+b(a-b)$
$= a(a)+a(-b)+b(a)+b(-b)$
$= a^2 -ab+ab-b^2$
$= a^2 -b^2$

b. $(2x+3y)(2x-3y)$
$= 2x(2x-3y)+3y(2x-3y)$
$= 2x(2x)+2x(-3y)+3y(2x)+3y(-3y)$
$= 4x^2 -6xy+6xy-9y^2$
$= 4x^2 -9y^2$

c. $(4x+7)(4x-7)$
$= 4x(4x-7)+7(4x-7)$
$= 4x(4x)+4x(-7)+7(4x)+7(-7)$
$= 16x^2 -28x+28x-49$
$= 16x^2 -49$

d. answers may vary

Section 10.6

Practice Problems

1. $(x+7)(x-5)$
$= (x)(x)+(x)(-5)+(7)(x)+(7)(-5)$
$= x^2 -5x+7x-35$
$= x^2 +2x-35$

2. $(6x-1)(x-4)$
$= 6x(x)+6x(-4)+(-1)(x)+(-1)(-4)$
$= 6x^2 -24x-x+4$
$= 6x^2 -25x+4$

3. $(2y^2 +3)(y-4) = 2y^3 -8y^2 +3y-12$

4. $(2x+9)^2 = (2x+9)(2x+9)$
$= (2x)(2x)+(2x)(9)+9(2x)+9(9)$
$= 4x^2 +18x+18x+81$
$= 4x^2 +36x+81$

5. $(y+3)^2 = y^2 +2(y)(3)+3^2 = y^2 +6y+9$

6. $(r-s)^2 = r^2 -2(r)(s)+s^2 = r^2 -2rs+s^2$

7. $(6x+5)^2 = (6x)^2 +2(6x)(5)+5^2$
$= 36x^2 +60x+25$

8. $(x^2 -3y)^2 = (x^2)^2 -2(x^2)(3y)+(3y)^2$
$= x^4 -6x^2 y+9y^2$

9. $(x+9)(x-9) = x^2 -9^2 = x^2 -81$

10. $(5+4y)(5-4y) = 5^2 -(4y)^2 = 25-16y^2$

11. $\left(x-\dfrac{1}{3}\right)\left(x+\dfrac{1}{3}\right) = x^2 -\left(\dfrac{1}{3}\right)^2 = x^2 -\dfrac{1}{9}$

12. $(3a-b)(3a+b) = (3a)^2 -b^2 = 9a^2 -b^2$

13. $(2x^2 -6y)(2x^2 +6y) = (2x^2)^2 -(6y)^2$
$= 4x^4 -36y^2$

14. $(7x-1)^2 = (7x)^2 -2(7x)(1)+1^2$
$= 49x^2 -14x+1$

15. $(5y+3)(2y-5)$
$= (5y)(2y)+(5y)(-5)+(3)(2y)+(3)(-5)$
$= 10y^2 -25y+6y-15$
$= 10y^2 -19y-15$

16. $(2a-1)(2a+1) = (2a)^2 -(1)^2 = 4a^2 -1$

17. $\left(5y-\dfrac{1}{9}\right)^2 = (5y)^2 -2(5y)\left(\dfrac{1}{9}\right)+\left(\dfrac{1}{9}\right)^2$
$= 25y^2 -\dfrac{10}{9}y+\dfrac{1}{81}$

Vocabulary and Readiness Check

1. $(x+4)^2 = x^2 +2(x)(4)+4^2$
$= x^2 +8x+16$
$\neq x^2 +16$
The statement is false.

2. The statement is true.

3. $(x+4)(x-4) = x^2 -4^2 = x^2 -16 \neq x^2 +16$
The statement is false.

4. $(x-1)(x^3 +3x-1) = x(x^3 +3x-1)-1(x^3 +3x-1)$
$= x^4 +3x^2 -x-x^3 -3x+1$
$= x^4 -x^3 +3x^2 -4x+1$
The product is a polynomial of degree 4, not 5.
The statement is false.

Exercise Set 10.6

1. $(x+3)(x+4) = x^2 +4x+3x+12 = x^2 +7x+12$

3. $(x-5)(x+10) = x^2 +10x-5x-50$
$= x^2 +5x-50$

5. $(5x-6)(x+2) = 5x^2 +10x-6x-12$
$= 5x^2 +4x-12$

7. $(y-6)(4y-1) = 4y^2 - y - 24y + 6$
$= 4y^2 - 25y + 6$

9. $(2x+5)(3x-1) = 6x^2 - 2x + 15x - 5$
$= 6x^2 + 13x - 5$

11. $(y^2+7)(6y+4) = 6y^3 + 4y^2 + 42y + 28$

13. $\left(x - \frac{1}{3}\right)\left(x + \frac{2}{3}\right) = x^2 + \frac{2}{3}x - \frac{1}{3}x - \frac{2}{9}$
$= x^2 + \frac{1}{3}x - \frac{2}{9}$

15. $(0.4-3a)(0.2-5a) = 0.08 - 2.0a - 0.6a + 15a^2$
$= 0.08 - 2.6a + 15a^2$

17. $(x+5y)(2x-y) = 2x^2 - xy + 10xy - 5y^2$
$= 2x^2 + 9xy - 5y^2$

19. $(x+2)^2 = x^2 + 2(2)(x) + 2^2 = x^2 + 4x + 4$

21. $(2a-3)^2 = (2a)^2 - 2(2a)(3) + (3)^2$
$= 4a^2 - 12a + 9$

23. $(3a-5)^2 = (3a)^2 - 2(3a)(5) + 5^2$
$= 9a^2 - 30a + 25$

25. $(x^2+0.5)^2 = (x^2)^2 + 2(x^2)(0.5) + (0.5)^2$
$= x^4 + x^2 + 0.25$

27. $\left(y - \frac{2}{7}\right)^2 = y^2 - 2(y)\left(\frac{2}{7}\right) + \left(\frac{2}{7}\right)^2$
$= y^2 - \frac{4}{7}y + \frac{4}{49}$

29. $(2x-1)^2 = (2x)^2 - 2(2x)(1) + (1)^2$
$= 4x^2 - 4x + 1$

31. $(5x+9)^2 = (5x)^2 + 2(5x)(9) + 9^2$
$= 25x^2 + 90x + 81$

33. $(3x-7y)^2 = (3x)^2 - 2(3x)(7y) + (7y)^2$
$= 9x^2 - 42xy + 49y^2$

35. $(4m+5n)^2 = (4m)^2 + 2(4m)(5n) + (5n)^2$
$= 16m^2 + 40mn + 25n^2$

37. $(5x^4-3)^2 = (5x^4)^2 - 2(5x^4)(3) + (3)^2$
$= 25x^8 - 30x^4 + 9$

39. $(a-7)(a+7) = a^2 - 7^2 = a^2 - 49$

41. $(x+6)(x-6) = (x)^2 - (6)^2 = x^2 - 36$

43. $(3x-1)(3x+1) = (3x)^2 - 1^2 = 9x^2 - 1$

45. $(x^2+5)(x^2-5) = (x^2)^2 - (5)^2 = x^4 - 25$

47. $(2y^2-1)(2y^2+1) = (2y^2)^2 - 1^2 = 4y^4 - 1$

49. $(4-7x)(4+7x) = (4)^2 - (7x)^2 = 16 - 49x^2$

51. $\left(3x - \frac{1}{2}\right)\left(3x + \frac{1}{2}\right) = (3x)^2 - \left(\frac{1}{2}\right)^2 = 9x^2 - \frac{1}{4}$

53. $(9x+y)(9x-y) = (9x)^2 - (y)^2 = 81x^2 - y^2$

55. $(2m+5n)(2m-5n) = (2m)^2 - (5n)^2$
$= 4m^2 - 25n^2$

57. $(a+5)(a+4) = a^2 + 4a + 5a + 20 = a^2 + 9a + 20$

59. $(a-7)^2 = a^2 - 2(a)(7) + 7^2 = a^2 - 14a + 49$

61. $(4a+1)(3a-1) = 12a^2 - 4a + 3a - 1$
$= 12a^2 - a - 1$

63. $(x+2)(x-2) = x^2 - 2^2 = x^2 - 4$

65. $(3a+1)^2 = (3a)^2 + 2(3a)(1) + (1)^2 = 9a^2 + 6a + 1$

67. $(x+y)(4x-y) = 4x^2 - xy + 4xy - y^2$
$= 4x^2 + 3xy - y^2$

69. $\left(\frac{1}{3}a^2 - 7\right)\left(\frac{1}{3}a^2 + 7\right) = \left(\frac{1}{3}a^2\right)^2 - 7^2$
$= \frac{1}{9}a^4 - 49$

71. $(3b+7)(2b-5) = 6b^2 - 15b + 14b - 35$
$$= 6b^2 - b - 35$$

73. $(x^2+10)(x^2-10) = (x^2)^2 - (10)^2 = x^4 - 100$

75. $(4x+5)(4x-5) = (4x)^2 - 5^2 = 16x^2 - 25$

77. $(5x-6y)^2 = (5x)^2 - 2(5x)(6y) + (6y)^2$
$$= 25x^2 - 60xy + 36y^2$$

79. $(2r-3s)(2r+3s) = (2r)^2 - (3s)^2 = 4r^2 - 9s^2$

81. $(2x+1)^2 = (2x)^2 + 2(2x)(1) + (1)^2 = 4x^2 + 4x + 1$

The area of the rug is $(4x^2 + 4x + 1)$ square feet.

83. $\dfrac{50b^{10}}{70b^5} = \dfrac{50}{70} \cdot \dfrac{b^{10}}{b^5} = \dfrac{5}{7}b^{10-5} = \dfrac{5}{7}b^5 = \dfrac{5b^5}{7}$

85. $\dfrac{8a^{17}b^5}{-4a^7b^{10}} = \dfrac{8}{-4} \cdot \dfrac{a^{17}}{a^7} \cdot \dfrac{b^5}{b^{10}}$
$$= -2a^{17-7}b^{5-10}$$
$$= -2a^{10}b^{-5}$$
$$= -\dfrac{2a^{10}}{b^5}$$

87. $\dfrac{2x^4y^{12}}{3x^4y^4} = \dfrac{2}{3} \cdot \dfrac{x^4}{x^4} \cdot \dfrac{y^{12}}{y^4}$
$$= \dfrac{2}{3}x^{4-4}y^{12-4}$$
$$= \dfrac{2}{3}x^0y^8$$
$$= \dfrac{2y^8}{3}$$

89. $(a-b)^2 = (a)^2 - 2(a)(b) + (b)^2 = a^2 - 2ab + b^2$
which is choice c.

91. $(a+b)^2 = (a)^2 + 2(a)(b) + (b)^2 = a^2 + 2ab + b^2$
which is choice d.

93. Since $x^2 \cdot x^2 = x^4$ and $3x^2 + 7x^2 = 10x^2$,
$(x^2+7)(x^2+3) = x^4 + 10x^2 + 21$ is a true
statement.

95. $(x^2-1)^2 - x^2 = ((x^2)^2 - 2(x^2)(1) + 1^2) - x^2$
$$= (x^4 - 2x^2 + 1) - x^2$$
$$= x^4 - 2x^2 + 1 - x^2$$
$$= x^4 - 3x^2 + 1$$

The area is $(x^4 - 3x^2 + 1)$ square meters.

97. $(5x-3)^2 - (x+1)^2$
$$= ((5x)^2 - 2(5x)(3) + 3^2) - (x^2 + 2x + 1^2)$$
$$= (25x^2 - 30x + 9) + (-x^2 - 2x - 1)$$
$$= 25x^2 - 30x + 9 - x^2 - 2x - 1$$
$$= 24x^2 - 32x + 8$$

The area is $(24x^2 - 32x + 8)$ square meters.

99. answers may vary

101. answers may vary

Integrated Review

1. $(5x^2)(7x^3) = (5 \cdot 7)(x^2 \cdot x^3) = 35x^5$

2. $(4y^2)(-8y^7) = (4 \cdot -8)(y^2 \cdot y^7) = -32y^9$

3. $-4^2 = -(4^2) = -16$

4. $(-4)^2 = (-4)(-4) = 16$

5. $(x-5)(2x+1) = 2x^2 + 1x - 10x - 5 = 2x^2 - 9x - 5$

6. $(3x-2)(x+5) = 3x^2 + 15x - 2x - 10$
$$= 3x^2 + 13x - 10$$

7. $(x-5) + (2x+1) = x - 5 + 2x + 1 = 3x - 4$

8. $(3x-2) + (x+5) = 3x - 2 + x + 5 = 4x + 3$

9. $\dfrac{7x^9y^{12}}{x^3y^{10}} = 7 \cdot x^{9-3} \cdot y^{12-10} = 7x^6y^2$

10. $\dfrac{20a^2b^8}{14a^2b^2} = \dfrac{20}{14}a^{2-2}b^{8-2} = \dfrac{10a^0b^6}{7} = \dfrac{10b^6}{7}$

11. $(12m^7n^6)^2 = 12^2 \cdot m^{7 \cdot 2}n^{6 \cdot 2} = 144m^{14}n^{12}$

12. $(4y^9z^{10})^3 = 4^3 \cdot y^{9 \cdot 3}z^{10 \cdot 3} = 64y^{27}z^{30}$

13. $(4y-3)(4y+3) = (4y)^2 - 3^2 = 16y^2 - 9$

14. $(7x-1)(7x+1) = (7x)^2 - 1^2 = 49x^2 - 1$

15. $(x^{-7}y^5)^9 = x^{-7 \cdot 9}y^{5 \cdot 9} = x^{-63}y^{45} = \dfrac{y^{45}}{x^{63}}$

16. $8^{-2} = \dfrac{1}{8^2} = \dfrac{1}{64}$

17. $(3^{-1}x^9)^3 = 3^{-1 \cdot 3}x^{9 \cdot 3} = 3^{-3}x^{27} = \dfrac{x^{27}}{3^3} = \dfrac{x^{27}}{27}$

18. $\dfrac{(r^7 s^{-5})^6}{(2r^{-4}s^{-4})^4} = \dfrac{r^{7 \cdot 6}s^{-5 \cdot 6}}{2^4 r^{-4 \cdot 4}s^{-4 \cdot 4}}$

$\qquad = \dfrac{r^{42}s^{-30}}{16r^{-16}s^{-16}}$

$\qquad = \dfrac{r^{42-(-16)}s^{-30-(-16)}}{16}$

$\qquad = \dfrac{r^{58}s^{-14}}{16}$

$\qquad = \dfrac{r^{58}}{16s^{14}}$

19. $(7x^2 - 2x + 3) - (5x^2 + 9) = (7x^2 - 2x + 3) + (-5x^2 - 9)$

$\qquad\qquad = 7x^2 - 2x + 3 - 5x^2 - 9$

$\qquad\qquad = 2x^2 - 2x - 6$

20. $(10x^2 + 7x - 9) - (4x^2 - 6x + 2) = (10x^2 + 7x - 9) + (-4x^2 + 6x - 2)$

$\qquad\qquad = 10x^2 + 7x - 9 - 4x^2 + 6x - 2$

$\qquad\qquad = 6x^2 + 13x - 11$

21. $0.7y^2 - 1.2 + 1.8y^2 - 6y + 1 = 2.5y^2 - 6y - 0.2$

22. $7.8x^2 - 6.8x - 3.3 + 0.6x^2 - 0.9 = 8.4x^2 - 6.8x - 4.2$

23. $(3y^2 - 6y + 1) - (y^2 + 2) = (3y^2 - 6y + 1) + (-y^2 - 2)$

$\qquad\qquad = 3y^2 - 6y + 1 - y^2 - 2$

$\qquad\qquad = 2y^2 - 6y - 1$

24. $(z^2 + 5) - (3z^2 - 1) + \left(8z^2 + 2z - \dfrac{1}{2}\right) = (z^2 + 5) + (-3z^2 + 1) + \left(8z^2 + 2z - \dfrac{1}{2}\right)$

$$= z^2 + 5 - 3z^2 + 1 + 8z^2 + 2z - \dfrac{1}{2}$$

$$= 6z^2 + 2z + \dfrac{11}{2}$$

25. $(x + 4)^2 = x^2 + 2(x)(4) + 4^2 = x^2 + 8x + 16$

26. $(y - 9)^2 = y^2 - 2(y)(9) + 9^2 = y^2 - 18x + 81$

27. $(x + 4) + (x + 4) = x + 4 + x + 4 = 2x + 8$

28. $(y - 9) + (y - 9) = y - 9 + y - 9 = 2y - 18$

29. $7x^2 - 6xy + 4(y^2 - xy) = 7x^2 - 6xy + 4y^2 - 4xy$

$$= 7x^2 - 10xy + 4y^2$$

30. $5a^2 - 3ab + 6(b^2 - a^2) = 5a^2 - 3ab + 6b^2 - 6a^2$

$$= -a^2 - 3ab + 6b^2$$

31. $(x - 3)(x^2 + 5x - 1) = x(x^2 + 5x - 1) + (-3)(x^2 + 5x - 1)$

$$= x(x^2) + x(5x) + x(-1) + (-3)(x^2) + (-3)(5x) + (-3)(-1)$$

$$= x^3 + 5x^2 - x - 3x^2 - 15x + 3$$

$$= x^3 + 2x^2 - 16x + 3$$

32. $(x + 1)(x^2 - 3x - 2) = x(x^2 - 3x - 2) + 1(x^2 - 3x - 2)$

$$= x(x^2) + x(-3x) + x(-2) + 1(x^2) + 1(-3x) + 1(-2)$$

$$= x^3 - 3x^2 - 2x + x^2 - 3x - 2$$

$$= x^3 - 2x^2 - 5x - 2$$

33. $(2x - 7)(3x + 10) = 6x^2 + 20x - 21x - 70$

$$= 6x^2 - x - 70$$

34. $(5x - 1)(4x + 5) = 20x^2 + 25x - 4x - 5$

$$= 20x^2 + 21x - 5$$

35. $(2x - 7)(x^2 - 6x + 1) = 2x(x^2 - 6x + 1) + (-7)(x^2 - 6x + 1)$

$$= 2x(x^2) + 2x(-6x) + 2x(1) + (-7)(x^2) + (-7)(-6x) + (-7)(1)$$

$$= 2x^3 - 12x^2 + 2x - 7x^2 + 42x - 7$$

$$= 2x^3 - 19x^2 + 44x - 7$$

36. $(5x-1)(x^2+2x-3) = 5x(x^2+2x-3)+(-1)(x^2+2x-3)$
$$= 5x(x^2)+5x(2x)+5x(-3)+(-1)(x^2)+(-1)(2x)+(-1)(-3)$$
$$= 5x^3+10x^2-15x-x^2-2x+3$$
$$= 5x^3+9x^2-17x+3$$

37. $\left(2x+\dfrac{5}{9}\right)\left(2x-\dfrac{5}{9}\right) = (2x)^2-\left(\dfrac{5}{9}\right)^2 = 4x^2-\dfrac{25}{81}$

38. $\left(12y+\dfrac{3}{7}\right)\left(12y-\dfrac{3}{7}\right) = (12y)^2-\left(\dfrac{3}{7}\right)^2$
$$= 144y^2-\dfrac{9}{49}$$

Section 10.7

Practice Problems

1. $\dfrac{25x^3+5x^2}{5x^2} = \dfrac{25x^3}{5x^2}+\dfrac{5x^2}{5x^2} = 5x+1$

2. $\dfrac{24x^7+12x^2-4x}{4x^2} = \dfrac{24x^7}{4x^2}+\dfrac{12x^2}{4x^2}-\dfrac{4x}{4x^2}$
$$= 6x^5+3-\dfrac{1}{x}$$

3. $\dfrac{12x^3y^3-18xy+6y}{3xy} = \dfrac{12x^3y^3}{3xy}-\dfrac{18xy}{3xy}+\dfrac{6y}{3xy}$
$$= 4x^2y^2-6+\dfrac{2}{x}$$

4.
$$
\begin{array}{r}
x+7 \\
x+5\overline{\smash{\big)}\,x^2+12x+35} \\
\underline{x^2+5x} \\
7x+35 \\
\underline{7x+35} \\
0
\end{array}
$$

Thus, $\dfrac{x^2+12x+35}{x+5} = x+7$.

5.

$$2x-1 \overline{\smash{\big)}\,\begin{aligned}4x+3\\ 8x^2+2x-7\end{aligned}}$$

$$\underline{8x^2-4x}$$
$$6x-7$$
$$\underline{6x-3}$$
$$-4$$

Thus, $\dfrac{8x^2+2x-7}{2x-1} = 4x+3+\dfrac{-4}{2x-1}$ or

$4x+3-\dfrac{4}{2x-1}$.

6. $15-2x^2 = -2x^2+0x+15$

$$x-3 \overline{\smash{\big)}\,\begin{aligned}-2x-6\\ -2x^2+0x+15\end{aligned}}$$

$$\underline{-2x^2+6x}$$
$$-6x+15$$
$$\underline{-6x+18}$$
$$-3$$

Thus, $\dfrac{15-2x^2}{x-3} = -2x-6+\dfrac{-3}{x-3}$ or

$-2x-6-\dfrac{3}{x-3}$.

7. $\dfrac{5-x+9x^3}{3x+2} = \dfrac{9x^3+0x^2-x+5}{3x+2}$

$$3x+2 \overline{\smash{\big)}\,\begin{aligned}3x^2-2x+1\\ 9x^3+0x^2-x+5\end{aligned}}$$

$$\underline{9x^3+6x^2}$$
$$-6x^2-x$$
$$\underline{-6x^2-4x}$$
$$3x+5$$
$$\underline{3x+2}$$
$$3$$

Thus, $\dfrac{5-x+9x^3}{3x+2} = 3x^2-2x+1+\dfrac{3}{3x+2}$.

8.

$$x-1 \overline{\smash{\big)}\,\begin{aligned}x^2+x+1\\ x^3+0x^2+0x-1\end{aligned}}$$

$$\underline{x^3-x^2}$$
$$x^2+0x$$
$$\underline{x^2-x}$$
$$x-1$$
$$\underline{x-1}$$
$$0$$

Thus, $\dfrac{x^3-1}{x-1} = x^2+x+1$.

Vocabulary and Readiness Check

1. In $6\overline{\smash{\big)}18}$, the 18 is the <u>dividend</u>, the 3 is the <u>quotient</u>, and the 6 is the <u>divisor</u>.

2. In $x+1 \overline{\smash{\big)}\,\begin{aligned}x+2\\ x^2+3x+2\end{aligned}}$, the $x+1$ is the <u>divisor</u>, the x^2+3x+2 is the <u>dividend</u>, and the $x+2$ is the <u>quotient</u>.

3. $\dfrac{a^6}{a^4} = a^{6-4} = a^2$

4. $\dfrac{p^8}{p^3} = p^{8-3} = p^5$

5. $\dfrac{y^2}{y} = \dfrac{y^2}{y^1} = y^{2-1} = y^1 = y$

6. $\dfrac{a^3}{a} = \dfrac{a^3}{a^1} = a^{3-1} = a^2$

Exercise Set 10.7

1. $\dfrac{12x^4+3x^2}{x} = \dfrac{12x^4}{x}+\dfrac{3x^2}{x} = 12x^3+3x$

3. $\dfrac{20x^3-30x^2+5x+5}{5} = \dfrac{20x^3}{5}-\dfrac{30x^2}{5}+\dfrac{5x}{5}+\dfrac{5}{5}$
$= 4x^3-6x^2+x+1$

5. $\dfrac{15p^3+18p^2}{3p} = \dfrac{15p^3}{3p}+\dfrac{18p^2}{3p} = 5p^2+6p$

7. $\dfrac{-9x^4 + 18x^5}{6x^5} = \dfrac{-9x^4}{6x^5} + \dfrac{18x^5}{6x^5} = \dfrac{-3}{2x} + 3$

9. $\dfrac{-9x^5 + 3x^4 - 12}{3x^3} = \dfrac{-9x^5}{3x^3} + \dfrac{3x^4}{3x^3} - \dfrac{12}{3x^3}$

$\qquad\qquad = -3x^2 + x - \dfrac{4}{x^3}$

11. $\dfrac{4x^4 - 6x^3 + 7}{-4x^4} = \dfrac{4x^4}{-4x^4} - \dfrac{6x^3}{-4x^4} + \dfrac{7}{-4x^4}$

$\qquad\qquad = -1 + \dfrac{3}{2x} - \dfrac{7}{4x^4}$

13.
$$\begin{array}{r}
x + 1 \\
x+3\overline{\smash{)}x^2 + 4x + 3} \\
\underline{x^2 + 3x} \\
x + 3 \\
\underline{x + 3} \\
0
\end{array}$$

$\dfrac{x^2 + 4x + 3}{x + 3} = x + 1$

15.
$$\begin{array}{r}
2x + 3 \\
x+5\overline{\smash{)}2x^2 + 13x + 15} \\
\underline{2x^2 + 10x} \\
3x + 15 \\
\underline{3x + 15} \\
0
\end{array}$$

$\dfrac{2x^2 + 13x + 15}{x + 5} = 2x + 3$

17.
$$\begin{array}{r}
2x + 1 \\
x-4\overline{\smash{)}2x^2 - 7x + 3} \\
\underline{2x^2 - 8x} \\
x + 3 \\
\underline{x - 4} \\
7
\end{array}$$

$\dfrac{2x^2 - 7x + 3}{x - 4} = 2x + 1 + \dfrac{7}{x - 4}$

19.
$$\begin{array}{r}
3a^2 - 3a + 1 \\
3a+2\overline{\smash{)}9a^3 - 3a^2 - 3a + 4} \\
\underline{9a^3 + 6a^2} \\
-9a^2 - 3a \\
\underline{-9a^2 - 6a} \\
3a + 4 \\
\underline{3a + 2} \\
2
\end{array}$$

$\dfrac{9a^3 - 3a^2 - 3a + 4}{3a + 2} = 3a^2 - 3a + 1 + \dfrac{2}{3a + 2}$

21.
$$\begin{array}{r}
4x + 3 \\
2x+1\overline{\smash{)}8x^2 + 10x + 1} \\
\underline{8x^2 + 4x} \\
6x + 1 \\
\underline{6x + 3} \\
-2
\end{array}$$

$\dfrac{8x^2 + 10x + 1}{2x + 1} = 4x + 3 - \dfrac{2}{2x + 1}$

23.
$$\begin{array}{r}
2x^2 + 6x - 5 \\
x-2\overline{\smash{)}2x^3 + 2x^2 - 17x + 8} \\
\underline{2x^3 - 4x^2} \\
6x^2 - 17x \\
\underline{6x^2 - 12x} \\
-5x + 8 \\
\underline{-5x + 10} \\
-2
\end{array}$$

$\dfrac{2x^3 + 2x^2 - 17x + 8}{x - 2} = 2x^2 + 6x - 5 - \dfrac{2}{x - 2}$

25.
$$\begin{array}{r}
x + 6 \\
x-6\overline{\smash{)}x^2 + 0x - 36} \\
\underline{x^2 - 6x} \\
6x - 36 \\
\underline{6x - 36} \\
0
\end{array}$$

$\dfrac{x^2 - 36}{x - 6} = x + 6$

27.

$$
\begin{array}{r}
x^2 + 3x + 9 \\
x - 3 \overline{\smash{\big)}\ x^3 + 0x^2 + 0x - 27} \\
\underline{x^3 - 3x^2} \\
3x^2 + 0x \\
\underline{3x^2 - 9x} \\
9x - 27 \\
\underline{9x - 27} \\
0
\end{array}
$$

$$\frac{x^3 - 27}{x - 3} = x^2 + 3x + 9$$

29. $1 - 3x^2 = -3x^2 + 0x + 1$

$$
\begin{array}{r}
-3x + 6 \\
x + 2 \overline{\smash{\big)}\ -3x^2 + 0x + 1} \\
\underline{-3x^2 - 6x} \\
6x + 1 \\
\underline{6x + 12} \\
-11
\end{array}
$$

$$\frac{1 - 3x^2}{x + 2} = -3x + 6 - \frac{11}{x + 2}$$

31.

$$
\begin{array}{r}
2b - 1 \\
2b - 1 \overline{\smash{\big)}\ -4b^2 - 4b - 5} \\
\underline{4b^2 - 2b} \\
-2b - 5 \\
\underline{-2b + 1} \\
-6
\end{array}
$$

$$\frac{-4b + 4b^2 - 5}{2b - 1} = 2b - 1 - \frac{6}{2b - 1}$$

33. $\dfrac{a^2b^2 - ab^3}{ab} = \dfrac{a^2b^2}{ab} - \dfrac{ab^3}{ab} = ab - b^2$

35.

$$
\begin{array}{r}
4x + 9 \\
2x - 3 \overline{\smash{\big)}\ 8x^2 + 6x - 27} \\
\underline{8x^2 - 12x} \\
18x - 27 \\
\underline{18x - 27} \\
0
\end{array}
$$

$$\frac{8x^2 + 6x - 27}{2x - 3} = 4x + 9$$

37. $\dfrac{2x^2y + 8x^2y^2 - xy^2}{2xy} = \dfrac{2x^2y}{2xy} + \dfrac{8x^2y^2}{2xy} - \dfrac{xy^2}{2xy}$

$$= x + 4xy - \frac{y}{2}$$

39.

$$
\begin{array}{r}
2b^2 + b + 2 \\
b + 4 \overline{\smash{\big)}\ 2b^3 + 9b^2 + 6b - 4} \\
\underline{2b^3 + 8b^2} \\
b^2 + 6b \\
\underline{b^2 + 4b} \\
2b - 4 \\
\underline{2b + 8} \\
-12
\end{array}
$$

$$\frac{2b^3 + 9b^2 + 6b - 4}{b + 4} = 2b^2 + b + 2 - \frac{12}{b + 4}$$

41.

$$
\begin{array}{r}
y^2 + 5y + 10 \\
y - 2 \overline{\smash{\big)}\ y^3 + 3y^2 + 0y + 4} \\
\underline{y^3 - 2y^2} \\
5y^2 + 0y \\
\underline{5y^2 - 10y} \\
10y + 4 \\
\underline{10y - 20} \\
24
\end{array}
$$

$$\frac{y^3 + 3y^2 + 4}{y - 2} = y^2 + 5y + 10 + \frac{24}{y - 2}$$

43.

$$
\begin{array}{r}
-6x - 12 \\
x - 2 \overline{\smash{\big)}\ -6x^2 + 0x + 5} \\
\underline{-6x^2 + 12x} \\
-12x + 5 \\
\underline{-12x + 24} \\
-19
\end{array}
$$

$$\frac{5 - 6x^2}{x - 2} = -6x - 12 - \frac{19}{x - 2}$$

45.

$$
\begin{array}{r}
x^3 - x^2 + x \\
x^2 + x \overline{\smash{\big)}\ x^5 + 0x^4 + 0x^3 + x^2} \\
\underline{x^5 + x^4} \\
-x^4 + 0x^3 \\
\underline{-x^4 - x^3} \\
x^3 + x^2 \\
\underline{x^3 + x^2} \\
0
\end{array}
$$

$$\frac{x^5 + x^2}{x^2 + x} = x^3 - x^2 + x$$

47. $\dfrac{12}{4} = 3$, so $12 = 4 \cdot 3$.

49. $\dfrac{20}{-5} = -4$, so $20 = -5 \cdot -4$.

51. $\dfrac{9x^2}{3x} = 3x$, so $9x^2 = 3x \cdot 3x$.

53. $\dfrac{36x^2}{4x} = 9x$, so $36x^2 = 4x \cdot 9x$.

55. $\dfrac{12x^3 + 4x - 16}{4} = \dfrac{12x^3}{4} + \dfrac{4x}{4} - \dfrac{16}{4}$
$\qquad\qquad\qquad = 3x^3 + x - 4$

The length of each side of the square is
$(3x^3 + x - 4)$ feet.

57.
$$
\begin{array}{r}
2x+5 \\
5x+3\overline{)10x^2+31x+15} \\
\underline{10x^2+6x} \\
25x+15 \\
\underline{25x+15} \\
0
\end{array}
$$

The height of the parallelogram is
$(2x + 5)$ meters.

59. answers may vary

61. $\dfrac{a+7}{7} = \dfrac{a}{7} + \dfrac{7}{7} = \dfrac{a}{7} + 1$ which is choice c.

Chapter 10 Vocabulary Check

1. A <u>term</u> is a number or the product of numbers and variables raised to powers.

2. The <u>FOIL</u> method may be used when multiplying two binomials.

3. A polynomial with exactly 3 terms is called a <u>trinomial</u>.

4. The <u>degree of polynomial</u> is the greatest degree of any term of the polynomial.

5. A polynomial with exactly 2 terms is called a <u>binomial</u>.

6. The <u>coefficient</u> of a term is its numerical factor.

7. The <u>degree of a term</u> is the sum of the exponents on the variables in the term.

8. A polynomial with exactly 1 term is called a <u>monomial</u>.

9. Monomials, binomials, and trinomials are all examples of <u>polynomials</u>.

10. The <u>distributive</u> property is used to multiply $2x(x - 4)$.

Chapter 10 Review

1. In 3^2, the base is 3 and the exponent is 2.

2. In $(-5)^4$, the base is -5 and the exponent is 4.

3. In -5^4, the base is 5 and the exponent is 4.

4. In x^6, the base is x and the exponent is 6.

5. $8^3 = 8 \cdot 8 \cdot 8 = 512$

6. $(-6)^2 = (-6)(-6) = 36$

7. $-6^2 = -(6 \cdot 6) = -36$

8. $-4^3 - 4^0 = -64 - 1 = -65$

9. $(3b)^0 = 1$

10. $\dfrac{8b}{8b} = 1$

11. $y^2 \cdot y^7 = y^{2+7} = y^9$

12. $x^9 \cdot x^5 = x^{9+5} = x^{14}$

13. $(2x^5)(-3x^6) = -6x^{5+6} = -6x^{11}$

14. $(-5y^3)(4y^4) = -20y^{3+4} = -20y^7$

15. $(x^4)^2 = x^{4 \cdot 2} = x^8$

16. $(y^3)^5 = y^{3 \cdot 5} = y^{15}$

17. $(3y^6)^4 = 3^4 \cdot y^{6 \cdot 4} = 81y^{24}$

18. $(2x^3)^3 = 2^3 \cdot x^{3 \cdot 3} = 8x^9$

19. $\dfrac{x^9}{x^4} = x^{9-4} = x^5$

20. $\dfrac{z^{12}}{z^5} = z^{12-5} = z^7$

21. $\dfrac{a^5 b^4}{ab} = a^{5-1} b^{4-1} = a^4 b^3$

22. $\dfrac{x^4 y^6}{xy} = x^{4-1} y^{6-1} = x^3 y^5$

23. $\dfrac{3x^4 y^{10}}{12xy^6} = \dfrac{3}{12} x^{4-1} y^{10-6} = \dfrac{1}{4} x^3 y^4 = \dfrac{x^3 y^4}{4}$

24. $\dfrac{2x^7 y^8}{8xy^2} = \dfrac{1}{4} x^{7-1} y^{8-2} = \dfrac{x^6 y^6}{4}$

25. $5a^7 (2a^4)^3 = 5a^7 (2^3 \cdot a^{4 \cdot 3})$
$\qquad\qquad = 5a^7 (8a^{12})$
$\qquad\qquad = 40a^{7+12}$
$\qquad\qquad = 40a^{19}$

26. $(2x)^2 (9x) = (2^2 x^2)(9x)$
$\qquad\qquad = 4x^2 (9x)$
$\qquad\qquad = 36x^{2+1}$
$\qquad\qquad = 36x^3$

27. $(-5a)^0 + 7^0 + 8^0 = 1 + 1 + 1 = 3$

28. $8x^0 + 9^0 = 8 \cdot 1 + 1 = 8 + 1 = 9$

29. $\left(\dfrac{3x^4}{4y}\right)^3 = \dfrac{3^3 x^{4 \cdot 3}}{4^3 y^{1 \cdot 3}} = \dfrac{27 x^{12}}{64 y^3}$; b

30. $\left(\dfrac{5a^6}{b^3}\right)^2 = \dfrac{5^2 a^{6 \cdot 2}}{b^{3 \cdot 2}} = \dfrac{25 a^{12}}{b^6}$; c

31. $7^{-2} = \dfrac{1}{7^2} = \dfrac{1}{49}$

32. $-7^{-2} = -\dfrac{1}{7^2} = -\dfrac{1}{49}$

33. $2x^{-4} = \dfrac{2}{x^4}$

34. $(2x)^{-4} = \dfrac{1}{(2x)^4} = \dfrac{1}{2^4 x^4} = \dfrac{1}{16x^4}$

35. $\left(\dfrac{1}{5}\right)^{-3} = (5)^3 = 125$

36. $\left(\dfrac{-2}{3}\right)^{-2} = \left(\dfrac{3}{-2}\right)^2 = \dfrac{9}{4}$

37. $2^0 + 2^{-4} = 1 + \dfrac{1}{2^4} = 1 + \dfrac{1}{16} = \dfrac{17}{16}$

38. $6^{-1} - 7^{-1} = \dfrac{1}{6} - \dfrac{1}{7} = \dfrac{7}{42} - \dfrac{6}{42} = \dfrac{1}{42}$

39. $\dfrac{x^5}{x^{-3}} = x^{5-(-3)} = x^8$

40. $\dfrac{z^4}{z^{-4}} = z^{4-(-4)} = z^8$

41. $\dfrac{r^{-3}}{r^{-4}} = r^{-3-(-4)} = r^1 = r$

42. $\dfrac{y^{-2}}{y^{-5}} = y^{-2-(-5)} = y^3$

43. $\left(\dfrac{bc^{-2}}{bc^{-3}}\right)^4 = (b^{1-1} c^{-2-(-3)})^4 = (b^0 c^1)^4 = c^4$

44. $\left(\dfrac{x^{-3} y^{-4}}{x^{-2} y^{-5}}\right)^{-3} = (x^{-3-(-2)} y^{-4-(-5)})^{-3}$
$\qquad\qquad = (x^{-1} y^1)^{-3}$
$\qquad\qquad = x^{-1 \cdot -3} y^{1 \cdot -3}$
$\qquad\qquad = x^3 y^{-3}$
$\qquad\qquad = \dfrac{x^3}{y^3}$

45. $\dfrac{x^{-4} y^{-6}}{x^2 y^7} = x^{-4-2} y^{-6-7} = x^{-6} y^{-13} = \dfrac{1}{x^6 y^{13}}$

46. $\dfrac{a^5 b^{-5}}{a^{-5} b^5} = a^{5-(-5)} b^{(-5)-5} = a^{10} b^{-10} = \dfrac{a^{10}}{b^{10}}$

47. $0.00027 = 2.7 \times 10^{-4}$

48. $0.8868 = 8.868 \times 10^{-1}$

49. $80,800,000 = 8.08 \times 10^{7}$

50. $868,000 = 8.68 \times 10^{5}$

51. $127,000,000 = 1.27 \times 10^{8}$

52. $150,000 = 1.5 \times 10^{5}$

53. $8.67 \times 10^{5} = 867,000$

54. $3.86 \times 10^{-3} = 0.00386$

55. $8.6 \times 10^{-4} = 0.00086$

56. $8.936 \times 10^{5} = 893,600$

57. $1.43128 \times 10^{15} = 1,431,280,000,000,000$

58. $1 \times 10^{-10} = 0.0000000001$

59. $(8 \times 10^{4})(2 \times 10^{-7}) = 16 \times 10^{-3} = 0.016$

60. $\dfrac{8 \times 10^{4}}{2 \times 10^{-7}} = 4 \times 10^{11} = 400,000,000,000$

61. The degree of $(y^{5} + 7x - 8x^{4})$ is 5.

62. The degree of $(9y^{2} + 30y + 25)$ is 2.

63. The degree of $(-14x^{2}y - 28x^{2}y^{3} - 42x^{2}y^{2})$ is 2 + 3 or 5.

64. The degree of $(6x^{2}y^{2}z^{2} + 5x^{2}y^{3} - 12xyz)$ is 2 + 2 + 2 or 6.

65.
$$-16t^{2} + 4000 = -16(0)^{2} + 4000$$
$$= 0 + 4000$$
$$= 4000$$

$$-16t^{2} + 4000 = -16(1)^{2} + 4000$$
$$= -16 + 4000$$
$$= 3984$$

$$-16t^2 + 4000 = -16(3)^2 + 4000$$
$$= -144 + 4000$$
$$= 3856$$
$$-16t^2 + 4000 = -16(5)^2 + 4000$$
$$= -400 + 4000$$
$$= 3600$$

t	0 seconds	1 second	3 seconds	5 seconds
$-16t^2 + 4000$	4000 feet	3984 feet	3856 feet	3600 feet

66. $2x^2 + 20x = 2(1)^2 + 20(1) = 2 + 20 = 22$
$2x^2 + 20x = 2(3)^2 + 20(3) = 18 + 60 = 78$
$2x^2 + 20x = 2(5.1)^2 + 20(5.1) = 52.02 + 102$
$\qquad = 154.02$
$2x^2 + 20x = 2(10)^2 + 20(10) = 200 + 200 = 400$

x	1	3	5.1	10
$2x^2 + 20x$	22	78	154.02	400

67. $7a^2 - 4a^2 - a^2 = (7 - 4 - 1)a^2 = 2a^2$

68. $9y + y - 14y = (9 + 1 - 14)y = -4y$

69. $6a^2 + 4a + 9a^2 = 6a^2 + 9a^2 + 4a = 15a^2 + 4a$

70. $21x^2 + 3x + x^2 + 6 = 21x^2 + x^2 + 3x + 6$
$\qquad = 22x^2 + 3x + 6$

71. $4a^2b - 3b^2 - 8q^2 - 10a^2b + 7q^2 = 4a^2b - 10a^2b - 3b^2 - 8q^2 + 7q^2$
$\qquad = -6a^2b - 3b^2 - q^2$

72. $2s^{14} + 3s^{13} + 12s^{12} - s^{10}$ cannot be combined.

73. $(3x^2 + 2x + 6) + (5x^2 + x) = 3x^2 + 2x + 6 + 5x^2 + x$
$\qquad = 3x^2 + 5x^2 + 2x + x + 6$
$\qquad = 8x^2 + 3x + 6$

74. $(2x^5 + 3x^4 + 4x^3 + 5x^2) + (4x^2 + 7x + 6) = 2x^5 + 3x^4 + 4x^3 + 5x^2 + 4x^2 + 7x + 6$
$\qquad = 2x^5 + 3x^4 + 4x^3 + 9x^2 + 7x + 6$

75. $(-5y^2 + 3) - (2y^2 + 4) = (-5y^2 + 3) + (-2y^2 - 4)$
$\qquad = -5y^2 + 3 - 2y^2 - 4$
$\qquad = -7y^2 - 1$

76. $(2m^7 + 3x^4 + 7m^6) - (8m^7 + 4m^2 + 6x^4) = (2m^7 + 3x^4 + 7m^6) + (-8m^7 - 4m^2 - 6x^4)$
$$= 2m^7 + 3x^4 + 7m^6 - 8m^7 - 4m^2 - 6x^4$$
$$= -6m^7 - 3x^4 + 7m^6 - 4m^2$$

77. $(3x^2 - 7xy + 7y^2) - (4x^2 - xy + 9y^2) = (3x^2 - 7xy + 7y^2) + (-4x^2 + xy - 9y^2)$
$$= 3x^2 - 7xy + 7y^2 - 4x^2 + xy - 9y^2$$
$$= -x^2 - 6xy - 2y^2$$

78. $(8x^6 - 5xy - 10y^2) - (7x^6 - 9xy - 12y^2) = (8x^6 - 5xy - 10y^2) + (-7x^6 + 9xy + 12y^2)$
$$= 8x^6 - 5xy - 10y^2 - 7x^6 + 9xy + 12y^2$$
$$= x^6 + 4xy + 2y^2$$

79. $(-9x^2 + 6x + 2) + (4x^2 - x - 1) = -9x^2 + 6x + 2 + 4x^2 - x - 1$
$$= -5x^2 + 5x + 1$$

80. $[(x^2 + 7x + 9) + (x^2 + 4)] - (4x^2 + 8x - 7) = (x^2 + 7x + 9) + (x^2 + 4) + (-4x^2 - 8x + 7)$
$$= x^2 + 7x + 9 + x^2 + 4 - 4x^2 - 8x + 7$$
$$= -2x^2 - x + 20$$

81. $6(x + 5) = 6(x) + 6(5) = 6x + 30$

82. $9(x - 7) = 9(x) + 9(-7) = 9x - 63$

83. $4(2a + 7) = 4(2a) + 4(7) = 8a + 28$

84. $9(6a - 3) = 9(6a) + 9(-3) = 54a - 27$

85. $-7x(x^2 + 5) = (-7x)(x^2) + (-7x)(5)$
$$= -7x^3 - 35x$$

86. $-8y(4y^2 - 6) = (-8y)(4y^2) + (-8y)(-6)$
$$= -32y^3 + 48y$$

87. $-2(x^3 - 9x^2 + x) = (-2)(x^3) + (-2)(-9x^2) + (-2)(x)$
$$= -2x^3 + 18x^2 - 2x$$

88. $-3a(a^2b + ab + b^2) = (-3a)(a^2b) + (-3a)(ab) + (-3a)(b^2)$
$$= -3a^3b - 3a^2b - 3ab^2$$

89. $(3a^3 - 4a + 1)(-2a) = (3a^3)(-2a) + (-4a)(-2a) + (1)(-2a)$
$$= -6a^4 + 8a^2 - 2a$$

90. $(6b^3 - 4b + 2)(7b) = (6b^3)(7b) + (-4b)(7b) + (2)(7b)$
$$= 42b^4 - 28b^2 + 14b$$

91. $(2x+2)(x-7) = 2x^2 - 14x + 2x - 14$
$$= 2x^2 - 12x - 14$$

92. $(2x-5)(3x+2) = 6x^2 + 4x - 15x - 10$
$$= 6x^2 - 11x - 10$$

93. $(4a-1)(a+7) = 4a^2 + 28a - a - 7$
$$= 4a^2 + 27a - 7$$

94. $(6a-1)(7a+3) = 42a^2 + 18a - 7a - 3$
$$= 42a^2 + 11a - 3$$

95. $(x+7)(x^3+4x-5) = x(x^3+4x-5) + 7(x^3+4x-5)$
$$= x(x^3) + x(4x) + x(-5) + 7(x^3) + 7(4x) + 7(-5)$$
$$= x^4 + 4x^2 - 5x + 7x^3 + 28x - 35$$
$$= x^4 + 7x^3 + 4x^2 + 23x - 35$$

96. $(x+2)(x^5+x+1) = x(x^5+x+1) + 2(x^5+x+1)$
$$= x(x^5) + x(x) + x(1) + 2(x^5) + 2(x) + 2(1)$$
$$= x^6 + x^2 + x + 2x^5 + 2x + 2$$
$$= x^6 + 2x^5 + x^2 + 3x + 2$$

97. $(x^2+2x+4)(x^2+2x-4) = x^2(x^2+2x-4) + 2x(x^2+2x-4) + 4(x^2+2x-4)$
$$= x^4 + 2x^3 - 4x^2 + 2x^3 + 4x^2 - 8x + 4x^2 + 8x - 16$$
$$= x^4 + 4x^3 + 4x^2 - 16$$

98. $(x^3+4x+4)(x^3+4x-4) = x^3(x^3+4x-4) + 4x(x^3+4x-4) + 4(x^3+4x-4)$
$$= x^6 + 4x^4 - 4x^3 + 4x^4 + 16x^2 - 16x + 4x^3 + 16x - 16$$
$$= x^6 + 8x^4 + 16x^2 - 16$$

99. $(x+7)^3 = (x+7)(x+7)^2$
$$= (x+7)(x^2 + 2(x)(7) + 7^2)$$
$$= (x+7)(x^2 + 14x + 49)$$
$$= x(x^2 + 14x + 49) + 7(x^2 + 14x + 49)$$
$$= x^3 + 14x^2 + 49x + 7x^2 + 98x + 343$$
$$= x^3 + 21x^2 + 147x + 343$$

100. $(2x-5)^3$
$$= (2x-5)(2x-5)^2$$
$$= (2x-5)((2x)^2 - (2)(2x)(5) + 5^2)$$
$$= (2x-5)(4x^2 - 20x + 25)$$
$$= 2x(4x^2 - 20x + 25) + (-5)(4x^2 - 20x + 25)$$
$$= 8x^3 - 40x^2 + 50x - 20x^2 + 100x - 125$$
$$= 8x^3 - 60x^2 + 150x - 125$$

101. $(x+7)^2 = x^2 + 2(x)(7) + 7^2 = x^2 + 14x + 49$

102. $(x-5)^2 = x^2 - 2(x)(5) + 5^2 = x^2 - 10x + 25$

103. $(3x-7)^2 = (3x)^2 - 2(3x)(7) + 7^2$
$$= 9x^2 - 42x + 49$$

104. $(4x+2)^2 = (4x)^2 + 2(4x)(2) + 2^2$
$$= 16x^2 + 16x + 4$$

105. $(5x-9)^2 = (5x)^2 - 2(5x)(9) + 9^2$
$$= 25x^2 - 90x + 81$$

106. $(5x+1)(5x-1) = (5x)^2 - 1^2 = 25x^2 - 1$

107. $(7x+4)(7x-4) = (7x)^2 - 4^2 = 49x^2 - 16$

108. $(a+2b)(a-2b) = a^2 - (2b)^2 = a^2 - 4b^2$

109. $(2x-6)(2x+6) = (2x)^2 - 6^2 = 4x^2 - 36$

110. $(4a^2 - 2b)(4a^2 + 2b) = (4a^2)^2 - (2b)^2$
$$= 16a^4 - 4b^2$$

111. $(3x-1)^2 = (3x)^2 - 2(3x)(1) + 1^2$
$$= 9x^2 - 6x + 1$$
The area is $(9x^2 - 6x + 1)$ square meters.

112. $(5x+2)(x-1) = 5x^2 - 5x + 2x - 2$
$$= 5x^2 - 3x - 2$$
The area is $(5x^2 - 3x - 2)$ square miles.

113. $\dfrac{x^2 + 21x + 49}{7x^2} = \dfrac{x^2}{7x^2} + \dfrac{21x}{7x^2} + \dfrac{49}{7x^2}$
$$= \dfrac{1}{7} + \dfrac{3}{x} + \dfrac{7}{x^2}$$

114. $\dfrac{5a^3 b - 15ab^2 + 20ab}{-5ab} = \dfrac{5a^3 b}{-5ab} + \dfrac{-15ab^2}{-5ab} + \dfrac{20ab}{-5ab}$
$$= -a^2 + 3b - 4$$

115.
$$\begin{array}{r}
a+1 \\
a-2 \overline{\smash{)}a^2 - a + 4} \\
\underline{a^2 - 2a} \\
a + 4 \\
\underline{a - 2} \\
6
\end{array}$$

$\dfrac{a^2 - a + 4}{a - 2} = a + 1 + \dfrac{6}{a-2}$

116.
$$\begin{array}{r}
4x \\
x+5 \overline{\smash{)}4x^2 + 20x + 7} \\
\underline{4x^2 + 20x} \\
7
\end{array}$$

$\dfrac{4x^2 + 20x + 7}{x + 5} = 4x + \dfrac{7}{x+5}$

117.
$$\begin{array}{r}
a^2 + 3a + 8 \\
a-2 \overline{\smash{)}a^3 + a^2 + 2a + 6} \\
\underline{a^3 - 2a^2} \\
3a^2 + 2a \\
\underline{3a^2 - 6a} \\
8a + 6 \\
\underline{8a - 16} \\
22
\end{array}$$

$\dfrac{a^3 + a^2 + 2a + 6}{a - 2} = a^2 + 3a + 8 + \dfrac{22}{a-2}$

118.
$$\begin{array}{r}
3b^2 - 4b \\
3b-2 \overline{\smash{)}9b^3 - 18b^2 + 8b - 1} \\
\underline{9b^3 - 6b^2} \\
-12b^2 + 8b \\
\underline{-12b^2 + 8b} \\
-1
\end{array}$$

$\dfrac{9b^3 - 18b^2 + 8b - 1}{3b - 2} = 3b^2 - 4b - \dfrac{1}{3b-2}$

119.

$$2x-1 \overline{)\,2x^3 - x^2 + 0x + 2 \atop 4x^4 - 4x^3 + x^2 + 4x - 3}$$

$$\underline{4x^4 - 2x^3}$$
$$-2x^3 + x^2$$
$$\underline{-2x^3 + x^2}$$
$$4x - 3$$
$$\underline{4x - 2}$$
$$-1$$

$$\frac{4x^4 - 4x^3 + x^2 + 4x - 3}{2x-1} = 2x^3 - x^2 + 2 - \frac{1}{2x-1}$$

120.

$$x-6 \overline{)\,x^2 - 16x - 117 \atop -x^3 - 10x^2 - 21x + 18}$$

$$\underline{-x^3 + 6x^2}$$
$$-16x^2 - 21x$$
$$\underline{-16x^2 + 96x}$$
$$-117x + 18$$
$$\underline{-117x + 702}$$
$$-684$$

$$\frac{-x^3 - 10x^2 - 21x + 18}{x-6} = -x^2 - 16x - 117 - \frac{684}{x-6}$$

121.

$$\frac{15x^3 - 3x^2 + 60}{3x^2} = \frac{15x^3}{3x^2} - \frac{3x^2}{3x^2} + \frac{60}{3x^2}$$
$$= 5x - 1 + \frac{20}{x^2}$$

The width is $\left(5x - 1 + \dfrac{20}{x^2}\right)$ feet.

122.

$$\frac{21a^3b^6 + 3a - 3}{3} = \frac{21a^3b^6}{3} + \frac{3a}{3} - \frac{3}{3}$$
$$= 7a^3b^6 + a - 1$$

The length of a side is $(7a^3b^6 + a - 1)$ units.

123. $3^3 = (3)(3)(3) = 27$

124. $\left(-\dfrac{1}{2}\right)^3 = \left(-\dfrac{1}{2}\right)\left(-\dfrac{1}{2}\right)\left(-\dfrac{1}{2}\right) = -\dfrac{1}{8}$

125. $(4xy^2)(x^3y^5) = 4x^{1+3}y^{2+5} = 4x^4y^7$

126. $\dfrac{18x^9}{27x^3} = \dfrac{2}{3}x^{9-3} = \dfrac{2x^6}{3}$

127. $\left(\dfrac{3a^4}{b^2}\right)^3 = \dfrac{3^3 a^{4\cdot 3}}{b^{2\cdot 3}} = \dfrac{27a^{12}}{b^6}$

128. $(2x^{-4}y^3)^{-4} = 2^{-4}x^{-4\cdot -4}y^{3\cdot -4} = \dfrac{x^{16}}{16y^{12}}$

129. $\dfrac{a^{-3}b^6}{9^{-1}a^{-5}b^{-2}} = 9a^{-3-(-5)}b^{6-(-2)} = 9a^2b^8$

130. $(-y^2 - 4) + (3y^2 - 6) = -y^2 - 4 + 3y^2 - 6$
$$= 2y^2 - 10$$

131. $(6x+2)+(5x-7) = 6x+2+5x-7 = 11x-5$

132. $(5x^2 + 2x - 6) - (-x - 4)$
$$= (5x^2 + 2x - 6) + (x + 4)$$
$$= 5x^2 + 2x - 6 + x + 4$$
$$= 5x^2 + 3x - 2$$

133. $(8y^2 - 3y + 1) - (3y^2 + 2)$
$$= (8y^2 - 3y + 1) + (-3y^2 - 2)$$
$$= 8y^2 - 3y + 1 - 3y^2 - 2$$
$$= 5y^2 - 3y - 1$$

134. $(2x+5)(3x-2) = 6x^2 - 4x + 15x - 10$
$$= 6x^2 + 11x - 10$$

135. $4x(7x^2 + 3) = 4x(7x^2) + 4x(3) = 28x^3 + 12x$

136. $(7x-2)(4x-9) = 28x^2 - 63x - 8x + 18$
$$= 28x^2 - 71x + 18$$

137. $(x-3)(x^2 + 4x - 6)$
$$= x(x^2 + 4x - 6) + (-3)(x^2 + 4x - 6)$$
$$= x^3 + 4x^2 - 6x - 3x^2 - 12x + 18$$
$$= x^3 + x^2 - 18x + 18$$

138. $(5x+4)^2 = (5x)^2 + 2(5x)(4) + 4^2$
$$= 25x^2 + 40x + 16$$

139. $(6x+3)(6x-3) = (6x)^2 - 3^2 = 36x^2 - 9$

140. $\dfrac{8a^4-2a^3+4a-5}{2a^3} = \dfrac{8a^4}{2a^3} - \dfrac{2a^3}{2a^3} + \dfrac{4a}{2a^3} - \dfrac{5}{2a^3}$

$\qquad\qquad\qquad = 4a - 1 + \dfrac{2}{a^2} - \dfrac{5}{2a^3}$

141.

$$
\begin{array}{r}
x-3 \\
x+5\overline{\smash{\big)}\,x^2+2x+10} \\
\underline{x^2+5x} \\
-3x+10 \\
\underline{-3x-15} \\
25
\end{array}
$$

$\qquad \dfrac{x^2+2x+10}{x+5} = x - 3 + \dfrac{25}{x+5}$

142.

$$
\begin{array}{r}
2x^2+7x+5 \\
2x-3\overline{\smash{\big)}\,4x^3+8x^2-11x+\ \ 4} \\
\underline{4x^3-6x^2} \\
14x^2-11x \\
\underline{14x^2-21x} \\
10x+\ \ 4 \\
\underline{10x-15} \\
19
\end{array}
$$

$\qquad \dfrac{4x^3+8x^2-11x+4}{2x-3} = 2x^2 + 7x + 5 + \dfrac{19}{2x-3}$

Chapter 10 Test

1. $2^5 = 2\cdot2\cdot2\cdot2\cdot2 = 32$

2. $(-3)^4 = (-3)(-3)(-3)(-3) = 81$

3. $-3^4 = -(3\cdot3\cdot3\cdot3) = -81$

4. $4^{-3} = \dfrac{1}{4^3} = \dfrac{1}{64}$

5. $(3x^2)(-5x^9) = 3(-5)(x^2 \cdot x^9)$

$\qquad\qquad\qquad = -15x^{2+9}$

$\qquad\qquad\qquad = -15x^{11}$

6. $\dfrac{y^7}{y^2} = y^{7-2} = y^5$

7. $\dfrac{r^{-8}}{r^{-3}} = r^{-8-(-3)} = r^{-5} = \dfrac{1}{r^5}$

8. $\left(\dfrac{4x^2y^3}{x^3y^{-4}}\right)^2 = \dfrac{4^2 x^{2\cdot2} y^{3\cdot2}}{x^{3\cdot2} y^{-4\cdot2}}$

$\qquad\qquad\qquad = \dfrac{16x^4 y^6}{x^6 y^{-8}}$

$\qquad\qquad\qquad = 16x^{4-6} y^{6-(-8)}$

$\qquad\qquad\qquad = 16x^{-2} y^{14}$

$\qquad\qquad\qquad = \dfrac{16y^{14}}{x^2}$

9. $\dfrac{6^2 x^{-4} y^{-1}}{6^3 x^{-3} y^7} = \dfrac{6^2}{6^3} \cdot \dfrac{x^{-4}}{x^{-3}} \cdot \dfrac{y^{-1}}{y^7}$

$\qquad\qquad\qquad = 6^{2-3} x^{-4-(-3)} y^{-1-7}$

$\qquad\qquad\qquad = 6^{-1} x^{-1} y^{-8}$

$\qquad\qquad\qquad = \dfrac{1}{6}\cdot\dfrac{1}{x}\cdot\dfrac{1}{y^8}$

$\qquad\qquad\qquad = \dfrac{1}{6xy^8}$

10. $563,000 = 5.63\times10^5$

11. $0.0000863 = 8.63\times10^{-5}$

12. $1.5\times10^{-3} = 0.0015$

13. $6.23\times10^4 = 62,300$

14. $(1.2\times10^5)(3\times10^{-7}) = 3.6\times10^{-2} = 0.036$

15. a. $4xy^2 + 7xyz + x^3y - 2$

Term	Numerical Coefficient	Degree of Terms
$4xy^2$	4	3
$7xyz$	7	3
x^3y	1	4
-2	-2	0

b. The degree of $4xy^2 + 7xyz + x^3y$ is $3 + 1$ or 4.

16. $5x^2 + 4x - 7x^2 + 11 + 8x$

$= (5-7)x^2 + (4+8)x + 11$

$= -2x^2 + 12x + 11$

17. $(8x^3 + 7x^2 + 4x - 7) + (8x^3 - 7x - 6)$

$= 8x^3 + 7x^2 + 4x - 7 + 8x^3 - 7x - 6$

$= 8x^3 + 8x^3 + 7x^2 + 4x - 7x - 7 - 6$

$= 16x^3 + 7x^2 - 3x - 13$

18.

$$\begin{array}{r} 5x^3 + x^2 + 5x - 2 \\ -\ (8x^3 - 4x^2 + x - 7) \\ \hline \end{array} \qquad \begin{array}{r} 5x^3 + x^2 + 5x - 2 \\ -8x^3 + 4x^2 - x + 7 \\ \hline -3x^3 + 5x^2 + 4x + 5 \end{array}$$

19. $[(8x^2 + 7x + 5) + (x^3 - 8)] - (4x + 2)$

$= (8x^2 + 7x + 5) + (x^3 - 8) + (-4x - 2)$

$= 8x^2 + 7x + 5 + x^3 - 8 - 4x - 2$

$= x^3 + 8x^2 + 3x - 5$

20. $(3x + 7)(x^2 + 5x + 2)$

$= 3x(x^2 + 5x + 2) + 7(x^2 + 5x + 2)$

$= 3x(x^2) + 3x(5x) + 3x(2) + 7(x^2) + 7(5x) + 7(2)$

$= 3x^3 + 15x^2 + 6x + 7x^2 + 35x + 14$

$= 3x^3 + 22x^2 + 41x + 14$

21. $3x^2(2x^2 - 3x + 7)$

$= 3x^2(2x^2) + 3x^2(-3x) + 3x^2(7)$

$= 6x^4 - 9x^3 + 21x^2$

22. $(x + 7)(3x - 5) = 3x^2 - 5x + 21x - 35$

$= 3x^2 + 16x - 35$

23. $\left(3x - \dfrac{1}{5}\right)\left(3x + \dfrac{1}{5}\right) = (3x)^2 - \left(\dfrac{1}{5}\right)^2 = 9x^2 - \dfrac{1}{25}$

24. $(4x - 2)^2 = (4x)^2 - 2(4x)(2) + 2^2$

$= 16x^2 - 16x + 4$

25. $(8x + 3)^2 = (8x)^2 + 2(8x)(3) + (3)^2$

$= 64x^2 + 48x + 9$

26. $(x^2 - 9b)(x^2 + 9b) = (x^2)^2 - (9b)^2 = x^4 - 81b^2$

27. $-16t^2 + 1001 = -16(0)^2 + 1001 = 1001$ ft

$= -16(1)^2 + 1001 = -16 + 1001$

$= 985$ ft

$= -16(3)^2 + 1001 = -144 + 1001$

$= 857$ ft

$= -16(5)^2 + 1001 = -400 + 1001$

$= 601$ ft

28. $(2x - 3)(2x + 3) = (2x)^2 - (3)^2$

$= 4x^2 - 9$

The area is $(2x - 3)(2x + 3)$ or $(4x^2 - 9)$ square inches.

29. $\dfrac{4x^2 + 2xy - 7x}{8xy} = \dfrac{4x^2}{8xy} + \dfrac{2xy}{8xy} - \dfrac{7x}{8xy}$

$= \dfrac{x}{2y} + \dfrac{1}{4} - \dfrac{7}{8y}$

30.

$$\begin{array}{r} x + 2 \\ x+5\ \overline{)\ x^2 + 7x + 10} \\ \underline{x^2 + 5x} \\ 2x + 10 \\ \underline{2x + 10} \\ 0 \end{array}$$

$\dfrac{x^2 + 7x + 10}{x + 5} = x + 2$

31.

$$\begin{array}{r} 9x^2 - 6x + 4 \\ 3x+2\ \overline{)\ 27x^3 + 0x^2 + 0x - 8} \\ \underline{27x^3 + 18x^2} \\ -18x^2 + 0x \\ \underline{-18x^2 - 12x} \\ 12x - 8 \\ \underline{12x + 8} \\ -16 \end{array}$$

$\dfrac{27x^3 - 8}{3x + 2} = 9x^2 - 6x + 4 - \dfrac{16}{3x + 2}$

Cumulative Review Chapters 1–10

1. $9^2 = 81$

2. $5^3 = 125$

3. $3^4 = 81$

4. $3^3 = 27$

5. a. $7 + x$

   b. $15 - x$

   c. $2x$

   d. $\dfrac{x}{5}$ or $x \div 5$

   e. $x - 2$

6. a. $x + 3$

   b. $3x$

   c. $2x$

   d. $10 - x$

   e. $5x + 7$

7. $2(3 + 7x) - 15 = 2(3) + 2(7x) - 15$
$$= 6 + 14x - 15$$
$$= 14x - 9$$

8. $5(x + 2) = 5 \cdot x + 5 \cdot 2 = 5x + 10$

9. $-2(x - 5) + 4(2x + 2) = -2x + 10 + 8x + 8$
$$= -2x + 8x + 10 + 8$$
$$= 6x + 18$$

10. $-2(y + 0.3z - 1)$
$$= (-2)(y) + (-2)(0.3z) + (-2)(-1)$$
$$= -2y - 0.6z + 2$$

11. $\quad y - 5 = -2 - 6$
$$y - 5 = -8$$
$$y - 5 + 5 = -8 + 5$$
$$y = -3$$

12. $\quad \dfrac{y}{7} = 20$
$$7 \cdot \dfrac{y}{7} = 20 \cdot 7$$
$$y = 140$$

13. $\quad 7(x - 2) = 9x - 6$
$$7x - 14 = 9x - 6$$
$$7x - 7x - 14 = 9x - 7x - 6$$
$$-14 = 2x - 6$$
$$-14 + 6 = 2x - 6 + 6$$
$$-8 = 2x$$
$$\dfrac{-8}{2} = \dfrac{2x}{2}$$
$$-4 = x$$

14. $6(2a - 1) - (11a + 6) = 7$
$$12a - 6 - 11a - 6 = 7$$
$$a - 12 = 7$$
$$a - 12 + 12 = 7 + 12$$
$$a = 19$$

15. $\quad \dfrac{3}{5}a = 9$
$$\dfrac{5}{3} \cdot \dfrac{3}{5}a = \dfrac{5}{3} \cdot 9$$
$$a = 15$$

16. $\quad \dfrac{2}{3}y = 16$
$$\dfrac{3}{2} \cdot \dfrac{2}{3}y = \dfrac{3}{2} \cdot 16$$
$$y = 24$$

17. $\quad 3y = -\dfrac{2}{11}$
$$\dfrac{1}{3} \cdot 3y = \dfrac{1}{3}\left(-\dfrac{2}{11}\right)$$
$$y = -\dfrac{2}{33}$$

18. $\quad 5y = -\dfrac{1}{5}$
$$\dfrac{1}{5} \cdot 5y = \dfrac{1}{5} \cdot -\dfrac{1}{5}$$
$$y = -\dfrac{1}{25}$$

19. $0.125 = \dfrac{125}{1000} = \dfrac{1}{8}$

20. $0.250 = \dfrac{250}{1000} = \dfrac{1}{4}$

21. $43.5 = 43 + \dfrac{5}{10} = 43 + \dfrac{1}{2} = 43\dfrac{1}{2}$

22. $10.75 = 10 + \dfrac{75}{100} = 10 + \dfrac{3}{4} = 10\dfrac{3}{4}$

23. $-105.083 = -\left(105 + \dfrac{83}{1000}\right) = -105\dfrac{83}{1000}$

24. $-31.07 = -\left(31 + \dfrac{7}{100}\right) = -31\dfrac{7}{100}$

25. $x - y = 2.8 - 0.92 = 1.88$

26. $x - y = -1.2 - 7.6 = -8.8$

27. $xy = 2.3 \cdot 0.44 = 1.012$

28. $xy = -6.1 \cdot 0.5 = -3.05$

29. a. $11, 112$

    b. $0, 11, 112$

    c. $-3, -2, 0, 11, 112$

    d. $-3, -2, 0, \dfrac{1}{4}, 11, 112$

    e. $\sqrt{2}$

    f. $-2, 0, \dfrac{1}{4}, 112, -3, 11, \sqrt{2}$

30. $-2\dfrac{1}{2} = -\dfrac{5}{2}$

$-2\dfrac{1}{2}$ is a rational number and a real number.

31. $0.25x + 0.10(x - 3) = 1.1$
$0.25x + 0.10x - 0.30 = 1.1$
$0.35x - 0.30 = 1.1$
$0.35x = 1.4$
$x = 4$

32. $0.6x - 10 = 1.4x - 14$
$10(0.6x - 10) = 10(1.4x - 14)$
$6x - 100 = 14x - 140$
$-100 = 8x - 140$
$40 = 8x$
$\dfrac{40}{8} = \dfrac{8x}{8}$
$5 = x$

33. $2(x + 4) = 4x - 12$
$2x + 8 = 4x - 12$
$8 = 2x - 12$
$20 = 2x$
$10 = x$
The number is 10.

34. $3(x - 2) = 5x - 10$
$3x - 6 = 5x - 10$
$-6 = 2x - 10$
$4 = 2x$
$\dfrac{4}{2} = \dfrac{2x}{2}$
$2 = x$
The number is 2.

35. $30 \cdot 2 + 2x = 140$
$60 + 2x = 140$
$2x = 80$
$x = 40$
The length is 40 feet.

36. Use $A = l \cdot w$ with $A = 2016$ and $l = 63$.
$2016 = 63w$
$\dfrac{2016}{63} = \dfrac{63w}{63}$
$32 = w$
The width is 32 feet.

37. $-4x + 7 \geq -9$
$-4x \geq -16$
$x \leq 4$
$\{x \mid x \leq 4\}$

38. $3x + 4 \geq 2x - 6$
$3x - 2x + 4 \geq 2x - 2x - 6$
$x + 4 \geq -6$
$x + 4 - 4 \geq -6 - 4$
$x \geq -10$
$\{x \mid x \geq -10\}$

39. a. $x^7 \cdot x^4 = x^{7+4} = x^{11}$

    b. $\left(\dfrac{t}{2}\right)^4 = \dfrac{t^4}{2^4} = \dfrac{t^4}{16}$

    c. $(9y^5)^2 = 9^2 y^{5 \cdot 2} = 81y^{10}$

40. a. $y \cdot y^5 = y^1 \cdot y^5 = y^{1+5} = y^6$

b. $\left(\dfrac{2}{3}\right)^3 = \dfrac{2^3}{3^3} = \dfrac{8}{27}$

c. $(8x^3)^2 = 8^2(x^3)^2 = 64x^{3\cdot2} = 64x^6$

41. $\left(\dfrac{3a^2}{b}\right)^{-3} = \dfrac{3^{-3}a^{2\cdot-3}}{b^{-3}} = \dfrac{3^{-3}a^{-6}}{b^{-3}} = \dfrac{b^3}{27a^6}$

42. $\left(\dfrac{2x^3}{y}\right)^{-2} = \dfrac{2^{-2}(x^3)^{-2}}{y^{-2}} = \dfrac{2^{-2}x^{-6}}{y^{-2}} = \dfrac{y^2}{4x^6}$

43. $(5y^3)^{-2} = 5^{-2}y^{3\cdot-2} = 5^{-2}y^{-6} = \dfrac{1}{25y^6}$

44. $(3x^7)^{-3} = 3^{-3}(x^7)^{-3} = 3^{-3}x^{-21} = \dfrac{1}{27x^{21}}$

45. $9x^3 + x^3 = (9+1)x^3 = 10x^3$

46. $9x^3 - x^3 = (9-1)x^3 = 8x^3$

47. $5x^2 + 6x - 9x - 3 = 5x^2 - 3x - 3$

48. $2x - x^2 + 5x - 4x^2 = -x^2 - 4x^2 + 2x + 5x$
$= -5x^2 + 7x$

49. $7x(x^2 + 2x + 5) = 7x(x^2) + 7x(2x) + 7x(5)$
$= 7x^3 + 14x^2 + 35x$

50. $-2x(x^2 - x + 1) = -2x(x^2) - (-2x)(x) + (-2x)(1)$
$= -2x^3 + 2x^2 - 2x$

51. $\dfrac{9x^5 - 12x^2 + 3x}{3x^2} = \dfrac{9x^5}{3x^2} - \dfrac{12x^2}{3x^2} + \dfrac{3x}{3x^2}$
$= 3x^3 - 4 + \dfrac{1}{x}$

52. $\dfrac{4x^7 - 12x^2 + 2x}{2x} = \dfrac{4x^7}{2x} - \dfrac{12x^2}{2x} + \dfrac{2x}{2x}$
$= 2x^6 - 6x + 1$

Chapter 11

Practice Problems

1. **a.** $45 = 3 \cdot 3 \cdot 5$
    $75 = 3 \cdot 5 \cdot 5$
    GCF $= 3 \cdot 5 = 15$

    b. $32 = 2 \cdot 2 \cdot 2 \cdot 2 \cdot 2$
    $33 = 3 \cdot 11$
    There are no common prime factors; thus, the GCF is 1.

    c. $14 = 2 \cdot 7$
    $24 = 2 \cdot 2 \cdot 2 \cdot 3$
    $60 = 2 \cdot 2 \cdot 3 \cdot 5$
    GCF $= 2$

2. **a.** The GCF is y^4, since 4 is the smallest exponent to which y is raised.

    b. The GCF is x^1 or x, since 1 is the smallest exponent on x.

3. **a.** $6x^2 = 2 \cdot 3 \cdot x^2$
    $9x^4 = 3 \cdot 3 \cdot x^4$
    $-12x^5 = -1 \cdot 2 \cdot 2 \cdot 3 \cdot x^5$
    GCF $= 3 \cdot x^2 = 3x^2$

    b. $-16y = -1 \cdot 2 \cdot 2 \cdot 2 \cdot 2 \cdot y$
    $-20y^6 = -1 \cdot 2 \cdot 2 \cdot 5 \cdot y^6$
    $40y^4 = 2 \cdot 2 \cdot 2 \cdot 5 \cdot y^4$
    GCF $= 2 \cdot 2 \cdot y = 4y$

    c. The GCF of a^5, a, and a^3 is a.
    The GCF of b^4, b^3, and b^2 is b^2.
    Thus, the GCF of a^5b^4, ab^3, and a^3b^2 is ab^2.

4. **a.** The GCF of terms $10y$ and 25 is 5.
    $10y + 25 = 5 \cdot 2y + 5 \cdot 5 = 5(2y + 5)$

    b. The GCF of x^4 and x^9 is x^4.
    $x^4 - x^9 = x^4(1) - x^4(x^5) = x^4(1 - x^5)$

5. $-10x^3 + 8x^2 - 2x = 2x(-5x^2) + 2x(4x) + 2x(-1)$
    $= 2x(-5x^2 + 4x - 1)$

6. $4x^3 + 12x = 4x(x^2 + 3)$

7. $\dfrac{2}{5}a^5 - \dfrac{4}{5}a^3 + \dfrac{1}{5}a^2 = \dfrac{1}{5}a^2(2a^3 - 4a + 1)$

8. $6a^3b + 3a^3b^2 + 9a^2b^4 = 3a^2b(2a + ab + 3b^3)$

9. $7(p + 2) + q(p + 2) = (p + 2)(7 + q)$

10. $ab + 7a + 2b + 14 = (ab + 7a) + (2b + 14)$
    $= a(b + 7) + 2(b + 7)$
    $= (b + 7)(a + 2)$

11. $28x^3 - 7x^2 + 12x - 3 = (28x^3 - 7x^2) + (12x - 3)$
    $= 7x^2(4x - 1) + 3(4x - 1)$
    $= (4x - 1)(7x^2 + 3)$

12. $2xy + 5y^2 - 4x - 10y$
    $= (2xy + 5y^2) + (-4x - 10y)$
    $= y(2x + 5y) - 2(2x + 5y)$
    $= (2x + 5y)(y - 2)$

13. $3x^2 + 4xy + 3x + 4y = (3x^2 + 4xy) + (3x + 4y)$
    $= x(3x + 4y) + 1(3x + 4y)$
    $= (3x + 4y)(x + 1)$

14. $4x^3 + x - 20x^2 - 5 = x(4x^2 + 1) - 5(4x^2 + 1)$
    $= (4x^2 + 1)(x - 5)$

15. $3xy - 4 + x - 12y = (3xy + x) + (-12y - 4)$
    $= x(3y + 1) - 4(3y + 1)$
    $= (3y + 1)(x - 4)$

16. $2x - 2 + x^3 - 3x^2 = 2(x - 1) + x^2(x - 3)$
    There is no common binomial factor that can now be factored out. This polynomial is not factorable by grouping.

Vocabulary and Readiness Check

1. Since $5 \cdot 4 = 20$, the numbers 5 and 4 are called <u>factors</u> of 20.

2. The <u>greatest common factor</u> of a list of integers is the largest integer that is a factor of all the integers in the list.

3. The greatest common factor of a list of common variables raised to powers is the variable raised to the <u>least</u> exponent in the list.

4. The process of writing a polynomial as a product is called <u>factoring</u>.

5. A factored form of $7x + 21 + xy + 3y$ is $7(x + 3) + y(x + 3)$. <u>false</u>

6. A factored form of $3x^3 + 6x + x^2 + 2$ is $3x(x^2 + 2)$. <u>false</u>

7. $14 = 2 \cdot 7$

8. $15 = 3 \cdot 5$

9. The GCF of 18 and 3 is 3.

10. The GCF of 7 and 35 is 7.

11. The GCF of 20 and 15 is 5.

12. The GCF of 6 and 15 is 3.

Exercise Set 11.1

1. $32 = 2 \cdot 2 \cdot 2 \cdot 2 \cdot 2$
$36 = 2 \cdot 2 \cdot 3 \cdot 3$
$GCF = 2 \cdot 2 = 4$

3. $18 = 2 \cdot 3 \cdot 3$
$42 = 2 \cdot 3 \cdot 7$
$84 = 2 \cdot 2 \cdot 3 \cdot 7$
$GCF = 2 \cdot 3 = 6$

5. $24 = 2 \cdot 2 \cdot 2 \cdot 3$
$14 = 2 \cdot 7$
$21 = 3 \cdot 7$
$GCF = 1$ since there are no common prime factors.

7. The GCF of y^2, y^4, and y^7 is y^2.

9. The GCF of z^7, z^9, and z^{11} is z^7.

11. The GCF of x^{10}, x, and x^3 is x.
The GCF of y^2, y^2, and y^3 is y^2.
Thus, the GCF of $x^{10}y^2$, xy^2, and x^3y^3 is xy^2.

13. $14x = 2 \cdot 7 \cdot x$
$21 = 3 \cdot 7$
$GCF = 7$

15. $12y^4 = 2 \cdot 2 \cdot 3 \cdot y^4$
$20y^3 = 2 \cdot 2 \cdot 5 \cdot y^3$
$GCF = 2 \cdot 2 \cdot y^3 = 4y^3$

17. $-10x^2 = -1 \cdot 2 \cdot 5 \cdot x^2$
$15x^3 = 3 \cdot 5 \cdot x^3$
$GCF = 5 \cdot x^2 = 5x^2$

19. $12x^3 = 2 \cdot 2 \cdot 3 \cdot x^3$
$-6x^4 = -1 \cdot 2 \cdot 3 \cdot x^4$
$3x^5 = 3 \cdot x^5$
$GCF = 3 \cdot x^3 = 3x^3$

21. $-18x^2y = -1 \cdot 2 \cdot 3 \cdot 3 \cdot x^2 \cdot y$
$9x^3y^3 = 3 \cdot 3 \cdot x^3 \cdot y^3$
$36x^3y = 2 \cdot 2 \cdot 3 \cdot 3 \cdot x^3 \cdot y$
$GCF = 3 \cdot 3 \cdot x^2 \cdot y = 9x^2y$

23. $20a^6b^2c^8 = 2 \cdot 2 \cdot 5 \cdot a^6 \cdot b^2 \cdot c^8$
$50a^7b = 2 \cdot 5 \cdot 5 \cdot a^7 \cdot b$
$GCF = 2 \cdot 5 \cdot a^6 \cdot b = 10a^6b$

25. $3a + 6 = 3(a + 2)$

27. $30x - 15 = 15(2x - 1)$

29. $x^3 + 5x^2 = x^2(x + 5)$

31. $6y^4 + 2y^3 = 2y^3(3y + 1)$

33. $32xy - 18x^2 = 2x(16y - 9x)$

35. $4x - 8y + 4 = 4(x - 2y + 1)$

37. $6x^3 - 9x^2 + 12x = 3x(2x^2 - 3x + 4)$

39. $a^7b^6 - a^3b^2 + a^2b^5 - a^2b^2$
$= a^2b^2(a^5b^4 - a + b^3 - 1)$

41. $5x^3y - 15x^2y + 10xy = 5xy(x^2 - 3x + 2)$

43. $8x^5 + 16x^4 - 20x^3 + 12 = 4(2x^5 + 4x^4 - 5x^3 + 3)$

45. $\frac{1}{3}x^4 + \frac{2}{3}x^3 - \frac{4}{3}x^5 + \frac{1}{3}x = \frac{1}{3}x(x^3 + 2x^2 - 4x^4 + 1)$

47. $y(x^2 + 2) + 3(x^2 + 2) = (x^2 + 2)(y + 3)$

49. $z(y + 4) + 3(y + 4) = (y + 4)(z + 3)$

51. $r(z^2 - 6) + (z - 6) = r(z^2 - 6) + 1(z^2 - 6)$
$ = (z^2 - 6)(r + 1)$

53. $-x - 7 = (-1)x + (-1)(7) = -1(x + 7)$

55. $-2 + z = -1(2) + (-1)(-z) = -1(2 - z)$

57. $3a - b + 2 = (-1)(-3a) + (-1)(b) - (-1)(2)$
$ = -1(-3a + b - 2)$

59. $x^3 + 2x^2 + 5x + 10 = x^2(x + 2) + 5(x + 2)$
$ = (x + 2)(x^2 + 5)$

61. $5x + 15 + xy + 3y = 5(x + 3) + y(x + 3)$
$ = (x + 3)(5 + y)$

63. $6x^3 - 4x^2 + 15x - 10 = 2x^2(3x - 2) + 5(3x - 2)$
$ = (3x - 2)(2x^2 + 5)$

65. $5m^3 + 6mn + 5m^2 + 6n$
$= m(5m^2 + 6n) + 1(5m^2 + 6n)$
$= (5m^2 + 6n)(m + 1)$

67. $2y - 8 + xy - 4x = 2(y - 4) + x(y - 4)$
$ = (y - 4)(2 + x)$

69. $2x^3 + x^2 + 8x + 4 = x^2(2x + 1) + 4(2x + 1)$
$ = (2x + 1)(x^2 + 4)$

71. $3x - 3 + x^3 - 4x^2 = 3(x - 1) + x^2(x - 4)$
The polynomial is not factorable by grouping.

73. $4x^2 - 8xy - 3x + 6y = 4x(x - 2y) - 3(x - 2y)$
$ = (x - 2y)(4x - 3)$

75. $5q^2 - 4pq - 5q + 4p = q(5q - 4p) - 1(5q - 4p)$
$ = (5q - 4p)(q - 1)$

77. $12x^2y - 42x^2 - 4y + 14$
$= 2(6x^2y - 21x^2 - 2y + 7)$
$= 2[3x^2(2y - 7) - 1(2y - 7)]$
$= 2(2y - 7)(3x^2 - 1)$

79. $6a^2 + 9ab^2 + 6ab + 9b^3$
$= 3(2a^2 + 3ab^2 + 2ab + 3b^3)$
$= 3[a(2a + 3b^2) + b(2a + 3b^2)]$
$= 3(2a + 3b^2)(a + b)$

81. $(x + 2)(x + 5) = x^2 + 5x + 2x + 10 = x^2 + 7x + 10$

83. $(b + 1)(b - 4) = b^2 - 4b + b - 4 = b^2 - 3b - 4$

85. $2 \cdot 6 = 12$
$2 + 6 = 8$
2 and 6 have a product of 12 and a sum of 8.

87. $-1 \cdot (-8) = 8$
$-1 + (-8) = -9$
-1 and -8 have a product of 8 and a sum of -9.

89. $-2 \cdot 5 = -10$
$-2 + 5 = 3$
-2 and 5 have a product of -10 and a sum of 3.

91. $-8 \cdot 3 = -24$
$-8 + 3 = -5$
-8 and 3 have a product of -24 and a sum of -5.

93. $-2x + 14 = -2(x - 7)$, which is choice d.

95. $(a + 6)(a + 2)$ is factored.

97. Since $5(2y + z) - b(2y + z) = (2y + z)(5 - b)$, the given expression is not factored.

99. a. $-1264x^2 + 5056x + 18,960$
$= -1264(1)^2 + 5056(1) + 18,960$
$= -1264(1) + 5056(1) + 18,960$
$= -1264 + 5056 + 18,960$
$= 22,752$

The cotton harvest in 2004 was approximately 22,752 thousand bales.

b. Let $x = 4$ for 2007.

$-1264x^2 + 5056x + 18,960$

$= -1264(4)^2 + 5056(4) + 18,960$

$= -1264(16) + 5056(4) + 18,960$

$= -20,224 + 20,224 + 18,960$

$= 18,960$

The cotton harvest in 2007 was approximately 18,960 thousand bales.

c. $-1264x^2 + 5056x + 18,960$

$= -1264(x^2 - 4x - 15)$

or $1264(-x^2 + 4x + 15)$

101. The area of the circle is πx^2. Since the sides of the square have length $2x$, the area of the square is $(2x)^2 = 4x^2$. The shaded region is the region inside the square but outside the circle. The area of the shaded region is $4x^2 - \pi x^2 = x^2(4 - \pi)$.

103.   Area = width · length

$5x^5 - 5x^2 = 5x^2(x^3 - 1)$

The length is $(x^3 - 1)$ units.

105. answers may vary

107. answers may vary

Section 11.2

Practice Problems

1.

Factors of 20	Sum of Factors
1, 20	21
2, 10	12
4, 5	9

Thus, $x^2 + 12x + 20 = (x + 10)(x + 2)$.

2. a.

Factors of 22	Sum of Factors
−1, −22	−23
−2, −11	−13

$x^2 - 23x + 22 = (x - 1)(x - 22)$

b.

Factors of 50	Sum of Factors
−1, −50	−51
−2, −25	−27
−5, −10	−15

$x^2 - 27x + 50 = (x - 2)(x - 25)$

3.

Factors of −36	Sum of Factors
−1, 36	35
1, −36	−35
−2, 18	16
2, −18	−16
−3, 12	9
3, −12	−9
−4, 9	5
4, −9	−5
−6, 6	0

$x^2 + 5x - 36 = (x + 9)(x - 4)$

4. a. Two factors of −40 whose sum is −3 are −8 and 5.

$q^2 - 3q - 40 = (q - 8)(q + 5)$

b. Two factors of −48 whose sum is 2 are 8 and −6.

$y^2 + 2y - 48 = (y + 8)(y - 6)$

5. Since there are no two numbers whose product is 15 and whose sum is 6, the polynomial is prime.

6. a. Two factors of $14y^2$ whose sum is $9y$ are $2y$ and $7y$.

$x^2 + 9xy + 14y^2 = (x + 2y)(x + 7y)$

b. Two factors of $30b^2$ whose sum is $-13b$ are $-3b$ and $-10b$.

$a^2 - 13ab + 30b^2 = (a - 3b)(a - 10b)$

7. Two factors of 12 whose sum is 8 are 6 and 2.

$x^4 + 8x^2 + 12 = (x^2 + 6)(x^2 + 2)$

8. $48 - 14x + x^2 = x^2 - 14x + 48$

Two factors of 48 whose sum is -14 are -6 and -8.

$x^2 - 14x + 48 = (x-6)(x-8)$

9. a. $4x^2 - 24x + 36 = 4(x^2 - 6x + 9)$

Two factors of 9 whose sum is -6 are -3 and -3.

$4(x^2 - 6x + 9) = 4(x-3)(x-3)$ or $4(x-3)^2$

b. $x^3 + 3x^2 - 4x = x(x^2 + 3x - 4)$

Two factors of -4 whose sum is 3 are 4 and -1.

$x(x^2 + 3x - 4) = x(x+4)(x-1)$

10. $5x^5 - 25x^4 - 30x^3 = 5x^3(x^2 - 5x - 6)$
$\qquad\qquad\qquad\quad = 5x^3(x+1)(x-6)$

Vocabulary and Readiness Check

1. To factor $x^2 + 7x + 6$, we look for two numbers whose product is 6 and whose sum is 7. <u>true</u>

2. We can write the factorization $(y + 2)(y + 4)$ also as $(y + 4)(y + 2)$. <u>true</u>

3. The factorization $(4x - 12)(x - 5)$ is completely factored. <u>false</u>

4. The factorization $(x + 2y)(x + y)$ may also be written as $(x + 2y)^2$. <u>false</u>

5. $x^2 + 9x + 20 = (x+4)(x+5)$

6. $x^2 + 12x + 35 = (x+5)(x+7)$

7. $x^2 - 7x + 12 = (x-4)(x-3)$

8. $x^2 - 13x + 22 = (x-2)(x-11)$

9. $x^2 + 4x + 4 = (x+2)(x+2)$

10. $x^2 + 10x + 24 = (x+6)(x+4)$

Exercise Set 11.2

1. Two factors of 6 whose sum is 7 are 6 and 1.

$x^2 + 7x + 6 = (x+6)(x+1)$

3. Two factors of 9 whose sum is -10 are -9 and -1.

$y^2 - 10y + 9 = (y-9)(y-1)$

5. Two factors of 9 whose sum is -6 are -3 and -3.

$x^2 - 6x + 9 = (x-3)(x-3)$ or $(x-3)^2$

7. Two factors of -18 whose sum is -3 are -6 and 3.

$x^2 - 3x - 18 = (x-6)(x+3)$

9. Two factors of -70 whose sum is 3 are 10 and -7.

$x^2 + 3x - 70 = (x+10)(x-7)$

11. Since there are no two numbers whose product is 2 and whose sum is 5, the polynomial is prime.

13. Two factors of $15y^2$ whose sum is $8y$ are $5y$ and $3y$.

$x^2 + 8xy + 15y^2 = (x+5y)(x+3y)$

15. Two factors of -15 whose sum is -2 are -5 and 3.

$a^4 - 2a^2 - 15 = (a^2 - 5)(a^2 + 3)$

17. $13 + 14m + m^2 = m^2 + 14m + 13$

Two factors of 13 whose sum is 14 are 13 and 1.

$13 + 14m + m^2 = m^2 + 14m + 13 = (m+13)(m+1)$

19. $10t - 24 + t^2 = t^2 + 10t - 24$

Two factors of -24 whose sum is 10 are -2 and 12.

$10t - 24 + t^2 = t^2 + 10t - 24 = (t-2)(t+12)$

21. Two factors of $16b^2$ whose sum is $-10b$ are $-2b$ and $-8b$.

$a^2 - 10ab + 16b^2 = (a-2b)(a-8b)$

23. $2z^2 + 20z + 32 = 2(z^2 + 10z + 16)$
$\qquad\qquad\qquad\quad = 2(z+8)(z+2)$

25. $2x^3 - 18x^2 + 40x = 2x(x^2 - 9x + 20)$
$\qquad\qquad\qquad\quad\; = 2x(x-5)(x-4)$

27. $x^2 - 3xy - 4y^2 = (x-4y)(x+y)$

29. $x^2 + 15x + 36 = (x + 12)(x + 3)$

31. $x^2 - x - 2 = (x - 2)(x + 1)$

33. $r^2 - 16r + 48 = (r - 12)(r - 4)$

35. $x^2 + xy - 2y^2 = (x + 2y)(x - y)$

37. $3x^2 + 9x - 30 = 3(x^2 + 3x - 10) = 3(x + 5)(x - 2)$

39. $3x^2 - 60x + 108 = 3(x^2 - 20x + 36)$
$ = 3(x - 18)(x - 2)$

41. $x^2 - 18x - 144 = (x - 24)(x + 6)$

43. $r^2 - 3r + 6$ is prime.

45. $x^2 - 8x + 15 = (x - 5)(x - 3)$

47. $6x^3 + 54x^2 + 120x = 6x(x^2 + 9x + 20)$
$ = 6x(x + 4)(x + 5)$

49. $4x^2y + 4xy - 12y = 4y(x^2 + x - 3)$

51. $x^2 - 4x - 21 = (x - 7)(x + 3)$

53. $x^2 + 7xy + 10y^2 = (x + 5y)(x + 2y)$

55. $64 + 24t + 2t^2 = 2t^2 + 24t + 64$
$ = 2(t^2 + 12t + 32)$
$ = 2(t + 8)(t + 4)$

57. $x^3 - 2x^2 - 24x = x(x^2 - 2x - 24)$
$ = x(x - 6)(x + 4)$

59. $2t^5 - 14t^4 + 24t^3 = 2t^3(t^2 - 7t + 12)$
$ = 2t^3(t - 4)(t - 3)$

61. $5x^3y - 25x^2y^2 - 120xy^3$
$ = 5xy(x^2 - 5xy - 24y^2)$
$ = 5xy(x - 8y)(x + 3y)$

63. $162 - 45m + 3m^2 = 3m^2 - 45m + 162$
$ = 3(m^2 - 15m + 54)$
$ = 3(m - 9)(m - 6)$

65. $-x^2 + 12x - 11 = -1(x^2 - 12x + 11)$
$ = -1(x - 11)(x - 1)$

67. $\dfrac{1}{2}y^2 - \dfrac{9}{2}y - 11 = \dfrac{1}{2}(y^2 - 9y - 22)$
$\phantom{\dfrac{1}{2}y^2 - \dfrac{9}{2}y - 11} = \dfrac{1}{2}(y - 11)(y + 2)$

69. $x^3y^2 + x^2y - 20x = x(x^2y^2 + xy - 20)$
$ = x(xy - 4)(xy + 5)$

71. $(2x + 1)(x + 5) = 2x^2 + 10x + x + 5$
$ = 2x^2 + 11x + 5$

73. $(5y - 4)(3y - 1) = 15y^2 - 5y - 12y + 4$
$ = 15y^2 - 17y + 4$

75. $(a + 3b)(9a - 4b) = 9a^2 - 4ab + 27ab - 12b^2$
$ = 9a^2 + 23ab - 12b^2$

77. $(x - 3)(x + 8) = x^2 + 8x - 3x - 24 = x^2 + 5x - 24$

79. answers may vary

81. $P = 2l + 2w$
$ = 2(x^2 + 10x) + 2(4x + 33)$
$ = 2x^2 + 20x + 8x + 66$
$ = 2x^2 + 28x + 66$
$ = 2(x^2 + 14x + 33)$
$ = 2(x + 3)(x + 11)$

83. $-16t^2 + 64t + 80 = -16(t^2 - 4t - 5)$
$ = -16(t - 5)(t + 1)$

85. $x^2 + \dfrac{1}{2}x + \dfrac{1}{16} = \left(x + \dfrac{1}{4}\right)\left(x + \dfrac{1}{4}\right)$ or $\left(x + \dfrac{1}{4}\right)^2$

87. $z^2(x + 1) - 3z(x + 1) - 70(x + 1)$
$ = (x + 1)(z^2 - 3z - 70)$
$ = (x + 1)(z - 10)(z + 7)$

89. The factors of c must sum to -16. Since c is positive, both factors must have the same sign.
$-1 + (-15) = -16; \; (-1)(-15) = 15$
$-2 + (-14) = -16; \; (-2)(-14) = 28$
$-3 + (-13) = -16; \; (-3)(-13) = 39$
$-4 + (-12) = -16; \; (-4)(-12) = 48$
$-5 + (-11) = -16; \; (-5)(-11) = 55$

$-6 + (-10) = -16; (-6)(-10) = 60$
$-7 + (-9) = -16; (-7)(-9) = 63$
$-8 + (-8) = -16; (-8)(-8) = 64$
The possible values of c are 15, 28, 39, 48, 55, 60, 63, and 64.

91. The factors of 20 must sum to b. Since 20 is positive and b is positive, both factors of 20 must be positive.
$1 + 20 = 21; (1)(20) = 20$
$2 + 10 = 12; (2)(10) = 20$
$4 + 5 = 9; (4)(5) = 20$
The possible values of b are 9, 12, and 21.

93. $x^{2n} + 8x^n - 20 = (x^n + 10)(x^n - 2)$

Section 11.3

Practice Problems

1. a. Factors of $5x^2$: $5x^2 = 5x \cdot x$
Factors of 10: $10 = 1 \cdot 10, 10 = 2 \cdot 5$
$5x^2 + 27x + 10 = (5x + 2)(x + 5)$

b. Factors of $4x^2$: $4x^2 = 4x \cdot x, \ 4x^2 = 2x \cdot 2x$
Factors of 5: $5 = 1 \cdot 5$
$4x^2 + 12x + 5 = (2x + 5)(2x + 1)$

2. a. Factors of $2x^2$: $2x^2 = 2x \cdot x$
Factors of 12: $12 = -1 \cdot -12, 12 = -2 \cdot -6,$
$12 = -3 \cdot -4$
$2x^2 - 11x + 12 = (2x - 3)(x - 4)$

b. Factors of $6x^2$: $6x^2 = 6x \cdot x, 6x^2 = 3x \cdot 2x$
Factors of 1: $1 = -1 \cdot -1$
$6x^2 - 5x + 1 = (3x - 1)(2x - 1)$

3. a. Factors of $3x^2$: $3x^2 = 3x \cdot x$
Factors of -5: $-5 = -5 \cdot 1, -5 = 1 \cdot -5$
$3x^2 + 14x - 5 = (3x - 1)(x + 5)$

b. Factors of $35x^2$: $35x^2 = 35x \cdot x,$
$35x^2 = 5x \cdot 7x$
Factors of -4: $-4 = -1 \cdot 4, -4 = 1 \cdot -4,$
$-4 = -2 \cdot 2$
$35x^2 + 4x - 4 = (5x + 2)(7x - 2)$

4. a. Factors of $14x^2$: $14x^2 = 14x \cdot x,$
$14x^2 = 7x \cdot 2x$
Factors of $-2y^2$: $-2y^2 = -2y \cdot y,$
$-2y^2 = 2y \cdot -y$
$14x^2 - 3xy - 2y^2 = (7x + 2y)(2x - y)$

b. Factors of $12a^2$: $12a^2 = 12a \cdot a,$
$12a^2 = 6a \cdot 2a, \ 12a^2 = 3a \cdot 4a$
Factors of $-3b^2$: $-3b^2 = -3b \cdot b,$
$-3b^2 = 3b \cdot -b$
$12a^2 - 16ab - 3b^2 = (6a + b)(2a - 3b)$

5. Factors of $2x^4$: $2x^4 = 2x^2 \cdot x^2$
Factors of -7: $-7 = -7 \cdot 1, -7 = 7 \cdot -1$
$2x^4 - 5x^2 - 7 = (2x^2 - 7)(x^2 + 1)$

6. a. $3x^3 + 17x^2 + 10x = x(3x^2 + 17x + 10)$
Factors of $3x^2$: $3x^2 = 3x \cdot x$
Factors of 10: $10 = 1 \cdot 10, 10 = 2 \cdot 5$
$x(3x^2 + 17x + 10) = x(3x + 2)(x + 5)$

b. $6xy^2 + 33xy - 18x = 3x(2y^2 + 11y - 6)$
Factors of $2y^2$: $2y^2 = 2y \cdot y$
Factors of -6: $-6 = 1 \cdot -6, -6 = -1 \cdot 6,$
$-6 = 2 \cdot -3, -6 = -2 \cdot 3$
$3x(2y^2 + 11y - 6) = 3x(2y - 1)(y + 6)$

7. $-5x^2 - 19x + 4 = -1(5x^2 + 19x - 4)$
Factors of $5x^2$: $5x^2 = 5x \cdot x$
Factors of -4: $-4 = -4 \cdot 1, -4 = 4 \cdot -1,$
$-4 = 2 \cdot -2$
$-1(5x^2 + 19x - 4) = -1(x + 4)(5x - 1)$

Vocabulary and Readiness Check

1. $2x^2 + 5x + 3$ factors as $(2x + 3)(x + 1)$, which is choice d.

2. $7x^2 + 9x + 2$ factors as $(7x + 2)(x + 1)$, which is choice b.

3. $3x^2 + 31x + 10$ factors as $(3x + 1)(x + 10)$, which is choice c.

4. $5x^2 + 61x + 12$ factors as $(5x + 1)(x + 12)$, which is choice a.

Exercise Set 11.3

1. $5x^2 = 5x \cdot x$
$8 = 2 \cdot 4$
$5x^2 + 22x + 8 = (5x + 2)(x + 4)$

3. $50x^2 = 5x \cdot 10x$
$-2 = 2 \cdot -1$
$50x^2 + 15x - 2 = (5x + 2)(10x - 1)$

5. $20x^2 = 5x \cdot 4x$
$-6 = 2 \cdot -3$
$20x^2 - 7x - 6 = (5x + 2)(4x - 3)$

7. Factors of $2x^2$: $2x^2 = 2x \cdot x$
Factors of 15: $15 = 1 \cdot 15$, $15 = 3 \cdot 5$
$2x^2 + 13x + 15 = (2x + 3)(x + 5)$

9. Factors of $8y^2$: $8y^2 = 8y \cdot y$, $8y^2 = 4y \cdot 2y$.
Factors of 9: $9 = -1 \cdot -9$, $-3 \cdot -3$.
$8y^2 - 17y + 9 = (y - 1)(8y - 9)$

11. Factors of $2x^2$: $2x^2 = 2x \cdot x$
Factors of -5: $-5 = 1 \cdot -5$, $-5 = -1 \cdot 5$
$2x^2 - 9x - 5 = (2x + 1)(x - 5)$

13. Factors of $20r^2$: $20r^2 = 20r \cdot r$, $20r^2 = 10r \cdot 2r$,
$20r^2 = 5r \cdot 4r$.
Factors of -8: $-8 = -1 \cdot 8$, $-8 = -2 \cdot 4$,
$-8 = -4 \cdot 2$, $-8 = -8 \cdot 1$
$20r^2 + 27r - 8 = (4r - 1)(5r + 8)$

15. Factors of $10x^2$: $10x^2 = 10x \cdot x$, $10x^2 = 5x \cdot 2x$
Factors of 3: $3 = 1 \cdot 3$
$10x^2 + 31x + 3 = (10x + 1)(x + 3)$

17. $x + 3x^2 - 2 = 3x^2 + x - 2$
Factors of $3x^2$: $3x^2 = 3x \cdot x$
Factors of -2: $-2 = -1 \cdot 2$, $-2 = 2 \cdot -1$
$3x^2 + x - 2 = (3x - 2)(x + 1)$

19. Factors of $6x^2$: $6x^2 = 6x \cdot x$, $6x^2 = 3x \cdot 2x$
Factors of $5y^2$: $5y^2 = -5y \cdot -y$
$6x^2 - 13xy + 5y^2 = (3x - 5y)(2x - y)$

21. Factors of $15m^2$: $15m^2 = 15m \cdot m$,
$15m^2 = 5m \cdot 3m$.
Factors of -15: $-15 = -1 \cdot 15$, $-15 = -3 \cdot 5$,
$-15 = -5 \cdot 3$, $-15 = -15 \cdot 1$
$15m^2 - 16m - 15 = (3m - 5)(5m + 3)$

23. $-9x + 20 + x^2 = x^2 - 9x + 20$
Factors of x^2: $x^2 = x \cdot x$
Factors of 20: $20 = -1 \cdot -20$, $20 = -2 \cdot -10$,
$20 = -4 \cdot -5$
$x^2 - 9x + 20 = (x - 4)(x - 5)$

25. Factors of $2x^2$: $2x^2 = 2x \cdot x$
Factors of -99: $-99 = -1 \cdot 99$, $-99 = -3 \cdot 33$,
$-99 = -9 \cdot 11$, $-99 = -11 \cdot 9$, $-99 = -33 \cdot 3$,
$-99 = -99 \cdot 1$
$2x^2 - 7x - 99 = (2x + 11)(x - 9)$

27. $-27t + 7t^2 - 4 = 7t^2 - 27t - 4$
Factors of $7t^2$: $7t^2 = 7t \cdot t$
Factors of -4: $-4 = -1 \cdot 4$, $-4 = 1 \cdot -4$,
$-4 = 2 \cdot -2$
$7t^2 - 27t - 4 = (7t + 1)(t - 4)$

29. Factors of $3a^2$: $3a^2 = 3a \cdot a$
Factors of $3b^2$: $3b^2 = b \cdot 3b$
$3a^2 + 10ab + 3b^2 = (3a + b)(a + 3b)$

31. Factors of $49p^2$: $49p^2 = 49p \cdot p$,
$49p^2 = 7p \cdot 7p$
Factors of -2: $-2 = -1 \cdot 2$, $-2 = 1 \cdot -2$
$49p^2 - 7p - 2 = (7p + 1)(7p - 2)$

33. Factors of $18x^2$: $18x^2 = 18x \cdot x$,
$18x^2 = 9x \cdot 2x$, $18x^2 = 6x \cdot 3x$
Factors of -14: $-14 = -1 \cdot 14$, $-14 = -2 \cdot 7$,
$-14 = -7 \cdot 2$, $-14 = -14 \cdot 1$
$18x^2 - 9x - 14 = (6x - 7)(3x + 2)$

35. Factors of $2m^2$: $2m^2 = 2m \cdot m$
Factors of 10: $10 = 1 \cdot 10$, $10 = 2 \cdot 5$
$2m^2 + 17m + 10$ is prime.

37. Factors of $24x^2$: $24x^2 = 24x \cdot x$,
$24x^2 = 12x \cdot 2x$, $24x^2 = 8x \cdot 3x$, $24x^2 = 6x \cdot 4x$
Factors of 12: $12 = 1 \cdot 12$, $12 = 2 \cdot 6$, $12 = 3 \cdot 4$
$24x^2 + 41x + 12 = (3x + 4)(8x + 3)$

39. $12x^3 + 11x^2 + 2x = x(12x^2 + 11x + 2)$
Factor of $12x^2$: $12x^2 = 12x \cdot x$, $12x^2 = 6x \cdot 2x$,
$12x^2 = 4x \cdot 3x$
Factors of 2: $2 = 1 \cdot 2$
$12x^3 + 11x^2 + 2x = x(3x + 2)(4x + 1)$

41. $21b^2 - 48b - 45 = 3(7b^2 - 16b - 15)$
Factors of $7b^2$: $7b^2 = 7b \cdot b$
Factors of -15: $-15 = -1 \cdot 15$, $-15 = -3 \cdot 5$,
$-15 = -5 \cdot 3$, $-15 = -15 \cdot 1$
$21b^2 - 48b - 45 = 3(7b + 5)(b - 3)$

43. $7z + 12z^2 - 12 = 12z^2 + 7z - 12$
Factors of $12z^2$: $12z^2 = 12z \cdot z$, $12z^2 = 6z \cdot 2z$,
$12z^2 = 4z \cdot 3z$
Factors of -12: $-12 = -12 \cdot 1$, $-12 = 12 \cdot -1$,
$-12 = -6 \cdot 2$, $-12 = 6 \cdot -2$, $-12 = -4 \cdot 3$,
$-12 = 4 \cdot -3$
$12z^2 + 7z - 12 = (3z + 4)(4z - 3)$

45. $6x^2y^2 - 2xy^2 - 60y^2 = 2y^2(3x^2 - x - 30)$
Factors of $3x^2$: $3x^2 = 3x \cdot x$
Factors of -30: $-30 = -1 \cdot 30$, $-30 = -2 \cdot 15$,
$-30 = -3 \cdot 10$, $-30 = -5 \cdot 6$, $-30 = -6 \cdot 5$,
$-30 = -10 \cdot 3$, $-30 = -15 \cdot 2$, $-30 = -30 \cdot 1$
$6x^2y^2 - 2xy^2 - 60y^2 = 2y^2(3x - 10)(x + 3)$

47. Factors of $4x^2$: $4x^2 = 4x \cdot x$, $4x^2 = 2x \cdot 2x$
Factors of -21: $-21 = -1 \cdot 21$, $-21 = 1 \cdot -21$,
$-21 = -7 \cdot 3$, $-21 = 7 \cdot -3$
$4x^2 - 8x - 21 = (2x - 7)(2x + 3)$

49. $3x^2 - 42x + 63 = 3(x^2 - 14x + 21)$
$x^2 - 14x + 21$ is prime, so $3(x^2 - 14x + 21)$ is a
factored form of $3x^2 - 42x + 63$.

51. Factors of $8x^2$: $8x^2 = 8x \cdot x$, $8x^2 = 4x \cdot 2x$
Factors of $-27y^2$: $-27y^2 = -27y \cdot y$,
$-27y^2 = 27y \cdot -y$, $-27y^2 = -9y \cdot 3y$,
$-27y^2 = 9y \cdot -3y$
$8x^2 + 6xy - 27y^2 = (4x + 9y)(2x - 3y)$

53. $-x^2 + 2x + 24 = -1(x^2 - 2x - 24)$
$\qquad\qquad\qquad\quad = -1(x - 6)(x + 4)$

55. $4x^3 - 9x^2 - 9x = x(4x^2 - 9x - 9)$
Factors of $4x^2$: $4x^2 = 4x \cdot x$, $4x^2 = 2x \cdot 2x$
Factors of -9: $-9 = -1 \cdot 9$, $-9 = 1 \cdot -9$,
$-9 = 3 \cdot -3$
$4x^3 - 9x^2 - 9x = x(4x + 3)(x - 3)$

57. Factors of $24x^2$: $24x^2 = 24x \cdot x$,
$24x^2 = 12x \cdot 2x$, $24x^2 = 8x \cdot 3x$, $24x^2 = 6x \cdot 4x$
Factors of 9: $9 = -1 \cdot -9$, $9 = -3 \cdot -3$
$24x^2 - 58x + 9 = (4x - 9)(6x - 1)$

59. $40a^2b + 9ab - 9b = b(40a^2 + 9a - 9)$
Factors of $40a^2$: $40a^2 = 40a \cdot a$,
$40a^2 = 20a \cdot 2a$, $40a^2 = 10a \cdot 4a$,
$40a^2 = 8a \cdot 5a$
Factors of -9: $-9 = -1 \cdot 9$, $-9 = 1 \cdot -9$,
$-9 = 3 \cdot -3$
$40a^2b + 9ab - 9b = b(8a - 3)(5a + 3)$

61. $30x^3 + 38x^2 + 12x = 2x(15x^2 + 19x + 6)$
Factors of $15x^2$: $15x^2 = 15x \cdot x$, $15x^2 = 5x \cdot 3x$
Factors of 6: $6 = 1 \cdot 6$, $6 = 2 \cdot 3$
$30x^3 + 38x^2 + 12x = 2x(3x + 2)(5x + 3)$

63. $6y^3 - 8y^2 - 30y = 2y(3y^2 - 4y - 15)$
Factors of $3y^2$: $3y^2 = 3y \cdot y$
Factors of -15: $-15 = -1 \cdot 15$, $-15 = 1 \cdot -15$,
$-15 = -3 \cdot 5$, $-15 = 3 \cdot -5$
$6y^3 - 8y^2 - 30y = 2y(3y + 5)(y - 3)$

65. $10x^4 + 25x^3 y - 15x^2 y^2 = 5x^2 (2x^2 + 5xy - 3y^2)$

Factors of $2x^2$: $2x^2 = 2x \cdot x$

Factors of $-3y^2$: $-3y^2 = -y \cdot 3y$,

$-3y^2 = -3y \cdot y$

$10x^4 + 25x^3 y - 15x^2 y^2 = 5x^2 (2x - y)(x + 3y)$

67. $-14x^2 + 39x - 10 = -1(14x^2 - 39x + 10)$

Factors of $14x^2$: $14x^2 = 14x \cdot x$, $14x^2 = 7x \cdot 2x$

Factors of 10: $10 = -1 \cdot -10$, $10 = -2 \cdot -5$

$-14x^2 + 39x - 10 = -1(2x - 5)(7x - 2)$

69. $16p^4 - 40p^3 + 25p^2 = p^2 (16p^2 - 40p + 25)$

Factors of $16p^2$: $16p^2 = 16p \cdot p$,

$16p^2 = 8p \cdot 2p$, $16p^2 = 4p \cdot 4p$

Factors of 25: $25 = -1 \cdot -25$, $25 = -5 \cdot -5$

$16p^4 - 40p^3 + 25p^2 = p^2 (4p - 5)(4p - 5)$ or

$p^2 (4p - 5)^2$

71. $-2x^2 + 9x + 5 = -1(2x^2 - 9x - 5)$

Factors of $2x^2$: $2x^2 = 2x \cdot x$

Factors of -5: $-5 = -1 \cdot 5$, $-5 = 1 \cdot -5$

$-2x^2 + 9x + 5 = -1(2x + 1)(x - 5)$

73. $-4 + 52x - 48x^2 = -48x^2 + 52x - 4$

$= -4(12x^2 - 13x + 1)$

Factors of $12x^2$: $12x^2 = 12x \cdot x$, $12x^2 = 6x \cdot 2x$,

$12x^2 = 4x \cdot 3x$

Factors of 1: $1 = -1 \cdot -1$

$-4 + 52x - 48x^2 = -4(12x - 1)(x - 1)$

75. Factors of $2t^4$: $2t^4 = 2t^2 \cdot t^2$

Factors of -27: $-27 = -1 \cdot 27$, $-27 = 1 \cdot -27$,

$-27 = -3 \cdot 9$, $-27 = 3 \cdot -9$

$2t^4 + 3t^2 - 27 = (2t^2 + 9)(t^2 - 3)$

77. Factors of $5x^2 y^2$: $5x^2 y^2 = 5xy \cdot xy$

Factors of 1: $1 = 1 \cdot 1$

There is no combination that gives the correct middle term, so $5x^2 y^2 + 20xy + 1$ is prime.

79. $6a^5 + 37a^3 b^2 + 6ab^4 = a(6a^4 + 37a^2 b^2 + 6b^4)$

Factors of $6a^4$: $6a^4 = 6a^2 \cdot a^2$, $6a^4 = 3a^2 \cdot 2a^2$

Factors of $6b^4$: $6b^4 = 6b^2 \cdot b^2$, $6b^4 = 3b^2 \cdot 2b^2$

$6a^5 + 37a^3 b^2 + 6ab^4 = a(6a^2 + b^2)(a^2 + 6b^2)$

81. $(x - 4)(x + 4) = (x)^2 - (4)^2 = x^2 - 16$

83. $(x + 2)^2 = x^2 + 2x(2) + 2^2 = x^2 + 4x + 4$

85. $(2x - 1)^2 = (2x)^2 - 2(2x)(1) + (1)^2 = 4x^2 - 4x + 1$

87. No.

$4x^2 = 2 \cdot 2 \cdot x \cdot x$

$19x = 19 \cdot x$

$12 = 2 \cdot 2 \cdot 3$

There is no common factor (other than 1).

89. $(3x^2 + 1) + (6x + 4) + (x^2 + 15x) = 4x^2 + 21x + 5$

$= (4x + 1)(x + 5)$

91. $4x^2 + 2x + \dfrac{1}{4} = \left(2x + \dfrac{1}{2}\right)\left(2x + \dfrac{1}{2}\right)$ or $\left(2x + \dfrac{1}{2}\right)^2$

93. $4x^2 (y - 1)^2 + 25x(y - 1)^2 + 25(y - 1)^2$

$= (y - 1)^2 (4x^2 + 25x + 25)$

$= (y - 1)^2 (4x + 5)(x + 5)$

95. Factors of $3x^2$: $3x^2 = 3x \cdot x$

Factors of -5: $-5 = -1 \cdot 5$, $-5 = 1 \cdot -5$

$(3x - 1)(x + 5) = 3x^2 + 14x - 5$

$(3x + 1)(x - 5) = 3x^2 - 14x - 5$

$(3x - 5)(x + 1) = 3x^2 - 2x - 5$

$(3x + 5)(x - 1) = 3x^2 + 2x - 5$

Since b is positive, the possible values are 2 and 14.

97. Note that $5 + 2 = 7$.

$(5x + 2)(x + 1) = 5x(x + 1) + 2(x + 1)$

$= 5x^2 + 5x + 2x + 2$

$= 5x^2 + 7x + 2$

If $c = 2$, then $5x^2 + 7x + c$ is factorable.

99. answers may vary

Section 11.4

Practice Problems

1. a. $3 \cdot 8 = 24$
         $12 \cdot 2 = 24$
         $12 + 2 = 14$

$$3x^2 + 14x + 8 = 3x^2 + 12x + 2x + 8$$
$$= 3x(x+4) + 2(x+4)$$
$$= (x+4)(3x+2)$$

b. $12 \cdot 5 = 60$
      $15 \cdot 4 = 60$
      $15 + 4 = 19$

$$12x^2 + 19x + 5 = 12x^2 + 15x + 4x + 5$$
$$= 3x(4x+5) + 1(4x+5)$$
$$= (4x+5)(3x+1)$$

2. a. $30x^2 - 26x + 4 = 2(15x^2 - 13x + 2)$

      $15 \cdot 2 = 30$
      $-3 \cdot -10 = 30$
      $-3 + (-10) = -13$

$$30x^2 - 26x + 4 = 2(15x^2 - 13x + 2)$$
$$= 2(15x^2 - 3x - 10x + 2)$$
$$= 2[3x(5x-1) - 2(5x-1)]$$
$$= 2(5x-1)(3x-2)$$

b. $6x^2 y - 7xy - 5y = y(6x^2 - 7x - 5)$

      $6 \cdot -5 = -30$
      $3 \cdot -10 = -30$
      $3 + (-10) = -7$

$$6x^2 y - 7xy - 5y = y(6x^2 - 7x - 5)$$
$$= y(6x^2 + 3x - 10x - 5)$$
$$= y[3x(2x+1) - 5(2x+1)]$$
$$= y(2x+1)(3x-5)$$

3. $12y^5 + 10y^4 - 42y^3 = 2y^3(6y^2 + 5y - 21)$
    $6 \cdot -21 = -126$
    $14 \cdot -9 = -126$
    $14 + (-9) = 5$
    $12y^5 + 10y^4 - 42y^3$
$$= 2y^3(6y^2 + 5y - 21)$$
$$= 2y^3(6y^2 + 14y - 9y - 21)$$
$$= 2y^3[2y(3y+7) - 3(3y+7)]$$
$$= 2y^3(3y+7)(2y-3)$$

Vocabulary and Readiness Check

1. $a = 1$, $b = 6$, $c = 8$
    $a \cdot c = 1 \cdot 8 = 8$
    $4 \cdot 2 = 8$ and $4 + 2 = 6$; choice a.

2. $a = 1$, $b = 11$, $c = 24$
    $a \cdot c = 1 \cdot 24 = 24$
    $8 \cdot 3 = 24$ and $8 + 3 = 11$; choice c.

3. $a = 2$, $b = 13$, $c = 6$
    $a \cdot c = 2 \cdot 6 = 12$
    $12 \cdot 1 = 12$ and $12 + 1 = 13$; choice b.

4. $a = 4$, $b = 8$, $c = 3$
    $a \cdot c = 4 \cdot 3 = 12$
    $2 \cdot 6 = 12$ and $2 + 6 = 8$; choice d.

Exercise Set 11.4

1. $x^2 + 3x + 2x + 6 = x(x+3) + 2(x+3)$
$$= (x+3)(x+2)$$

3. $y^2 + 8y - 2y - 16 = y(y+8) - 2(y+8)$
$$= (y+8)(y-2)$$

5. $8x^2 - 5x - 24x + 15 = x(8x-5) - 3(8x-5)$
$$= (8x-5)(x-3)$$

7. $5x^4 - 3x^2 + 25x^2 - 15 = x^2(5x^2 - 3) + 5(5x^2 - 3)$
$$= (5x^2 - 3)(x^2 + 5)$$

9. a. $9 \cdot 2 = 18$
      $9 + 2 = 11$
      9 and 2 are numbers whose product is 18
      and whose sum is 11.

b. $11x = 9x + 2x$

c. $6x^2 + 11x + 3 = 6x^2 + 9x + 2x + 3$
$$= 3x(2x+3) + 1(2x+3)$$
$$= (2x+3)(3x+1)$$

11. a. $-3 \cdot -20 = 60$
      $-3 + (-20) = -23$
      -3 and -20 are numbers whose product is
      60 and whose sum is -23.

b. $-23x = -3x - 20x$

c. $15x^2 - 23x + 4 = 15x^2 - 3x - 20x + 4$
$$= 3x(5x-1) - 4(5x-1)$$
$$= (5x-1)(3x-4)$$

13. $21 \cdot 2 = 42$
$14 \cdot 3 = 42$
$14 + 3 = 17$
$21y^2 + 17y + 2 = 21y^2 + 14y + 3y + 2$
$$= 7y(3y+2) + 1(3y+2)$$
$$= (3y+2)(7y+1)$$

15. $7 \cdot -11 = -77$
$-11 \cdot 7 = -77$
$-11 + 7 = -4$
$7x^2 - 4x - 11 = 7x^2 - 11x + 7x - 11$
$$= x(7x-11) + 1(7x-11)$$
$$= (7x-11)(x+1)$$

17. $10 \cdot 2 = 20$
$-4 \cdot -5 = 20$
$-4 + (-5) = -9$
$10x^2 - 9x + 2 = 10x^2 - 4x - 5x + 2$
$$= 2x(5x-2) - 1(5x-2)$$
$$= (5x-2)(2x-1)$$

19. $2 \cdot 5 = 10$
$-5 \cdot -2 = 10$
$-5 + (-2) = -7$
$2x^2 - 7x + 5 = 2x^2 - 5x - 2x + 5$
$$= x(2x-5) - 1(2x-5)$$
$$= (2x-5)(x-1)$$

21. $12x + 4x^2 + 9 = 4x^2 + 12x + 9$
$4 \cdot 9 = 36$
$6 \cdot 6 = 36$
$6 + 6 = 12$
$4x^2 + 12x + 9 = 4x^2 + 6x + 6x + 9$
$$= 2x(2x+3) + 3(2x+3)$$
$$= (2x+3)(2x+3) \text{ or } (2x+3)^2$$

23. $4 \cdot -21 = -84$
$6 \cdot -14 = -84$
$6 + (-14) = -8$
$4x^2 - 8x - 21 = 4x^2 + 6x - 14x - 21$
$$= 2x(2x+3) - 7(2x+3)$$
$$= (2x+3)(2x-7)$$

25. $10 \cdot 12 = 120$
$-8 \cdot -15 = 120$
$-8 + (-15) = -23$
$10x^2 - 23x + 12 = 10x^2 - 8x - 15x + 12$
$$= 2x(5x-4) - 3(5x-4)$$
$$= (5x-4)(2x-3)$$

27. $2x^3 + 13x^2 + 15x = x(2x^2 + 13x + 15)$
$2 \cdot 15 = 30$
$3 \cdot 10 = 30$
$3 + 10 = 13$
$2x^3 + 13x^2 + 15x = x(2x^2 + 13x + 15)$
$$= x(2x^2 + 3x + 10x + 15)$$
$$= x[x(2x+3) + 5(2x+3)]$$
$$= x(2x+3)(x+5)$$

29. $16y^2 - 34y + 18 = 2(8y^2 - 17y + 9)$
$8 \cdot 9 = 72$
$-9 \cdot -8 = 72$
$-9 + (-8) = -17$
$16y^2 - 34y + 18 = 2(8y^2 - 17y + 9)$
$$= 2(8y^2 - 9y - 8y + 9)$$
$$= 2[y(8y-9) - 1(8y-9)]$$
$$= 2(8y-9)(y-1)$$

31. $-13x + 6 + 6x^2 = 6x^2 - 13x + 6$
$6 \cdot 6 = 36$
$-9 \cdot -4 = 36$
$-9 + (-4) = -13$
$6x^2 - 13x + 6 = 6x^2 - 9x - 4x + 6$
$$= 3x(2x-3) - 2(2x-3)$$
$$= (2x-3)(3x-2)$$

33. $54a^2 - 9a - 30 = 3(18a^2 - 3a - 10)$
$18 \cdot -10 = -180$
$12 \cdot -15 = -180$
$12 + (-15) = -3$
$54a^2 - 9a - 30 = 3(18a^2 - 3a - 10)$
$$= 3(18a^2 + 12a - 15a - 10)$$
$$= 3[6a(3a+2) - 5(3a+2)]$$
$$= 3(3a+2)(6a-5)$$

35. $20a^3 + 37a^2 + 8a = a(20a^2 + 37a + 8)$

$20 \cdot 8 = 160$
$5 \cdot 32 = 160$
$5 + 32 = 37$
$20a^3 + 37a^2 + 8a = a(20a^2 + 37a + 8)$
$\qquad\qquad = a(20a^2 + 5a + 32a + 8)$
$\qquad\qquad = a[5a(4a+1) + 8(4a+1)]$
$\qquad\qquad = a(4a+1)(5a+8)$

37. $12x^3 - 27x^2 - 27x = 3x(4x^2 - 9x - 9)$

$4 \cdot -9 = -36$
$3 \cdot -12 = -36$
$3 + (-12) = -9$
$12x^3 - 27x^2 - 27x = 3x(4x^2 - 9x - 9)$
$\qquad\qquad = 3x(4x^2 + 3x - 12x - 9)$
$\qquad\qquad = 3x[x(4x+3) - 3(4x+3)]$
$\qquad\qquad = 3x(4x+3)(x-3)$

39. $3x^2 y + 4xy^2 + y^3 = y(3x^2 + 4xy + y^2)$

$3 \cdot y^2 = 3y^2$
$y \cdot 3y = 3y^2$
$y + 3y = 4y$
$3x^2 y + 4xy^2 + y^3 = y(3x^2 + 4xy + y^2)$
$\qquad\qquad = y(3x^2 + xy + 3xy + y^2)$
$\qquad\qquad = y[x(3x+y) + y(3x+y)]$
$\qquad\qquad = y(3x+y)(x+y)$

41. $20 \cdot 1 = 20$
There are no factors of 20 which sum to 7, so
$20z^2 + 7z + 1$ is prime.

43. $24a^2 - 6ab - 30b^2 = 6(4a^2 - ab - 5b^2)$

$4 \cdot -5b^2 = -20b^2$
$4b \cdot -5b = -20b^2$
$4b + (-5b) = -b$
$24a^2 - 6ab - 30b^2 = 6(4a^2 - ab - 5b^2)$
$\qquad\qquad = 6(4a^2 + 4ab - 5ab - 5b^2)$
$\qquad\qquad = 6[4a(a+b) - 5b(a+b)]$
$\qquad\qquad = 6(a+b)(4a-5b)$

45. $15p^4 + 31p^3 q + 2p^2 q^2$
$= p^2(15p^2 + 31pq + 2q^2)$
$15 \cdot 2q^2 = 30q^2$
$q \cdot 30q = 30q^2$

$q + 30q = 31q$
$15p^4 + 31p^3 q + 2p^2 q^2$
$= p^2(15p^2 + 31pq + 2q^2)$
$= p^2(15p^2 + pq + 30pq + 2q^2)$
$= p^2[p(15p+q) + 2q(15p+q)]$
$= p^2(15p+q)(p+2q)$

47. $35 + 12x + x^2 = x^2 + 12x + 35$
$1 \cdot 35 = 35$
$7 \cdot 5 = 35$
$7 + 5 = 12$
$x^2 + 12x + 35 = x^2 + 7x + 5x + 35$
$\qquad\qquad = x(x+7) + 5(x+7)$
$\qquad\qquad = (x+7)(x+5)$ or $(7+x)(5+x)$

49. $6 - 11x + 5x^2 = 5x^2 - 11x + 6$
$5 \cdot 6 = 30$
$-6 \cdot -5 = 30$
$-6 + (-5) = -11$
$5x^2 - 11x + 6 = 5x^2 - 6x - 5x + 6$
$\qquad\qquad = x(5x-6) - 1(5x-6)$
$\qquad\qquad = (5x-6)(x-1)$ or $(6-5x)(1-x)$

51. $(x-2)(x+2) = x^2 - 2^2 = x^2 - 4$

53. $(y+4)(y+4) = (y+4)^2$
$\qquad\qquad = (y)^2 + 2(y)(4) + (4)^2$
$\qquad\qquad = y^2 + 8y + 16$

55. $(9z+5)(9z-5) = (9z)^2 - 5^2 = 81z^2 - 25$

57. $(4x-3)^2 = (4x)^2 - 2(4x)(3) + (3)^2$
$\qquad\qquad = 16x^2 - 24x + 9$

59. $5(2x^2 + 9x + 9) = 10x^2 + 45x + 45$
$2 \cdot 9 = 18$
$3 \cdot 6 = 18$
$3 + 6 = 9$
$5(2x^2 + 9x + 9) = 5(2x^2 + 3x + 6x + 9)$
$\qquad\qquad = 5[x(2x+3) + 3(2x+3)]$
$\qquad\qquad = 5(2x+3)(x+3)$

The perimeter is $10x^2 + 45x + 45$ or
$5(2x + 3)(x + 3)$.

61. $x^{2n} + 2x^n + 3x^n + 6 = x^n(x^n + 2) + 3(x^n + 2)$
$$= (x^n + 2)(x^n + 3)$$

63. $3 \cdot -35 = -105$
$-5 \cdot 21 = -105$
$-5 + 21 = 16$
$3x^{2n} + 16x^n - 35 = 3x^{2n} - 5x^n + 21x^n - 35$
$$= x^n(3x^n - 5) + 7(3x^n - 5)$$
$$= (3x^n - 5)(x^n + 7)$$

65. answers may vary

Section 11.5

Practice Problems

1. a. Since $36 = 6^2$ and $12x = 2 \cdot 6 \cdot x$,
$x^2 + 12x + 36$ is a perfect square trinomial.

b. Since $100 = 10^2$ and $20x = 2 \cdot 10 \cdot x$,
$x^2 + 20x + 100$ is a perfect square trinomial.

2. a. Since $9x^2 = (3x)^2$ and $25 = 5^2$, but
$20x \neq 2 \cdot 3x \cdot 5$, the polynomial is not a
perfect square trinomial.

b. Since $4x^2 = (2x)^2$, but 11 is not a perfect
square, the polynomial is not a perfect
square trinomial.

3. a. Since $25x^2 = (5x)^2$ and $1 = 1^2$, and
$2 \cdot 5x \cdot 1 = 10x$ which is the opposite of
$-10x$, the trinomial is a perfect square
trinomial.

b. Since $9x^2 = (3x)^2$ and $49 = 7^2$, and
$2 \cdot 3x \cdot 7 = 42x$ which is the opposite of
$-42x$, the trinomial is a perfect square
trinomial.

4. $x^2 + 16x + 64 = (x)^2 + 2 \cdot x \cdot 8 + 8^2$
$$= (x + 8)^2$$

5. $9r^2 + 24rs + 16s^2 = (3r)^2 + 2 \cdot 3r \cdot 4s + (4s)^2$
$$= (3r + 4s)^2$$

6. $9n^4 - 6n^2 + 1 = (3n^2)^2 - 2 \cdot 3n^2 \cdot 1 + 1^2$
$$= (3n^2 - 1)^2$$

7. Notice that this trinomial is not a perfect square
trinomial.
$9x^2 = (3x)^2$ and $4 = 2^2$, but $2 \cdot 3x \cdot 2 = 12x$ and
$12x$ is not the middle term $15x$.
Factor by grouping.
$9 \cdot 4 = 36$
$3 \cdot 12 = 36$
$3 + 12 = 15$
$9x^2 + 15x + 4 = 9x^2 + 3x + 12x + 4$
$$= 3x(3x + 1) + 4(3x + 1)$$
$$= (3x + 1)(3x + 4)$$

8. a. $8n^2 + 40n + 50 = 2(4n^2 + 20n + 25)$
$$= 2[(2n)^2 + 2 \cdot 2n \cdot 5 + 5^2]$$
$$= 2(2n + 5)^2$$

b. $12x^3 - 84x^2 + 147x$
$$= 3x(4x^2 - 28x + 49)$$
$$= 3x[(2x)^2 - 2 \cdot 2x \cdot 7 + 7^2]$$
$$= 3x(2x - 7)^2$$

9. $x^2 - 9 = x^2 - 3^2 = (x - 3)(x + 3)$

10. $a^2 - 16 = a^2 - 4^2 = (a - 4)(a + 4)$

11. $c^2 - \dfrac{9}{25} = c^2 - \left(\dfrac{3}{5}\right)^2 = \left(c - \dfrac{3}{5}\right)\left(c + \dfrac{3}{5}\right)$

12. $s^2 + 9$ is prime since it is the sum of two
squares.

13. $9s^2 - 1 = (3s)^2 - 1^2 = (3s - 1)(3s + 1)$

14. $16x^2 - 49y^2 = (4x)^2 - (7y)^2$
$$= (4x - 7y)(4x + 7y)$$

15. $p^4 - 81 = (p^2)^2 - 9^2$
$$= (p^2 + 9)(p^2 - 9)$$
$$= (p^2 + 9)(p + 3)(p - 3)$$

16. $9x^3 - 25x = x(9x^2 - 25)$
$$= x[(3x)^2 - 5^2]$$
$$= x(3x - 5)(3x + 5)$$

17. $48x^4 - 3 = 3(16x^4 - 1)$
$$= 3[(4x^2)^2 - 1^2]$$
$$= 3(4x^2 + 1)(4x^2 - 1)$$
$$= 3(4x^2 + 1)(2x + 1)(2x - 1)$$

18. $-9x^2 + 100 = -1(9x^2 - 100)$
$$= -1[(3x)^2 - 10^2]$$
$$= -1(3x - 10)(3x + 10)$$

19. $121 - m^2 = 11^2 - m^2 = (11 + m)(11 - m)$
or
$$121 - m^2 = -m^2 + 121$$
$$= -1(m^2 - 121)$$
$$= -1(m^2 - 11^2)$$
$$= -1(m + 11)(m - 11)$$

Calculator Explorations

	$x^2 - 2x + 1$	$x^2 - 2x - 1$	$(x-1)^2$
$x = 5$	16	14	16
$x = -3$	16	14	16
$x = 2.7$	2.89	0.89	2.89
$x = -12.1$	171.61	169.61	171.61
$x = 0$	1	1	1

Vocabulary and Readiness Check

1. A <u>perfect square trinomial</u> is a trinomial that is the square of a binomial.

2. The term $25y^2$ written as a square is $\underline{(5y)^2}$.

3. The expression $x^2 + 10x + 25y^2$ is called a <u>perfect square trinomial</u>.

4. The expression $x^2 - 49$ is called a <u>difference of two squares</u>.

5. The factorization $(x + 5y)(x + 5y)$ may also be written as $\underline{(x + 5y)^2}$.

6. The factorization $(x - 5y)(x + 5y)$ may also be written as $(x - 5y)^2$. <u>false</u>

7. The trinomial $x^2 - 6x - 9$ is a perfect square trinomial. <u>false</u>

8. The binomial $y^2 + 9$ factors as $(y + 3)^2$. <u>false</u>

9. $64 = 8^2$

10. $9 = 3^2$

11. $121a^2 = (11a)^2$

12. $81b^2 = (9b)^2$

13. $36p^4 = (6p^2)^2$

14. $4q^4 = (2q^2)^2$

Exercise Set 11.5

1. Since $64 = 8^2$ and $16x = 2 \cdot 8 \cdot x$, $x^2 + 16x + 64$ is a perfect square trinomial.

3. Since $25 = 5^2$ but $5y \neq 2 \cdot 5 \cdot y$, $y^2 + 5y + 25$ is not a perfect square trinomial.

5. Since $1 = 1^2$ and $-2m = -2 \cdot 1 \cdot m$, $m^2 - 2m + 1$ is a perfect square trinomial.

7. Since $49 = 7^2$ but $16a \neq 2 \cdot 7 \cdot a$, $a^2 - 16a + 49$ is not a perfect square trinomial.

9. $4x^2 = (2x)^2$ but $8y^2$ is not a perfect square, so $4x^2 + 12xy + 8y^2$ is not a perfect square trinomial.

11. $25a^2 = (5a)^2$, $16b^2 = (4b)^2$, and $40ab = 2 \cdot 5a \cdot 4b$, so $25a^2 - 40ab + 16b^2$ is a perfect square trinomial.

13. $x^2 + 22x + 121 = x^2 + 2 \cdot x \cdot 11 + 11^2$
$$= (x + 11)^2$$

15. $x^2 - 16x + 64 = x^2 - 2 \cdot x \cdot 8 + 8^2 = (x - 8)^2$

17. $16a^2 - 24a + 9 = (4a)^2 - 2 \cdot 4a \cdot 3 + 3^2$
$$= (4a - 3)^2$$

19. $x^4 + 4x^2 + 4 = (x^2)^2 + 2 \cdot x^2 \cdot 2 + 2^2 = (x^2 + 2)^2$

21. $2n^2 - 28n + 98 = 2(n^2 - 14n + 49)$
$$= 2[n^2 - 2 \cdot n \cdot 7 + 7^2]$$
$$= 2(n - 7)^2$$

23. $16y^2 + 40y + 25 = (4y)^2 + 2 \cdot 4y \cdot 5 + 5^2$
$$= (4y + 5)^2$$

25. $x^2 y^2 - 10xy + 25 = (xy)^2 - 2 \cdot xy \cdot 5 + 5^2$
$$= (xy - 5)^2$$

27. $m^3 + 18m^2 + 81m = m(m^2 + 18m + 81)$
$$= m(m^2 + 2 \cdot m \cdot 9 + 9^2)$$
$$= m(m + 9)^2$$

29. Since $1 = 1^2$ and $x^4 = (x^2)^2$, but $6x^2 \neq 2 \cdot 1 \cdot x^2$, the polynomial is not a perfect square trinomial. Since there are no factors of $1 \cdot 1 = 1$ that sum to 6, the trinomial is prime.

31. $9x^2 - 24xy + 16y^2 = (3x)^2 - 2 \cdot 3x \cdot 4y + (4y)^2$
$$= (3x - 4y)^2$$

33. $x^2 - 4 = x^2 - (2)^2 = (x + 2)(x - 2)$

35. $81 - p^2 = 9^2 - p^2 = (9 + p)(9 - p)$
or
$81 - p^2 = -p^2 + 81$
$$= -1(p^2 - 81)$$
$$= -1(p - 9^2)$$
$$= -1(p + 9)(p - 9)$$

37. $-4r^2 + 1 = -1(4r^2 - 1)$
$$= -1[(2r)^2 - 1^2]$$
$$= -1(2r + 1)(2r - 1)$$

39. $9x^2 - 16 = (3x)^2 - 4^2 = (3x + 4)(3x - 4)$

41. $16r^2 + 1$ is the sum of two squares, which is prime.

43. $-36 + x^2 = -1(36 - x^2)$
$$= -1(6^2 - x^2)$$
$$= -1(6 + x)(6 - x)$$
or
$-36 + x^2 = x^2 - 36$
$$= x^2 - 6^2$$
$$= (x - 6)(x + 6)$$

45. $m^4 - 1 = (m^2)^2 - 1^2$
$$= (m^2 + 1)(m^2 - 1)$$
$$= (m^2 + 1)(m^2 - 1^2)$$
$$= (m^2 + 1)(m + 1)(m - 1)$$

47. $x^2 - 169y^2 = x^2 - (13y)^2 = (x^2 + 13y)(x - 13y)$

49. $18r^2 - 8 = 2(9r^2 - 4)$
$$= 2[(3r)^2 - 2^2]$$
$$= 2(3r + 2)(3r - 2)$$

51. $9xy^2 - 4x = x(9y^2 - 4)$
$$= x[(3y)^2 - 2^2]$$
$$= x(3y + 2)(3y - 2)$$

53. $16x^4 - 64x^2 = 16x^2(x^2 - 4)$
$$= 16x^2(x^2 - 2^2)$$
$$= 16x^2(x + 2)(x - 2)$$

55. $xy^3 - 9xyz^2 = xy(y^2 - 9z^2)$
$$= xy[y^2 - (3z)^2]$$
$$= xy(y - 3z)(y + 3z)$$

57. $36x^2 - 64y^2 = 4(9x^2 - 16y^2)$
$$= 4[(3x)^2 - (4y)^2]$$
$$= 4(3x + 4y)(3x - 4y)$$

59. $144 - 81x^2 = 9(16 - 9x^2)$
$$= 9[4^2 - (3x)^2]$$
$$= 9(4 - 3x)(4 + 3x)$$

61. $25y^2 - 9 = (5y)^2 - 3^2 = (5y + 3)(5y - 3)$

63. $121m^2 - 100n^2 = (11m)^2 - (10n)^2$
$$= (11m + 10n)(11m - 10n)$$

65. $x^2 y^2 - 1 = (xy)^2 - 1^2 = (xy+1)(xy-1)$

67. $x^2 - \dfrac{1}{4} = x^2 - \left(\dfrac{1}{2}\right)^2 = \left(x - \dfrac{1}{2}\right)\left(x + \dfrac{1}{2}\right)$

69. $49 - \dfrac{9}{25}m^2 = 7^2 - \left(\dfrac{3}{5}m\right)^2$

$\qquad = \left(7 + \dfrac{3}{5}m\right)\left(7 - \dfrac{3}{5}m\right)$

71. $81a^2 - 25b^2 = (9a)^2 - (5b)^2 = (9a+5b)(9a-5b)$

73. $x^2 + 14xy + 49y^2 = x^2 + 2 \cdot x \cdot 7y + (7y)^2$

$\qquad = (x+7y)^2$

75. $32n^4 - 112n^2 + 98 = 2(16n^4 - 56n^2 + 49)$

$\qquad = 2[(4n^2)^2 - 2 \cdot 4n^2 \cdot 7 + 7^2]$

$\qquad = 2(4n^2 - 7)^2$

77. $x^6 - 81x^2 = x^2(x^4 - 81)$

$\qquad = x^2[(x^2)^2 - 9^2]$

$\qquad = x^2(x^2 + 9)(x^2 - 9)$

$\qquad = x^2(x^2 + 9)[(x)^2 - 3^2]$

$\qquad = x^2(x^2 + 9)(x+3)(x-3)$

79. $64p^3 q - 81pq^3 = pq(64p^2 - 81q^2)$

$\qquad = pq[(8p)^2 - (9q)^2]$

$\qquad = pq(8p - 9q)(8p + 9q)$

81. $x - 6 = 0$

$\quad x - 6 + 6 = 0 + 6$

$\qquad\quad x = 6$

83. $2m + 4 = 0$

$\quad 2m + 4 - 4 = 0 - 4$

$\qquad\quad 2m = -4$

$\qquad\quad \dfrac{2m}{2} = \dfrac{-4}{2}$

$\qquad\quad m = -2$

85. $5z - 1 = 0$

$\quad 5z - 1 + 1 = 0 + 1$

$\qquad\quad 5z = 1$

$\qquad\quad \dfrac{5z}{5} = \dfrac{1}{5}$

$\qquad\quad z = \dfrac{1}{5}$

87. $x^2 - \dfrac{2}{3}x + \dfrac{1}{9} = x^2 - 2 \cdot x \cdot \dfrac{1}{3} + \left(\dfrac{1}{3}\right)^2 = \left(x - \dfrac{1}{3}\right)^2$

89. $(x+2)^2 - y^2 = [(x+2) + y][(x+2) - y]$

$\qquad = (x+2+y)(x+2-y)$

91. $a^2(b-4) - 16(b-4) = (b-4)(a^2 - 16)$

$\qquad = (b-4)(a^2 - 4^2)$

$\qquad = (b-4)(a-4)(a+4)$

93. $(x^2 + 6x + 9) - 4y^2$

$\quad = (x^2 + 2 \cdot x \cdot 3 + 3^2) - 4y^2$

$\quad = (x+3)^2 - 4y^2$

$\quad = (x+3)^2 - (2y)^2$

$\quad = [(x+3) + 2y][(x+3) - 2y]$

$\quad = (x+3+2y)(x+3-2y)$

95. $x^{2n} - 100 = (x^n)^2 - 10^2 = (x^n + 10)(x^n - 10)$

97. $x^2 = x^2$ and $16 = 4^2$.

$(x+4)^2 = x^2 + 2 \cdot x \cdot 4 + 4^2 = x^2 + 8x + 16,$ so the number 8 makes the given expression a perfect square trinomial.

99. answers may vary

101. The difference of two squares is the result of multiplying binomials of the form $(x + a)$ and $(x - a)$, so multiplying $(x - 6)$ by $(x + 6)$ results in the difference of two squares.

103. $(a+b)^2 = a^2 + 2 \cdot a \cdot b + b^2 = a^2 + 2ab + b^2$

105. a. $2704 - 16t^2 = 2704 - 16(3)^2$

$\qquad = 2704 - 16 \cdot 9$

$\qquad = 2704 - 144$

$\qquad = 2560$

After 3 seconds, the filter is 2560 feet above the river.

b. $2704 - 16t^2 = 2704 - 16(7)^2$
$= 2704 - 16 \cdot 49$
$= 2704 - 784$
$= 1920$

After 7 seconds, the filter is 1920 feet above the river.

c. The filter lands in the river when its height is 0 feet.

$2704 - 16t^2 = 0$
$(52 + 4t)(52 - 4t) = 0$
$52 + 4t = 0 \quad$ or $\quad 52 - 4t = 0$
$\quad 4t = -52 \qquad\qquad -4t = -52$
$\qquad t = -13 \qquad\qquad\quad t = 13$

Discard $t = -13$ since time cannot be negative. The filter lands in the river after 13 seconds.

d. $2704 - 16t^2 = 16(169 - t^2)$
$= 16[(13)^2 - t^2]$
$= 16(13 - t)(13 + t)$

107. a. $1600 - 16t^2 = 1600 - 16(3)^2$
$= 1600 - 16 \cdot 9$
$= 1600 - 144$
$= 1456$

After 3 seconds, the height of the bolt is 1456 feet.

b. $1600 - 16t^2 = 1600 - 16(7)^2$
$= 1600 - 16(49)$
$= 1600 - 784$
$= 816$

After 7 seconds, the height of the bolt is 816 feet.

c. The bolt hits the ground when its height is 0 feet.

$1600 - 16t^2 = 0$
$(40 - 4t)(40 + 4t) = 0$
$40 - 4t = 0 \quad$ or $\quad 40 + 4t = 0$
$\quad -4t = -40 \qquad\qquad 4t = -40$
$\qquad t = 10 \qquad\qquad\quad t = -10$

Discard $t = -10$ since time cannot be negative. The bolt hits the ground after 10 seconds.

d. $1600 - 16t^2 = 16(100 - t^2)$
$= 16(10^2 - t^2)$
$= 16(10 + t)(10 - t)$

Integrated Review

1–76. Factoring methods may vary.

1. $x^2 + x - 12 = (x - 3)(x + 4)$

2. $x^2 - 10x + 16 = (x - 8)(x - 2)$

3. $x^2 + 2x + 1 = x^2 + 2 \cdot x \cdot 1 + 1^2$
$= (x + 1)^2$

4. $x^2 - 6x + 9 = x^2 - 2 \cdot x \cdot 3 + 3^2$
$= (x - 3)^2$

5. $x^2 - x - 6 = (x + 2)(x - 3)$

6. $x^2 + x - 2 = (x + 2)(x - 1)$

7. $x^2 + x - 6 = (x + 3)(x - 2)$

8. $x^2 + 7x + 12 = (x + 3)(x + 4)$

9. $x^2 - 7x + 10 = (x - 5)(x - 2)$

10. $x^2 - x - 30 = (x - 6)(x + 5)$

11. $2x^2 - 98 = 2(x^2 - 49)$
$= 2(x^2 - 7^2)$
$= 2(x - 7)(x + 7)$

12. $3x^2 - 75 = 3(x^2 - 25)$
$= 3(x^2 - 5^2)$
$= 3(x - 5)(x + 5)$

13. $x^2 + 3x + 5x + 15 = x(x + 3) + 5(x + 3)$
$= (x + 3)(x + 5)$

14. $3y - 21 + xy - 7x = 3(y - 7) + x(y - 7)$
$= (y - 7)(3 + x)$

15. $x^2 + 6x - 16 = (x + 8)(x - 2)$

16. $x^2 - 3x - 28 = (x - 7)(x + 4)$

17. $4x^3 + 20x^2 - 56x = 4x(x^2 + 5x - 14)$
$= 4x(x + 7)(x - 2)$

18. $6x^3 - 6x^2 - 120x = 6x(x^2 - x - 20)$
$\qquad\qquad\qquad\quad = 6x(x-5)(x+4)$

19. $12x^2 + 34x + 24 = 2(6x^2 + 17x + 12)$
$\qquad\qquad\qquad\quad = 2(3x+4)(2x+3)$

20. $24a^2 + 18ab - 15b^2 = 3(8a^2 + 6ab - 5b^2)$
$\qquad\qquad\qquad\qquad\quad = 3(2a-b)(4a+5b)$

21. $4a^2 - b^2 = (2a)^2 - b^2 = (2a+b)(2a-b)$

22. $x^2 - 25y^2 = x^2 - (5y)^2 = (x+5y)(x-5y)$

23. $28 - 13x - 6x^2 = (4-3x)(7+2x)$

24. $20 - 3x - 2x^2 = (5-2x)(4+x)$

25. $4 - 2x + x^2$ is prime.

26. $a + a^2 - 3$ is prime.

27. $6y^2 + y - 15 = (3y+5)(2y-3)$

28. $4x^2 - x - 5 = (4x-5)(x+1)$

29. $18x^3 - 63x^2 + 9x = 9x(2x^2 - 7x + 1)$

30. $12a^3 - 24a^2 + 4a = 4a(3a^2 - 6a + 1)$

31. $16a^2 - 56a + 49 = (4a)^2 - 2 \cdot 4a \cdot 7 + 7^2$
$\qquad\qquad\qquad\quad = (4a-7)^2$

32. $25p^2 - 70p + 49 = (5p)^2 - 2 \cdot 5p \cdot 7 + 7^2$
$\qquad\qquad\qquad\quad = (5p-7)^2$

33. $14 + 5x - x^2 = (7-x)(2+x)$

34. $3 - 2x - x^2 = (3+x)(1-x)$

35. $3x^4 y + 6x^3 y - 72x^2 y = 3x^2 y(x^2 + 2x - 24)$
$\qquad\qquad\qquad\qquad\quad = 3x^2 y(x+6)(x-4)$

36. $2x^3 y + 8x^2 y^2 - 10xy^3 = 2xy(x^2 + 4xy - 5y^2)$
$\qquad\qquad\qquad\qquad\qquad = 2xy(x+5y)(x-y)$

37. $12x^3 y + 243xy = 3xy(4x^2 + 81)$

38. $6x^3 y^2 + 8xy^2 = 2xy^2(3x^2 + 4)$

39. $2xy - 72x^3 y = 2xy(1 - 36x^2)$
$\qquad\qquad\quad = 2xy[1 - (6x)^2]$
$\qquad\qquad\quad = 2xy(1-6x)(1+6x)$

40. $2x^3 - 18x = 2x(x^2 - 9)$
$\qquad\qquad\quad = 2x(x^2 - 3^2)$
$\qquad\qquad\quad = 2x(x-3)(x+3)$

41. $x^3 + 6x^2 - 4x - 24 = x^2(x+6) - 4(x+6)$
$\qquad\qquad\qquad\qquad = (x+6)(x^2 - 4)$
$\qquad\qquad\qquad\qquad = (x+6)(x+2)(x-2)$

42. $x^3 - 2x^2 - 36x + 72 = x^2(x-2) - 36(x-2)$
$\qquad\qquad\qquad\qquad = (x-2)(x^2 - 36)$
$\qquad\qquad\qquad\qquad = (x-2)(x-6)(x+6)$

43. $6a^3 + 10a^2 = 2a^2(3a+5)$

44. $4n^2 - 6n = 2n(2n-3)$

45. $3x^3 - x^2 + 12x - 4 = x^2(3x-1) + 4(3x-1)$
$\qquad\qquad\qquad\qquad = (3x-1)(x^2 + 4)$

46. $x^3 - 2x^2 + 3x - 6 = x^2(x-2) + 3(x-2)$
$\qquad\qquad\qquad\qquad = (x-2)(x^2 + 3)$

47. $6x^2 + 18xy + 12y^2 = 6(x^2 + 3xy + 2y^2)$
$\qquad\qquad\qquad\qquad = 6(x+2y)(x+y)$

48. $12x^2 + 46xy - 8y^2 = 2(6x^2 + 23xy - 4y^2)$
$\qquad\qquad\qquad\qquad = 2(x+4y)(6x-y)$

49. $5(x+y) + x(x+y) = (x+y)(5+x)$

50. $7(x-y) + y(x-y) = (x-y)(7+y)$

51. $14t^2 - 9t + 1 = (7t-1)(2t-1)$

52. $3t^2 - 5t + 1$ is prime.

53. $-3x^2 - 2x + 5 = -1(3x^2 + 2x - 5)$
$\qquad\qquad\qquad = -1(3x+5)(x-1)$

54. $-7x^2 - 19x + 6 = -1(7x^2 + 19x - 6)$
$= -1(7x - 2)(x + 3)$

55. $1 - 8a - 20a^2 = (1 - 10a)(1 + 2a)$

56. $1 - 7a - 60a^2 = (1 + 5a)(1 - 12a)$

57. $x^4 - 10x^2 + 9 = (x^2 - 9)(x^2 - 1)$
$= (x - 3)(x + 3)(x - 1)(x + 1)$

58. $x^4 - 13x^2 + 36 = (x^2 - 9)(x^2 - 4)$
$= (x - 3)(x + 3)(x - 2)(x + 2)$

59. $x^2 - 23x + 120 = (x - 15)(x - 8)$

60. $y^2 + 22y + 96 = (y + 16)(y + 6)$

61. $25p^2 - 70pq + 49q^2 = (5p)^2 - 2 \cdot 5p \cdot 7q + (7q)^2$
$= (5p - 7q)^2$

62. $16a^2 - 56ab + 49b^2 = (4a)^2 - 2 \cdot 4a \cdot 7b + (7b)^2$
$= (4a - 7b)^2$

63. $x^2 - 14x - 48$ is prime.

64. $7x^2 + 24xy + 9y^2 = (7x + 3y)(x + 3y)$

65. $-x^2 - x + 30 = -1(x^2 + x - 30) = -1(x - 5)(x + 6)$

66. $-x^2 + 6x - 8 = -1(x^2 - 6x + 8)$
$= -1(x - 2)(x - 4)$

67. $3rs - s + 12r - 4 = s(3r - 1) + 4(3r - 1)$
$= (3r - 1)(s + 4)$

68. $x^3 - 2x^2 + x - 2 = x^2(x - 2) + 1(x - 2)$
$= (x - 2)(x^2 + 1)$

69. $4x^2 - 8xy - 3x + 6y = 4x(x - 2y) - 3(x - 2y)$
$= (x - 2y)(4x - 3)$

70. $4x^2 - 2xy - 7yz + 14xz = 2x(2x - y) - 7z(y - 2x)$
$= 2x(2x - y) + 7z(2x - y)$
$= (2x - y)(2x + 7z)$

71. $x^2 + 9xy - 36y^2 = (x + 12y)(x - 3y)$

72. $3x^2 + 10xy - 8y^2 = (3x - 2y)(x + 4y)$

73. $x^4 - 14x^2 - 32 = (x^2 + 2)(x^2 - 16)$
$= (x^2 + 2)(x + 4)(x - 4)$

74. $x^4 - 22x^2 - 75 = (x^2 + 3)(x^2 - 25)$
$= (x^2 + 3)(x + 5)(x - 5)$

75. answers may vary

76. Yes; $9x^2 + 81y^2 = 9(x^2 + 9y^2)$

Section 11.6

Practice Problems

1. $(x - 7)(x + 2) = 0$
$x - 7 = 0$ or $x + 2 = 0$
$x = 7$ $x = -2$
The solutions are 7 and −2.

2. $(x - 10)(3x + 1) = 0$
$x - 10 = 0$ or $3x + 1 = 0$
$x = 10$ $3x = -1$
$x = -\dfrac{1}{3}$
The solutions are 10 and $-\dfrac{1}{3}$.

3. a. $y(y + 3) = 0$
$y = 0$ or $y + 3 = 0$
$y = -3$
The solutions are 0 and −3.

b. $x(4x - 3) = 0$
$x = 0$ or $4x - 3 = 0$
$4x = 3$
$x = \dfrac{3}{4}$
The solutions are 0 and $\dfrac{3}{4}$.

4. $x^2 - 3x - 18 = 0$
$(x - 6)(x + 3) = 0$
$x - 6 = 0$ or $x + 3 = 0$
$x = 6$ $x = -3$
The solutions are 6 and −3.

5.
$$9x^2 - 24x = -16$$
$$9x^2 - 24x + 16 = 0$$
$$(3x - 4)(3x - 4) = 0$$
$$3x - 4 = 0 \quad \text{or} \quad 3x - 4 = 0$$
$$3x = 4 \qquad\qquad 3x = 4$$
$$x = \frac{4}{3} \qquad\qquad x = \frac{4}{3}$$

The solution is $\frac{4}{3}$.

6. a.
$$x(x - 4) = 5$$
$$x^2 - 4x = 5$$
$$x^2 - 4x - 5 = 0$$
$$(x - 5)(x + 1) = 0$$
$$x - 5 = 0 \quad \text{or} \quad x + 1 = 0$$
$$x = 5 \qquad\qquad x = -1$$
The solutions are 5 and −1.

b.
$$x(3x + 7) = 6$$
$$3x^2 + 7x = 6$$
$$3x^2 + 7x - 6 = 0$$
$$(3x - 2)(x + 3) = 0$$
$$3x - 2 = 0 \quad \text{or} \quad x + 3 = 0$$
$$3x = 2 \qquad\qquad x = -3$$
$$x = \frac{2}{3}$$

The solutions are $\frac{2}{3}$ and −3.

7.
$$2x^3 - 18x = 0$$
$$2x(x^2 - 9) = 0$$
$$2x(x - 3)(x + 3) = 0$$
$$2x = 0 \quad \text{or} \quad x - 3 = 0 \quad \text{or} \quad x + 3 = 0$$
$$x = 0 \qquad\qquad x = 3 \qquad\qquad x = -3$$
The solutions are 0, 3, and −3.

8. $(x + 3)(3x^2 - 20x - 7) = 0$
$$x + 3 = 0 \quad \text{or} \quad 3x^2 - 20x - 7 = 0$$
$$x = -3 \qquad\qquad (3x + 1)(x - 7) = 0$$
$$3x + 1 = 0 \quad \text{or} \quad x - 7 = 0$$
$$3x = -1 \qquad\qquad x = 7$$
$$x = -\frac{1}{3}$$

The solutions are −3, $-\frac{1}{3}$, and 7.

Vocabulary and Readiness Check

1. An equation that can be written in the form $ax^2 + bx + c = 0,$ (with $a \neq 0$), is called a <u>quadratic</u> equation.

2. If the product of two numbers is 0, then at least one of the numbers must be <u>0</u>.

3. The solutions to $(x - 3)(x + 5) = 0$ are <u>3, −5</u>.

4. If $a \cdot b = 0$, then <u>$a = 0$ or $b = 0$</u>.

Exercise Set 11.6

1. $(x - 2)(x + 1) = 0$
$$x - 2 = 0 \quad \text{or} \quad x + 1 = 0$$
$$x = 2 \qquad\qquad x = -1$$
The solutions are 2 and −1.

3. $(x - 6)(x - 7) = 0$
$$x - 6 = 0 \quad \text{or} \quad x - 7 = 0$$
$$x = 6 \qquad\qquad x = 7$$
The solutions are 6 and 7.

5. $(x + 9)(x + 17) = 0$
$$x + 9 = 0 \quad \text{or} \quad x + 17 = 0$$
$$x = -9 \qquad\qquad x = -17$$
The solutions are −9 and −17.

7. $x(x + 6) = 0$
$$x = 0 \quad \text{or} \quad x + 6 = 0$$
$$x = -6$$
The solutions are 0 and −6.

9. $3x(x - 8) = 0$
$$3x = 0 \quad \text{or} \quad x - 8 = 0$$
$$x = 0 \qquad\qquad x = 8$$
The solutions are 0 and 8.

11. $(2x + 3)(4x - 5) = 0$
$$2x + 3 = 0 \quad \text{or} \quad 4x - 5 = 0$$
$$2x = -3 \qquad\qquad 4x = 5$$
$$x = -\frac{3}{2} \qquad\qquad x = \frac{5}{4}$$

The solutions are $-\frac{3}{2}$ and $\frac{5}{4}$.

13. $(2x - 7)(7x + 2) = 0$

$2x - 7 = 0$ or $7x + 2 = 0$

$2x = 7$ $7x = -2$

$x = \dfrac{7}{2}$ $x = -\dfrac{2}{7}$

The solutions are $\dfrac{7}{2}$ and $-\dfrac{2}{7}$.

15. $\left(x - \dfrac{1}{2}\right)\left(x + \dfrac{1}{3}\right) = 0$

$x - \dfrac{1}{2} = 0$ or $x + \dfrac{1}{3} = 0$

$x = \dfrac{1}{2}$ $x = -\dfrac{1}{3}$

The solutions are $\dfrac{1}{2}$ and $-\dfrac{1}{3}$.

17. $(x + 0.2)(x + 1.5) = 0$

$x + 0.2 = 0$ or $x + 1.5 = 0$

$x = -0.2$ $x = -1.5$

The solutions are -0.2 and -1.5.

19. $x^2 - 13x + 36 = 0$

$(x - 9)(x - 4) = 0$

$x - 9 = 0$ or $x - 4 = 0$

$x = 9$ $x = 4$

The solutions are 9 and 4.

21. $x^2 + 2x - 8 = 0$

$(x + 4)(x - 2) = 0$

$x + 4 = 0$ or $x - 2 = 0$

$x = -4$ $x = 2$

The solutions are -4 and 2.

23. $x^2 - 7x = 0$

$x(x - 7) = 0$

$x = 0$ or $x - 7 = 0$

$x = 7$

The solutions are 0 and 7.

25. $x^2 + 20x = 0$

$x(x + 20) = 0$

$x = 0$ or $x + 20 = 0$

$x = -20$

The solutions are 0 and -20.

27. $x^2 = 16$

$x^2 - 16 = 0$

$(x - 4)(x + 4) = 0$

$x - 4 = 0$ or $x + 4 = 0$

$x = 4$ $x = -4$

The solutions are 4 and -4.

29. $x^2 - 4x = 32$

$x^2 - 4x - 32 = 0$

$(x - 8)(x + 4) = 0$

$x - 8 = 0$ or $x + 4 = 0$

$x = 8$ $x = -4$

The solutions are 8 and -4.

31. $(x + 4)(x - 9) = 4x$

$x^2 - 5x - 36 = 4x$

$x^2 - 9x - 36 = 0$

$(x + 3)(x - 12) = 0$

$x + 3 = 0$ or $x - 12 = 0$

$x = -3$ $x = 12$

The solutions are -3 and 12.

33. $x(3x - 1) = 14$

$3x^2 - x = 14$

$3x^2 - x - 14 = 0$

$3x^2 - 7x + 6x - 14 = 0$

$x(3x - 7) + 2(3x - 7) = 0$

$(3x - 7)(x + 2) = 0$

$3x - 7 = 0$ or $x + 2 = 0$

$3x = 7$ $x = -2$

$x = \dfrac{7}{3}$

The solutions are $\dfrac{7}{3}$ and -2.

35. $3x^2 + 19x - 72 = 0$

$(3x - 8)(x + 9) = 0$

$3x - 8 = 0$ or $x + 9 = 0$

$3x = 8$ $x = -9$

$x = \dfrac{8}{3}$

The solutions are $\dfrac{8}{3}$ and -9.

37.
$$4x^3 - x = 0$$
$$x(4x^2 - 1) = 0$$
$$x[(2x)^2 - (1)^2] = 0$$
$$x(2x+1)(2x-1) = 0$$
$x = 0$ or $2x+1 = 0$ or $2x-1 = 0$
$$2x = -1 \qquad 2x = 1$$
$$x = -\frac{1}{2} \qquad x = \frac{1}{2}$$
The solutions are 0, $-\dfrac{1}{2}$, and $\dfrac{1}{2}$.

39.
$$4(x-7) = 6$$
$$4x - 28 = 6$$
$$4x = 34$$
$$x = \frac{34}{4}$$
$$x = \frac{17}{2}$$
The solution is $\dfrac{17}{2}$.

41.
$$(4x-3)(16x^2 - 24x + 9) = 0$$
$$(4x-3)[(4x)^2 - 2 \cdot 4x \cdot 3 + (3)^2] = 0$$
$$(4x-3)(4x-3)^2 = 0$$
$$(4x-3)(4x-3)(4x-3) = 0$$
$$4x - 3 = 0$$
$$4x = 3$$
$$x = \frac{3}{4}$$
The solution is $\dfrac{3}{4}$.

43.
$$4y^2 - 1 = 0$$
$$(2y-1)(2y+1) = 0$$
$2y - 1 = 0$ or $2y + 1 = 0$
$$2y = 1 \qquad 2y = -1$$
$$y = \frac{1}{2} \qquad y = -\frac{1}{2}$$
The solutions are $\dfrac{1}{2}$ and $-\dfrac{1}{2}$.

45.
$$(2x+3)(2x^2 - 5x - 3) = 0$$
$$(2x+3)(2x^2 + x - 6x - 3) = 0$$
$$(2x+3)[x(2x+1) - 3(2x+1)] = 0$$
$$(2x+3)(2x+1)(x-3) = 0$$

$2x+3 = 0$ or $2x+1 = 0$ or $x-3 = 0$
$$2x = -3 \qquad 2x = -1 \qquad x = 3$$
$$x = -\frac{3}{2} \qquad x = -\frac{1}{2}$$
The solutions are $-\dfrac{3}{2}$, $-\dfrac{1}{2}$, and 3.

47.
$$x^2 - 15 = -2x$$
$$x^2 + 2x - 15 = 0$$
$$(x+5)(x-3) = 0$$
$x + 5 = 0$ or $x - 3 = 0$
$$x = -5 \qquad x = 3$$
The solutions are -5 and 3.

49.
$$30x^2 - 11x = 30$$
$$30x^2 - 11x - 30 = 0$$
$$30x^2 + 25x - 36x - 30 = 0$$
$$5x(6x+5) - 6(6x+5) = 0$$
$$(6x+5)(5x-6) = 0$$
$6x + 5 = 0$ or $5x - 6 = 0$
$$6x = -5 \qquad 5x = 6$$
$$x = -\frac{5}{6} \qquad x = \frac{6}{5}$$
The solutions are $-\dfrac{5}{6}$ and $\dfrac{6}{5}$.

51.
$$5x^2 - 6x - 8 = 0$$
$$(5x+4)(x-2) = 0$$
$5x + 4 = 0$ or $x - 2 = 0$
$$5x = -4 \qquad x = 2$$
$$x = -\frac{4}{5}$$
The solutions are $-\dfrac{4}{5}$ and 2.

53.
$$6y^2 - 22y - 40 = 0$$
$$2(3y^2 - 11y - 20) = 0$$
$$2(3y^2 + 4y - 15y - 20) = 0$$
$$2[y(3y+4) - 5(3y+4)] = 0$$
$$2(3y+4)(y-5) = 0$$
$3y + 4 = 0$ or $y - 5 = 0$
$$3y = -4 \qquad y = 5$$
$$y = -\frac{4}{3}$$
The solutions are $-\dfrac{4}{3}$ and 5.

55. $(y-2)(y+3)=6$

$y^2+y-6=6$

$y^2+y-12=0$

$(y+4)(y-3)=0$

$y+4=0$ or $y-3=0$

$y=-4$ $y=3$

The solutions are -4 and 3.

57. $x^3-12x^2+32x=0$

$x(x^2-12x+32)=0$

$x(x-8)(x-4)=0$

$x=0$ or $x-8=0$ or $x-4=0$

$x=8$ $x=4$

The solutions are 0, 8, and 4.

59. $x^2+14x+49=0$

$(x+7)(x+7)=0$

$x+7=0$

$x=-7$

The solution is -7.

61. $12y=8y^2$

$0=8y^2-12y$

$0=4y(2y-3)$

$4y=0$ or $2y-3=0$

$y=0$ $2y=3$

$y=\dfrac{3}{2}$

The solutions are 0 and $\dfrac{3}{2}$.

63. $7x^3-7x=0$

$7x(x^2-1)=0$

$7x(x-1)(x+1)=0$

$7x=0$ or $x-1=0$ or $x+1=0$

$x=0$ $x=1$ $x=-1$

The solutions are 0, 1, and -1.

65. $3x^2+8x-11=13-6x$

$3x^2+14x-11=13$

$3x^2+14x-24=0$

$3x^2+18x-4x-24=0$

$3x(x+6)-4(x+6)=0$

$(x+6)(3x-4)=0$

$x+6=0$ or $3x-4=0$

$x=-6$ $3x=4$

$x=\dfrac{4}{3}$

The solutions are -6 and $\dfrac{4}{3}$.

67. $3x^2-20x=-4x^2-7x-6$

$7x^2-13x+6=0$

$(7x-6)(x-1)=0$

$7x-6=0$ or $x-1=0$

$7x=6$ $x=1$

$x=\dfrac{6}{7}$

The solutions are $\dfrac{6}{7}$ and 1.

69. $\dfrac{3}{5}+\dfrac{4}{9}=\dfrac{3\cdot9}{5\cdot9}+\dfrac{4\cdot5}{9\cdot5}=\dfrac{27}{45}+\dfrac{20}{45}=\dfrac{47}{45}$

71. $\dfrac{7}{10}-\dfrac{5}{12}=\dfrac{7\cdot6}{10\cdot6}-\dfrac{5\cdot5}{12\cdot5}=\dfrac{42}{60}-\dfrac{25}{60}=\dfrac{17}{60}$

73. $\dfrac{4}{5}\cdot\dfrac{7}{8}=\dfrac{4\cdot7}{5\cdot8}=\dfrac{4\cdot7}{5\cdot4\cdot2}=\dfrac{7}{5\cdot2}=\dfrac{7}{10}$

75. The equation must first be written in standard form.

$x(x-2)=8$

$x^2-2x=8$

$x^2-2x-8=0$

$(x-4)(x+2)=0$

$x-4=0$ or $x+2=0$

$x=4$ $x=-2$

The solutions are 4 and -2.

77. answers may vary, for example $(x-6)(x+1)=0$

79. answers may vary, for example

$(x-5)(x-7)=0$

$x^2-7x-5x+35=0$

$x^2-12x+35=0$

81. a.

Time, x (seconds)	Height, y (feet)
0	$-16(0)^2 + 20(0) + 300 = 300$
1	$-16(1)^2 + 20(1) + 300 = 304$
2	$-16(2)^2 + 20(2) + 300 = 276$
3	$-16(3)^2 + 20(3) + 300 = 216$
4	$-16(4)^2 + 20(4) + 300 = 124$
5	$-16(5)^2 + 20(5) + 300 = 0$
6	$-16(6)^2 + 20(6) + 300 = -156$

    b. When the compass strikes the ground, its height is 0 feet, so it strikes the ground after 5 seconds.

    c. The maximum height listed in the table is 304 feet, after 1 second.

83.
$$(x-3)(3x+4) = (x+2)(x-6)$$
$$3x^2 + 4x - 9x - 12 = x^2 - 6x + 2x - 12$$
$$3x^2 - 5x - 12 = x^2 - 4x - 12$$
$$2x^2 - x = 0$$
$$x(2x-1) = 0$$
$$x = 0 \quad \text{or} \quad 2x - 1 = 0$$
$$x = \frac{1}{2}$$

The solutions are 0 and $\frac{1}{2}$.

85.
$$(2x-3)(x+8) = (x-6)(x+4)$$
$$2x^2 + 16x - 3x - 24 = x^2 + 4x - 6x - 24$$
$$2x^2 + 13x - 24 = x^2 - 2x - 24$$
$$x^2 + 15x = 0$$
$$x(x+15) = 0$$
$$x = 0 \quad \text{or} \quad x + 15 = 0$$
$$x = -15$$

The solutions are 0 and -15.

Section 11.7

Practice Problems

1. The diver will be at a height of 0 when he or she reaches the pool.
$$h = -16t^2 + 64$$
$$0 = -16t^2 + 64$$
$$0 = -16(t^2 - 4)$$
$$0 = -16(t-2)(t+2)$$
$$t - 2 = 0 \quad \text{or} \quad t + 2 = 0$$
$$t = 2 \qquad\qquad t = -2$$
It takes the diver 2 seconds to reach the pool.

2. Let x be the number.
$$x^2 - 2x = 63$$
$$x^2 - 2x - 63 = 0$$
$$(x-9)(x+7) = 0$$
$$x - 9 = 0 \quad \text{or} \quad x + 7 = 0$$
$$x = 9 \qquad\qquad x = -7$$
The numbers are 9 and -7.

3. Let x be the width. Then $x + 5$ is the length.
$$\text{Area} = \text{length} \cdot \text{width}$$
$$176 = (x+5) \cdot x$$
$$176 = x^2 + 5x$$
$$0 = x^2 + 5x - 176$$
$$0 = (x+16)(x-11)$$
$$x + 16 = 0 \quad \text{or} \quad x - 11 = 0$$
$$x = -16 \qquad\qquad x = 11$$
The width is 11 feet and the length is $x + 5 = 11 + 5 = 16$ feet.

4. Let x be the first odd integer. Then $x + 2$ is the next consecutive odd integer.
$$x(x+2) = x + (x+2) + 23$$
$$x^2 + 2x = 2x + 25$$
$$x^2 = 25$$
$$x^2 - 25 = 0$$
$$(x+5)(x-5) = 0$$
$$x + 5 = 0 \quad \text{or} \quad x - 5 = 0$$
$$x = -5 \qquad\qquad x = 5$$
$$x + 2 = -3 \qquad x + 2 = 7$$
The two consecutive odd integers are -5 and -3 or 5 and 7.

5. Let x be the length of one leg. Then $x - 7$ is the length of the other leg.

$$x^2 + (x-7)^2 = 13^2$$
$$x^2 + x^2 - 14x + 49 = 169$$
$$2x^2 - 14x - 120 = 0$$
$$2(x^2 - 7x - 60) = 0$$
$$2(x+5)(x-12) = 0$$
$$x + 5 = 0 \quad \text{or} \quad x - 12 = 0$$
$$x = -5 \qquad\qquad x = 12$$

Discard $x = -5$ since length cannot be negative. If $x = 12$, then $x - 7 = 5$. The lengths of the legs are 5 meters and 12 meters.

Exercise Set 11.7

1. Let x be the width of the rectangle, then the length is $x + 4$.

3. Let x be the first odd integer, then the next consecutive odd integer is $x + 2$.

5. Let x be the base of the triangle, then the height is $4x + 1$.

7. area = $(\text{side})^2$

$$121 = x^2$$
$$0 = x^2 - 121$$
$$0 = (x-11)(x+11)$$
$$x - 11 = 0 \quad \text{or} \quad x + 11 = 0$$
$$x = 11 \qquad\qquad x = -11$$

Discard $x = -11$ since length cannot be negative. The length of its sides are 11 units.

9. The perimeter is the sum of the lengths of the sides.

$$(x+5) + (x^2 - 3x) + (3x - 8) + (x + 3) = 120$$
$$x^2 + 2x = 120$$
$$x^2 + 2x - 120 = 0$$
$$(x+12)(x-10) = 0$$
$$x + 12 = 0 \quad \text{or} \quad x - 10 = 0$$
$$x = -12 \qquad\qquad x = 10$$

For $x = -12$, $x + 5$, $x + 3$, and $3x - 8$ are negative. Since lengths cannot be negative, $x = 10$ is the only solution that works in this context.
$x + 3 = 10 + 3 = 13$
$x + 5 = 10 + 5 = 15$
$x^2 - 3x = (10)^2 - 3(10) = 100 - 30 = 70$
$3x - 8 = 3(10) - 8 = 30 - 8 = 22$
The sides have lengths 13 cm, 15 cm, 70 cm, and 22 cm.

11. Area = base · height

$$96 = (x+5)(x-5)$$
$$96 = x^2 - 25$$
$$0 = x^2 - 121$$
$$0 = (x+11))(x-11)$$
$$x + 11 = 0 \quad \text{or} \quad x - 11 = 0$$
$$x = -11 \qquad\qquad x = 11$$

For $x = -11$, $x + 5$ and $x - 5$ are negative. Since lengths cannot be negative, $x = 11$ is the only solution that works in this context.
$x + 5 = 11 + 5 = 16$
$x - 5 = 11 - 5 = 6$
The base is 16 miles and the height is 6 miles.

13. The object will hit the ground when its height is 0.

$$0 = -16t^2 + 64t + 80$$
$$0 = -16(t^2 - 4t - 5)$$
$$0 = -16(t-5)(t+1)$$
$$0 = t - 5 \quad \text{or} \quad 0 = t + 1$$
$$5 = t \qquad\qquad -1 = t$$

Since the time t cannot be negative, we discard $t = -1$. The object hits the ground after 5 seconds.

15. Let x be the width. Then $2x - 7$ is the length.
Area = length · width

$$30 = (2x - 7) \cdot (x)$$
$$30 = 2x^2 - 7x$$
$$0 = 2x^2 - 7x - 30$$
$$0 = (2x + 5)(x - 6)$$
$$2x + 5 = 0 \quad \text{or} \quad x - 6 = 0$$
$$x = -\frac{5}{2} \qquad\qquad x = 6$$

Discard $x = -\frac{5}{2}$ since length cannot be negative.

The width is 6 cm and the length is
$2x - 7 = 2(6) - 7 = 12 - 7 = 5$ cm.

17. $D = \frac{1}{2}n(n-3)$

$$= \frac{1}{2}(12)(12 - 3)$$
$$= \frac{1}{2}(12)(9)$$
$$= 54$$

A polygon with 12 sides has 54 diagonals.

19.
$$D = \frac{1}{2}n(n-3)$$
$$35 = \frac{1}{2}n(n-3)$$
$$2 \cdot 35 = 2 \cdot \frac{1}{2}n(n-3)$$
$$70 = n(n-3)$$
$$70 = n^2 - 3n$$
$$0 = n^2 - 3n - 70$$
$$0 = (n-10)(n+7)$$
$$n - 10 = 0 \quad \text{or} \quad n + 7 = 0$$
$$n = 10 \qquad\qquad n = -7$$
Discard $n = -7$. The polygon has 10 sides.

21. Let x be the number.
$$x + x^2 = 132$$
$$x^2 + x - 132 = 0$$
$$(x+12)(x-11) = 0$$
$$x + 12 = 0 \quad \text{or} \quad x - 11 = 0$$
$$x = -12 \qquad\qquad x = 11$$
The number is -12 or 11.

23. Let x be the first number. Then $x + 1$ is the next consecutive number.
$$x(x+1) = 210$$
$$x^2 + x = 210$$
$$x^2 + x - 210 = 0$$
$$(x-14)(x+15) = 0$$
$$x - 14 = 0 \quad \text{or} \quad x + 15 = 0$$
$$x = 14 \qquad\qquad x = -15$$
Discard $x = -15$. The room numbers are 14 and $x + 1 = 14 + 1 = 15$.

25. Use the Pythagorean theorem where $x = $ hypotenuse, $(x - 1) = $ one leg, and $5 = $ other leg.
$$x^2 = (x-1)^2 + 5^2$$
$$x^2 = x^2 - 2x + 1 + 25$$
$$x^2 = x^2 - 2x + 26$$
$$0 = -2x + 26$$
$$2x = 26$$
$$x = 13$$
The length of the ladder is 13 feet.

27.
$$(x+3)^2 = 64$$
$$x^2 + 6x + 9 = 64$$
$$x^2 + 6x - 55 = 0$$
$$(x-5)(x+11) = 0$$
$$x - 5 = 0 \quad \text{or} \quad x + 11 = 0$$
$$x = 5 \qquad\qquad x = -11$$
Discard $x = -11$. The original square had sides of 5 inches.

29. Let x be the length of the shorter leg. Then the length of the other leg is $x + 4$ and the length of the hypotenuse is $x + 8$.
$$(x+8)^2 = x^2 + (x+4)^2$$
$$x^2 + 16x + 64 = x^2 + x^2 + 8x + 16$$
$$0 = x^2 - 8x - 48$$
$$0 = (x-12)(x+4)$$
$$0 = x - 12 \quad \text{or} \quad 0 = x + 4$$
$$12 = x \qquad\qquad -4 = x$$
Discard $x = -4$ since length cannot be negative.
$x + 4 = 12 + 4 = 16$
$x + 8 = 12 + 8 = 20$
The lengths of the sides are 12 mm, 16 mm, and 20 mm.

31.
$$\text{area} = \frac{1}{2} \cdot \text{base} \cdot \text{height}$$
$$100 = \frac{1}{2} \cdot 2x \cdot x$$
$$100 = x^2$$
$$0 = x^2 - 100$$
$$0 = (x-10)(x+10)$$
$$x - 10 = 0 \quad \text{or} \quad x + 10 = 0$$
$$x = 10 \qquad\qquad x = -10$$
Discard $x = -10$. The height is 10 kilometers.

33. Let x be the length of the shorter leg. Then $x + 12$ is the length of the longer leg and $2x - 12$ is the length of the hypotenuse.
$$(2x-12)^2 = x^2 + (x+12)^2$$
$$4x^2 - 48x + 144 = x^2 + x^2 + 24x + 144$$
$$2x^2 - 72x = 0$$
$$2x(x-36) = 0$$
$$2x = 0 \quad \text{or} \quad x - 36 = 0$$
$$x = 0 \qquad\qquad x = 36$$
Discard $x = 0$ since the length must be positive. The shorter leg of the triangle has length 36 feet.

35. When the object reaches the ground, the height is 0.

$$h = -16t^2 + 1444$$
$$0 = -16t^2 + 1444$$
$$0 = -4(4t^2 - 361)$$
$$0 = -4(2t - 19)(2t + 19)$$
$$2t - 19 = 0 \quad \text{or} \quad 2t + 19 = 0$$
$$t = \frac{19}{2} \qquad\qquad t = -\frac{19}{2}$$

Discard $t = -\frac{19}{2}$ since time must be positive.

The object reaches the ground after $\frac{19}{2}$ or 9.5 seconds.

37. Use $A = P(1 + r)^2$ when $P = 100$ and $A = 144$.

$$144 = 100(1 + r)^2$$
$$144 = 100(1 + 2r + r^2)$$
$$144 = 100 + 200r + 100r^2$$
$$0 = 100r^2 + 200r - 44$$
$$0 = 4(25r^2 + 50r - 11)$$
$$0 = 4(5r - 1)(5r + 11)$$
$$0 = 5r - 1 \quad \text{or} \quad 0 = 5r + 11$$
$$1 = 5r \qquad\qquad -11 = 5r$$
$$\frac{1}{5} = r \qquad\qquad -\frac{11}{5} = r$$

Discard $r = -\frac{11}{5}$ since the interest rate must be

positive. The interest rate is $\frac{1}{5} = 0.20 = 20\%$.

39. Let x be the length. Then $x - 7$ is the width.
area = length · width
$$120 = x(x - 7)$$
$$0 = x^2 - 7x - 120$$
$$0 = (x - 15)(x + 8)$$
$$x - 15 = 0 \quad \text{or} \quad x + 8 = 0$$
$$x = 15 \qquad\qquad x = -8$$
Discard $x = -8$ since length is positive. The length is 15 miles and the width is
$x - 7 = 15 - 7 = 8$ miles.

41. Let $C = 9500$ in $C = x^2 - 15x + 50$.

$$9500 = x^2 - 15x + 50$$
$$0 = x^2 - 15x - 9450$$
$$0 = (x + 90)(x - 105)$$
$$0 = x + 90 \quad \text{or} \quad 0 = x - 105$$
$$-90 = x \qquad\qquad 105 = x$$
Discard $x = -90$ since the number of units manufactured cannot be negative.
105 units are manufactured at a cost of \$9500.

43. From the graph, there were approximately 2 million, or 2,000,000, visitors to Glacier National Park in 2004.

45. From the graph, there were approximately 1.95 million, or 1,950,000, visitors to Glacier National Park in 2006.

47. From the graph, the lines intersect at approximately 2003.

49. answers may vary

51. Since x is the width of the rectangle, the length is $x + 6$.

$$x^2 + x(x + 6) = 176$$
$$x^2 + x^2 + 6x = 176$$
$$2x^2 + 6x - 176 = 0$$
$$2(x^2 + 3x - 88) = 0$$
$$2(x - 8)(x + 11) = 0$$
$$x - 8 = 0 \quad \text{or} \quad x + 11 = 0$$
$$x = 8 \qquad\qquad x = -11$$
Discard $x = -11$ since length cannot be negative. The side of the square is 8 meters.

53. Let x be one of the numbers. Since the numbers sum to 25, the other number is $25 - x$.

$$x^2 + (25 - x)^2 = 325$$
$$x^2 + 625 - 50x + x^2 = 325$$
$$2x^2 - 50x + 300 = 0$$
$$2(x^2 - 25x + 150) = 0$$
$$2(x - 10)(x - 15) = 0$$
$$x - 10 = 0 \quad \text{or} \quad x - 15 = 0$$
$$x = 10 \qquad\qquad x = 15$$
If $x = 10$, then $25 - x = 25 - 10 = 15$.
If $x = 15$, then $25 - x = 25 - 15 = 10$.
The numbers are 10 and 15.

55. Dimensions of total area:

length $= x + 6 + 4 + 4 = x + 14$

width $= x + 4 + 4 = x + 8$

Total area = pool area $+ 576$

$(x+14)(x+8) = x(x+6) + 576$

$x^2 + 22x + 112 = x^2 + 6x + 576$

$22x + 112 = 6x + 576$

$16x = 464$

$x = 29$

$x + 6 = 29 + 6 = 35$

The pool is 29 meters by 35 meters.

Chapter 11 Vocabulary Check

1. An equation that can be written in the form $ax^2 + bx + c = 0$ (with a not 0) is called a <u>quadratic equation</u>.

2. <u>Factoring</u> is the process of writing an expression as a product.

3. The <u>greatest common factor</u> of a list of terms is the product of all common factors.

4. A trinomial that is the square of some binomial is called a <u>perfect square trinomial</u>.

5. In a right triangle, the side opposite the right angle is called the <u>hypotenuse</u>.

6. In a right triangle, each side adjacent to the right angle is called a <u>leg</u>.

7. The Pythagorean theorem states that $(\text{leg})^2 + (\text{leg})^2 = (\underline{\text{hypotenuse}})^2$.

Chapter 11 Review

1. $6x^2 - 15x = 3x \cdot 2x - 3x \cdot 5 = 3x(2x - 5)$

2. $4x^5 + 2x - 10x^4 = 2x \cdot 2x^4 + 2x \cdot 1 - 2x \cdot 5x^3$
$= 2x(2x^4 + 1 - 5x^3)$

3. $5m + 30 = 5 \cdot m + 5 \cdot 6 = 5(m + 6)$

4. $20x^3 + 12x^2 + 24x = 4x \cdot 5x^2 + 4x \cdot 3x + 4x \cdot 6$
$= 4x(5x^2 + 3x + 6)$

5. $3x(2x + 3) - 5(2x + 3) = (2x + 3)(3x - 5)$

6. $5x(x+1) - (x+1) = 5x(x+1) - 1 \cdot (x+1)$
$= (x+1)(5x - 1)$

7. $3x^2 - 3x + 2x - 2 = 3x(x-1) + 2(x-1)$
$= (x-1)(3x+2)$

8. $3a^2 + 9ab + 3b^2 + ab = 3a(a+3b) + b(3b+a)$
$= (a+3b)(3a+b)$

9. $10a^2 + 5ab + 7b^2 + 14ab$
$= 5a(2a+b) + 7b(b+2a)$
$= (2a+b)(5a+7b)$

10. $6x^2 + 10x - 3x - 5 = 2x(3x+5) - 1(3x+5)$
$= (3x+5)(2x-1)$

11. $x^2 + 6x + 8 = (x+4)(x+2)$

12. $x^2 - 11x + 24 = (x-8)(x-3)$

13. $x^2 + x + 2$ is prime.

14. $x^2 - 5x - 6 = (x-6)(x+1)$

15. $x^2 + 2x - 8 = (x+4)(x-2)$

16. $x^2 + 4xy - 12y^2 = (x+6y)(x-2y)$

17. $x^2 + 8xy + 15y^2 = (x+5y)(x+3y)$

18. $72 - 18x - 2x^2 = 2(36 - 9x - x^2)$
$= 2(3-x)(12+x)$

  or

$72 - 18x - 2x^2 = -2x^2 - 18x + 72$
$= -2(x^2 + 9x - 36)$
$= -2(x-3)(x+12)$

19. $32 + 12x - 4x^2 = 4(8 + 3x - x^2)$

  or

$32 + 12x - 4x^2 = -4x^2 + 12x + 32$
$= -4(x^2 - 3x - 8)$

20. $5y^3 - 50y^2 + 120y = 5y(y^2 - 10y + 24)$
$= 5y(y-6)(y-4)$

21. To factor $x^2 + 2x - 48$, think of two numbers whose product is -48 and whose sum is 2.

22. The first step to factor $3x^2 + 15x + 30$ is to factor out the GCF, 3.

23. Factors of $2x^2$: $2x \cdot x$
Factors of 6: $6 = 1 \cdot 6$, $6 = 2 \cdot 3$
$2x^2 + 13x + 6 = (2x + 1)(x + 6)$

24. Factors of $4x^2$: $4x^2 = 4x \cdot x$, $4x^2 = 2x \cdot 2x$
Factors of -3: $-3 = -1 \cdot 3$, $-3 = 1 \cdot -3$
$4x^2 + 4x - 3 = (2x + 3)(2x - 1)$

25. Factors of $6x^2$: $6x^2 = 6x \cdot x$, $6x^2 = 3x \cdot 2x$
Factors of $-4y^2$: $-4y^2 = -4y \cdot y$,
$-4y^2 = 4y \cdot -y$, $-4y^2 = -2y \cdot 2y$
$6x^2 + 5xy - 4y^2 = (3x + 4y)(2x - y)$

26. $x^2 - x + 2$ is prime.

27. $2 \cdot -39 = -78$
$3 \cdot -26 = -78$
$3 + (-26) = -23$
$2x^2 - 23x - 39 = 2x^2 + 3x - 26x - 39$
$\qquad = x(2x + 3) - 13(2x + 3)$
$\qquad = (2x + 3)(x - 13)$

28. $18 \cdot -20y^2 = -360y^2$
$15y \cdot -24y = -360y^2$
$15y + (-24y) = -9y$
$18x^2 - 9xy - 20y^2 = 18x^2 + 15xy - 24xy - 20y^2$
$\qquad = 3x(6x + 5y) - 4y(6x + 5y)$
$\qquad = (6x + 5y)(3x - 4y)$

29. $10y^3 + 25y^2 - 60y = 5y(2y^2 + 5y - 12)$
$2 \cdot -12 = -24$
$-3 \cdot 8 = -24$
$-3 + 8 = 5$
$10y^3 + 25y^2 - 60y = 5y(2y^2 + 5y - 12)$
$\qquad = 5y(2y^2 - 3y + 8y - 12)$
$\qquad = 5y[y(2y - 3) + 4(2y - 3)]$
$\qquad = 5y(2y - 3)(y + 4)$

30. $60y^3 - 39y^2 + 6y = 3y(20y^2 - 13y + 2)$
$20 \cdot 2 = 40$
$-5 \cdot -8 = 40$
$-5 + (-8) = -13$
$60y^3 - 39y^2 + 6y = 3y(20y^2 - 13y + 2)$
$\qquad = 3y(20y^2 - 5y - 8y + 2)$
$\qquad = 3y[5y(4y - 1) - 2(4y - 1)]$
$\qquad = 3y(4y - 1)(5y - 2)$

31. $(x^2 - 2) + (x^2 - 4x) + (3x^2 - 5x)$
$= x^2 - 2 + x^2 - 4x + 3x^2 - 5x$
$= 5x^2 - 9x - 2$
$5 \cdot -2 = -10$
$1 \cdot -10 = -10$
$1 + (-10) = -9$
$5x^2 - 9x - 2 = 5x^2 + x - 10x - 2$
$\qquad = x(5x + 1) - 2(5x + 1)$
$\qquad = (5x + 1)(x - 2)$
The perimeter is $5x^2 - 9x - 2$ or
$(5x + 1)(x - 2)$.

32. $2(2x^2 + 3) + 2(6x^2 - 14x) = 4x^2 + 6 + 12x^2 - 28x$
$\qquad = 16x^2 - 28x + 6$
$\qquad = 2(8x^2 - 14x + 3)$
$8 \cdot 3 = 24$
$-2 \cdot -12 = 24$
$-2 + (-12) = -14$
$2(8x^2 - 14x + 3) = 2(8x^2 - 2x - 12x + 3)$
$\qquad = 2[2x(4x - 1) - 3(4x - 1)]$
$\qquad = 2(4x - 1)(2x - 3)$
The perimeter is $16x^2 - 28x + 6$ or
$2(4x - 1)(2x - 3)$.

33. Since $9 = 3^2$ and $6x = 2 \cdot 3 \cdot x$, $x^2 + 6x + 9$ is a perfect square trinomial.

34. Since $64 = 8^2$, but $8x \neq 2 \cdot 8 \cdot x$, $x^2 + 8x + 64$ is not a perfect square trinomial.

35. $9m^2 = (3m)^2$ and $16 = 4^2$, but $2 \cdot 3m \cdot 4 \neq 12m$, so $9m^2 - 12m + 16$ is not a perfect square trinomial.

36. Since $4y^2 = (2y)^2$ and $49 = 7^2$ and

$2 \cdot 2y \cdot 7 = 28y$, $4y^2 - 28y + 49$ is a perfect square trinomial.

37. Yes; $x^2 - 9$ or $x^2 - 3^2$ is the difference of two squares.

38. No; $x^2 + 16$ or $x^2 + 4^2$ is the sum of two squares.

39. Yes; $4x^2 - 25y^2$ or $(2x)^2 - (5y)^2$ is the difference of two squares.

40. No; $9a^3 - 1$ is not the difference of two squares [note: $9a^2 - 1$ or $(3a)^2 - 1^2$ is the difference of two squares.]

41. $x^2 - 81 = x^2 - 9^2 = (x - 9)(x + 9)$

42. $x^2 + 12x + 36 = x^2 + 2 \cdot x \cdot 6 + 6^2 = (x + 6)^2$

43. $4x^2 - 9 = (2x)^2 - 3^2 = (2x - 3)(2x + 3)$

44. $9t^2 - 25s^2 = (3t)^2 - (5s)^2 = (3t - 5s)(3t + 5s)$

45. $16x^2 = (4x)^2$ and y^2 are both perfect squares, but they are added instead of subtracted, so the polynomial is prime.

46. $n^2 - 18n + 81 = n^2 - 2 \cdot n \cdot 9 + 9^2 = (n - 9)^2$

47. $3r^2 + 36r + 108 = 3(r^2 + 12 + 36)$
$= 3(r^2 + 2 \cdot r \cdot 6 + 6^2)$
$= 3(r + 6)^2$

48. $9y^2 - 42y + 49 = (3y)^2 - 2 \cdot 3y \cdot 7 + 7^2$
$= (3y - 7)^2$

49. $5m^8 - 5m^6 = 5m^6(m^2 - 1)$
$= 5m^6(m^2 - 1^2)$
$= 5m^6(m + 1)(m - 1)$

50. $4x^2 - 28xy + 49y^2 = (2x)^2 - 2 \cdot 2x \cdot 7y + (7y)^2$
$= (2x - 7y)^2$

51. $3x^2y + 6xy^2 + 3y^3 = 3y(x^2 + 2xy + y^2)$
$= 3y(x + y)^2$

52. $16x^4 - 1 = (4x^2)^2 - 1^2$
$= (4x^2 - 1)(4x^2 + 1)$
$= [(2x)^2 - 1^2](4x^2 + 1)$
$= (2x - 1)(2x + 1)(4x^2 + 1)$

53. $(x + 6)(x - 2) = 0$
$x + 6 = 0$ or $x - 2 = 0$
$x = -6$ $\qquad x = 2$
The solutions are -6 and 2.

54. $(x - 7)(x + 11) = 0$
$x - 7 = 0$ or $x + 11 = 0$
$x = 7$ $\qquad x = -11$
The solutions are 7 and -11.

55. $3x(x + 1)(7x - 2) = 0$
$3x = 0$ or $x + 1 = 0$ or $7x - 2 = 0$
$x = 0$ $\qquad x = -1$ $\qquad x = \dfrac{2}{7}$

The solutions are 0, -1, and $\dfrac{2}{7}$.

56. $4(5x + 1)(x + 3) = 0$
$5x + 1 = 0$ or $x + 3 = 0$
$x = -\dfrac{1}{5}$ $\qquad x = -3$

The solutions are $-\dfrac{1}{5}$ and -3.

57. $x^2 + 8x + 7 = 0$
$(x + 7)(x + 1) = 0$
$x + 7 = 0$ or $x + 1 = 0$
$x = -7$ $\qquad x = -1$
The solutions are -7 and -1.

58. $x^2 - 2x - 24 = 0$
$(x + 4)(x - 6) = 0$
$x + 4 = 0$ or $x - 6 = 0$
$x = -4$ $\qquad x = 6$
The solutions are -4 and 6.

59. $x^2 + 10x = -25$

$x^2 + 10x + 25 = 0$

$(x+5)^2 = 0$

$x+5 = 0$

$x = -5$

The solution is -5.

60. $x(x-10) = -16$

$x^2 - 10x = -16$

$x^2 - 10x + 16 = 0$

$(x-2)(x-8) = 0$

$x-2 = 0$ or $x-8 = 0$

$x = 2$ $x = 8$

The solutions are 2 and 8.

61. $(3x-1)(9x^2+3x+1) = 0$

$3x-1 = 0$ or $9x^2+3x+1 = 0$

$x = \dfrac{1}{3}$ $9x^2+3x+1 > 0$

The solution is $\dfrac{1}{3}$.

62. $56x^2 - 5x - 6 = 0$

$(7x+2)(8x-3) = 0$

$7x+2 = 0$ or $8x-3 = 0$

$x = -\dfrac{2}{7}$ $x = \dfrac{3}{8}$

The solutions are $-\dfrac{2}{7}$ and $\dfrac{3}{8}$.

63. $m^2 = 6m$

$m^2 - 6m = 0$

$m(m-6) = 0$

$m = 0$ or $m-6 = 0$

$m = 6$

The solutions are 0 and 6.

64. $r^2 = 25$

$r^2 - 25 = 0$

$(r-5)(r+5) = 0$

$r-5 = 0$ or $r+5 = 0$

$r = 5$ $r = -5$

The solutions are 5 and -5.

65. $(x-4)(x-5) = 0$

$x^2 - 9x + 20 = 0$

66. $[x-(-1)][x-(-1)] = 0$

$(x+1)(x+1) = 0$

$x^2 + 2x + 1 = 0$

67. Let x be the width. Then $2x$ is the length.

perimeter $= 2 \cdot$ length $+ 2 \cdot$ width

$24 = 2(2x) + 2x$

$24 = 4x + 2x$

$24 = 6x$

$4 = x$

$8 = 2x$

The dimensions are 4 inches by 8 inches. The choice is c.

68. Let x be the width. Then $3x + 1$ is the length.

area $=$ length $\cdot$ width

$80 = (3x+1) \cdot x$

$80 = 3x^2 + x$

$0 = 3x^2 + x - 80$

$0 = (3x+16)(x-5)$

$3x+16 = 0$ or $x-5 = 0$

$x = -\dfrac{16}{3}$ $x = 5$

Discard $x = -\dfrac{16}{3}$ since length cannot be

negative. The dimensions are 5 meters by $3x + 1 = 3(5) + 1 = 15 + 1 = 16$ meters. The choice is d.

69. area $=$ side^2

$81 = x^2$

$0 = x^2 - 81$

$0 = (x-9)(x+9)$

$x-9 = 0$ or $x+9 = 0$

$x = 9$ $x = -9$

Discard $x = -9$ since length cannot be negative. The length of each side is 9 units.

70. The perimeter is the sum of the sides.

$(2x+3) + (3x+1) + (x^2-3x) + (x+3) = 47$

$x^2 + 3x + 7 = 47$

$x^2 + 3x - 40 = 0$

$(x-5)(x+8) = 0$

$x-5 = 0$ or $x+8 = 0$

$x = 5$ $x = -8$

Discard $x = -8$ since, for example, $x + 3$ would be negative.

$2x + 3 = 2(5) + 3 = 10 + 3 = 13$

$3x + 1 = 3(5) + 1 = 15 + 1 = 16$

$x^2 - 3x = 5^2 - 3(5) = 25 - 15 = 10$

$x + 3 = 5 + 3 = 8$

The lengths of the sides are 13 units, 16 units, 10 units, and 8 units.

71. Let x be the width. Then $2x - 15$ is the length.

area = length $\cdot$ width

$500 = (2x - 15) \cdot x$

$500 = 2x^2 - 15x$

$0 = 2x^2 - 15x - 500$

$0 = (2x + 25)(x - 20)$

$2x + 25 = 0 \qquad$ or $\quad x - 20 = 0$

$\qquad x = -\dfrac{25}{2} \qquad\qquad x = 20$

Discard $x = -\dfrac{25}{2}$ since length cannot be negative. The width is 20 inches and the length is $2 \cdot 20 - 15 = 40 - 15 = 25$ inches.

72. Let x be the height. Then $4x$ is the base.

area $= \dfrac{1}{2} \cdot$ base $\cdot$ height

$162 = \dfrac{1}{2} \cdot 4x \cdot x$

$162 = 2x^2$

$0 = 2x^2 - 162$

$0 = 2(x^2 - 81)$

$0 = 2(x - 9)(x + 9)$

$x - 9 = 0 \quad$ or $\quad x + 9 = 0$

$\quad x = 9 \qquad\qquad x = -9$

Discard $x = -9$ since length cannot be negative. The height is 9 yards and the base is $4x = 4(9) = 36$ yards.

73. Let x be the first positive integer. Then $x + 1$ is the next consecutive integer.

$x(x + 1) = 380$

$x^2 + x = 380$

$x^2 + x - 380 = 0$

$(x + 20)(x - 19) = 0$

$x + 20 = 0 \qquad$ or $\quad x - 19 = 0$

$\quad x = -20 \qquad\qquad x = 19$

Discard $x = -20$ since it is not positive. The integers are 19 and $19 + 1 = 20$.

74. Let x be the first positive even integer. Then $x + 2$ is the next consecutive even integer.

$x(x + 2) = 440$

$x^2 + 2x = 440$

$x^2 + 2x - 440 = 0$

$(x + 22)(x - 20) = 0$

$x + 22 = 0 \qquad$ or $\quad x - 20 = 0$

$\quad x = -22 \qquad\qquad x = 20$

Discard $x = -22$ since it is not positive. The integers are 20 and $20 + 2 = 22$.

75. a.

$$h = -16t^2 + 440t$$

$$2800 = -16t^2 + 440t$$

$$16t^2 - 440t + 2800 = 0$$

$$8(2t^2 - 55t + 350) = 0$$

$$8(2t - 35)(t - 10) = 0$$

$2t - 35 = 0 \qquad$ or $\quad t - 10 = 0$

$\quad t = \dfrac{35}{2}$ or $17.5 \qquad\qquad t = 10$

The rocket reaches a height of 2800 feet at 10 seconds on the way up and at 17.5 seconds on the way down.

b. The height is 0 when the rocket reaches the ground.

$h = -16t^2 + 440t$

$0 = -16t^2 + 440t$

$0 = -8t(2t - 55)$

$-8t = 0 \quad$ or $\quad 2t - 55 = 0$

$\quad t = 0 \qquad\qquad 2t = 55$

$\qquad\qquad\qquad\qquad t = 27.5$

The rocket reaches the ground again after 27.5 seconds.

76. Let x be the length of the longer leg. Then $x + 8$ is the length of the hypotenuse and $x - 8$ is the length of the shorter leg.

$(x + 8)^2 = (x - 8)^2 + x^2$

$x^2 + 16x + 64 = x^2 - 16x + 64 + x^2$

$0 = x^2 - 32x$

$0 = x(x - 32)$

$x = 0 \quad$ or $\quad x - 32 = 0$

$\qquad\qquad\qquad x = 32$

The longer leg is 32 centimeters.

77. $6x + 24 = 6 \cdot x + 6 \cdot 4 = 6(x + 4)$

78. $7x - 63 = 7 \cdot x - 7 \cdot 9 = 7(x - 9)$

79. $11x(4x-3)-6(4x-3)=(4x-3)(11x-6)$

80. $2x(x-5)-(x-5)=2x(x-5)-1(x-5)$
$$=(x-5)(2x-1)$$

81. $3x^3-4x^2+6x-8=x^2(3x-4)+2(3x-4)$
$$=(3x-4)(x^2+2)$$

82. $xy+2x-y-2=x(y+2)-1(y+2)$
$$=(y+2)(x-1)$$

83. $2x^2+2x-24=2(x^2+x-12)=2(x+4)(x-3)$

84. $3x^3-30x^2+27x=3x(x^2-10x+9)$
$$=3x(x-9)(x-1)$$

85. $4x^2-81=(2x)^2-9^2=(2x+9)(2x-9)$

86. $2x^2-18=2(x^2-9)$
$$=2(x^2-3^2)$$
$$=2(x-3)(x+3)$$

87. $16x^2-24x+9=(4x)^2-2\cdot 4x\cdot 3+3^2=(4x-3)^2$

88. $5x^2+20x+20=5(x^2+4x+4)$
$$=5(x^2+2\cdot x\cdot 2+2^2)$$
$$=5(x+2)^2$$

89. $2x^2-x-28=0$
$$(2x+7)(x-4)=0$$
$$2x+7=0 \quad \text{or} \quad x-4=0$$
$$x=-\frac{7}{2} \qquad\qquad x=4$$

The solutions are $-\dfrac{7}{2}$ and 4.

90. $x^2-2x=15$
$$x^2-2x-15=0$$
$$(x+3)(x-5)=0$$
$$x+3=0 \quad \text{or} \quad x-5=0$$
$$x=-3 \qquad\qquad x=5$$
The solutions are -3 and 5.

91. $2x(x+7)(x+4)=0$
$$2x=0 \quad \text{or} \quad x+7=0 \quad \text{or} \quad x+4=0$$
$$x=0 \qquad\qquad x=-7 \qquad\qquad x=-4$$

92. $x(x-5)=-6$
$$x^2-5x=-6$$
$$x^2-5x+6=0$$
$$(x-3)(x-2)=0$$
$$x-3=0 \quad \text{or} \quad x-2=0$$
$$x=3 \qquad\qquad x=2$$
The solutions are 3 and 2.

93. $x^2=16x$
$$x^2-16x=0$$
$$x(x-16)=0$$
$$x=0 \quad \text{or} \quad x-16=0$$
$$x=16$$
The solutions are 0 and 16.

94. The perimeter is the sum of the sides.
$$(x^2+3)+2x+(4x+5)=48$$
$$x^2+6x+8=48$$
$$x^2+6x-40=0$$
$$(x-4)(x+10)=0$$
$$x-4=0 \quad \text{or} \quad x+10=0$$
$$x=4 \qquad\qquad x=-10$$
Discard $x=-10$ since length, such as $2x=2(-10)=-20$ cannot be negative.
$$x^2+3=4^2+3=16+3=19$$
$$2x=2\cdot 4=8$$
$$4x+5=4\cdot 4+5=16+5=21$$
The lengths are 19 inches, 8 inches, and 21 inches.

95. Let x be the length. Then $x-4$ is the width.
area = length · width
$$12=x(x-4)$$
$$12=x^2-4x$$
$$0=x^2-4x-12$$
$$0=(x-6)(x+2)$$
$$x-6=0 \quad \text{or} \quad x+2=0$$
$$x=6 \qquad\qquad x=-2$$
Discard $x=-2$ since length cannot be negative. The length is 6 inches and the width is $x-4=6-4=2$ inches.

Chapter 11 Test

1. $9x^2-3x=3x(3x-1)$

2. $x^2+11x+28=(x+7)(x+4)$

3. $49-m^2=7^2-m^2=(7-m)(7+m)$

4. $y^2 + 22y + 121 = y^2 + 2 \cdot y \cdot 11 + 11^2$
$$= (y + 11)^2$$

5. $x^4 - 16 = (x^2)^2 - (4)^2$
$$= (x^2 + 4)(x^2 - 4)$$
$$= (x^2 + 4)[(x)^2 - (2)^2]$$
$$= (x^2 + 4)(x + 2)(x - 2)$$

6. $4(a + 3) - y(a + 3) = (a + 3)(4 - y)$

7. $x^2 + 4$ is prime.

8. $y^2 - 8y - 48 = (y - 12)(y + 4)$

9. $3a^2 + 3ab - 7a - 7b = 3a(a + b) - 7(a + b)$
$$= (a + b)(3a - 7)$$

10. $3x^2 - 5x + 2 = (3x - 2)(x - 1)$

11. $180 - 5x^2 = 5(36 - x^2)$
$$= 5(6^2 - x^2)$$
$$= 5(6 - x)(6 + x)$$

12. $3x^3 - 21x^2 + 30x = 3x(x^2 - 7x + 10)$
$$= 3x(x - 5)(x - 2)$$

13. $6t^2 - t - 5 = 6t^2 + 5t - 6t - 5$
$$= t(6t + 5) - 1(6t + 5)$$
$$= (6t + 5)(t - 1)$$

14. $xy^2 - 7y^2 - 4x + 28 = y^2(x - 7) - 4(x - 7)$
$$= (x - 7)(y^2 - 4)$$
$$= (x - 7)(y - 2)(y + 2)$$

15. $x - x^5 = x(1 - x^4)$
$$= x[1^2 - (x^2)^2]$$
$$= x(1 + x^2)(1 - x^2)$$
$$= x(1 + x^2)(1 + x)(1 - x)$$

16. $x^2 + 14xy + 24y^2 = x^2 + 12xy + 2xy + 24y^2$
$$= x(x + 12y) + 2y(x + 12y)$$
$$= (x + 12y)(x + 2y)$$

17. $(x - 3)(x + 9) = 0$
$x - 3 = 0$ or $x + 9 = 0$
     $x = 3$ $x = -9$
The solutions are 3 and –9.

18. $x^2 + 5x = 14$
   $x^2 + 5x - 14 = 0$
   $(x + 7)(x - 2) = 0$
$x + 7 = 0$ or $x - 2 = 0$
    $x = -7$ $x = 2$
The solutions are –7 and 2.

19. $x(x + 6) = 7$
      $x^2 + 6x = 7$
   $x^2 + 6x - 7 = 0$
   $(x + 7)(x - 1) = 0$
$x + 7 = 0$ or $x - 1 = 0$
    $x = -7$ $x = 1$
The solutions are –7 and 1.

20. $3x(2x - 3)(3x + 4) = 0$
$3x = 0$ or $2x - 3 = 0$ or $3x + 4 = 0$
  $x = 0$ $x = \dfrac{3}{2}$ $x = -\dfrac{4}{3}$

The solutions are 0, $\dfrac{3}{2}$, and $-\dfrac{4}{3}$.

21. $5t^3 - 45t = 0$
      $5t(t^2 - 9) = 0$
$5t[(t)^2 - (3)^2] = 0$
  $5t(t + 3)(t - 3) = 0$
$5t = 0$ or $t + 3 = 0$ or $t - 3 = 0$
  $t = 0$ $t = -3$ $t = 3$
The solutions are 0, –3, and 3.

22. $t^2 - 2t - 15 = 0$
   $(t + 3)(t - 5) = 0$
   $t + 3 = 0$ or $t - 5 = 0$
      $t = -3$ $t = 5$
The solutions are –3 and 5.

23. $6x^2 = 15x$
   $6x^2 - 15x = 0$
   $3x(2x - 5) = 0$

$3x = 0$ or $2x - 5 = 0$
$x = 0$ $x = \dfrac{5}{2}$

The solutions are 0 and $\dfrac{5}{2}$.

24. Let x be the height. Then the base is $x + 9$.

$$\text{area} = \dfrac{1}{2} \cdot \text{base} \cdot \text{height}$$

$$68 = \dfrac{1}{2} \cdot (x + 9) \cdot x$$

$$2 \cdot 68 = 2 \cdot \dfrac{1}{2} \cdot (x + 9) \cdot x$$

$$136 = x(x + 9)$$

$$136 = x^2 + 9x$$

$$0 = x^2 + 9x - 136$$

$$0 = (x + 17)(x - 8)$$

$x + 17 = 0$ or $x - 8 = 0$
$x = -17$ $x = 8$

Discard $x = -17$ since length cannot be negative.
The height is 8 feet and the base is
$x + 9 = 8 + 9 = 17$ feet.

25. $(x - 1)(x + 2) = 54$

$$x^2 + 2x - x - 2 = 54$$

$$x^2 + x - 56 = 0$$

$$(x + 8)(x - 7) = 0$$

$x + 8 = 0$ or $x - 7 = 0$
$x = -8$ $x = 7$

Discard $x = -8$ since length cannot be negative.
$x - 1 = 7 - 1 = 6$
$x + 2 = 7 + 2 = 9$
The width of the rectangle is 6 units and the
length is 9 units.

26. The object is at a height of 0 when it reaches the ground.

$$h = -16t^2 + 784$$

$$0 = -16t^2 + 784$$

$$0 = -16(t^2 - 49)$$

$$0 = -16(t - 7)(t + 7)$$

$t - 7 = 0$ or $t + 7 = 0$
$t = 7$ $t = -7$

Discard $t = -7$ since time cannot be negative.
The object reaches the ground after 7 seconds.

27. Let x be the length of the shorter leg. Then
$x + 10$ is the length of the hypotenuse and
$x + 10 - 5 = x + 5$ is the length of the longer leg.

$$x^2 + (x + 5)^2 = (x + 10)^2$$

$$x^2 + x^2 + 10x + 25 = x^2 + 20x + 100$$

$$x^2 - 10x - 75 = 0$$

$$(x - 15)(x + 5) = 0$$

$x - 15 = 0$ or $x + 5 = 0$
$x = 15$ $x = -5$

Discard $x = -5$ since length cannot be negative.
The shorter leg is 15 cm, the longer leg is
$15 + 5 = 20$ cm, and the hypotenuse is
$15 + 10 = 25$ cm.

28. The height of the object is 0 when it reaches the ground.

$$h = -16t^2 + 1089$$

$$0 = -16t^2 + 1089$$

$$0 = -1(16t^2 - 1089)$$

$$0 = -1[(4t)^2 - 33^2]$$

$$0 = -1(4t - 33)(4t + 33)$$

$4t - 33 = 0$ or $4t + 33 = 0$

$t = \dfrac{33}{4}$ or 8.25 $t = -\dfrac{33}{4}$

Discard $t = -\dfrac{33}{4}$ since time cannot be negative.

The object reaches the ground after
8.25 seconds.

Cumulative Review Chapters 1–11

1. $x + 2y - z = 3 + 2(-5) - (-4)$
            $= 3 - 10 + 4$
            $= -3$

2. $5x - y = 5(-2) - 4 = -10 - 4 = -14$

3. $7 - x^2 = 7 - (-4)^2 = 7 - 16 = -9$

4. $x^3 - y^3 = (-2)^3 - 4^3 = -8 - 64 = -72$

5. $-8 = n + 1$
        $-8 - 1 = n + 1 - 1$
            $-9 = n$

6. $-8x = 72$
        $\dfrac{-8x}{-8} = \dfrac{72}{-8}$
            $x = -9$

7. $2y - 6 + 4y + 8 = 2y + 4y - 6 + 8 = 6y + 2$

8. $-5a - 3 + a + 2 = -5a + a - 3 + 2 = -4a - 1$

9. $4x + 2 - 5x + 3 = 4x - 5x + 2 + 3 = -x + 5$

10. $2x + 5x - 6 = 7x - 6$

11.
$$3(3x-5) = 10x$$
$$9x - 15 = 10x$$
$$9x - 9x - 15 = 10x - 9x$$
$$-15 = x$$

12.
$$2(7x-1) = 15x$$
$$14x - 2 = 15x$$
$$14x - 14x - 2 = 15x - 14x$$
$$-2 = x$$

13.
$$3(2x-6)+6 = 0$$
$$6x - 18 + 6 = 0$$
$$6x - 12 = 0$$
$$6x - 12 + 12 = 0 + 12$$
$$6x = 12$$
$$\frac{6x}{6} = \frac{12}{6}$$
$$x = 2$$

14.
$$4(x+3)-12 = 0$$
$$4x + 12 - 12 = 0$$
$$4x = 0$$
$$\frac{4x}{4} = \frac{0}{4}$$
$$x = 0$$

15.
$$\frac{x-5}{3} = \frac{x+2}{5}$$
$$15\left(\frac{x-5}{3}\right) = 15\left(\frac{x+2}{5}\right)$$
$$5(x-5) = 3(x+2)$$
$$5x - 25 = 3x + 6$$
$$2x - 25 = 6$$
$$2x = 31$$
$$\frac{2x}{2} = \frac{31}{2}$$
$$x = \frac{31}{2}$$

16.
$$\frac{x+1}{2} = \frac{x-7}{3}$$
$$6\left(\frac{x+1}{2}\right) = 6\left(\frac{x-7}{3}\right)$$
$$3(x+1) = 2(x-7)$$
$$3x + 3 = 2x - 14$$
$$x + 3 = -14$$
$$x = -17$$

17. a. Nine is less than or equal to eleven is translated as $9 \le 11$.

b. Eight is greater than one is translated as $8 > 1$.

c. Three is not equal to four is translated as $3 \ne 4$.

18. a. Five is greater than or equal to one is translated as $5 \ge 1$.

b. Two is not equal to negative four translates as $2 \ne -4$.

19.
$$3(x-4) = 3x - 12$$
$$3x - 12 = 3x - 12$$
$$-3x + 3x - 12 = -3x + 3x - 12$$
$$-12 = -12$$
Since this results in a true statement, the solution is every real number.

20.
$$2(x+5) = 2x + 9$$
$$2x + 10 = 2x + 9$$
$$10 = 9$$
Since $10 = 9$ is a false statement, there is no solution.

21.
$$V = lwh$$
$$\frac{V}{wh} = \frac{lwh}{wh}$$
$$\frac{V}{wh} = l \text{ or } l = \frac{V}{wh}$$

22.
$$3x - 2y = 5$$
$$3x = 2y + 5$$
$$\frac{3x}{3} = \frac{2y+5}{3}$$
$$x = \frac{2y+5}{3}$$

23. $(5^3)^6 = 5^{3 \cdot 6} = 5^{18}$

24. $(7^9)^2 = 7^{9 \cdot 2} = 7^{18}$

25. $(y^8)^2 = y^{8 \cdot 2} = y^{16}$

26. $(x^{11})^3 = x^{11 \cdot 3} = x^{33}$

27. $\dfrac{(x^3)^4 x}{x^7} = \dfrac{x^{3\cdot 4} \cdot x^1}{x^7}$

$= \dfrac{x^{12} \cdot x^1}{x^7}$

$= \dfrac{x^{12+1}}{x^7}$

$= \dfrac{x^{13}}{x^7}$

$= x^{13-7}$

$= x^6$

28. $\dfrac{(y^3)^9 \cdot y}{y^6} = \dfrac{y^{3\cdot 9} \cdot y^1}{y^6}$

$= \dfrac{y^{27} \cdot y^1}{y^6}$

$= \dfrac{y^{27+1}}{y^6}$

$= \dfrac{y^{28}}{y^6}$

$= y^{28-6}$

$= y^{22}$

29. $(y^{-3} z^6)^{-6} = y^{-3\cdot-6} z^{6\cdot-6} = y^{18} z^{-36} = \dfrac{y^{18}}{z^{36}}$

30. $(xy^{-4})^{-2} = x^{-2}(y^{-4})^{-2} = x^{-2} y^8 = \dfrac{y^8}{x^2}$

31. $\dfrac{x^{-7}}{(x^4)^3} = \dfrac{x^{-7}}{x^{4\cdot3}} = \dfrac{x^{-7}}{x^{12}} = \dfrac{1}{x^{12-(-7)}} = \dfrac{1}{x^{12+7}} = \dfrac{1}{x^{19}}$

32. $\dfrac{(y^2)^5}{y^{-3}} = \dfrac{y^{10}}{y^{-3}} = y^{10-(-3)} = y^{10+3} = y^{13}$

33. $-3x + 7x = (-3 + 7)x = 4x$

34. $y + y = 2y$

35. $11x^2 + 5 + 2x^2 - 7 = 11x^2 + 2x^2 + 5 - 7$
$= 13x^2 - 2$

36. $8y - y^2 + 4y - y^2 = 8y + 4y - y^2 - y^2$
$= 12y - 2y^2$

37. $(2x - y)^2$
$= (2x - y)(2x - y)$
$= 2x(2x) + 2x(-y) + (-y)(2x) + (-y)(-y)$
$= 4x^2 - 2xy - 2xy + y^2$
$= 4x^2 - 4xy + y^2$

38. $(3x + 1)^2 = (3x + 1)(3x + 1)$
$= 3x(3x) + 3x(1) + 1(3x) + 1(1)$
$= 9x^2 + 3x + 3x + 1$
$= 9x^2 + 6x + 1$

39. $(t + 2)^2 = t^2 + 2(t)(2) + 2^2 = t^2 + 4t + 4$

40. $(x - 4)^2 = x^2 - 2(x)(4) + 4^2 = x^2 - 8x + 16$

41. $(x^2 - 7y)^2 = (x^2)^2 - 2(x^2)(7y) + (7y)^2$
$= x^4 - 14x^2 y + 49y^2$

42. $(x^2 + 7y)^2 = (x^2)^2 + 2(x^2)(7y) + (7y)^2$
$= x^4 + 14x^2 y + 49y^2$

43. $\dfrac{8x^2 y^2 - 16xy + 2x}{4xy} = \dfrac{8x^2 y^2}{4xy} - \dfrac{16xy}{4xy} + \dfrac{2x}{4xy}$
$= 2xy - 4 + \dfrac{1}{2y}$

44. $\dfrac{20a^2 b^3 - 5ab + 10b}{5ab} = \dfrac{20a^2 b^3}{5ab} - \dfrac{5ab}{5ab} + \dfrac{10b}{5ab}$
$= 4ab^2 - 1 + \dfrac{2}{a}$

45. $5(x + 3) + y(x + 3) = (x + 3)(5 + y)$

46. $9(y - 2) + x(y - 2) = (y - 2)(9 + x)$

47. $x^4 + 5x^2 + 6 = x^4 + 2x^2 + 3x^2 + 6$
$= x^2(x^2 + 2) + 3(x^2 + 2)$
$= (x^2 + 2)(x^2 + 3)$

48. $x^4 - 4x^2 - 5 = x^4 + x^2 - 5x^2 - 5$
$= x^2(x^2 + 1) - 5(x^2 + 1)$
$= (x^2 + 1)(x^2 - 5)$

49.
$$6x^2 - 2x - 20 = 2(3x^2 - x - 10)$$
$$= 2(3x^2 - 6x + 5x - 10)$$
$$= 2[3x(x-2) + 5(x-2)]$$
$$= 2(x-2)(3x+5)$$

50.
$$10x^2 + 25x + 10 = 5(2x^2 + 5x + 2)$$
$$= 5(2x^2 + 4x + x + 2)$$
$$= 5[2x(x+2) + 1(x+2)]$$
$$= 5(x+2)(2x+1)$$

51. The height is 0 when the diver reaches the ocean.
$$h = -16t^2 + 144$$
$$0 = -16t^2 + 144$$
$$0 = -16(t^2 - 9)$$
$$0 = -16(t-3)(t+3)$$
$$t - 3 = 0 \quad \text{or} \quad t + 3 = 0$$
$$t = 3 \qquad\qquad t = -3$$
Discard $t = -3$ since time cannot be negative.
The diver reaches the ocean after 3 seconds.

52.
$$x^2 + 2x = 120$$
$$x^2 + 2x - 120 = 0$$
$$(x+12)(x-10) = 0$$
$$x + 12 = 0 \quad \text{or} \quad x - 10 = 0$$
$$x = -12 \qquad\qquad x = 10$$
The number is -12 or 10.

Chapter 12

Practice Problems

1. a. $\dfrac{x-3}{5x+1} = \dfrac{4-3}{5(4)+1} = \dfrac{1}{20+1} = \dfrac{1}{21}$

b. $\dfrac{x-3}{5x+1} = \dfrac{(-3)-3}{5(-3)+1} = \dfrac{-6}{-15+1} = \dfrac{-6}{-14} = \dfrac{3}{7}$

2. a. $x+8=0$
$\quad\quad x=-8$

When $x=-8$, the expression $\dfrac{x}{x+8}$ is undefined.

b. $x^2+5x+4=0$
$(x+4)(x+1)=0$
$x+4=0 \quad$ or $\quad x+1=0$
$\quad x=-4 \quad\quad\quad\quad x=-1$
When $x=-4$ or $x=-1$, the expression
$\dfrac{x-3}{x^2+5x+4}$ is undefined.

c. The denominator of $\dfrac{x^2-3x+2}{5}$ is never 0, so there are no values of x for which this expression is undefined.

3. $\dfrac{x^4+x^3}{5x+5} = \dfrac{x^3(x+1)}{5(x+1)} = \dfrac{x^3}{5}$

4. $\dfrac{x^2+11x+18}{x^2+x-2} = \dfrac{(x+9)(x+2)}{(x-1)(x+2)} = \dfrac{x+9}{x-1}$

5. $\dfrac{x^2+10x+25}{x^2+5x} = \dfrac{(x+5)(x+5)}{x(x+5)} = \dfrac{x+5}{x}$

6. $\dfrac{x+5}{x^2-25} = \dfrac{x+5}{(x+5)(x-5)} = \dfrac{1}{x-5}$

7. a. $\dfrac{x+4}{4+x} = \dfrac{x+4}{x+4} = 1$

b. $\dfrac{x-4}{4-x} = \dfrac{x-4}{(-1)(x-4)} = \dfrac{1}{-1} = -1$

8. $-\dfrac{3x+7}{x-6} = \dfrac{-(3x+7)}{x-6} = \dfrac{-3x-7}{x-6}$ or $\dfrac{3x+7}{-(x-6)} = \dfrac{3x+7}{-x+6}$

Vocabulary and Readiness Check

1. A <u>rational expression</u> is an expression that can be written in the form $\dfrac{P}{Q}$ where P and Q are polynomials and $Q \neq 0$.

2. The expression $\dfrac{x+3}{3+x}$ simplifies to <u>1</u>.

3. The expression $\dfrac{x-3}{3-x}$ simplifies to <u>-1</u>.

4. A rational expression is undefined for values that make the denominator <u>0</u>.

5. The expression $\dfrac{7x}{x-2}$ is undefined for $x = \underline{2}$.

6. The process of writing a rational expression in lowest terms is called <u>simplifying</u>.

7. For a rational expression, $-\dfrac{a}{b} = \dfrac{-a}{\underline{b}} = \dfrac{a}{\underline{-b}}$.

8. $\dfrac{x}{x+7}$ cannot be simplified.

9. Since $3+x = x+3$, $\dfrac{3+x}{x+3}$ can be simplified.

10. Since $5-x = -1(x-5)$, $\dfrac{5-x}{x-5}$ can be simplified.

11. $\dfrac{x+2}{x+8}$ cannot be simplified.

Exercise Set 12.1

1. $\dfrac{x+5}{x+2} = \dfrac{2+5}{2+2} = \dfrac{7}{4}$

432

3. $\dfrac{y^3}{y^2-1} = \dfrac{(-2)^3}{(-2)^2-1} = \dfrac{-8}{4-1} = -\dfrac{8}{3}$

5. $\dfrac{x^2+8x+2}{x^2-x-6} = \dfrac{2^2+8(2)+2}{2^2-2-6}$

$= \dfrac{4+16+2}{4-2-6}$

$= \dfrac{22}{-4}$

$= -\dfrac{11}{2}$

7. a. $A = \dfrac{3x+400}{x} = \dfrac{3(1)+400}{1} = 403$

The cost of producing 1 DVD is $403.

b. $A = \dfrac{3(100)+400}{100} = \dfrac{300+400}{100} = \dfrac{700}{100} = 7$

The average cost for producing 100 DVDs is $7.

c. decrease; answers may vary

9. $2x = 0$

$x = 0$

$\dfrac{7}{2x}$ is undefined for $x = 0$.

11. $x + 2 = 0$

$x = -2$

$\dfrac{x+3}{x+2}$ is undefined for $x = -2$.

13. $2x - 5 = 0$

$2x = 5$

$x = \dfrac{5}{2}$

$\dfrac{x-4}{2x-5}$ is undefined for $x = \dfrac{5}{2}$.

15. $15x^2 + 30x = 0$

$15x(x+2) = 0$

$15x = 0$ or $x + 2 = 0$

$x = 0$ $x = -2$

$\dfrac{9x^3+4}{15x^2+30x}$ is undefined for $x = 0$ and $x = -2$.

17. Since $4 \neq 0$, there are no values of x for which $\dfrac{x^2-5x-2}{4}$ is undefined.

19. $x^2 - 5x - 6 = 0$

$(x-6)(x+1) = 0$

$x - 6 = 0$ or $x + 1 = 0$

$x = 6$ $x = -1$

$\dfrac{3x^2+9}{x^2-5x-6}$ is undefined for $x = 6$ and $x = -1$.

21. $3x^2 + 13x + 14 = 0$

$(x+2)(3x+7) = 0$

$x + 2 = 0$ or $3x + 7 = 0$

$x = -2$ $3x = -7$

$x = -\dfrac{7}{3}$

$\dfrac{x}{3x^2+13x+14}$ is undefined for $x = -2$ and $x = -\dfrac{7}{3}$.

23. $\dfrac{x+7}{7+x} = \dfrac{x+7}{x+7} = 1$

25. $\dfrac{x-7}{7-x} = \dfrac{-1(-x+7)}{7-x} = \dfrac{-1(7-x)}{7-x} = -1$

27. $\dfrac{2}{8x+16} = \dfrac{2}{8(x+2)} = \dfrac{1}{4(x+2)}$

29. $\dfrac{x-2}{x^2-4} = \dfrac{x-2}{(x+2)(x-2)} = \dfrac{1}{x+2}$

31. $\dfrac{2x-10}{3x-30} = \dfrac{2(x-5)}{3(x-10)}$ can't be simplified.

33. $\dfrac{-5a-5b}{a+b} = \dfrac{-5(a+b)}{a+b} = -5$

35. $\dfrac{7x+35}{x^2+5x} = \dfrac{7(x+5)}{x(x+5)} = \dfrac{7}{x}$

37. $\dfrac{x+5}{x^2-4x-45} = \dfrac{x+5}{(x-9)(x+5)} = \dfrac{1}{x-9}$

39. $\dfrac{5x^2+11x+2}{x+2} = \dfrac{(5x+1)(x+2)}{x+2} = 5x+1$

41. $\dfrac{x^3+7x^2}{x^2+5x-14} = \dfrac{x^2(x+7)}{(x-2)(x+7)} = \dfrac{x^2}{x-2}$

43. $\dfrac{14x^2-21x}{2x-3} = \dfrac{7x(2x-3)}{2x-3} = 7x$

45. $\dfrac{x^2+7x+10}{x^2-3x-10} = \dfrac{(x+5)(x+2)}{(x+2)(x-5)} = \dfrac{x+5}{x-5}$

47. $\dfrac{3x^2+7x+2}{3x^2+13x+4} = \dfrac{(3x+1)(x+2)}{(3x+1)(x+4)} = \dfrac{x+2}{x+4}$

49. $\dfrac{2x^2-8}{4x-8} = \dfrac{2(x^2-4)}{4(x-2)} = \dfrac{2(x+2)(x-2)}{2\cdot 2(x-2)} = \dfrac{x+2}{2}$

51. $\dfrac{4-x^2}{x-2} = \dfrac{-(x^2-4)}{x-2} = \dfrac{-(x+2)(x-2)}{x-2} = -(x+2)$

53. $\dfrac{x^2-1}{x^2-2x+1} = \dfrac{(x+1)(x-1)}{(x-1)^2} = \dfrac{x+1}{x-1}$

55. $\dfrac{x^2+xy+2x+2y}{x+2} = \dfrac{x(x+y)+2(x+y)}{x+2}$
$= \dfrac{(x+2)(x+y)}{x+2}$
$= x+y$

57. $\dfrac{5x+15-xy-3y}{2x+6} = \dfrac{5(x+3)-y(x+3)}{2(x+3)}$
$= \dfrac{(x+3)(5-y)}{2(x+3)}$
$= \dfrac{5-y}{2}$

59. $\dfrac{2xy+5x-2y-5}{3xy+4x-3y-4} = \dfrac{x(2y+5)-1(2y+5)}{x(3y+4)-1(3y+4)}$
$= \dfrac{(2y+5)(x-1)}{(3y+4)(x-1)}$
$= \dfrac{2y+5}{3y+4}$

61. $-\dfrac{x-10}{x+8} = \dfrac{-(x-10)}{x+8}$
$= \dfrac{-x+10}{x+8}$
$= \dfrac{x-10}{-(x+8)}$
$= \dfrac{x-10}{-x-8}$

63. $-\dfrac{5y-3}{y-12} = \dfrac{-(5y-3)}{y-12}$
$= \dfrac{-5y+3}{y-12}$
$= \dfrac{5y-3}{-(y-12)}$
$= \dfrac{5y-3}{-y+12}$

65. $\dfrac{9-x^2}{x-3} = \dfrac{9-x^2}{-(3-x)}$
$= \dfrac{(3+x)(3-x)}{-(3-x)}$
$= \dfrac{3+x}{-1}$
$= -3-x$
The given answer is correct.

67. $\dfrac{7-34x-5x^2}{25x^2-1} = \dfrac{(7+x)(1-5x)}{(5x+1)(5x-1)}$
$= \dfrac{(7+x)(1-5x)}{-(5x+1)(1-5x)}$
$= \dfrac{7+x}{-5x-1}$
The given answer is correct.

69. $\dfrac{1}{3}\cdot\dfrac{9}{11} = \dfrac{1\cdot 9}{3\cdot 11} = \dfrac{1\cdot 3\cdot 3}{3\cdot 11} = \dfrac{3}{11}$

71. $\dfrac{1}{3}\div\dfrac{1}{4} = \dfrac{1}{3}\cdot\dfrac{4}{1} = \dfrac{1\cdot 4}{3\cdot 1} = \dfrac{4}{3}$

73. $\dfrac{13}{20}\div\dfrac{2}{9} = \dfrac{13}{20}\cdot\dfrac{9}{2} = \dfrac{13\cdot 9}{20\cdot 2} = \dfrac{117}{40}$

75. $\dfrac{5a-15}{5} = \dfrac{5(a-3)}{5} = a-3$
The given answer is correct.

77. $\dfrac{1+2}{1+3} = \dfrac{3}{4} \neq \dfrac{2}{3}$

The given answer is incorrect.

79. answers may vary

81. answers may vary

83. Use $C = \dfrac{DA}{A+12}$ with $A = 8$ and $D = 1000$.

$C = \dfrac{DA}{A+12} = \dfrac{1000 \cdot 8}{8+12} = \dfrac{8000}{20} = 400$

The child should receive a dose of 400 milligrams.

85. Use $C = \dfrac{100W}{L}$ with $W = 5$ and $L = 6.4$.

$C = \dfrac{100W}{L} = \dfrac{100(5)}{6.4} = \dfrac{500}{6.4} = 78.125$

The cephalic index is 78.125. The skull is medium.

87. Use $S = \dfrac{h+d+2t+3r}{b}$ with $h = 187$, $d = 44$, $t = 0$, $r = 37$, and $b = 524$.

$S = \dfrac{187+44+2(0)+3(37)}{524} = \dfrac{342}{524} \approx 0.6527$

Pujols' slugging percentage was about 65.3%.

Section 12.2

Practice Problems

1. a. $\dfrac{16y}{3} \cdot \dfrac{1}{x^2} = \dfrac{16y \cdot 1}{3 \cdot x^2} = \dfrac{16y}{3x^2}$

   b. $\dfrac{-5a^3}{3b^3} \cdot \dfrac{2b^2}{15a} = \dfrac{-5a^3 \cdot 2b^2}{3b^3 \cdot 15a}$

$$= \dfrac{-5 \cdot a^3 \cdot 2 \cdot b^2}{3 \cdot b^3 \cdot 3 \cdot 5 \cdot a}$$

$$= -\dfrac{2a^2}{9b}$$

2. $\dfrac{3x+6}{14} \cdot \dfrac{7x^2}{x^3+2x^2} = \dfrac{3(x+2) \cdot 7x^2}{2 \cdot 7 \cdot x^2(x+2)} = \dfrac{3}{2}$

3. $\dfrac{4x+8}{7x^2-14x} \cdot \dfrac{3x^2-5x-2}{9x^2-1} = \dfrac{4(x+2)}{7x(x-2)} \cdot \dfrac{(3x+1)(x-2)}{(3x+1)(3x-1)}$

$$= \dfrac{4(x+2)(3x+1)(x-2)}{7x(x-2)(3x+1)(3x-1)}$$

$$= \dfrac{4(x+2)}{7x(3x-1)}$$

4. $\dfrac{7x^2}{6} \div \dfrac{x}{2y} = \dfrac{7x^2}{6} \cdot \dfrac{2y}{x} = \dfrac{7 \cdot x \cdot x \cdot 2 \cdot y}{2 \cdot 3 \cdot x} = \dfrac{7xy}{3}$

5. $\dfrac{(x-4)^2}{6} \div \dfrac{3x-12}{2} = \dfrac{(x-4)^2}{6} \cdot \dfrac{2}{3x-12}$

$\qquad = \dfrac{(x-4)(x-4) \cdot 2}{2 \cdot 3 \cdot 3 \cdot (x-4)}$

$\qquad = \dfrac{x-4}{9}$

6. $\dfrac{10x+4}{x^2-4} \div \dfrac{5x^3+2x^2}{x+2} = \dfrac{10x+4}{x^2-4} \cdot \dfrac{x+2}{5x^3+2x^2}$

$\qquad = \dfrac{2(5x+2)(x+2)}{(x-2)(x+2) \cdot x^2(5x+2)}$

$\qquad = \dfrac{2}{x^2(x-2)}$

7. $\dfrac{3x^2-10x+8}{7x-14} \div \dfrac{9x-12}{21}$

$\quad = \dfrac{3x^2-10x+8}{7x-14} \cdot \dfrac{21}{9x-12}$

$\quad = \dfrac{(3x-4)(x-2) \cdot 3 \cdot 7}{7(x-2) \cdot 3(3x-4)}$

$\quad = 1$

8. a. $\dfrac{x+3}{x} \cdot \dfrac{7}{x+3} = \dfrac{(x+3) \cdot 7}{x \cdot (x+3)} = \dfrac{7}{x}$

   b. $\dfrac{x+3}{x} \div \dfrac{7}{x+3} = \dfrac{x+3}{x} \cdot \dfrac{x+3}{7} = \dfrac{(x+3)^2}{7x}$

   c. $\dfrac{3-x}{x^2+6x+5} \cdot \dfrac{2x+10}{x^2-7x+12}$

$\qquad = \dfrac{(3-x) \cdot 2(x+5)}{(x+5)(x+1) \cdot (x-4)(x-3)}$

$\qquad = \dfrac{-1(x-3) \cdot 2}{(x+1)(x-4)(x-3)}$

$\qquad = -\dfrac{2}{(x+1)(x-4)}$

9. $288 \text{ sq in.} = \dfrac{288 \text{ sq in.}}{1} \cdot \dfrac{1 \text{ sq ft}}{144 \text{ sq in.}} = 2 \text{ sq ft}$

10. $3.5 \text{ sq ft} = \dfrac{3.5 \text{ sq ft}}{1} \cdot \dfrac{144 \text{ sq in.}}{1 \text{ sq ft}} = 504 \text{ sq in.}$

11. $61,000 \text{ sq yd} = 61,000 \text{ sq yd} \cdot \dfrac{9 \text{ sq ft}}{1 \text{ sq yd}}$

$\qquad = 549,000 \text{ sq ft}$

12. 102.7 feet/second

$\quad = \dfrac{102.7 \text{ feet}}{1 \text{ second}} \cdot \dfrac{3600 \text{ seconds}}{1 \text{ hour}} \cdot \dfrac{1 \text{ mile}}{5280 \text{ feet}}$

$\quad = \dfrac{102.7 \cdot 3600}{5280} \text{ miles/hour}$

$\quad \approx 70.0 \text{ miles/hour}$

Vocabulary and Readiness Check

1. The expressions $\dfrac{x}{2y}$ and $\dfrac{2y}{x}$ are called

   <u>reciprocals</u>.

2. $\dfrac{a}{b} \cdot \dfrac{c}{d} = \dfrac{a \cdot c}{\underline{b \cdot d}}$

3. $\dfrac{a}{b} \div \dfrac{c}{d} = \dfrac{a \cdot d}{\underline{b \cdot c}}$

4. $\dfrac{x}{7} \cdot \dfrac{x}{6} = \dfrac{x^2}{\underline{42}}$

5. $\dfrac{x}{7} \div \dfrac{x}{6} = \dfrac{6}{\underline{7}}$

Exercise Set 12.2

1. $\dfrac{3x}{y^2} \cdot \dfrac{7y}{4x} = \dfrac{3 \cdot 7 \cdot x \cdot y}{4 \cdot x \cdot y \cdot y} = \dfrac{21}{4y}$

3. $\dfrac{8x}{2} \cdot \dfrac{x^5}{4x^2} = \dfrac{2 \cdot 4 \cdot x \cdot x \cdot x \cdot x \cdot x \cdot x \cdot x}{2 \cdot 4 \cdot x \cdot x} = x^4$

5. $-\dfrac{5a^2b}{30a^2b^2} \cdot b^3 = -\dfrac{5a^2b}{30a^2b^2} \cdot \dfrac{b^3}{1}$

$\qquad = -\dfrac{5 \cdot a^2b \cdot b \cdot b^2}{5 \cdot 6 \cdot a^2 \cdot b^2}$

$\qquad = -\dfrac{b \cdot b}{6}$

$\qquad = -\dfrac{b^2}{6}$

7. $\dfrac{x}{2x-14} \cdot \dfrac{x^2-7x}{5} = \dfrac{x}{2(x-7)} \cdot \dfrac{x(x-7)}{5}$

$\qquad\qquad\qquad = \dfrac{x \cdot x}{2 \cdot 5}$

$\qquad\qquad\qquad = \dfrac{x^2}{10}$

9. $\dfrac{6x+6}{5} \cdot \dfrac{10}{36x+36} = \dfrac{6(x+1)}{5} \cdot \dfrac{10}{36(x+1)}$

$\qquad\qquad\qquad = \dfrac{6 \cdot 10}{5 \cdot 36}$

$\qquad\qquad\qquad = \dfrac{6 \cdot 2 \cdot 5}{5 \cdot 6 \cdot 2 \cdot 3}$

$\qquad\qquad\qquad = \dfrac{1}{3}$

11. $\dfrac{(m+n)^2}{m-n} \cdot \dfrac{m}{m^2+mn} = \dfrac{(m+n)(m+n)}{m-n} \cdot \dfrac{m}{m(m+n)}$

$\qquad\qquad\qquad\qquad = \dfrac{m+n}{m-n}$

13. $\dfrac{x^2-25}{x^2-3x-10} \cdot \dfrac{x+2}{x} = \dfrac{(x+5)(x-5)}{(x+2)(x-5)} \cdot \dfrac{x+2}{x}$

$\qquad\qquad\qquad\qquad = \dfrac{x+5}{x}$

15. $\dfrac{x^2+6x+8}{x^2+x-20} \cdot \dfrac{x^2+2x-15}{x^2+8x+16}$

$\qquad = \dfrac{(x+4)(x+2)}{(x+5)(x-4)} \cdot \dfrac{(x+5)(x-3)}{(x+4)(x+4)}$

$\qquad = \dfrac{(x+2)(x-3)}{(x-4)(x+4)}$

17. $\dfrac{5x^7}{2x^5} \div \dfrac{15x}{4x^3} = \dfrac{5x^7}{2x^5} \cdot \dfrac{4x^3}{15x}$

$\qquad\qquad\quad = \dfrac{5 \cdot x^5 \cdot x \cdot x}{2 \cdot x^5} \cdot \dfrac{2 \cdot 2 \cdot x^3}{5 \cdot 3 \cdot x}$

$\qquad\qquad\quad = \dfrac{2 \cdot x \cdot x^3}{3}$

$\qquad\qquad\quad = \dfrac{2x^4}{3}$

19. $\dfrac{8x^2}{y^3} \div \dfrac{4x^2 y^3}{6} = \dfrac{8x^2}{y^3} \cdot \dfrac{6}{4x^2 y^3}$

$\qquad\qquad\quad = \dfrac{2 \cdot 4 \cdot 6 \cdot x \cdot x}{4 \cdot x \cdot x \cdot y \cdot y \cdot y \cdot y \cdot y \cdot y}$

$\qquad\qquad\quad = \dfrac{2 \cdot 6}{y \cdot y \cdot y \cdot y \cdot y \cdot y}$

$\qquad\qquad\quad = \dfrac{12}{y^6}$

21. $\dfrac{(x-6)(x+4)}{4x} \div \dfrac{2x-12}{8x^2} = \dfrac{(x-6)(x+4)}{4x} \cdot \dfrac{8x^2}{2x-12}$

$\qquad\qquad\qquad = \dfrac{(x-6)(x+4)}{4x} \cdot \dfrac{4x \cdot 2 \cdot x}{2(x-6)}$

$\qquad\qquad\qquad = \dfrac{x(x+4)}{1}$

$\qquad\qquad\qquad = x(x+4)$

23. $\dfrac{3x^2}{x^2-1} \div \dfrac{x^5}{(x+1)^2} = \dfrac{3x^2}{x^2-1} \cdot \dfrac{(x+1)^2}{x^5}$

$\qquad\qquad\qquad = \dfrac{3x^2}{(x-1)(x+1)} \cdot \dfrac{(x+1)(x+1)}{x^2 \cdot x^3}$

$\qquad\qquad\qquad = \dfrac{3(x+1)}{x^3(x-1)}$

25. $\dfrac{m^2-n^2}{m+n} \div \dfrac{m}{m^2+nm} = \dfrac{m^2-n^2}{m+n} \cdot \dfrac{m^2+nm}{m}$

$\qquad\qquad\qquad = \dfrac{(m+n)(m-n)}{m+n} \cdot \dfrac{m(m+n)}{m}$

$\qquad\qquad\qquad = (m-n)(m+n)$

$\qquad\qquad\qquad = m^2 - n^2$

27. $\dfrac{x+2}{7-x} \div \dfrac{x^2-5x+6}{x^2-9x+14} = \dfrac{x+2}{7-x} \cdot \dfrac{x^2-9x+14}{x^2-5x+6}$

$\qquad\qquad\qquad = \dfrac{x+2}{7-x} \cdot \dfrac{(x-7)(x-2)}{(x-3)(x-2)}$

$\qquad\qquad\qquad = \dfrac{x+2}{-(x-7)} \cdot \dfrac{(x-7)(x-2)}{(x-3)(x-2)}$

$\qquad\qquad\qquad = -\dfrac{x+2}{x-3}$

29. $\dfrac{x^2+7x+10}{x-1} \div \dfrac{x^2+2x-15}{x-1}$

$= \dfrac{x^2+7x+10}{x-1} \cdot \dfrac{x-1}{x^2+2x-15}$

$= \dfrac{(x+5)(x+2)}{x-1} \cdot \dfrac{x-1}{(x+5)(x-3)}$

$= \dfrac{x+2}{x-3}$

31. $\dfrac{5x-10}{12} \div \dfrac{4x-8}{8} = \dfrac{5x-10}{12} \cdot \dfrac{8}{4x-8}$

$= \dfrac{5(x-2)}{2\cdot 6} \cdot \dfrac{4\cdot 2}{4(x-2)}$

$= \dfrac{5}{6}$

33. $\dfrac{x^2+5x}{8} \cdot \dfrac{9}{3x+15} = \dfrac{x(x+5)}{8} \cdot \dfrac{3\cdot 3}{3(x+5)} = \dfrac{3x}{8}$

35. $\dfrac{7}{6p^2+q} \div \dfrac{14}{18p^2+3q} = \dfrac{7}{6p^2+q} \cdot \dfrac{18p^2+3q}{14}$

$= \dfrac{7}{6p^2+q} \cdot \dfrac{3(6p^2+q)}{7\cdot 2}$

$= \dfrac{3}{2}$

37. $\dfrac{3x+4y}{x^2+4xy+4y^2} \cdot \dfrac{x+2y}{2} = \dfrac{3x+4y}{(x+2y)^2} \cdot \dfrac{x+2y}{2}$

$= \dfrac{3x+4y}{2(x+2y)}$

39. $\dfrac{(x+2)^2}{x-2} \div \dfrac{x^2-4}{2x-4} = \dfrac{(x+2)^2}{x-2} \cdot \dfrac{2x-4}{x^2-4}$

$= \dfrac{(x+2)(x+2)}{x-2} \cdot \dfrac{2(x-2)}{(x-2)(x+2)}$

$= \dfrac{2(x+2)}{x-2}$

41. $\dfrac{x^2-4}{24x} \div \dfrac{2-x}{6xy} = \dfrac{x^2-4}{24x} \cdot \dfrac{6xy}{2-x}$

$= \dfrac{(x+2)(x-2)}{6\cdot 4\cdot x} \cdot \dfrac{6\cdot x\cdot y}{-1(x-2)}$

$= \dfrac{y(x+2)}{-4}$

$= -\dfrac{y(x+2)}{4}$

43. $\dfrac{a^2+7a+12}{a^2+5a+6} \cdot \dfrac{a^2+8a+15}{a^2+5a+4}$

$= \dfrac{(a+4)(a+3)}{(a+3)(a+2)} \cdot \dfrac{(a+5)(a+3)}{(a+4)(a+1)}$

$= \dfrac{(a+5)(a+3)}{(a+2)(a+1)}$

45. $\dfrac{5x-20}{3x^2+x} \cdot \dfrac{3x^2+13x+4}{x^2-16}$

$= \dfrac{5(x-4)}{x(3x+1)} \cdot \dfrac{(x+4)(3x+1)}{(x+4)(x-4)}$

$= \dfrac{5}{x}$

47. $\dfrac{8n^2-18}{2n^2-5n+3} \div \dfrac{6n^2+7n-3}{n^2-9n+8}$

$= \dfrac{8n^2-18}{2n^2-5n+3} \cdot \dfrac{n^2-9n+8}{6n^2+7n-3}$

$= \dfrac{2(4n^2-9)}{(2n-3)(n-1)} \cdot \dfrac{(n-8)(n-1)}{(3n-1)(2n+3)}$

$= \dfrac{2(2n-3)(2n+3)}{(2n-3)(n-1)} \cdot \dfrac{(n-8)(n-1)}{(3n-1)(2n+3)}$

$= \dfrac{2(n-8)}{3n-1}$

49. 10 square feet

$= \dfrac{10 \text{ square feet}}{1} \cdot \dfrac{144 \text{ square inches}}{1 \text{ square foot}}$

$= 1440$ square inches

51. 45 square feet $= \dfrac{45 \text{ square feet}}{1} \cdot \dfrac{1 \text{ square yard}}{9 \text{ square feet}}$

$= 5$ square yards

53. 3 cubic yards $= \dfrac{3 \text{ cubic yards}}{1} \cdot \dfrac{27 \text{ cubic feet}}{1 \text{ cubic yard}}$

$= 81$ cubic feet

55. $\dfrac{50 \text{ miles}}{1 \text{ hour}} = \dfrac{50 \text{ miles}}{1 \text{ hour}} \cdot \dfrac{5280 \text{ feet}}{1 \text{ mile}} \cdot \dfrac{1 \text{ hour}}{3600 \text{ seconds}}$

≈ 73 feet per second

57. 6.3 square yards

$= \dfrac{6.3 \text{ square yards}}{1} \cdot \dfrac{9 \text{ square feet}}{1 \text{ square yard}}$

$= 56.7$ square feet

59. 133,500 square yards

$$= \frac{133{,}500 \text{ square yards}}{1} \cdot \frac{9 \text{ square feet}}{1 \text{ square yard}}$$

$$= 1{,}201{,}500 \text{ square feet}$$

61. 359.2 feet per second

$$= \frac{359.2 \text{ feet}}{1 \text{ second}} \cdot \frac{3600 \text{ seconds}}{1 \text{ hour}} \cdot \frac{1 \text{ mile}}{5280 \text{ feet}}$$

$$\approx 244.9 \text{ miles per hour}$$

63. $\dfrac{1}{5} + \dfrac{4}{5} = \dfrac{1+4}{5} = \dfrac{5}{5} = 1$

65. $\dfrac{9}{9} - \dfrac{19}{9} = \dfrac{9-19}{9} = \dfrac{-10}{9} = -\dfrac{10}{9}$

67. $\dfrac{6}{5} + \left(\dfrac{1}{5} - \dfrac{8}{5} \right) = \dfrac{6}{5} + \left(-\dfrac{7}{5} \right) = -\dfrac{1}{5}$

69. $\dfrac{4}{a} \cdot \dfrac{1}{b} = \dfrac{4 \cdot 1}{a \cdot b} = \dfrac{4}{ab}$

The statement is true.

71. $\dfrac{x}{5} \cdot \dfrac{x+3}{4} = \dfrac{x^2+3x}{20} \neq \dfrac{2x+3}{20}$

The statement is false.

73. $\dfrac{2x}{x^2-25} \cdot \dfrac{x+5}{9x} = \dfrac{2 \cdot x}{(x+5)(x-5)} \cdot \dfrac{x+5}{9 \cdot x}$

$$= \dfrac{2}{9(x-5)}$$

The area is $\dfrac{2}{9(x-5)}$ square feet.

75. $\left(\dfrac{x^2-y^2}{x^2+y^2} \div \dfrac{x^2-y^2}{3x} \right) \cdot \dfrac{x^2+y^2}{6}$

$$= \dfrac{x^2-y^2}{x^2+y^2} \cdot \dfrac{3x}{x^2-y^2} \cdot \dfrac{x^2+y^2}{6}$$

$$= \dfrac{3x}{6}$$

$$= \dfrac{x}{2}$$

77. $\left(\dfrac{2a+b}{b^2} \cdot \dfrac{3a^2-2ab}{ab+2b^2} \right) \div \dfrac{a^2-3ab+2b^2}{5ab-10b^2}$

$$= \dfrac{2a+b}{b^2} \cdot \dfrac{3a^2-2ab}{ab+2b^2} \cdot \dfrac{5ab-10b^2}{a^2-3ab+2b^2}$$

$$= \dfrac{2a+b}{b^2} \cdot \dfrac{a(3a-2b)}{b(a+2b)} \cdot \dfrac{5 \cdot b(a-2b)}{(a-b)(a-2b)}$$

$$= \dfrac{5a(2a+b)(3a-2b)}{b^2(a-b)(a+2b)}$$

79. answers may vary

81. $\$2000 \text{ US} = \dfrac{\$2000 \text{ US}}{1} \cdot \dfrac{1 \text{ euro}}{\$1.3595 \text{ US}}$

$$= \dfrac{2000}{1.3595} \text{ euros}$$

$$\approx 1471.129 \text{ euros}$$

On that day, $2000 US was worth 1471.13 euros.

Section 12.3

Practice Problems

1. $\dfrac{8x}{3y} + \dfrac{x}{3y} = \dfrac{8x+x}{3y} = \dfrac{9x}{3y} = \dfrac{3x}{y}$

2. $\dfrac{3x}{3x-7} - \dfrac{7}{3x-7} = \dfrac{3x-7}{3x-7} = \dfrac{1}{1} \text{ or } 1$

3. $\dfrac{2x^2+5x}{x+2} - \dfrac{4x+6}{x+2} = \dfrac{2x^2+5x-(4x+6)}{x+2}$

$$= \dfrac{2x^2+5x-4x-6}{x+2}$$

$$= \dfrac{2x^2+x-6}{x+2}$$

$$= \dfrac{(2x-3)(x+2)}{x+2}$$

$$= 2x-3$$

4. a. $\dfrac{2}{9}, \dfrac{7}{15}$

$9 = 3^2$ and $15 = 3 \cdot 5$

$\text{LCD} = 3^2 \cdot 5 = 9 \cdot 5 = 45$

b. $\dfrac{5}{6x^3}, \dfrac{11}{8x^5}$

$6x^3 = 2 \cdot 3 \cdot x^3$ and $8x^5 = 2^3 \cdot x^5$

$\text{LCD} = 3 \cdot 2^3 \cdot x^5 = 3 \cdot 8 \cdot x^5 = 24x^5$

5. $\dfrac{3a}{a+5}, \dfrac{7a}{a-5}$

LCD $= (a+5)(a-5)$

6. $\dfrac{7x^2}{(x-4)^2}, \dfrac{5x}{3x-12}$

$(x-4)^2 = (x-4)(x-4)$ and $3x-12 = 3(x-4)$

LCD $= 3(x-4)(x-4) = 3(x-4)^2$

7. $\dfrac{y+5}{y^2+2y-3}, \dfrac{y+4}{y^2-3y+2}$

$y^2+2y-3 = (y+3)(y-1)$

$y^2-3y+2 = (y-2)(y-1)$

LCD $= (y+3)(y-2)(y-1)$

8. $\dfrac{6}{x-4}, \dfrac{9}{4-x}$

$(4-x) = -(x-4)$

LCD $= (x-4)$ or $(4-x)$

9. $\dfrac{2x}{5y} = \dfrac{2x}{5y} \cdot 1 = \dfrac{2x}{5y} \cdot \dfrac{4x^2y}{4x^2y} = \dfrac{8x^3y}{20x^2y^2}$

10. $\dfrac{3}{x^2-25} = \dfrac{3}{(x-5)(x+5)}$

$= \dfrac{3}{(x-5)(x+5)} \cdot \dfrac{x-3}{x-3}$

$= \dfrac{3(x-3)}{(x-5)(x+5)(x-3)}$

$= \dfrac{3x-9}{(x-5)(x+5)(x-3)}$

Vocabulary and Readiness Check

1. $\dfrac{7}{11} + \dfrac{2}{11} = \dfrac{9}{\underline{11}}$

2. $\dfrac{7}{11} - \dfrac{2}{11} = \dfrac{5}{\underline{11}}$

3. $\dfrac{a}{b} + \dfrac{c}{b} = \dfrac{a+c}{\underline{b}}$

4. $\dfrac{a}{b} - \dfrac{c}{b} = \dfrac{a-c}{\underline{b}}$

5. $\dfrac{5}{x} - \dfrac{6+x}{x} = \dfrac{5-(6+x)}{\underline{x}}$

Exercise Set 12.3

1. $\dfrac{a}{13} + \dfrac{9}{13} = \dfrac{a+9}{13}$

3. $\dfrac{4m}{3n} + \dfrac{5m}{3n} = \dfrac{4m+5m}{3n} = \dfrac{9m}{3n} = \dfrac{3m}{n}$

5. $\dfrac{4m}{m-6} - \dfrac{24}{m-6} = \dfrac{4m-24}{m-6} = \dfrac{4(m-6)}{m-6} = 4$

7. $\dfrac{9}{3+y} + \dfrac{y+1}{3+y} = \dfrac{9+y+1}{3+y} = \dfrac{y+10}{3+y}$

9. $\dfrac{5x^2+4x}{x-1} - \dfrac{2x+3}{x-1} = \dfrac{5x^2+4x-(2x+3)}{x-1}$

$= \dfrac{5x^2+2x-3}{x-1}$

$= \dfrac{(5x-3)(x+1)}{x-1}$

11. $\dfrac{4a}{a^2+2a-15} - \dfrac{12}{a^2+2a-15} = \dfrac{4a-12}{a^2+2a-15}$

$= \dfrac{4(a-3)}{(a+5)(a-3)}$

$= \dfrac{4}{a+5}$

13. $\dfrac{2x+3}{x^2-x-30} - \dfrac{x-2}{x^2-x-30} = \dfrac{2x+3-(x-2)}{x^2-x-30}$

$= \dfrac{x+5}{(x-6)(x+5)}$

$= \dfrac{1}{x-6}$

15. $2x = 2 \cdot x$

$4x^3 = 2^2 \cdot x^3$

LCD $= 2^2 \cdot x^3 = 4x^3$

17. $8x = 2 \cdot 2 \cdot 2 \cdot x$

$2x+4 = 2(x+2)$

LCD $= 2 \cdot 2 \cdot 2 \cdot x(x+2) = 8x(x+2)$

19. $x+3 = x+3$

$x-2 = x-2$

LCD $= (x+3)(x-2)$

21. $x + 6 = x + 6$
$3x + 18 = 3(x + 6)$
LCD $= 3(x + 6)$

23. $(x - 6)^2 = (x - 6)(x - 6)$
$5x - 30 = 5(x - 6)$
LCD $= 5(x - 6)(x - 6) = 5(x - 6)^2$

25. $3x + 3 = 3(x + 1)$
$2x^2 + 4x + 2 = 2(x^2 + 2x + 1) = 2(x + 1)^2$
LCD $= 2 \cdot 3 \cdot (x + 1)^2 = 6(x + 1)^2$

27. $8 - x = -(x - 8)$
LCD $= x - 8$ or $8 - x$

29. $x^2 + 3x - 4 = (x - 1)(x + 4)$
$x^2 + 2x - 3 = (x - 1)(x + 3)$
LCD $= (x - 1)(x + 4)(x + 3)$

31. $3x^2 + 4x + 1 = (3x + 1)(x + 1)$
$2x^2 - x - 1 = (2x + 1)(x - 1)$
LCD $= (3x + 1)(x + 1)(2x + 1)(x - 1)$

33. $x^2 - 16 = (x + 4)(x - 4)$
$2x^3 - 8x^2 = 2x^2(x - 4)$
LCD $= 2x^2(x + 4)(x - 4)$

35. $\dfrac{3}{2x} = \dfrac{3 \cdot 2x}{2x \cdot 2x} = \dfrac{6x}{4x^2}$

37. $\dfrac{6}{3a} = \dfrac{6 \cdot 4b^2}{3a \cdot 4b^2} = \dfrac{24b^2}{12ab^2}$

39. $\dfrac{9}{2x + 6} = \dfrac{9}{2(x + 3)} = \dfrac{9y}{2(x + 3)y} = \dfrac{9y}{2y(x + 3)}$

41. $\dfrac{9a + 2}{5a + 10} = \dfrac{9a + 2}{5(a + 2)} = \dfrac{(9a + 2) \cdot b}{5(a + 2) \cdot b} = \dfrac{9ab + 2b}{5b(a + 2)}$

43. $\dfrac{x}{x^3 + 6x^2 + 8x} = \dfrac{x}{x(x^2 + 6x + 8)}$
$\phantom{\dfrac{x}{x^3 + 6x^2 + 8x}} = \dfrac{x}{x(x + 4)(x + 2)}$
$\phantom{\dfrac{x}{x^3 + 6x^2 + 8x}} = \dfrac{x(x + 1)}{x(x + 4)(x + 2)(x + 1)}$
$\phantom{\dfrac{x}{x^3 + 6x^2 + 8x}} = \dfrac{x^2 + x}{x(x + 4)(x + 2)(x + 1)}$

45. $\dfrac{9y - 1}{15x^2 - 30} = \dfrac{(9y - 1) \cdot 2}{(15x^2 - 30) \cdot 2} = \dfrac{18y - 2}{30x^2 - 60}$

47. $\dfrac{5x}{7} + \dfrac{9x}{7} = \dfrac{5x + 9x}{7} = \dfrac{14x}{7} = 2x$

49. $\dfrac{x + 3}{4} \div \dfrac{2x - 1}{4} = \dfrac{x + 3}{4} \cdot \dfrac{4}{2x - 1} = \dfrac{x + 3}{2x - 1}$

51. $\dfrac{x^2}{x - 6} - \dfrac{5x + 6}{x - 6} = \dfrac{x^2 - (5x + 6)}{x - 6}$
$\phantom{\dfrac{x^2}{x - 6} - \dfrac{5x + 6}{x - 6}} = \dfrac{x^2 - 5x - 6}{x - 6}$
$\phantom{\dfrac{x^2}{x - 6} - \dfrac{5x + 6}{x - 6}} = \dfrac{(x - 6)(x + 1)}{x - 6}$
$\phantom{\dfrac{x^2}{x - 6} - \dfrac{5x + 6}{x - 6}} = x + 1$

53. $\dfrac{x^2 + 5x}{x^2 - 25} \cdot \dfrac{3x - 15}{x^2} = \dfrac{x(x + 5)}{(x + 5)(x - 5)} \cdot \dfrac{3(x - 5)}{x^2} = \dfrac{3}{x}$

55. $\dfrac{x^3 + 7x^2}{3x^3 - x^2} \div \dfrac{5x^2 + 36x + 7}{9x^2 - 1}$
$= \dfrac{x^3 + 7x^2}{3x^3 - x^2} \cdot \dfrac{9x^2 - 1}{5x^2 + 36x + 7}$
$= \dfrac{x^2(x + 7)}{x^2(3x - 1)} \cdot \dfrac{(3x - 1)(3x + 1)}{(5x + 1)(x + 7)}$
$= \dfrac{3x + 1}{5x + 1}$

57. $\dfrac{2}{3} + \dfrac{5}{7} = \dfrac{2 \cdot 7}{3 \cdot 7} + \dfrac{5 \cdot 3}{7 \cdot 3} = \dfrac{14}{21} + \dfrac{15}{21} = \dfrac{29}{21}$

59. $\dfrac{2}{6} - \dfrac{3}{4} = \dfrac{2 \cdot 2}{6 \cdot 2} - \dfrac{3 \cdot 3}{4 \cdot 3} = \dfrac{4}{12} - \dfrac{9}{12} = -\dfrac{5}{12}$

61. $\dfrac{1}{12} + \dfrac{3}{20} = \dfrac{1 \cdot 5}{12 \cdot 5} + \dfrac{3 \cdot 3}{20 \cdot 3} = \dfrac{5}{60} + \dfrac{9}{60} = \dfrac{14}{60} = \dfrac{7}{30}$

63. $4a - 20 = 4(a - 5)$

$(a-5)^2 = (a-5)(a-5)$

$LCD = 4(a-5)(a-5) = 4(a-5)^2$; d

65. answers may vary

67. The perimeter of a square is 4 times the side length.

$4 \cdot \dfrac{5}{x-2} = \dfrac{4}{1} \cdot \dfrac{5}{x-2} = \dfrac{20}{x-2}$

The perimeter is $\dfrac{20}{x-2}$ meters.

69. answers may vary

71. $88 = 2^3 \cdot 11$

$4332 = 2^2 \cdot 3 \cdot 19^2$

$LCD = 2^3 \cdot 3 \cdot 11 \cdot 19^2 = 95,304$ Earth days

73. answers may vary

75. answers may vary

Section 12.4

Practice Problems

1. a. $\dfrac{y}{5} - \dfrac{3y}{15} = \dfrac{y \cdot 3}{5 \cdot 3} - \dfrac{3y}{15} = \dfrac{3y - 3y}{15} = \dfrac{0}{15} = 0$

b. $\dfrac{5}{8x} + \dfrac{11}{10x^2} = \dfrac{5 \cdot 5x}{8x \cdot 5x} + \dfrac{11 \cdot 4}{10x^2 \cdot 4}$

$= \dfrac{25x}{40x^2} + \dfrac{44}{40x^2}$

$= \dfrac{25x + 44}{40x^2}$

2. $\dfrac{10x}{x^2 - 9} - \dfrac{5}{x+3} = \dfrac{10x}{(x-3)(x+3)} - \dfrac{5(x-3)}{(x+3)(x-3)}$

$= \dfrac{10x - 5(x-3)}{(x+3)(x-3)}$

$= \dfrac{10x - 5x + 15}{(x+3)(x-3)}$

$= \dfrac{5x + 15}{(x+3)(x-3)}$

$= \dfrac{5(x+3)}{(x+3)(x-3)}$

$= \dfrac{5}{x-3}$

3. $\dfrac{5}{7x} + \dfrac{2}{x+1} = \dfrac{5(x+1)}{7x(x+1)} + \dfrac{2(7x)}{(x+1)(7x)}$

$= \dfrac{5(x+1) + 2(7x)}{7x(x+1)}$

$= \dfrac{5x + 5 + 14x}{7x(x+1)}$

$= \dfrac{19x + 5}{7x(x+1)}$

4. $\dfrac{10}{x-6} - \dfrac{15}{6-x} = \dfrac{10}{x-6} - \dfrac{15}{-(x-6)}$

$= \dfrac{10}{x-6} - \dfrac{-15}{x-6}$

$= \dfrac{10 - (-15)}{x-6}$

$= \dfrac{25}{x-6}$

5. $2 + \dfrac{x}{x+5} = \dfrac{2}{1} + \dfrac{x}{x+5}$

$= \dfrac{2(x+5)}{1(x+5)} + \dfrac{x}{x+5}$

$= \dfrac{2x + 10 + x}{x+5}$

$= \dfrac{3x + 10}{x+5}$

6. $\dfrac{4}{3x^2 + 2x} - \dfrac{3x}{12x + 8} = \dfrac{4}{x(3x+2)} - \dfrac{3x}{4(3x+2)}$

$= \dfrac{4(4)}{x(3x+2)(4)} - \dfrac{3x(x)}{4(3x+2)(x)}$

$= \dfrac{16 - 3x^2}{4x(3x+2)}$

7. $\dfrac{6x}{x^2+4x+4} + \dfrac{x}{x^2-4}$

$= \dfrac{6x}{(x+2)(x+2)} + \dfrac{x}{(x+2)(x-2)}$

$= \dfrac{6x(x-2)}{(x+2)(x+2)(x-2)} + \dfrac{x(x+2)}{(x+2)(x-2)(x+2)}$

$= \dfrac{6x(x-2)+x(x+2)}{(x+2)^2(x-2)}$

$= \dfrac{6x^2-12x+x^2+2x}{(x+2)^2(x-2)}$

$= \dfrac{7x^2-10x}{(x+2)^2(x-2)}$

$= \dfrac{x(7x-10)}{(x+2)^2(x-2)}$

Vocabulary and Readiness Check

1. $\dfrac{3}{7x} + \dfrac{5}{7} = \dfrac{3}{7x} + \dfrac{5 \cdot x}{7 \cdot x} = \dfrac{3+5x}{7x};\ b$

2. $\dfrac{1}{x} + \dfrac{2}{x^2} = \dfrac{1 \cdot x}{x \cdot x} + \dfrac{2}{x^2} = \dfrac{x+2}{x^2};\ a$

Exercise Set 12.4

1. $\dfrac{4}{2x} + \dfrac{9}{3x} = \dfrac{4 \cdot 3}{2x \cdot 3} + \dfrac{9 \cdot 2}{3x \cdot 2} = \dfrac{12}{6x} + \dfrac{18}{6x} = \dfrac{30}{6x} = \dfrac{5}{x}$

3. $\dfrac{15a}{b} + \dfrac{6b}{5} = \dfrac{15a \cdot 5}{b \cdot 5} + \dfrac{6b \cdot b}{5 \cdot b}$

$= \dfrac{75a}{5b} + \dfrac{6b^2}{5b}$

$= \dfrac{75a+6b^2}{5b}$

5. $\dfrac{3}{x} + \dfrac{5}{2x^2} = \dfrac{3 \cdot 2x}{x \cdot 2x} + \dfrac{5}{2x^2} = \dfrac{6x}{2x^2} + \dfrac{5}{2x^2} = \dfrac{6x+5}{2x^2}$

7. $\dfrac{6}{x+1} + \dfrac{10}{2x+2} = \dfrac{6}{x+1} + \dfrac{10}{2(x+1)}$

$= \dfrac{6}{x+1} + \dfrac{5}{x+1}$

$= \dfrac{11}{x+1}$

9. $\dfrac{3}{x+2} - \dfrac{2x}{x^2-4} = \dfrac{3(x-2)}{(x+2)(x-2)} - \dfrac{2x}{(x+2)(x-2)}$

$= \dfrac{3x-6-2x}{(x+2)(x-2)}$

$= \dfrac{x-6}{(x+2)(x-2)}$

11. $\dfrac{3}{4x} + \dfrac{8}{x-2} = \dfrac{3(x-2)}{4x(x-2)} + \dfrac{8(4x)}{(x-2)(4x)}$

$= \dfrac{3x-6+32x}{4x(x-2)}$

$= \dfrac{35x-6}{4x(x-2)}$

13. $\dfrac{6}{x-3} + \dfrac{8}{3-x} = \dfrac{6}{x-3} + \dfrac{8}{-(x-3)}$

$= \dfrac{6}{x-3} + \dfrac{-8}{x-3}$

$= \dfrac{6+(-8)}{x-3}$

$= \dfrac{-2}{x-3}$

$= -\dfrac{2}{x-3}$

15. $\dfrac{9}{x-3} + \dfrac{9}{3-x} = \dfrac{9}{x-3} + \dfrac{9}{-(x-3)}$

$= \dfrac{9}{x-3} + \dfrac{-9}{x-3}$

$= \dfrac{0}{x-3}$

$= 0$

17. $\dfrac{-8}{x^2-1} - \dfrac{7}{1-x^2} = \dfrac{-8}{x^2-1} - \dfrac{7}{-(x^2-1)}$

$= \dfrac{-8}{x^2-1} - \dfrac{-7}{x^2-1}$

$= \dfrac{-8-(-7)}{x^2-1}$

$= \dfrac{-1}{x^2-1}$

$= -\dfrac{1}{x^2-1}$

19. $\dfrac{5}{x} + 2 = \dfrac{5}{x} + \dfrac{2}{1} = \dfrac{5}{x} + \dfrac{2 \cdot x}{1 \cdot x} = \dfrac{5+2x}{x}$

21. $\dfrac{5}{x-2}+6 = \dfrac{5}{x-2}+\dfrac{6}{1}$

$\qquad = \dfrac{5}{x-2}+\dfrac{6(x-2)}{1(x-2)}$

$\qquad = \dfrac{5+6x-12}{x-2}$

$\qquad = \dfrac{6x-7}{x-2}$

23. $\dfrac{y+2}{y+3}-2 = \dfrac{y+2}{y+3}-\dfrac{2}{1}$

$\qquad = \dfrac{y+2}{y+3}-\dfrac{2(y+3)}{1(y+3)}$

$\qquad = \dfrac{y+2}{y+3}-\dfrac{2y+6}{y+3}$

$\qquad = \dfrac{y+2-(2y+6)}{y+3}$

$\qquad = \dfrac{y+2-2y-6}{y+3}$

$\qquad = \dfrac{-y-4}{y+3}$

$\qquad = \dfrac{-(y+4)}{y+3}$

$\qquad = -\dfrac{y+4}{y+3}$

25. $\dfrac{-x+2}{x}-\dfrac{x-6}{4x} = \dfrac{4(-x+2)}{4x}-\dfrac{x-6}{4x}$

$\qquad = \dfrac{-4x+8-(x-6)}{4x}$

$\qquad = \dfrac{-4x+8-x+6}{4x}$

$\qquad = \dfrac{-5x+14}{4x}$ or $-\dfrac{5x-14}{4x}$

27. $\dfrac{5x}{x+2}-\dfrac{3x-4}{x+2} = \dfrac{5x-(3x-4)}{x+2}$

$\qquad = \dfrac{5x-3x+4}{x+2}$

$\qquad = \dfrac{2x+4}{x+2}$

$\qquad = \dfrac{2(x+2)}{x+2}$

$\qquad = 2$

29. $\dfrac{3x^4}{7}-\dfrac{4x^2}{21} = \dfrac{3x^4 \cdot 3}{7 \cdot 3}-\dfrac{4x^2}{21}$

$\qquad = \dfrac{9x^4}{21}-\dfrac{4x^2}{21}$

$\qquad = \dfrac{9x^4-4x^2}{21}$

31. $\dfrac{1}{x+3}-\dfrac{1}{(x+3)^2} = \dfrac{1\cdot(x+3)}{(x+3)(x+3)}-\dfrac{1}{(x+3)(x+3)}$

$\qquad = \dfrac{x+3-1}{(x+3)^2}$

$\qquad = \dfrac{x+2}{(x+3)^2}$

33. $\dfrac{4}{5b}+\dfrac{1}{b-1} = \dfrac{4(b-1)}{5b(b-1)}+\dfrac{1\cdot 5b}{(b-1)(5b)}$

$\qquad = \dfrac{4b-4}{5b(b-1)}+\dfrac{5b}{5b(b-1)}$

$\qquad = \dfrac{4b-4+5b}{5b(b-1)}$

$\qquad = \dfrac{9b-4}{5b(b-1)}$

35. $\dfrac{2}{m}+1 = \dfrac{2}{m}+\dfrac{m}{m} = \dfrac{2+m}{m}$

37. $\dfrac{2x}{x-7}-\dfrac{x}{x-2} = \dfrac{2x(x-2)}{(x-7)(x-2)}-\dfrac{x(x-7)}{(x-2)(x-7)}$

$\qquad = \dfrac{2x^2-4x-(x^2-7x)}{(x-7)(x-2)}$

$\qquad = \dfrac{2x^2-4x-x^2+7x}{(x-7)(x-2)}$

$\qquad = \dfrac{x^2+3x}{(x-7)(x-2)}$

$\qquad = \dfrac{x(x+3)}{(x-7)(x-2)}$

39. $\dfrac{6}{1-2x}-\dfrac{4}{2x-1} = \dfrac{6}{1-2x}-\dfrac{4}{-(1-2x)}$

$\qquad = \dfrac{6}{1-2x}-\dfrac{-4}{1-2x}$

$\qquad = \dfrac{6+4}{1-2x}$

$\qquad = \dfrac{10}{1-2x}$

41. $\dfrac{7}{(x+1)(x-1)}+\dfrac{8}{(x+1)^2}$

$=\dfrac{7(x+1)}{(x+1)(x-1)(x+1)}+\dfrac{8(x-1)}{(x+1)^2(x-1)}$

$=\dfrac{7x+7+8x-8}{(x+1)^2(x-1)}$

$=\dfrac{15x-1}{(x+1)^2(x-1)}$

43. $\dfrac{x}{x^2-1}-\dfrac{2}{x^2-2x+1}$

$=\dfrac{x(x-1)}{(x-1)(x+1)(x-1)}-\dfrac{2(x+1)}{(x-1)^2(x+1)}$

$=\dfrac{x^2-x-2x-2}{(x-1)^2(x+1)}$

$=\dfrac{x^2-3x-2}{(x-1)^2(x+1)}$

45. $\dfrac{3a}{2a+6}-\dfrac{a-1}{a+3}=\dfrac{3a}{2(a+3)}-\dfrac{(a-1)(2)}{(a+3)(2)}$

$=\dfrac{3a-(2a-2)}{2(a+3)}$

$=\dfrac{3a-2a+2}{2(a+3)}$

$=\dfrac{a+2}{2(a+3)}$

47. $\dfrac{y-1}{2y+3}+\dfrac{3}{(2y+3)^2}=\dfrac{(y-1)(2y+3)}{(2y+3)^2}+\dfrac{3}{(2y+3)^2}$

$=\dfrac{2y^2+3y-2y-3+3}{(2y+3)^2}$

$=\dfrac{2y^2+y}{(2y+3)^2}$

$=\dfrac{y(2y+1)}{(2y+3)^2}$

49. $\dfrac{5}{2-x}+\dfrac{x}{2x-4}=\dfrac{5}{-(x-2)}+\dfrac{x}{2(x-2)}$

$=\dfrac{-5(2)}{(x-2)(2)}+\dfrac{x}{2(x-2)}$

$=\dfrac{-10+x}{2(x-2)}$

$=\dfrac{x-10}{2(x-2)}$

51. $\dfrac{15}{x^2+6x-19}+\dfrac{2}{x+3}=\dfrac{15}{(x+3)^2}+\dfrac{2(x+3)}{(x+3)(x+3)}$

$=\dfrac{15+2x+6}{(x+3)^2}$

$=\dfrac{2x+21}{(x+3)^2}$

53. $\dfrac{13}{x^2-5x+6}-\dfrac{5}{x-3}$

$=\dfrac{13}{(x-3)(x-2)}-\dfrac{5(x-2)}{(x-3)(x-2)}$

$=\dfrac{13-(5x-10)}{(x-3)(x-2)}$

$=\dfrac{13-5x+10}{(x-3)(x-2)}$

$=\dfrac{-5x+23}{(x-3)(x-2)}$

55. $\dfrac{70}{m^2-100}+\dfrac{7}{2(m+10)}$

$=\dfrac{70\cdot2}{(m-10)(m+10)2}+\dfrac{7(m-10)}{2(m+10)(m-10)}$

$=\dfrac{140+7m-70}{2(m-10)(m+10)}$

$=\dfrac{7m+70}{2(m-10)(m+10)}$

$=\dfrac{7(m+10)}{2(m-10)(m+10)}$

$=\dfrac{7}{2(m-10)}$

57. $\dfrac{x+8}{x^2-5x-6}+\dfrac{x+1}{x^2-4x-5}$

$=\dfrac{x+8}{(x+1)(x-6)}+\dfrac{x+1}{(x+1)(x-5)}$

$=\dfrac{(x+8)(x-5)+(x+1)(x-6)}{(x+1)(x-6)(x-5)}$

$=\dfrac{x^2+3x-40+x^2-5x-6}{(x+1)(x-6)(x-5)}$

$=\dfrac{2x^2-2x-46}{(x+1)(x-6)(x-5)}$

$=\dfrac{2(x^2-x-23)}{(x+1)(x-6)(x-5)}$

59. $\dfrac{5}{4n^2-12n+8}-\dfrac{3}{3n^2-6n}=\dfrac{5\cdot 3n}{4(n-2)(n-1)3n}-\dfrac{3(n-1)\cdot 4}{3n(n-2)(n-1)4}$

$\qquad\qquad\qquad\qquad\qquad\quad =\dfrac{15n-12n+12}{12n(n-2)(n-1)}$

$\qquad\qquad\qquad\qquad\qquad\quad =\dfrac{3n+12}{12n(n-2)(n-1)}$

$\qquad\qquad\qquad\qquad\qquad\quad =\dfrac{3(n+4)}{12n(n-2)(n-1)}$

$\qquad\qquad\qquad\qquad\qquad\quad =\dfrac{n+4}{4n(n-2)(n-1)}$

61. $\dfrac{15x}{x+8}\cdot\dfrac{2x+16}{3x}=\dfrac{5\cdot 3x}{x+8}\cdot\dfrac{2(x+8)}{3x}=\dfrac{5\cdot 2}{1}=10$

63. $\dfrac{8x+7}{3x+5}-\dfrac{2x-3}{3x+5}=\dfrac{8x+7-(2x-3)}{3x+5}$

$\qquad\qquad\qquad\qquad =\dfrac{8x+7-2x+3}{3x+5}$

$\qquad\qquad\qquad\qquad =\dfrac{6x+10}{3x+5}$

$\qquad\qquad\qquad\qquad =\dfrac{2(3x+5)}{3x+5}$

$\qquad\qquad\qquad\qquad =2$

65. $\dfrac{5a+10}{18}\div\dfrac{a^2-4}{10a}=\dfrac{5a+10}{18}\cdot\dfrac{10a}{a^2-4}$

$\qquad\qquad\qquad\qquad =\dfrac{5(a+2)}{9\cdot 2}\cdot\dfrac{2\cdot 5a}{(a+2)(a-2)}$

$\qquad\qquad\qquad\qquad =\dfrac{5\cdot 5a}{9(a-2)}$

$\qquad\qquad\qquad\qquad =\dfrac{25a}{9(a-2)}$

67. $\dfrac{5}{x^2-3x+2}+\dfrac{1}{x-2}=\dfrac{5}{(x-2)(x-1)}+\dfrac{1(x-1)}{(x-2)(x-1)}$

$\qquad\qquad\qquad\qquad\quad =\dfrac{5+x-1}{(x-2)(x-1)}$

$\qquad\qquad\qquad\qquad\quad =\dfrac{x+4}{(x-2)(x-1)}$

69. $3x+5=7$

$\qquad 3x=2$

$\qquad\;\, x=\dfrac{2}{3}$

71. $2x^2 - x - 1 = 0$

$(2x+1)(x-1) = 0$

$2x+1 = 0 \quad$ or $\quad x-1 = 0$

$\quad 2x = -1 \qquad\qquad x = 1$

$\qquad x = -\dfrac{1}{2}$

73. $4(x+6) + 3 = -3$

$\quad 4x + 24 + 3 = -3$

$\qquad 4x + 27 = -3$

$\qquad\quad 4x = -30$

$\qquad\quad x = \dfrac{-30}{4}$

$\qquad\quad x = -\dfrac{15}{2}$

75. $\dfrac{3}{x} - \dfrac{2x}{x^2-1} + \dfrac{5}{x+1} = \dfrac{3}{x} - \dfrac{2x}{(x-1)(x+1)} + \dfrac{5}{x+1}$

$\qquad\qquad = \dfrac{3(x-1)(x+1)}{x(x-1)(x+1)} - \dfrac{2x \cdot x}{(x-1)(x+1)x} + \dfrac{5 \cdot x(x-1)}{(x+1)x(x-1)}$

$\qquad\qquad = \dfrac{3x^2 - 3 - 2x^2 + 5x^2 - 5x}{x(x-1)(x+1)}$

$\qquad\qquad = \dfrac{6x^2 - 5x - 3}{x(x-1)(x+1)}$

77. $\dfrac{5}{x^2-4} + \dfrac{2}{x^2-4x+4} - \dfrac{3}{x^2-x-6} = \dfrac{5}{(x+2)(x-2)} + \dfrac{2}{(x-2)^2} - \dfrac{3}{(x+2)(x-3)}$

$\qquad\qquad = \dfrac{5(x-2)(x-3) + 2(x+2)(x-3) - 3(x-2)^2}{(x+2)(x-2)^2(x-3)}$

$\qquad\qquad = \dfrac{5(x^2-5x+6) + 2(x^2-x-6) - 3(x^2-4x+4)}{(x-2)^2(x+2)(x-3)}$

$\qquad\qquad = \dfrac{5x^2 - 25x + 30 + 2x^2 - 2x - 12 - 3x^2 + 12x - 12}{(x-2)^2(x+2)(x-3)}$

$\qquad\qquad = \dfrac{4x^2 - 15x + 6}{(x-2)^2(x+2)(x-3)}$

79. $\dfrac{9}{x^2+9x+14} - \dfrac{3x}{x^2+10x+21} + \dfrac{x+4}{x^2+5x+6} = \dfrac{9}{(x+2)(x+7)} - \dfrac{3x}{(x+3)(x+7)} + \dfrac{x+4}{(x+2)(x+3)}$

$\qquad\qquad = \dfrac{9(x+3)}{(x+2)(x+7)(x+3)} - \dfrac{3x(x+2)}{(x+3)(x+7)(x+2)} + \dfrac{(x+4)(x+7)}{(x+2)(x+3)(x+7)}$

$\qquad\qquad = \dfrac{9x + 27 - 3x^2 - 6x + x^2 + 7x + 4x + 28}{(x+2)(x+7)(x+3)}$

$\qquad\qquad = \dfrac{-2x^2 + 14x + 55}{(x+2)(x+7)(x+3)}$

81. $\dfrac{3}{x+4} - \dfrac{1}{x-4} = \dfrac{3(x-4)-1(x+4)}{(x+4)(x-4)}$

$\qquad\qquad\qquad = \dfrac{3x-12-x-4}{(x+4)(x-4)}$

$\qquad\qquad\qquad = \dfrac{2x-16}{(x+4)(x-4)}$

$\qquad\qquad\qquad = \dfrac{2(x-8)}{(x+4)(x-4)}$

The other piece of the board measures $\dfrac{2(x-8)}{(x+4)(x-4)}$ inches.

83. $1 - \dfrac{G}{P} = \dfrac{P}{P} - \dfrac{G}{P} = \dfrac{P-G}{P}$

85. answers may vary

87. $90 - \dfrac{40}{x} = \dfrac{90}{1} - \dfrac{40}{x}$

$\qquad\qquad\quad = \dfrac{90x}{x} - \dfrac{40}{x}$

$\qquad\qquad\quad = \dfrac{90x-40}{x}$

The complement measures $\left(\dfrac{90x-40}{x}\right)^{\circ}$.

89. answers may vary

Section 12.5

Practice Problems

1. The LCD is 20.

$$\dfrac{x}{4} + \dfrac{4}{5} = \dfrac{1}{20}$$

$$20\left(\dfrac{x}{4} + \dfrac{4}{5}\right) = 20\left(\dfrac{1}{20}\right)$$

$$20\left(\dfrac{x}{4}\right) + 20\left(\dfrac{4}{5}\right) = 20\left(\dfrac{1}{20}\right)$$

$$5x + 16 = 1$$

$$5x = -15$$

$$x = -3$$

The solution is -3.

2. The LCD is 15.

$$\frac{x+2}{3} - \frac{x-1}{5} = \frac{1}{15}$$

$$15\left(\frac{x+2}{3} - \frac{x-1}{5}\right) = 15\left(\frac{1}{15}\right)$$

$$15\left(\frac{x+2}{3}\right) - 15\left(\frac{x-1}{5}\right) = 15\left(\frac{1}{15}\right)$$

$$5(x+2) - 3(x-1) = 1$$

$$5x + 10 - 3x + 3 = 1$$

$$2x + 13 = 1$$

$$2x = -12$$

$$x = -6$$

The solution is −6.

3. The LCD is x.

$$2 + \frac{6}{x} = x + 7$$

$$x\left(2 + \frac{6}{x}\right) = x(x+7)$$

$$x(2) + x\left(\frac{6}{x}\right) = x \cdot x + x \cdot 7$$

$$2x + 6 = x^2 + 7x$$

$$0 = x^2 + 5x - 6$$

$$0 = (x+6)(x-1)$$

$$x + 6 = 0 \quad \text{or} \quad x - 1 = 0$$

$$x = -6 \qquad\qquad x = 1$$

Neither −6 nor 1 makes the denominator 0 in the original equation. Both −6 and 1 are solutions.

4. The LCD is $(x + 3)(x - 3)$.

$$\frac{2}{x+3} + \frac{3}{x-3} = \frac{-2}{x^2 - 9}$$

$$(x+3)(x-3)\left(\frac{2}{x+3} + \frac{3}{x-3}\right) = (x+3)(x-3)\left(\frac{-2}{x^2 - 9}\right)$$

$$(x+3)(x-3) \cdot \frac{2}{x+3} + (x+3)(x-3) \cdot \frac{3}{x-3} = (x+3)(x-3)\left(\frac{-2}{x^2 - 9}\right)$$

$$2(x-3) + 3(x+3) = -2$$

$$2x - 6 + 3x + 9 = -2$$

$$5x + 3 = -2$$

$$5x = -5$$

$$x = -1$$

The solution is −1.

5. The LCD is $x - 1$.

$$\frac{5x}{x-1} = \frac{5}{x-1} + 3$$

$$(x-1)\left(\frac{5x}{x-1}\right) = (x-1)\left(\frac{5}{x-1} + 3\right)$$

$$(x-1) \cdot \frac{5x}{x-1} = (x-1) \cdot \frac{5}{x-1} + (x-1) \cdot 3$$

$$5x = 5 + 3(x-1)$$

$$5x = 5 + 3x - 3$$

$$2x = 2$$

$$x = 1$$

1 makes the denominator 0 in the original equation. Therefore 1 is *not* a solution and this equation has no solution.

6. The LCD is $x + 3$.

$$x - \frac{6}{x+3} = \frac{2x}{x+3} + 2$$

$$(x+3)\left(x - \frac{6}{x+3}\right) = (x+3)\left(\frac{2x}{x+3} + 2\right)$$

$$(x+3)(x) - (x+3)\left(\frac{6}{x+3}\right) = (x+3)\left(\frac{2x}{x+3}\right) + (x+3)(2)$$

$$(x+3)(x) - 6 = 2x + 2(x+3)$$

$$x^2 + 3x - 6 = 2x + 2x + 6$$

$$x^2 - x - 12 = 0$$

$$(x-4)(x+3) = 0$$

$$x - 4 = 0 \quad \text{or} \quad x + 3 = 0$$
$$x = 4 \qquad\qquad x = 3$$

$x = 3$ can't be a solution of the original equation. The only solution is 4.

7. The LCD is abx.

$$\frac{1}{a} + \frac{1}{b} = \frac{1}{x}$$

$$abx\left(\frac{1}{a} + \frac{1}{b}\right) = abx\left(\frac{1}{x}\right)$$

$$abx\left(\frac{1}{a}\right) + abx\left(\frac{1}{b}\right) = abx\left(\frac{1}{x}\right)$$

$$bx + ax = ab$$

$$bx = ab - ax$$

$$bx = a(b - x)$$

$$\frac{bx}{b-x} = \frac{a(b-x)}{b-x}$$

$$\frac{bx}{b-x} = a$$

Vocabulary and Readiness Check

1. $4\left(\dfrac{3x}{2}+5\right)=4\left(\dfrac{1}{4}\right)$

$4\left(\dfrac{3x}{2}\right)+4\cdot5=4\left(\dfrac{1}{4}\right)$

$6x+20=1$

The correct choice is c.

2. $5x\left(\dfrac{1}{x}-\dfrac{3}{5x}\right)=5x(2)$

$5x\left(\dfrac{1}{x}\right)-5x\left(\dfrac{3}{5x}\right)=5x(2)$

$5-3=10x$

The correct choice is b.

3. The LCD of $\dfrac{9}{x}, \dfrac{3}{4},$ and $\dfrac{1}{12}=\dfrac{1}{3\cdot4}$ is $12x$; b.

4. The LCD of $\dfrac{8}{3x}, \dfrac{1}{x},$ and $\dfrac{7}{9}=\dfrac{7}{3\cdot3}$ is $9x$; d.

5. The LCD of $\dfrac{9}{x-1}$ and $\dfrac{7}{(x-1)^2}$ is $(x-1)^2$; a.

6. The LCD of $\dfrac{1}{x-2}, \dfrac{3}{x^2-4}=\dfrac{3}{(x+2)(x-2)},$ and

$8=\dfrac{8}{1}$ is (x^2-4); c.

Exercise Set 12.5

1. The LCD is 5.

$\dfrac{x}{5}+3=9$

$5\left(\dfrac{x}{5}+3\right)=5(9)$

$x+15=45$

$x=30$

Check: $\dfrac{x}{5}+3=9$

$\dfrac{30}{5}+3\overset{?}{=}9$

$6+3\overset{?}{=}9$

$9=9$ True

The solution is 30.

3. The LCD is 12.

$\dfrac{x}{2}+\dfrac{5x}{4}=\dfrac{x}{12}$

$12\left(\dfrac{x}{2}+\dfrac{5x}{4}\right)=12\left(\dfrac{x}{12}\right)$

$6x+15x=x$

$21x=x$

$20x=0$

$x=0$

Check: $\dfrac{x}{2}+\dfrac{5x}{4}=\dfrac{x}{12}$

$\dfrac{0}{2}+\dfrac{5(0)}{4}\overset{?}{=}\dfrac{0}{12}$

$0+0\overset{?}{=}0$

$0=0$ True

The solution is 0.

5. The LCD is x.

$2-\dfrac{8}{x}=6$

$x\left(2-\dfrac{8}{x}\right)=x(6)$

$2x-8=6x$

$-8=4x$

$-2=x$

Check: $2-\dfrac{8}{x}=6$

$2-\dfrac{8}{-2}\overset{?}{=}6$

$2-(-4)\overset{?}{=}6$

$2+4=6$

$6=6$ True

The solution is -2.

7. The LCD is x.

$2+\dfrac{10}{x}=x+5$

$x\left(2+\dfrac{10}{x}\right)=x(x+5)$

$2x+10=x^2+5x$

$0=x^2+3x-10$

$0=(x+5)(x-2)$

$x+5=0$ or $x-2=0$

$x=-5$ $x=2$

Check -5: $2+\dfrac{10}{x}=x+5$

$2+\dfrac{10}{-5}\overset{?}{=}-5+5$

$2+(-2)\overset{?}{=}-5+5$

$0=0$ True

Check 2: $2 + \dfrac{10}{x} = x + 5$

$$2 + \frac{10}{2} \stackrel{?}{=} 2 + 5$$

$$2 + 5 \stackrel{?}{=} 2 + 5$$

$$7 = 7 \quad \text{True}$$

The solutions are -5 and 2.

9. The LCD is $5 \cdot 2 = 10$.

$$\frac{a}{5} = \frac{a-3}{2}$$

$$10\left(\frac{a}{5}\right) = 10\left(\frac{a-3}{2}\right)$$

$$2a = 5(a-3)$$

$$2a = 5a - 15$$

$$-3a = -15$$

$$a = 5$$

Check: $\dfrac{a}{5} = \dfrac{a-3}{2}$

$$\frac{5}{5} \stackrel{?}{=} \frac{5-3}{2}$$

$$1 \stackrel{?}{=} \frac{2}{2}$$

$$1 = 1 \quad \text{True}$$

The solution is 5.

11. The LCD is $5 \cdot 2 = 10$.

$$\frac{x-3}{5} + \frac{x-2}{2} = \frac{1}{2}$$

$$10\left(\frac{x-3}{5} + \frac{x-2}{2}\right) = 10\left(\frac{1}{2}\right)$$

$$2(x-3) + 5(x-2) = \frac{10}{2}$$

$$2x - 6 + 5x - 10 = 5$$

$$7x - 16 = 5$$

$$7x = 21$$

$$x = 3$$

Check: $\dfrac{x-3}{5} + \dfrac{x-2}{2} = \dfrac{1}{2}$

$$\frac{3-3}{5} + \frac{3-2}{2} \stackrel{?}{=} \frac{1}{2}$$

$$\frac{0}{5} + \frac{1}{2} \stackrel{?}{=} \frac{1}{2}$$

$$\frac{1}{2} = \frac{1}{2} \quad \text{True}$$

The solution is 3.

13. The LCD is $2a - 5$.

$$\frac{3}{2a-5} = -1$$

$$(2a-5)\left(\frac{3}{2a-5}\right) = (2a-5)(-1)$$

$$3 = -2a + 5$$

$$-2 = -2a$$

$$1 = a$$

Check: $\dfrac{3}{2a-5} = -1$

$$\frac{3}{2(1)-5} \stackrel{?}{=} -1$$

$$\frac{3}{2-5} \stackrel{?}{=} -1$$

$$\frac{3}{-3} \stackrel{?}{=} -1$$

$$-1 = -1 \quad \text{True}$$

The solution is 1.

15. The LCD is $y - 4$.

$$\frac{4y}{y-4} + 5 = \frac{5y}{y-4}$$

$$(y-4)\left(\frac{4y}{y-4} + 5\right) = (y-4)\left(\frac{5y}{y-4}\right)$$

$$4y + 5(y-4) = 5y$$

$$4y + 5y - 20 = 5y$$

$$9y - 20 = 5y$$

$$-20 = -4y$$

$$5 = y$$

Check: $\dfrac{4y}{y-4} + 5 = \dfrac{5y}{y-4}$

$$\frac{4 \cdot 5}{5-4} + 5 \stackrel{?}{=} \frac{5 \cdot 5}{5-4}$$

$$\frac{20}{1} + 5 \stackrel{?}{=} \frac{25}{1}$$

$$25 = 25 \quad \text{True}$$

The solution is 5.

17. The LCD is $a - 3$.

$$2 + \frac{3}{a-3} = \frac{a}{a-3}$$

$$(a-3)\left(2 + \frac{3}{a-3}\right) = (a-3)\frac{a}{a-3}$$

$$2(a-3) + 3 = a$$

$$2a - 6 + 3 = a$$

$$2a - 3 = a$$

$$-3 = -a$$

$$3 = a$$

Check: $2 + \dfrac{3}{a-3} = \dfrac{a}{a-3}$

$2 + \dfrac{3}{3-3} \overset{?}{=} \dfrac{3}{3-3}$

$2 + \dfrac{3}{0} \overset{?}{=} \dfrac{3}{0}$

Since $\dfrac{3}{0}$ is undefined, $a = 3$ does not check and the equation has no solution.

19. The LCD is $(x+3)(x-3) = x^2 - 9$.

$$\dfrac{1}{x+3} + \dfrac{6}{x^2-9} = 1$$

$$(x^2-9)\left(\dfrac{1}{x+3} + \dfrac{6}{x^2-9}\right) = 1(x^2-9)$$

$$(x-3) + 6 = x^2 - 9$$

$$x + 3 = x^2 - 9$$

$$0 = x^2 - x - 12$$

$$0 = (x-4)(x+3)$$

$x - 4 = 0$ or $x + 3 = 0$

$x = 4$ $x = -3$

Check 4: $\dfrac{1}{x+3} + \dfrac{6}{x^2-9} = 1$

$\dfrac{1}{4+3} + \dfrac{6}{4^2-9} \overset{?}{=} 1$

$\dfrac{1}{7} + \dfrac{6}{16-9} \overset{?}{=} 1$

$\dfrac{1}{7} + \dfrac{6}{7} \overset{?}{=} 1$

$\dfrac{7}{7} = 1$ True

Check -3: $\dfrac{1}{x+3} + \dfrac{6}{x^2-9} = 1$

$\dfrac{1}{-3+3} + \dfrac{6}{(-3)^2-9} \overset{?}{=} 1$

$\dfrac{1}{0} + \dfrac{6}{0} \overset{?}{=} 1$

Since $\dfrac{1}{0}$ and $\dfrac{6}{0}$ are undefined, $x = -3$ does not check. The solution is 4.

21. The LCD is $y + 4$.

$$\dfrac{2y}{y+4} + \dfrac{4}{y+4} = 3$$

$$(y+4)\left(\dfrac{2y}{y+4} + \dfrac{4}{y+4}\right) = (y+4)(3)$$

$$2y + 4 = 3y + 12$$

$$4 = y + 12$$

$$-8 = y$$

Check: $\dfrac{2y}{y+4} + \dfrac{4}{y+4} = 3$

$\dfrac{2(-8)}{-8+4} + \dfrac{4}{-8+4} \overset{?}{=} 3$

$\dfrac{-16}{-4} + \dfrac{4}{-4} \overset{?}{=} 3$

$4 - 1 \overset{?}{=} 3$

$3 = 3$ True

The solution is -8.

23. The LCD is $(x+2)(x-2) = x^2 - 4$.

$$\dfrac{2x}{x+2} - 2 = \dfrac{x-8}{x-2}$$

$$(x^2-4)\left(\dfrac{2x}{x+2} - 2\right) = (x^2-4)\left(\dfrac{x-8}{x-2}\right)$$

$$2x(x-2) - 2(x^2-4) = (x+2)(x-8)$$

$$2x^2 - 4x - 2x^2 + 8 = x^2 - 8x + 2x - 16$$

$$-4x + 8 = x^2 - 6x - 16$$

$$0 = x^2 - 2x - 24$$

$$0 = (x-6)(x+4)$$

$x - 6 = 0$ or $x + 4 = 0$

$x = 6$ $x = -4$

Check 6: $\dfrac{2x}{x+2} - 2 = \dfrac{x-8}{x-2}$

$\dfrac{2(6)}{6+2} - 2 \overset{?}{=} \dfrac{6-8}{6-2}$

$\dfrac{12}{8} - 2 \overset{?}{=} \dfrac{-2}{4}$

$\dfrac{3}{2} - \dfrac{4}{2} \overset{?}{=} -\dfrac{1}{2}$

$-\dfrac{1}{2} = -\dfrac{1}{2}$ True

Check -4: $\quad \dfrac{2x}{x+2} - 2 = \dfrac{x-8}{x-2}$

$$\dfrac{2(-4)}{-4+2} - 2 \stackrel{?}{=} \dfrac{-4-8}{-4-2}$$

$$\dfrac{-8}{-2} - 2 \stackrel{?}{=} \dfrac{-12}{-6}$$

$$4 - 2 \stackrel{?}{=} 2$$

$$2 = 2 \quad \text{True}$$

The solutions are 6 and -4.

25. The LCD is $2y$.

$$\dfrac{2}{y} + \dfrac{1}{2} = \dfrac{5}{2y}$$

$$2y\left(\dfrac{2}{y} + \dfrac{1}{2}\right) = 2y\left(\dfrac{5}{2y}\right)$$

$$2(2) + y(1) = 5$$

$$4 + y = 5$$

$$y = 1$$

The solution $y = 1$ checks.

27. The LCD is $(a-6)(a-1)$.

$$\dfrac{a}{a-6} = \dfrac{-2}{a-1}$$

$$(a-6)(a-1)\left(\dfrac{a}{a-6}\right) = (a-6)(a-1)\left(\dfrac{-2}{a-1}\right)$$

$$a(a-1) = -2(a-6)$$

$$a^2 - a = -2a + 12$$

$$a^2 + a - 12 = 0$$

$$(a+4)(a-3) = 0$$

$$a+4 = 0 \quad \text{or} \quad a-3 = 0$$

$$a = -4 \qquad\qquad a = 3$$

The solutions $a = -4$ and $a = 3$ check.

29. The LCD is $2x \cdot 3 = 6x$.

$$\dfrac{11}{2x} + \dfrac{2}{3} = \dfrac{7}{2x}$$

$$6x\left(\dfrac{11}{2x} + \dfrac{2}{3}\right) = 6x\left(\dfrac{7}{2x}\right)$$

$$3(11) + 2x(2) = 3(7)$$

$$33 + 4x = 21$$

$$4x = -12$$

$$x = -3$$

The solution $x = -3$ checks.

31. The LCD is $(x-2)(x+2)$.

$$\dfrac{2}{x-2} + 1 = \dfrac{x}{x+2}$$

$$(x-2)(x+2)\left(\dfrac{2}{x-2} + 1\right) = (x-2)(x+2)\left(\dfrac{x}{x+2}\right)$$

$$2(x+2) + 1(x-2)(x+2) = x(x-2)$$

$$2x + 4 + x^2 - 4 = x^2 - 2x$$

$$4x = 0$$

$$x = 0$$

The solution $x = 0$ checks.

33. The LCD is 6.

$$\dfrac{x+1}{3} - \dfrac{x-1}{6} = \dfrac{1}{6}$$

$$6\left(\dfrac{x+1}{3} - \dfrac{x-1}{6}\right) = 6\left(\dfrac{1}{6}\right)$$

$$2(x+1) - (x-1) = 1$$

$$2x + 2 - x + 1 = 1$$

$$x + 3 = 1$$

$$x = -2$$

The solution $x = -2$ checks.

35. The LCD is $6(t-4)$.

$$\dfrac{t}{t-4} = \dfrac{t+4}{6}$$

$$6(t-4)\left(\dfrac{t}{t-4}\right) = 6(t-4)\left(\dfrac{t+4}{6}\right)$$

$$6t = (t-4)(t+4)$$

$$6t = t^2 - 16$$

$$0 = t^2 - 6t - 16$$

$$0 = (t-8)(t+2)$$

$$t-8 = 0 \quad \text{or} \quad t+2 = 0$$

$$t = 8 \qquad\qquad t = -2$$

The solutions $t = 8$ and $t = -2$ check.

37. $2y + 2 = 2(y+1)$

$4y + 4 = 4(y+1) = 2 \cdot 2(y+1)$

The LCD is $4(y+1)$.

$$\dfrac{y}{2y+2} + \dfrac{2y-16}{4y+4} = \dfrac{2y-3}{y+1}$$

$$4(y+1)\left(\dfrac{y}{2(y+1)} + \dfrac{2y-16}{4(y+1)}\right) = 4(y+1)\left(\dfrac{2y-3}{y+1}\right)$$

$$2y + 2y - 16 = 4(2y-3)$$

$$4y - 16 = 8y - 12$$

$$-16 = 4y - 12$$

$$-4 = 4y$$

$$-1 = y$$

The solution $y = -1$ makes the denominators $2y + 2$, $4y + 4$, and $y + 1$ zero, so the equation has no solution.

39. $r^2 + 5r - 14 = (r+7)(r-2)$

The LCD is $(r+7)(r-2)$.

$$\frac{4r-4}{r^2+5r-14} + \frac{2}{r+7} = \frac{1}{r-2}$$

$$(r+7)(r-2)\left(\frac{4r-4}{(r+7)(r-2)} + \frac{2}{r+7}\right) = (r+7)(r-2)\left(\frac{1}{r-2}\right)$$

$$4r-4+2(r-2) = 1(r+7)$$
$$4r-4+2r-4 = r+7$$
$$6r-8 = r+7$$
$$5r = 15$$
$$r = 3$$

The solution $r = 3$ checks.

41. $x^2 + x - 6 = (x+3)(x-2)$

The LCD is $(x+3)(x-2)$.

$$\frac{x+1}{x+3} = \frac{x^2-11x}{x^2+x-6} - \frac{x-3}{x-2}$$

$$(x+3)(x-2)\left(\frac{x+1}{x+3}\right) = (x+3)(x-2)\left(\frac{x^2-11x}{x^2+x-6} - \frac{x-3}{x-2}\right)$$

$$(x-2)(x+1) = x^2-11x-(x+3)(x-3)$$
$$x^2-x-2 = x^2-11x-(x^2-9)$$
$$x^2-x-2 = x^2-11x-x^2+9$$
$$x^2-x-2 = -11x+9$$
$$x^2+10x-11 = 0$$
$$(x+11)(x-1) = 0$$
$$x+11 = 0 \quad \text{or} \quad x-1 = 0$$
$$x = -11 \qquad x = 1$$

The solutions $x = -11$ and $x = 1$ check.

43. The LCD is I.

$$R = \frac{E}{I}$$
$$I(R) = I\left(\frac{E}{I}\right)$$
$$IR = E$$
$$I = \frac{E}{R}$$

45. The LCD is $B + E$.

$$T = \frac{2U}{B+E}$$
$$(B+E)T = (B+E)\left(\frac{2U}{B+E}\right)$$
$$BT + ET = 2U$$
$$BT = 2U - ET$$
$$B = \frac{2U - ET}{T}$$

47. The LCD is h^2.

$$B = \frac{705w}{h^2}$$

$$h^2(B) = h^2\left(\frac{705w}{h^2}\right)$$

$$Bh^2 = 705w$$

$$\frac{Bh^2}{705} = w$$

49. The LCD is G.

$$N = R + \frac{V}{G}$$

$$G(N) = G\left(R + \frac{V}{G}\right)$$

$$GN = GR + V$$

$$GN - GR = V$$

$$G(N - R) = V$$

$$G = \frac{V}{N - R}$$

51. The LCD is πr.

$$\frac{C}{\pi r} = 2$$

$$\pi r\left(\frac{C}{\pi r}\right) = \pi r(2)$$

$$C = 2\pi r$$

$$\frac{C}{2\pi} = r$$

53. The LCD is $3xy$.

$$\frac{1}{y} + \frac{1}{3} = \frac{1}{x}$$

$$3xy\left(\frac{1}{y} + \frac{1}{3}\right) = 3xy\left(\frac{1}{x}\right)$$

$$3x + xy = 3y$$

$$x(3 + y) = 3y$$

$$x = \frac{3y}{3 + y}$$

55. The reciprocal of x is $\frac{1}{x}$.

57. The reciprocal of x, added to the reciprocal of 2 is $\frac{1}{x} + \frac{1}{2}$.

59. $\frac{1}{3}$ of the tank is filled in 1 hour.

61. $a^2 + 4a + 3 = (a+3)(a+1)$

$a^2 + a - 6 = (a+3)(a-2)$

$a^2 - a - 2 = (a+1)(a-2)$

The LCD is $(a+3)(a+1)(a-2)$.

$$\frac{4}{a^2+4a+3} + \frac{2}{a^2+a-6} - \frac{3}{a^2-a-2} = 0$$

$$(a+3)(a+1)(a-2)\left(\frac{4}{a^2+4a+3} + \frac{2}{a^2+a-6} - \frac{3}{a^2-a-2}\right) = (a+3)(a+1)(a-2)(0)$$

$$4(a-2) + 2(a+1) - 3(a+3) = 0$$

$$4a - 8 + 2a + 2 - 3a - 9 = 0$$

$$3a - 15 = 0$$

$$3a = 15$$

$$a = 5$$

The solution $a = 5$ checks.

63. $\frac{20x}{3} + \frac{32x}{6} = 180$

The LCD is 6.

$$6\left(\frac{20x}{3} + \frac{32x}{6}\right) = 6(180)$$

$$2(20x) + 32x = 1080$$

$$40x + 32x = 1080$$

$$72x = 1080$$

$$x = 15$$

$$\frac{20x}{3} = \frac{20(15)}{3} = 100°$$

$$\frac{32x}{6} = \frac{32(15)}{6} = 80°$$

The angles measure $100°$ and $80°$.

65. $\frac{450}{x} + \frac{150}{x} = 90$

The LCD is x.

$$x\left(\frac{450}{x} + \frac{150}{x}\right) = x(90)$$

$$450 + 150 = 90x$$

$$600 = 90x$$

$$\frac{600}{90} = x$$

$$\frac{20}{3} = x$$

$$\frac{450}{x} = 450 \div \frac{20}{3} = \frac{450}{1} \cdot \frac{3}{20} = \frac{1350}{20} = 67.5$$

$$\frac{150}{x} = 150 \div \frac{20}{3} = \frac{150}{1} \cdot \frac{3}{20} = \frac{450}{20} = 22.5$$

The angles measure $22.5°$ and $67.5°$.

67. No; multiplying both terms in the expressions by 4 changes the value of the original expressions.

Integrated Review

1. $\dfrac{1}{x}+\dfrac{2}{3}=\dfrac{1\cdot3}{x\cdot3}+\dfrac{2\cdot x}{3\cdot x}=\dfrac{3}{3x}+\dfrac{2x}{3x}=\dfrac{3+2x}{3x}$

This is an expression.

2. $\dfrac{3}{a}+\dfrac{5}{6}=\dfrac{3\cdot6}{a\cdot6}+\dfrac{5\cdot a}{6\cdot a}=\dfrac{18}{6a}+\dfrac{5a}{6a}=\dfrac{18+5a}{6a}$

This is an expression.

3. $\dfrac{1}{x}+\dfrac{2}{3}=\dfrac{3}{x}$

$3x\left(\dfrac{1}{x}+\dfrac{2}{3}\right)=3x\left(\dfrac{3}{x}\right)$

$3+2x=9$

$2x=6$

$x=3$

This is an equation.

4. $\dfrac{3}{a}+\dfrac{5}{6}=1$

$6a\left(\dfrac{3}{a}+\dfrac{5}{6}\right)=6a(1)$

$18+5a=6a$

$18=a$

This is an equation.

5. $\dfrac{2}{x+1}-\dfrac{1}{x}=\dfrac{2\cdot x}{(x+1)\cdot x}-\dfrac{1\cdot(x+1)}{x\cdot(x+1)}$

$=\dfrac{2x}{x(x+1)}-\dfrac{x+1}{x(x+1)}$

$=\dfrac{2x-x-1}{x(x+1)}$

$=\dfrac{x-1}{x(x+1)}$

This is an expression.

6. $\dfrac{4}{x-3}-\dfrac{1}{x}=\dfrac{4\cdot x}{(x-3)\cdot x}-\dfrac{1\cdot(x-3)}{x\cdot(x-3)}$

$=\dfrac{4x}{x(x-3)}-\dfrac{x-3}{x(x-3)}$

$=\dfrac{4x-x+3}{x(x-3)}$

$=\dfrac{3x+3}{x(x-3)}$

$=\dfrac{3(x+1)}{x(x-3)}$

This is an expression.

7. $\dfrac{2}{x+1}-\dfrac{1}{x}=1$

$x(x+1)\left(\dfrac{2}{x+1}-\dfrac{1}{x}\right)=x(x+1)(1)$

$2x-(x+1)=x(x+1)$

$2x-x-1=x^2+x$

$x-1=x^2+x$

$0=x^2+1$

There are no solutions. This is an equation.

8. $\dfrac{4}{x-3}-\dfrac{1}{x}=\dfrac{6}{x(x-3)}$

$x(x-3)\left(\dfrac{4}{x-3}-\dfrac{1}{x}\right)=x(x-3)\left(\dfrac{6}{x(x-3)}\right)$

$4x-1(x-3)=6$

$4x-x+3=6$

$3x=3$

$x=1$

This is an equation.

9. $\dfrac{15x}{x+8}\cdot\dfrac{2x+16}{3x}=\dfrac{3\cdot5x}{x+8}\cdot\dfrac{2(x+8)}{3x}=5\cdot2=10$

This is an expression.

10. $\dfrac{9z+5}{15}\cdot\dfrac{5z}{81z^2-25}=\dfrac{9z+5}{3\cdot5}\cdot\dfrac{5z}{(9z+5)(9z-5)}$

$=\dfrac{z}{3(9z-5)}$

This is an expression.

11. $\dfrac{2x+3}{x-3}+\dfrac{3x+6}{x-3}=\dfrac{2x+1+3x+6}{x-3}=\dfrac{5x+7}{x-3}$

This is an expression.

12. $\dfrac{4p-3}{2p+7}+\dfrac{3p+8}{2p+7}=\dfrac{4p-3+3p+8}{2p+7}=\dfrac{7p+5}{2p+7}$

This is an expression.

13. $\dfrac{x+5}{7}=\dfrac{8}{2}$

$14\left(\dfrac{x+5}{7}\right)=14\left(\dfrac{8}{2}\right)$

$2(x+5)=7(8)$

$2x+10=56$

$2x=46$

$x=23$

This is an equation.

14.
$$\frac{1}{2} = \frac{x+1}{8}$$
$$8\left(\frac{1}{2}\right) = 8\left(\frac{x+1}{8}\right)$$
$$4 = x+1$$
$$3 = x$$
This is an equation.

15.
$$\frac{5a+10}{18} \div \frac{a^2-4}{10a} = \frac{5a+10}{18} \cdot \frac{10a}{a^2-4}$$
$$= \frac{5(a+2)}{2 \cdot 9} \cdot \frac{2 \cdot 5a}{(a+2)(a-2)}$$
$$= \frac{5 \cdot 5a}{9(a-2)}$$
$$= \frac{25a}{9(a-2)}$$
This is an expression.

16.
$$\frac{9}{x^2-1} \div \frac{12}{3x+3} = \frac{9}{x^2-1} \cdot \frac{3x+3}{12}$$
$$= \frac{9}{(x-1)(x+1)} \cdot \frac{3(x+1)}{3 \cdot 4}$$
$$= \frac{9}{4(x-1)}$$

17.
$$\frac{x+2}{3x-1} + \frac{5}{(3x-1)^2} = \frac{(x+2)(3x-1)}{(3x-1)(3x-1)} + \frac{5}{(3x-1)^2}$$
$$= \frac{(x+2)(3x-1)+5}{(3x-1)^2}$$
$$= \frac{3x^2-x+6x-2+5}{(3x-1)^2}$$
$$= \frac{3x^2+5x+3}{(3x-1)^2}$$
This is an expression.

18.
$$\frac{4}{(2x-5)^2} + \frac{x+1}{2x-5} = \frac{4}{(2x-5)^2} + \frac{(x+1)(2x-5)}{(2x-5)(2x-5)}$$
$$= \frac{4+(x+1)(2x-5)}{(2x-5)^2}$$
$$= \frac{4+2x^2-5x+2x-5}{(2x-5)^2}$$
$$= \frac{2x^2-3x-1}{(2x-5)^2}$$
This is an expression.

19.
$$\frac{x-7}{x} - \frac{x+2}{5x} = \frac{(x-7) \cdot 5}{x \cdot 5} - \frac{x+2}{5x}$$
$$= \frac{5x-35-x-2}{5x}$$
$$= \frac{4x-37}{5x}$$
This is an expression.

20.
$$\frac{10x-9}{x} - \frac{x-4}{3x} = \frac{(10x-9) \cdot 3}{x \cdot 3} - \frac{x-4}{3x}$$
$$= \frac{3(10x-9)-x+4}{3x}$$
$$= \frac{30x-27-x+4}{3x}$$
$$= \frac{29x-23}{3x}$$
This is an expression.

21.
$$\frac{3}{x+3} = \frac{5}{x^2-9} - \frac{2}{x-3}$$
$$(x^2-9)\left(\frac{3}{x+3}\right) = (x^2-9)\left(\frac{5}{x^2-9} - \frac{2}{x-3}\right)$$
$$3(x-3) = 5-2(x+3)$$
$$3x-9 = 5-2x-6$$
$$3x-9 = -2x-1$$
$$5x = 8$$
$$x = \frac{8}{5}$$
This is an equation.

22.
$$\frac{9}{x^2-4} + \frac{2}{x+2} = \frac{-1}{x-2}$$
$$(x^2-4)\left(\frac{9}{x^2-4} + \frac{2}{x+2}\right) = (x^2-4)\left(\frac{-1}{x-2}\right)$$
$$9+2(x-2) = -1(x+2)$$
$$9+2x-4 = -x-2$$
$$2x+5 = -x-2$$
$$3x = -7$$
$$x = -\frac{7}{3}$$
This is an equation.

23. answers may vary

24. answers may vary

Section 12.6

Practice Problems

1. $\dfrac{x}{2} - \dfrac{1}{3} = \dfrac{x}{6}$

$6\left(\dfrac{x}{2} - \dfrac{1}{3}\right) = 6\left(\dfrac{x}{6}\right)$

$3x - 2 = x$

$2x = 2$

$x = 1$

The number is 1.

2.

	Hours to Complete Total Job	Part of Job Completed in 1 Hour
Andrew	2	$\dfrac{1}{2}$
Timothy	3	$\dfrac{1}{3}$
Together	x	$\dfrac{1}{x}$

$\dfrac{1}{2} + \dfrac{1}{3} = \dfrac{1}{x}$

$6x\left(\dfrac{1}{2}\right) + 6x\left(\dfrac{1}{3}\right) = 6x\left(\dfrac{1}{x}\right)$

$3x + 2x = 6$

$5x = 6$

$x = \dfrac{6}{5} = 1\dfrac{1}{5}$ hr

Together they can sort one batch in $1\dfrac{1}{5}$ hours.

3.

	distance	=	rate	·	time
Car	600		$x + 15$		$\dfrac{600}{x+15}$
Motorcycle	450		x		$\dfrac{450}{x}$

$\dfrac{600}{x+15} = \dfrac{450}{x}$

$600x = 450(x+15)$

$600x = 450x + 6750$

$150x = 6750$

$x = 45$

$x + 15 = 45 + 15 = 60$

The speed of the motorcycle is 45 mph. The speed of the car is 60 mph.

Vocabulary and Readiness Check

1. The time to complete the job working together will be less than both of the individual times. The answer is c.

2. The time to fill the pond with both pipes on at the same time will be less than both of the individual times. The answer is a.

3. A number: x

   The reciprocal of the number: $\dfrac{1}{x}$

   The reciprocal of the number, decreased by 3:

   $\dfrac{1}{x} - 3$

4. A number: y

   The reciprocal of the number: $\dfrac{1}{y}$

   The reciprocal of the number, increased by 2:

   $\dfrac{1}{y} + 2$

5. A number: z
   The sum of the number and 5: $z + 5$
   The reciprocal of the sum of the number and 5:

   $\dfrac{1}{z+5}$

6. A number: x
   The difference of the number and 1: $x - 1$
   The reciprocal of the difference of the number

   and 1: $\dfrac{1}{x-1}$

7. A number: y
   Twice the number: $2y$

   Eleven divided by twice the number: $\dfrac{11}{2y}$

8. A number: z
   Triple the number: $3z$

   Negative 10 divided by triple the number: $\dfrac{-10}{3y}$

Exercise Set 12.6

1. Let x be the number.

   $$3\left(\frac{1}{x}\right) = 9\left(\frac{1}{6}\right)$$
   $$\frac{3}{x} = \frac{9}{6}$$
   $$3(6) = 9x$$
   $$18 = 9x$$
   $$2 = x$$

   The number is 2.

3. Let x be the number.

   $$\frac{2x+3}{x+1} = \frac{3}{2}$$
   $$2(2x+3) = 3(x+1)$$
   $$4x+6 = 3x+3$$
   $$x = -3$$

   The number is -3.

5. Let x be the time in hours that it takes them to complete the job working together.

   The experienced surveyor completes $\dfrac{1}{4}$ of the job in 1 hour. The apprentice surveyor completes $\dfrac{1}{5}$ of the job in 1 hour. Together, they complete $\dfrac{1}{x}$ of the job in 1 hour.

   $$\frac{1}{4} + \frac{1}{5} = \frac{1}{x}$$

   The LCD is $4 \cdot 5 \cdot x = 20x$.

   $$20x\left(\frac{1}{4} + \frac{1}{5}\right) = 20x\left(\frac{1}{x}\right)$$
   $$5x + 4x = 20$$
   $$9x = 20$$
   $$x = \frac{20}{9}$$

   It takes them $\dfrac{20}{9} = 2\dfrac{2}{9}$ hours to survey the roadbed together.

7. Let x be the time in minutes that it takes the two belts to complete the job working together. The first belt completes $\dfrac{1}{2}$ of the job in 1 minute.

   The smaller belt completes $\dfrac{1}{6}$ of the job in

1 minute. Together, they complete $\dfrac{1}{x}$ of the job in 1 minute.

$$\frac{1}{2}+\frac{1}{6}=\frac{1}{x}$$

The LCD is $6x$.

$$6x\left(\frac{1}{2}+\frac{1}{6}\right)=6x\left(\frac{1}{x}\right)$$
$$3x+x=6$$
$$4x=6$$
$$x=\frac{6}{4}=\frac{3}{2}=1\frac{1}{2}$$

It will take $1\dfrac{1}{2}$ minutes to move the cans to the storage when both belts are used.

9. Let r be her jogging rate.

	distance	=	rate	·	time
Trip to park	12		r		$\dfrac{12}{r}$
Return trip	18		r		$\dfrac{18}{r}$

Since the return trip took 1 hour longer,

$\dfrac{18}{r}=1+\dfrac{12}{r}$. The LCD is r.

$$r\left(\frac{18}{r}\right)=r\left(1+\frac{12}{r}\right)$$
$$18=r+12$$
$$6=r$$

Her jogging rate is 6 miles per hour.

11. Let x be the speed for the first portion.

	distance	=	rate	·	time
1st portion	20		x		$\dfrac{20}{x}$
2nd portion	16		$x-2$		$\dfrac{16}{x-2}$

$$\frac{20}{x}=\frac{16}{x-2}$$

The LCD is $x(x-2)$.

$$x(x-2)\left(\frac{20}{x}\right)=x(x-2)\left(\frac{16}{x-2}\right)$$
$$20(x-2)=16x$$
$$20x-40=16x$$
$$4x=40$$
$$x=10$$

The cyclist's speed for first portion is 10 mph and the speed for the second portion is 8 mph.

13. Let n be the number.

$$\frac{1}{4}=\frac{n}{8}$$
$$8\left(\frac{1}{4}\right)=8\left(\frac{n}{8}\right)$$
$$2=n$$

The number is 2.

15. Let x be the time in hours that it takes Marcus and Tony to do the job working together.

Marcus lays $\dfrac{1}{6}$ of a slab in 1 hour. Tony lays $\dfrac{1}{4}$ of a slab in 1 hour. Together, they lay $\dfrac{1}{x}$ of the slab in 1 hour.

$$\frac{1}{6}+\frac{1}{4}=\frac{1}{x}$$

The LCD is $12x$.

$$12x\left(\frac{1}{6}+\frac{1}{4}\right)=12x\left(\frac{1}{x}\right)$$
$$2x+3x=12$$
$$5x=12$$
$$x=\frac{12}{5}$$

It will take Tony and Marcus $\dfrac{12}{5}$ hours to lay the slab, so the labor estimate should be

$$\frac{12}{5}(\$45)=\$108.$$

17. Let w be the speed of the wind.

	distance	=	rate	·	time
With wind	400		$230+w$		$\dfrac{400}{230+w}$
Against wind	336		$230-w$		$\dfrac{336}{230-w}$

$$\frac{400}{230+w} = \frac{336}{230-w}$$
$$400(230-w) = 336(230+w)$$
$$92,000 - 400w = 77,280 + 336w$$
$$14,720 = 736w$$
$$20 = w$$

The speed of the wind is 20 mph.

19. Let x be the number.

$$\frac{2}{x-3} - \frac{4}{x+3} = 8 \cdot \frac{1}{x^2-9}$$

The LCD is $x^2 - 9 = (x+3)(x-3)$.

$$(x+3)(x-3)\left(\frac{2}{x-3} - \frac{4}{x+3}\right) = (x^2-9)\left(\frac{8}{x^2-9}\right)$$
$$2(x+3) - 4(x-3) = 8$$
$$2x+6-4x+12 = 8$$
$$-2x+18 = 8$$
$$-2x = -10$$
$$x = 5$$

The solution $x = 5$ checks, so the number is 5.

21. Let x be the rate in still air.

	distance	=	rate	·	time
With wind	630		$x + 35$		$\frac{630}{x+35}$
Against wind	455		$x - 35$		$\frac{455}{x-35}$

$$\frac{630}{x+35} = \frac{455}{x-35}$$
$$630(x-35) = 455(x+35)$$
$$630x - 22,050 = 455x + 15,925$$
$$175x = 37,975$$
$$x = 217$$

The plane flies at a rate of 217 mph in still air.

23. Let x be the number.

$$\frac{x}{3} - 1 = \frac{5}{3}$$
$$3\left(\frac{x}{3} - 1\right) = 3\left(\frac{5}{3}\right)$$
$$x - 3 = 5$$
$$x = 8$$

The number is 8.

25. Let x be the rate of the slower hiker. Then the rate of the faster hiker is $x + 1.1$. In 2 hours, the slower hiker walks $2x$ miles, while the faster hiker walks $2(x + 1.1)$ miles.

$$2x + 2(x + 1.1) = 11$$
$$2x + 2x + 2.2 = 11$$
$$4x + 2.2 = 11$$
$$4x = 8.8$$
$$x = 2.2$$

$x + 1.1 = 2.2 + 1.1 = 3.3$

The hikers walk 2.2 miles per hour and 3.3 miles per hour.

27. Let x be the time it takes for the second worker to do the same job alone.

$$\frac{1}{3} + \frac{1}{x} = \frac{1}{\frac{3}{2}}$$
$$\frac{1}{3} + \frac{1}{x} = \frac{2}{3}$$
$$3x\left(\frac{1}{3} + \frac{1}{x}\right) = 3x\left(\frac{2}{3}\right)$$
$$x + 3 = 2x$$
$$3 = x$$

It will take the second worker 3 hours to get the job done.

29.

	r	$\times$	t	$=$	d
With wind	$16 + x$		$\frac{48}{16+x}$		48
Into wind	$16 - x$		$\frac{16}{16-x}$		16

$$\frac{48}{16+x} = \frac{16}{16-x}$$
$$42(16 - x) = 16(16 + x)$$
$$768 - 48x = 256 + 16x$$
$$512 = 64x$$
$$8 = x$$

The rate of the wind is 8 mph.

31. Let x be the speed of the second car.

	distance	$=$	rate	$\cdot$	time
one car	224		$x + 14$		$\frac{224}{x+14}$
second car	175		x		$\frac{175}{x}$

$$\frac{224}{x+14} = \frac{175}{x}$$
$$224x = 175(x + 14)$$
$$224x = 175x + 2450$$
$$49x = 2450$$
$$x = 50$$

$x + 14 = 50 + 14 = 64$

The speed of one car is 64 miles per hour and the speed of the second car is 50 miles per hour.

33. Let x be the speed of the plane in still air.

	distance	$=$	rate	$\cdot$	time
with wind	2160		$x + 30$		$\frac{2160}{x+30}$
against wind	1920		$x - 30$		$\frac{1920}{x-30}$

$$\frac{2160}{x+30} = \frac{1920}{x-30}$$
$$2160(x - 30) = 1920(x + 30)$$
$$2160x - 64,800 = 1920x + 57,600$$
$$240x = 122,400$$
$$x = 510$$

The speed of the plane in still air is 510 miles per hour.

35. Let t be the time in hours that the jet plane travels.

	distance	$=$	rate	$\cdot$	time
jet plane	$500t$		500		t
propeller plane	$200(t + 2)$		200		$t + 2$

$$500t = 200(t + 2)$$
$$500t = 200t + 400$$
$$300t = 400$$
$$t = \frac{400}{300}$$
$$t = \frac{4}{3}$$

$$\text{distance} = 500t = 500\left(\frac{4}{3}\right) = 666\frac{2}{3}$$

The planes are $666\frac{2}{3}$ miles from the starting point.

37. Let x be the time that it takes the third pipe to fill the pool alone.

$$\frac{1}{20}+\frac{1}{15}+\frac{1}{x}=\frac{1}{6}$$

$$60x\left(\frac{1}{20}+\frac{1}{15}+\frac{1}{x}\right)=60x\left(\frac{1}{6}\right)$$

$$3x+4x+60=10x$$
$$7x+60=10x$$
$$60=3x$$
$$20=x$$

It will take the third pipe 20 hours to do the job

39. Let r be the motorcycle's speed.

	distance	=	rate	·	time
car	280		$r+10$		$\frac{280}{r+10}$
motorcycle	240		r		$\frac{240}{r}$

$$\frac{280}{r+10}=\frac{240}{r}$$
$$280r=240(r+10)$$
$$280r=240r+2400$$
$$40r=2400$$
$$r=60$$
$$r+10=60+10=70$$

The motorcycle's speed was 60 miles per hour and the car's speed was 70 miles per hour.

41. Let x be the time for the third cook to prepare the same number of pies.

$$\frac{1}{6}+\frac{1}{7}+\frac{1}{x}=\frac{1}{2}$$

$$42x\left(\frac{1}{6}+\frac{1}{7}+\frac{1}{x}\right)=42x\left(\frac{1}{2}\right)$$

$$7x+6x+42=21x$$
$$13x+42=21x$$
$$42=8x$$
$$\frac{42}{8}=x$$

$$\frac{42}{8}=\frac{21}{4}=5\frac{1}{4}$$

It will take the third cook $5\frac{1}{4}$ hours to prepare the pies working alone.

43. $\dfrac{\frac{3}{4}+\frac{1}{4}}{\frac{3}{8}+\frac{13}{8}}=\dfrac{\frac{4}{4}}{\frac{16}{8}}=\dfrac{1}{2}$

45. $\dfrac{\frac{2}{5}+\frac{1}{5}}{\frac{7}{10}+\frac{7}{10}}=\dfrac{\frac{3}{5}}{\frac{14}{10}}=\dfrac{3}{5}\div\dfrac{14}{10}=\dfrac{3}{5}\cdot\dfrac{10}{14}=\dfrac{3\cdot2\cdot5}{5\cdot2\cdot7}=\dfrac{3}{7}$

47. Let x be the time in minutes that it takes for the faster pump to fill the tank, so it fills $\dfrac{1}{x}$ of the tank in 1 minute. It takes the slower pump $3x$ minutes to fill the tank, so the slower pump fills $\dfrac{1}{3x}$ of the tank in 1 minute. Together, the pumps fill $\dfrac{1}{21}$ of the tank in 1 minute.

$$\frac{1}{x}+\frac{1}{3x}=\frac{1}{21}$$

$$21x\left(\frac{1}{x}+\frac{1}{3x}\right)=21x\left(\frac{1}{21}\right)$$

$$21+7=x$$
$$28=x$$
$$3x=3(28)=84$$

The faster pump fills the tank in 28 minutes, while the slower pump takes 84 minutes.

49. answers will vary

51. $D=RT$

$$\frac{D}{T}=\frac{RT}{T}$$

$$\frac{D}{T}=R \text{ or } R=\frac{D}{T}$$

53. Let t be the time it takes for the hyena to overtake the giraffe.

$$0.5+32t=40t$$
$$0.5=8t$$
$$0.0625=t$$

$$0.0625 \text{ hr}\cdot\frac{60 \text{ min}}{1 \text{ hr}}=3.75 \text{ min}$$

It will take the hyena 3.75 minutes to overtake the giraffe.

Section 12.7

Practice Problems

1. $\dfrac{\frac{3}{7}}{\frac{5}{9}}=\dfrac{3}{7}\div\dfrac{5}{9}=\dfrac{3}{7}\cdot\dfrac{9}{5}=\dfrac{27}{35}$

2. $\dfrac{\frac{3}{4}-\frac{2}{3}}{\frac{1}{2}+\frac{3}{8}} = \dfrac{\frac{3(3)}{4(3)}-\frac{2(4)}{3(4)}}{\frac{1(4)}{2(4)}+\frac{3}{8}}$

$= \dfrac{\frac{9}{12}-\frac{8}{12}}{\frac{4}{8}+\frac{3}{8}}$

$= \dfrac{\frac{1}{12}}{\frac{7}{8}}$

$= \dfrac{1}{12}\cdot\dfrac{8}{7}$

$= \dfrac{1\cdot 2\cdot 4}{3\cdot 4\cdot 7}$

$= \dfrac{2}{21}$

3. $\dfrac{\frac{2}{5}-\frac{1}{x}}{\frac{2x}{15}-\frac{1}{3}} = \dfrac{\frac{2(x)}{5(x)}-\frac{1(5)}{x(5)}}{\frac{2x}{15}-\frac{1(5)}{3(5)}}$

$= \dfrac{\frac{2x}{5x}-\frac{5}{5x}}{\frac{2x}{15}-\frac{5}{15}}$

$= \dfrac{\frac{2x-5}{5x}}{\frac{2x-5}{15}}$

$= \dfrac{2x-5}{5x}\cdot\dfrac{15}{2x-5}$

$= \dfrac{2x-15}{5x}\cdot\dfrac{3\cdot 5}{2x-15}$

$= \dfrac{3}{x}$

4. The LCD is 24.

$\dfrac{\frac{3}{4}-\frac{2}{3}}{\frac{1}{2}+\frac{3}{8}} = \dfrac{24\left(\frac{3}{4}-\frac{2}{3}\right)}{24\left(\frac{1}{2}+\frac{3}{8}\right)}$

$= \dfrac{24\left(\frac{3}{4}\right)-24\left(\frac{2}{3}\right)}{24\left(\frac{1}{2}\right)+24\left(\frac{3}{8}\right)}$

$= \dfrac{18-16}{12+9}$

$= \dfrac{2}{21}$

5. The LCD is y.

$\dfrac{1+\frac{x}{y}}{\frac{2x+1}{y}} = \dfrac{y\left(1+\frac{x}{y}\right)}{y\left(\frac{2x+1}{y}\right)} = \dfrac{y(1)+y\left(\frac{x}{y}\right)}{y\left(\frac{2x+1}{y}\right)} = \dfrac{y+x}{2x+1}$

6. The LCD is $6xy$.

$\dfrac{\frac{5}{6y}+\frac{y}{x}}{\frac{y}{3}-x} = \dfrac{6xy\left(\frac{5}{6y}+\frac{y}{x}\right)}{6xy\left(\frac{y}{3}-x\right)}$

$= \dfrac{6xy\left(\frac{5}{6y}\right)+6xy\left(\frac{y}{x}\right)}{6xy\left(\frac{y}{3}\right)-6xy(x)}$

$= \dfrac{5x+6y^2}{2xy^2-6x^2y}$

$= \dfrac{5x+6y^2}{2xy(y-3x)}$

Vocabulary and Readiness Check

1. The LCD for $\dfrac{1}{4}=\dfrac{1}{2\cdot 2}$, $\dfrac{1}{2}$, $\dfrac{1}{3}$, and $\dfrac{1}{2}$ is

$2\cdot 2\cdot 3 = 12$; c.

2. The LCD for $\dfrac{3}{5}$, $\dfrac{2}{3}$, $\dfrac{1}{10}=\dfrac{1}{2\cdot 5}$, and $\dfrac{1}{6}=\dfrac{1}{2\cdot 3}$ is

$2\cdot 3\cdot 5 = 30$; b.

3. The LCD for $\dfrac{5}{2x^2}$, $\dfrac{3}{16x}=\dfrac{3}{2\cdot 2\cdot 2\cdot 2\cdot x}$,

$\dfrac{x}{8}=\dfrac{x}{2\cdot 2\cdot 2}$, and $\dfrac{3}{4x}=\dfrac{3}{2\cdot 2\cdot x}$ is

$2\cdot 2\cdot 2\cdot 2\cdot x^2 = 16x^2$; a.

4. The LCD for $\dfrac{11}{6}=\dfrac{11}{2\cdot 3}$, $\dfrac{10}{x^2}$, $\dfrac{7}{9}=\dfrac{7}{3\cdot 3}$, and $\dfrac{5}{x}$

is $2\cdot 3\cdot 3\cdot x^2 = 18x^2$; c.

Exercise Set 12.7

1. $\dfrac{\frac{1}{2}}{\frac{3}{4}} = \dfrac{1}{2}\div\dfrac{3}{4} = \dfrac{1}{2}\cdot\dfrac{4}{3} = \dfrac{1\cdot 4}{2\cdot 3} = \dfrac{2}{3}$

3. $\dfrac{-\frac{4x}{9}}{-\frac{2x}{3}} = -\dfrac{4x}{9}\div-\dfrac{2x}{3} = -\dfrac{4x}{9}\cdot\dfrac{3}{-2x} = \dfrac{4x\cdot 3}{9\cdot 2x} = \dfrac{2}{3}$

5. $\dfrac{\frac{1+x}{6}}{\frac{1+x}{3}} = \dfrac{1+x}{6}\div\dfrac{1+x}{3} = \dfrac{1+x}{6}\cdot\dfrac{3}{1+x} = \dfrac{3(1+x)}{6(1+x)} = \dfrac{1}{2}$

466

7. $\dfrac{\frac{1}{2}+\frac{2}{3}}{\frac{5}{9}-\frac{5}{6}} = \dfrac{18\left(\frac{1}{2}+\frac{2}{3}\right)}{18\left(\frac{5}{9}-\frac{5}{6}\right)} = \dfrac{9+12}{10-15} = \dfrac{21}{-5} = -\dfrac{21}{5}$

9. $\dfrac{2+\frac{7}{10}}{1+\frac{3}{5}} = \dfrac{10\left(2+\frac{7}{10}\right)}{10\left(1+\frac{3}{5}\right)} = \dfrac{20+7}{10+6} = \dfrac{27}{16}$

11. $\dfrac{\frac{1}{3}}{\frac{1}{2}-\frac{1}{4}} = \dfrac{12\left(\frac{1}{3}\right)}{12\left(\frac{1}{2}-\frac{1}{4}\right)} = \dfrac{4}{6-3} = \dfrac{4}{3}$

13. $\dfrac{-\frac{2}{9}}{-\frac{14}{3}} = -\dfrac{2}{9} \div \left(-\dfrac{14}{3}\right) = -\dfrac{2}{9}\cdot\left(-\dfrac{3}{14}\right) = \dfrac{2\cdot 3}{9\cdot 14} = \dfrac{1}{21}$

15. $\dfrac{-\frac{5}{12x^2}}{\frac{25}{16x^3}} = \dfrac{-5}{12x^2} \div \dfrac{25}{16x^3}$

$= -\dfrac{5}{12x^2}\cdot\dfrac{16x^3}{25}$

$= -\dfrac{5\cdot 16x^3}{12x^2 \cdot 25}$

$= -\dfrac{4x}{15}$

17. $\dfrac{\frac{m}{n}-1}{\frac{m}{n}+1} = \dfrac{n\left(\frac{m}{n}-1\right)}{n\left(\frac{m}{n}+1\right)} = \dfrac{m-n}{m+n}$

19. $\dfrac{\frac{1}{5}-\frac{1}{x}}{\frac{7}{10}+\frac{1}{x^2}} = \dfrac{10x^2\left(\frac{1}{5}-\frac{1}{x}\right)}{10x^2\left(\frac{7}{10}+\frac{1}{x^2}\right)}$

$= \dfrac{2x^2-10x}{7x^2+10}$

$= \dfrac{2x(x-5)}{7x^2+10}$

21. $\dfrac{1+\frac{1}{y-2}}{y+\frac{1}{y-2}} = \dfrac{(y-2)\left(1+\frac{1}{y-2}\right)}{(y-2)\left(y+\frac{1}{y-2}\right)}$

$= \dfrac{y-2+1}{(y-2)y+1}$

$= \dfrac{y-1}{y^2-2y+1}$

$= \dfrac{y-1}{(y-1)^2}$

$= \dfrac{1}{y-1}$

23. $\dfrac{\frac{4y-8}{16}}{\frac{6y-12}{4}} = \dfrac{16\left(\frac{4y-8}{16}\right)}{16\left(\frac{6y-12}{4}\right)} = \dfrac{4y-8}{24y-48} = \dfrac{4(y-2)}{24(y-2)} = \dfrac{1}{6}$

25. $\dfrac{\frac{x}{y}+1}{\frac{x}{y}-1} = \dfrac{y\left(\frac{x}{y}+1\right)}{y\left(\frac{x}{y}-1\right)} = \dfrac{x+y}{x-y}$

27. $\dfrac{1}{2+\frac{1}{3}} = \dfrac{3(1)}{3\left(2+\frac{1}{3}\right)} = \dfrac{3}{6+1} = \dfrac{3}{7}$

29. $\dfrac{\frac{ax+ab}{x^2-b^2}}{\frac{x+b}{x-b}} = \dfrac{ax+ab}{x^2-b^2} \div \dfrac{x+b}{x-b}$

$= \dfrac{ax+ab}{x^2-b^2}\cdot\dfrac{x-b}{x+b}$

$= \dfrac{a(x+b)}{(x+b)(x-b)}\cdot\dfrac{x-b}{x+b}$

$= \dfrac{a}{x+b}$

31. $\dfrac{-\frac{3+y}{4}}{\frac{8+y}{28}} = \dfrac{28\left(\frac{-3+y}{4}\right)}{28\left(\frac{8+y}{28}\right)}$

$= \dfrac{-21+7y}{8+y}$

$= \dfrac{7y-21}{8+y}$

$= \dfrac{7(y-3)}{8+y}$

33. $\dfrac{3+\frac{12}{x}}{1-\frac{16}{x^2}} = \dfrac{x^2\left(3+\frac{12}{x}\right)}{x^2\left(1-\frac{16}{x^2}\right)}$

$= \dfrac{3x^2+12x}{x^2-16}$

$= \dfrac{3x(x+4)}{(x+4)(x-4)}$

$= \dfrac{3x}{x-4}$

35. $\dfrac{\frac{8}{x+4}+2}{\frac{12}{x+4}-2} = \dfrac{(x+4)\left(\frac{8}{x+4}+2\right)}{(x+4)\left(\frac{12}{x+4}-2\right)}$

$= \dfrac{8+2x+8}{12-2x-8}$

$= \dfrac{2x+16}{-2x+4}$

$= \dfrac{2(x+8)}{2(-x+2)}$

$= -\dfrac{x+8}{x-2}$

37. $\dfrac{\frac{s}{r}+\frac{r}{s}}{\frac{s}{r}-\frac{r}{s}} = \dfrac{rs\left(\frac{s}{r}+\frac{r}{s}\right)}{rs\left(\frac{s}{r}-\frac{r}{s}\right)} = \dfrac{s^2+r^2}{s^2-r^2}$

39. $\dfrac{\frac{6}{x-5}+\frac{x}{x-2}}{\frac{3}{x-6}-\frac{2}{x-5}} = \dfrac{\frac{6(x-2)}{(x-5)(x-2)}+\frac{x(x-5)}{(x-2)(x-5)}}{\frac{3(x-5)}{(x-6)(x-5)}-\frac{2(x-6)}{(x-5)(x-6)}}$

$= \dfrac{\frac{6x-12+x^2-5x}{(x-5)(x-2)}}{\frac{3x-15-2x+12}{(x-6)(x-5)}}$

$= \dfrac{\frac{x^2+x-12}{(x-5)(x-2)}}{\frac{x-3}{(x-6)(x-5)}}$

$= \dfrac{(x+4)(x-3)}{(x-5)(x-2)} \cdot \dfrac{(x-6)(x-5)}{x-3}$

$= \dfrac{(x-6)(x+4)}{x-2}$

41. The longest bar corresponds to Lindsay Davenport, so Lindsay Davenport has won the most prize money in her career.

43. $22-20.3 = 1.7$
The approximate spread in lifetime prize money between Lindsay Davenport and Venus Williams is $1.7 million.

45. answers may vary

47. $\dfrac{\frac{1}{3}+\frac{3}{4}}{2} = \dfrac{\frac{1\cdot4}{3\cdot4}+\frac{3\cdot3}{4\cdot3}}{2} = \dfrac{\frac{4}{12}+\frac{9}{12}}{2} = \dfrac{\frac{13}{12}}{2} = \dfrac{13}{12}\cdot\dfrac{1}{2} = \dfrac{13}{24}$

49. $\dfrac{1}{\frac{1}{R_1}+\frac{1}{R_2}} = \dfrac{R_1R_2(1)}{R_1R_2\left(\frac{1}{R_1}+\frac{1}{R_2}\right)} = \dfrac{R_1R_2}{R_2+R_1}$

51. $\dfrac{x^{-1}+2^{-1}}{x^{-2}-4^{-1}} = \dfrac{\frac{1}{x}+\frac{1}{2}}{\frac{1}{x^2}-\frac{1}{4}}$

$= \dfrac{\frac{1\cdot2}{x\cdot2}+\frac{1\cdot x}{2\cdot x}}{\frac{1\cdot4}{x^2\cdot4}-\frac{1\cdot x^2}{4\cdot x^2}}$

$= \dfrac{\frac{2+x}{2x}}{\frac{4-x^2}{4x^2}}$

$= \dfrac{2+x}{2x}\cdot\dfrac{4x^2}{4-x^2}$

$= \dfrac{2+x}{2x}\cdot\dfrac{4x^2}{(2-x)(2+x)}$

$= \dfrac{2x}{2-x}$

53. $\dfrac{y^{-2}}{1-y^{-2}} = \dfrac{\frac{1}{y^2}}{1-\frac{1}{y^2}} = \dfrac{y^2\left(\frac{1}{y^2}\right)}{y^2\left(1-\frac{1}{y^2}\right)} = \dfrac{1}{y^2-1}$

55. $t = \dfrac{d}{r} = \dfrac{\frac{20x}{3}}{\frac{5x}{9}} = \dfrac{20x}{3}\cdot\dfrac{9}{5x} = 12$
The time is 12 hours.

Chapter 12 Vocabulary Check

1. A <u>rational expression</u> is an expression that can be written in the form $\dfrac{P}{Q}$, where P and Q are polynomials and Q is not 0.

2. In a <u>complex fraction</u>, the numerator or denominator or both may contain fractions.

3. For a rational expression, $-\dfrac{a}{b} = \dfrac{-a}{\underline{b}} = \dfrac{a}{\underline{-b}}$.

4. A rational expression is undefined when the <u>denominator</u> is 0.

5. The process of writing a rational expression in lowest terms is called <u>simplifying</u>.

6. The expressions $\dfrac{2x}{7}$ and $\dfrac{7}{2x}$ are called <u>reciprocals</u>.

7. The <u>least common denominator</u> of a list of rational expressions is a polynomial of least degree whose factors include all factors of the denominators in the list.

8. A <u>unit</u> fraction is a fraction that equals 1.

Chapter 12 Review

1.
$$x^2 - 4 = 0$$
$$(x-2)(x+2) = 0$$
$$x - 2 = 0 \quad \text{or} \quad x + 2 = 0$$
$$x = 2 \qquad\qquad x = -2$$
The expression $\dfrac{x+5}{x^2-4}$ is undefined for $x = 2$ and $x = -2$.

2.
$$4x^2 - 4x - 15 = 0$$
$$(2x-5)(2x+3) = 0$$
$$2x - 5 = 0 \quad \text{or} \quad 2x + 3 = 0$$
$$2x = 5 \qquad\qquad 2x = 3$$
$$x = \frac{5}{2} \qquad\qquad x = -\frac{3}{2}$$
The expression $\dfrac{5x+9}{4x^2-4x-15}$ is undefined for $x = \dfrac{5}{2}$ and $x = -\dfrac{3}{2}$.

3. Replace z with -2.
$$\frac{2-z}{z+5} = \frac{2-(-2)}{-2+5} = \frac{4}{3}$$

4. Replace x with 5 and y with 7.
$$\frac{x^2 + xy - y^2}{x+y} = \frac{(5)^2 + (5)(7) - (7)^2}{5+7}$$
$$= \frac{25 + 35 - 49}{12}$$
$$= \frac{11}{12}$$

5. $\dfrac{2x+6}{x^2+3x} = \dfrac{2(x+3)}{x(x+3)} = \dfrac{2}{x}$

6. $\dfrac{3x-12}{x^2-4x} = \dfrac{3(x-4)}{x(x-4)} = \dfrac{3}{x}$

7. $\dfrac{x+2}{x^2-3x-10} = \dfrac{x+2}{(x-5)(x+2)} = \dfrac{1}{x-5}$

8. $\dfrac{x+4}{x^2+5x+4} = \dfrac{x+4}{(x+4)(x+1)} = \dfrac{1}{x+1}$

9.
$$\frac{x^3-4x}{x^2+3x+2} = \frac{x(x^2-4)}{(x+2)(x+1)}$$
$$= \frac{x(x-2)(x+2)}{(x+2)(x+1)}$$
$$= \frac{x(x-2)}{x+1}$$

10.
$$\frac{5x^2-125}{x^2+2x-15} = \frac{5(x^2-25)}{(x+5)(x-3)}$$
$$= \frac{5(x-5)(x+5)}{(x+5)(x-3)}$$
$$= \frac{5(x-5)}{x-3}$$

11. $\dfrac{x^2-x-6}{x^2-3x-10} = \dfrac{(x-3)(x+2)}{(x-5)(x+2)} = \dfrac{x-3}{x-5}$

12. $\dfrac{x^2-2x}{x^2+2x-8} = \dfrac{x(x-2)}{(x+4)(x-2)} = \dfrac{x}{x+4}$

13.
$$\frac{x^2+xa+xb+ab}{x^2-xc+bx-bc} = \frac{(x^2+xa)+(xb+ab)}{(x^2-xc)+(bx-bc)}$$
$$= \frac{x(x+a)+b(x+a)}{x(x-c)+b(x-c)}$$
$$= \frac{(x+b)(x+a)}{(x+b)(x-c)}$$
$$= \frac{x+a}{x-c}$$

14.
$$\frac{x^2+5x-2x-10}{x^2-3x-2x+6} = \frac{(x^2+5x)+(-2x-10)}{(x^2-3x)+(-2x+6)}$$
$$= \frac{x(x+5)-2(x+5)}{x(x-3)-2(x-3)}$$
$$= \frac{(x-2)(x+5)}{(x-2)(x-3)}$$
$$= \frac{x+5}{x-3}$$

15. $\dfrac{15x^3y^2}{z} \cdot \dfrac{z}{5xy^3} = \dfrac{3 \cdot 5 \cdot x \cdot x^2 \cdot y^2 \cdot z}{z \cdot 5 \cdot x \cdot y \cdot y^2} = \dfrac{3x^2}{y}$

16. $\dfrac{-y^3}{8} \cdot \dfrac{9x^2}{y^3} = -\dfrac{y^3 \cdot 9x^2}{8 \cdot y^3} = -\dfrac{9x^2}{8}$

17. $\dfrac{x^2-9}{x^2-4} \cdot \dfrac{x-2}{x+3} = \dfrac{(x-3)(x+3)}{(x-2)(x+2)} \cdot \dfrac{x-2}{x+3} = \dfrac{x-3}{x+2}$

18. $\dfrac{2x+5}{x-6} \cdot \dfrac{2x}{-x+6} = \dfrac{2x+5}{x-6} \cdot \dfrac{2x}{-(x-6)} = \dfrac{-2x(2x+5)}{(x-6)^2}$

19. $\dfrac{x^2-5x-24}{x^2-x-12} \div \dfrac{x^2-10x+16}{x^2+x-6}$

$= \dfrac{x^2-5x-24}{x^2-x-12} \cdot \dfrac{x^2+x-6}{x^2-10x+16}$

$= \dfrac{(x-8)(x+3)}{(x-4)(x+3)} \cdot \dfrac{(x+3)(x-2)}{(x-8)(x-2)}$

$= \dfrac{x+3}{x-4}$

20. $\dfrac{4x+4y}{xy^2} \div \dfrac{3x+3y}{x^2y} = \dfrac{4x+4y}{xy^2} \cdot \dfrac{x^2y}{3x+3y}$

$= \dfrac{4(x+y)}{xy^2} \cdot \dfrac{x^2y}{3(x+y)}$

$= \dfrac{4x}{3y}$

21. $\dfrac{x^2+x-42}{x-3} \cdot \dfrac{(x-3)^2}{x+7} = \dfrac{(x+7)(x-6)}{x-3} \cdot \dfrac{(x-3)^2}{x+7}$

$= (x-6)(x-3)$

22. $\dfrac{2a+2b}{3} \cdot \dfrac{a-b}{a^2-b^2} = \dfrac{2(a+b)}{3} \cdot \dfrac{a-b}{(a-b)(a+b)}$

$= \dfrac{2}{3}$

23. $\dfrac{2x^2-9x+9}{8x-12} \div \dfrac{x^2-3x}{2x} = \dfrac{2x^2-9x+9}{8x-12} \cdot \dfrac{2x}{x^2-3x}$

$= \dfrac{(2x-3)(x-3)}{4(2x-3)} \cdot \dfrac{2x}{x(x-3)}$

$= \dfrac{1}{2}$

24. $\dfrac{x^2-y^2}{x^2+xy} \div \dfrac{3x^2-2xy-y^2}{3x^2+6x}$

$= \dfrac{x^2-y^2}{x^2+xy} \cdot \dfrac{3x^2+6x}{3x^2-2xy-y^2}$

$= \dfrac{(x-y)(x+y)}{x(x+y)} \cdot \dfrac{3x(x+2)}{(3x+y)(x-y)}$

$= \dfrac{3(x+2)}{3x+y}$

25. $\dfrac{x}{x^2+9x+14} + \dfrac{7}{x^2+9x+14} = \dfrac{x+7}{x^2+9x+14}$

$= \dfrac{x+7}{(x+7)(x+2)}$

$= \dfrac{1}{x+2}$

26. $\dfrac{x}{x^2+2x-15} + \dfrac{5}{x^2+2x-15} = \dfrac{x+5}{x^2+2x-15}$

$= \dfrac{x+5}{(x+5)(x-3)}$

$= \dfrac{1}{x-3}$

27. $\dfrac{4x-5}{3x^2} - \dfrac{2x+5}{3x^2} = \dfrac{4x-5-2x-5}{3x^2}$

$= \dfrac{2x-10}{3x^2}$

$= \dfrac{2(x-5)}{3x^2}$

28. $\dfrac{9x+7}{6x^2} - \dfrac{3x+4}{6x^2} = \dfrac{9x+7-3x-4}{6x^2}$

$= \dfrac{6x+3}{6x^2}$

$= \dfrac{3(2x+1)}{6x^2}$

$= \dfrac{2x+1}{2x^2}$

29. The LCD is $2 \cdot 7 \cdot x$ or $14x$.

30. $x^2-5x-24 = (x-8)(x+3)$

$x^2+11x+24 = (x+8)(x+3)$

The LCD is $(x+3)(x+8)(x-8)$.

31. $\dfrac{5}{7x} = \dfrac{5 \cdot 2x^2y}{7x \cdot 2x^2y} = \dfrac{10x^2y}{14x^3y}$

32. $\dfrac{9}{4y} = \dfrac{9 \cdot 4y^2 x}{4y \cdot 4y^2 x} = \dfrac{36y^2 x}{16y^3 x}$

33.
$$\dfrac{x+2}{x^2+11x+18} = \dfrac{x+2}{(x+2)(x+9)}$$
$$= \dfrac{(x+2)(x-5)}{(x+2)(x+9)(x-5)}$$
$$= \dfrac{x^2-3x-10}{(x+2)(x-5)(x+9)}$$

34.
$$\dfrac{3x-5}{x^2+4x+4} = \dfrac{3x-5}{(x+2)^2}$$
$$= \dfrac{(3x-5)(x+3)}{(x+2)^2(x+3)}$$
$$= \dfrac{3x^2+4x-15}{(x+2)^2(x+3)}$$

35. $\dfrac{4}{5x^2} + \dfrac{6}{y} = \dfrac{4y}{5x^2 y} + \dfrac{6 \cdot 5x^2}{y \cdot 5x^2} = \dfrac{4y+30x^2}{5x^2 y}$

36.
$$\dfrac{2}{x-3} - \dfrac{4}{x-1} = \dfrac{2(x-1)-4(x-3)}{(x-3)(x-1)}$$
$$= \dfrac{2x-2-4x+12}{(x-3)(x-1)}$$
$$= \dfrac{-2x+10}{(x-3)(x-1)}$$

37. $\dfrac{4}{x+3} - 2 = \dfrac{4-2(x+3)}{x+3} = \dfrac{4-2x-6}{x+3} = \dfrac{-2x-2}{x+3}$

38.
$$\dfrac{3}{x^2+2x-8} + \dfrac{2}{x^2-3x+2} = \dfrac{3}{(x+4)(x-2)} + \dfrac{2}{(x-2)(x-1)}$$
$$= \dfrac{3(x-1)+2(x+4)}{(x+4)(x-2)(x-1)}$$
$$= \dfrac{3x-3+2x+8}{(x+4)(x-2)(x-1)}$$
$$= \dfrac{5x+5}{(x+4)(x-2)(x-1)}$$
$$= \dfrac{5(x+1)}{(x+4)(x-2)(x-1)}$$

39. $\dfrac{2x-5}{6x+9} - \dfrac{4}{2x^2+3x} = \dfrac{2x-5}{3(2x+3)} - \dfrac{4}{x(2x+3)}$

$$= \dfrac{x(2x-5)-4(3)}{3x(2x+3)}$$

$$= \dfrac{2x^2-5x-12}{3x(2x+3)}$$

$$= \dfrac{(2x+3)(x-4)}{3x(2x+3)}$$

$$= \dfrac{x-4}{3x}$$

40. $\dfrac{x-1}{x^2-2x+1} - \dfrac{x+1}{x-1} = \dfrac{x-1}{(x-1)(x-1)} - \dfrac{x+1}{x-1}$

$$= \dfrac{1}{x-1} - \dfrac{x+1}{x-1}$$

$$= \dfrac{1-x-1}{x-1}$$

$$= -\dfrac{x}{x-1}$$

41. $\dfrac{n}{10} = 9 - \dfrac{n}{5}$

$$10\left(\dfrac{n}{10}\right) = 10\left(9 - \dfrac{n}{5}\right)$$

$$n = 90 - 2n$$

$$3n = 90$$

$$n = 30$$

The solution is 30.

42. $\dfrac{2}{x+1} - \dfrac{1}{x-2} = -\dfrac{1}{2}$

$$2(x+1)(x-2)\left(\dfrac{2}{x+1} - \dfrac{1}{x-2}\right) = 2(x+1)(x-2)\left(-\dfrac{1}{2}\right)$$

$$2 \cdot 2(x-2) - 2(x+1) = -1(x+1)(x-2)$$

$$4x - 8 - 2x - 2 = -(x^2 - x - 2)$$

$$2x - 10 = -x^2 + x + 2$$

$$x^2 + x - 12 = 0$$

$$(x+4)(x-3) = 0$$

$$x+4=0 \quad \text{or} \quad x-3=0$$

$$x=-4 \qquad\quad x=3$$

The solutions are −4 and 3.

43.
$$\frac{y}{2y+2}+\frac{2y-16}{4y+4}=\frac{y-3}{y+1}$$
$$\frac{y}{2(y+1)}+\frac{2y-16}{4(y+1)}=\frac{y-3}{y+1}$$
$$4(y+1)\left(\frac{y}{2(y+1)}+\frac{2y-16}{4(y+1)}\right)=4(y+1)\left(\frac{y-3}{y+1}\right)$$
$$2y+2y-16=4(y-3)$$
$$4y-16=4y-12$$
$$0y=4$$
$$0=4;\text{ no solution}$$

44.
$$\frac{2}{x-3}-\frac{4}{x+3}=\frac{8}{x^2-9}$$
$$(x^2-9)\left(\frac{2}{x-3}-\frac{4}{x+3}\right)=(x^2-9)\left(\frac{8}{x^2-9}\right)$$
$$2(x+3)-4(x-3)=8$$
$$2x+6-4x+12=8$$
$$-2x+18=8$$
$$-2x=-10$$
$$x=5$$
The solution is 5.

45.
$$\frac{x-3}{x+1}-\frac{x-6}{x+5}=0$$
$$(x+1)(x+5)\left(\frac{x-3}{x+1}-\frac{x-6}{x+5}\right)=(x+1)(x+5)0$$
$$(x+5)(x-3)-(x+1)(x-6)=0$$
$$x^2+2x-15-x^2+5x+6=0$$
$$7x-9=0$$
$$7x=9$$
$$x=\frac{9}{7}$$

The solution is $\frac{9}{7}$.

46.
$$x+5=\frac{6}{x}$$
$$x(x+5)=x\left(\frac{6}{x}\right)$$
$$x^2+5x=6$$
$$x^2+5x-6=0$$
$$(x+6)(x-1)=0$$
$$x+6=0\quad\text{or}\quad x-1=0$$
$$x=-6\qquad\qquad x=1$$
The solutions are -6 and 1.

47. Let n be the number.
$$5\left(\frac{1}{n}\right)=\frac{3}{2}\left(\frac{1}{n}\right)+\frac{7}{6}$$
$$\frac{5}{n}=\frac{3}{2n}+\frac{7}{6}$$
$$6n\left(\frac{5}{n}\right)=6n\left(\frac{3}{2n}+\frac{7}{6}\right)$$
$$30=9+7n$$
$$21=7n$$
$$3=n$$
The number is 3.

48. Let n be the number.
$$\frac{1}{n}=\frac{1}{4-n}$$
$$n(4-n)\left(\frac{1}{n}\right)=n(4-n)\left(\frac{1}{4-n}\right)$$
$$4-n=n$$
$$4=2n$$
$$2=n$$
The number is 2.

49. Let x be the speed of the faster car.

	distance	=	rate	·	time
Faster car	90		x		$\frac{90}{x}$
Slower car	60		$x-10$		$\frac{60}{x-10}$

The times are equal.
$$\frac{90}{x}=\frac{60}{x-10}$$
$$90(x-10)=60x$$
$$90x-900=60x$$
$$30x=900$$
$$x=30$$
$$x-10=20$$
The faster car is traveling at 30 mph and the slower car is traveling at 20 mph.

50. Let x be the speed of the boat in still water.

	distance	=	rate	·	time
Upstream	48		$x-4$		$\frac{48}{x-4}$
Downstream	72		$x+4$		$\frac{72}{x+4}$

The times are equal.

$$\frac{48}{x-4} = \frac{72}{x+4}$$
$$48(x+4) = 72(x-4)$$
$$48x+192 = 72x-288$$
$$480 = 24x$$
$$20 = x$$

The speed of the boat in still water is 20 mph.

51. Let x be the time for Maria alone. Together, Mark and Maria complete $\frac{1}{5}$ of the job in 1 hour. Individually, they complete $\frac{1}{7}$ and $\frac{1}{x}$ of the job in 1 hour.

$$\frac{1}{5} = \frac{1}{7} + \frac{1}{x}$$
$$35x\left(\frac{1}{5}\right) = 35x\left(\frac{1}{7} + \frac{1}{x}\right)$$
$$7x = 5x + 35$$
$$2x = 35$$
$$x = \frac{35}{2} = 17\frac{1}{2}$$

It will take Maria $17\frac{1}{2}$ hours to manicure Mr. Sturgeon's lawn alone.

52. Let x be the time for the pipes to fill the pond working together. Pipe A fills $\frac{1}{20}$ of the pond in 1 day, pipe B fills $\frac{1}{15}$ of the pond in 1 day, and together they fill $\frac{1}{x}$ of the pond in one day.

$$\frac{1}{20} + \frac{1}{15} = \frac{1}{x}$$
$$60x\left(\frac{1}{20} + \frac{1}{15}\right) = 60x\left(\frac{1}{x}\right)$$
$$3x + 4x = 60$$
$$7x = 60$$
$$x = \frac{60}{7} = 8\frac{4}{7}$$

It takes $8\frac{4}{7}$ days to fill the pond using both pipes.

53. $\dfrac{\frac{5x}{27}}{-\frac{10xy}{21}} = \dfrac{5x}{27} \div -\dfrac{10xy}{21}$

$$= \frac{5x}{27} \cdot \frac{-21}{10xy}$$
$$= -\frac{5 \cdot x \cdot 3 \cdot 7}{3 \cdot 9 \cdot 2 \cdot 5 \cdot x \cdot y}$$
$$= -\frac{7}{18y}$$

54. $\dfrac{\frac{3}{5} + \frac{2}{7}}{\frac{1}{5} + \frac{5}{6}} = \dfrac{\frac{3 \cdot 7}{5 \cdot 7} + \frac{2 \cdot 5}{7 \cdot 5}}{\frac{1 \cdot 6}{5 \cdot 6} + \frac{5 \cdot 5}{6 \cdot 5}}$

$$= \frac{\frac{21+10}{35}}{\frac{6+25}{30}}$$
$$= \frac{\frac{31}{35}}{\frac{31}{30}}$$
$$= \frac{31}{35} \div \frac{31}{30}$$
$$= \frac{31}{35} \cdot \frac{30}{31}$$
$$= \frac{31 \cdot 5 \cdot 6}{5 \cdot 7 \cdot 31}$$
$$= \frac{6}{7}$$

55. $\dfrac{3 - \frac{1}{y}}{2 - \frac{1}{y}} = \dfrac{y\left(3 - \frac{1}{y}\right)}{y\left(2 - \frac{1}{y}\right)} = \dfrac{3y-1}{2y-1}$

56. $\dfrac{\frac{6}{x+2} + 4}{\frac{8}{x+2} - 4} = \dfrac{(x+2)\left(\frac{6}{x+2} + 4\right)}{(x+2)\left(\frac{8}{x+2} - 4\right)}$

$$= \frac{6 + 4(x+2)}{8 - 4(x+2)}$$
$$= \frac{6 + 4x + 8}{8 - 4x - 8}$$
$$= \frac{4x+14}{-4x}$$
$$= -\frac{2(2x+7)}{2 \cdot 2x}$$
$$= -\frac{2x+7}{2x}$$

57. $\dfrac{4x+12}{8x^2 + 24x} = \dfrac{4(x+3)}{8x(x+3)} = \dfrac{1}{2x}$

58. $\dfrac{x^3-6x^2+9x}{x^2+4x-21} = \dfrac{x(x^2-6x+9)}{(x+7)(x-3)}$

$\qquad\qquad\qquad = \dfrac{x(x-3)(x-3)}{(x+7)(x-3)}$

$\qquad\qquad\qquad = \dfrac{x(x-3)}{x+7}$

59. $\dfrac{x^2+9x+20}{x^2-25} \cdot \dfrac{x^2-9x+20}{x^2+8x+16}$

$\qquad = \dfrac{(x+4)(x+5)}{(x-5)(x+5)} \cdot \dfrac{(x-4)(x-5)}{(x+4)(x+4)}$

$\qquad = \dfrac{x-4}{x+4}$

60. $\dfrac{x^2-x-72}{x^2-x-30} \div \dfrac{x^2+6x-27}{x^2-9x+18}$

$\qquad = \dfrac{x^2-x-72}{x^2-x-30} \cdot \dfrac{x^2-9x+18}{x^2+6x-27}$

$\qquad = \dfrac{(x-9)(x+8)}{(x-6)(x+5)} \cdot \dfrac{(x-6)(x-3)}{(x+9)(x-3)}$

$\qquad = \dfrac{(x-9)(x+8)}{(x+5)(x+9)}$

61. $\dfrac{x}{x^2-36} + \dfrac{6}{x^2-36} = \dfrac{x+6}{x^2-36}$

$\qquad\qquad\qquad\qquad = \dfrac{x+6}{(x+6)(x-6)}$

$\qquad\qquad\qquad\qquad = \dfrac{1}{x-6}$

62. $\dfrac{5x-1}{4x} - \dfrac{3x-2}{4x} = \dfrac{5x-1-3x+2}{4x} = \dfrac{2x+1}{4x}$

63. $\dfrac{3x}{x^2+9x+14} - \dfrac{6x}{x^2+4x-21}$

$\qquad = \dfrac{3x}{(x+7)(x+2)} - \dfrac{6x}{(x+7)(x-3)}$

$\qquad = \dfrac{3x(x-3)}{(x+7)(x+2)(x-3)} - \dfrac{6x(x+2)}{(x+7)(x-3)(x+2)}$

$\qquad = \dfrac{3x^2-9x-6x^2-12x}{(x+7)(x+2)(x-3)}$

$\qquad = \dfrac{-3x^2-21x}{(x+7)(x+2)(x-3)}$

$\qquad = \dfrac{-3x(x+7)}{(x+7)(x+2)(x-3)}$

$\qquad = -\dfrac{3x}{(x+2)(x-3)}$

64. $\dfrac{4}{3x^2+8x-3} + \dfrac{2}{3x^2-7x+2}$

$\qquad = \dfrac{4}{(3x-1)(x+3)} + \dfrac{2}{(3x-1)(x-2)}$

$\qquad = \dfrac{4(x-2)}{(3x-1)(x+3)(x-2)} + \dfrac{2(x+3)}{(3x-1)(x-2)(x+3)}$

$\qquad = \dfrac{4x-8+2x+6}{(3x-1)(x+3)(x-2)}$

$\qquad = \dfrac{6x-2}{(3x-1)(x+3)(x-2)}$

$\qquad = \dfrac{2(3x-1)}{(3x-1)(x+3)(x-2)}$

$\qquad = \dfrac{2}{(x+3)(x-2)}$

65. $\dfrac{4}{a-1} + 2 = \dfrac{3}{a-1}$

$\qquad (a-1)\left(\dfrac{4}{a-1}+2\right) = (a-1)\left(\dfrac{3}{a-1}\right)$

$\qquad\qquad 4+2(a-1) = 3$

$\qquad\qquad 4+2a-2 = 3$

$\qquad\qquad 2+2a = 3$

$\qquad\qquad 2a = 1$

$\qquad\qquad a = \dfrac{1}{2}$

The solution is $\dfrac{1}{2}$.

66.
$$\frac{x}{x+3}+4=\frac{x}{x+3}$$
$$(x+3)\left(\frac{x}{x+3}+4\right)=(x+3)\left(\frac{x}{x+3}\right)$$
$$x+4(x+3)=x$$
$$x+4x+12=x$$
$$5x+12=x$$
$$4x+12=0$$
$$4x=-12$$
$$x=-3$$

-3 makes the denominator $x+3$ zero. Therefore there is no solution.

67. Let n be the number.
$$\frac{2n}{3}-\frac{1}{6}=\frac{n}{2}$$
$$6\left(\frac{2n}{3}-\frac{1}{6}\right)=6\left(\frac{n}{2}\right)$$
$$4n-1=3n$$
$$n-1=0$$
$$n=1$$
The number is 1.

68. Let x be the time to paint the shed together. Mr. Crocker can paint $\frac{1}{3}$ of the shed in one day, and his son can paint $\frac{1}{4}$. Together, they can paint $\frac{1}{x}$.

$$\frac{1}{3}+\frac{1}{4}=\frac{1}{x}$$
$$12x\left(\frac{1}{3}+\frac{1}{4}\right)=12x\left(\frac{1}{x}\right)$$
$$4x+3x=12$$
$$7x=12$$
$$x=\frac{12}{7}\text{ or }1\frac{5}{7}$$

It will take $1\frac{5}{7}$ days to paint the shed when they work together.

69. $\dfrac{\frac{1}{4}}{\frac{1}{3}+\frac{1}{2}}=\dfrac{12\left(\frac{1}{4}\right)}{12\left(\frac{1}{3}+\frac{1}{2}\right)}=\dfrac{3}{4+6}=\dfrac{3}{10}$

70. $\dfrac{4+\frac{2}{x}}{6+\frac{3}{x}}=\dfrac{x\left(4+\frac{2}{x}\right)}{x\left(6+\frac{3}{x}\right)}=\dfrac{4x+2}{6x+3}=\dfrac{2(2x+1)}{3(2x+1)}=\dfrac{2}{3}$

Chapter 12 Test

1. $x^2+4x+3=0$
$(x+1)(x+3)=0$
$x+1=0$ or $x+3=0$
$x=-1$ $\qquad x=-3$

The expression $\dfrac{x+5}{x^2+4x+3}$ is undefined for $x=-1$ and $x=-3$.

2. a. $C=\dfrac{100x+3000}{x}=\dfrac{100(200)+3000}{200}=\$115$

b. $C=\dfrac{100x+3000}{x}$
$\quad=\dfrac{100(1000)+3000}{1000}$
$\quad=\$103$

3. $\dfrac{3x-6}{5x-10}=\dfrac{3(x-2)}{5(x-2)}=\dfrac{3}{5}$

4. $\dfrac{x+6}{x^2+12x+36}=\dfrac{x+6}{(x+6)(x+6)}=\dfrac{1}{x+6}$

5. $\dfrac{7-x}{x-7}=\dfrac{-(x-7)}{x-7}=-1$

6. $\dfrac{y-x}{x^2-y^2}=\dfrac{-(x-y)}{(x-y)(x+y)}=-\dfrac{1}{x+y}$

7. $\dfrac{2m^3-2m^2-12m}{m^2-5m+6}=\dfrac{2m(m^2-m-6)}{(m-3)(m-2)}$
$\qquad=\dfrac{2m(m-3)(m+2)}{(m-3)(m-2)}$
$\qquad=\dfrac{2m(m+2)}{m-2}$

8. $\dfrac{ay+3a+2y+6}{ay+3a+5y+15}=\dfrac{(ay+3a)+(2y+6)}{(ay+3a)+(5y+15)}$
$\qquad=\dfrac{a(y+3)+2(y+3)}{a(y+3)+5(y+3)}$
$\qquad=\dfrac{(a+2)(y+3)}{(a+5)(y+3)}$
$\qquad=\dfrac{a+2}{a+5}$

9.
$$\frac{x^2-13x+42}{x^2+10x+21} \div \frac{x^2-4}{x^2+x-6}$$
$$= \frac{x^2-13x+42}{x^2+10x+21} \cdot \frac{x^2+x-6}{x^2-4}$$
$$= \frac{(x-6)(x-7)}{(x+3)(x+7)} \cdot \frac{(x+3)(x-2)}{(x+2)(x-2)}$$
$$= \frac{(x-6)(x-7)}{(x+7)(x+2)}$$

10. $\dfrac{3}{x-1} \cdot (5x-5) = \dfrac{3}{x-1} \cdot 5(x-1) = 15$

11.
$$\frac{y^2-5y+6}{2y+4} \cdot \frac{y+2}{2y-6} = \frac{(y-3)(y-2)}{2(y+2)} \cdot \frac{y+2}{2(y-3)}$$
$$= \frac{y-2}{4}$$

12. $\dfrac{5}{2x+5} - \dfrac{6}{2x+5} = \dfrac{5-6}{2x+5} = -\dfrac{1}{2x+5}$

13.
$$\frac{5a}{a^2-a-6} - \frac{2}{a-3}$$
$$= \frac{5a}{(a-3)(a+2)} - \frac{2}{a-3}$$
$$= \frac{5a}{(a-3)(a+2)} - \frac{2(a+2)}{(a-3)(a+2)}$$
$$= \frac{5a-2(a+2)}{(a-3)(a+2)}$$
$$= \frac{5a-2a-4}{(a-3)(a+2)}$$
$$= \frac{3a-4}{(a-3)(a+2)}$$

14.
$$\frac{6}{x^2-1} + \frac{3}{x+1} = \frac{6}{(x-1)(x+1)} + \frac{3}{x+1}$$
$$= \frac{6}{(x-1)(x+1)} + \frac{3(x-1)}{(x+1)(x-1)}$$
$$= \frac{6+3x-3}{(x+1)(x-1)}$$
$$= \frac{3x+3}{(x+1)(x-1)}$$
$$= \frac{3(x+1)}{(x+1)(x-1)}$$
$$= \frac{3}{x-1}$$

15.
$$\frac{x^2-9}{x^2-3x} \div \frac{x^2+4x+1}{2x+10} = \frac{x^2-9}{x^2-3x} \cdot \frac{2x+10}{x^2+4x+1}$$
$$= \frac{(x-3)(x+3)}{x(x-3)} \cdot \frac{2(x+5)}{x^2+4x+1}$$
$$= \frac{2(x+3)(x+5)}{x(x^2+4x+1)}$$

16.
$$\frac{x+2}{x^2+11x+18} + \frac{5}{x^2-3x-10}$$
$$= \frac{x+2}{(x+9)(x+2)} + \frac{5}{(x-5)(x+2)}$$
$$= \frac{(x+2)(x-5)}{(x+9)(x+2)(x-5)} + \frac{5(x+9)}{(x-5)(x+2)(x+9)}$$
$$= \frac{x^2-3x-10+5x+45}{(x+9)(x+2)(x-5)}$$
$$= \frac{x^2+2x+35}{(x+9)(x+2)(x-5)}$$

17.
$$\frac{4y}{y^2+6y+5} - \frac{3}{y^2+5y+4}$$
$$= \frac{4y}{(y+5)(y+1)} - \frac{3}{(y+1)(y+4)}$$
$$= \frac{4y(y+4)-3(y+5)}{(y+1)(y+5)(y+4)}$$
$$= \frac{4y^2+16y-3y-15}{(y+1)(y+5)(y+4)}$$
$$= \frac{4y^2+13y-15}{(y+1)(y+5)(y+4)}$$

18. The LCD is $3 \cdot 5 \cdot y = 15y$.
$$\frac{4}{y} - \frac{5}{3} = -\frac{1}{5}$$
$$15y\left(\frac{4}{y} - \frac{5}{3}\right) = 15y\left(-\frac{1}{5}\right)$$
$$60 - 25y = -3y$$
$$60 = 22y$$
$$\frac{60}{22} = y$$
$$\frac{30}{11} = y$$

The solution is $\dfrac{30}{11}$.

19.
$$\frac{5}{y+1} = \frac{4}{y+2}$$
$$5(y+2) = 4(y+1)$$
$$5y+10 = 4y+4$$
$$y = -6$$
The solution is −6.

20. The LCD is $2(a-3)$.
$$\frac{a}{a-3} = \frac{3}{a-3} - \frac{3}{2}$$
$$2(a-3)\left(\frac{a}{a-3}\right) = 2(a-3)\left(\frac{3}{a-3} - \frac{3}{2}\right)$$
$$2a = 6 - 3(a-3)$$
$$2a = 6 - 3a + 9$$
$$5a = 15$$
$$a = 3$$
Since $a = 3$ causes the denominator $a-3$ to be 0, the equation has no solution.

21. The LCD is $x^2 - 25 = (x+5)(x-5)$.
$$\frac{10}{x^2-25} = \frac{3}{x+5} + \frac{1}{x-5}$$
$$(x^2-25)\left(\frac{10}{x^2-25}\right) = (x+5)(x-5)\left(\frac{3}{x+5} + \frac{1}{x-5}\right)$$
$$10 = 3(x-5) + 1(x+5)$$
$$10 = 3x - 15 + x + 5$$
$$10 = 4x - 10$$
$$20 = 4x$$
$$5 = x$$
Since $x = 5$ causes the denominators $x^2 - 25$ and $x - 5$ to be 0, the equation has no solution.

22.
$$x - \frac{14}{x-1} = 4 - \frac{2x}{x-1}$$
$$(x-1)\left(x - \frac{14}{x-1}\right) = (x-1)\left(4 - \frac{2x}{x-1}\right)$$
$$x(x-1) - 14 = 4(x-1) - 2x$$
$$x^2 - x - 14 = 4x - 4 - 2x$$
$$x^2 - x - 14 = 2x - 4$$
$$x^2 - 3x - 10 = 0$$
$$(x-5)(x+2) = 0$$
$$x - 5 = 0 \quad \text{or} \quad x + 2 = 0$$
$$x = 5 \qquad\qquad x = -2$$
The solutions are 5 and −2.

23.
$$\frac{\frac{5x^2}{yz^2}}{\frac{10x}{z^3}} = \frac{5x^2}{yz^2} \div \frac{10x}{z^3}$$
$$= \frac{5x^2}{yz^2} \cdot \frac{z^3}{10x}$$
$$= \frac{5 \cdot x \cdot x \cdot z \cdot z^2}{y \cdot z^2 \cdot 2 \cdot 5 \cdot x}$$
$$= \frac{xz}{2y}$$

24.
$$\frac{\frac{b}{a} - \frac{a}{b}}{\frac{1}{b} + \frac{1}{a}} = \frac{\left(\frac{b}{a} - \frac{a}{b}\right)ab}{\left(\frac{1}{b} + \frac{1}{a}\right)ab}$$
$$= \frac{b^2 - a^2}{a+b}$$
$$= \frac{(b-a)(b+a)}{a+b}$$
$$= b - a$$

25.
$$\frac{5 - \frac{1}{y^2}}{\frac{1}{y} + \frac{2}{y^2}} = \frac{y^2\left(5 - \frac{1}{y^2}\right)}{y^2\left(\frac{1}{y} + \frac{2}{y^2}\right)} = \frac{5y^2 - 1}{y+2}$$

26. Let n be the number.
$$n + 5\left(\frac{1}{n}\right) = 6$$
$$n + \frac{5}{n} = 6$$
$$n\left(n + \frac{5}{n}\right) = n(6)$$
$$n^2 + 5 = 6n$$
$$n^2 - 6n + 5 = 0$$
$$(n-5)(n-1) = 0$$
$$n - 5 = 0 \quad \text{or} \quad n - 1 = 0$$
$$n = 5 \qquad\qquad n = 1$$
The number is 1 or 5.

27. Let x be the speed of the boat in still water. Let $x + 2$ be the speed of the boat going downstream. Let $x - 2$ be the speed of the boat going upstream.

	distance	=	rate	·	time
Upstream	14		$x-2$		$\frac{14}{x-2}$
Downstream	16		$x+2$		$\frac{16}{x+2}$

$$\frac{14}{x-2} = \frac{16}{x+2}$$
$$14(x+2) = 16(x-2)$$
$$14x + 28 = 16x - 32$$
$$60 = 2x$$
$$30 = x$$

The speed of the boat in still water is 30 mph.

28. Let x be the time in hours that it takes for both inlet pipes together to fill the tank.

The first pipe fills $\dfrac{1}{12}$ of the tank in 1 hour, the second pipe fills $\dfrac{1}{15}$ of the tank in 1 hour, and the two pipes fill $\dfrac{1}{x}$ of the tank in 1 hour.

$$\frac{1}{12} + \frac{1}{15} = \frac{1}{x}$$

The LCD is $60x$.

$$60x\left(\frac{1}{12} + \frac{1}{15}\right) = 60x\left(\frac{1}{x}\right)$$
$$5x + 4x = 60$$
$$9x = 60$$
$$x = \frac{60}{9}$$
$$x = \frac{20}{3}$$

It takes both pipes $\dfrac{20}{3} = 6\dfrac{2}{3}$ hours to fill the tank.

Cumulative Review Chapters 1–12

1. $\dfrac{7}{20} = \dfrac{7}{20} \cdot 100\% = \dfrac{700}{20}\% = 35\%$

2. $\dfrac{4}{5} = \dfrac{4}{5} \cdot 100\% = \dfrac{400}{5}\% = 80\%$

3. $\dfrac{2}{3} = \dfrac{2}{3} \cdot 100\% = \dfrac{200}{3}\% = 66\dfrac{2}{3}\%$

4. $\dfrac{1}{9} = \dfrac{1}{9} \cdot 100\% = \dfrac{100}{9}\% = 11\dfrac{1}{9}\%$

5. $2\dfrac{1}{4} = \dfrac{9}{4} = \dfrac{9}{4} \cdot 100\% = \dfrac{900}{4}\% = 225\%$

6. $3\dfrac{3}{4} = \dfrac{15}{4} = \dfrac{15}{4} \cdot 100\% = \dfrac{1500}{4}\% = 375\%$

7. $2 \cdot (z \cdot 5) = 2 \cdot (5 \cdot z)$ illustrates the commutative property of multiplication.

8. $3 + y = y + 3$ illustrates the commutative property of addition.

9. $(x + 7) + 9 = x + (7 + 9)$ illustrates the associative property of addition.

10. $(x \cdot 7) \cdot 9 = x \cdot (7 \cdot 9)$ illustrates the associative property of multiplication.

11. Let x be the length of the shorter piece. Then $4x$ is the length of the longer piece.
$$x + 4x = 10$$
$$5x = 10$$
$$x = 2$$
$$4x = 4(2) = 8$$
The shorter piece is 2 feet. The longer piece is 8 feet.

12. Let x be the length of the longer pieces. Then $x - 3$ is the length of the shorter piece.
$$x + x + x - 3 = 45$$
$$3x - 3 = 45$$
$$3x = 48$$
$$x = 16$$
$$x - 3 = 16 - 3 = 13$$
The longer pieces both have length 16 feet. The shorter piece has length 13 feet.

13.
$$y = mx + b$$
$$y - b = mx$$
$$\frac{y - b}{m} = x$$

14.
$$y = mx + b$$
$$y - mx = b$$

15.
$$x + 4 \le -6$$
$$x + 4 - 4 \le -6 - 4$$
$$x \le -10$$

16. $x - 1 > -10$
$$x > -9$$
$$\{x | x > -9\}$$

17. $\dfrac{x^5}{x^2} = x^{5-2} = x^3$

18. $\dfrac{x^9}{x} = \dfrac{x^9}{x^1} = x^{9-1} = x^8$

19. $\dfrac{4^7}{4^3} = 4^{7-3} = 4^4 = 256$

20. $\dfrac{7^{12}}{7^4} = 7^{12-4} = 7^8 = 5,764,801$

21. $\dfrac{(-3)^5}{(-3)^2} = (-3)^{5-2} = (-3)^3 = -27$

22. $\dfrac{(-4)^9}{(-4)^7} = (-4)^{9-7} = (-4)^2 = 16$

23. $\dfrac{2x^5 y^2}{xy} = \dfrac{2}{1} \cdot \dfrac{x^5}{x} \cdot \dfrac{y^2}{y} = 2x^{5-1} y^{2-1} = 2x^4 y$

24. $\dfrac{13a^5 b}{a^4} = 13b \cdot \dfrac{a^5}{a^4} = 13b \cdot a^{5-4} = 13b \cdot a^1 = 13ab$

25. $2x^{-3} = 2 \cdot \dfrac{1}{x^3} = \dfrac{2}{x^3}$

26. $9x^{-2} = 9 \cdot \dfrac{1}{x^2} = \dfrac{9}{x^2}$

27. $(-2)^{-4} = \dfrac{1}{(-2)^4} = \dfrac{1}{16}$

28. $(-3)^{-3} = \dfrac{1}{(-3)^3} = \dfrac{1}{-27} = -\dfrac{1}{27}$

29. $5x(2x^3 + 6) = 5x(2x^3) + 5x(6) = 10x^4 + 30x$

30. $3y(4y^2 - 2) = 3y(4y^2) - 3y(2) = 12y^3 - 6y$

31. $-3x^2(5x^2 + 6x - 1)$
$= -3x^2(5x^2) + (-3x^2)(6x) - (-3x^2)(1)$
$= -15x^4 - 18x^3 + 3x^2$

32. $-5y(7y^2 - 3y + 1)$
$= -5y(7y^2) - (-5y)(3y) + (-5y)(1)$
$= -35y^3 + 15y^2 - 5y$

33. $\dfrac{4x^2 + 7 + 8x^3}{2x + 3} = 4x^2 - 4x + 6 - \dfrac{11}{2x+3}$

$$
\begin{array}{r}
4x^2 - 4x + 6 \\
2x+3 \overline{)\, 8x^3 + 4x^2 + 0x^1 + 7} \\
\underline{8x^3 + 12x^2 } \\
-8x^2 + 0x^1 \\
\underline{-8x^2 - 12x } \\
12x + 7 \\
\underline{12x + 18} \\
-11
\end{array}
$$

34. $\dfrac{6x^2 - 7x + 4}{2x + 1} = 3x - 5 + \dfrac{9}{2x+1}$

$$
\begin{array}{r}
3x - 5 \\
2x+1 \overline{)\, 6x^2 - 7x + 4} \\
\underline{6x^2 + 3x } \\
-10x + 4 \\
\underline{-10x - 5} \\
9
\end{array}
$$

35. $x^2 + 7x + 12 = (x+4)(x+3)$

36. $x^2 + 17x + 70 = (x+7)(x+10)$

37. $25x^2 + 20xy + 4y^2 = (5x+2y)(5x+2y)$
$ = (5x+2y)^2$

38. $36a^2 - 48ab + 16b^2$
$= 4(9a^2 - 12ab + 4b^2)$
$= 4[(3a)^2 - 2 \cdot 3a \cdot 2b + (2b)^2]$
$= 4(3a - 2b)^2$

39. $x^2 - 9x - 22 = 0$
$(x-11)(x+2) = 0$
$x - 11 = 0 \quad \text{or} \quad x + 2 = 0$
$x = 11 x = -2$
The solutions are 11 and −2.

40. $x^2 + 2x - 15 = 0$
$(x+5)(x-3) = 0$
$x + 5 = 0 \quad \text{or} \quad x - 3 = 0$
$x = -5 x = 3$
The solutions are −5 and 3.

41. $\dfrac{x^2+x}{3x} \cdot \dfrac{6}{5x+5} = \dfrac{x(x+1)}{3x} \cdot \dfrac{2 \cdot 3}{5(x+1)} = \dfrac{2}{5}$

42. $\dfrac{3x-12}{2} \div \dfrac{5x-20}{4x} = \dfrac{3x-12}{2} \cdot \dfrac{4x}{5x-20}$

$\qquad\qquad\qquad = \dfrac{3(x-4)}{2} \cdot \dfrac{2 \cdot 2x}{5(x-4)}$

$\qquad\qquad\qquad = \dfrac{3 \cdot 2x}{5}$

$\qquad\qquad\qquad = \dfrac{6x}{5}$

43. $\dfrac{3x^2+2x}{x-1} - \dfrac{10x-5}{x-1} = \dfrac{3x^2+2x-10x+5}{x-1}$

$\qquad\qquad\qquad\quad = \dfrac{3x^2-8x+5}{x-1}$

$\qquad\qquad\qquad\quad = \dfrac{(3x-5)(x-1)}{x-1}$

$\qquad\qquad\qquad\quad = 3x-5$

44. $\dfrac{4x}{x+2} + \dfrac{8}{x+2} = \dfrac{4x+8}{x+2} = \dfrac{4(x+2)}{x+2} = 4$

45. $\dfrac{6x}{x^2-4} - \dfrac{3}{x+2} = \dfrac{6x}{(x+2)(x-2)} - \dfrac{3(x-2)}{(x+2)(x-2)}$

$\qquad\qquad\qquad = \dfrac{6x-3x+6}{(x+2)(x-2)}$

$\qquad\qquad\qquad = \dfrac{3x+6}{(x+2)(x-2)}$

$\qquad\qquad\qquad = \dfrac{3(x+2)}{(x+2)(x-2)}$

$\qquad\qquad\qquad = \dfrac{3}{x-2}$

46. $\dfrac{2}{x-3} + \dfrac{5x}{x^2-9} = \dfrac{2(x+3)}{(x-3)(x+3)} + \dfrac{5x}{(x-3)(x+3)}$

$\qquad\qquad\qquad = \dfrac{2x+6+5x}{(x-3)(x+3)}$

$\qquad\qquad\qquad = \dfrac{7x+6}{x^2-9}$

47. $\dfrac{t-4}{2} - \dfrac{t-3}{9} = \dfrac{5}{18}$

$18\left(\dfrac{t-4}{2} - \dfrac{t-3}{9}\right) = 18\left(\dfrac{5}{18}\right)$

$9(t-4) - 2(t-3) = 5$

$9t-36-2t+6 = 5$

$7t-30 = 5$

$7t = 35$

$t = 5$

The solution is 5.

48. $\dfrac{y}{2} - \dfrac{y}{4} = \dfrac{1}{6}$

$12\left(\dfrac{y}{2} - \dfrac{y}{4}\right) = 12 \cdot \dfrac{1}{6}$

$6y-3y = 2$

$3y = 2$

$y = \dfrac{2}{3}$

The solution is $\dfrac{2}{3}$.

49. Let x be the time in hours for Sam and Frank to complete the tour together. Sam completes $\dfrac{1}{3}$ of a tour in 1 hour, and Frank completes $\dfrac{1}{7}$ of a tour in 1 hour. Together, they complete $\dfrac{1}{x}$ of a tour in 1 hour.

$\dfrac{1}{3} + \dfrac{1}{7} = \dfrac{1}{x}$

$21x\left(\dfrac{1}{3} + \dfrac{1}{7}\right) = 21x\left(\dfrac{1}{x}\right)$

$7x+3x = 21$

$10x = 21$

$x = \dfrac{21}{10} = 2\dfrac{1}{10}$

Sam and Frank can complete a quality control tour together in $2\dfrac{1}{10}$ hours.

50. Let x be the time in hours for both machines to complete the task together. The first machine completes $\dfrac{1}{18}$ of the task in 1 hour and the second machine completes $\dfrac{1}{12}$ of the task in 1 hour. Together, the machines complete $\dfrac{1}{x}$ of the task in 1 hour.

$$\frac{1}{18}+\frac{1}{12}=\frac{1}{x}$$
$$36x\left(\frac{1}{18}+\frac{1}{12}\right)=36x\cdot\frac{1}{x}$$
$$2x+3x=36$$
$$5x=36$$
$$x=\frac{36}{5}$$

Both machines can complete the task in $\dfrac{36}{5}=7\dfrac{1}{5}$ hours.

51.
$$\frac{\dfrac{1}{z}-\dfrac{1}{2}}{\dfrac{1}{3}-\dfrac{z}{6}}=\frac{\dfrac{2}{2z}-\dfrac{z}{2z}}{\dfrac{2}{6}-\dfrac{z}{6}}$$
$$=\frac{\dfrac{2-z}{2z}}{\dfrac{2-z}{6}}$$
$$=\frac{2-z}{2z}\div\frac{2-z}{6}$$
$$=\frac{2-z}{2z}\cdot\frac{6}{2-z}$$
$$=\frac{2\cdot3\cdot(2-z)}{2\cdot z\cdot(2-z)}$$
$$=\frac{3}{z}$$

52.
$$\frac{\dfrac{x}{9}-\dfrac{1}{x}}{1+\dfrac{3}{x}}=\frac{\dfrac{x^2}{9x}-\dfrac{9}{9x}}{\dfrac{x}{x}+\dfrac{3}{x}}$$
$$=\frac{\dfrac{x^2-9}{9x}}{\dfrac{x+3}{x}}$$
$$=\frac{x^2-9}{9x}\div\frac{x+3}{x}$$
$$=\frac{x^2-9}{9x}\cdot\frac{x}{x+3}$$
$$=\frac{x\cdot(x-3)\cdot(x+3)}{9\cdot x\cdot(x+3)}$$
$$=\frac{x-3}{9}$$

Chapter 13

Practice Problems

1. a. Point (4, 2) lies in quadrant I.

   b. Point (−1, −3) lies in quadrant III.

   c. Point (2, −2) lies in quadrant IV.

   d. Point (−5, 1) lies in quadrant II.

   e. Point (0, 3) lies on the *y*-axis.

   f. Point (3, 0) lies on the *x*-axis.

   g. Point (0, −4) lies on the *y*-axis.

   h. Point $\left(-2\frac{1}{2},\ 0\right)$ lies on the *x*-axis.

   i. Point $\left(1,\ -3\frac{3}{4}\right)$ lies in quadrant IV.

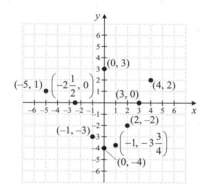

2. a. (2003, 1376), (2004, 1817), (2005, 1264), (2006, 1106), (2007, 1093), (2008, 1621)

b.

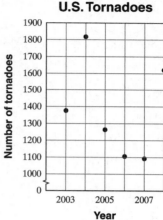

U.S. Tornadoes

c. The number of tornadoes varies greatly from year to year.

3. a. $x + 2y = 8$
In (0,), the *x*-coordinate is 0.
$0 + 2y = 8$
$\quad 2y = 8$
$\quad\ \ y = 4$
The ordered pair is (0, 4).

   b. $x + 2y = 8$
In (, 3) the *y*-coordinate is 3.
$x + 2(3) = 8$
$\quad x + 6 = 8$
$\quad\quad\ x = 2$
The ordered pair is (2, 3).

   c. $x + 2y = 8$
In (−4,), the *x*-coordinate is −4.
$-4 + 2y = 8$
$\quad\ \ 2y = 12$
$\quad\ \ \ y = 6$
The ordered pair is (−4, 6).

4. a. Let $x = -3$
$y = -2x$
$y = -2(-3)$
$y = 6$

   b. Let $y = 0$.
$y = -2x$
$0 = -2x$
$0 = x$

c. Let $y = 10$.
$$y = -2x$$
$$10 = -2x$$
$$-5 = x$$

The ordered pairs are $(-3, 6)$, $(0, 0)$, and $(-5, 10)$.

	x	y
a.	-3	6
b.	0	0
c.	-5	10

5. a. Let $x = -3$.
$$y = \frac{1}{3}x - 1$$
$$y = \frac{1}{3}(-3) - 1$$
$$y = -1 - 1$$
$$y = -2$$

b. Let $x = 0$.
$$y = \frac{1}{3}x - 1$$
$$y = \frac{1}{3}(0) - 1$$
$$y = 0 - 1$$
$$y = -1$$

c. Let $y = 0$.
$$0 = \frac{1}{3}x - 1$$
$$1 = \frac{1}{3}x$$
$$3(1) = x$$
$$3 = x$$

The ordered pairs are $(-3, -2)$, $(0, -1)$, and $(3, 0)$.

	x	y
a.	-3	-2
b.	0	-1
c.	3	0

6. When $x = 1$,
$$y = -50x + 400$$
$$y = -50(1) + 400$$
$$y = -50 + 400$$
$$y = 350$$

When $x = 2$,
$$y = -50x + 400$$
$$y = -50(2) + 400$$
$$y = -100 + 400$$
$$y = 300$$

When $x = 3$,
$$y = -50x + 400$$
$$y = -50(3) + 400$$
$$y = -150 + 400$$
$$y = 250$$

When $x = 4$,
$$y = -50x + 400$$
$$y = -50(4) + 400$$
$$y = -200 + 400$$
$$y = 200$$

When $x = 5$,
$$y = -50x + 400$$
$$y = -50(5) + 400$$
$$y = -250 + 400$$
$$y = 150$$

When $x = 6$,
$$y = -50x + 400$$
$$y = -50(6) + 400$$
$$y = -300 + 400$$
$$y = 100$$

When $x = 7$,
$$y = -50x + 400$$
$$y = -50(7) + 400$$
$$y = -350 + 400$$
$$y = 50$$

The completed table is shown.

x	1	2	3	4	5	6	7
y	350	300	250	200	150	100	50

Vocabulary and Readiness Check

1. The horizontal axis is called the <u>x-axis</u>.

2. The vertical axis is called the <u>y-axis</u>.

3. The intersection of the horizontal axis and the vertical axis is a point called the <u>origin</u>.

4. The axes divide the plane into regions, called <u>quadrants</u>. There are <u>four</u> of these regions.

5. In the ordered pair of numbers (−2, 5), the number −2 is called the <u>*x*-coordinate</u> and the number 5 is called the <u>*y*-coordinate</u>.

6. Each ordered pair of numbers corresponds to <u>one</u> point in the plane.

7. An ordered pair is a <u>solution</u> of an equation in two variables if replacing the variables by the coordinates of the ordered pair results in a true statement.

8. The graph of paired data as points in a rectangular coordinate system is called a <u>scatter diagram</u>.

Exercise Set 13.1

1.

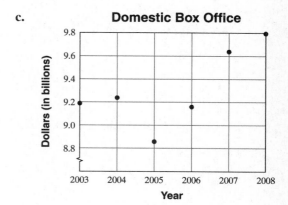

(1, 5) and (3.7, 2.2) are in quadrant I.

$\left(-1, 4\frac{1}{2}\right)$ is in quadrant II.

(−5, −2) is in quadrant III.

(2, −4) and $\left(\frac{1}{2}, -3\right)$ are in quadrant IV.

(−3, 0) lies on the *x*-axis.
(0, −1) lies on the *y*-axis.

3. Point *A* is at the origin, so its coordinates are (0, 0).

5. Point *C* is 3 units right and 2 units up from the origin, so its coordinates are (3, 2).

7. Point *E* is 2 units left and 2 units down from the origin, so its coordinates are (−2, −2).

9. Point *G* is 2 units right and 1 unit down from the origin, so its coordinates are (2, −1).

11. Point *B* is on the *y*-axis and 3 units down from the origin, so its coordinates are (0, −3).

13. Point *D* is 1 unit right and 3 units up from the origin, so its coordinates are (1, 3).

15. Point *F* is 3 units left and 1 unit down from the origin, so its coordinates are (−3, −1).

17. a. The ordered pairs are (2003, 9.17), (2004, 9.22), (2005, 8.83), (2006, 9.14), (2007, 9.63), (2008, 9.79).

b. The ordered pair (2006, 9.14) indicates that the domestic box office in 2006 was $9.14 billion.

c.

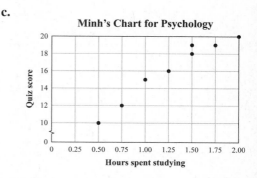

d. answers may vary

19. a. The ordered pairs are (0.50, 10), (0.75, 12), (1.00, 15), (1.25, 16), (1.50, 18), (1.50, 19), (1.75, 19), and (2.00, 20).

b. The ordered pair (1.25, 16) indicates that when Minh studied 1.25 hours, her quiz score was 16.

c.

d. answers may vary

21. $x - 4y = 4$

In (, −2), the y-coordinate is −2.

$x - 4(-2) = 4$

$x + 8 = 4$

$x = -4$

In (4,), the x-coordinate is 4.

$4 - 4y = 4$

$-4y = 0$

$y = 0$

The completed coordinates are (−4, −2) and (4, 0).

23. $y = \dfrac{1}{4}x - 3$

In (−8,), the x-coordinate is −8.

$y = \dfrac{1}{4}(-8) - 3 = -2 - 3 = -5$

In (, 1), the y-coordinate is 1.

$1 = \dfrac{1}{4}x - 3$

$4 = \dfrac{1}{4}x$

$16 = x$

The completed coordinates are (−8, −5) and (16, 1).

25. $y = -7x$

$-\dfrac{1}{7}y = x$

$x = -\frac{1}{7}y$	$y = -7x$
0	$-7(0) = 0$
−1	$-7(-1) = 7$
$-\frac{1}{7}(2) = -\frac{2}{7}$	2

27. $-y + 2 = x$

$-y = x - 2$

$y = -x + 2$

$x = -y + 2$	$y = -x + 2$
0	$-0 + 2 = 2$
$-0 + 2 = 2$	0
−3	$-(-3) + 2 = 3 + 2 = 5$

29. $y = \dfrac{1}{2}x$

$2y = x$

$x = 2y$	$y = \frac{1}{2}x$
0	$\frac{1}{2}(0) = 0$
–6	$\frac{1}{2}(-6) = -3$
$2(1) = 2$	1

31. $x + 3y = 6$ $3y = -x + 6$

       $x = -3y + 6$ $y = -\dfrac{1}{3}x + 2$

$x = -3y + 6$	$y = -\frac{1}{3}x + 2$
0	$-\frac{1}{3}(0) + 2 = 0 + 2 = 2$
$-3(0) + 6 = 0 + 6 = 6$	0
$-3(1) + 6 = -3 + 6 = 3$	1

33. $y = 2x - 12$

     $y + 12 = 2x$

$\dfrac{1}{2}(y + 12) = x$

$x = \frac{1}{2}(y + 12)$	$y = 2x - 12$
0	$2(0) - 12 = 0 - 12 = -12$
$\frac{1}{2}(-2 + 12) = \frac{1}{2}(10) = 5$	–2
3	$2(3) - 12 = 6 - 12 = -6$

35. $2x + 7y = 5$ $7y = -2x + 5$

     $2x = -7y + 5$ $y = \dfrac{-2x + 5}{7}$

       $x = \dfrac{-7y + 5}{2}$

$x = \frac{-7y+5}{2}$	$y = \frac{-2x+5}{7}$
0	$\frac{-2(0)+5}{7} = \frac{5}{7}$
$\frac{-7(0)+5}{2} = \frac{5}{2}$	0
$\frac{-7(1)+5}{2} = \frac{-2}{2} = -1$	1

37. $x = -5y$

$y = 0:\ x = -5(0) = 0$

$y = 1:\ x = -5(1) = -5$

$x = 10:\ 10 = -5y$

$\qquad\qquad -2 = y$

The ordered pairs are (0, 0), (−5, 1), and (10, −2).

x	y
0	0
−5	1
10	−2

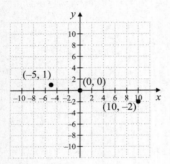

39. $y = \dfrac{1}{3}x + 2$

$x = 0:\ y = \dfrac{1}{3}(0) + 2 = 0 + 2 = 2$

$x = -3:\ y = \dfrac{1}{3}(-3) + 2 = -1 + 2 = 1$

$y = 0:\quad 0 = \dfrac{1}{3}x + 2$

$\qquad\qquad -2 = \dfrac{1}{3}x$

$\qquad\qquad -6 = x$

The ordered pairs are (0, 2), (−3, 1), and (−6, 0).

x	y
0	2
−3	1
−6	0

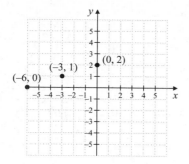

41. a.

x	100	200	300
$y = 80x + 5000$	$80(100) + 5000$ $= 8000 + 5000$ $= 13,000$	$80(200) + 5000$ $= 16,000 + 5000$ $= 21,000$	$80(300) + 5000$ $= 24,000 + 5000$ $= 29,000$

b. Find x when $y = 8600$.
$$8600 = 80x + 5000$$
$$3600 = 80x$$
$$45 = x$$
45 computer desks can be produced for \$8600.

43. a.

x	1	3	5
$y = 0.2x + 5.39$	$0.2(1) + 5.39$ $= 0.2 + 5.39$ $= 5.59$	$0.2(3) + 5.39$ $= 0.6 + 5.39$ $= 5.99$	$0.2(5) + 5.39$ $= 1 + 5.39$ $= 6.39$

b. Find x when $y = 6.40$.
$$6.40 = 0.2x + 5.39$$
$$1.01 = 0.2x$$
$$5.05 = x$$
$$5 \approx x$$
$$2000 + 5 = 2005$$
The average cinema admission price was \$6.40 in 2005.

c. Find x when $y = 8.00$.
$$8.00 = 0.2x + 5.39$$
$$2.61 = 0.2x$$
$$13.05 = x$$
$$13 \approx x$$
$$2000 + 13 = 2013$$
The average cinema admission price is predicted to be \$8.00 in 2013.

45. $x + y = 5$
$$y = 5 - x$$

47. $2x + 4y = 5$
$$4y = 5 - 2x$$
$$y = \frac{5 - 2x}{4}$$

49. $10x = -5y$
$-2x = y$
$y = -2x$

51. False; point $(-1, 5)$ lies in quadrant II.

53. True

55. Points in quadrant III are to the left and down from the origin, so the x- and y-coordinates are negative. (negative, negative) corresponds to quadrant III.

57. Points in quadrant IV are to the right and down from the origin, so the x-coordinate is positive and the y-coordinate is negative. (positive, negative) corresponds to quadrant IV.

59. The origin corresponds to $(0, 0)$.

61. If the x-coordinate of a point is 0, the point is neither to the left nor to the right of the origin, so it is on the y-axis.

63. no; answers may vary

65. answers may vary

67. answers may vary

69. A point four units to right of the y-axis and seven units below the x-axis has coordinates $(4, -7)$.

71. The length of the rectangle is $3 - (-1) = 4$ and the width of the rectangle is $5 - (-4) = 9$.
Perimeter $= 2(\text{length}) + 2(\text{width})$
$= 2(4) + 2(9)$
$= 8 + 18$
$= 26$
The perimeter is 26 units.

73. The revenues are approximately \$47 billion, \$53 billion, \$59 billion, and \$63 billion.

Section 13.2

Practice Problems

1. $x + 3y = 6$
$x = 0$: $0 + 3y = 6$
$3y = 6$
$y = 2$

$x = 3$: $3 + 3y = 6$
$3y = 3$
$y = 1$
$y = 0$: $x + 3(0) = 6$
$x + 0 = 6$
$x = 6$
The ordered pairs are $(0, 2)$, $(3, 1)$, and $(6, 0)$.

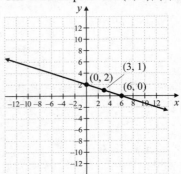

2. $-2x + 4y = 8$
$x = -2$: $-2(-2) + 4y = 8$
$4 + 4y = 8$
$4y = 4$
$y = 1$
$x = 0$: $-2(0) + 4y = 8$
$0 + 4y = 8$
$4y = 8$
$y = 2$
$x = 2$: $-2(2) + 4y = 8$
$-4 + 4y = 8$
$4y = 12$
$y = 3$
The ordered pairs are $(-2, 1)$, $(0, 2)$, and $(2, 3)$.

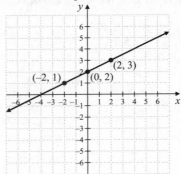

3. $y = 2x$
$x = -2$: $y = 2(-2) = -4$
$x = 0$: $y = 2(0) = 0$
$x = 3$: $y = 2(3) = 6$
The ordered pairs are $(-2, -4)$, $(0, 0)$, and $(3, 6)$.

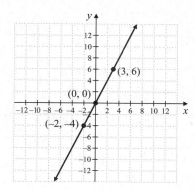

4. $y = -\dfrac{1}{2}x + 4$

$x = -6$: $y = -\dfrac{1}{2}(-6) + 4 = 3 + 4 = 7$

$x = 0$: $-\dfrac{1}{2}(0) + 4 = 0 + 4 = 4$

$x = 4$: $y = -\dfrac{1}{2}(4) + 4 = -2 + 4 = 2$

The ordered pairs are $(-6, 7)$, $(0, 4)$, and $(4, 2)$.

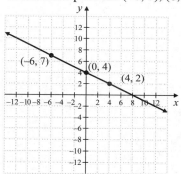

5. The equation $x = 3$ can be written in standard form as $x + 0y = 3$. No matter what value replaces y, x is always 3. It is a vertical line. Plot points $(3, 2)$, $(3, 0)$, and $(3, -4)$, for example.

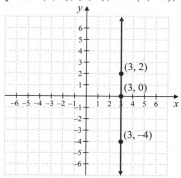

6. $x = 2015 - 2003 = 12$
Find 12 on the x-axis. Move vertically upward to the line and then horizontally to the left. In 2015, we predict that there will be 2840 thousand registered nurses.

Calculator Explorations

1. $y = -3x + 7$

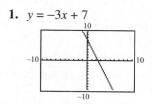

2. $y = -x + 5$

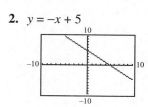

3. $y = 2.5x - 7.9$

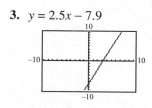

4. $y = -1.3x + 5.2$

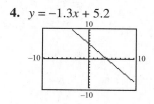

5. $y = -\dfrac{3}{10}x + \dfrac{32}{5}$

6. $y = \dfrac{2}{9}x - \dfrac{22}{3}$

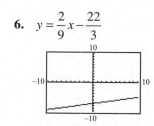

Exercise Set 13.2

1. $x - y = 6$

$y = 0$: $x - 0 = 6$

$\qquad x = 6$

$x = 4$: $4 - y = 6$

$\qquad -y = 2$

$\qquad y = -2$

$y = -1$: $x - (-1) = 6$

$\qquad x + 1 = 6$

$\qquad x = 5$

The ordered pairs are (6, 0), (4, −2), and (5, −1).

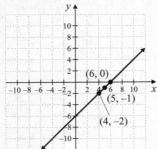

3. $y = -4x$

$x = 1$: $y = -4(1) = -4$

$x = 0$: $y = 4(0) = 0$

$x = -1$: $y = -4(-1) = 4$

The ordered pairs are (1, −4), (0, 0), and (−1, 4).

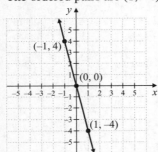

5. $y = \dfrac{1}{3}x$

$x = 0$: $y = \dfrac{1}{3}(0) = 0$

$x = 6$: $y = \dfrac{1}{3}(6) = 2$

$x = -3$: $y = \dfrac{1}{3}(-3) = -1$

The ordered pairs are (0, 0), (6, 2), and (−3, −1).

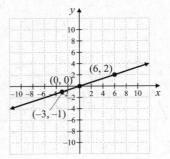

7. $y = -4x + 3$

$x = 0$: $y = -4(0) + 3 = 0 + 3 = 3$

$x = 1$: $y = -4(1) + 3 = -4 + 3 = -1$

$x = 2$: $y = -4(2) + 3 = -8 + 3 = -5$

The ordered pairs are (0, 3), (1, −1), and (2, −5).

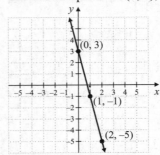

9. $x + y = 1$

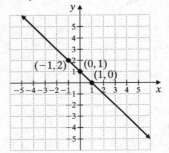

11. $x - y = -2$

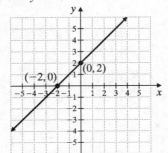

13. $x - 2y = 6$

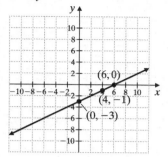

15. $y = 6x + 3$

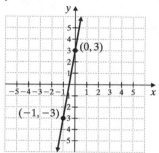

17. $x = -4$

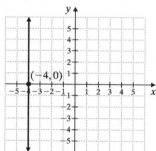

19. $y = 3$

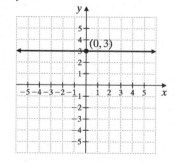

21. $y = x$

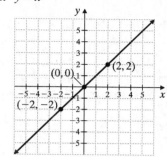

23. $x = -3y$

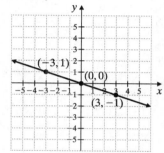

25. $x + 3y = 9$

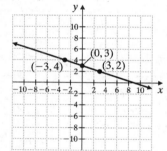

27. $y = \dfrac{1}{2}x + 2$

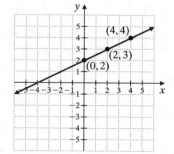

29. $3x - 2y = 12$

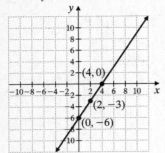

31. $y = -3.5x + 4$

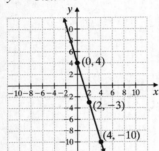

33. a.

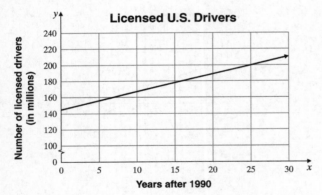

b. $x = 20: y = 2.2(20) + 145 = 44 + 145 = 189$
Yes, the point (20, 189) lies on the line. answers may vary

35. a.

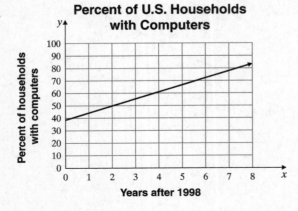

494

b. $x = 5$: $y = 5.6(5) + 38.5 = 28 + 38.5 = 66.5$
   The ordered pair is (5, 66.5).

c. Year $= x + 1998 = 5 + 1998 = 2003$
   In 2003, 66.5% of U.S. households had at least one computer.

37. The fourth vertex is the bottom-right corner of the rectangle. The x-coordinate must line the point up with the top-right corner, and the y-coordinate must line the point up with the bottom-left corner. The coordinates are $(4, -1)$.

39. $x - y = -3$
   $x = 0$: $0 - y = -3$
   $y = 3$
   $y = 0$: $x - 0 = -3$
   $x = -3$

x	y
0	3
-3	0

41. $y = 2x$
   $x = 0$: $y = 2(0) = 0$
   $y = 0$: $0 = 2x$
   $0 = x$

x	y
0	0
0	0

43. $y = 5x$
   $y = 5x + 4$

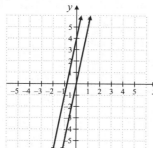

45. $y = -2x$
   $y = -2x - 3$

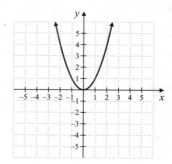

47. $y = x^2$

$x = 0$: $y = 0^2 = 0$

$x = 1$: $y = 1^2 = 1$

$x = -1$: $y = (-1)^2 = 1$

$x = 2$: $y = 2^2 = 4$

$x = -2$: $y = (-2)^2 = 4$

x	y
0	0
1	1
-1	1
2	4
-2	4

49. The perimeter is the distance around.
   $x + 5 + y + 5 = 22$
   $x + y + 10 = 22$
   $x + y = 12$
   $x = 3$: $3 + y = 12$
   $y = 9$
   If x is 3 centimeters, then y is 9 centimeters.

51. yes; answers may vary

Section 13.3

Practice Problems

1. x-intercept: $(2, 0)$
   y-intercept: $(0, -4)$

2. x-intercepts: $(-4, 0)$, $(2, 0)$
   y-intercept: $(0, 2)$

3. x-intercept and y-intercept: $(0, 0)$

4. $2x - y = 4$
   $y = 0$: $2x - 0 = 4$
   $\qquad\quad 2x = 4$
   $\qquad\quad\; x = 2$
   x-intercept: $(2, 0)$
   $x = 0$: $2(0) - y = 4$
   $\qquad\quad 0 - y = 4$
   $\qquad\quad\;\; -y = 4$
   $\qquad\quad\;\;\;\; y = -4$
   y-intercept: $(0, -4)$

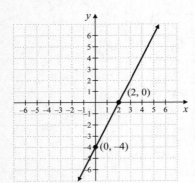

5. $y = 3x$
   $y = 0$: $0 = 3x$
   $\qquad\quad 0 = x$
   x-intercept: $(0, 0)$
   $x = 0$: $y = 3(0)$
   $\qquad\quad y = 0$
   y-intercept: $(0, 0)$
   Let $x = 1$ to find a second point.
   $x = 1$: $y = 3$
   $(1, 3)$ is another point on the line.

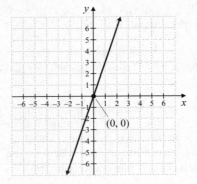

6. $x = -3$
   The graph of $x = -3$ is a vertical line with x-intercept $(-3, 0)$.

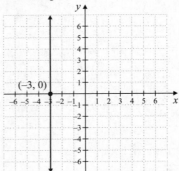

7. $y = 4$
   The graph of $y = 4$ is a horizontal line with y-intercept $(0, 4)$.

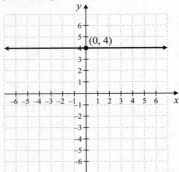

Calculator Explorations

1. $x = 3.78y$

496

2. $-2.61y = x$

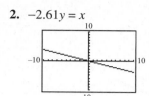

3. $3x + 7y = 21$

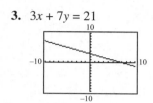

4. $-4x + 6y = 12$

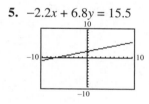

5. $-2.2x + 6.8y = 15.5$

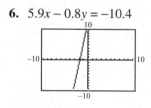

6. $5.9x - 0.8y = -10.4$

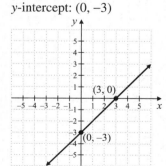

Vocabulary and Readiness Check

1. An equation that can be written in the form $Ax + By = C$ is called a <u>linear</u> equation in two variables.

2. The form $Ax + By = C$ is called <u>standard</u> form.

3. The graph of the equation $y = -1$ is a <u>horizontal</u> line.

4. The graph of the equation $x = 5$ is a <u>vertical</u> line.

5. A point where a graph crosses the y-axis is called a <u>y-intercept</u>.

6. A point where a graph crosses the x-axis is called an <u>x-intercept</u>.

7. Given an equation of a line, to find the x-intercept (if there is one), let <u>y</u> = 0 and solve for <u>x</u>.

8. Given an equation of a line, to find the y-intercept (if there is one), let <u>x</u> = 0 and solve for <u>y</u>.

9. False; a horizontal line (other than $y = 0$) has no x-intercept and a vertical line (other than $x = 0$) has no y-intercept.

10. True

11. True

12. False; $x = 5$: $y = 5(5) = 25$, so the point (5, 1) is not on the graph of $y = 5x$.

Exercise Set 13.3

1. x-intercept: $(-1, 0)$
y-intercept: $(0, 1)$

3. x-intercepts: $(-2, 0)$, $(2, 0)$
y-intercept: $(0, -2)$

5. x-intercepts: $(-2, 0)$, $(1, 0)$, $(3, 0)$
y-intercept: $(0, 3)$

7. x-intercepts: $(-1, 0)$, $(1, 0)$
y-intercepts: $(0, 1)$, $(0, -2)$

9. $x - y = 3$
$y = 0$: $x - 0 = 0$
$\qquad\quad x = 3$
x-intercept: $(3, 0)$
$x = 0$: $0 - y = 3$
$\qquad\quad -y = 3$
$\qquad\quad\; y = -3$
y-intercept: $(0, -3)$

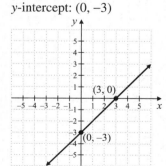

11. $x = 5y$
$y = 0: x = 5(0) = 0$
x-intercept: $(0, 0)$
$x = 0: 0 = 5y$
$\qquad 0 = y$
y-intercept: $(0, 0)$
Let $y = 1$ to find a second point.
$y = 1: x = 5$
$(5, 1)$ is another point on the line.

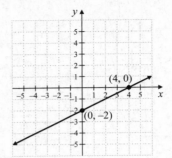

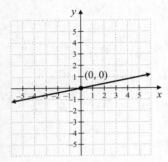

13. $-x + 2y = 6$
$y = 0: -x + 2(0) = 6$
$\qquad\qquad -x = 6$
$\qquad\qquad x = -6$
x-intercept: $(-6, 0)$
$x = 0: -0 + 2y = 6$
$\qquad\qquad 2y = 6$
$\qquad\qquad y = 3$
y-intercept: $(0, 3)$

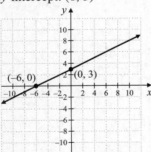

15. $2x - 4y = 8$
$y = 0: 2x - 4(0) = 8$
$\qquad\qquad 2x - 0 = 8$
$\qquad\qquad 2x = 8$
$\qquad\qquad x = 4$
x-intercept: $(4, 0)$
$x = 0: 2(0) - 4y = 8$
$\qquad\qquad 0 - 4y = 8$
$\qquad\qquad -4y = 8$
$\qquad\qquad y = -2$
y-intercept: $(0, -2)$

17. $y = 2x$
$y = 0: 0 = 2x$
$\qquad\quad 0 = x$
x-intercept: $(0, 0)$
$(0, 0)$ is also the y-intercept. Let $x = 1$ to find a second point.
$x = 1: y = 2(1)$
$\qquad\quad y = 2$
$(1, 2)$ is another point on the line.

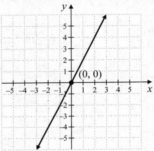

19. $y = 3x + 6$
$y = 0: 0 = 3x + 6$
$\qquad\quad -6 = 3x$
$\qquad\quad -2 = x$
x-intercept: $(-2, 0)$
$x = 0: y = 3(0) + 6$
$\qquad\quad y = 0 + 6$
$\qquad\quad y = 6$
y-intercept: $(0, 6)$

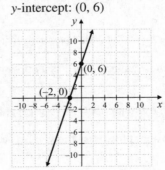

21. The graph of $x = -1$ is a vertical line with
x-intercept $(-1, 0)$.

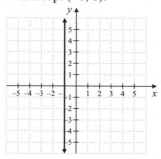

23. The graph of $y = 0$ is a horizontal line with
y-intercept $(0, 0)$.

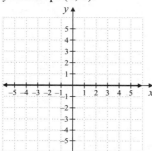

25. $y + 7 = 0$
   $\quad\quad y = -7$

The graph of $y = -7$ is a horizontal line with
y-intercept $(0, -7)$.

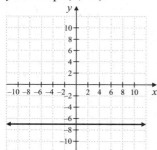

27. $x + 3 = 0$
   $\quad\quad x = -3$
The graph of $x = -3$ is a vertical line with
x-intercept $(0, -3)$.

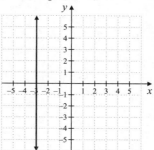

29. $x = y$
$y = 0: x = 0$
x-intercept: $(0, 0)$
$(0, 0)$ is also the y-intercept. Let $x = 3$ to find a
second point.
$x = 3: 3 = y$
$(3, 3)$ is another point on the line.

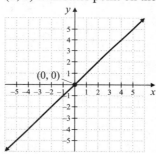

31. $x + 8y = 8$
   $y = 0: \ x + 8(0) = 8$
   $\quad\quad\quad x + 0 = 8$
   $\quad\quad\quad\quad\ \ x = 8$
x-intercept: $(8, 0)$
$x = 0: \ 0 + 8y = 8$
   $\quad\quad\quad 8y = 8$
   $\quad\quad\quad\ \ y = 1$
y-intercept: $(0, 1)$

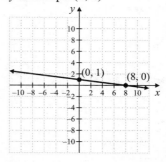

33. $5 = 6x - y$

$y = 0$: $5 = 6x - 0$

$\qquad 5 = 6x$

$\qquad \dfrac{5}{6} = x$

x-intercept: $\left(\dfrac{5}{6}, 0\right)$

$x = 0$: $5 = 6(0) - y$

$\qquad 5 = -y$

$\qquad -5 = y$

y-intercept: $(0, -5)$

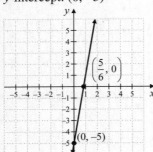

35. $-x + 10y = 11$

$y = 0$: $-x + 10(0) = 11$

$\qquad -x + 0 = 11$

$\qquad -x = 11$

$\qquad x = -11$

x-intercept: $(-11, 0)$

$x = 0$: $-0 + 10y = 11$

$\qquad 10y = 11$

$\qquad y = \dfrac{11}{10}$

y-intercept: $\left(0, \dfrac{11}{10}\right)$

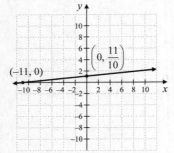

37. $x = -4\dfrac{1}{2}$

This is a vertical line with x-intercept $\left(-4\dfrac{1}{2}, 0\right)$.

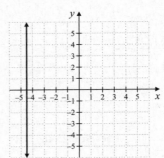

39. $y = 3\dfrac{1}{4}$

This is a horizontal line with y-intercept $\left(0, 3\dfrac{1}{4}\right)$.

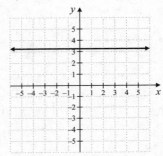

41. $y = -\dfrac{2}{3}x + 1$

$y = 0$: $0 = -\dfrac{2}{3}x + 1$

$\qquad \dfrac{2}{3}x = 1$

$\qquad x = \dfrac{3}{2}$

x-intercept: $\left(\dfrac{3}{2}, 0\right)$

$x = 0$: $y = -\dfrac{2}{3}(0) + 1$

$\qquad y = 1$

y-intercept: $(0, 1)$

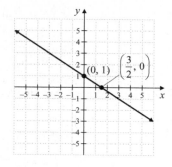

43. $4x - 6y + 2 = 0$

$y = 0: \quad 4x - 6(0) + 2 = 0$

$\qquad 4x - 0 + 2 = 0$

$\qquad\qquad 4x = -2$

$\qquad\qquad x = -\dfrac{1}{2}$

x-intercept: $\left(-\dfrac{1}{2}, 0\right)$

$x = 0: \quad 4(0) - 6y + 2 = 0$

$\qquad\qquad 0 - 6y + 2 = 0$

$\qquad\qquad\quad -6y = -2$

$\qquad\qquad\quad\quad y = \dfrac{1}{3}$

y-intercept: $\left(0, \dfrac{1}{3}\right)$

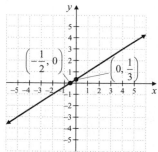

45. $\dfrac{-6-3}{2-8} = \dfrac{-9}{-6} = \dfrac{3}{2}$

47. $\dfrac{-8-(-2)}{-3-(-2)} = \dfrac{-8+2}{-3+2} = \dfrac{-6}{-1} = 6$

49. $\dfrac{0-6}{5-0} = \dfrac{-6}{5} = -\dfrac{6}{5}$

51. The graph of $y = 3$ is a horizontal line with y-intercept $(0, 3)$. This is graph c.

53. The graph of $x = 3$ is a vertical line with x-intercept $(3, 0)$. This is graph a.

55. The line can be on the x-axis or the y-axis so it can have infinitely many x- and y-intercepts.

57. A circle can have no x- and y-intercepts. That is, it does not have to intersect the axes.

59. answers may vary

61. $3x + 6y = 1200$

$x = 0: \quad 3(0) + 6y = 1200$

$\qquad\qquad\qquad 6y = 1200$

$\qquad\qquad\qquad\ y = 200$

The ordered pair $(0, 200)$ corresponds to manufacturing 0 chairs and 200 desks.

63. Manufacturing 50 desks corresponds to $y = 50$.

$3x + 6y = 1200$

$y = 50: \quad 3x + 6(50) = 1200$

$\qquad\qquad\quad 3x + 300 = 1200$

$\qquad\qquad\qquad\quad 3x = 900$

$\qquad\qquad\qquad\quad\ x = 300$

When 50 desks are manufactured, 300 chairs can be manufactured.

65.

The equation of the line is $y = -4$.

67. a. $y = -1.9x + 59$

$y = 0: \quad 0 = -1.9x + 59$

$\qquad\qquad 1.9x = 59$

$\qquad\qquad\quad x \approx 31.1$

The x-intercept is $(31.1, 0)$.

b. The x-intercept of $(31.1, 0)$ means that 31.1 years after 2003, there may be no newspaper circulation.

Section 13.4

Practice Problems

1. $m = \dfrac{y_2 - y_1}{x_2 - x_1} = \dfrac{-1 - 3}{4 - (-2)} = \dfrac{-4}{6} = -\dfrac{2}{3}$

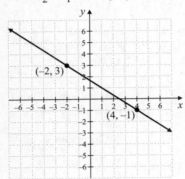

2. $m = \dfrac{y_2 - y_1}{x_2 - x_1} = \dfrac{5 - 1}{3 - (-2)} = \dfrac{4}{5}$

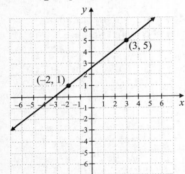

3. $5x + 4y = 10$

$4y = -5x + 10$

$y = -\dfrac{5}{4}x + \dfrac{10}{4}$

The slope is $-\dfrac{5}{4}$.

4. $-y = -2x + 7$

$\dfrac{-y}{-1} = \dfrac{-2x}{-1} + \dfrac{7}{-1}$

$y = 2x - 7$

The slope is 2.

5. $y = 3$ is a horizontal line. Horizontal lines have a slope of 0.

6. $x = -2$ is a vertical line. Vertical lines have undefined slopes.

7. a. $\begin{aligned} x + y &= 5 \\ y &= -x + 5 \end{aligned}$ $\begin{aligned} 2x + y &= 5 \\ y &= -2x + 5 \end{aligned}$

slope $= -1$ slope $= -2$

The slopes are not the same, so the lines are not parallel. The product, $(-1)(-2) = 2$, is not -1, so the lines are not perpendicular.

b. $\begin{aligned} 5y &= 2x - 3 \\ y &= \dfrac{2}{5}x - \dfrac{3}{5} \end{aligned}$ $\begin{aligned} 5x + 2y &= 1 \\ 2y &= -5x + 1 \\ y &= -\dfrac{5}{2}x + \dfrac{1}{2} \end{aligned}$

slope $= \dfrac{2}{5}$ slope $= -\dfrac{5}{2}$

The slopes are not the same, so the lines are not parallel. The product, $\left(\dfrac{2}{5}\right)\left(-\dfrac{5}{2}\right) = -1$, is -1, so the lines are perpendicular.

c. $y = 2x + 1$ $\begin{aligned} 4x - 2y &= 8 \\ -2y &= -4x + 8 \\ y &= \dfrac{-4x}{-2} + \dfrac{8}{-2} \\ y &= 2x - 4 \end{aligned}$

slope $= 2$ slope $= 2$

The slopes are the same, so the lines are parallel.

8. $\text{grade} = \dfrac{\text{rise}}{\text{run}} = \dfrac{3}{20} = 0.15 = 15\%$

The grade is 15%.

9. $m = \dfrac{240 - 120}{1990 - 1980} = \dfrac{120}{10} = 12$

Each year the sales of food and drink from restaurants increases by \$12 billion.

Calculator Explorations

1.

The lines are parallel since they all have a slope of 3.8. The graph of $y = 3.8x - 3$ is the graph of $y = 3.8x$ moved 3 units down with a y-intercept of -3. The graph of $y = 3.8x + 9$ is the graph of $y = 3.8x$ moved 9 units up with a y-intercept of 9.

2.

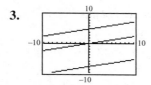

The lines are parallel since they all have a slope of -4.9. The graph of $y = -4.9x + 1$ is the graph of $y = -4.9x$ moved 1 unit up with a y-intercept of 1. The graph of $y = -4.9x + 8$ is the graph of $y = -4.9x$ moved 8 units up with a y-intercept of 8.

3.

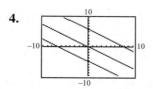

The lines are parallel since they all have a slope of $\frac{1}{4}$. The graph of $y = \frac{1}{4}x + 5$ is the graph of $y = \frac{1}{4}x$ moved 5 units up with a y-intercept of 5. The graph of $y = \frac{1}{4}x - 8$ is the graph of $y = \frac{1}{4}x$ moved 8 units down with a y-intercept of -8.

4.

The lines are parallel since they all have a slope of $-\frac{3}{4}$. The graph of $y = -\frac{3}{4}x - 5$ is the graph of $y = -\frac{3}{4}x$ moved 5 units down with a y-intercept of -5. The graph of $y = -\frac{3}{4}x + 6$ is the graph of $y = -\frac{3}{4}x$ moved 6 units up with a y-intercept of 6.

Vocabulary and Readiness Check

1. The measure of the steepness or tilt of a line is called <u>slope</u>.

2. If an equation is written in the form $y = mx + b$, the value of the letter <u>m</u> is the value of the slope of the graph.

3. The slope of a horizontal line is <u>0</u>.

4. The slope of a vertical line is <u>undefined</u>.

5. If the graph of a line moves upward from left to right, the line has <u>positive</u> slope.

6. If the graph of a line moves downward from left to right, the line has <u>negative</u> slope.

7. Given two points of a line, slope $= \dfrac{\text{change in } \underline{y}}{\text{change in } \underline{x}}$.

8. The line slants downward, so its slope is negative.

9. The line slants upward, so its slope is positive.

10. The line is vertical, so its slope is undefined.

11. The line is horizontal, so its slope is 0.

12. Since $m = \dfrac{7}{6}$ is positive, the line slants upward.

13. Since $m = -3$ is negative, the line slants downward.

14. Since $m = 0$, the line is horizontal.

15. Since m is undefined, the line is vertical.

Exercise Set 13.4

1. $m = \dfrac{y_2 - y_1}{x_2 - x_1} = \dfrac{-2 - 5}{6 - (-1)} = \dfrac{-7}{7} = -1$

3. $m = \dfrac{y_2 - y_1}{x_2 - x_1} = \dfrac{3 - 4}{5 - 1} = \dfrac{-1}{4} = -\dfrac{1}{4}$

5. $m = \dfrac{y_2 - y_1}{x_2 - x_1} = \dfrac{1 - 1}{-2 - 5} = \dfrac{0}{-7} = 0$

7. $m = \dfrac{y_2 - y_1}{x_2 - x_1} = \dfrac{5 - 3}{-4 - (-4)} = \dfrac{5 - 3}{-4 + 4} = \dfrac{2}{0}$
The slope is undefined.

9. $(x_1, y_1) = (-1, 2), (x_2, y_2) = (2, -2)$

$$m = \frac{y_2 - y_1}{x_2 - x_1} = \frac{-2-2}{2-(-1)} = \frac{-4}{3} = -\frac{4}{3}$$

11. $(x_1, y_1) = (1, -2), (x_2, y_2) = (3, 3)$

$$m = \frac{y_2 - y_1}{x_2 - x_1} = \frac{3-(-2)}{3-1} = \frac{3+2}{3-1} = \frac{5}{2}$$

13. Line 1 has a positive slope and line 2 has a negative slope, so line 1 has the greater slope.

15. Line 2 is steeper, so it has the greater slope.

17. $y = 5x - 2$
The slope is $m = 5$.

19. $y = -0.3x + 2.5$
The slope is $m = -0.3$.

21. $2x + y = 7$
$\quad\quad y = -2x + 7$
The slope is $m = -2$.

23. The line is vertical, so it has an undefined slope.

25. $2x - 3y = 10$
$\quad -3y = -2x + 10$
$\quad\quad y = \frac{2}{3}x - \frac{10}{3}$
The slope is $m = \frac{2}{3}$.

27. $x = 1$ is a vertical line, so its slope is undefined.

29. $\quad x = 2y$
$\quad \frac{1}{2}x = y$
$\quad\quad y = \frac{1}{2}x$
The slope is $m = \frac{1}{2}$.

31. $y = -3$ is a horizontal line, so its slope is 0.

33. $-3x - 4y = 6$
$\quad\quad -4y = 3x + 6$
$\quad\quad\quad y = -\frac{3}{4}x - \frac{3}{2}$
The slope is $m = -\frac{3}{4}$.

35. $20x - 5y = 1.2$
$\quad\quad -5y = -20x + 1.2$
$\quad\quad\quad y = \frac{-20x}{-5} + \frac{1.2}{-5}$
$\quad\quad\quad y = 4x - 0.24$
The slope is $m = 4$.

37. $y = \frac{2}{9}x + 3$

$y = -\frac{2}{9}x$

$\frac{2}{9} \neq -\frac{2}{9}$, so the lines are not parallel.

$\left(\frac{2}{9}\right)\left(-\frac{2}{9}\right) = -\frac{4}{81} \neq -1$, so the lines are not perpendicular.
The lines are neither parallel nor perpendicular.

39. $x - 3y = -6$
$\quad -3y = -x - 6$
$\quad\quad y = \frac{1}{3}x + 2$
$y = 3x - 9$

$\frac{1}{3} \neq 3$, so the lines are not parallel.

$\left(\frac{1}{3}\right)(3) = 1 \neq -1$, so the lines are not perpendicular. The lines are neither parallel nor perpendicular.

41. $\quad 6x = 5y + 1$
$\quad -5y = -6x + 1$
$\quad\quad y = \frac{6}{5}x - \frac{1}{5}$
$\quad -12x + 10y = 1$
$\quad\quad 10y = 12x + 1$
$\quad\quad\quad y = \frac{6}{5}x + \frac{1}{10}$

Both lines have slope $\frac{6}{5}$ and the y-intercepts are different, so they are parallel.

43. $6 + 4x = 3y$
$\quad 2 + \frac{4}{3}x = y$ or $y = \frac{4}{3}x + 2$

$$3x + 4y = 8$$
$$4y = -3x + 8$$
$$y = -\frac{3}{4}x + 2$$

$\left(\frac{4}{3}\right)\left(-\frac{3}{4}\right) = -1$, so the lines are perpendicular.

45. $m = \dfrac{y_2 - y_1}{x_2 - x_1} = \dfrac{0 - (-3)}{0 - (-3)} = \dfrac{3}{3} = 1$

    a. The slope of a parallel line is 1.

    b. The slope of a perpendicular line is

        $-\dfrac{1}{1} = -1$.

47. $m = \dfrac{y_2 - y_1}{x_2 - x_1} = \dfrac{5 - (-4)}{3 - (-8)} = \dfrac{5 + 4}{3 + 8} = \dfrac{9}{11}$

    a. The slope of a parallel line is $\dfrac{9}{11}$.

    b. The slope of a perpendicular line is

        $-\dfrac{1}{\frac{9}{11}} = -\dfrac{11}{9}$.

49. $\text{slope} = \dfrac{\text{rise}}{\text{run}} = \dfrac{6 \text{ feet}}{10 \text{ feet}} = \dfrac{3}{5}$

    The pitch of the roof is $\dfrac{3}{5}$.

51. $\text{slope} = \dfrac{\text{rise}}{\text{run}} = \dfrac{2}{16} = 0.125 = 12.5\%$

    The grade of the road is 12.5%

53. $\text{grade} = \dfrac{\text{rise}}{\text{run}} = \dfrac{2580 \text{ meters}}{6450 \text{ meters}} = 0.40 = 40\%$

    The grade of the track is 40%.

55. Canton Avenue:

    $\text{grade} = \dfrac{\text{rise}}{\text{run}} = \dfrac{11 \text{ meters}}{30 \text{ meters}} \approx 0.37 = 37\%$

    The grade of Canton Avenue is 37%.
    Baldwin Street:

    $\text{grade} = \dfrac{\text{rise}}{\text{run}} = \dfrac{1 \text{ meter}}{2.86 \text{ meters}} \approx 0.35 = 35\%$

    The grade of Baldwin Street is 35%.

57. $m = \dfrac{y_2 - y_1}{x_2 - x_1} = \dfrac{112 - 109.5}{2007 - 2005} = \dfrac{2.5}{2} = \dfrac{5}{4}$

    Every 4 years there are/should be 5 million more U.S. households with televisions.

59. $m = \dfrac{y_2 - y_1}{x_2 - x_1} = \dfrac{9.4 - 8.8}{2008 - 2004} = \dfrac{0.6}{4} = 0.15$

    Every year, the median age of automobiles in the United States increases by 0.15 year.

61. $y - (-6) = 2(x - 4)$
       $y + 6 = 2x - 8$
          $y = 2x - 14$

63. $y - 1 = -6(x - (-2))$
    $y - 1 = -6(x + 2)$
    $y - 1 = -6x - 12$
       $y = -6x - 11$

65. $(x_1, y_1) = (0, 0)$, $(x_2, y_2) = (1, 1)$

    $m = \dfrac{y_2 - y_1}{x_2 - x_1} = \dfrac{1 - 0}{1 - 0} = \dfrac{1}{1} = 1$
    The slope is $m = 1$; d.

67. The line is vertical, so its slope is undefined; b.

69. $(x_1, y_1) = (2, 0)$, $(x_2, y_2) = (4, -1)$

    $m = \dfrac{y_2 - y_1}{x_2 - x_1} = \dfrac{-1 - 0}{4 - 2} = \dfrac{-1}{2} = -\dfrac{1}{2}$
    The slope is $m = -\dfrac{1}{2}$; e.

71. $m = \dfrac{y_2 - y_1}{x_2 - x_1} = \dfrac{0 - 1}{0 - 2} = \dfrac{-1}{-2} = \dfrac{1}{2}$

    $\dfrac{-1 - 1}{-2 - 2} = \dfrac{-2}{-4} = \dfrac{1}{2}$; $\dfrac{-2 - 1}{-4 - 2} = \dfrac{-3}{-6} = \dfrac{1}{2}$
    $\dfrac{-1 - 0}{-2 - 0} = \dfrac{-1}{-2} = \dfrac{1}{2}$; $\dfrac{-2 - 0}{-4 - 0} = \dfrac{-2}{-4} = \dfrac{1}{2}$
    $\dfrac{-2 - (-1)}{-4 - (-2)} = \dfrac{-2 + 1}{-4 + 2} = \dfrac{-1}{-2} = \dfrac{1}{2}$

73. answers may vary

75. From the graph, for year 2004 the average miles per gallon was 29.5.

77. The lowest point on the graph corresponds to 1999. The average fuel economy for that year was 28.3 miles per gallon.

79. Of the line segments listed, the line from 2006 to 2007 is the steepest and therefore has the greatest slope.

81. $\text{pitch} = \dfrac{\text{rise}}{\text{run}}$

$$\dfrac{2}{5} = \dfrac{4}{\frac{x}{2}}$$

$$2 \cdot \dfrac{x}{2} = 5 \cdot 4$$

$$x = 20$$

83. a.   (2004, 2025) and (2007, 2208)

b. $m = \dfrac{y_2 - y_1}{x_2 - x_1}$

$$= \dfrac{2208 - 2025}{2007 - 2004}$$

$$= \dfrac{183}{3}$$

$$= 61$$

The slope is 61.

c.   For the years 2004 through 2007, the number of heart transplants increased at a rate of 61 per year.

85. Slope through (1, 3) and (2, 1):

$$m = \dfrac{1-3}{2-1} = \dfrac{-2}{1} = -2$$

Slope through (−4, 0) and (−3, −2):

$$m = \dfrac{-2-0}{-3-(-4)} = \dfrac{-2}{-3+4} = \dfrac{-2}{1} = -2$$

Slope through (1, 3) and (−4, 0):

$$m = \dfrac{0-3}{-4-1} = \dfrac{-3}{-5} = \dfrac{3}{5}$$

Slope through (2, 1) and (−3, −2):

$$m = \dfrac{-2-1}{-3-2} = \dfrac{-3}{-5} = \dfrac{3}{5}$$

Opposite sides are parallel and their slopes are equal.

87. $m = \dfrac{y_2 - y_1}{x_2 - x_1} = \dfrac{4.5 - 1.2}{-2.2 - (-3.8)} = \dfrac{3.3}{1.6} = 2.0625$

89. $m = \dfrac{y_2 - y_1}{x_2 - x_1} = \dfrac{-2.9 - (-10.1)}{9.8 - 14.3} = \dfrac{7.2}{-4.5} = -1.6$

91.

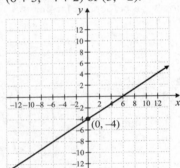

As the slope becomes larger, the line becomes steeper.

Section 13.5

Practice Problems

1. $y = mx + b$

$$y = \dfrac{3}{5}x + (-2)$$

$$y = \dfrac{3}{5}x - 2$$

2. From $y = \dfrac{2}{3}x - 4,$ the *y*-intercept is (0, −4). The slope is $\dfrac{2}{3},$ so another point on the graph is

(0 + 3, −4 + 2) or (3, −2).

3. $3x + y = 2$

$$y = -3x + 2$$

The slope is $-3 = \dfrac{-3}{1}$ and the *y*-intercept is (0, 2). Another point on the graph is (0 + 1, 2 − 3) or (1, −1).

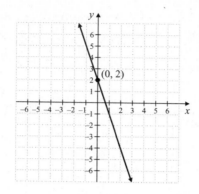

4.
$$y - y_1 = m(x - x_1)$$
$$y - (-4) = -3(x - 2)$$
$$y + 4 = -3(x - 2)$$
$$y + 4 = -3x + 6$$
$$y = -3x + 2$$

5.
$$m = \frac{-2 - 3}{5 - 1} = \frac{-5}{4}$$
$$y - y_1 = m(x - x_1)$$
$$y - 3 = \frac{-5}{4}(x - 1)$$
$$4(y - 3) = 4\left[\frac{-5}{4}(x - 1)\right]$$
$$4(y - 3) = -5(x - 1)$$
$$4y - 12 = -5x + 5$$
$$5x + 4y = 17$$

6. a. $(10, 200), (9, 250)$
$$m = \frac{y_2 - y_1}{x_2 - x_1} = \frac{250 - 200}{9 - 10} = \frac{50}{-1} = -50$$
$$y - y_1 = m(x - x_1)$$
$$y - 200 = -50(x - 10)$$
$$y - 200 = -50x + 500$$
$$y = -50x + 700$$

b. Let $x = 7.50$.
$$y = -50x + 700$$
$$y = -50(7.50) + 700$$
$$y = -375 + 700$$
$$y = 325$$
The predicted weekly sales is 325.

Calculator Explorations

1.

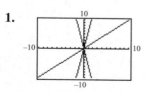

2.

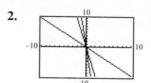

3.

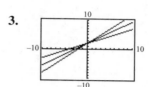

4.

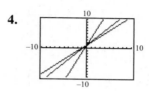

Vocabulary and Readiness Check

1. The form $y = mx + b$ is called <u>slope-intercept</u> form. When a linear equation in two variables is written in this form, <u>m</u> is the slope of its graph and $(0, \underline{b})$ is its y-intercept.

2. The form $y - y_1 = m(x - x_1)$ is called <u>point-slope</u> form. When a linear equation in two variables is written in this form, <u>m</u> is the slope of its graph and $\underline{(x_1, y_1)}$ is a point on the graph.

3. $y - 7 = 4(x + 3)$; <u>point-slope</u> form

4. $5x - 9y = 11$; <u>standard</u> form

5. $y = \frac{3}{4}x - \frac{1}{3}$; <u>slope-intercept</u> form

6. $y + 2 = \frac{-1}{3}(x - 2)$; <u>point-slope</u> form

7. $y = \frac{1}{2}$; <u>horizontal</u> line

8. $x = -17$; <u>vertical</u> line

Exercise Set 13.5

1. $y = mx + b$
$y = 5x + 3$

3. $y = mx + b$

$y = -4x + \left(-\dfrac{1}{6}\right)$

$y = -4x - \dfrac{1}{6}$

5. $y = mx + b$

$y = \dfrac{2}{3}x + 0$

$y = \dfrac{2}{3}x$

7. $y = mx + b$

$y = 0x + (-8)$

$y = -8$

9. $y = mx + b$

$y = -\dfrac{1}{5}x + \dfrac{1}{9}$

11. From $y = 2x + 1$, the y-intercept is $(0, 1)$. The slope is 2 or $\dfrac{2}{1}$, so another point on the graph is $(0 + 1, 1 + 2)$ or $(1, 3)$.

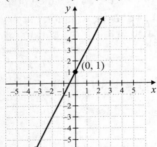

13. From $y = \dfrac{2}{3}x + 5$, the y-intercept is $(0, 5)$. The slope is $\dfrac{2}{3}$, so another point on the graph is $(0 + 3, 5 + 2)$ or $(3, 7)$.

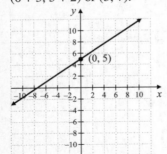

15. From $y = -5x$, the y-intercept is $(0, 0)$. The slope is -5 or $\dfrac{-5}{1}$, so another point on the graph is $(0 + 1, 0 + (-5))$ or $(1, -5)$.

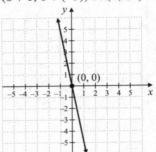

17. $4x + y = 6$

$y = -4x + 6$

The slope is $-4 = \dfrac{-4}{1}$ and the y-intercept is $(0, 6)$. Another point on the graph is $(0 + 1, 6 - 4)$ or $(1, 2)$.

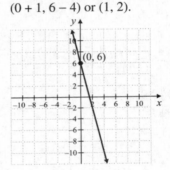

19. $4x - 7y = -14$

$-7y = -4x - 14$

$y = \dfrac{4}{7}x + 2$

The slope is $\dfrac{4}{7}$ and the y-intercept is $(0, 2)$.

Another point on the graph is $(0 + 7, 2 + 4)$ or $(7, 6)$.

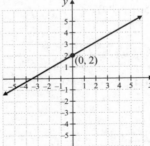

21. $x = \frac{5}{4}y$

$\frac{4}{5}x = y$

$y = \frac{4}{5}x + 0$

The slope is $\frac{4}{5}$ and the y-intercept is $(0, 0)$.

Another point on the graph is $(0 + 5, 0 + 4)$ or $(5, 4)$.

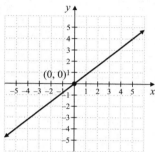

23. $y - y_1 = m(x - x_1)$
$y - 2 = 6(x - 2)$
$y - 2 = 6x - 12$
$y = 6x - 10$
$-6x + y = -10$

25. $y - y_1 = m(x - x_1)$
$y - (-5) = -8[x - (-1)]$
$y + 5 = -8(x + 1)$
$y + 5 = -8x - 8$
$y = -8x - 13$
$8x + y = -13$

27. $y - y_1 = m(x - x_1)$
$y - (-6) = \frac{3}{2}(x - 5)$
$y + 6 = \frac{3}{2}(x - 5)$
$2(y + 6) = 2\left[\frac{3}{2}(x - 5)\right]$
$2y + 12 = 3x - 15$
$2y = 3x - 27$
$-3x + 2y = -27$ or $3x - 2y = 27$

29. $y - y_1 = m(x - x_1)$
$y - 0 = -\frac{1}{2}[x - (-3)]$
$y = -\frac{1}{2}(x + 3)$
$2y = -1(x + 3)$
$2y = -x - 3$
$x + 2y = -3$

31. $m = \frac{y_2 - y_1}{x_2 - x_1} = \frac{6 - 2}{5 - 3} = \frac{4}{2} = 2$
$y - y_1 = m(x - x_1)$
$y - 2 = 2(x - 3)$
$y - 2 = 2x - 6$
$y + 4 = 2x$
$4 = 2x - y$
$2x - y = 4$

33. $m = \frac{y_2 - y_1}{x_2 - x_1} = \frac{-5 - 3}{-2 - (-1)} = \frac{-8}{-1} = 8$
$y - y_1 = m(x - x_1)$
$y - 3 = 8[x - (-1)]$
$y - 3 = 8(x + 1)$
$y - 3 = 8x + 8$
$y - 11 = 8x$
$-11 = 8x - y$
$8x - y = -11$

35. $m = \frac{y_2 - y_1}{x_2 - x_1} = \frac{-1 - 3}{-1 - 2} = \frac{-4}{-3} = \frac{4}{3}$
$y - y_1 = m(x - x_1)$
$y - 3 = \frac{4}{3}(x - 2)$
$3(y - 3) = 4(x - 2)$
$3y - 9 = 4x - 8$
$3y - 1 = 4x$
$-1 = 4x - 3y$
$4x - 3y = -1$

37. $m = \frac{y_2 - y_1}{x_2 - x_1} = \frac{\frac{1}{13} - 0}{-\frac{1}{8} - 0} = \frac{\frac{1}{13}}{-\frac{1}{8}} = \frac{1}{13}\left(-\frac{8}{1}\right) = -\frac{8}{13}$
$y - y_1 = m(x - x_1)$
$y - 0 = -\frac{8}{13}(x - 0)$
$y = -\frac{8}{13}x$
$13y = -8x$
$8x + 13y = 0$

39. $y = mx + b$

$$y = -\frac{1}{2}x + \frac{5}{3}$$

41. $m = \dfrac{y_2 - y_1}{x_2 - x_1} = \dfrac{10 - 7}{7 - 10} = \dfrac{3}{-3} = -1$

$y - y_1 = m(x - x_1)$
$y - 7 = -1(x - 10)$
$y - 7 = -x + 10$
$\quad y = -x + 17$

43. A line with undefined slope is a vertical line. This one has an x-intercept of $\left(-\dfrac{3}{4}, 0\right)$. The equation is $x = -\dfrac{3}{4}$.

45. $y - y_1 = m(x - x_1)$
$y - 9 = 1[x - (-7)]$
$y - 9 = x + 7$
$\quad y = x + 16$

47. $y = mx + b$
$y = -5x + 7$

49. A line parallel to $y = 5$ is a horizontal line.
$y = 2$

51. $m = \dfrac{y_2 - y_1}{x_2 - x_1} = \dfrac{3 - 0}{2 - 0} = \dfrac{3}{2}$

$y - y_1 = m(x - x_1)$

$y - 0 = \dfrac{3}{2}(x - 0)$

$\quad y = \dfrac{3}{2}x$

53. A line perpendicular to the y-axis is a horizontal line.
$y = -3$

55. $y - y_1 = m(x - x_1)$

$y - (-2) = -\dfrac{4}{7}[x - (-1)]$

$y + 2 = -\dfrac{4}{7}(x + 1)$

$y + 2 = -\dfrac{4}{7}x - \dfrac{4}{7}$

$\quad y = -\dfrac{4}{7}x - \dfrac{4}{7} - \dfrac{14}{7}$

$\quad y = -\dfrac{4}{7}x - \dfrac{18}{7}$

57. a. The ordered pairs are (0, 302) and (4, 322).

b. $m = \dfrac{y_2 - y_1}{x_2 - x_1} = \dfrac{322 - 302}{4 - 0} = \dfrac{20}{4} = 5$

$y - y_1 = m(x - x_1)$
$y - 302 = 5(x - 0)$
$y - 302 = 5x$
$\quad y = 5x + 302$

c. 2005 corresponds to $x = 2$.
$x = 2$: $y = 5(2) + 302 = 10 + 302 = 312$
There were approximately 312 million magazine subscriptions in 2005.

59. a. The ordered pairs are (1, 32) and (3, 96).

$m = \dfrac{s_2 - s_1}{t_2 - t_1} = \dfrac{96 - 32}{3 - 1} = \dfrac{64}{2} = 32$

$s - s_1 = m(t - t_1)$
$s - 32 = 32(t - 1)$
$s - 32 = 32t - 32$
$\quad s = 32t$

b. $t = 4$: $s = 32(4)$
$\quad s = 128$
The speed of the rock 4 seconds after it was dropped is 128 feet per second.

61. a. The ordered pairs are (3, 353,000) and (0, 83,000).

$m = \dfrac{y_2 - y_1}{x_2 - x_1} = \dfrac{83,000 - 353,000}{0 - 3}$

$\qquad = \dfrac{-270,000}{-3}$

$\qquad = 90,000$

$y - y_1 = m(x - x_1)$
$y - 353,000 = 90,000(x - 3)$
$y - 353,000 = 90,000x - 270,000$
$\qquad y = 90,000x + 83,000$

b. The year 2009 is 5 years past 2004.
$x = 2009 - 2004 = 5$
$y = 90{,}000(5) + 83{,}000$
$y = 450{,}000 + 83{,}000$
$y = 533{,}000$
533,000 vehicles are predicted for 2009.

63. a. The ordered pairs are (4, 5540) and (0, 5700).
$$m = \frac{y_2 - y_1}{x_2 - x_1} = \frac{5700 - 5540}{0 - 4} = \frac{160}{-4} = -40$$
$y - y_1 = m(x - x_1)$
$y - 5700 = -40(x - 0)$
$y - 5700 = -40x$
$\qquad\quad y = -40x + 5700$

b. The year 2010 is 7 years past 2003, so it corresponds to $x = 7$.
$x = 7:\ y = -40(7) + 5700$
$\qquad\quad y = -280 + 5700$
$\qquad\quad y = 5420$

5420 cinema sites are predicted for 2010.

65. a. The ordered pairs are (3, 10,000) and (5, 8000).
$$m = \frac{S_2 - S_1}{p_2 - p_1}$$
$$= \frac{8000 - 10{,}000}{5 - 3}$$
$$= \frac{-2000}{2}$$
$$= -1000$$
$S - S_1 = m(p - p_1)$
$S - 10{,}000 = -1000(p - 3)$
$S - 10{,}000 = -1000p + 3000$
$\qquad\quad S = -1000p + 13{,}000$

b. $p = 3.50:\ S = -1000(3.50) + 13{,}000$
$\qquad\qquad\quad S = -3500 + 13{,}000$
$\qquad\qquad\quad S = 9500$
9500 Fun Noodles will be sold when the price is $3.50 each.

67. $x = 2:\ x^2 - 3x + 1 = 2^2 - 3(2) + 1 = 4 - 6 + 1 = -1$

69. $x = -1:\ x^2 - 3x + 1 = (-1)^2 - 3(-1) + 1$
$\qquad\qquad\qquad\qquad\quad = 1 + 3 + 1$
$\qquad\qquad\qquad\qquad\quad = 5$

71. The graph of $y = 2x + 1$ has slope $m = 2$ and y-intercept (0, 1). This is graph b.

73. The graph of $y = -3x - 2$ has slope $m = -3$ and y-intercept (0, −2). This is graph d.

75. The slope of the line $y = 3x - 1$ is $m = 3$.
$y - y_1 = m(x - x_1)$
$y - 2 = 3[x - (-1)]$
$y - 2 = 3(x + 1)$
$y - 2 = 3x + 3$
$\ \ -5 = 3x - y$
$3x - y = -5$

77. a. A line parallel to the line $y = 3x - 1$ will have slope 3.
$y - y_1 = m(x - x_1)$
$y - 2 = 3[x - (-1)]$
$y - 2 = 3(x + 1)$
$y - 2 = 3x + 3$
$\quad y = 3x + 5$
$\ \ -5 = 3x - y$
$3x - y = -5$

b. A line perpendicular to the line $y = 3x - 1$ will have slope $-\dfrac{1}{3}$.
$y - y_1 = m(x - x_1)$
$y - 2 = -\dfrac{1}{3}[x - (-1)]$
$y - 2 = -\dfrac{1}{3}(x + 1)$
$3y - 6 = -1(x + 1)$
$3y - 6 = -x - 1$
$\quad 3y = -x + 5$
$x + 3y = 5$

Integrated Review

1. Select two points on the line, such as (0, 0) and (1, 2).
$$m = \frac{y_2 - y_1}{x_2 - x_1} = \frac{2 - 0}{1 - 0} = \frac{2}{1} = 2$$

2. Horizontal lines have slopes of $m = 0$.

3. Select two points on the line, such as (0, 1) and (−3, 3).
$$m = \frac{y_2 - y_1}{x_2 - x_1} = \frac{3 - 1}{-3 - 0} = \frac{2}{-3} = -\frac{2}{3}$$

4. Vertical lines have undefined slopes.

5. $y = -2x$
   $y = 0:\ 0 = -2x$
   $\qquad\quad 0 = x$
   The x-intercept is $(0, 0)$.
   $x = 0:\ y = -2(0) = 0$
   The y-intercept is $(0, 0)$.
   Find another point, for example let $x = 1$.
   $y = -2(1) = -2$
   Another point on the line is $(1, -2)$.

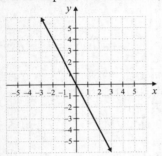

6. $x + y = 3$
   $y = 0:\ x + 0 = 3$
   $\qquad\qquad x = 3$
   The x-intercept is $(3, 0)$.
   $x = 0:\ 0 + y = 3$
   $\qquad\qquad y = 3$
   The y-intercept is $(0, 3)$.

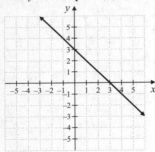

7. The graph of $x = -1$ is a vertical line with an x-intercept of $(-1, 0)$.

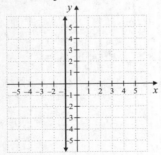

8. The graph of $y = 4$ is a horizontal line with a y-intercept of $(0, 4)$.

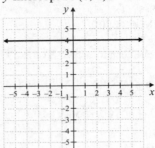

9. $x - 2y = 6$
   $y = 0:\ x - 2(0) = 6$
   $\qquad\qquad x - 0 = 6$
   $\qquad\qquad\quad x = 6$
   The x-intercept is $(6, 0)$.
   $x = 0:\ 0 - 2y = 6$
   $\qquad\qquad -2y = 6$
   $\qquad\qquad\quad y = -3$
   The y-intercept is $(0, -3)$.

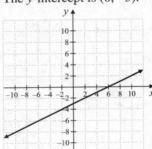

10. $y = 3x + 2$
    $y = 0:\quad 0 = 3x + 2$
    $\qquad\qquad -2 = 3x$
    $\qquad\qquad -\dfrac{2}{3} = x$
    The x-intercept is $\left(-\dfrac{2}{3}, 0\right)$.
    $x = 0:\ y = 3(0) + 2$
    $\qquad\qquad y = 0 + 2$
    $\qquad\qquad y = 2$
    The y-intercept is $(0, 2)$.

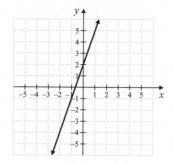

11. $y = -\dfrac{3}{4}x + 3$

$y = 0:$ $0 = -\dfrac{3}{4}x + 3$

$\qquad\qquad -3 = -\dfrac{3}{4}x$

$\qquad\qquad\quad 4 = x$

The x-intercept is $(4, 0)$.

$x = 0:$ $y = -\dfrac{3}{4}(0) + 3$

$\qquad\qquad y = 0 + 3$

$\qquad\qquad y = 3$

The y-intercept is $(0, 3)$.

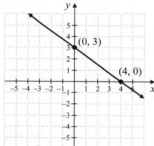

12. $5x - 2y = 8$

$y = 0:$ $5x - 2(0) = 8$

$\qquad\qquad 5x - 0 = 8$

$\qquad\qquad\quad 5x = 8$

$\qquad\qquad\quad\; x = \dfrac{8}{5}$

The x-intercept is $\left(\dfrac{8}{5}, 0\right)$.

$x = 0:$ $5(0) - 2y = 8$

$\qquad\qquad 0 - 2y = 8$

$\qquad\qquad\; -2y = 8$

$\qquad\qquad\quad\; y = -4$

The y-intercept is $(0, -4)$.

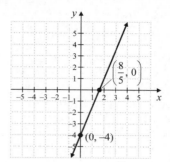

13. $y = mx + b$
$\quad y = 3x - 1$
$\quad$ The slope is $m = 3$.

14. $y = mx + b$
$\quad y = -6x + 2$
$\quad$ The slope is $m = -6$.

15. $y = mx + b$
$\quad 7x + 2y = 11$
$\qquad\quad 2y = -7x + 11$
$\qquad\quad\; y = -\dfrac{7}{2}x + \dfrac{11}{2}$

$\quad$ The slope is $m = -\dfrac{7}{2}$.

16. $y = mx + b$
$\quad 2x - y = 0$
$\qquad -y = -2x$
$\qquad\;\; y = 2x$
$\qquad\;\; y = 2x + 0$
$\quad$ The slope is $m = 2$.

17. The graph of $x = 2$ is a vertical line. Vertical lines have undefined slopes.

18. The graph of $y = -4$ is a horizontal line. Horizontal lines have slopes of $m = 0$.

19. $y = mx + b$

$\quad y = 2x + \left(-\dfrac{1}{3}\right)$

$\quad y = 2x - \dfrac{1}{3}$

20. $y - y_1 = m(x - x_1)$
$\quad\; y - 3 = -4[x - (-1)]$
$\quad\; y - 3 = -4(x + 1)$
$\quad\; y - 3 = -4x - 4$
$\qquad\;\; y = -4x - 1$

513

21. $m = \dfrac{y_2 - y_1}{x_2 - x_1} = \dfrac{-3-0}{-1-2} = \dfrac{-3}{-3} = 1$

$y - y_1 = m(x - x_1)$

$y - 0 = 1(x - 2)$

$y = x - 2$

$-x + y = -2$ or $x - y = 2$

22. $6x - y = 7$ $\qquad\qquad$ $2x + 3y = 4$

$\quad -y = -6x + 7$ $\qquad\qquad$ $3y = -2x + 4$

$\quad\quad y = 6x - 7$ $\qquad\qquad$ $y = -\dfrac{2}{3}x + \dfrac{4}{3}$

$m = 6$ $\qquad\qquad\qquad$ $m = -\dfrac{2}{3}$

Since $6 \neq -\dfrac{2}{3}$, the lines are not parallel. Since

$6\left(-\dfrac{2}{3}\right) = -4 \neq -1$, the lines are not

perpendicular. The lines are neither parallel nor perpendicular.

23. $3x - 6y = 4$ $\qquad\qquad$ $y = -2x$

$\quad -6y = -3x + 4$ $\qquad\quad$ $m = -2$

$\quad\quad y = \dfrac{1}{2}x - \dfrac{2}{3}$

$m = \dfrac{1}{2}$

Since $\left(\dfrac{1}{2}\right)(-2) = -1$, the lines are perpendicular.

24. a. The ordered pairs are (2002, 2133) and (2007, 3478).

b. $m = \dfrac{y_2 - y_1}{x_2 - x_1} = \dfrac{3478 - 2133}{2007 - 2002} = \dfrac{1345}{5} = 269$

c. For the years 2002 through 2007, the amount of yogurt produced increased at a rate of 269 million pounds per year.

Section 13.6

Practice Problems

1. The domain is the set of x-coordinates: $\{-3, 4, 7\}$.
The range is the set of y-coordinates: $\{0, 1, 5, 6\}$.

2. a. Each x-value is only assigned to one y-value, so the relation is a function.

b. The x-value 1 is paired with two y-values, 4 and -3, so this set of ordered pairs is not a function.

3. a. This is the graph of the relation $\{(-3, -2), (-1, -1), (0, 0), (1, 1)\}$.
Each x-coordinate has exactly one y-value, so this is the graph of a function.

b. This is the graph of the relation $\{(-1, -1), (-1, 2), (1, 0), (3, 1)\}$.
The x-value -1 is paired with two y-values, -1 and 2, so this is not the graph of a function.

4. a. No vertical line will intersect the graph more than once, so the graph is the graph of a function.

b. No vertical line will intersect the graph more than once, so the graph is the graph of a function.

c. Vertical lines can be drawn that intersect the graph in two points, so the graph is not the graph of a function.

d. A vertical line can be drawn that intersects this line at every point, so the graph is not the graph of a function.

5. a, b, and **c** are functions because their graphs are nonvertical lines. **d** is not a function because its graph is a vertical line.

6. a. According to the graph, the time of the sunrise on March 1st is 6:30 A.M.

b. According to the graph, the sun rises at 6 A.M. in the middle of March and the middle of September.

7. $f(x) = x^2 + 1$

a. $f(1) = 1^2 + 1 = 1 + 1 = 2$
Ordered pair: (1, 2)

b. $f(-3) = (-3)^2 + 1 = 9 + 1 = 10$
$(-3, 10)$

c. $f(0) = 0^2 + 1 = 0 + 1 = 1$
$(0, 1)$

8. a. In this function, x can be any real number. The domain of $h(x)$ is the set of all real numbers.

b. Since we cannot divide by 0, the domain of $f(x)$ is the set of all real numbers except 0.

9. a. The x-values go from -4 to 6, so the domain is $-4 \le x \le 6$.
The y-values go from -2 to 3, so the range is $-2 \le y \le 3$.

b. There are no restrictions on the x-values, so the domain is all real numbers.
The y-values are all less than or equal to 3, so the range is $y \le 3$.

Vocabulary and Readiness Check

1. A set of ordered pairs is called a <u>relation</u>.

2. A set of ordered pairs that assigns to each x-value exactly one y-value is called a <u>function</u>.

3. The set of all y-coordinates of a relation is called the <u>range</u>.

4. The set of all x-coordinates of a relation is called the <u>domain</u>.

5. All linear equations are functions except those whose graphs are <u>vertical</u> lines.

6. All linear equations are functions except those whose equations are of the form <u>$x = c$</u>.

7. If $f(3) = 7$, the corresponding ordered pair is <u>(3, 7)</u>.

8. The domain of $f(x) = x + 5$ is <u>all real numbers</u>.

9. For the function $y = mx + b$, the dependent variable is <u>y</u> and the independent variable is <u>x</u>.

Exercise Set 13.6

1. The domain is the set of x-coordinates: $\{-7, 0, 2, 10\}$.
The range is the set of y-coordinates: $\{-7, 0, 4, 10\}$.

3. The domain is the set of x-coordinates: $\{0, 1, 5\}$
The range is the set of y-coordinates: $\{-2\}$

5. Each x-value is only assigned to one y-value, so the relation is a function.

7. The x-value -1 is paired with more than one y-value, 0, 6, and 8, so the relation is not a function.

9. The vertical line $x = 1$ will intersect the graph in two points, so the graph is not the graph of a function.

11. No vertical line will intersect the graph more than once, so the graph is the graph of a function.

13. No vertical line will intersect the graph more than once, so the graph is the graph of a function.

15. Vertical lines can be drawn that intersect the graph in two points, so the graph is not the graph of a function.

17. If $x = -1$, the relation is not also a function; a.

19. $y - x = 7$
The graph of this linear equation is not a vertical line, so the equation describes a function.

21. $y = 6$
The graph of this linear equation is not a vertical line, so the equation describes a function.

23. $x = -2$
The graph of this linear equation is a vertical line, so the equation does not describe a function.

25. $x = y^2$
$y = 1: \ x = (1)^2 = 1$
$y = -1: \ x = (-1)^2 = 1$
Since there is an x-value that is paired with two y-values, the equation does not describe a function.

27. On June 1, the graph shows sunset to be at approximately 9:30 P.M.

29. At 3 P.M., the graph shows this happens on January 1 and December 1.

31. The graph passes the vertical line test, so it is the graph of a function.

33. Before October 1996, the graph shows the minimum wage was \$4.25 per hour.

35. According to the graph, the minimum wage will increase to over $7.00 in 2009.

37. yes; answers may vary

39. According to the graph, the postage would be $1.50.

41. From the graph, it would cost $1 to mail a large envelope that weighs more than 1 ounce and less than or equal to 2 ounces.

43. yes; answers may vary

45. $f(x) = 2x - 5$
$f(-2) = 2(-2) - 5 = -4 - 5 = -9$
$f(0) = 2(0) - 5 = 0 - 5 = -5$
$f(3) = 2(3) - 5 = 6 - 5 = 1$

47. $f(x) = x^2 + 2$
$f(-2) = (-2)^2 + 2 = 4 + 2 = 6$
$f(0) = 0^2 + 2 = 0 + 2 = 2$
$f(3) = 3^2 + 2 = 9 + 2 = 11$

49. $f(x) = 3x$
$f(-2) = 3(-2) = -6$
$f(0) = 3(0) = 0$
$f(3) = 3(3) = 9$

51. $f(x) = |x|$
$f(-2) = |-2| = 2$
$f(0) = |0| = 0$
$f(3) = |3| = 3$

53. $h(x) = -5x$
$h(-1) = -5(-1) = 5$
$h(0) = -5(0) = 0$
$h(4) = -5(4) = -20$

55. $h(x) = 2x^2 + 3$
$h(-1) = 2(-1)^2 + 3 = 2(1) + 3 = 2 + 3 = 5$
$h(0) = 2(0)^2 + 3 = 2(0) + 3 = 0 + 3 = 3$
$h(4) = 2(4)^2 + 3 = 2(16) + 3 = 32 + 3 = 35$

57. The ordered-pair solution corresponding to $f(3) = 6$ is $(3, 6)$.

59. The ordered-pair solution corresponding to
$g(0) = -\dfrac{1}{2}$ is $\left(0, -\dfrac{1}{2}\right)$.

61. The ordered-pair solution corresponding to $h(-2) = 9$ is $(-2, 9)$.

63. The domain of $f(x)$ is all real numbers.

65. $x + 5$ cannot be 0.
$x + 5 = 0$
$x = -5$
The domain of $f(x)$ is all real numbers except -5.

67. The domain is all real numbers. The range is $y \geq -4$.

69. The domain is all real numbers. The range is all real numbers.

71. The domain is all real numbers. The range is $\{2\}$.

73. When $x = 0$, $y = -1$, so the ordered-pair solution is $(0, -1)$.

75. When $x = 0$, $y = -1$, so $f(0) = -1$.

77. When $y = 0$, $x = -1$ and $x = 5$.

79. $2x + 5 < 7$
$2x < 2$
$x < 1$

81. $-x + 6 \leq 9$
$-x \leq 3$
$x \geq -3$

83. $\dfrac{3}{x} + \dfrac{3}{2x} + \dfrac{5}{x} = \dfrac{3 \cdot 2}{x \cdot 2} + \dfrac{3}{2x} + \dfrac{5 \cdot 2}{x \cdot 2}$
$= \dfrac{6}{2x} + \dfrac{3}{2x} + \dfrac{10}{2x}$
$= \dfrac{6 + 3 + 10}{2x}$
$= \dfrac{19}{2x}$

The perimeter is $\dfrac{19}{2x}$ meters.

85. A function f evaluated at -5 as 12 is written as $f(-5) = 12$.

87. answers may vary

89. $y = x + 7$ written in function notation is $f(x) = x + 7$.

91. $f(x) = \dfrac{136}{25}x$

    a. $f(35) = \dfrac{136}{25}(35) = \dfrac{4760}{25} = \dfrac{952}{5} = 190.4$

    The proper dosage for a 35-pound dog is 190.4 milligrams.

    b. $f(70) = \dfrac{136}{25}(70) = \dfrac{9520}{25} = \dfrac{1904}{5} = 380.8$

    The proper dosage for a 70-pound dog is 380.8 milligrams.

Section 13.7

Practice Problems

  1. $x - 4y > 8$

    a. $(-3, 2):\ -3 - 4(2) > 8$
                 $-3 - 8 > 8$
                     $-11 > 8$ False
    $(-3, 2)$ is not a solution of the inequality.

    b. $(9, 0):\ 9 - 4(0) > 8$
                   $9 - 0 > 8$
                     $9 > 8$ True
    $(9, 0)$ is a solution of the inequality.

  2. Graph the boundary line, $x - y = 3$, with a dashed line.
    Test $(0, 0):\ x - y > 3$
                $0 - 0 > 3$
                  $0 > 3$ False
    Shade the half-plane not containing $(0, 0)$.

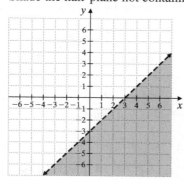

  3. Graph the boundary line, $x - 4y = 4$, with a solid line.
    Test $(0, 0):\ x - 4y \le 4$
               $0 - 4(0) \le 4$
                 $0 - 0 \le 4$
                   $0 \le 4$ True
    Shade the half-plane containing $(0, 0)$.

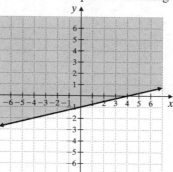

  4. Graph the boundary line, $y = 3x$, with a dashed line.
    Test $(1, 1):\ y < 3x$
                $1 < 3(1)$
                $1 < 3$ True
    Shade the half-plane containing $(1, 1)$.

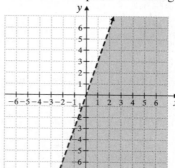

  5. Graph the boundary line, $3x + 2y = 12$, with a solid line.
    Test $(0, 0):$ $3x + 2y \ge 12$
                $3(0) + 2(0) \ge 12$
                 $0 + 0 \ge 12$
                   $0 \ge 12$ False
    Shade the half-plane not containing $(0, 0)$.

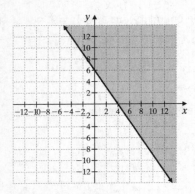

6. Graph the boundary line, $x = 2$, with a dashed line.

Test $(0, 0)$: $x < 2$

$0 < 2$ True

Shade the half-plane containing $(0, 0)$.

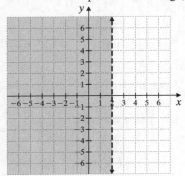

7. Graph the boundary line, $y = \dfrac{1}{4}x + 3$, with a solid line.

Test $(0, 0)$: $y \geq \dfrac{1}{4}x + 3$

$0 \geq \dfrac{1}{4}(0) + 3$

$0 \geq 0 + 3$

$0 \geq 3$ False

Shade the half-plane not containing $(0, 0)$.

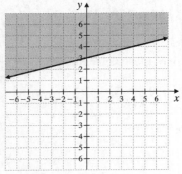

Vocabulary and Readiness Check

1. The statement $5x - 6y < 7$ is an example of a <u>linear inequality in two variables</u>.

2. A boundary line divides a plane into two regions called <u>half-planes</u>.

3. The graph of $5x - 6y < 7$ include its corresponding boundary line. <u>false</u>

4. When graphing a linear inequality, to determine which side of the boundary line to shade, choose a point *not* on the boundary line. <u>true</u>

5. The boundary line for the inequality $5x - 6y < 7$ is the graph of $5x - 6y = 7$. <u>true</u>

6. The graph shown is <u>$y < 2$</u>.

Exercise Set 13.7

1. $x - y > 3$

$(0, 3)$: $0 - 3 > 3$

$-3 > 3$ False

$(0, 3)$ is not a solution of the inequality.

$(2, -1)$: $2 - (-1) > 3$

$2 + 1 > 3$

$3 > 3$ False

$(2, -1)$ is not a solution of the inequality.

3. $3x - 5y \leq -4$

$(2, 3)$: $3(2) - 5(3) \leq -4$

$6 - 15 \leq -4$

$-9 \leq -4$ True

$(2, 3)$ is a solution of the inequality.

$(-1, -1)$: $3(-1) - 5(-1) \leq -4$

$-3 + 5 \leq -4$

$2 \leq -4$ False

$(-1, -1)$ is not a solution of the inequality.

5. $x < -y$

$(0, 2)$: $0 < -2$ False

$(0, 2)$ is not a solution of the inequality.

$(-5, 1)$: $-5 < -1$ True

$(-5, 1)$ is a solution of the inequality.

7. Graph the boundary line, $x + y = 1$, with a solid line.

Test $(0, 0)$: $x + y \leq 1$

$0 + 0 \leq 1$

$0 \leq 1$ True

Shade the half-plane containing $(0, 0)$.

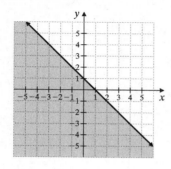

9. Graph the boundary line, $2x - y = -4$, with a dashed line.

Test $(0, 0)$: $2x - y > -4$
$2(0) - 0 > -4$
$0 - 0 > -4$
$0 > -4$ True

Shade the half-plane containing $(0, 0)$.

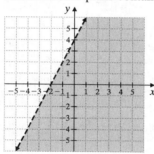

11. Graph the boundary line, $y = 2x$, with a solid line.

Test $(1, 1)$: $y \geq 2x$
$1 \geq 2(1)$
$1 \geq 2$ False

Shade the half-plane not containing $(1, 1)$.

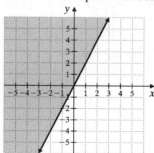

13. Graph the boundary line, $x = -3y$, with a dashed line.

Test $(1, 1)$: $x < -3y$
$1 < -3(1)$
$1 < -3$ False

Shade the half-plane not containing $(1, 1)$.

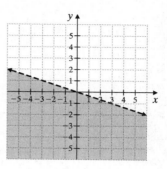

15. Graph the boundary line, $y = x + 5$, with a solid line.

Test $(0, 0)$: $y \geq x + 5$
$0 \geq 0 + 5$
$0 \geq 5$ False

Shade the half-plane not containing $(0, 0)$.

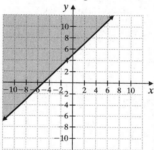

17. Graph the boundary line, $y = 4$, with a dashed line.

Test $(0, 0)$: $y < 4$
$0 < 4$ True

Shade the half-plane containing $(0, 0)$.

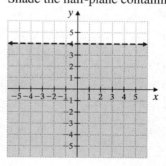

19. Graph the boundary line, $x = -3$, with a solid line.

Test $(0, 0)$: $x \geq -3$
$0 \geq -3$ True

Shade the half-plane containing $(0, 0)$.

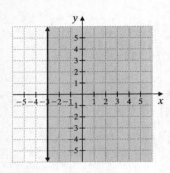

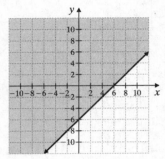

21. Graph the boundary line, $5x + 2y = 10$, with a solid line.

Test $(0, 0)$: $5x + 2y \leq 10$

$$5(0) + 2(0) \leq 10$$

$$0 + 0 \leq 10$$

$$0 \leq 10 \quad \text{True}$$

Shade the half-plane containing $(0, 0)$.

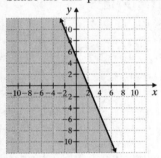

23. Graph the boundary line, $x = y$, with a dashed line.

Test $(1, 4)$: $x > y$

$$1 > 4 \quad \text{False}$$

Shade the half-plane not containing $(1, 4)$.

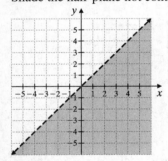

25. Graph the boundary line, $x - y = 6$, with a solid line.

Test $(0, 0)$: $x - y \leq 6$

$$0 - 0 \leq 6$$

$$0 \leq 6 \quad \text{True}$$

Shade the half-plane containing $(0, 0)$.

27. Graph the boundary line, $x = 0$, with a solid line.

Test $(1, 1)$: $x \geq 0$

$$1 \geq 0 \quad \text{True}$$

Shade the half-plane containing $(1, 1)$.

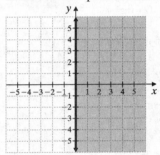

29. Shade the boundary line, $2x + 7y = 5$, with a dashed line.

Test $(0, 0)$: $2x + 7y > 5$

$$2(0) + 7(0) > 5$$

$$0 + 0 > 5$$

$$0 > 5 \quad \text{False}$$

Shade the half-plane not containing $(0, 0)$.

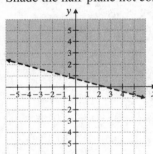

31. Graph the boundary line, $y = \dfrac{1}{2}x - 4$, with a solid line.

Test $(0, 0)$: $y \geq \dfrac{1}{2}x - 4$

$$0 \geq \dfrac{1}{2}(0) - 4$$

$$0 \geq 0 - 4$$

$$0 \geq -4 \quad \text{True}$$

Shade the half-plane containing (0, 0).

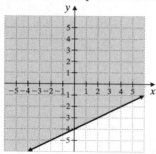

33. The point of intersection appears to be $(-2, 1)$.

35. The point of intersection appears to be $(-3, -1)$.

37. The graph is the half-plane with the dashed boundary line $x = 2$. The choice is a.

39. The graph is the half-plane with the dashed boundary line $y = 2$. The choice is b.

41. answers may vary

43. Test $(1, 1)$: $3x + 4y < 8$

$$3(1) + 4(1) < 8$$
$$3 + 4 < 8$$
$$7 < 8 \quad \text{True}$$

$(1, 1)$ is included in the graph of $3x + 4y < 8$.

45. Test $(1, 1)$: $y \geq -\dfrac{1}{2}x$

$$1 \geq -\dfrac{1}{2}(1)$$
$$1 \geq -\dfrac{1}{2} \quad \text{True}$$

$(1, 1)$ is included in the graph of $y \geq -\dfrac{1}{2}x$.

47. a. The sum of the number of days, x, times \$30, and the number of miles, y, times \$0.15, must be at most \$500.
$$30x + 0.15y \leq 500$$

b.

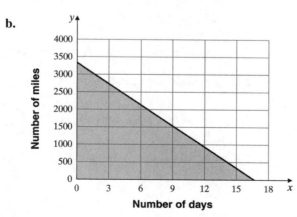

c. answers may vary

Section 13.8

Practice Problems

1. Use (4, 8).
$$y = kx$$
$$8 = k \cdot 4$$
$$\frac{8}{4} = \frac{k \cdot 4}{4}$$
$$2 = k$$
Since $k = 2$, the equation is $y = 2x$.

2. Let $y = 15$ and $x = 45$.
$$y = kx$$
$$15 = k(45)$$
$$\frac{15}{45} = \frac{k(45)}{45}$$
$$\frac{1}{3} = k$$
The equation is $y = \frac{1}{3}x$.

Let $x = 3$.
$$y = \frac{1}{3}x$$
$$y = \frac{1}{3} \cdot 3$$
$$y = 1$$
Thus, when x is 3, y is 1.

3. Use $(-1, -2)$ and $(0, 0)$.
$$\text{slope} = \frac{0 - (-2)}{0 - (-1)} = \frac{2}{1} = 2$$
Thus, $k = 2$ and the variation equation is $y = 2x$.

4. Use (4, 5).
$$y = \frac{k}{x}$$
$$5 = \frac{k}{4}$$
$$4 \cdot 5 = 4 \cdot \frac{k}{4}$$
$$20 = k$$
Since $k = 20$, the equation is $y = \frac{20}{x}$.

5. Let $y = 4$ and $x = 0.8$.
$$y = \frac{k}{x}$$
$$4 = \frac{k}{0.8}$$
$$0.8(4) = 0.8\left(\frac{k}{0.8}\right)$$
$$3.2 = k$$
The equation is $y = \frac{3.2}{x}$.

Let $x = 20$.
$$y = \frac{3.2}{20}$$
$$y = 0.16$$
Thus, when x is 20, y is 0.16.

6. $A = kr^2$
$$49\pi = k(7)^2$$
$$49\pi = 49k$$
$$\pi = k$$
The formula for the area of a circle is $A = \pi r^2$.
Let $r = 4$.
$$A = \pi r^2$$
$$A = \pi \cdot 4^2$$
$$A = 16\pi$$
The area is 16π square feet.

7. $d = kt^2$
$$144 = k(3)^2$$
$$144 = 9k$$
$$16 = k$$
The equation is $d = 16t^2$.
Let $t = 5$.
$$d = 16t^2$$
$$d = 16 \cdot 5^2$$
$$d = 16 \cdot 25$$
$$d = 400$$
The object will fall 400 feet in 5 seconds.

Vocabulary and Readiness Check

1. $y = \frac{k}{x}$, where k is a constant. <u>inverse</u>

2. $y = kx$, where k is a constant. <u>direct</u>

3. $y = 5x$ <u>direct</u>

4. $y = \dfrac{5}{x}$ <u>inverse</u>

5. $y = \dfrac{7}{x^2}$ <u>inverse</u>

6. $y = 6.5x^4$ <u>direct</u>

7. $y = \dfrac{11}{x}$ <u>inverse</u>

8. $y = 18x$ <u>direct</u>

9. $y = 12x^2$ <u>direct</u>

10. $y = \dfrac{20}{x^3}$ <u>inverse</u>

Exercise Set 13.8

1. $y = kx$
$3 = k(6)$
$\dfrac{1}{2} = k$
$y = \dfrac{1}{2}x$

3. $y = kx$
$12 = k(2)$
$6 = k$
$y = 6x$

5. $m = \dfrac{y_2 - y_1}{x_2 - x_1} = \dfrac{3 - 0}{1 - 0} = \dfrac{3}{1} = 3$
$y = 3x$

7. $m = \dfrac{y_2 - y_1}{x_2 - x_1} = \dfrac{2 - 0}{3 - 0} = \dfrac{2}{3}$
$y = \dfrac{2}{3}x$

9. $y = \dfrac{k}{x}$
$7 = \dfrac{k}{1}$
$7 = k$
$y = \dfrac{7}{x}$

11. $y = \dfrac{k}{x}$
$0.05 = \dfrac{k}{10}$
$0.5 = k$
$y = \dfrac{0.5}{x}$

13. y varies directly as x is written as $y = kx$.

15. h varies inversely as t is written as $h = \dfrac{k}{t}$.

17. z varies directly as x^2 is written as $z = kx^2$.

19. y varies inversely as z^3 is written as $y = \dfrac{k}{z^3}$.

21. x varies inversely as $\sqrt{y}$ is written as $x = \dfrac{k}{\sqrt{y}}$.

23. $y = kx$
$y = 20$ when $x = 5$: $20 = k(5)$
$\qquad\qquad\qquad\qquad 4 = k$
$y = 4x$
$x = 10$: $y = 4(10) = 40$
$y = 40$ when $x = 10$.

25. $y = \dfrac{k}{x}$
$y = 5$ when $x = 60$: $5 = \dfrac{k}{60}$
$\qquad\qquad\qquad\qquad 300 = k$
$y = \dfrac{300}{x}$
$x = 100$: $y = \dfrac{300}{100} = 3$
$y = 3$ when $x = 100$.

27. $z = kx^2$
$z = 96$ when $x = 4$: $96 = k(4)^2$
$\qquad\qquad\qquad\qquad 96 = 16k$
$\qquad\qquad\qquad\qquad\quad 6 = k$
$z = 6x^2$
$x = 3$: $z = 6(3)^2 = 6(9) = 54$
$z = 54$ when $x = 3$.

29. $a = \dfrac{k}{b^3}$

$a = \dfrac{3}{2}$ when $b = 2$: $\quad \dfrac{3}{2} = \dfrac{k}{2^3}$

$$\dfrac{3}{2} = \dfrac{k}{8}$$
$$12 = k$$

$a = \dfrac{12}{b^3}$

$b = 3$: $\quad a = \dfrac{12}{3^3} = \dfrac{12}{27} = \dfrac{4}{9}$

$a = \dfrac{4}{9}$ when $b = 3$.

31. Let p be the paycheck amount when h hours are worked.
$p = kh$
$p = 166.50$ when $h = 18$: $166.50 = k(18)$
$\qquad\qquad\qquad\qquad\qquad\quad 9.25 = k$

$p = 9.25h$
$h = 10$: $p = 9.25(10) = 92.50$
The pay is \$92.50 for 10 hours.

33. Let c be the cost per headphone when h headphones are manufactured.

$c = \dfrac{k}{h}$

$c = 9$ when $h = 5000$: $\qquad 9 = \dfrac{k}{5000}$
$\qquad\qquad\qquad\qquad\qquad 45,000 = k$

$c = \dfrac{45,000}{h}$

$h = 7500$: $c = \dfrac{45,000}{7500} = 6$

The cost to manufacture 7500 headphones is \$6 per headphone.

35. Let d be the distance when a weight of w is attached.
$d = kw$
$d = 4$ when $w = 60$: $\quad 4 = k(60)$
$\qquad\qquad\qquad\qquad\quad \dfrac{1}{15} = k$

$d = \dfrac{1}{15}w$

$w = 80$: $d = \dfrac{1}{15}(80) = 5\dfrac{1}{3}$

The spring stretches $5\dfrac{1}{3}$ inches when 80 pounds is attached to the spring.

37. Let w be the weight of an object when it is d miles from the center of the Earth.

$w = \dfrac{k}{d^2}$

$w = 180$ when $d = 4000$:

$$180 = \dfrac{k}{4000^2}$$
$$180 = \dfrac{k}{16,000,000}$$
$$2,880,000,000 = k$$

$$w = \dfrac{2,880,000,000}{d^2}$$

$d = 4010$: $w = \dfrac{2,880,000,000}{4010^2}$

$\qquad\qquad\quad = \dfrac{2,880,000,000}{16,080,100}$

$\qquad\qquad\quad \approx 179.1$

The man will weigh about 179.1 pounds when he is 10 miles above the surface of the Earth.

39. $d = kt^2$

$d = 64$ when $t = 2$: $\quad 64 = k(2)^2$
$\qquad\qquad\qquad\qquad\quad 64 = 4k$
$\qquad\qquad\qquad\qquad\quad 16 = k$

$d = 16t^2$

$t = 10$: $d = 16(10)^2 = 16(100) = 1600$
He will fall 1600 feet in 10 seconds.

41. $\quad -3x + 4y = 7$
$\qquad \underline{3x - 2y = 9}$
$\qquad\qquad\quad 2y = 16$

43. $\quad 5x - 0.4y = 0.7$
$\qquad \underline{-9x + 0.4y = -0.2}$
$\qquad -4x \qquad\quad = 0.5$

45. If y varies directly as x, then $y = kx$. If x is tripled, to become $3x$, then $y = k(3x) = 3(kx)$, and y is multiplied by 3.

47. If p varies directly with the square root of l, then $p = k\sqrt{l}$. If l is quadrupled, to become $4l$, then $k\sqrt{4l} = 2\left(k\sqrt{l}\right)$, and p is doubled.

Chapter 13 Vocabulary Check

1. An ordered pair is a <u>solution</u> of an equation in two variables if replacing the variables by the coordinates of the ordered pair results in a true statement.

2. The vertical number line in the rectangular coordinate system is called the <u>y-axis</u>.

3. A <u>linear</u> equation can be written in the form $Ax + By = C$.

4. A(n) <u>x-intercept</u> is a point of the graph where the graph crosses the x-axis.

5. The form $Ax + By = C$ is called <u>standard</u> form.

6. A(n) <u>y-intercept</u> is a point of the graph where the graph crosses the y-axis.

7. A set of ordered pairs that assigns to each x-value exactly one y-value is called a <u>function</u>.

8. The equation $y = 7x - 5$ is written in <u>slope-intercept</u> form.

9. The set of all x-coordinates of a relation is called the <u>domain</u> of the relation.

10. The set of all y-coordinates of a relation is called the <u>range</u> of the relation.

11. The set of ordered pairs is called a <u>relation</u>.

12. The equation $y + 1 = 7(x - 2)$ is written in <u>point-slope</u> form.

13. To find an x-intercept of a graph, let <u>y</u> = 0.

14. The horizontal number line in the rectangular coordinate system is called the <u>x-axis</u>.

15. To find a y-intercept of a graph, let <u>x</u> = 0.

16. The <u>slope</u> of a line measures the steepness or tilt of a line.

17. The equation $y = kx$ is an example of <u>direct</u> variation.

18. The equation $y = \dfrac{k}{x}$ is an example of <u>inverse</u> variation.

Chapter 13 Review

1–6.

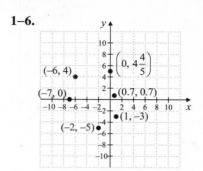

7. $-2 + y = 6x$
   In $(7, \ )$, the x-coordinate is 7.
   $-2 + y = 6(7)$
   $-2 + y = 42$
   $y = 44$

   The ordered-pair solution is $(7, 44)$.

8. $y = 3x + 5$
   In $(\ , -8)$, the y-coordinate is -8.
   $-8 = 3x + 5$
   $-13 = 3x$
   $-\dfrac{13}{3} = x$

   The ordered-pair solution is $\left(-\dfrac{13}{3}, -8\right)$.

9. $9 = -3x + 4y$
   $y = 0:\quad 9 = -3x + 4(0)$
   $\qquad\qquad 9 = -3x + 0$
   $\qquad\qquad 9 = -3x$
   $\qquad\quad -3 = x$

   $y = 3:\quad 9 = -3x + 4(3)$
   $\qquad\qquad 9 = -3x + 12$
   $\qquad\quad -3 = -3x$
   $\qquad\qquad 1 = x$

   $x = 9:\quad 9 = -3(9) + 4y$
   $\qquad\qquad 9 = -27 + 4y$
   $\qquad\quad 36 = 4y$
   $\qquad\qquad 9 = y$

x	y
-3	0
1	3
9	9

10. $y = 5$ for each value of x.

x	y
7	5
−7	5
0	5

11. $x = 2y$

$y = 0: \ x = 2(0)$
$\quad\quad\quad x = 0$

$y = 5: \ x = 2(5)$
$\quad\quad\quad x = 10$

$y = -5: \ x = 2(-5)$
$\quad\quad\quad\quad x = -10$

x	y
0	0
10	5
−10	−5

12. a. $y = 5x + 2000$
$x = 1: y = 5(1) + 2000 = 5 + 2000 = 2005$

$x = 100: \ y = 5(100) + 2000$
$\quad\quad\quad\quad\quad = 500 + 2000$
$\quad\quad\quad\quad\quad = 2500$

$x = 1000: \ y = 5(1000) + 2000$
$\quad\quad\quad\quad\quad\quad = 5000 + 2000$
$\quad\quad\quad\quad\quad\quad = 7000$

x	1	100	1000
y	2005	2500	7000

b. Let $y = 6430$ and solve for x.
$6430 = 5x + 2000$
$4430 = 5x$
$\ 886 = x$
886 compact disc holders can be produced for $6430.

13. $x - y = 1$

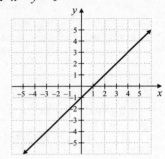

14. $x + y = 6$

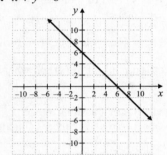

15. $x - 3y = 12$

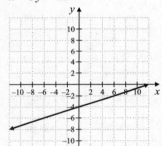

16. $5x - y = -8$

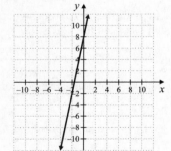

17. $x = 3y$

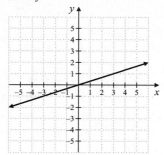

18. $y = -2x$

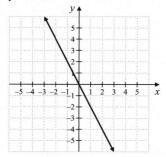

19. The x-intercept is $(4, 0)$.
The y-intercept is $(0, -2)$.

20. The x-intercepts are $(-2, 0)$ and $(2, 0)$.
The y-intercepts are $(0, 2)$ and $(0, -2)$.

21. $y = -3$ is a horizontal line with y-intercept $(0, -3)$.

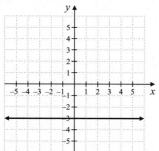

22. $x = 5$ is a vertical line with x-intercept $(5, 0)$.

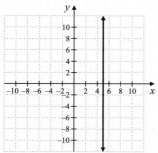

23. $x - 3y = 12$
$y = 0$: $x - 3(0) = 12$
$x - 0 = 12$
$x = 12$
x-intercept: $(12, 0)$
$x = 0$: $0 - 3y = 12$
$-3y = 12$
$y = -4$
y-intercept: $(0, -4)$

24. $-4x + y = 8$
$y = 0$: $-4x + 0 = 8$
$-4x = 8$
$x = -2$
x-intercept: $(-2, 0)$
$x = 0$: $-4(0) + y = 8$
$0 + y = 8$
$y = 8$
y-intercept: $(0, 8)$

25. $(x_1, y_1) = (-1, 2)$, $(x_2, y_2) = (3, -1)$
$$m = \frac{y_2 - y_1}{x_2 - x_1} = \frac{-1 - 2}{3 - (-1)} = \frac{-3}{3 + 1} = -\frac{3}{4}$$

26. $(x_1, y_1) = (-2, -2)$, $(x_2, y_2) = (3, -1)$
$$m = \frac{y_2 - y_1}{x_2 - x_1} = \frac{-1 - (-2)}{3 - (-2)} = \frac{-1 + 2}{3 + 2} = \frac{1}{5}$$

27. When $m = 0$, the line is horizontal. The choice is d.

28. The slope is $m = -1$. The choice is b.

29. When the slope is undefined, the line is vertical. The choice is c.

30. The slope is $m = 4$. The choice is a.

31. $m = \dfrac{y_2 - y_1}{x_2 - x_1} = \dfrac{8 - 5}{6 - 2} = \dfrac{3}{4}$

32. $m = \dfrac{y_2 - y_1}{x_2 - x_1} = \dfrac{2 - 7}{1 - 4} = \dfrac{-5}{-3} = \dfrac{5}{3}$

33. $m = \dfrac{y_2 - y_1}{x_2 - x_1} = \dfrac{-9 - 3}{-2 - 1} = \dfrac{-12}{-3} = 4$

34. $m = \dfrac{y_2 - y_1}{x_2 - x_1} = \dfrac{-6 - 1}{3 - (-4)} = \dfrac{-6 - 1}{3 + 4} = \dfrac{-7}{7} = -1$

35. $y = mx + b$
$y = 3x + 7$
The slope is $m = 3$.

36. $y = mx + b$
$x - 2y = 4$
$-2y = -x + 4$
$y = \dfrac{1}{2}x - 2$

The slope is $m = \dfrac{1}{2}$.

37. $y = mx + b$
$y = -2$
$y = 0x - 2$
The slope is $m = 0$.

38. $x = 0$ is a vertical line. The slope is undefined.

39. $x - y = -6$ $x + y = 3$
$\quad -y = -x - 6$ $\quad y = -x + 3$
$\quad\quad y = x + 6$

$m = 1$ $m = -1$
Since $(1)(-1) = -1$, the lines are perpendicular.

40. $3x + y = 7$ $-3x - y = 10$
$\quad\quad y = -3x + 7$ $\quad -y = 3x + 10$
$\quad\quad\quad\quad\quad\quad\quad\quad y = -3x - 10$

$m = -3$ $m = -3$
Since the slopes are equal, the lines are parallel.

41. $y = 4x + \dfrac{1}{2}$ $4x + 2y = 1$
$\quad\quad\quad\quad\quad\quad\quad 2y = -4x + 1$
$\quad\quad\quad\quad\quad\quad\quad\quad y = -2x + \dfrac{1}{2}$

$m = 4$ $m = -2$
Since $4 \neq -2$ and $(4)(-2) = -8 \neq -1$, the lines are neither parallel nor perpendicular.

42. $y = 6x - \dfrac{1}{3}$ $x + 6y = 6$
$\quad\quad\quad\quad\quad\quad\quad 6y = -x + 6$
$\quad\quad\quad\quad\quad\quad\quad\quad y = -\dfrac{1}{6}x + 1$

$m = 6$ $m = -\dfrac{1}{6}$

Since $(6)\left(-\dfrac{1}{6}\right) = -1,$ the lines are perpendicular.

43. $m = \dfrac{y_2 - y_1}{x_2 - x_1} = \dfrac{1.5 - 1.4}{2008 - 2004} = \dfrac{0.1}{4} = 0.025$

Every 1 year, 0.025 million more students (25,000) graduate with a bachelor's degree.

44. $m = \dfrac{y_2 - y_1}{x_2 - x_1} = \dfrac{16,600 - 14,800}{2007 - 2004} = \dfrac{1800}{3} = 600$

Every 1 year, 600 more people get kidney transplants.

45. $y = mx + b$
$x - 6y = -1$
$\quad -6y = -x - 1$
$\quad\quad y = \dfrac{1}{6}x + \dfrac{1}{6}$

$m = \dfrac{1}{6}$; y-intercept $\left(0, \dfrac{1}{6}\right)$

46. $y = mx + b$
$3x + y = 7$
$\quad\quad y = -3x + 7$

$m = -3$; y-intercept $(0, 7)$

47. $y = mx + b$
$y = -5x + \dfrac{1}{2}$

48. $y = mx + b$
$y = \dfrac{2}{3}x + 6$

49. $y = mx + b$
$y = 2x + 1$
$m = 2$, y-intercept $(0, 1)$
The choice is d.

50. $y = mx + b$
$y = -4x$
$y = -4x + 0$
$m = -4$; y-intercept $(0, 0)$
The choice is c.

51. $y = mx + b$
$y = 2x$
$y = 2x + 0$
$m = 2$; y-intercept $(0, 0)$
The choice is a.

52. $y = mx + b$
$y = 2x - 1$
$m = 2$; y-intercept $(0, -1)$
The choice is b.

53. $y - y_1 = m(x - x_1)$
$y - 0 = 4(x - 2)$
$y = 4x - 8$

$-4x + y = -8$

54. $y - y_1 = m(x - x_1)$
$y - (-5) = -3(x - 0)$
$y + 5 = -3x$
$y = -3x - 5$
$3x + y = -5$

55. $y - y_1 = m(x - x_1)$
$y - 4 = \dfrac{3}{5}(x - 1)$
$5(y - 4) = 5 \cdot \dfrac{3}{5}(x - 1)$
$5y - 20 = 3(x - 1)$
$5y - 20 = 3x - 3$
$5y = 3x + 17$
$-3x + 5y = 17$

56. $y - y_1 = m(x - x_1)$
$y - 3 = -\dfrac{1}{3}[x - (-3)]$
$3y - 9 = -1[x - (-3)]$
$3y - 9 = -(x + 3)$
$3y - 9 = -x - 3$
$3y = -x + 6$
$x + 3y = 6$

57. $m = \dfrac{y_2 - y_1}{x_2 - x_1} = \dfrac{-7 - 7}{2 - 1} = \dfrac{-14}{1} = -14$
$y - y_1 = m(x - x_1)$
$y - 7 = -14(x - 1)$
$y - 7 = -14x + 14$
$y = -14x + 21$

58. $m = \dfrac{y_2 - y_1}{x_2 - x_1} = \dfrac{6 - 5}{-4 - (-2)} = \dfrac{6 - 5}{-4 + 2} = \dfrac{1}{-2} = -\dfrac{1}{2}$
$y - y_1 = m(x - x_1)$
$y - 5 = -\dfrac{1}{2}[x - (-2)]$
$y - 5 = -\dfrac{1}{2}(x + 2)$
$2(y - 5) = 2\left(-\dfrac{1}{2}\right)(x + 2)$
$2y - 10 = -1(x + 2)$
$2y - 10 = -x - 2$
$2y = -x + 8$
$y = -\dfrac{1}{2}x + 4$

59. The *x*-value 7 is paired with two *y*-values, 1 and 5, so the relation is not a function.

60. Each *x*-value is only assigned to one *y*-value, so the relation is a function.

61. No vertical line will intersect the graph more than once, so the graph is the graph of a function.

62. No vertical line will intersect the graph more than once, so the graph is the graph of a function.

63. The vertical line $x = 3$ will intersect the graph at more than one point, so the graph is not the graph of a function.

64. No vertical line will intersect the graph more than once, so the graph is the graph of a function.

65. $f(x) = -2x + 6$
$f(0) = -2(0) + 6 = 0 + 6 = 6$

66. $f(x) = -2x + 6$
$f(-2) = -2(-2) + 6 = 4 + 6 = 10$

67. $f(x) = -2x + 6$
$f\left(\dfrac{1}{2}\right) = -2\left(\dfrac{1}{2}\right) + 6 = -1 + 6 = 5$

68. $f(x) = -2x + 6$
$f\left(-\dfrac{1}{2}\right) = -2\left(-\dfrac{1}{2}\right) + 6 = 1 + 6 = 7$

69. Graph the boundary line, $x + 6y = 6$, with a dashed line.
Test $(0, 0)$: $x + 6y < 6$
$0 + 6(0) < 6$
$0 + 0 < 6$
$0 < 6$ True
Shade the half-plane containing $(0, 0)$.

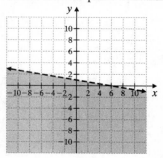

70. Graph the boundary line, $x + y = -2$, with a dashed line.

Test $(0, 0)$: $x + y > -2$

$$0 + 0 > -2$$
$$0 > -2 \quad \text{True}$$

Shade the half-plane containing $(0, 0)$.

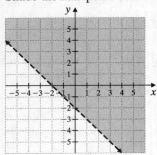

71. Graph the boundary line, $y = -7$, with a solid line.

Test $(0, 0)$: $y \geq -7$

$$0 \geq -7 \quad \text{True}$$

Shade the half-plane containing $(0, 0)$.

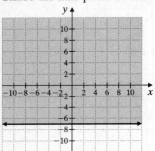

72. Graph the boundary line, $y = -4$, as a solid line.

Test $(0, 0)$: $y \leq -4$

$$0 \leq -4 \quad \text{False}$$

Shade the half-plane not containing $(0, 0)$.

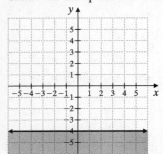

73. Graph the boundary line, $-x = y$, as a solid line.

Test $(1, 1)$: $-x \leq y$

$$-1 \leq 1 \quad \text{True}$$

Shade the half-plane containing $(1, 1)$.

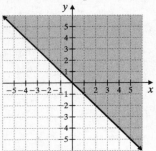

74. Graph the boundary line, $x = -y$, as a solid line.

Test $(1, 1)$: $x \geq -y$

$$1 \geq -1 \quad \text{True}$$

Shade the half-plane containing $(1, 1)$.

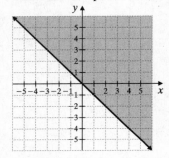

75. $y = kx$

$y = 40$ when $x = 4$: $\quad 40 = k(4)$

$$10 = k$$

$y = 10x$

$x = 11$: $y = 10(11) = 110$

$y = 110$ when $x = 11$.

76. $y = \dfrac{k}{x}$

$y = 4$ when $x = 6$: $\quad 4 = \dfrac{k}{6}$

$$24 = k$$

$y = \dfrac{24}{x}$

$x = 48$: $y = \dfrac{24}{48} = \dfrac{1}{2}$

$y = \dfrac{1}{2}$ when $x = 48$.

77. $y = \dfrac{k}{x^3}$

$y = 12.5$ when $x = 2$: $12.5 = \dfrac{k}{2^3}$

$$12.5 = \dfrac{k}{8}$$

$$100 = k$$

$y = \dfrac{100}{x^3}$

$x = 3$: $y = \dfrac{100}{3^3} = \dfrac{100}{27}$

$y = \dfrac{100}{27}$ when $x = 3$.

78. $y = kx^2$

$y = 175$ when $x = 5$: $175 = k(5)^2$

$$175 = 25k$$

$$7 = k$$

$y = 7x^2$

$x = 10$: $y = 7(10)^2 = 7(100) = 700$

$y = 700$ when $x = 10$.

79. Let c be the cost for manufacturing m milliliters.

$c = \dfrac{k}{m}$

$c = 6600$ when $m = 3000$: $\quad 6600 = \dfrac{k}{3000}$

$$19,800,000 = k$$

$c = \dfrac{19,800,000}{m}$

Let $m = 5000$: $c = \dfrac{19,800,000}{5000} = 3960$

It costs \$3960 to manufacture 5000 milliliters.

80. Let d be the distance when a weight of w is attached.

$d = kw$

$d = 8$ when $w = 150$: $\quad 8 = k(150)$

$$\dfrac{4}{75} = k$$

$d = \dfrac{4}{75}w$

Let $w = 90$: $d = \dfrac{4}{75} \cdot 90 = 4\dfrac{4}{5}$

The spring stretches $4\dfrac{4}{5}$ inches when 90 pounds is attached.

81. $2x - 5y = 9$

$y = 1$: $2x - 5(1) = 9$

$$2x - 5 = 9$$

$$2x = 14$$

$$x = 7$$

$x = 2$: $2(2) - 5y = 9$

$$4 - 5y = 9$$

$$-5y = 5$$

$$y = -1$$

$y = -3$: $2x - 5(-3) = 9$

$$2x + 15 = 9$$

$$2x = -6$$

$$x = -3$$

x	y
7	1
2	−1
−3	−3

82. $x = -3y$

$x = 0$: $0 = -3y$

$$0 = y$$

$y = 1$: $x = -3(1)$

$$x = -3$$

$x = 6$: $6 = -3y$

$$-2 = y$$

x	y
0	0
−3	1
6	−2

83. $2x - 3y = 6$

$y = 0$: $2x - 3(0) = 6$

$$2x - 0 = 6$$

$$2x = 6$$

$$x = 3$$

x-intercept: $(3, 0)$

$x = 0$: $2(0) - 3y = 6$

$$0 - 3y = 6$$

$$-3y = 6$$

$$y = -2$$

y-intercept: $(0, -2)$

84. $-5x + y = 10$
$\quad y = 0:\ -5x + 0 = 10$
$\qquad\qquad\quad -5x = 10$
$\qquad\qquad\qquad\ \ x = -2$
$\quad$ *x*-intercept: $(-2, 0)$
$\quad x = 0:\ -5(0) + y = 10$
$\qquad\qquad\quad\ \ 0 + y = 10$
$\qquad\qquad\qquad\qquad y = 10$
$\quad$ *y*-intercept: $(0, 10)$

85. $x - 5y = 10$
$\quad y = 0:\ x - 5(0) = 10$
$\qquad\qquad\quad\ x - 0 = 10$
$\qquad\qquad\qquad\ \ \ x = 10$
$\quad$ *x*-intercept: $(10, 0)$
$\quad x = 0:\ 0 - 5y = 10$
$\qquad\qquad\quad -5y = 10$
$\qquad\qquad\qquad\ \ y = -2$
$\quad$ *y*-intercept: $(0, -2)$

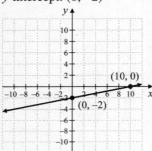

86. $x + y = 4$
$\quad y = 0:\ x + 0 = 4$
$\qquad\qquad\qquad x = 4$
$\quad$ *x*-intercept: $(4, 0)$
$\quad x = 0:\ 0 + y = 4$
$\qquad\qquad\qquad\ y = 4$
$\quad$ *y*-intercept: $(0, 4)$

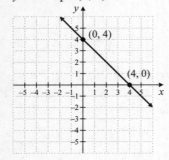

87. $y = -4x$
$\quad y = 0:\ 0 = -4x$
$\qquad\qquad\quad\ 0 = x$
$\quad$ *x*-intercept: $(0, 0)$
$\quad$ The *y*-intercept is also $(0, 0)$. Find another point.
$\quad$ Let $x = 1$.
$\quad y = -4(1) = -4$
$\quad$ Another point is $(1, -4)$.

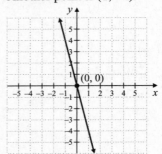

88. $2x + 3y = -6$
$\quad y = 0:\ 2x + 3(0) = -6$
$\qquad\qquad\quad\ \ 2x + 0 = -6$
$\qquad\qquad\qquad\qquad 2x = -6$
$\qquad\qquad\qquad\qquad\ \ x = -3$
$\quad$ *x*-intercept: $(-3, 0)$
$\quad x = 0:\ 2(0) + 3y = -6$
$\qquad\qquad\quad\ \ \ 0 + 3y = -6$
$\qquad\qquad\qquad\qquad\ \ 3y = -6$
$\qquad\qquad\qquad\qquad\qquad y = -2$
$\quad$ *y*-intercept: $(0, -2)$

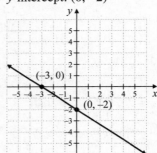

89. $x = 3$ is a vertical line with *x*-intercept $(3, 0)$.

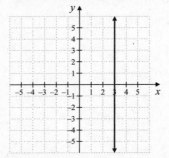

90. $y = -2$ is a horizontal line with y-intercept $(0, -2)$.

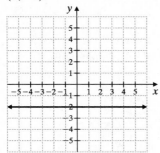

91. $m = \dfrac{y_2 - y_1}{x_2 - x_1} = \dfrac{2 - (-5)}{-4 - 3} = \dfrac{2 + 5}{-4 - 3} = \dfrac{7}{-7} = -1$

92. $m = \dfrac{y_2 - y_1}{x_2 - x_1} = \dfrac{-8 - 3}{-6 - 1} = \dfrac{-11}{-7} = \dfrac{11}{7}$

93. $(x_1, y_1) = (0, -4), (x_2, y_2) = (2, 0)$

$m = \dfrac{y_2 - y_1}{x_2 - x_1} = \dfrac{0 - (-4)}{2 - 0} = \dfrac{4}{2} = 2$

94. $(x_1, y_1) = (0, 2), (x_2, y_2) = (6, 0)$

$m = \dfrac{y_2 - y_1}{x_2 - x_1} = \dfrac{0 - 2}{6 - 0} = \dfrac{-2}{6} = -\dfrac{1}{3}$

95. $y = mx + b$

$-2x + 3y = -15$

$3y = 2x - 15$

$y = \dfrac{2}{3}x - 5$

$m = \dfrac{2}{3};\ y\text{-intercept: } (0, -5)$

96. $y = mx + b$

$6x + y - 2 = 0$

$6x + y = 2$

$y = -6x + 2$

$m = -6;\ y\text{-intercept: } (0, 2)$

97. $y - y_1 = m(x - x_1)$

$y - (-7) = -5(x - 3)$

$y + 7 = -5x + 15$

$y = -5x + 8$

$5x + y = 8$

98. $y - y_1 = m(x - x_1)$

$y - 6 = 3(x - 0)$

$y - 6 = 3x$

$-6 = 3x - y$

$3x - y = -6$

99. $m = \dfrac{y_2 - y_1}{x_2 - x_1} = \dfrac{5 - 9}{-2 - (-3)} = \dfrac{5 - 9}{-2 + 3} = \dfrac{-4}{1} = -4$

$y - y_1 = m(x - x_1)$

$y - 9 = -4[x - (-3)]$

$y - 9 = -4(x + 3)$

$y - 9 = -4x - 12$

$y = -4x - 3$

$4x + y = -3$

100. $m = \dfrac{y_2 - y_1}{x_2 - x_1} = \dfrac{-9 - 1}{5 - 3} = \dfrac{-10}{2} = -5$

$y - y_1 = m(x - x_1)$

$y - 1 = -5(x - 3)$

$y - 1 = -5x + 15$

$y = -5x + 16$

$5x + y = 16$

Chapter 13 Test

1. $12y - 7x = 5$

$x = 1:\ 12y - 7(1) = 5$

$\quad\quad\quad\quad 12y - 7 = 5$

$\quad\quad\quad\quad\quad 12y = 12$

$\quad\quad\quad\quad\quad\quad y = 1$

The ordered pair is $(1, 1)$.

2. $y = 17$ for each value of x. The ordered pair is $(-4, 17)$.

3. $(x_1, y_1) = (-1, -1), (x_2, y_2) = (4, 1)$

$m = \dfrac{y_2 - y_1}{x_2 - x_1} = \dfrac{1 - (-1)}{4 - (-1)} = \dfrac{1 + 1}{4 + 1} = \dfrac{2}{5}$

4. The slope of a horizontal line is $m = 0$.

5. $m = \dfrac{y_2 - y_1}{x_2 - x_1} = \dfrac{2 - (-5)}{-1 - 6} = \dfrac{7}{-7} = -1$

6. $m = \dfrac{y_2 - y_1}{x_2 - x_1} = \dfrac{-1 - (-8)}{-1 - 0} = \dfrac{-1 + 8}{-1} = \dfrac{7}{-1} = -7$

7. $y = mx + b$
$-3x + y = 5$
$\quad y = 3x + 5$
$m = 3$

8. $x = 6$ is a vertical line. The slope of a vertical line is undefined.

9. $2x + y = 8$
$y = 0: \; 2x + 0 = 8$
$\qquad 2x = 8$
$\qquad x = 4$
x-intercept: $(4, 0)$
$x = 0: \; 2(0) + y = 8$
$\qquad y = 8$
y-intercept: $(0, 8)$

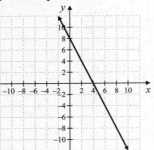

10. $-x + 4y = 5$
$y = 0: \; -x + 4(0) = 5$
$\qquad -x + 0 = 5$
$\qquad -x = 5$
$\qquad x = -5$
x-intercept: $(-5, 0)$
$x = 0: \; -0 + 4y = 5$
$\qquad 4y = 5$
$\qquad y = \dfrac{5}{4}$
y-intercept: $\left(0, \dfrac{5}{4}\right)$

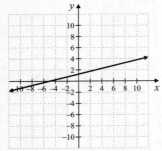

11. Graph the boundary line, $x - y = -2$, with a solid line.
Test $(0, 0)$: $x - y \geq -2$
$\qquad 0 - 0 \geq -2$
$\qquad 0 \geq -2$ True
Shade the half-plane containing $(0, 0)$.

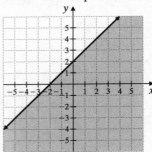

12. Graph the boundary line, $y = -4x$, with a solid line.
Test $(1, 1)$: $y \geq -4x$
$\qquad 1 \geq -4(1)$
$\qquad 1 \geq -4$ True
Shade the half-plane containing $(1, 1)$.

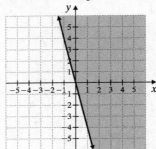

13. $5x - 7y = 10$
$y = 0: \; 5x - 7(0) = 10$
$\qquad 5x - 0 = 10$
$\qquad 5x = 10$
$\qquad x = 2$
x-intercept: $(2, 0)$
$x = 0: \; 5(0) - 7y = 10$
$\qquad 0 - 7y = 10$
$\qquad -7y = 10$
$\qquad y = -\dfrac{10}{7}$
y-intercept: $\left(0, -\dfrac{10}{7}\right)$

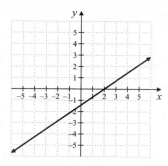

14. Graph the boundary line, $2x - 3y = -6$, with a dashed line.

Test $(0, 0)$:
$$2x - 3y > -6$$
$$2(0) - 3(0) > -6$$
$$0 - 0 > -6$$
$$0 > -6 \quad \text{True}$$

Shade the half-plane containing $(0, 0)$.

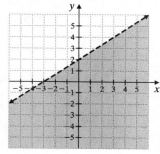

15. Graph the boundary line, $6x + y = -1$, with a dashed line.

Test $(0, 0)$:
$$6x + y > -1$$
$$6(0) + 0 > -1$$
$$0 + 0 > -1$$
$$0 > -1 \quad \text{True}$$

Shade the half-plane containing $(0, 0)$.

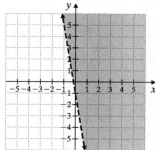

16. The graph of $y = -1$ is a horizontal line with a y-intercept of $(0, -1)$.

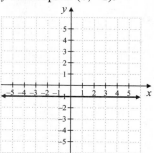

17. $y = 2x - 6$
The slope is $m = 2$ and the y-intercept is $(0, -6)$.
$$-4x = 2y$$
$$-2x = y$$
$$y = -2x + 0$$

The slope is $m = -2$ and the y-intercept is $(0, 0)$. Since the slopes are different, the lines are not parallel. Since $2(-2) = -4 \neq -1$, the lines are not perpendicular. The lines are neither parallel nor perpendicular.

18.
$$y - y_1 = m(x - x_1)$$
$$y - 2 = -\frac{1}{4}(x - 2)$$
$$4(y - 2) = 4\left(-\frac{1}{4}\right)(x - 2)$$
$$4y - 8 = -1(x - 2)$$
$$4y - 8 = -x + 2$$
$$4y = -x + 10$$
$$x + 4y = 10$$

19. $m = \dfrac{y_2 - y_1}{x_2 - x_1} = \dfrac{-7 - 0}{6 - 0} = \dfrac{-7}{6} = -\dfrac{7}{6}$
$$y - y_1 = m(x - x_1)$$
$$y - 0 = -\frac{7}{6}(x - 0)$$
$$y = -\frac{7}{6}x$$
$$6y = 6\left(-\frac{7}{6}x\right)$$
$$6y = -7x$$
$$7x + 6y = 0$$

20. $m = \dfrac{y_2 - y_1}{x_2 - x_1} = \dfrac{3 - (-5)}{1 - 2} = \dfrac{3 + 5}{-1} = -8$

$y - y_1 = m(x - x_1)$

$y - (-5) = -8(x - 2)$

$y + 5 = -8x + 16$

$y = -8x + 11$

$8x + y = 11$

21. $m = \dfrac{1}{8}$; $b = 12$

$y = \dfrac{1}{8}x + 12$

$8y = x + 8(12)$

$8y = x + 96$

$x - 8y = -96$

22. Each *x*-value is only assigned to one *y*-value, so the relation is a function.

23. The *x*-value −3 is assigned to two *y*-values, −3 and 2, so the relation is not a function. Note that the *x*-value 0 is also assigned to two *y*-values, 5 and 0.

24. No vertical line will intersect the graph more than once, so the graph is the graph of a function.

25. No vertical line will intersect the graph more than once, so the graph is the graph of a function.

26. $f(x) = 2x - 4$

   a. $f(-2) = 2(-2) - 4 = -4 - 4 = -8$

   b. $f(0.2) = 2(0.2) - 4 = 0.4 - 4 = -3.6$

   c. $f(0) = 2(0) - 4 = 0 - 4 = -4$

27. $f(x) = x^3 - x$

   a. $f(-1) = (-1)^3 - (-1) = -1 + 1 = 0$

   b. $f(0) = 0^3 - 0 = 0 - 0 = 0$

   c. $f(4) = 4^3 - 4 = 64 - 4 = 60$

28. $2x + 2(2y) = 42$

$2(x + 2y) = 2(21)$

$x + 2y = 21$

Let $y = 8$: $x + 2(8) = 21$

$x + 16 = 21$

$x = 5$

When $y = 8$ meters, $x = 5$ meters.

29. a. The ordered pairs are (2003, 66.0), (2004, 65.4), (2005, 65.4), (2006, 65.6), (2007, 64.9).

   b.

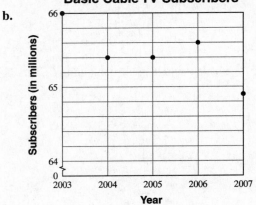

Basic Cable TV Subscribers

30. $m = \dfrac{y_2 - y_1}{x_2 - x_1} = \dfrac{1400 - 1484}{2007 - 2004} = \dfrac{-84}{3} = -28$

Every 1 year, 28 million fewer movie tickets are sold.

31. $y = kx$

$y = 10$ when $x = 15$: $10 = k(15)$

$\dfrac{2}{3} = k$

$y = \dfrac{2}{3}x$

Let $x = 42$: $y = \dfrac{2}{3}(42) = 28$

When $x = 42$, $y = 28$.

32. $y = \dfrac{k}{x^2}$

$y = 8$ when $x = 5$: $8 = \dfrac{k}{5^2}$

$8 = \dfrac{k}{25}$

$200 = k$

$$y = \frac{200}{x^2}$$

Let $x = 15$: $y = \frac{200}{15^2} = \frac{200}{225} = \frac{8}{9}$

When $x = 15$, $y = \frac{8}{9}$.

Cumulative Review Chapters 1–13

1. Area = length $\cdot$ width
    $= (380 \text{ miles}) \cdot (280 \text{ miles})$
    $= 106,400 \text{ square miles}$

    The area of Colorado is about 106,400 square miles.

2. $21 \cdot 7 = 147$
    There are 147 trees in the orchard.

3. $1 + (-10) + (-8) + 9 = -9 + (-8) + 9$
    $\qquad\qquad\qquad\qquad = -17 + 9$
    $\qquad\qquad\qquad\qquad = -8$

4. $-2 + (-7) + 3 + (-4) = -9 + 3 + (-4)$
    $\qquad\qquad\qquad\qquad\quad = -6 + (-4)$
    $\qquad\qquad\qquad\qquad\quad = -10$

5. $\dfrac{8}{3x} = \dfrac{8}{3x} \cdot \dfrac{8}{8} = \dfrac{8 \cdot 8}{3x \cdot 8} = \dfrac{64}{24x}$

6. $\dfrac{3}{2c} = \dfrac{3}{2c} \cdot \dfrac{4}{4} = \dfrac{3 \cdot 4}{2c \cdot 4} = \dfrac{12}{8c}$

7. $\begin{array}{r} 14 \\ -8\frac{3}{7} \\ \hline \end{array}$ $\qquad$ $\begin{array}{r} 13\frac{7}{7} \\ -8\frac{3}{7} \\ \hline 5\frac{4}{7} \end{array}$

8. $\begin{array}{r} 15 \\ -4\frac{2}{5} \\ \hline \end{array}$ $\qquad$ $\begin{array}{r} 14\frac{5}{5} \\ -4\frac{2}{5} \\ \hline 10\frac{3}{5} \end{array}$

9. $-2x + 5 = -2(3.8) + 5 = -7.6 + 5 = -2.6$

10. $6x - 1 = 6(-2.1) - 1 = -12.6 - 1 = -13.6$

11. $\begin{array}{r} 3.142 \approx 3.14 \\ 7\overline{)22.000} \\ \underline{21} \\ 10 \\ \underline{7} \\ 30 \\ \underline{28} \\ 20 \\ \underline{14} \\ 6 \end{array}$

    $\dfrac{7}{22} \approx 3.14$

12. $\begin{array}{r} 1.9473 \approx 1.947 \\ 19\overline{)37.0000} \\ \underline{19} \\ 18\ 0 \\ \underline{17\ 1} \\ 90 \\ \underline{76} \\ 140 \\ \underline{133} \\ 70 \\ \underline{57} \\ 13 \end{array}$

    $\dfrac{37}{19} \approx 1.947$

13. $2x < -4$
    $\dfrac{2x}{2} < \dfrac{-4}{2}$
    $x < -2$

14. $3x \le -9$
    $\dfrac{3x}{3} \le \dfrac{-9}{3}$
    $x \le -3$
    $\{x | x \le -3\}$

15. **a.** The degree of the trinomial $-2t^2 + 3t + 6$ is 2, the greatest degree of any of its terms.

    b. The degree of the binomial $15x - 10$ or $15x^1 - 10$ is 1.

c. The degree of the polynomial
$7x + 3x^3 + 2x^2 - 1$ is 3. It is not a monomial, binomial, nor a trinomial, so the answer is none of these.

16. a. The degree of the binomial $-7y + 2$ or $-7y^1 + 2$ is 1.

b. The degree of the trinomial $8x - x^2 - 1$ is 2, the greatest degree of any of its terms.

c. The degree of the polynomial
$9y^3 - 6y + 2 + y^2$ is 3. It is not a monomial, binomial, or trinomial, so the answer is none of these.

17. $(-2x^2 + 5x - 1) + (-2x^2 + x + 3)$
$= -2x^2 + 5x - 1 - 2x^2 + x + 3$
$= (-2x^2 - 2x^2) + (5x + x) + (-1 + 3)$
$= -4x^2 + 6x + 2$

18. $(9x - 5) + (x^2 - 6x + 5)$
$= 9x - 5 + x^2 - 6x + 5$
$= x^2 + (9x - 6x) + (-5 + 5)$
$= x^2 + 3x$

19. $(3y + 1)^2 = (3y + 1)(3y + 1)$
$= (3y)(3y) + (3y)(1) + 1(3y) + 1(1)$
$= 9y^2 + 3y + 3y + 1$
$= 9y^2 + 6y + 1$

20. $(2x - 5)^2$
$= (2x - 5)(2x - 5)$
$= (2x)(2x) + (2x)(-5) + (-5)(2x) + (-5)(-5)$
$= 4x^2 - 10x - 10x + 25$
$= 4x^2 - 20x + 25$

21. $-9a^5 + 18a^2 - 3a = 3a(-3a^4) + 3a(6a) + 3a(-1)$
$= 3a(-3a^4 + 6a - 1)$

22. $2x^5 - x^3 = x^3 \cdot 2x^2 - x^3 \cdot 1 = x^3(2x^2 - 1)$

23. $x^2 + 4x - 12$
Look for two numbers whose product is -12 and whose sum is 4.
$x^2 + 4x - 12 = (x - 2)(x + 6)$

24. $x^2 + 4x - 21$
Look for two numbers whose product is -21 and whose sum is 4.
$x^2 + 4x - 21 = (x - 3)(x + 7)$

25. Factors of $8x^2$: $8x^2 = 8x \cdot x$, $8x^2 = 4x \cdot 2x$
Factors of 5: $5 = -1 \cdot -5$
$8x^2 - 22x + 5 = (4x - 1)(2x - 5)$

26. Factors of $15x^2$: $15x^2 = 15x \cdot x$, $15x^2 = 5x \cdot 3x$
Factors of -2: $-2 = -2 \cdot 1$, $-2 = 2 \cdot -1$
$15x^2 + x - 2 = (5x + 2)(3x - 1)$

27.
$$4x^2 - 28x = -49$$
$$4x^2 - 28x + 49 = 0$$
$$(2x)^2 - 2 \cdot 2x \cdot 7 + 7^2 = 0$$
$$(2x - 7)^2 = 0$$
$$2x - 7 = 0$$
$$2x = 7$$
$$x = \frac{7}{2}$$
The solution is $\frac{7}{2}$.

28.
$$x^2 - 9x = -14$$
$$x^2 - 9x + 14 = 0$$
$$(x - 2)(x - 7) = 0$$
$$x - 2 = 0 \quad \text{or} \quad x - 7 = 0$$
$$x = 2 \qquad\qquad x = 7$$
The solutions are 2 and 7.

29. $\dfrac{2x^2 - 11x + 5}{5x - 25} \div \dfrac{4x - 2}{10} = \dfrac{2x^2 - 11x + 5}{5x - 25} \cdot \dfrac{10}{4x - 2}$
$= \dfrac{(2x - 1)(x - 5) \cdot 2 \cdot 5}{5(x - 5) \cdot 2(2x - 1)}$
$= \dfrac{1}{1}$ or 1

30. $\dfrac{3x^2 + 17x - 6}{5x + 5} \cdot \dfrac{2x + 2}{4x + 24}$
$= \dfrac{(3x - 1) \cdot (x + 6) \cdot 2 \cdot (x + 1)}{5 \cdot (x + 1) \cdot 2 \cdot 2(x + 6)}$
$= \dfrac{3x - 1}{5 \cdot 2}$
$= \dfrac{3x - 1}{10}$

31. $\dfrac{4b}{9a} = \dfrac{4b}{9a} \cdot 1 = \dfrac{4b}{9a} \cdot \dfrac{3ab}{3ab} = \dfrac{4b(3ab)}{9a(3ab)} = \dfrac{12ab^2}{27a^2 b}$

32. $\dfrac{7x}{11y} = \dfrac{7x}{11y} \cdot 1$

$\qquad = \dfrac{7x}{11y} \cdot \dfrac{9x^2 y}{9x^2 y}$

$\qquad = \dfrac{7x(9x^2 y)}{11y(9x^2 y)}$

$\qquad = \dfrac{63x^3 y}{99x^2 y^2}$

33. $1 + \dfrac{m}{m+1} = \dfrac{1}{1} + \dfrac{m}{m+1}$

$\qquad = \dfrac{1(m+1)}{1(m+1)} + \dfrac{m}{m+1}$

$\qquad = \dfrac{m+1+m}{m+1}$

$\qquad = \dfrac{2m+1}{m+1}$

34. $1 - \dfrac{m}{m+1} = \dfrac{1}{1} - \dfrac{m}{m+1}$

$\qquad = \dfrac{1(m+1)}{1(m+1)} - \dfrac{m}{m+1}$

$\qquad = \dfrac{m+1-m}{m+1}$

$\qquad = \dfrac{1}{m+1}$

35. $3 - \dfrac{6}{x} = x + 8$

$\qquad x\left(3 - \dfrac{6}{x}\right) = x(x+8)$

$\qquad 3x - 6 = x^2 + 8x$

$\qquad 0 = x^2 + 5x + 6$

$\qquad 0 = (x+3)(x+2)$

$\qquad x + 3 = 0 \quad$ or $\quad x + 2 = 0$

$\qquad x = -3 \qquad\qquad x = -2$

The solutions are -3 and -2.

36. $2 + \dfrac{10}{x} = x + 5$

$\qquad x\left(2 + \dfrac{10}{x}\right) = x(x+5)$

$\qquad 2x + 10 = x^2 + 5x$

$\qquad 0 = x^2 + 3x - 10$

$\qquad 0 = (x+5)(x-2)$

$\qquad x + 5 = 0 \quad$ or $\quad x - 2 = 0$

$\qquad x = -5 \qquad\qquad x = 2$

The solutions are -5 and 2.

37. $\dfrac{\frac{x+1}{y}}{\frac{x}{y}+2} = \dfrac{y\left(\frac{x+1}{y}\right)}{y\left(\frac{x}{y}+2\right)} = \dfrac{y\left(\frac{x+1}{y}\right)}{y\left(\frac{x}{y}\right)+y(2)} = \dfrac{x+1}{x+2y}$

38. $\dfrac{\frac{x}{2}+2}{\frac{x}{2}-2} = \dfrac{2\left(\frac{x}{2}+2\right)}{2\left(\frac{x}{2}-2\right)} = \dfrac{x+4}{x-4}$

39. $3x + y = 12$

    a. In $(0, \ )$, the *x*-coordinate is 0.

$\qquad x = 0: \ 3(0) + y = 12$

$\qquad\qquad\qquad 0 + y = 12$

$\qquad\qquad\qquad\quad y = 12$

    The ordered-pair solution is $(0, 12)$.

    b. In $(\ , 6)$, the *y*-coordinate is 6.

$\qquad y = 6: \ 3x + 6 = 12$

$\qquad\qquad\qquad 3x = 6$

$\qquad\qquad\qquad\ x = 2$

    The ordered-pair solution is $(2, 6)$.

    c. In $(-1, \ )$, the *x*-coordinate is -1.

$\qquad x = -1: \ 3(-1) + y = 12$

$\qquad\qquad\qquad -3 + y = 12$

$\qquad\qquad\qquad\qquad y = 15$

    The ordered-pair solution is $(-1, 15)$.

40. $-x + 4y = -20$

    a. In $(0, \ )$, the *x*-coordinate is 0.

$\qquad x = 0: \ -0 + 4y = -20$

$\qquad\qquad\qquad 4y = -20$

$\qquad\qquad\qquad\ y = -5$

    The ordered pair solution is $(0, -5)$.

b. In (, 0), the y-coordinate is 0.

$$y = 0:\ -x + 4(0) = -20$$
$$-x + 0 = -20$$
$$-x = -20$$
$$x = 20$$

The ordered-pair solution is (20, 0).

c. In (, −2), the y-coordinate is −2.

$$y = -2:\ -x + 4(-2) = -20$$
$$-x - 8 = -20$$
$$-x = -12$$
$$x = 12$$

The ordered pair solution is (12, −2).

41. $2x + y = 5$

$$y = 0:\ 2x + 0 = 5$$
$$2x = 5$$
$$x = \frac{5}{2}$$

The x-intercept is $\left(\dfrac{5}{2}, 0\right)$.

$$x = 0:\ 2(0) + y = 5$$
$$0 + y = 5$$
$$y = 5$$

The y-intercept is (0, 5).

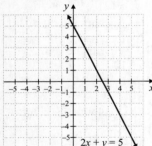

42. $y = -2x$

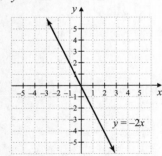

43. $y = mx + b$

$$-2x + 3y = 11$$
$$3y = 2x + 11$$
$$y = \frac{2}{3}x + \frac{11}{3}$$

The slope is $m = \dfrac{2}{3}$.

44. $y = mx + b$

$$7x + 4y = 10$$
$$4y = -7x + 10$$
$$y = -\frac{7}{4}x + \frac{5}{2}$$

The slope is $m = -\dfrac{7}{4}$.

45.
$$y - y_1 = m(x - x_1)$$
$$y - 5 = -2[x - (-1)]$$
$$y - 5 = -2(x + 1)$$
$$y - 5 = -2x - 2$$
$$y = -2x + 3$$
$$2x + y = 3$$

46.
$$y - y_1 = m(x - x_1)$$
$$y - (-7) = -5(x - 2)$$
$$y + 7 = -5x + 10$$
$$y = -5x + 3$$
$$5x + y = 3$$

47. $g(x) = x^2 - 3$

a. $g(2) = 2^2 - 3 = 4 - 3 = 1$

The ordered pair is (2, 1).

b. $g(-2) = (-2)^2 - 3 = 4 - 3 = 1$

The ordered pair is (−2, 1).

c. $g(0) = 0^2 - 3 = 0 - 3 = -3$

The ordered pair is (0, −3).

48. $f(x) = 3x^2 + 2$

a. $f(0) = 3(0)^2 + 2 = 3 \cdot 0 + 2 = 0 + 2 = 2$

The ordered pair is (0, 2).

b. $f(4) = 3(4)^2 + 2 = 3 \cdot 16 + 2 = 48 + 2 = 50$

The ordered pair is (4, 50).

c. $f(-1) = 3(-1)^2 + 2 = 3 \cdot 1 + 2 = 3 + 2 = 5$

The ordered pair is (−1, 5).

Chapter 14

Section 14.1

Practice Problems

1.

$5x - 2y = -3$	$y = 3x$
$5(3) - 2(9) = -3$	$9 = 3(3)$
$15 - 18 = -3$	$9 = 9$
$-3 = -3$	

(3, 9) is a solution of the system.

2.

$2x - y = 8$	$x + 3y = 4$
$2(3) - (-2) = 8$	$3 + 3(-2) = 4$
$6 + 2 = 8$	$3 + -6 = 4$
$8 = 8$	$-3 \neq 4$

(3, −2) is not a solution of the system.

3.

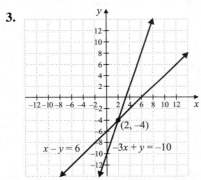

(2, −4) is a solution of the system.

4.

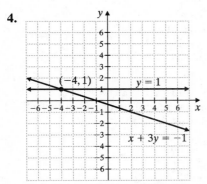

(−4, 1) is a solution of the system.

5.

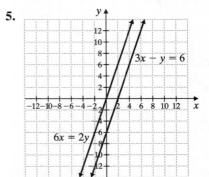

There are no solution because the lines are parallel.

6.

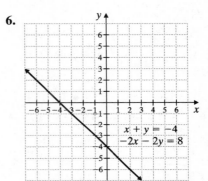

There are an infinite number of solutions because it is the same line.

7.

$5x + 4y = 6$	$x - y = 3$
$4y = -5x + 6$	$-y = -x + 3$
$y = -\dfrac{5}{4}x + \dfrac{3}{2}$	$y = x - 3$

The slope of the first line is $-\dfrac{5}{4}$, while the slope of the second line is 1. Since the slopes are not equal, the system has one solution.

8.

$-\dfrac{2}{3}x + y = 6$	$3y = 2x + 5$
$y = \dfrac{2}{3}x + 6$	$y = \dfrac{2}{3}x + \dfrac{5}{3}$

Both lines have slope $\dfrac{2}{3}$, but the y-intercepts are different. The lines are parallel, so the system has no solution.

Calculator Explorations

1. $y = -2.68x + 1.21$
    $y = 5.22x - 1.68$

    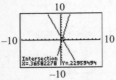

    (0.37, 0.23) is the approximate point of intersection.

2. $y = 4.25x + 3.89$
    $y = -1.88x + 3.21$

    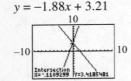

    (−0.11, 3.42) is the approximate point of intersection.

3. $4.3x - 2.9y = 5.6 \rightarrow y = -(5.6 - 4.3x)/2.9$
    $8.1x + 7.6y = -14.1 \rightarrow y = (-14.1 - 8.1x)/7.6$

    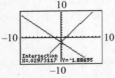

    (0.03, −1.89) is the approximate point of intersection.

4. $-3.6x - 8.6y = 10 \rightarrow y = -(10 + 3.6x)/8.6$
    $-4.5x + 9.6y = -7.7 \rightarrow y = (-7.7 + 4.5x)/9.6$

    (−0.41, −0.99) is the approximate point of intersection.

Vocabulary and Readiness Check

1. In a system of linear equations in two variables, if the graphs of the equations are the same, the equations are <u>dependent</u> equations.

2. Two or more linear equations are called a <u>system of linear equations</u>.

3. A system of equations that has at least one solution is called a <u>consistent</u> system.

4. A <u>solution</u> of a system of two equations in two variables is an ordered pair of numbers that is a solution of both equations in the system.

5. A system of equations that has no solution is called an <u>inconsistent</u> system.

6. In a system of linear equations in two variables, if the graphs of the equations are different, the equations are <u>independent</u> equations.

7. The lines intersect at (−1, 3); therefore there is one solution.

8. Since the lines are parallel and do not intersect, there is no solutions.

9. Since the lines are the same, there is an infinite number of solutions.

10. The lines intersect at (3, 4); therefore there is one solution.

Exercise Set 14.1

1. **a.** First equation:
    $x + y = 8$
    $2 + 4 \overset{?}{=} 8$
    $6 = 8$ False
    (2, 4) is not a solution of the first equation, so it is not a solution of the system.

    b. First equation:
    $x + y = 8$
    $5 + 3 \overset{?}{=} 8$
    $8 = 8$ True
    Second equation:
    $3x + 2y = 21$
    $3(5) + 2(3) \overset{?}{=} 21$
    $15 + 6 \overset{?}{=} 21$
    $21 = 21$ True
    Since (5, 3) is a solution of both equations, it is a solution of the system.

3. **a.** First equation:
    $3x - y = 5$
    $3(3) - 4 \overset{?}{=} 5$
    $9 - 4 \overset{?}{=} 5$
    $5 = 5$ True
    Second equation:
    $x + 2y = 11$
    $3 + 2(4) \overset{?}{=} 11$
    $3 + 8 \overset{?}{=} 11$
    $11 = 11$ True
    Since (3, 4) is a solution of both equations, it is a solution of the system.

b. First equation:
$$3x - y = 5$$
$$3(0) - (-5) \overset{?}{=} 5$$
$$0 + 5 \overset{?}{=} 5$$
$$5 = 5 \quad \text{True}$$
Second equation:
$$x + 2y = 11$$
$$0 + 2(-5) \overset{?}{=} 11$$
$$0 + (-10) \overset{?}{=} 11$$
$$-10 = 11 \quad \text{False}$$
$(0, -5)$ is not a solution of the second equation, so it is not a solution of the system.

5. a. First equation:
$$2y = 4x + 6$$
$$2(-3) \overset{?}{=} 4(-3) + 6$$
$$-6 \overset{?}{=} -12 + 6$$
$$-6 = -6 \quad \text{True}$$
Second equation:
$$2x - y = -3$$
$$2(-3) - (-3) \overset{?}{=} -3$$
$$-6 + 3 \overset{?}{=} -3$$
$$-3 = -3 \quad \text{True}$$
$(-3, -3)$ is a solution of both equations, it is a solution of the system.

b. First equation:
$$2y = 4x + 6$$
$$2(3) \overset{?}{=} 4(0) + 6$$
$$6 \overset{?}{=} 0 + 6$$
$$6 = 6 \quad \text{True}$$
Second equation:
$$2x - y = -3$$
$$2(0) - 3 \overset{?}{=} -3$$
$$0 - 3 \overset{?}{=} -3$$
$$-3 = -3 \quad \text{True}$$
Since $(0, 3)$ is a solution of both equations, it is a solution of the system.

7. a. First equation:
$$-2 = x - 7y$$
$$-2 \overset{?}{=} -2 - 7(0)$$
$$-2 \overset{?}{=} -2 - 0$$
$$-2 = -2 \quad \text{True}$$
Second equation:
$$6x - y = 13$$
$$6(-2) - 0 \overset{?}{=} 13$$
$$-12 - 0 \overset{?}{=} 13$$
$$-12 = 13 \quad \text{False}$$
$(-2, 0)$ is not a solution of the second equation, so it is not a solution of the system.

b. First equation:
$$-2 = x - 7y$$
$$-2 \overset{?}{=} \frac{1}{2} - 7\left(\frac{5}{14}\right)$$
$$-2 \overset{?}{=} \frac{1}{2} - \frac{5}{2}$$
$$-2 = -\frac{4}{2}$$
$$-2 = -2 \quad \text{True}$$
Second equation:
$$6x - y = 13$$
$$6\left(\frac{1}{2}\right) - \frac{5}{14} \overset{?}{=} 13$$
$$\frac{42}{14} - \frac{5}{14} \overset{?}{=} 13$$
$$\frac{37}{14} = 13 \quad \text{False}$$
$\left(\frac{1}{2}, \frac{5}{14}\right)$ is not a solution of the second equation, so it is not a solution of the system.

9.

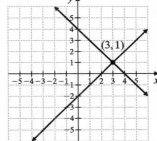

First equation:
$$x + y = 4$$
$$3 + 1 \overset{?}{=} 4$$
$$4 = 4 \quad \text{True}$$
Second equation:
$$x - y = 2$$
$$3 - 1 \overset{?}{=} 2$$
$$2 = 2 \quad \text{True}$$
The solution of the system is $(3, 1)$.

11.

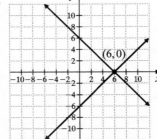

First equation:
$x + y = 6$
$6 + 0 \overset{?}{=} 6$
$\quad 6 = 6$ True
Second equation:
$-x + y = -6$
$-6 + 0 = -6$
$\quad\quad -6 = -6$ True
The solution of the system is (6, 0).

13.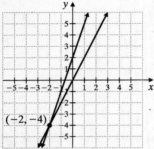

First equation:
$\quad y = 2x$
$-4 \overset{?}{=} 2(-2)$
$-4 = -4$ True
Second equation:
$\quad 3x - y = -2$
$3(-2) - (-4) \overset{?}{=} -2$
$\quad -6 + 4 \overset{?}{=} -2$
$\quad\quad -2 = -2$ True
The solution of the system is (−2, −4).

15.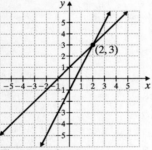

First equation:
$\quad y = x + 1$
$3 \overset{?}{=} 2 + 1$
$3 = 3$ True
Second equation:
$\quad y = 2x - 1$
$3 \overset{?}{=} 2(2) - 1$
$3 \overset{?}{=} 4 - 1$
$3 = 3$ True
The solution of the system is (2, 3).

17.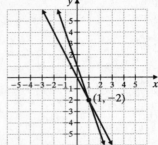

First equation:
$\quad 2x + y = 0$
$2(1) + (-2) \overset{?}{=} 0$
$\quad 2 - 2 \overset{?}{=} 0$
$\quad\quad 0 = 0$ True
Second equation:
$\quad 3x + y = 1$
$3(1) + (-2) \overset{?}{=} 1$
$\quad 3 - 2 \overset{?}{=} 1$
$\quad\quad 1 = 1$ True
The solution of the system is (1, −2).

19.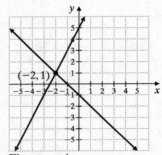

First equation:
$\quad y = -x - 1$
$1 \overset{?}{=} -(-2) - 1$
$1 \overset{?}{=} 2 - 1$
$1 = 1$ True
Second equation:
$\quad y = 2x + 5$
$1 \overset{?}{=} 2(-2) + 5$
$1 \overset{?}{=} -4 + 5$
$1 = 1$ True
The solution of the system is (−2, 1).

21.

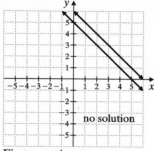

no solution

First equation:

$x + y = 5$

$y = -x + 5$

Second equation:

$x + y = 6$

$y = -x + 6$

The lines have the same slope, but different y-intercepts, so they are parallel. The system has no solution.

23.

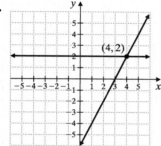

(4, 2)

First equation:

$2x - y = 6$

$2(4) - 2 \stackrel{?}{=} 6$

$8 - 2 \stackrel{?}{=} 6$

$6 = 6$ True

Second equation:

$y = 2$

$2 = 2$ True

The solution of the system is (4, 2).

25.

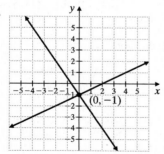

(0, −1)

First equation:

$x - 2y = 2$

$0 - 2(-1) \stackrel{?}{=} 2$

$0 + 2 \stackrel{?}{=} 2$

$2 = 2$ True

Second equation:

$3x + 2y = -2$

$3(0) + 2(-1) \stackrel{?}{=} -2$

$0 - 2 \stackrel{?}{=} -2$

$-2 = -2$ True

The solution of the system is (0, −1).

27.

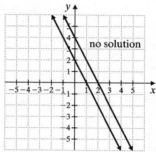

no solution

First equation:

$2x + y = 4$

$y = -2x + 4$

Second equation:

$6x = -3y + 6$

$3y = -6x + 6$

$y = -2x + 2$

The lines have the same slope, but different y-intercepts, so they are parallel. The system has no solution.

29.

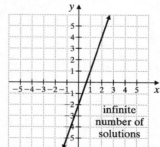

infinite number of solutions

First equation:

$y - 3x = -2$

$y = 3x - 2$

Second equation:

$6x - 2y = 4$

$-2y = -6x + 4$

$y = 3x - 2$

The graphs of the equations are the same line, so the system has an infinite number of solutions.

31.

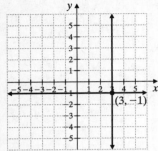

First equation:

$x = 3$

$3 = 3$ True

Second equation:

$y = -1$

$-1 = -1$ True

The solution of the system is $(3, -1)$.

33.

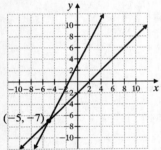

First equation:

$y = x - 2$

$-7 \stackrel{?}{=} -5 - 2$

$-7 = -7$ True

Second equation:

$y = 2x + 3$

$-7 \stackrel{?}{=} 2(-5) + 3$

$-7 \stackrel{?}{=} -10 + 3$

$-7 = -7$ True

The solution of the system is $(-5, -7)$.

35.

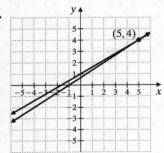

First equation:

$2x - 3y = -2$

$2(5) - 3(4) \stackrel{?}{=} -2$

$10 - 12 \stackrel{?}{=} -2$

$-2 = -2$ True

Second equation:

$-3x + 5y = 5$

$-3(5) + 5(4) \stackrel{?}{=} 5$

$-15 + 20 \stackrel{?}{=} 5$

$5 = 5$ True

The solution of the system is $(5, 4)$.

37.

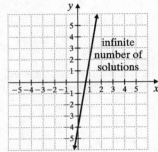

First equation:

$6x - y = 4$

$-y = -6x + 4$

$y = 6x - 4$

Second equation:

$\dfrac{1}{2}y = -2 + 3x$

$y = -4 + 6x$

$y = 6x - 4$

The graphs of the equations are the same line, so the system has an infinite number of solutions.

39. $4x + y = 24$ $x + 2y = 2$

$ y = -4x + 24$ $2y = -x + 2$

$ y = -\dfrac{1}{2}x + 1$

a.   The slopes of the lines are different, so the lines intersect.

b.   The system has one solution.

41. $2x + y = 0$ $2y = 6 - 4x$

$ y = -2x$ $ y = -2x + 3$

a.   The lines have the same slope, but different y-intercepts, so the lines are parallel.

b.   The system has no solution.

43. $6x - y = 4$ $\dfrac{1}{2}y = -2 + 3x$
    $6x - 4 = y$
                                   $y = 6x - 4$

a.   The lines are identical.

b.   The system has an infinite number of solutions.

45. $x = 5$ $y = -2$
    vertical line   horizontal line

a.   The slopes of the lines are different, so the lines intersect.

b.   The system has one solution.

47. $3y - 2x = 3$ $x + 2y = 9$
    $3y = 2x + 3$ $2y = -x + 9$
    $y = \dfrac{2}{3}x + 1$ $y = -\dfrac{1}{2}x + \dfrac{9}{2}$

a.   The slopes of the lines are different, so the lines intersect.

b.   The system has one solution.

49. $6y + 4x = 6$ $3y - 3 = -2x$
    $6y = -4x + 6$ $3y = -2x + 3$
    $y = -\dfrac{2}{3}x + 1$ $y = -\dfrac{2}{3}x + 1$

a.   The lines are identical.

b.   The system has an infinite number of solutions.

51. $x + y = 4$ $x + y = 3$
    $y = -x + 4$ $y = -x + 3$

a.   The lines have the same slope, but different y-intercepts, so the lines are parallel.

b.   The system has no solution.

53. $5(x - 3) + 3x = 1$
    $5x - 15 + 3x = 1$
            $8x = 16$
             $x = 2$

55. $4\left(\dfrac{y+1}{2}\right) + 3y = 0$
    $2(y + 1) + 3y = 0$
    $2y + 2 + 3y = 0$
        $5y + 2 = 0$
          $5y = -2$
           $y = -\dfrac{2}{5}$

57. $8a - 2(3a - 1) = 6$
    $8a - 6a + 2 = 6$
          $2a = 4$
           $a = 2$

59. Answers may vary. Possible answer:

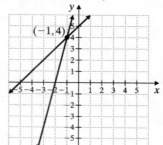

61. Answers may vary. Possible answer:

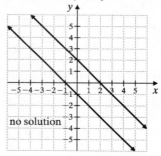

63. The lines cross at a point between 1988 and 1989, and again between 2001 and 2002. The number of pounds of imported fishery products was equal to the domestic catch between 1988 and 1989, and also between 2001 and 2002.

65. The average attendance per game for the Texas Rangers was greater than the average attendance per game for the Minnesota Twins in 2004, 2005, 2006, 2007, and 2008.

67. answers may vary

69. answers may vary

71. a. (4, 9) appears in both tables, so it is a
solution of the system.

b.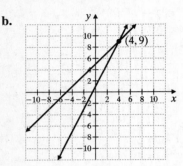

c. Yes; the two lines intersect at (4, 9).

Section 14.2

Practice Problems

1. $\begin{cases} 2x+3y=13 \\ x=y+4 \end{cases}$

Substitute $y + 4$ for x in the first equation and
solve for y.
$$2(y+4)+3y=13$$
$$2y+8+3y=13$$
$$5y=5$$
$$y=1$$
Solve for x.
$$x=y+4=1+4=5$$
The solution of the system is (5, 1).

2. $\begin{cases} 4x-y=2 \\ y=5x \end{cases}$

Substitute $5x$ for y in the first equation and solve
for x.
$$4x-5x=2$$
$$-x=2$$
$$x=-2$$
Solve for y.
$$y=5x=5(-2)=-10$$
The solution of the system is (−2, −10).

3. $\begin{cases} 3x+y=5 \\ 3x-2y=-7 \end{cases}$

Solve the first equation for y.
$$3x+y=5$$
$$y=-3x+5$$
Substitute $-3x + 5$ for y in the second equation.

$$3x-2y=-7$$
$$3x-2(-3x+5)=-7$$
$$3x+6x-10=-7$$
$$9x=3$$
$$x=\frac{3}{9}=\frac{1}{3}$$
Solve for y.
$$y=-3x+5=-3\left(\frac{1}{3}\right)+5=-1+5=4$$
The solution of the system is $\left(\frac{1}{3},\ 4\right)$.

4. $\begin{cases} 5x-2y=6 \\ -3x+y=-3 \end{cases}$

Solve the second equation for y.
$$-3x+y=-3$$
$$y=3x-3$$
Substitute $3x - 3$ for y in the first equation.
$$5x-2y=6$$
$$5x-2(3x-3)=6$$
$$5x-6x+6=6$$
$$-x=0$$
$$x=0$$
Solve for y.
$$y=3x-3=3(0)-3=0-3=-3$$
The solution of the system is (0, −3).

5. $\begin{cases} -x+3y=6 \\ y=\dfrac{1}{3}x+2 \end{cases}$

Substitute $\dfrac{1}{3}x+2$ for y in the first equation.
$$-x+3y=6$$
$$-x+3\left(\frac{1}{3}x+2\right)=6$$
$$-x+x+6=6$$
$$0x=0$$
$$0=0$$
The statement $0 = 0$ indicates that this system
has an infinite number of solutions. It is a graph
of the same line.

6. $\begin{cases} 2x-3y=6 \\ -4x+6y=12 \end{cases}$
$$2x-3y=6$$
$$-3y=-2x+6$$
$$y=\frac{2}{3}x-2$$

Substitute $\frac{2}{3}x - 2$ for y in the second equation.

$$-4x + 6y = 12$$
$$-4x + 6\left(\frac{2}{3}x - 2\right) = 12$$
$$-4x + 4x - 12 = 12$$
$$-12 = 12$$

The statement $-12 = 12$ indicates that this system has no solution. It is a graph of parallel lines.

Vocabulary and Readiness Check

1. $x = 1$: $y = 4(1) = 4$
   The solution is $(1, 4)$.

2. $0 = 34$ is a false statement. The system has no solution.

3. $0 = 0$ is a true statement. The system has an infinite number of solutions.

4. $y = 0$: $x = 0 + 5 = 5$
   The solution is $(5, 0)$.

5. $x = 0$: $0 + y = 0$
   $$y = 0$$
   The solution is $(0, 0)$.

6. $0 = 0$ is a true statement. The system has an infinite number of solutions.

Exercise Set 14.2

1. $\begin{cases} x + y = 3 \\ x = 2y \end{cases}$

   Substitute $2y$ for x in the first equation and solve for y.
   $$x + y = 3$$
   $$2y + y = 3$$
   $$3y = 3$$
   $$y = 1$$
   Now solve for x.
   $x = 2y = 2(1) = 2$
   The solution of the system is $(2, 1)$.

3. $\begin{cases} x + y = 6 \\ y = -3x \end{cases}$

   Substitute $-3x$ for y in the first equation and solve for x.
   $$x + y = 6$$
   $$x + (-3x) = 6$$
   $$-2x = 6$$
   $$x = -3$$

Now solve for y.
$y = -3x = -3(-3) = 9$
The solution of the system is $(-3, 9)$.

5. $\begin{cases} y = 3x + 1 \\ 4y - 8x = 12 \end{cases}$

   Substitute $3x + 1$ for y in the second equation and solve for x.
   $$4y - 8x = 12$$
   $$4(3x + 1) - 8x = 12$$
   $$12x + 4 - 8x = 12$$
   $$4x + 4 = 12$$
   $$4x = 8$$
   $$x = 2$$
   Now solve for y.
   $y = 3x + 1 = 3(2) + 1 = 6 + 1 = 7$
   The solution of the system is $(2, 7)$.

7. $\begin{cases} y = 2x + 9 \\ y = 7x + 10 \end{cases}$

   Substitute $2x + 9$ for y in the second equation and solve for x.
   $$y = 7x + 10$$
   $$2x + 9 = 7x + 10$$
   $$-5x = 1$$
   $$y = -\frac{1}{5}$$
   Now solve for y.
   $$y = 2x + 9 = 2\left(-\frac{1}{5}\right) + 9 = \frac{-2}{5} + \frac{45}{5} = \frac{43}{5}$$
   The solution of the system is $\left(-\frac{1}{5}, \frac{43}{5}\right)$.

9. $\begin{cases} 3x - 4y = 10 \\ y = x - 3 \end{cases}$

   Substitute $x - 3$ for y in the first equation and solve for x.
   $$3x - 4y = 10$$
   $$3x - 4(x - 3) = 10$$
   $$3x - 4x + 12 = 10$$
   $$-x + 12 = 10$$
   $$-x = -2$$
   $$x = 2$$
   Now solve for y.
   $y = x - 3 = 2 - 3 = -1$
   The solution of the system is $(2, -1)$.

11. $\begin{cases} x+2y=6 \\ 2x+3y=8 \end{cases}$

Solve the first equation for x.

$x+2y=6$

$\quad x=-2y+6$

Substitute $-2y+6$ for x in the second equation and solve for y.

$2x+3y=8$

$2(-2y+6)+3y=8$

$-4y+12+3y=8$

$\quad\quad\quad -y=-4$

$\quad\quad\quad\quad y=4$

Now solve for x.

$x=-2y+6=-2(4)+6=-8+6=-2$

The solution of the system is $(-2, 4)$.

13. $\begin{cases} 3x+2y=16 \\ x=3y-2 \end{cases}$

Substitute $3y-2$ for x in the first equation and solve for y.

$3x+2y=16$

$3(3y-2)+2y=16$

$9y-6+2y=16$

$11y-6=16$

$11y=22$

$y=2$

Now solve for x.

$x=3y-2=3(2)-2=6-2=4$

The solution of the system is $(4, 2)$.

15. $\begin{cases} 2x-5y=1 \\ 3x+y=-7 \end{cases}$

Solve the second equation for y.

$3x+y=-7$

$\quad y=-3x-7$

Substitute $-3x-7$ for y in the first equation and solve for y.

$2x-5y=1$

$2x-5(-3x-7)=1$

$2x+15x+35=1$

$17x=-34$

$x=-2$

Now solve for y.

$y=-3x-7=-3(-2)-7=6-7=-1$

The solution of the system is $(-2, -1)$.

17. $\begin{cases} 4x+2y=5 \\ -2x=y+4 \end{cases}$

Solve the second equation for x.

$-2x=y+4$

$x=-\dfrac{1}{2}y-2$

Substitute $-\dfrac{1}{2}y-2$ for x in the first equation and solve for y.

$4x+2y=5$

$4\left(-\dfrac{1}{2}y-2\right)+2y=5$

$-2y-8+2y=5$

$-8=5$ False

Since the statement $-8=5$ is false, the system has no solution.

19. $\begin{cases} 4x+y=11 \\ 2x+5y=1 \end{cases}$

Solve the first equation for y.

$4x+y=11$

$\quad y=-4x+11$

Substitute $-4x+11$ for y in the second equation and solve for y.

$2x+5y=1$

$2x+5(-4x+11)=1$

$2x+(-20x)+55=1$

$-18x=-54$

$x=3$

Now solve for y.

$y=-4x+11=-4(3)+11=-12+11=-1$

The solution of the system is $(3, -1)$.

21. $\begin{cases} x+2y+5=-4+5y-x \\ 2x+x=y+4 \end{cases}$

Simplify each equation.

$\begin{cases} 2x+9=3y \\ 3x=y+4 \end{cases}$

Solve the second simplified equation for y.

$3x=y+4$

$3x-4=y$

Substitute $3x-4$ for y in the first simplified equation and solve for x.

$2x+9=3y$

$2x+9=3(3x-4)$

$2x+9=9x-12$

$2x+21=9x$

$21=7x$

$3=x$

Now solve for y.

$y=3x-4=3(3)-4=9-4=5$

The solution of the system is $(3, 5)$.

23. $\begin{cases} 6x - 3y = 5 \\ x + 2y = 0 \end{cases}$

Solve the second equation for x.

$x + 2y = 0$

$\quad x = -2y$

Substitute $-2y$ for x in the first equation and solve for y.

$6x - 3y = 5$

$6(-2y) - 3y = 5$

$\quad -12y - 3y = 5$

$\quad\quad -15y = 5$

$\quad\quad y = -\dfrac{5}{15} = -\dfrac{1}{3}$

Now solve for x.

$x = -2y = -2\left(-\dfrac{1}{3}\right) = \dfrac{2}{3}$

The solution of the system is $\left(\dfrac{2}{3}, -\dfrac{1}{3}\right)$.

25. $\begin{cases} 3x - y = 1 \\ 2x - 3y = 10 \end{cases}$

Solve the first equation for y.

$3x - y = 1$

$\quad -y = -3x + 1$

$\quad y = 3x - 1$

Substitute $3x - 1$ for y in the second equation and solve for x.

$2x - 3y = 10$

$2x - 3(3x - 1) = 10$

$2x - 9x + 3 = 10$

$\quad -7x + 3 = 10$

$\quad\quad -7x = 7$

$\quad\quad x = -1$

Now solve for y.

$y = 3x - 1 = 3(-1) - 1 = -3 - 1 = -4$

The solution of the system is $(-1, -4)$.

27. $\begin{cases} -x + 2y = 10 \\ -2x + 3y = 18 \end{cases}$

Solve the first equation for x.

$-x + 2y = 10$

$\quad 2y - 10 = x$

Substitute $2y - 10$ for x in the second equation and solve for y.

$-2x + 3y = 18$

$-2(2y - 10) + 3y = 18$

$\quad -4y + 20 + 3y = 18$

$\quad\quad -y + 20 = 18$

$\quad\quad\quad 2 = y$

Now solve for x.

$x = 2y - 10 = 2(2) - 10 = 4 - 10 = -6$

The solution of the system is $(-6, 2)$.

29. $\begin{cases} 5x + 10y = 20 \\ 2x + 6y = 10 \end{cases}$

Solve the first equation for x. (Note that the second equation could also be easily solved for x.)

$5x + 10y = 20$

$\quad 5x = -10y + 20$

$\quad x = -2y + 4$

Substitute $-2y + 4$ for x in the second equation and solve for y.

$2x + 6y = 10$

$2(-2y + 4) + 6y = 10$

$\quad -4y + 8 + 6y = 10$

$\quad\quad 2y + 8 = 10$

$\quad\quad 2y = 2$

$\quad\quad y = 1$

Now solve for x.

$x = -2y + 4 = -2(1) + 4 = -2 + 4 = 2$

The solution of the system is $(2, 1)$.

31. $\begin{cases} 3x + 6y = 9 \\ 4x + 8y = 16 \end{cases}$

Solve the first equation for x.

$3x + 6y = 9$

$\quad 3x = -6y + 9$

$\quad x = -2y + 3$

Substitute $-2y + 3$ for x in the second equation and solve for y.

$4x + 8y = 16$

$4(-2y + 3) + 8y = 16$

$\quad -8y + 12 + 8y = 16$

$\quad\quad 0 = 4 \quad$ False

Since the statement $0 = 4$ is false, the system has no solution.

33. $\begin{cases} \dfrac{1}{3}x - y = 2 \\ x - 3y = 6 \end{cases}$

Solve the second equation for x.

$x - 3y = 6$

$\quad x = 3y + 6$

Substitute $3y + 6$ for x in the first equation and solve for y.

$$\frac{1}{3}x - y = 2$$

$$\frac{1}{3}(3y + 6) - y = 2$$

$$y + 2 - y = 2$$

$$2 = 2$$

Since 2 = 2 is a true statement, the two equations in the original system are equivalent. The system has an infinite number of solutions.

35. $\begin{cases} x = \dfrac{3}{4}y - 1 \\ 8x - 5y = -6 \end{cases}$

Substitute $\dfrac{3}{4}y - 1$ for x in the second equation

and solve for y.

$$8x - 5y = -6$$

$$8\left(\frac{3}{4}y - 1\right) - 5y = -6$$

$$6y - 8 - 5y = -6$$

$$y = 2$$

Now solve for x.

$$x = \frac{3}{4}y - 1 = \frac{3}{4}(2) - 1 = \frac{3}{2} - 1 = \frac{1}{2}$$

The solution of the system is $\left(\dfrac{1}{2}, 2\right)$.

37.
$$3x + 2y = 6$$
$$-2(3x + 2y) = -2(6)$$
$$-6x - 4y = -12$$

39.
$$-4x + y = 3$$
$$3(-4x + y) = 3(3)$$
$$-12x + 3y = 9$$

41.
$$\begin{array}{r} 3n + 6m \\ +\ 2n - 6m \\ \hline 5n \end{array}$$

43.
$$\begin{array}{r} -5a - 7b \\ 5a - 8b \\ \hline -15b \end{array}$$

45. $\begin{cases} -5y + 6y = 3x + 2(x - 5) - 3x + 5 \\ 4(x + y) - x + y = -12 \end{cases}$

Simplify each equation.

$$\begin{cases} y = 2x - 5 \\ 3x + 5y = -12 \end{cases}$$

Substitute $2x - 5$ for y in the second simplified equation and solve for x.

$$3x + 5y = -12$$
$$3x + 5(2x - 5) = -12$$
$$3x + 10x - 25 = -12$$
$$13x - 25 = -12$$
$$13x = 13$$
$$x = 1$$

Now solve for y.

$$y = 2x - 5 = 2(1) - 5 = 2 - 5 = -3$$

The solution of the system is $(1, -3)$.

47. answers may vary

49. no; answers may vary

51. c; answers may vary

53. Using a graphing calculator, the solution of the system is $(-2.6, 1.3)$.

55. Using a graphing calculator, the solution of the system is $(3.28, 2.1)$.

57. a. $\begin{cases} y = -1.1x + 7.1 \\ y = 1.9x + 4.7 \end{cases}$

Substitute $-1.1x + 7.1$ for y in the second equation and solve for x.

$$y = 1.9x + 4.7$$
$$-1.1x + 7.1 = 1.9x + 4.7$$
$$-1.1x + 2.4 = 1.9x$$
$$2.4 = 3x$$
$$0.8 = x$$

Now solve for y.

$$y = -1.1x + 7.1$$
$$= -1.1(0.8) + 7.1$$
$$= -0.88 + 7.1$$
$$= 6.22$$
$$\approx 6$$

The rounded solution is $(0.8, 6)$.

b. In about 0.8 year after 2000, the sales of DVD and VHS units were both approximately \$6 billion.

c.

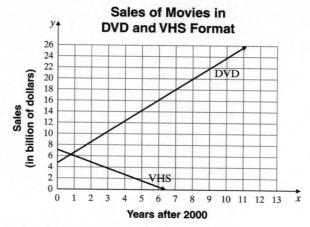

Sales of Movies in DVD and VHS Format

(Note: Not enough BluRay years of data to include in graph.)
answers may vary

d. 2007 corresponds to $x = 7$.
$x = 7$: $y = -1.1(7) + 7.1 = -7.7 + 7.1 = -0.6$
answers may vary

Section 14.3

Practice Problems

1. $\begin{cases} x + y = 13 \\ x - y = 5 \end{cases}$

Add the equations to eliminate y; then solve for x.

$\begin{aligned} x + y &= 13 \\ \underline{x - y} &= \underline{5} \\ 2x\phantom{{}+y} &= 18 \\ x\phantom{{}+y} &= 9 \end{aligned}$

Now solve for y.
$x + y = 13$
$9 + y = 13$
$\phantom{9 +{}} y = 4$

The solution of the system is $(9, 4)$.

2. $\begin{cases} 2x - y = -6 \\ -x + 4y = 17 \end{cases}$

Multiply the first equation by 4.

$\begin{cases} 4(2x - y) = 4(-6) \\ -x + 4y = 17 \end{cases} \Rightarrow \begin{cases} 8x - 4y = -24 \\ -x + 4y = 17 \end{cases}$

Add the equations to eliminate y; then solve for x.

$\begin{aligned} 8x - 4y &= -24 \\ \underline{-x + 4y} &= \underline{17} \\ 7x\phantom{{}+4y} &= -7 \\ x\phantom{{}+4y} &= -1 \end{aligned}$

Now solve for y.

$$2x - y = -6$$
$$2(-1) - y = -6$$
$$-2 - y = -6$$
$$-y = -4$$
$$y = 4$$

The solution of the system is $(-1, 4)$.

3. $\begin{cases} x - 3y = -2 \\ -3x + 9y = 5 \end{cases}$

Multiply the first equation by 3.

$\begin{cases} 3(x - 3y) = 3(-2) \\ -3x + 9y = 5 \end{cases}$ $\Rightarrow$ $\begin{cases} 3x - 9y = -6 \\ -3x + 9y = 5 \end{cases}$

Add the equations to eliminate y; then solve for x.

$$\begin{array}{r} 3x - 9y = -6 \\ -3x + 9y = 5 \\ \hline 0 = -1 \end{array}$$

Since the statement $0 = -1$ is false, there is no solution to the system.

4. $\begin{cases} 2x + 5y = 1 \\ -4x - 10y = -2 \end{cases}$

Multiply the first equation by 2.

$\begin{cases} 2(2x + 5y) = 2(1) \\ -4x - 10y = -2 \end{cases}$ $\Rightarrow$ $\begin{cases} 4x + 10y = 2 \\ -4x - 10y = -2 \end{cases}$

Add the equations to eliminate y; then solve for x.

$$\begin{array}{r} 4x + 10y = 2 \\ -4x - 10y = -2 \\ \hline 0 = 0 \end{array}$$

Since the statement $0 = 0$ is true, there are an infinite number of solutions.

5. $\begin{cases} 4x + 5y = 14 \\ 3x - 2y = -1 \end{cases}$

Multiply the first equation by 2 and multiply the second equation by 5.

$\begin{cases} 2(4x + 5y) = 2(14) \\ 5(3x - 2y) = 5(-1) \end{cases}$ $\Rightarrow$ $\begin{cases} 8x + 10y = 28 \\ 15x - 10y = -5 \end{cases}$

Add the equations to eliminate y; then solve for x.

$$\begin{array}{r} 8x + 10y = 28 \\ 15x - 10y = -5 \\ \hline 23x = 23 \\ x = 1 \end{array}$$

Now solve for y.

$$4x + 5y = 14$$
$$4(1) + 5y = 14$$
$$5y = 10$$
$$y = 2$$

The solution of the system is $(1, 2)$.

6. $\begin{cases} -\dfrac{x}{3} + y = \dfrac{4}{3} \\ \dfrac{x}{2} - \dfrac{5}{2}y = -\dfrac{1}{2} \end{cases}$

Multiply the first equation by 3 and the second equation by 2.

$\begin{cases} 3\left(-\dfrac{x}{3} + y\right) = 3\left(\dfrac{4}{3}\right) \\ 2\left(\dfrac{x}{2} - \dfrac{5}{2}y\right) = 2\left(-\dfrac{1}{2}\right) \end{cases}$ $\Rightarrow$ $\begin{cases} -x + 3y = 4 \\ x - 5y = -1 \end{cases}$

Add the equations to eliminate x; then solve for y.

$$\begin{array}{r} -x + 3y = 4 \\ x - 5y = -1 \\ \hline -2y = 3 \\ y = -\dfrac{3}{2} \end{array}$$

Now solve for y through elimination. Multiply the first equation by 15 and the second equation by 6.

$\begin{cases} 15\left(-\dfrac{x}{3} + y\right) = 15\left(\dfrac{4}{3}\right) \\ 6\left(\dfrac{x}{2} - \dfrac{5}{2}y\right) = 6\left(-\dfrac{1}{2}\right) \end{cases}$ $\Rightarrow$ $\begin{cases} -5x + 15y = 20 \\ 3x - 15y = -3 \end{cases}$

Add the equations to eliminate y; then solve for x.

$$\begin{array}{r} -5x + 15y = 20 \\ 3x - 15y = -3 \\ \hline -2x = 17 \\ x = -\dfrac{17}{2} \end{array}$$

The solution to the system is $\left(-\dfrac{17}{2}, -\dfrac{3}{2}\right)$.

Vocabulary and Readiness Check

1. $\begin{cases} 3x - 2y = -9 \\ x + 5y = 14 \end{cases}$

Multiply the second equation by -3, then add the resulting equations.

$$\begin{array}{r} 3x - 2y = -9 \\ -3x - 15y = -42 \\ \hline -17y = -51 \end{array}$$

The y's are not eliminated; the statement is false.

2. $\begin{cases} 3x - 2y = -9 \\ x + 5y = 14 \end{cases}$

Multiply the second equation by –3, then add the resulting equations.

$$3x - 2y = -9$$
$$\underline{-3x - 15y = -42}$$
$$-17y = -51$$

The statement is true.

3. $\begin{cases} 3x - 2y = -9 \\ x + 5y = 14 \end{cases}$

Multiply the first equation by 5 and the second equation by 2, then add the two new equations.

$$15x - 10y = -45$$
$$\underline{2x + 10y = \;\; 28}$$
$$17x \qquad = -17$$

The statement is true.

4. $\begin{cases} 3x - 2y = -9 \\ x + 5y = 14 \end{cases}$

Multiply the first equation by 5 and the second equation by –2, then add the two new equations.

$$15x - 10y = -45$$
$$\underline{-2x - 10y = -28}$$
$$13x - 20y = -73$$

The y's are not eliminated; the statement is false.

Exercise Set 14.3

1. $\begin{cases} 3x + y = 5 \\ 6x - y = 4 \end{cases}$

Add the equations to eliminate y; then solve for x.

$$3x + y = 5$$
$$\underline{6x - y = 4}$$
$$9x \quad = 9$$
$$x = 1$$

Now solve for y.

$$3x + y = 5$$
$$3(1) + y = 5$$
$$3 + y = 5$$
$$y = 2$$

The solution of the system is (1, 2).

3. $\begin{cases} x - 2y = 8 \\ -x + 5y = -17 \end{cases}$

Add the equations to eliminate x; then solve for y.

$$x - 2y = 8$$
$$\underline{-x + 5y = -17}$$
$$3y = -9$$
$$y = -3$$

Now solve for x.

$$x - 2y = 8$$
$$x - 2(-3) = 8$$
$$x + 6 = 8$$
$$x = 2$$

The solution of the system is (2, –3).

5. $\begin{cases} 3x + y = -11 \\ 6x - 2y = -2 \end{cases}$

Multiply the first equation by 2.

$$\begin{cases} 2(3x + y) = 2(-11) \\ 6x - 2y = -2 \end{cases} \rightarrow \begin{cases} 6x + 2y = -22 \\ 6x - 2y = -2 \end{cases}$$

Add the equations to eliminate y; then solve for x.

$$6x + 2y = -22$$
$$\underline{6x - 2y = -2}$$
$$12x \qquad = -24$$
$$x = -2$$

Now solve for y.

$$3x + y = -11$$
$$3(-2) + y = -11$$
$$-6 + y = -11$$
$$y = -5$$

The solution of the system is (–2, –5).

7. $\begin{cases} 3x + 2y = 11 \\ 5x - 2y = 29 \end{cases}$

Add the equations to eliminate y; then solve for x.

$$3x + 2y = 11$$
$$\underline{5x - 2y = 29}$$
$$8x = 40$$
$$x = 5$$

Now solve for y.

$$3x + 2y = 11$$
$$3(5) + 2y = 11$$
$$15 + 2y = 11$$
$$2y = -4$$
$$y = -2$$

The solution of the system is (5, –2).

9. $\begin{cases} x + 5y = 18 \\ 3x + 2y = -11 \end{cases}$

Multiply the first equation by –3.

$$\begin{cases} -3(x + 5y) = -3(18) \\ 3x + 2y = -11 \end{cases} \rightarrow \begin{cases} -3x - 15y = -54 \\ 3x + 2y = -11 \end{cases}$$

Add the equations to eliminate x; then solve for y.

$$-3x - 15y = -54$$
$$\underline{3x + 2y = -11}$$
$$-13y = -65$$
$$y = 5$$

Now solve for x.

$$x + 5y = 18$$
$$x + 5(5) = 18$$
$$x + 25 = 18$$
$$x = -7$$

The solution of the system is $(-7, 5)$.

11. $\begin{cases} x + y = 6 \\ x - y = 6 \end{cases}$

Add the equations to eliminate y; then solve for x.

$$x + y = 6$$
$$\underline{x - y = 6}$$
$$2x = 12$$
$$x = 6$$

Now solve for y.

$$x + y = 6$$
$$6 + y = 6$$
$$y = 0$$

The solution of the system is $(6, 0)$.

13. $\begin{cases} 2x + 3y = 0 \\ 4x + 6y = 3 \end{cases}$

Multiply the first equation by -2.

$$\begin{cases} -2(2x + 3y) = -2(0) \\ 4x + 6y = 3 \end{cases} \rightarrow \begin{cases} -4x - 6y = 0 \\ 4x + 6y = 3 \end{cases}$$

Add the equations to eliminate x.

$$-4x - 6y = 0$$
$$\underline{4x + 6y = 3}$$
$$0 = 3$$

Since the statement $0 = 3$ is false, the system has no solution.

15. $\begin{cases} -x + 5y = -1 \\ 3x - 15y = 3 \end{cases}$

Multiply the first equation by 3.

$$\begin{cases} 3(-x + 5y) = 3(-1) \\ 3x - 15y = 3 \end{cases} \rightarrow \begin{cases} -3x + 15y = -3 \\ 3x - 15y = 3 \end{cases}$$

Add the equations to eliminate x.

$$-3x + 15y = -3$$
$$\underline{3x - 15y = 3}$$
$$0 = 0$$

Since the statement $0 = 0$ is true, the system has an infinite number of solutions.

17. $\begin{cases} 3x - 2y = 7 \\ 5x + 4y = 8 \end{cases}$

Multiply the first equation by 2.

$$\begin{cases} 2(3x - 2y) = 2(7) \\ 5x + 4y = 8 \end{cases} \rightarrow \begin{cases} 6x - 4y = 14 \\ 5x + 4y = 8 \end{cases}$$

Add the equations to eliminate y; then solve for x.

$$6x - 4y = 14$$
$$\underline{5x + 4y = 8}$$
$$11x = 22$$
$$x = 2$$

Now solve for y.

$$3x - 2y = 7$$
$$3(2) - 2y = 7$$
$$6 - 2y = 7$$
$$-2y = 1$$
$$y = -\frac{1}{2}$$

The solution of the system is $\left(2, -\frac{1}{2}\right)$.

19. $\begin{cases} 8x = -11y - 16 \\ 2x + 3y = -4 \end{cases} \rightarrow \begin{cases} 8x + 11y = -16 \\ 2x + 3y = -4 \end{cases}$

Multiply the second equation by -4.

$$\begin{cases} 8x + 11y = -16 \\ -4(2x + 3y) = -4(-4) \end{cases} \rightarrow \begin{cases} 8x + 11y = -16 \\ -8x - 12y = 16 \end{cases}$$

Add the equations to eliminate x; then solve for y.

$$8x + 11y = -16$$
$$\underline{-8x - 12y = 16}$$
$$-y = 0$$
$$y = 0$$

Now solve for x.

$$8x + 11y = -16$$
$$8x + 11(0) = -16$$
$$8x = -16$$
$$x = -2$$

The solution of the system is $(-2, 0)$.

21. $\begin{cases} 4x - 3y = 7 \\ 7x + 5y = 2 \end{cases}$

Multiply the first equation by 5 and the second equation by 3.

$$\begin{cases} 5(4x - 3y) = 5(7) \\ 3(7x + 5y) = 3(2) \end{cases} \rightarrow \begin{cases} 20x - 15y = 35 \\ 21x + 15y = 6 \end{cases}$$

Add the equations to eliminate y; then solve for x.

$$20x - 15y = 35$$
$$\underline{21x + 15y = 6}$$
$$41x \qquad = 41$$
$$\qquad x = 1$$

Now solve for y.

$$4x - 3y = 7$$
$$4(1) - 3y = 7$$
$$4 - 3y = 7$$
$$-3y = 3$$
$$y = -1$$

The solution of the system is $(1, -1)$.

23. $\begin{cases} 4x - 6y = 8 \\ 6x - 9y = 12 \end{cases}$

Multiply the first equation by -3 and the second equation by 2.

$$\begin{cases} -3(4x - 6y) = -3(8) \\ 2(6x - 9y) = 2(12) \end{cases} \rightarrow \begin{cases} -12x + 18y = -24 \\ 12x - 18y = 24 \end{cases}$$

Add the equations to eliminate x.

$$-12x + 18y = -24$$
$$\underline{12x - 18y = 24}$$
$$0 = 0$$

Since the statement $0 = 0$ is true, the system has an infinite number of solutions.

25. $\begin{cases} 2x - 5y = 4 \\ 3x - 2y = 4 \end{cases}$

Multiply the first equation by -3 and the second equation by 2.

$$\begin{cases} -3(2x - 5y) = -3(4) \\ 2(3x - 2y) = 2(4) \end{cases} \rightarrow \begin{cases} -6x + 15y = -12 \\ 6x - 4y = 8 \end{cases}$$

Add the equations to eliminate x; then solve for y.

$$-6x + 15y = -12$$
$$\underline{6x - 4y = 8}$$
$$11y = -4$$
$$y = -\frac{4}{11}$$

Multiply the first original equation by -2 and the second original equation by 5.

$$\begin{cases} -2(2x - 5y) = -2(4) \\ 5(3x - 2y) = 5(4) \end{cases} \rightarrow \begin{cases} -4x + 10y = -8 \\ 15x - 10y = 20 \end{cases}$$

Add the equations to eliminate y; then solve for x.

$$-4x + 10y = -8$$
$$\underline{15x - 10y = 20}$$
$$11x \qquad = 12$$
$$x = \frac{12}{11}$$

The solution of the system is $\left(\dfrac{12}{11}, -\dfrac{4}{11}\right)$.

27. $\begin{cases} \dfrac{x}{3} + \dfrac{y}{6} = 1 \\ \dfrac{x}{2} - \dfrac{y}{4} = 0 \end{cases}$

Multiply the first equation by 6 and the second equation by 4.

$$\begin{cases} 6\left(\dfrac{x}{3} + \dfrac{y}{6}\right) = 6(1) \\ 4\left(\dfrac{x}{2} - \dfrac{y}{4}\right) = 4(0) \end{cases} \rightarrow \begin{cases} 2x + y = 6 \\ 2x - y = 0 \end{cases}$$

Add the equations to eliminate y; then solve for x.

$$2x + y = 6$$
$$\underline{2x - y = 0}$$
$$4x = 6$$
$$x = \frac{6}{4} = \frac{3}{2}$$

Multiply the original first equation by 6 and the second original equation by -4.

$$\begin{cases} 6\left(\dfrac{x}{3} + \dfrac{y}{6}\right) = 6(1) \\ -4\left(\dfrac{x}{2} - \dfrac{y}{4}\right) = -4(0) \end{cases} \rightarrow \begin{cases} 2x + y = 6 \\ -2x + y = 0 \end{cases}$$

Add the equations to eliminate x; then solve for y.

$$2x + y = 6$$
$$\underline{-2x + y = 0}$$
$$2y = 6$$
$$y = 3$$

The solution of the system is $\left(\dfrac{3}{2}, 3\right)$.

29. $\begin{cases} \dfrac{10}{3}x + 4y = -4 \\ 5x + 6y = -6 \end{cases}$

Multiply the first equation by 3 and the second equation by -2.

$$\begin{cases} 3\left(\dfrac{10}{3}x + 4y\right) = 3(-4) \\ -2(5x + 6y) = -2(-6) \end{cases} \rightarrow \begin{cases} 10x + 12y = -12 \\ -10x - 12y = 12 \end{cases}$$

Add the equations to eliminate x.

$$10x + 12y = -12$$
$$\underline{-10x - 12y = 12}$$
$$0 = 0$$

Since the statement $0 = 0$ is true, the system has an infinite number of solutions.

31. $\begin{cases} x - \dfrac{y}{3} = -1 \\ -\dfrac{x}{2} + \dfrac{y}{8} = \dfrac{1}{4} \end{cases}$

Multiply the first equation by 3 and the second equation by 8.

$\begin{cases} 3\left(x - \dfrac{y}{3}\right) = 3(-1) \\ 8\left(-\dfrac{x}{2} + \dfrac{y}{8}\right) = 8\left(\dfrac{1}{4}\right) \end{cases} \rightarrow \begin{cases} 3x - y = -3 \\ -4x + y = 2 \end{cases}$

Add the equations to eliminate y; then solve for x.

$\begin{array}{r} 3x - y = -3 \\ -4x + y = 2 \\ \hline -x = -1 \\ x = 1 \end{array}$

Now solve for y.

$x - \dfrac{y}{3} = -1$

$1 - \dfrac{y}{3} = -1$

$-\dfrac{y}{3} = -2$

$y = 6$

The solution of the system is $(1, 6)$.

33. $\begin{cases} -4(x + 2) = 3y \\ 2x - 2y = 3 \end{cases}$

Rewrite the first equation.

$-4(x + 2) = 3y$

$-4x - 8 = 3y$

$-4x = 3y + 8$

$-4x - 3y = 8$

$\begin{cases} -4x - 3y = 8 \\ 2x - 2y = 3 \end{cases}$

Multiply the second equation by 2.

$\begin{cases} -4x - 3y = 8 \\ 2(2x - 2y) = 2(3) \end{cases} \rightarrow \begin{cases} -4x - 3y = 8 \\ 4x - 4y = 6 \end{cases}$

Add the equations to eliminate x; then solve for y.

$\begin{array}{r} -4x - 3y = 8 \\ 4x - 4y = 6 \\ \hline -7y = 14 \\ y = -2 \end{array}$

Now solve for x.

$2x - 2y = 3$

$2x - 2(-2) = 3$

$2x + 4 = 3$

$2x = -1$

$x = -\dfrac{1}{2}$

The solution of the system is $\left(-\dfrac{1}{2}, -2\right)$.

35. $\begin{cases} \dfrac{x}{3} - y = 2 \\ -\dfrac{x}{2} + \dfrac{3y}{2} = -3 \end{cases}$

Multiply the first equation by 3 and the second by 2.

$\begin{cases} 3\left(\dfrac{x}{3} - y\right) = 3(2) \\ 2\left(-\dfrac{x}{2} + \dfrac{3y}{2}\right) = 2(-3) \end{cases} \rightarrow \begin{cases} x - 3y = 6 \\ -x + 3y = -6 \end{cases}$

Add the equations to eliminate y.

$\begin{array}{r} x - 3y = 6 \\ -x + 3y = -6 \\ \hline 0 = 0 \end{array}$

Since the statement $0 = 0$ is true, the system has an infinite number of solutions.

37. $\begin{cases} \dfrac{3}{5}x - y = -\dfrac{4}{5} \\ 3x + \dfrac{y}{2} = -\dfrac{9}{5} \end{cases}$

Multiply the first equation by 5 and the second equation by 10 to eliminate fractions.

$\begin{cases} 5\left(\dfrac{3}{5}x - y\right) = 5\left(-\dfrac{4}{5}\right) \\ 10\left(3x + \dfrac{y}{2}\right) = 10\left(-\dfrac{9}{5}\right) \end{cases} \rightarrow \begin{cases} 3x - 5y = -4 \\ 30x + 5y = -18 \end{cases}$

Add the equations to eliminate y; then solve for x.

$\begin{array}{r} 3x - 5y = -4 \\ 30x + 5y = -18 \\ \hline 33x = -22 \\ x = -\dfrac{22}{33} = -\dfrac{2}{3} \end{array}$

Now use the equation $3x - 5y = -4$ to solve for y.

$$3x - 5y = -4$$
$$3\left(-\frac{2}{3}\right) - 5y = -4$$
$$-2 - 5y = -4$$
$$-5y = -2$$
$$y = \frac{2}{5}$$

The solution of the system is $\left(-\frac{2}{3}, \frac{2}{5}\right)$.

39. $\begin{cases} 3.5x + 2.5y = 17 \\ -1.5x - 7.5y = -33 \end{cases}$

Multiply the first equation by 30 and the second equation by 10.

$\begin{cases} 30(3.5x + 2.5y) = 30(17) \\ 10(-1.5x - 7.5y) = 10(-33) \end{cases}$

$\rightarrow \begin{cases} 105x + 75y = 510 \\ -15x - 75y = -330 \end{cases}$

Add the equations to eliminate y; then solve for x.

$$\begin{array}{r} 105x + 75y = 510 \\ -15x - 75y = -330 \\ \hline 90x \qquad\quad = 180 \\ x = 2 \end{array}$$

Now solve for y.
$$3.5x + 2.5y = 17$$
$$3.5(2) + 2.5y = 17$$
$$7 + 2.5y = 17$$
$$2.5y = 10$$
$$y = 4$$

The solution of the system is $(2, 4)$.

41. $\begin{cases} 0.02x + 0.04y = 0.09 \\ -0.1x + 0.3y = 0.8 \end{cases}$

Multiply the first equation by 100 and the second equation by 10 to eliminate decimals.

$\begin{cases} 100(0.02x + 0.04y) = 100(0.09) \\ 10(-0.1x + 0.3y) = 10(0.8) \end{cases}$

$\rightarrow \begin{cases} 2x + 4y = 9 \\ -x + 3y = 8 \end{cases}$

Multiply the second equation by 2.

$\begin{cases} 2x + 4y = 9 \\ 2(-x + 3y) = 2(8) \end{cases} \rightarrow \begin{cases} 2x + 4y = 9 \\ -2x + 6y = 16 \end{cases}$

Add the equations to eliminate x; then solve for y.

$$\begin{array}{r} 2x + 4y = 9 \\ -2x + 6y = 16 \\ \hline 10y = 25 \\ y = 2.5 \end{array}$$

Use the equation $-x + 3y = 8$ to solve for x.
$$-x + 3y = 8$$
$$-x + 3(2.5) = 8$$
$$-x + 7.5 = 8$$
$$-x = 0.5$$
$$x = -0.5$$

The solution of the system is $(-0.5, 2.5)$.

43. Twice a number, added to 6, is 3 less than the number is written as $2x + 6 = x - 3$.

45. Three times a number, subtracted from 20, is 2 is written as $20 - 3x = 2$.

47. The product of 4 and the sum of a number and 6 is twice the number is written as $4(x + 6) = 2x$.

49. To eliminate the variable y, multiply the second equation by 2.
$$3x - y = -12$$
$$2(3x - y) = 2(-12)$$
$$6x - 2y = -24$$

51. b; answers may vary

53. answers may vary

55. a. When $b = 15$, the system has an infinite number of solutions.

b. When b is any real number except 15, the system has no solutions.

57. $\begin{cases} 2x + 3y = 14 \\ 3x - 4y = -69.1 \end{cases}$

Multiply the first equation by -3 and the second equation by 2.

$\begin{cases} -3(2x + 3y) = -3(14) \\ 2(3x - 4y) = 2(-69.1) \end{cases}$

$\rightarrow \begin{cases} -6x - 9y = -42 \\ 6x - 8y = -138.2 \end{cases}$

Add the equations to eliminate x; then solve for y.

$$\begin{array}{r} -6x - 9y = -42 \\ 6x - 8y = -138.2 \\ \hline -17y = -180.2 \\ y = 10.6 \end{array}$$

Now solve for x.

$$2x + 3y = 14$$
$$2x + 3(10.6) = 14$$
$$2x + 31.8 = 14$$
$$2x = -17.8$$
$$x = -8.9$$

The solution of the system is (−8.9, 10.6).

59. a.
$$\begin{cases} 9.1x - y = -295 \\ 14x - y = -262 \end{cases}$$

Multiply the second equation by −1.
$$\begin{cases} 9.1x - y = -295 \\ -1(14x - y) = -1(-262) \end{cases}$$
$$\rightarrow \begin{cases} 9.1x - y = -295 \\ -14x + y = 262 \end{cases}$$

Add the equations to eliminate y; then solve for x.

$$9.1x - y = -295$$
$$\underline{-14x + y = 262}$$
$$-4.9x \quad\quad = -33$$
$$x \approx 6.7 \quad \text{or } 7$$

Now solve for y.
$$9.1x - y = -295$$
$$9.1(7) - y = -295$$
$$63.7 - y = -295$$
$$y = 358.7 \text{ or } 359$$

The solution is (7, 359) or (7, 360). (Note that (7, 360) is the result if you use the second equation when solving for y.)

b. The solution (7, 359) means that in about 2013 (2006 + 7) the number of pharmacy technician jobs will be approximately equal to the number of network system analyst jobs.

c. There will be about 359 thousand (or 360 thousand) such jobs.

Integrated Review

1.
$$\begin{cases} 2x - 3y = -11 \\ y = 4x - 3 \end{cases}$$

Substitute $4x - 3$ for y in the first equation and solve for x.
$$2x - 3y = -11$$
$$2x - 3(4x - 3) = -11$$
$$2x - 12x + 9 = -11$$
$$-10x = -20$$
$$x = 2$$

Now solve for y.
$$y = 4x - 3 = 4(2) - 3 = 8 - 3 = 5$$
The solution to the system is (2, 5).

2.
$$\begin{cases} 4x - 5y = 6 \\ y = 3x - 10 \end{cases}$$

Substitute $3x - 10$ for y in the first equation and solve for x.
$$4x - 5y = 6$$
$$4x - 5(3x - 10) = 6$$
$$4x - 15x + 50 = 6$$
$$-11x = -44$$
$$x = 4$$

Now solve for y.
$$y = 3x - 10 = 3(4) - 10 = 12 - 10 = 2$$
The solution of the system is (4, 2).

3.
$$\begin{cases} x + y = 3 \\ x - y = 7 \end{cases}$$

Add the equations to eliminate y; then solve for x.
$$x + y = 3$$
$$\underline{x - y = 7}$$
$$2x \quad\; = 10$$
$$x = 5$$

Now solve for y.
$$x + y = 3$$
$$5 + y = 3$$
$$y = -2$$
The solution of the system is (5, −2).

4.
$$\begin{cases} x - y = 20 \\ x + y = -8 \end{cases}$$

Add the equations to eliminate y; then solve for x.
$$x - y = 20$$
$$\underline{x + y = -8}$$
$$2x = 12$$
$$x = 6$$

Now solve for y.
$$x + y = -8$$
$$6 + y = -8$$
$$y = -14$$
The solution of the system is (6, −14).

5.
$$\begin{cases} x + 2y = 1 \\ 3x + 4y = -1 \end{cases}$$

Solve the first equation for x.
$$x + 2y = 1$$
$$x = -2y + 1$$

Substitute $-2y + 1$ for x in the second equation and solve for y.

$$3x + 4y = -1$$
$$3(-2y + 1) + 4y = -1$$
$$-6y + 3 + 4y = -1$$
$$-2y = -4$$
$$y = 2$$

Now solve for x.
$$x = -2y + 1 = -2(2) + 1 = -4 + 1 = -3$$
The solution of the system is $(-3, 2)$.

6. $\begin{cases} x + 3y = 5 \\ 5x + 6y = -2 \end{cases}$

Solve the first equation for x.
$$x + 3y = 5$$
$$x = -3y + 5$$

Substitute $-3y + 5$ for x in the second equation and solve for y.
$$5x + 6y = -2$$
$$5(-3y + 5) + 6y = -2$$
$$-15y + 25 + 6y = -2$$
$$-9y = -27$$
$$y = 3$$

Now solve for x.
$$x = -3y + 5 = -3(3) + 5 = -9 + 5 = -4$$
The solution of the system is $(-4, 3)$.

7. $y = x + 3$
$3x = 2y - 6$

Substitute $x + 3$ for y in the second equation and solve for x.
$$3x = 2y - 6$$
$$3x = 2(x + 3) - 6$$
$$3x = 2x + 6 - 6$$
$$x = 0$$

Now solve for y.
$$y = x + 3 = 0 + 3 = 3$$
The solution of the system is $(0, 3)$.

8. $\begin{cases} y = -2x \\ 2x - 3y = -16 \end{cases}$

Substitute $-2x$ for y in the second equation and solve for x.
$$2x - 3y = -16$$
$$2x - 3(-2x) = -16$$
$$2x + 6x = -16$$
$$8x = -16$$
$$x = -2$$

Now solve for y.
$$y = -2x = -2(-2) = 4$$
The solution of the system is $(-2, 4)$.

9. $\begin{cases} y = 2x - 3 \\ y = 5x - 18 \end{cases}$

Substitute $2x - 3$ for y in the second equation and solve for x.
$$y = 5x - 18$$
$$2x - 3 = 5x - 18$$
$$15 = 3x$$
$$5 = x$$

Now solve for y.
$$y = 2x - 3 = 2(5) - 3 = 10 - 3 = 7$$
The solution of the system is $(5, 7)$.

10. $\begin{cases} y = 6x - 5 \\ y = 4x - 11 \end{cases}$

Substitute $6x - 5$ for y in the second equation and solve for x.
$$y = 4x - 11$$
$$6x - 5 = 4x - 11$$
$$2x = -6$$
$$x = -3$$

Now solve for y.
$$y = 6x - 5 = 6(-3) - 5 = -18 - 5 = -23$$
The solution of the system is $(-3, -23)$.

11. $\begin{cases} x + \dfrac{1}{6}y = \dfrac{1}{2} \\ 3x + 2y = 3 \end{cases}$

Multiply the first equation by 6 to eliminate fractions.
$$6\left(x + \frac{1}{6}y\right) = 6\left(\frac{1}{2}\right)$$
$$6x + y = 3$$

Now solve for y.
$$y = -6x + 3$$

Substitute $-6x + 3$ for y in the second equation and solve for x.
$$3x + 2y = 3$$
$$3x + 2(-6x + 3) = 3$$
$$3x - 12x + 6 = 3$$
$$-9x = -3$$
$$x = \frac{3}{9} = \frac{1}{3}$$

Now solve for y.
$$y = -6x + 3 = -6\left(\frac{1}{3}\right) + 3 = -2 + 3 = 1$$

The solution of the system is $\left(\dfrac{1}{3}, 1\right)$.

12. $x + \dfrac{1}{3}y = \dfrac{5}{12}$

$8x + 3y = 4$

Multiply the first equation by 12 to eliminate fractions.

$12\left(x + \dfrac{1}{3}y\right) = 12\left(\dfrac{5}{12}\right)$

$12x + 4y = 5$

Multiply the revised first equation by -3 and the second original equation by 4.

$\begin{cases} -3(12x + 4y) = -3(5) \\ 4(8x + 3y) = 4(4) \end{cases} \rightarrow \begin{cases} -36x - 12y = -15 \\ 32x + 12y = 16 \end{cases}$

Add the equations to eliminate y; then solve for x.

$\begin{array}{r} -36x - 12y = -15 \\ 32x + 12y = 16 \\ \hline -4x\qquad\ = 1 \end{array}$

$x = -\dfrac{1}{4}$

Now solve for y.

$8x + 3y = 4$

$8\left(-\dfrac{1}{4}\right) + 3y = 4$

$-2 + 3y = 4$

$3y = 6$

$y = 2$

The solution of the system is $\left(-\dfrac{1}{4}, 2\right)$.

13. $\begin{cases} x - 5y = 1 \\ -2x + 10y = 3 \end{cases}$

Solve the first equation for x.

$x - 5y = 1$

$x = 5y + 1$

Substitute $5y + 1$ for x in the second equation and then solve for y.

$-2x + 10y = 3$

$-2(5y + 1) + 10y = 3$

$-10y - 2 + 10y = 3$

$-2 = 3$

Since the statement is false, the system has no solution.

14. $\begin{cases} -x + 2y = 3 \\ 3x - 6y = -9 \end{cases}$

Solve the first equation for x.

$-x + 2y = 3$

$x = 2y - 3$

Substitute $2y - 3$ for x in the second equation and solve for y.

$3x - 6y = -9$

$3(2y - 3) - 6y = -9$

$6y - 9 - 6y = -9$

$0 = 0$

Since the statement $0 = 0$ is true, the system has an infinite number of solutions.

15. $\begin{cases} 0.2x - 0.3y = -0.95 \\ 0.4x + 0.1y = 0.55 \end{cases}$

Multiply both equations by 100 to eliminate decimals.

$\begin{cases} 100(0.2x - 0.3y) = 100(-0.95) \\ 100(0.4x + 0.1y) = 100(0.55) \end{cases}$

$\rightarrow \begin{cases} 20x - 30y = -95 \\ 40x + 10y = 55 \end{cases}$

Multiply the second revised equation by 3.

$\begin{cases} 20x - 30y = -95 \\ 3(40x + 10y) = 3(55) \end{cases} \rightarrow \begin{cases} 20x - 30y = -95 \\ 120x + 30y = 165 \end{cases}$

Add the equations to eliminate y; then solve for x.

$\begin{array}{r} 20x - 30y = -95 \\ 120x + 30y = 165 \\ \hline 140x\qquad = 70 \end{array}$

$x = 0.5$

Now solve for y.

$0.4x + 0.1y = 0.55$

$0.4(0.5) + 0.1y = 0.55$

$0.2 + 0.1y = 0.55$

$0.1y = 0.35$

$y = 3.5$

The solution of the system is $(0.5, 3.5)$.

16. $\begin{cases} 0.08x - 0.04y = -0.11 \\ 0.02x - 0.06y = -0.09 \end{cases}$

Multiply both equations by 100 to eliminate decimals.

$\begin{cases} 100(0.08x - 0.04y) = 100(-0.11) \\ 100(0.02x - 0.06y = 100(-0.09) \end{cases}$

$\rightarrow \begin{cases} 8x - 4y = -11 \\ 2x - 6y = -9 \end{cases}$

Multiply the second revised equation by -4.

$\begin{cases} 8x - 4y = -11 \\ -4(2x - 6y) = -4(-9) \end{cases} \rightarrow \begin{cases} 8x - 4y = -11 \\ -8x + 24y = 36 \end{cases}$

Add the equations to eliminate x; then solve for y.

$\begin{array}{r} 8x - 4y = -11 \\ -8x + 24y = 36 \\ \hline 20y = 25 \\ y = 1.25 \end{array}$

Now solve for x.

$$0.08x - 0.04y = -0.11$$
$$0.08x - 0.04(1.25) = -0.11$$
$$0.08x - 0.05 = -0.11$$
$$0.08x = -0.06$$
$$x = -0.75$$

The solution of the system is $(-0.75, 1.25)$.

17. $\begin{cases} x = 3y - 7 \\ 2x - 6y = -14 \end{cases}$

Substitute $3y - 7$ for x in the second equation and solve for y.
$$2x - 6y = -14$$
$$2(3y - 7) - 6y = -14$$
$$6y - 14 - 6y = -14$$
$$0 = 0$$

Since the statement $0 = 0$ is true, the system has an infinite number of solutions.

18. $\begin{cases} y = \dfrac{x}{2} - 3 \\ 2x - 4y = 0 \end{cases}$

Substitute $\dfrac{x}{2} - 3$ for y in the second equation and solve for x.
$$2x - 4y = 0$$
$$2x - 4\left(\dfrac{x}{2} - 3\right) = 0$$
$$2x - 2x + 12 = 0$$
$$12 = 0$$

Since the statement $12 = 0$ is false, the system has no solution.

19. $\begin{cases} 2x + 5y = -1 \\ 3x - 4y = 33 \end{cases}$

Multiply the first equation by 3 and the second equation by -2.
$$\begin{cases} 3(2x + 5y) = 3(-1) \\ -2(3x - 4y) = -2(33) \end{cases} \rightarrow \begin{cases} 6x + 15y = -3 \\ -6x + 8y = -66 \end{cases}$$

Add the equations to eliminate x; then solve for y.
$$\begin{array}{r} 6x + 15y = -3 \\ -6x + 8y = -66 \\ \hline 23y = -69 \\ y = -3 \end{array}$$

Now solve for x.
$$2x + 5y = -1$$
$$2x + 5(-3) = -1$$
$$2x - 15 = -1$$
$$2x = 14$$
$$x = 7$$

The solution of the system is $(7, -3)$.

20. $\begin{cases} 7x - 3y = 2 \\ 6x + 5y = -21 \end{cases}$

Multiply the first equation by 5 and the second equation by 3.
$$\begin{cases} 5(7x - 3y) = 5(2) \\ 3(6x + 5y) = 3(-21) \end{cases} \rightarrow \begin{cases} 35x - 15y = 10 \\ 18x + 15y = -63 \end{cases}$$

Add the equations to eliminate y; then solve for x.
$$\begin{array}{r} 35x - 15y = 10 \\ 18x + 15y = -63 \\ \hline 53x = -53 \\ x = -1 \end{array}$$

Now solve for y.
$$7x - 3y = 2$$
$$7(-1) - 3y = 2$$
$$-7 - 3y = 2$$
$$-3y = 9$$
$$y = -3$$

The solution of the system is $(-1, -3)$.

21. answers may vary

22. answers may vary

Section 14.4

Practice Problems

1. $\begin{cases} x + y = 50 \\ x - y = 22 \end{cases}$

Add the equations to eliminate y; then solve for x.
$$\begin{array}{r} x + y = 50 \\ x - y = 22 \\ \hline 2x = 72 \\ x = 36 \end{array}$$

Now solve for y.
$$x + y = 50$$
$$36 + y = 50$$
$$y = 14$$

The two numbers are 36 and 14.

2. $\begin{cases} A + C = 587 \\ 7A + 5C = 3379 \end{cases}$

Multiply the first equation by -5.
$$\begin{cases} -5(A + C) = -5(587) \\ 7A + 5C = 3379 \end{cases} \rightarrow \begin{cases} -5A - 5C = -2935 \\ 7A + 5C = 3379 \end{cases}$$

Add the equations to eliminate C; then solve for A.

$-5A - 5C = -2935$
$\underline{7A + 5C = 3379}$
$2A \quad\quad = 444$
$\quad\quad A = 222$

Now solve for C.

$A + C = 587$
$222 + C = 587$
$\quad\quad C = 365$

There were 222 adults and 365 children.

3.

	r	$\cdot\ t\ =$	d
Faster car	x	3	$3x$
Slower car	y	3	$3y$

$3x + 3y = 440$
$x = y + 10$

Substitute $y + 1$ for x in the first equation and solve for y.

$3x + 3y = 440$
$3(y + 10) + 3y = 440$
$3y + 30 + 3y = 440$
$6y = 410$
$y = 68\frac{1}{3}$

Now solve for x.

$x = y + 10 = 68\frac{1}{3} + 10 = 78\frac{1}{3}$

One car's speed is $68\frac{1}{3}$ mph and the other car's speed is $78\frac{1}{3}$ mph.

4. Let x be the liters of 20% solution.
Let y be the liters of 70% solution.

$\begin{cases} x + y = 50 \\ 0.2x + 0.7y = 0.6(50) \end{cases}$

Multiply the first equation by -2 and the second equation by 10.

$\begin{cases} -2(x + y) = -2(50) \\ 10(0.2x + 0.7y) = 10(30) \end{cases}$

$\rightarrow \begin{cases} -2x - 2y = -100 \\ 2x + 7y = 300 \end{cases}$

Add the equations to eliminate x; then solve for y.

$-2x - 2y = -100$
$\underline{2x + 7y = 300}$
$5y = 200$
$y = 40$

Now solve for x.

$x + y = 50$
$x + 40 = 50$
$x = 10$

10 liters of the 20% alcohol solution and 40 liters of the 70% alcohol solution make 50 liters of the 60% alcohol solution.

Exercise Set 14.4

1. In choice b, the length is not 3 feet longer than the width. In choice a, the perimeter is $2(8 + 5) = 2(13) = 26$ feet, not 30 feet. Choice c gives the solution, since $9 = 6 + 3$ and $2(9 + 6) = 2(15) = 30$.

3. In choice a, the total cost is $2(3) + 3(4) = 6 + 12 = \$18$, not \$17. In choice c, the total cost is $2(2) + 3(5) = 4 + 15 = \$19$, not \$17. Choice b gives the solution, since $2(4) + 3(3) = 8 + 9 = \$17$ and $5(4) + 4(3) = 20 + 12 = \$32$.

5. In choice b, the total number of coins is $20 + 44 = 64$, not 100. In choice c, the total value of the coins is $60(0.10) + 40(0.25) = 6.00 + 10.00 = \$16.00$, not \$13.00. Choice a gives the solution, since $80 + 20 = 100$ and $80(0.10) + 20(0.25) = 8.00 + 5.00 = \$13.00$.

7. Let x be the first number and y the second.
$\begin{cases} x + y = 15 \\ x - y = 7 \end{cases}$

9. Let x be the amount in the larger account and y be the amount in the smaller account.
$\begin{cases} x + y = 6500 \\ x = y + 800 \end{cases}$

11. Let x be the first number and y be the second.
$x + y = 83$
$x - y = 17$

Add the equations to eliminate y then solve for x.

$x + y = 83$
$\underline{x - y = 17}$
$2x \quad\quad = 100$
$\quad x = 50$

Now solve for y.

$x + y = 83$
$50 + y = 83$
$y = 33$

The numbers are 50 and 33.

13. Let x be the first number and y the second.
$$\begin{cases} x + 2y = 8 \\ 2x + y = 25 \end{cases}$$
Solve the first equation for x.
$$x + 2y = 8$$
$$x = 8 - 2y$$
Substitute $8 - 2y$ for x in the second equation and solve for y.
$$2x + y = 25$$
$$2(8 - 2y) + y = 25$$
$$16 - 4y + y = 25$$
$$16 - 3y = 25$$
$$-3y = 9$$
$$y = -3$$
Now solve for x.
$$x = 8 - 2y = 8 - 2(-3) = 8 + 6 = 14$$
The numbers are 14 and −3.

15. Let x be the number of runs that Ryan Howard batted in and y be the number that Josh Hamilton batted in.
$$\begin{cases} y = x - 16 \\ x + y = 276 \end{cases}$$
Substitute $x - 16$ for y in the second equation and solve for x.
$$x + y = 276$$
$$x + x - 16 = 276$$
$$2x = 292$$
$$x = 146$$
Now solve for y.
$$y = x - 16 = 146 - 16 = 130$$
Ryan Howard batted in 146 runs and Josh Hamilton batted in 130 runs.

17. Let a be the price of an adult's ticket and c be the price of a child's ticket.
$$\begin{cases} 3a + 4c = 159 \\ 2a + 3c = 112 \end{cases}$$
Multiply the first equation by −2 and the second equation by 3.
$$\begin{cases} -2(3a + 4c) = -2(159) \\ 3(2a + 3c) = 3(112) \end{cases} \rightarrow \begin{cases} -6a - 8c = -318 \\ 6a + 9c = 336 \end{cases}$$
Add the equations to eliminate a and solve for c.
$$\begin{array}{r} -6a - 8c = -318 \\ 6a + 9c = 336 \\ \hline c = 18 \end{array}$$
Now solve for a.

$$2a + 3c = 112$$
$$2a + 3(18) = 112$$
$$2a + 54 = 112$$
$$2a = 58$$
$$a = 29$$
The price of an adult's ticket is $29 and the price of a child's ticket is $18.

19. Let x be quarters and y be nickels.
$$\begin{cases} x + y = 80 \\ 0.25x + 0.05y = 14.60 \end{cases}$$
Solve the first equation in terms of y.
$$x + y = 80$$
$$y = -x + 80$$
Substitute $-x + 80$ for y in the second equation and solve for x.
$$0.25x + 0.05y = 14.60$$
$$0.25x + 0.05(-x + 80) = 14.60$$
$$0.25x - 0.05x + 4 = 14.60$$
$$0.20x = 10.60$$
$$x = 53$$
Now solve for y.
$$y = -x + 80 = -53 + 80 = 27$$
There are 53 quarters and 27 nickels.

21. Let x be the value of one McDonald's share and let y be the value of one Ohio Art Company share.
$$\begin{cases} 35x + 69y = 2360 \\ x = y + 60 \end{cases}$$
Substitute $y + 60$ for x in the first equation and solve for y.
$$35x + 69y = 2360$$
$$35(y + 60) + 69y = 2360$$
$$35y + 2100 + 69y = 2360$$
$$2100 + 104y = 2360$$
$$104y = 260$$
$$y = 2.5$$
Now solve for x.
$$x = y + 60 = 2.5 + 60 = 62.5$$
On that day, the closing price of the McDonald's stock was $62.5 per share and the closing price of The Ohio Art Company stock was $2.50 per share.

23. Let x be the daily fee and y be the mileage charge.
$$\begin{cases} 4x + 450y = 240.50 \\ 3x + 200y = 146.00 \end{cases}$$
Multiply the first equation by 3 and the second by −4.

$$\begin{cases} 3(4x+450y)=3(240.50) \\ -4(3x+200y)=-4(146.00) \end{cases}$$

$$\rightarrow \begin{cases} 12x+1350y=721.5 \\ -12x-800y=-584 \end{cases}$$

Add the equations to eliminate x and solve for y.

$$12x+1350y=721.5$$
$$\underline{-12x-800y=-584}$$
$$550y=137.5$$
$$y=0.25$$

Now solve for x.
$$3x+200y=146$$
$$3x+200(0.25)=146$$
$$3x+50=146$$
$$3x=96$$
$$x=32$$

There is a \$32 daily fee and a \$0.25 per mile mileage charge.

25. $\begin{cases} 18=2(x+y) \\ 18=\dfrac{9}{2}(x-y) \end{cases}$

Multiply the first equation by $\dfrac{1}{2}$ and the second

equation by $\dfrac{2}{9}$.

$$\begin{cases} \dfrac{1}{2}(18)=\dfrac{1}{2}[2(x+y)] \\ \dfrac{2}{9}(18)=\dfrac{2}{9}\left[\dfrac{9}{2}(x-y)\right] \end{cases} \rightarrow \begin{cases} 9=x+y \\ 4=x-y \end{cases}$$

Add the equations to eliminate y; then solve for x.

$$9=x+y$$
$$\underline{4=x-y}$$
$$13=2x$$
$$6.5=x$$

Now solve for y.
$$9=x+y$$
$$9=6.5+y$$
$$2.5=y$$

The rate that Pratap can row in still water is 6.5 miles per hour and the rate of the current is 2.5 miles per hour.

27. Let x = rate of flight in still wind.
Then y = rate of wind.

$$\begin{cases} 780=\dfrac{3}{2}(x+y) \\ 780=2(x-y) \end{cases}$$

Multiply the first equation by $\dfrac{2}{3}$ and the second

equation by $\dfrac{1}{2}$.

$$\begin{cases} \dfrac{2}{3}(780)=\dfrac{2}{3}\left[\dfrac{3}{2}(x+y)\right] \\ \dfrac{1}{2}(780)=\dfrac{1}{2}[2(x-y)] \end{cases} \rightarrow \begin{cases} 520=x+y \\ 390=x-y \end{cases}$$

Add the equations to eliminate y; then solve for x.

$$520=x+y$$
$$\underline{390=x-y}$$
$$910=2x$$
$$455=x$$

Now solve for y.
$$780=2(x-y)$$
$$780=2(455)-2y$$
$$780=910-2y$$
$$-130=-2y$$
$$65=y$$

The speed of the plane in still air is 455 mph and the speed of the wind is 65 mph.

29. Let x be the number of hours that Kevin spent on his bicycle and y be the number of hours he spent walking. Then the distance he rode was $40x$ miles and the distance he walked was $4y$ miles.

$$\begin{cases} x+y=6 \\ 40x+4y=186 \end{cases}$$

Solve the first equation for y.
$$x+y=6$$
$$y=6-x$$

Substitute $6-x$ for y in the second equation and solve for x.
$$40x+4y=186$$
$$40x+4(6-x)=186$$
$$40x+24-4x=186$$
$$36x+24=186$$
$$36x=162$$
$$x=4.5$$

Kevin spent 4.5 hours on his bike.

31. Let x be ounces of 4% solution, and let y be ounces of 12% solution.

$$\begin{cases} x+y=12 \\ 0.04x+0.12y=0.09(12) \end{cases}$$

Solve the first equation in terms of x.
$$x+y=12$$
$$x=-y+12$$

Substitute $-y+12$ for x in the second equation and solve for y.

$$0.04x + 0.12y = 1.08$$
$$0.04(-y+12) + 0.12y = 1.08$$
$$-0.04y + 0.48 + 0.12y = 1.08$$
$$0.08y = 0.60$$
$$y = 7.5$$

Now solve for x.
$$x = -y + 12 = -7.5 + 12 = 4.5$$
Darren will need 4.5 ounces of the 4% solution and 7.5 ounces of the 12% solution to make 12 ounces of the 9% solution.

33. Let x be the number of pounds of high-quality coffee, and let y be the number of pounds of the cheaper coffee.
$$\begin{cases} x + y = 200 \\ 4.95x + 2.65y = 200(3.95) \end{cases}$$

Solve the first equation for x.
$$x + y = 200$$
$$x = 200 - y$$

Substitute $200 - y$ for x in the second equation and solve for y.
$$4.95x + 2.65y = 200(3.95)$$
$$4.95(200 - y) + 2.65y = 790$$
$$990 - 4.95y + 2.65y = 790$$
$$990 - 2.30y = 790$$
$$-2.30y = -200$$
$$y = \frac{200}{2.30}$$
$$y \approx 87$$

$$x = 200 - y \approx 200 - 87 = 113$$
Wayne should blend 113 pounds of the coffee that sells for \$4.95 per pound with 87 pounds of the cheaper coffee.

35. Let x be one angle, and let y be the other angle.
$$x + y = 90$$
$$y = 2x$$

Substitute $2x$ for y in the first equation and solve for x.
$$x + y = 90$$
$$x + 2x = 90$$
$$3x = 90$$
$$x = 30$$
Now solve for y.
$$y = 2x = 2(30) = 60$$
One angle is 30° and the other is 60°.

37. Let x be the measure of one angle and y be the measure of the other.
$$\begin{cases} x + y = 90 \\ x = 10 + 3y \end{cases}$$

Substitute $10 + 3y$ for x in the first equation and

solve for y.
$$x + y = 90$$
$$10 + 3y + y = 90$$
$$10 + 4y = 90$$
$$4y = 80$$
$$y = 20$$
$$x = 10 + 3y = 10 + 3(20) = 10 + 60 = 70$$
The angles measure 20° and 70°.

39. Let x be the number of pieces sold at the original price, and let y be the number of pieces sold at the discounted price.
$$\begin{cases} x + y = 90 \\ 9.5x + 7.5y = 721 \end{cases}$$

Solve the first equation in terms of x.
$$x + y = 90$$
$$x = -y + 90$$

Substitute $-y + 90$ for x in the second equation and solve for y.
$$9.5x + 7.5y = 721$$
$$9.5(-y + 90) + 7.5y = 721$$
$$-9.5y + 855 + 7.5y = 721$$
$$-2.0y = -134$$
$$y = 67$$

Now solve for x.
$$x = -y + 90 = -67 + 90 = 23$$
They sold 23 pieces at \$9.50 each and 67 pieces at \$7.50 each.

41. Let x be the rate of the faster group and y be the rate of the slower group.
$$\begin{cases} 240x + 240y = 1200 \\ y = x - \frac{1}{2} \end{cases}$$

Substitute $x - \frac{1}{2}$ for y in the fist equation and solve for x.
$$240x + 240y = 1200$$
$$240x + 240\left(x - \frac{1}{2}\right) = 1200$$
$$240x + 240x - 120 = 1200$$
$$480x - 120 = 1200$$
$$480x = 1320$$
$$x = 2.75$$

$$y = x - \frac{1}{2} = x - 0.5 = 2.75 - 0.5 = 2.25$$

The hiking rates are $2.75 = 2\frac{3}{4}$ miles per hour

and $2.25 = 2\frac{1}{4}$ miles per hour.

43. Let x be the number of gallons of 30% solution and y be the number of gallons of 60% solution.

$$\begin{cases} x + y = 150 \\ 0.3x + 0.6y = 0.5(150) \end{cases}$$

Solve the first equation in terms of x.

$x = 150 - y$

Substitute $150 - y$ for x in the second equation and solve for y.

$$0.3x + 0.6y = 0.5(150)$$
$$0.3x + 0.6y = 75$$
$$0.3(150 - y) + 0.6y = 75$$
$$45 - 0.3y + 0.6y = 75$$
$$0.3y = 30$$
$$y = 100$$

Now solve for x.

$x = 150 - y = 150 - 100 = 50$

Combining 50 gallons of the 30% solution and 100 gallons of the 60% solution is necessary to create 150 gallons of a 50% solution.

45. Let x be the length and y the width.

$$\begin{cases} 2(x + y) = 144 \\ x = y + 12 \end{cases}$$

Substitute $y + 12$ for x in the first equation and solve for y.

$$2(x + y) = 144$$
$$2(y + 12 + y) = 144$$
$$2(2y + 12) = 144$$
$$4y + 24 = 144$$
$$4y = 120$$
$$y = 30$$

$x = y + 12 = 30 + 12 = 42$

The length is 42 inches and the width is 30 inches.

47. $4^2 = 4 \cdot 4 = 16$

49. $(6x)^2 = (6x)(6x) = 36x^2$

51. $(10y^3)^2 = (10y^3)(10y^3) = 100y^6$

53. The price of the result must be between $0.49 and $0.65, so choice a is the only possibility.

55. $y + 2x = 33$
$\qquad y = 2x - 3$

Substitute $2x - 3$ for y in the first equation and solve for y.

$$y + 2x = 33$$
$$2x - 3 + 2x = 33$$
$$4x = 36$$
$$x = 9$$

Now solve for y.

$y = 2x - 3 = 2(9) - 3 = 18 - 3 = 15$

The width is 9 feet and the length is 15 feet.

Chapter 14 Vocabulary Check

1. In a system of linear equations in two variables, if the graphs of the equations are the same, the equations are <u>dependent</u> equations.

2. Two or more linear equations are called a <u>system of linear equations</u>.

3. A system of equations that has at least one solution is called a(n) <u>consistent</u> system.

4. A <u>solution</u> of a system of two equations in two variables is an ordered pair of numbers that is a solution of both equations in the system.

5. Two algebraic methods for solving systems of equations are <u>addition</u> and <u>substitution</u>.

6. A system of equations that has no solution is called a(n) <u>inconsistent</u> system.

7. In a system of linear equations in two variables, if the graphs of the equations are different, the equations are <u>independent</u> equations.

Chapter 14 Review

1. a. $\begin{cases} 2x - 3y = 12 \\ 3x + 4y = 1 \end{cases}$

First equation:
$$2x - 3y = 12$$
$$2(12) - 3(4) \stackrel{?}{=} 12$$
$$24 - 12 \stackrel{?}{=} 12$$
$$12 = 12 \quad \text{True}$$

Second equation:
$$3x + 4y = 1$$
$$3(12) - 4(4) \stackrel{?}{=} 1$$
$$36 - 16 \stackrel{?}{=} 1$$
$$20 = 1 \quad \text{False}$$

$(12, 4)$ is not a solution of the system.

b. First equation:
$$2x - 3y = 12$$
$$2(3) - 3(-2) \stackrel{?}{=} 12$$
$$6 + 6 \stackrel{?}{=} 12$$
$$12 = 12 \quad \text{True}$$

Second equation:
$$3x + 4y = 1$$
$$3(3) + 4(-2) \overset{?}{=} 1$$
$$9 - 8 \overset{?}{=} 1$$
$$1 = 1 \quad \text{True}$$
$(3, -2)$ is a solution of the system.

2. a. $\begin{cases} 2x + 3y = 1 \\ 3y - x = 4 \end{cases}$

    First equation:
$$2x + 3y = 1$$
$$2(2) + 3(2) \overset{?}{=} 1$$
$$4 + 6 \overset{?}{=} 1$$
$$10 = 1 \quad \text{False}$$
$(2, 2)$ is not a solution of the system.

b. First equation:
$$2x + 3y = 1$$
$$2(-1) + 3(1) \overset{?}{=} 1$$
$$-2 + 3 \overset{?}{=} 1$$
$$1 = 1 \quad \text{True}$$
Second equation:
$$3y - x = 4$$
$$3(1) - (-1) \overset{?}{=} 4$$
$$3 + 1 \overset{?}{=} 4$$
$$4 = 4 \quad \text{True}$$
$(-1, 1)$ is a solution of the system.

3. a. $\begin{cases} 5x - 6y = 18 \\ 2y - x = -4 \end{cases}$

    First equation:
$$5x - 6y = 18$$
$$5(-6) - 6(-8) \overset{?}{=} 18$$
$$-30 + 48 \overset{?}{=} 18$$
$$18 = 18 \quad \text{True}$$
Second equation:
$$2y - x = -4$$
$$2(-8) - (-6) \overset{?}{=} -4$$
$$-16 + 6 \overset{?}{=} -4$$
$$-10 = -4 \quad \text{False}$$
$(-6, -8)$ is not a solution of the system.

b. First equation:
$$5x - 6y = 18$$
$$5(3) - 6\left(\frac{5}{2}\right) \overset{?}{=} 18$$
$$15 - 15 \overset{?}{=} 18$$
$$0 = 18 \quad \text{False}$$
$\left(3, \dfrac{5}{2}\right)$ is not a solution of the system.

4. a. $\begin{cases} 4x + y = 0 \\ -8x - 5y = 9 \end{cases}$

    First equation:
$$4x + y = 0$$
$$4\left(\frac{3}{4}\right) + (-3) \overset{?}{=} 0$$
$$3 - 3 \overset{?}{=} 0$$
$$0 = 0 \quad \text{True}$$
Second equation:
$$-8x - 5y = 9$$
$$-8\left(\frac{3}{4}\right) - 5(-3) \overset{?}{=} 9$$
$$-6 + 15 \overset{?}{=} 9$$
$$9 = 9 \quad \text{True}$$
$\left(\dfrac{3}{4}, -3\right)$ is a solution of the system.

b. First equation:
$$4x + y = 0$$
$$4(-2) + 8 \overset{?}{=} 0$$
$$-8 + 8 \overset{?}{=} 0$$
$$0 = 0 \quad \text{True}$$
Second equation:
$$-8x - 5y = 9$$
$$-8(-2) - 5(8) \overset{?}{=} 9$$
$$16 - 40 \overset{?}{=} 9$$
$$-24 = 9 \quad \text{False}$$
$(-2, 8)$ is not a solution of the system.

5. $\begin{cases} x + y = 5 \\ x - y = 1 \end{cases}$

The solution of the system is $(3, 2)$.

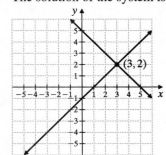

6. $\begin{cases} x + y = 3 \\ x - y = -1 \end{cases}$

The solution of the system is (1, 2).

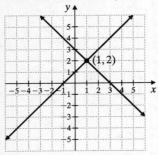

7. $\begin{cases} x = 5 \\ y = -1 \end{cases}$

The solution of the system is (5, −1).

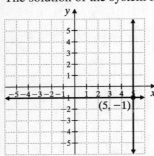

8. $\begin{cases} x = -3 \\ y = 2 \end{cases}$

The solution of the system is (−3, 2).

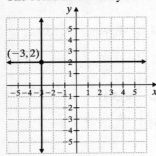

9. $\begin{cases} 2x + y = 5 \\ x = -3y \end{cases}$

The solution of the system is (3, −1).

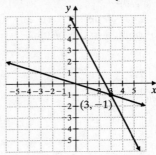

10. $\begin{cases} 3x + y = -2 \\ y = -5x \end{cases}$

The solution of the system is (1, −5).

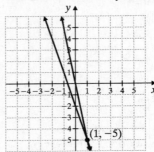

11. $\begin{cases} y = 3x \\ -6x + 2y = 6 \end{cases}$

There are no solutions to the system because the lines are parallel.

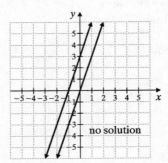

12. $\begin{cases} x - 2y = 2 \\ -2x + 4y = -4 \end{cases}$

Since they are the same lines, there are an infinite number of solutions.

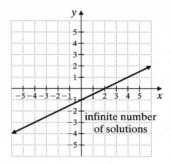

infinite number of solutions

13. $\begin{cases} y = 2x + 6 \\ 3x - 2y = -11 \end{cases}$

Substitute $2x + 6$ for y in the second equation and solve for x.
$$3x - 2y = -11$$
$$3x - 2(2x + 6) = -11$$
$$3x - 4x - 12 = -11$$
$$-x = 1$$
$$x = -1$$
Now solve for y.
$$y = 2x + 6 = 2(-1) + 6 = -2 + 6 = 4$$
The solution of the system is $(-1, 4)$.

14. $\begin{cases} y = 3x - 7 \\ 2x - 3y = 7 \end{cases}$

Substitute $3x - 7$ for y in the second equation and solve for x.
$$2x - 3y = 7$$
$$2x - 3(3x - 7) = 7$$
$$2x - 9x + 21 = 7$$
$$-7x = -14$$
$$x = 2$$
Now solve for y.
$$y = 3x - 7 = 3(2) - 7 = 6 - 7 = -1$$
The solution of the system is $(2, -1)$.

15. $\begin{cases} x + 3y = -3 \\ 2x + y = 4 \end{cases}$

Solve the second equation in terms of y.
$$2x + y = 4$$
$$y = -2x + 4$$
Substitute $-2x + 4$ for y in the first equation and solve for x.
$$x + 3y = -3$$
$$x + 3(-2x + 4) = -3$$
$$x - 6x + 12 = -3$$
$$-5x = -15$$
$$x = 3$$
Now solve for y.
$$y = -2x + 4 = -2(3) + 4 = -6 + 4 = -2$$
The solution of the system is $(3, -2)$.

16. $\begin{cases} 3x + y = 11 \\ x + 2y = 12 \end{cases}$

Solve the first equation in terms of y.
$$3x + y = 11$$
$$y = -3x + 11$$
Substitute $-3x + 11$ for y in the second equation and solve for x.
$$x + 2y = 12$$
$$x + 2(-3x + 11) = 12$$
$$x - 6x + 22 = 12$$
$$-5x = -10$$
$$x = 2$$
Now solve for y.
$$y = -3x + 11 = -3(2) + 11 = -6 + 11 = 5$$
The solution of the system is $(2, 5)$.

17. $\begin{cases} 4y = 2x + 6 \\ x - 2y = -3 \end{cases}$

Solve the second equation in terms of x.
$$x - 2y = -3$$
$$x = 2y - 3$$
Substitute $2y - 3$ for x in the first equation and solve for y.
$$4y = 2x + 6$$
$$4y = 2(2y - 3) + 6$$
$$4y = 4y - 6 + 6$$
$$0 = 0$$
Since the statement $0 = 0$ is true, there are an infinite number of solutions for the system.

18. $\begin{cases} 9x = 6y + 3 \\ 6x - 4y = 2 \end{cases}$

Solve the first equation in terms of x.
$$9x = 6y + 3$$
$$x = \frac{6}{9}y + \frac{3}{9}$$
$$x = \frac{2}{3}y + \frac{1}{3}$$
Substitute $\frac{2}{3}y + \frac{1}{3}$ for x in the second equation and solve for y.
$$6x - 4y = 2$$
$$6\left(\frac{2}{3}y + \frac{1}{3}\right) - 4y = 2$$
$$4y + 2 - 4y = 2$$
$$0 = 0$$
Since the statement $0 = 0$ is true, there are an infinite number of solutions for the system.

19. $\begin{cases} x+y=6 \\ y=-x-4 \end{cases}$

Substitute $-x - 4$ for y in the first equation and solve for x.
$$x+y=6$$
$$x+(-x-4)=6$$
$$0=10 \quad \text{False}$$
Since the statement $0 = 10$ is false, there is no solution for the system.

20. $\begin{cases} -3x+y=6 \\ y=3x+2 \end{cases}$

Substitute $3x + 2$ for y in the first equation and solve for x.
$$-3x+y=6$$
$$-3x+3x+2=6$$
$$2=6 \quad \text{False}$$
Since the statement $2 = 6$ is false, there is no solution for the system.

21. $\begin{cases} 2x+3y=-6 \\ x-3y=-12 \end{cases}$

Add the equations to eliminate y and solve for x.
$$\begin{aligned} 2x+3y&=-6 \\ x-3y&=-12 \\ \hline 3x&=-18 \\ x&=-6 \end{aligned}$$
Now solve for y.
$$x-3y=-12$$
$$-6-3y=-12$$
$$-3y=-6$$
$$y=2$$
The solution for the system is $(-6, 2)$.

22. $\begin{cases} 4x+y=15 \\ -4x+3y=-19 \end{cases}$

Add the equations to eliminate x and solve for y.
$$\begin{aligned} 4x+y&=15 \\ -4x+3y&=-19 \\ \hline 4y&=-4 \\ y&=-1 \end{aligned}$$
Now solve for x.
$$4x+y=15$$
$$4x-1=15$$
$$4x=16$$
$$x=4$$
The solution for the system is $(4, -1)$.

23. $\begin{cases} 2x-3y=-15 \\ x+4y=31 \end{cases}$

Multiply the second equation by -2.

$$\begin{cases} 2x-3y=-15 \\ -2(x+4y)=-2(31) \end{cases} \rightarrow \begin{cases} 2x-3y=-15 \\ -2x-8y=-62 \end{cases}$$

Add the equations to eliminate x and solve for y.
$$\begin{aligned} 2x-3y&=-15 \\ -2x-8y&=-62 \\ \hline -11y&=-77 \\ y&=7 \end{aligned}$$
Now solve for x.
$$x+4y=31$$
$$x+4(7)=31$$
$$x+28=31$$
$$x=3$$
The solution of the system is $(3, 7)$.

24. $\begin{cases} x-5y=-22 \\ 4x+3y=4 \end{cases}$

Multiply the first equation by -4.

$$\begin{cases} -4(x-5y)=-4(-22) \\ 4x+3y=4 \end{cases} \rightarrow \begin{cases} -4x+20y=88 \\ 4x+3y=4 \end{cases}$$

Add the equations to eliminate x and solve for y.
$$\begin{aligned} -4x+20y&=88 \\ 4x+3y&=4 \\ \hline 23y&=92 \\ y&=4 \end{aligned}$$
Now solve for x.
$$x-5y=-22$$
$$x-5(4)=-22$$
$$x-20=-22$$
$$x=-2$$
The solution of the system is $(-2, 4)$.

25. $\begin{cases} 2x-6y=-1 \\ -x+3y=\dfrac{1}{2} \end{cases}$

Multiply the second equation by 2.

$$\begin{cases} 2x-6y=-1 \\ 2(-x+3y)=2\left(\dfrac{1}{2}\right) \end{cases} \rightarrow \begin{cases} 2x-6y=-1 \\ -2x+6y=1 \end{cases}$$

Add the equations to eliminate x.
$$\begin{aligned} 2x-6y&=-1 \\ -2x+6y&=1 \\ \hline 0&=0 \end{aligned}$$
Since the statement $0 = 0$ is true, there are an infinite number of solutions for the system.

26. $\begin{cases} 0.6x-0.3y=-1.5 \\ 0.04x-0.02y=-0.1 \end{cases}$

Multiply the first equation by 10 and the second by 100 to eliminate decimals.

$$\begin{cases} 10(0.6x - 0.3y) = 10(-1.5) \\ 100(0.04x - 0.02y) = 100(-0.1) \end{cases}$$

$$\rightarrow \begin{cases} 6x - 3y = -15 \\ 4x - 2y = -10 \end{cases}$$

Multiply the first revised equation by 2 and the second revised equation by −3.

$$\begin{cases} 2(6x - 3y) = 2(-15) \\ -3(4x - 2y) = -3(-10) \end{cases} \rightarrow \begin{cases} 12x - 6y = -30 \\ -12x + 6y = 30 \end{cases}$$

Add the equations to eliminate y.

$$\begin{array}{r} 12x - 6y = -30 \\ -12x + 6y = 30 \\ \hline 0 = 0 \end{array}$$

Since the statement $0 = 0$ is true, there are an infinite number of solutions for the system.

27. $\begin{cases} \dfrac{3}{4}x + \dfrac{2}{3}y = 2 \\ \\ x + \dfrac{y}{3} = 6 \end{cases}$

Multiply the first equation by 12 and the second by 3 to eliminate fractions.

$$\begin{cases} 12\left(\dfrac{3}{4}x + \dfrac{2}{3}y\right) = 12(2) \\ \\ 3\left(x + \dfrac{y}{3}\right) = 3(6) \end{cases} \rightarrow \begin{cases} 9x + 8y = 24 \\ 3x + y = 18 \end{cases}$$

Multiply the second revised equation by −3.

$$\begin{cases} 9x + 8y = 24 \\ -3(3x + y) = -3(18) \end{cases} \rightarrow \begin{cases} 9x + 8y = 24 \\ -9x - 3y = -54 \end{cases}$$

Add the equations to eliminate x and solve for y.

$$\begin{array}{r} 9x + 8y = 24 \\ -9x - 3y = -54 \\ \hline 5y = -30 \\ y = -6 \end{array}$$

Now solve for x.

$$x + \frac{y}{3} = 6$$
$$x + \left(\frac{-6}{3}\right) = 6$$
$$x + (-2) = 6$$
$$x = 8$$

The solution of the system is $(8, -6)$.

28. $\begin{cases} 10x + 2y = 0 \\ 3x + 5y = 33 \end{cases}$

Multiply the first equation by 5 and the second by −2.

$$\begin{cases} 5(10x + 2y) = 5(0) \\ -2(3x + 5y) = -2(33) \end{cases} \rightarrow \begin{cases} 50x + 10y = 0 \\ -6x - 10y = -66 \end{cases}$$

Add the equations to eliminate y and solve for x.

$$\begin{array}{r} 50x + 10y = 0 \\ -6x - 10y = -66 \\ \hline 44x = -66 \end{array}$$

$$x = \frac{-66}{44} = -\frac{3}{2}$$

Now solve for y.

$$10x + 2y = 0$$
$$10\left(-\frac{3}{2}\right) + 2y = 0$$
$$-15 + 2y = 0$$
$$2y = 15$$
$$y = \frac{15}{2}$$

The solution of the system is $\left(-\dfrac{3}{2}, \dfrac{15}{2}\right)$.

29. Let x be the smaller number and y be the larger.

$$\begin{cases} x + y = 16 \\ 3y - x = 72 \end{cases}$$

Solve the first equation in terms of y.

$$x + y = 16$$
$$y = -x + 16$$

Substitute $-x + 16$ for y in the second equation and solve for x.

$$3y - x = 72$$
$$3(-x + 16) - x = 72$$
$$-3x + 48 - x = 72$$
$$-4x = 24$$
$$x = -6$$

Now solve for y.

$$y = -x + 16 = -(-6) + 16 = 6 + 16 = 22$$

The two numbers are −6 and 22.

30. Let x be the number of orchestra seats and y be the number of balcony seats.

$$\begin{cases} x + y = 360 \\ 45x + 35y = 15{,}150 \end{cases}$$

Solve the first equation in terms of x.

$$x = -y + 360$$

Substitute $-y + 360$ for x in the second equation and solve for y.

$$45x + 35y = 15{,}150$$
$$45(-y + 360) + 35y = 15{,}150$$
$$-45y + 16{,}200 + 35y = 15{,}150$$
$$-10y = -1050$$
$$y = 105$$

Now solve for x.

$$x + y = 360$$
$$x + 105 = 360$$
$$x = 255$$

There are 255 orchestra seats and 105 balcony seats.

31. Let x be the rate of the current and y be the speed in still water.

$$19(x - y) = 340$$
$$14(x + y) = 340$$

Multiply the first equation by $\dfrac{1}{19}$ and the second by $\dfrac{1}{14}$.

$$\begin{cases} \dfrac{1}{19}[19(x-y)] = \dfrac{1}{19}(340) \\ \dfrac{1}{14}[14(x+y)] = \dfrac{1}{14}(340) \end{cases} \rightarrow \begin{cases} x - y = 17.9 \\ x + y = 24.3 \end{cases}$$

Add the equations to eliminate y and solve for x.

$$\begin{array}{r} x - y = 17.9 \\ x + y = 24.3 \\ \hline 2x = 42.2 \end{array}$$
$$x = 21.1$$

Now solve for x.

$$x + y = 24.3$$
$$21.1 + y = 24.3$$
$$y = 3.2$$

The speed in still water is 21.1 mph and the current of the river is 3.2 mph.

32. Let x = number of cc of 6% acid solution and y = number of cc of 14% acid solution.

$$x + y = 50$$
$$0.06x + 0.14y = 0.12(50) \rightarrow 0.06x + 0.14y = 6$$

Solve the first equation in terms of x.

$$x + y = 50$$
$$x = -y + 50$$

Substitute $-y + 50$ for x in the second equation and solve for y.

$$0.06x + 0.14y = 6$$
$$0.06(-y + 50) + 0.14y = 6$$
$$-0.06y + 3 + 0.14y = 6$$
$$0.08y = 3$$
$$y = 37.5$$

Now solve for x.

$$x = -y + 50 = -37.5 + 50 = 12.5$$

12.5 cc of the 6% solution and 37.5 cc of the 14% solution are needed to make 50 cc of the 12% solution.

33. Let x be the cost of an egg and y be the cost of a strip of bacon.

$$\begin{cases} 3x + 4y = 3.80 \\ 2x + 3y = 2.75 \end{cases}$$

Multiply the first equation by 2 and the second by -3.

$$\begin{cases} 2(3x + 4y) = 2(3.80) \\ -3(2x + 3y) = -3(2.75) \end{cases} \rightarrow \begin{cases} 6x + 8y = 7.60 \\ -6x - 9y = -8.25 \end{cases}$$

Add the equations to eliminate x and solve for y.

$$\begin{array}{r} 6x + 8y = 7.60 \\ -6x - 9y = -8.25 \\ \hline -y = -0.65 \end{array}$$
$$y = 0.65$$

Now solve for x.

$$2x + 3y = 2.75$$
$$2x + 3(0.65) = 2.75$$
$$2x + 1.95 = 2.75$$
$$2x = 0.80$$
$$x = 0.40$$

Each egg costs \$0.40 and each strip of bacon costs \$0.65.

34. Let x be time spent jogging, and let y be the time spent walking.

$$\begin{cases} x + y = 3 \\ 7.5x + 4y = 15 \end{cases}$$

Solve the first equation in terms of x.

$$x + y = 3$$
$$x = -y + 3$$

Substitute $-y + 3$ for x in the second equation and solve for y.

$$7.5x + 4y = 15$$
$$7.5(-y + 3) + 4y = 15$$
$$-7.5y + 22.5 + 4y = 15$$
$$-3.5y = -7.5$$
$$y = 2.14$$

Now solve for x.

$$x + y = 3$$
$$x + 2.14 = 3$$
$$x = 0.86$$

He spent 0.86 hour jogging and 2.14 hours walking.

35. $\begin{cases} x - 2y = 1 \\ 2x + 3y = -12 \end{cases}$

The solution to the system is $(-3, -2)$.

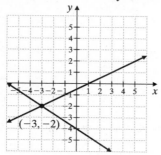

$(-3, -2)$

36. $\begin{cases} 3x - y = -4 \\ 6x - 2y = -8 \end{cases}$

The system has an infinite number of solutions because it is the same line.

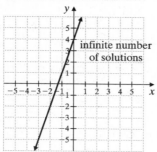

infinite number of solutions

37. $\begin{cases} x + 4y = 11 \\ 5x - 9y = -3 \end{cases}$

Solve the first equation in terms of x.

$x + 4y = 11$

$x = -4y + 11$

Substitute $-4y + 11$ for x in the second equation and solve for y.

$5x - 9y = -3$

$5(-4y + 11) - 9y = -3$

$-20y + 55 - 9y = -3$

$-29y = -58$

$y = 2$

Now solve for x.

$x = -4y + 11 = -4(2) + 11 = -8 + 11 = 3$

The solution of the system is $(3, 2)$.

38. $\begin{cases} x + 9y = 16 \\ 3x - 8y = 13 \end{cases}$

Solve the first equation in terms of x.

$x + 9y = 16$

$x = -9y + 16$

Substitute $-9y + 16$ for x in the second equation

and solve for y.

$3x - 8y = 13$

$3(-9y + 16) - 8y = 13$

$-27y + 48 - 8y = 13$

$-35y = -35$

$y = 1$

Now solve for x.

$x = -9y + 16 = -9(1) + 16 = -9 + 16 = 7$

The solution of the system is $(7, 1)$.

39. $y = -2x$

$4x + 7y = -15$

Substitute $-2x$ for y in the second equation and solve for x.

$4x + 7y = -15$

$4x + 7(-2x) = -15$

$4x - 14x = -15$

$-10x = -15$

$x = \dfrac{-15}{-10} = \dfrac{3}{2}$

Now solve for y.

$y = -2x = -2\left(\dfrac{3}{2}\right) = -3$

The solution of the system is $\left(\dfrac{3}{2}, -3\right)$.

40. $\begin{cases} 3y = 2x + 15 \\ -2x + 3y = 21 \end{cases} \quad \rightarrow \quad \begin{cases} 2x - 3y = -15 \\ -2x + 3y = 21 \end{cases}$

Add the equations to eliminate x.

$\quad 2x - 3y = -15$

$\underline{-2x + 3y = 21}$

$\qquad\qquad 0 = 6 \quad$ False

Since the statement $0 = 6$ in false, there is no solution for the system.

41. $\begin{cases} 3x - y = 4 \\ 4y = 12x - 16 \end{cases}$

Solve the first equation in terms of y.

$3x - y = 4$

$3x - 4 = y$

Substitute $3x - 4$ for y in the second equation and solve for x.

$4y = 12x - 16$

$4(3x - 4) = 12x - 16$

$12x - 16 = 12x - 16$

$0 = 0$

Since the statement $0 = 0$ is true, there are an infinite number of solutions for the system.

42. $\begin{cases} x + y = 19 \\ x - y = -3 \end{cases}$

Add the equations to eliminate y and solve for x.

$\begin{array}{r} x + y = 19 \\ \underline{x - y = -3} \\ 2x = 16 \\ x = 8 \end{array}$

Now solve for y.

$x + y = 19$
$8 + y = 19$
$y = 11$

The solution of the system is (8, 11).

43. $\begin{cases} x - 3y = -11 \\ 4x + 5y = -10 \end{cases}$

Solve the first equation in terms of x.

$x - 3y = -11$
$x = 3y - 11$

Substitute $3y - 11$ for x in the second equation and solve for y.

$4x + 5y = -10$
$4(3y - 11) + 5y = -10$
$12y - 44 + 5y = -10$
$17y = 34$
$y = 2$

Now solve for x.
$x = 3y - 11 = 3(2) - 11 = 6 - 11 = -5$
The solution of the system is (−5, 2).

44. $\begin{cases} -x - 15y = 44 \\ 2x + 3y = 20 \end{cases}$

Solve the first equation in terms of x.

$-x - 15y = 44$
$-15y - 44 = x$

Substitute $-15y - 44$ for x in the second equation and solve for y.

$2x + 3y = 20$
$2(-15y - 44) + 3y = 20$
$-30y - 88 + 3y = 20$
$-27y = 108$
$y = -4$

Now solve for x.
$x = -15y - 44 = -15(-4) - 44 = 60 - 44 = 16$
The solution of the system is (16, −4).

45. $\begin{cases} 2x + y = 3 \\ 6x + 3y = 9 \end{cases}$

Solve the first equation in terms of y.

$2x + y = 3$
$y = -2x + 3$

Substitute $-2x + 3$ for y in the second equation and solve for x.

$6x + 3y = 9$
$6x + 3(-2x + 3) = 9$
$6x - 6x + 9 = 9$
$0 = 0$

Since the statement $0 = 0$ is true, there are an infinite number of solutions for the system.

46. $\begin{cases} -3x + y = 5 \\ -3x + y = -2 \end{cases}$

Solve the first equation in terms of y.

$-3x + y = 5$
$y = 3x + 5$

Substitute $3x + 5$ for y in the second equation and solve for x.

$-3x + y = -2$
$-3x + 3x + 5 = -2$
$5 = -2$ False

Since the statement $5 = -2$ is false, there is no solution for the system.

47. Let x be the smaller number and y be the larger number.

$\begin{cases} x + y = 12 \\ 3x + y = 20 \end{cases}$

Solve the first equation in terms of y.

$x + y = 12$
$y = -x + 12$

Substitute $-x + 12$ for y in the second equation and solve for x.

$3x + y = 20$
$3x + (-x + 12) = 20$
$2x + 12 = 20$
$2x = 8$
$x = 4$

Now solve for y.
$y = -x + 12 = -4 + 12 = 8$
The two numbers are 4 and 8.

48. Let x be the smaller number and y be the larger number.

$\begin{cases} x - y = -18 \\ 2x - y = -23 \end{cases}$

Solve the first equation in terms of x.

$x - y = -18$
$x = y - 18$

Substitute $y - 18$ for x in the second equation and solve for y.

$$2x - y = -23$$
$$2(y - 18) - y = -23$$
$$2y - 36 - y = -23$$
$$y = 13$$

Now solve for x.

$$x = y - 18 = 13 - 18 = -5$$

The two numbers are -5 and 13.

49. Let x be nickels and y be dimes.

$$x + y = 65$$
$$0.05x + 0.1y = 5.30$$

Solve the first equation in terms of x.

$$x + y = 65$$
$$x = -y + 65$$

Substitute $-y + 65$ for x in the second equation and solve for y.

$$0.05x + 0.1y = 5.30$$
$$0.05(-y + 65) + 0.1y = 5.30$$
$$-0.05y + 3.25 + 0.1y = 5.30$$
$$0.05y = 2.05$$
$$y = 41$$

Now solve for x.

$$x = -y + 65 = -41 + 65 = 24.$$

There are 24 nickels and 41 dimes.

50. Let x be the number of 13¢ stamps and y be the number of 22¢ stamps.

$$\begin{cases} x + y = 26 \\ 0.13x + 0.22y = 4.19 \end{cases}$$

Solve the first equation in terms of x.

$$x + y = 26$$
$$x = -y + 26$$

Substitute $-y + 26$ for x in the second equation and solve for y.

$$0.13x + 0.22y = 4.19$$
$$0.13(-y + 26) + 0.22y = 4.19$$
$$-0.13y + 3.38 + 0.22y = 4.19$$
$$0.09y = 0.81$$
$$y = 9$$

Now solve for x.

$$x = -y + 26 = -9 + 26 = 17$$

They purchased 17 13¢ stamps and 9 22¢ stamps.

Chapter 14 Test

1. False; a system of two linear equations can have no solutions, exactly one solution, or infinitely many solutions.

2. False; a solution has to be a solution to both equations to be a solution of the system.

3. True; when the resulting statement is false the system has no solutions.

4. False; when $3x = 0 \rightarrow x = 0$; the system does have a solution.

5. First equation:

$$2x - 3y = 5$$
$$2(1) - 3(-1) \overset{?}{=} 5$$
$$2 + 3 \overset{?}{=} 5$$
$$5 = 5 \quad \text{True}$$

Second equation:

$$6x + y = 1$$
$$6(1) + (-1) \overset{?}{=} 1$$
$$6 - 1 \overset{?}{=} 1$$
$$5 = 1 \quad \text{False}$$

Since the statement $5 = 1$ is false, $(1, -1)$ is not a solution of the system.

6. $\begin{cases} 4x - 3y = 24 \\ 4x + 5y = -8 \end{cases}$

First equation:

$$4x - 3y = 24$$
$$4(3) - 3(-4) \overset{?}{=} 24$$
$$12 + 12 \overset{?}{=} 24$$
$$24 = 24 \quad \text{True}$$

Second equation:

$$4x + 5y = -8$$
$$4(3) + 5(-4) \overset{?}{=} -8$$
$$12 - 20 \overset{?}{=} -8$$
$$-8 = -8 \quad \text{True}$$

$(3, -4)$ is a solution of the system.

7. $\begin{cases} x - y = 2 \\ 3x - y = -2 \end{cases}$

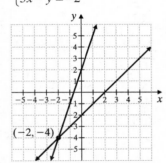

$(-2, -4)$

8. $\begin{cases} y = -3x \\ 3x + y = 6 \end{cases}$

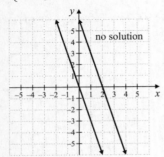

no solution

9. $\begin{cases} 3x - 2y = -14 \\ y = x + 5 \end{cases}$

Substitute $x + 5$ for y in the first equation and solve for x.

$$3x - 2y = -14$$
$$3x - 2(x + 5) = -14$$
$$3x - 2x - 10 = -14$$
$$x - 10 = -14$$
$$x = -4$$
$$y = x + 5 = -4 + 5 = 1$$

The solution of the system is $(-4, 1)$.

10. $\begin{cases} \dfrac{1}{2}x + 2y = -\dfrac{15}{4} \\ 4x = -y \end{cases}$

Multiply the second equation by -1.
$$(-1)4x = (-1)(-y)$$
$$-4x = y$$

Substitute $-4x$ for y in the first equation.

$$\frac{1}{2}x + 2y = -\frac{15}{4}$$
$$\frac{1}{2}x + 2(-4x) = -\frac{15}{4}$$
$$\frac{1}{2}x - 8x = -\frac{15}{4}$$
$$4\left(\frac{1}{2}x - 8x\right) = 4\left(-\frac{15}{4}\right)$$
$$2x - 32x = -15$$
$$-30x = -15$$
$$x = \frac{15}{30} = \frac{1}{2}$$

Now solve for y.
$$y = -4x = -4\left(\frac{1}{2}\right) = -2$$

The solution of the system is $\left(\dfrac{1}{2}, -2\right)$.

11. $\begin{cases} x + y = 28 \\ x - y = 12 \end{cases}$

Add the equations to eliminate y.
$$\begin{array}{r} x + y = 28 \\ \underline{x - y = 12} \\ 2x \quad\;\; = 40 \\ x = 20 \end{array}$$

Now solve for y.
$$x + y = 28$$
$$20 + y = 28$$
$$y = 8$$

The solution of the system is $(20, 8)$.

12. $\begin{cases} 4x - 6y = 7 \\ -2x + 3y = 0 \end{cases}$

Multiply the second equation by 2.
$$\begin{cases} 4x - 6y = 7 \\ 2(-2x + 3y) = 2(0) \end{cases} \rightarrow \begin{cases} 4x - 6y = 7 \\ -4x + 6y = 0 \end{cases}$$

Add the equations to eliminate x.
$$\begin{array}{r} 4x - 6y = 7 \\ \underline{-4x + 6y = 0} \\ 0 = 7 \end{array}$$

Since the statement $0 = 7$ is false, the system has no solution.

13. $\begin{cases} 3x + y = 7 \\ 4x + 3y = 1 \end{cases}$

Solve the first equation for y.
$$3x + y = 7$$
$$y = 7 - 3x$$

Substitute $7 - 3x$ for y in the second equation and solve for x.
$$4x + 3y = 1$$
$$4x + 3(7 - 3x) = 1$$
$$4x + 21 - 9x = 1$$
$$21 - 5x = 1$$
$$-5x = -20$$
$$x = 4$$
$$y = 7 - 3x = 7 - 3(4) = 7 - 12 = -5$$

The solution of the system is $(4, -5)$.

14. $\begin{cases} 3(2x + y) = 4x + 20 \\ x - 2y = 3 \end{cases}$

Simplify the first equation.
$$3(2x + y) = 4x + 20$$
$$6x + 3y = 4x + 20$$
$$2x + 3y = 20$$
$$\begin{cases} 2x + 3y = 20 \\ x - 2y = 3 \end{cases}$$

Multiply the second equation by -2.

$$\begin{cases} 2x+3y=20 \\ -2(x-2y)=-2(3) \end{cases} \rightarrow \begin{cases} 2x+3y=20 \\ -2x+4y=-6 \end{cases}$$

Add the equations to eliminate x; then solve for y.

$$\begin{array}{r} 2x+3y=20 \\ -2x+4y=-6 \\ \hline 7y=14 \\ y=2 \end{array}$$

Now solve for x.

$$x-2y=3$$
$$x-2(2)=3$$
$$x-4=3$$
$$x=7$$

The solution of the system is $(7, 2)$.

15. $\begin{cases} \dfrac{x-3}{2}=\dfrac{2-y}{4} \\ \dfrac{7-2x}{3}=\dfrac{y}{2} \end{cases}$

Multiply the first equation by 4 and the second equation by 6 to eliminate fractions and simplify.

$$\begin{cases} 4\left(\dfrac{x-3}{2}\right)=4\left(\dfrac{2-y}{4}\right) \\ 6\left(\dfrac{7-2x}{3}\right)=6\left(\dfrac{y}{2}\right) \end{cases} \rightarrow \begin{cases} 2x-6=2-y \\ 14-4x=3y \end{cases}$$

$$\rightarrow \begin{cases} 2x+y=8 \\ 4x+3y=14 \end{cases}$$

Multiply the first revised equation by -3.

$$\begin{cases} -3(2x+y)=-3(8) \\ 4x+3y=14 \end{cases} \rightarrow \begin{cases} -6x-3y=-24 \\ 4x+3y=14 \end{cases}$$

Add the equations to eliminate y.

$$\begin{array}{r} -6x-3y=-24 \\ 4x+3y=14 \\ \hline -2x\quad\quad=-10 \\ x=5 \end{array}$$

Now solve for y.

$$2x+y=8$$
$$2(5)+y=8$$
$$10+y=8$$
$$y=-2$$

The solution of the system is $(5, -2)$.

16. $\begin{cases} 8x-4y=12 \\ y=2x-3 \end{cases}$

Substitute $2x-3$ for y in the first equation and solve for x.

$$8x-4y=12$$
$$8x-4(2x-3)=12$$
$$8x-8x+12=12$$
$$0=0$$

Since the statement $0=0$ is true, the system has an infinite number of solutions.

17. $\begin{cases} 0.01x-0.06y=-0.23 \\ 0.2x+0.4y=0.2 \end{cases}$

Multiply the first equation by 100 and the second equation by 10 to eliminate decimals.

$$\begin{cases} 100(0.01x-0.06y)=100(-0.23) \\ 10(0.2x+0.4y)=10(0.2) \end{cases}$$

$$\rightarrow \begin{cases} x-6y=-23 \\ 2x+4y=2 \end{cases}$$

Multiply the first equation by -2.

$$\begin{cases} -2(x-6y)=-2(-23) \\ 2x+4y=2 \end{cases} \rightarrow \begin{cases} -2x+12y=46 \\ 2x+4y=2 \end{cases}$$

Add the equations to eliminate x; then solve for y.

$$\begin{array}{r} -2x+12y=46 \\ 2x+4y=2 \\ \hline 16y=48 \\ y=3 \end{array}$$

Now solve for x.

$$x-6y=-23$$
$$x-6(3)=-23$$
$$x-18=-23$$
$$x=-5$$

The solution of the system is $(-5, 3)$.

18. $\begin{cases} x-\dfrac{2}{3}y=3 \\ -2x+3y=10 \end{cases}$

Solve the first equation in terms of x.

$$x-\frac{2}{3}y=3$$
$$x=\frac{2}{3}y+3$$

Substitute $\dfrac{2}{3}y+3$ for x in the second equation and solve for y.

$$-2x + 3y = 10$$

$$-2\left(\frac{2}{3}y + 3\right) + 3y = 10$$

$$-\frac{4}{3}y - 6 + 3y = 10$$

$$-4y - 18 + 9y = 30$$

$$5y = 48$$

$$y = \frac{48}{5}$$

Now solve for x.

$$x = \frac{2}{3}y + 3 = \frac{2}{3}\left(\frac{48}{5}\right) + 3 = \frac{32}{5} + \frac{15}{5} = \frac{47}{5}$$

The solution of the system is $\left(\frac{47}{5}, \frac{48}{5}\right)$.

19. Let x be the first number and the y be the second.

$$\begin{cases} x + y = 124 \\ x - y = 32 \end{cases}$$

Add the equations to eliminate y then solve for x.

$$\begin{array}{r} x + y = 124 \\ x - y = 32 \\ \hline 2x \phantom{{}-y} = 156 \\ x = 78 \end{array}$$

Now solve for y.

$$x + y = 124$$

$$78 + y = 124$$

$$y = 46$$

The numbers are 78 and 46.

20. Let x = number of cc of 12% solution and y = number of cc of 16% solution.

$$\begin{cases} x + 80 = y \\ 0.12x + 0.22(80) = 0.16y \end{cases}$$

Substitute $x + 80$ for y in the second equation; then solve for x.

$$0.12x + 17.6 = 0.16y$$

$$0.12x + 17.6 = 0.16(x + 80)$$

$$0.12x + 17.6 = 0.16x + 12.8$$

$$4.8 = 0.04x$$

$$120 = x$$

120 cc of the 12% saline is needed to make the 16% solution.

21. Let t be the number of farms in Texas and let m be the number of farms in Missouri.

$$\begin{cases} t + m = 336 \\ t = m + 116 \end{cases}$$

Substitute $m + 116$ for t in the first equation and solve for m.

$$t + m = 336$$

$$m + 116 + m = 336$$

$$2m + 116 = 336$$

$$2m = 220$$

$$m = 110$$

$$t = m + 116 = 110 + 116 = 226$$

There are 226 thousand farms in Texas and 110 thousand in Missouri.

22. Let x be speed of one hiker and y be the speed of the other hiker.

$$\begin{cases} 4x + 4y = 36 \\ y = 2x \end{cases}$$

Substitute $2x$ for y in the first equation; then solve for x.

$$4x + 4y = 36$$

$$4x + 4(2x) = 36$$

$$4x + 8x = 36$$

$$12x = 36$$

$$x = 3$$

Now solve for y.

$$y = 2x = 2(3) = 6$$

One hiker hikes at 3 mph and the other hikes at 6 mph.

23. Purchases of country music were equal to purchases of rap/hip-hop music in 1999, between 2003 and 2004, between 2004 and 2005, and between 2005 and 2006.

24. There were more purchases of country music than of rap/hip-hop music in 1998, 2004, 2006, and 2007.

Cumulative Review Chapters 1–14

1. $8 - 15 = 8 + (-15) = -7$

2. $4 - 7 = 4 + (-7) = -3$

3. $-4 - (-5) = -4 + 5 = 1$

4. $3 - (-2) = 3 + 2 = 5$

5.
$$7x = 6x + 4$$
$$7x - 6x = 6x - 6x + 4$$
$$x = 4$$

6.
$$4x = -2 + 3x$$
$$4x - 3x = -2 + 3x - 3x$$
$$x = -2$$

7. "1.2 is 30% of what number?" translates as $1.2 = 30\% \cdot x$.

8. "9 is 45% of what number?" translates as
$9 = 45\% \cdot x$.

9. $x \cdot 50 = 8$

$$\frac{50x}{50} = \frac{8}{50}$$
$$x = 0.16 = 16\%$$

16% of 50 is 8.

10. $x \cdot 16 = 4$

$$\frac{16x}{16} = \frac{4}{16}$$
$$x = 0.25 = 25\%$$

25% of 16 is 4.

11. Let x be the number of freshmen at Slidell High.
31 is 4% of what number?
$$31 = 4\% \cdot x$$
$$31 = 0.04x$$
$$\frac{31}{0.04} = \frac{0.04x}{0.04}$$
$$775 = x$$
There are 775 freshmen at Slidell High.

12. Let x be the number of apples in the shipment.
29 is 2% of what number?
$$29 = 2\% \cdot x$$
$$29 = 0.02x$$
$$\frac{29}{0.02} = \frac{0.02x}{0.02}$$
$$1450 = x$$
There are 1450 apples in the shipment.

13. $-2(x-5)+10 = -3(x+2)+x$
$$-2x+10+10 = -3x-6+x$$
$$-2x+20 = -2x-6$$
$$20 = -6$$
Since the statement $20 = -6$ is false, the equation has no solution.

14. $4(4y+2) = 2(1+6y)+8$
$$16y+8 = 2+12y+8$$
$$16y+8 = 12y+10$$
$$4y+8 = 10$$
$$4y = 2$$
$$\frac{4y}{4} = \frac{2}{4}$$
$$y = \frac{1}{2}$$

15. $-5x+7 < 2(x-3)$
$$-5x+7 < 2x-6$$
$$13 < 7x$$
$$\frac{13}{7} < x$$
$$\left\{ x \middle| x > \frac{13}{7} \right\}$$

16. $-7x+4 \le 3(4-x)$
$$-7x+4 \le 12-3x$$
$$4 \le 12+4x$$
$$-8 \le 4x$$
$$-2 \le x$$
$$\{x | x \ge -2\}$$

17. $\left(\dfrac{m}{n}\right)^7 = \dfrac{m^7}{n^7}$ where $n \ne 0$

18. $(-5x^3)(-7x^4) = -5(-7)x^3 \cdot x^4 = 35x^{3+4} = 35x^7$

19. $\left(\dfrac{2x^4}{3y^5}\right)^4 = \dfrac{2^4 x^{4\cdot4}}{3^4 y^{5\cdot4}} = \dfrac{16x^{16}}{81y^{20}}$ where $y \ne 0$

20. $\left(\dfrac{5x^2}{4y^3}\right)^2 = \dfrac{5^2 x^{2\cdot2}}{4^2 y^{3\cdot2}} = \dfrac{25x^4}{16y^6}$ where $y \ne 0$

21. $(2x^3 + 8x^2 - 6x) - (2x^3 - x^2 + 1)$
$$= 2x^3 + 8x^2 - 6x - 2x^3 + x^2 - 1$$
$$= 9x^2 - 6x - 1$$

22. $(7x+1)-(-x-3) = (7x+1)+(x+3)$
$$= 7x+x+1+3$$
$$= 8x+4$$

23.
$$\begin{array}{r} 2x+4 \\ 3x-1 \overline{)6x^2+10x-5} \\ \underline{6x^2-2x} \\ 12x-5 \\ \underline{12x-4} \\ -1 \end{array}$$

$$\frac{6x^2+10x-1}{3x-1} = 2x+4-\frac{1}{3x-1}$$

24.

$$\begin{array}{r} 3x+2 \\ x-1\overline{\smash{\big)}\,3x^2-x-4} \\ \underline{3x^2-3x} \\ 2x-4 \\ \underline{2x-2} \\ -2 \end{array}$$

$$\frac{3x^2-x-4}{x-1}=3x+2-\frac{2}{x-1}$$

25.
$$x(2x-7)=4$$
$$2x^2-7x=4$$
$$2x^2-7x-4=0$$
$$(2x+1)(x-4)=0$$
$$2x+1=0 \quad \text{or} \quad x-4=0$$
$$2x=-1 \qquad\qquad x=4$$
$$x=-\frac{1}{2}$$

The solutions are $x=-\dfrac{1}{2}$ or $x=4$.

26.
$$x(x-5)=24$$
$$x^2-5x=24$$
$$x^2-5x-24=0$$
$$(x+3)(x-8)=0$$
$$x+3=0 \quad \text{or} \quad x-8=0$$
$$x=-3 \qquad\qquad x=8$$
The solutions are -3 and 8.

27. $x=$ one leg
$x+2=$ other leg
$x+4=$ hypotenuse
$$x^2+(x+2)^2=(x+4)^2$$
$$x^2+x^2+4x+4=x^2+8x+16$$
$$x^2-4x-12=0$$
$$(x-6)(x+2)=0$$
$$x-6=0 \quad \text{or} \quad x+2=0$$
$$x=6 \qquad\qquad x=-2$$
Discard $x=-2$ because length cannot be negative.
one leg: $x=6$
other leg: $x+2=6+2=8$
hypotenuse: $x+4=6+4=10$
The lengths of the sides of the right triangle are 6, 8, and 10 units.

28. Let x be the number.
$$x+x^2=132$$
$$x^2+x-132=0$$
$$(x+12)(x-11)=0$$
$$x+12=0 \quad \text{or} \quad x-11=0$$
$$x=-12 \qquad\qquad x=11$$
The number is -12 or 11.

29. $\dfrac{2y}{2y-7}-\dfrac{7}{2y-7}=\dfrac{2y-7}{2y-7}=1$

30. $\dfrac{x^2+3}{x+9}+\dfrac{9x-3}{x+9}=\dfrac{x^2+3+9x-3}{x+9}$
$$=\frac{x^2+9x}{x+9}$$
$$=\frac{x(x+9)}{x+9}$$
$$=x$$

31. $y=mx+b$
If $y=-1$, then $m=0$.

32. Pick any 2 points on the line $x=2$.
Let $(x_1,y_1)=(2,0)$ and $(x_2,y_2)=(2,5)$.
$$m=\frac{y_2-y_1}{x_2-x_1}=\frac{5-0}{2-2}=\frac{5}{0}=\text{ undefined}$$

33. $m=\dfrac{y_2-y_1}{x_2-x_1}=\dfrac{4-5}{-3-2}=\dfrac{-1}{-5}=\dfrac{1}{5}$
$$y-y_1=m(x-x_1)$$
$$y-5=\frac{1}{5}(x-2)$$
$$y-5=\frac{1}{5}x-\frac{2}{5}$$
$$5(y-5)=5\left(\frac{1}{5}x-\frac{2}{5}\right)$$
$$5y-25=x-2$$
$$-x+5y=23$$

34. $m=\dfrac{y_2-y_1}{x_2-x_1}=\dfrac{5-(-6)}{-6-5}=\dfrac{11}{-11}=-1$
$$y-y_1=m(x-x_1)$$
$$y-(-6)=-1(x-5)$$
$$y+6=-x+5$$
$$y=-x-1$$
$$x+y=-1$$

35. $\{(0, 2), (3, 3), (-1, 0), (3, -2)\}$
Domain: $\{-1, 0, 3\}$
Range: $\{-2, 0, 2, 3\}$

36. $\{(2, 3), (2, 0), (2, -2), (2, 4)\}$
Domain: $\{2\}$
Range: $\{-2, 0, 3, 4\}$

37. $\begin{cases} x + 2y = 7 \\ 2x + 2y = 13 \end{cases}$

Multiply the first equation by -1.
$\begin{cases} -1(x + 2y) = -1(7) \\ 2x + 2y = 13 \end{cases} \rightarrow \begin{cases} -x - 2y = -7 \\ 2x + 2y = 13 \end{cases}$
Add the equations to eliminate y; then solve for x.
$\begin{array}{r} -x - 2y = -7 \\ 2x + 2y = 13 \\ \hline x \quad\quad = 6 \end{array}$
Now solve for y.
$x + 2y = 7$
$6 + 2y = 7$
$2y = 1$
$y = \dfrac{1}{2}$
The solution of the system is $\left(6, \dfrac{1}{2}\right)$.

38. $\begin{cases} 3y = x + 6 \\ 4x + 12y = 0 \end{cases}$

Solve the first equation for x.
$3y - 6 = x$
Substitute $3y - 6$ for x in the second equation and solve for y.
$4x + 12y = 0$
$4(3y - 6) + 12y = 0$
$12y - 24 + 12y = 0$
$24y - 24 = 0$
$24y = 24$
$y = 1$
Now solve for x.
$3y = x + 6$
$3(1) = x + 6$
$3 = x + 6$
$-3 = x$
The solution of the system is $(-3, 1)$.

39. $\begin{cases} -x - \dfrac{y}{2} = \dfrac{5}{2} \\ \dfrac{x}{6} - \dfrac{y}{2} = 0 \end{cases}$

Multiply the first equation by -6 and the second equation by 6.
$\begin{cases} -6\left(-x - \dfrac{y}{2}\right) = -6\left(\dfrac{5}{2}\right) \\ 6\left(\dfrac{x}{6} - \dfrac{y}{2}\right) = 6(0) \end{cases} \rightarrow \begin{cases} 6x + 3y = -15 \\ x - 3y = 0 \end{cases}$

Add the equations to eliminate y; then solve for x.
$\begin{array}{r} 6x + 3y = -15 \\ x - 3y = 0 \\ \hline 7x \quad\quad = -15 \\ x = -\dfrac{15}{7} \end{array}$
Now solve for y.
$-x - \dfrac{y}{2} = \dfrac{5}{2}$
$-\left(-\dfrac{15}{7}\right) - \dfrac{y}{2} = \dfrac{5}{2}$
$14\left(\dfrac{15}{7} - \dfrac{y}{2}\right) = 14\left(\dfrac{5}{2}\right)$
$30 - 7y = 35$
$-7y = 5$
$y = -\dfrac{5}{7}$

The solution of the system is $\left(-\dfrac{15}{7}, -\dfrac{5}{7}\right)$.

40. $\begin{cases} x - \dfrac{3y}{8} = -\dfrac{3}{2} \\ x + \dfrac{y}{9} = \dfrac{13}{3} \end{cases}$

Multiply the first equation by 8 and the second equation by 9.
$\begin{cases} 8\left(x - \dfrac{3y}{8}\right) = 8\left(-\dfrac{3}{2}\right) \\ 9\left(x + \dfrac{y}{9}\right) = 9\left(\dfrac{13}{3}\right) \end{cases} \rightarrow \begin{cases} 8x - 3y = -12 \\ 9x + y = 39 \end{cases}$

Multiply the second equation by 3.
$\begin{cases} 8x - 3y = -12 \\ 3(9x + y) = 3(39) \end{cases} \rightarrow \begin{cases} 8x - 3y = -12 \\ 27x + 3y = 117 \end{cases}$

Add the equations to eliminate y, then solve for x.

$$8x - 3y = -12$$
$$\underline{27x + 3y = 117}$$
$$35x \quad\quad = 105$$
$$x = 3$$

Now solve for y.
$$8x - 3y = -12$$
$$8(3) - 3y = -12$$
$$24 - 3y = -12$$
$$-3y = -36$$
$$y = 12$$

The solution of the system is (3, 12).

41. Let x be the first number and y be the second.
$$\begin{cases} x + y = 37 \\ x - y = 21 \end{cases}$$

Add the equations to eliminate y; then solve for x.
$$x + y = 37$$
$$\underline{x - y = 21}$$
$$2x \quad\quad = 58$$
$$x = 29$$

Now solve for y.
$$x + y = 37$$
$$29 + y = 37$$
$$y = 8$$

The two numbers are 29 and 8.

42. Let x be the first number and y be the second.
$$\begin{cases} x + y = 75 \\ x - y = 9 \end{cases}$$

Add the equations to eliminate y, then solve for x.
$$x + y = 75$$
$$\underline{x - y = 9}$$
$$2x \quad\quad = 84$$
$$x = 42$$

Now solve for y.
$$x + y = 75$$
$$42 + y = 75$$
$$y = 33$$

The two numbers are 42 and 33.

Chapter 15

Section 15.1

Practice Problems

1. $\sqrt{100} = 10$, because $10^2 = 100$ and 10 is positive.

2. $-\sqrt{81} = -9$. The negative sign in front of the radical indicates the negative square root of 81.

3. $\sqrt{\dfrac{25}{81}} = \dfrac{5}{9}$, because $\left(\dfrac{5}{9}\right)^2 = \dfrac{25}{81}$ and $\dfrac{5}{9}$ is positive.

4. $\sqrt{1} = 1$, because $1^2 = 1$ and 1 is positive.

5. $\sqrt{0.81} = 0.9$ because $(0.9)^2 = 0.81$ and 0.9 is positive.

6. $\sqrt[3]{27} = 3$ because $3^3 = 27$.

7. $\sqrt[3]{-8} = -2$ because $(-2)^3 = -8$.

8. $\sqrt[3]{\dfrac{1}{64}} = \dfrac{1}{4}$ because $\left(\dfrac{1}{4}\right)^3 = \dfrac{1}{64}$.

9. $\sqrt[4]{-16}$ is not a real number since the index 4 is even and the radicand -16 is negative.

10. $\sqrt[5]{-1} = -1$ because $(-1)^5 = -1$.

11. $\sqrt[4]{256} = 4$ because $4^4 = 256$ and 4 is positive.

12. $\sqrt[6]{-1}$ is not a real number because the index 6 is even and the radicand -1 is negative.

13. To three decimal places, $\sqrt{22} \approx 4.690$.

14. $\sqrt{z^8} = z^4$ because $(z^4)^2 = z^8$.

15. $\sqrt{x^{20}} = x^{10}$ because $(x^{10})^2 = x^{20}$.

16. $\sqrt{4x^6} = 2x^3$ because $(2x^3)^2 = 4x^6$.

17. $\sqrt[3]{8y^{12}} = 2y^4$ because $(2y^4)^3 = 8y^{12}$.

18. $\sqrt[3]{-64x^9 y^{24}} = -4x^3 y^8$ because $(-4x^3 y^8)^3 = -64x^9 y^{24}$.

19. $\sqrt[3]{-64x^9 y^{24}} = -4x^3 y^8$ because $(-4x^3 y^8)^3 = -64x^9 y^{24}$.

Calculator Explorations

1. $\sqrt{6} \approx 2.449$; since 6 is between perfect squares 4 and 9, $\sqrt{6}$ is between $\sqrt{4} = 2$ and $\sqrt{9} = 3$.

2. $\sqrt{14} \approx 3.742$; since 14 is between perfect squares 9 and 16, $\sqrt{14}$ is between $\sqrt{9} = 3$ and $\sqrt{16} = 4$.

3. $\sqrt{11} \approx 3.317$; since 11 is between perfect squares 9 and 16, $\sqrt{11}$ is between $\sqrt{9} = 3$ and $\sqrt{16} = 4$.

4. $\sqrt{200} \approx 14.142$; since 200 is between perfect squares 196 and 225, $\sqrt{200}$ is between $\sqrt{196} = 14$ and $\sqrt{225} = 15$.

5. $\sqrt{82} \approx 9.055$; since 82 is between perfect squares 81 and 100, $\sqrt{82}$ is between $\sqrt{81} = 9$ and $\sqrt{100} = 10$.

6. $\sqrt{46} \approx 6.782$; since 46 is between perfect squares 36 and 49, $\sqrt{46}$ is between $\sqrt{36} = 6$ and $\sqrt{49} = 7$.

7. $\sqrt[3]{40} \approx 3.420$

8. $\sqrt[3]{71} \approx 4.141$

9. $\sqrt[4]{20} \approx 2.115$

10. $\sqrt[4]{15} \approx 1.968$

11. $\sqrt[5]{18} \approx 1.783$

12. $\sqrt[6]{2} \approx 1.122$

Vocabulary and Readiness Check

1. The symbol $\sqrt{}$ is used to denote the positive, or <u>principal</u>, square root.

2. In the expression $\sqrt[4]{16}$, the number 4 is called the <u>index</u>, the number 16 is called the <u>radicand</u>, and $\sqrt{}$ is called the <u>radical sign</u>.

3. The reverse operation of squaring a number is finding a <u>square root</u> of a number.

4. For a positive number a,
$-\sqrt{a}$ is the <u>negative</u> square root of a and
$\sqrt{a}$ is the <u>positive</u> square root of a.

5. An nth root of a number a is a number whose nth <u>power</u> is a.

6. $\sqrt{4} = 2$; the statement is false.

7. $\sqrt{-9}$ is not a real number; the statement is false.

8. $\sqrt{1000} \approx 31.623$; the statement is false.

9. True

10. True

Exercise Set 15.1

1. $\sqrt{16} = 4$, because $4^2 = 16$ and 4 is positive.

3. $\sqrt{\dfrac{1}{25}} = \dfrac{1}{5}$, because $\left(\dfrac{1}{5}\right)^2 = \dfrac{1}{25}$ and $\dfrac{1}{5}$ is positive.

5. $-\sqrt{100} = -10$. The negative sign indicates the negative square root of 100.

7. $\sqrt{-4}$ is not a real number, because there is no real number whose square is -4.

9. $-\sqrt{121} = -11$. The negative sign indicates the negative square root of 121.

11. $\sqrt{\dfrac{9}{25}} = \dfrac{3}{5}$, because $\left(\dfrac{3}{5}\right)^2 = \dfrac{9}{25}$ and $\dfrac{3}{5}$ is positive.

13. $\sqrt{900} = 30$, because $30^2 = 900$ and 30 is positive.

15. $\sqrt{144} = 12$, because $12^2 = 144$ and 12 is positive.

17. $\sqrt{\dfrac{1}{100}} = \dfrac{1}{10}$, because $\left(\dfrac{1}{10}\right)^2 = \dfrac{1}{100}$ and $\dfrac{1}{10}$ is positive.

19. $\sqrt{0.25} = 0.5$, because $0.5^2 = 0.25$ and 0.5 is positive.

21. $\sqrt[3]{125} = 5$, because $5^3 = 125$.

23. $\sqrt[3]{-64} = -4$, because $(-4)^3 = -64$.

25. $-\sqrt[3]{8} = -2$, because $2^3 = 8$.

27. $\sqrt[3]{\dfrac{1}{8}} = \dfrac{1}{2}$, because $\left(\dfrac{1}{2}\right)^3 = \dfrac{1}{8}$.

29. $\sqrt[3]{-125} = -5$, because $(-5)^3 = -125$.

31. $\sqrt[5]{32} = 2$, because $2^5 = 32$.

33. $\sqrt{81} = 9$, because $9^2 = 81$ and 9 is positive.

35. $\sqrt[4]{-16}$ is not a real number since the index 4 is even and the radicand -16 is negative.

37. $\sqrt[3]{-\dfrac{27}{64}} = -\dfrac{3}{4}$, because $\left(-\dfrac{3}{4}\right)^3 = -\dfrac{27}{64}$.

39. $-\sqrt[4]{625} = -5$, because $5^4 = 625$.

41. $\sqrt[6]{1} = 1$, because $1^6 = 1$ and 1 is positive.

43. $\sqrt{7} \approx 2.646$

45. $\sqrt{37} \approx 6.083$

47. $\sqrt{136} \approx 11.662$

49. $\sqrt{2} \approx 1.41$
$90\sqrt{2} \approx 90(1.41) = 126.90$
The distance from home plate to second base is approximately 126.90 feet.

51. $\sqrt{m^2} = m$, because $m^2 = m^2$.

53. $\sqrt{x^4} = x^2$, because $(x^2)^2 = x^4$.

55. $\sqrt{9x^8} = 3x^4$, because $(3x^4)^2 = 9x^8$.

57. $\sqrt{81x^2} = 9x$ because $(9x)^2 = 81x^2$.

59. $\sqrt{a^2b^4} = ab^2$, because $(ab^2)^2 = a^2b^4$.

61. $\sqrt{16a^6b^4} = 4a^3b^2$, because $(4a^3b^2)^2 = 16a^6b^4$

63. $\sqrt[3]{a^6b^{18}} = a^2b^6$, because $(a^2b^6)^3 = a^6b^{18}$.

65. $\sqrt[3]{-8x^3y^{27}} = -2xy^9$, because
$(-2xy^9)^3 = -8x^3y^{27}$

67. $\sqrt{\dfrac{x^6}{36}} = \dfrac{x^3}{6}$, because $\left(\dfrac{x^3}{6}\right)^2 = \dfrac{x^6}{36}$.

69. $\sqrt{\dfrac{25y^2}{9}} = \dfrac{5y}{3}$, because $\left(\dfrac{5y}{3}\right)^2 = \dfrac{25y^2}{9}$.

71. $50 = 25 \cdot 2$

73. $32 = 16 \cdot 2$ or
$32 = 4 \cdot 8$

75. $28 = 4 \cdot 7$

77. $27 = 9 \cdot 3$

79. a. $\sqrt[7]{-1}$ is a real number because the index is odd.

    b. $\sqrt[3]{-125}$ is a real number because the index is odd.

    c. $\sqrt[6]{-128}$ is not a real number because the index is even and the radicand is negative.

    d. $\sqrt[8]{-1}$ is not a real number because the index is even and the radicand is negative.

81. The length of the side is $\sqrt{49}$. Since $7^2 = 49$, $\sqrt{49} = 7$ and the sides of the square have length 7 miles.

83. The length of a side is $\sqrt{9.61}$ inches. Since $(3.1)^2 = 9.61$, $\sqrt{9.61} = 3.1$. The length of a side is 3.1 inches.

85. $\sqrt{\sqrt{81}} = \sqrt{9} = 3$, since $3^2 = 9$ and $9^2 = 81$.

87. $\sqrt{\sqrt{10,000}} = 10$ since $10^2 = 100$ and $100^2 = 10,000$.

89. Since $\sqrt{18}$ is between $\sqrt{16}$ and $\sqrt{25}$, then $\sqrt{18}$ is between 4 and 5.

91. Since $\sqrt{80}$ is between $\sqrt{64}$ and $\sqrt{81}$, then $\sqrt{80}$ is between 8 and 9.

93. $T = 2\pi\sqrt{\dfrac{L}{g}} = 2\pi\sqrt{\dfrac{30}{32}} \approx 2(3.14)(0.968) \approx 6.1$

The period of the pendulum is 6.1 seconds.

95. answers may vary

97.

x	$y = \sqrt{x}$
0	$\sqrt{0} = 0$
1	$\sqrt{1} = 1$
3	$\sqrt{3} \approx 1.7$
4	$\sqrt{4} = 2$
9	$\sqrt{9} = 3$

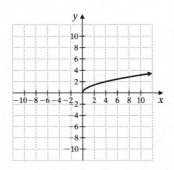

99. $\sqrt{x^2} = |x|$

101. $\sqrt{(x+2)^2} = |x+2|$

103. The graph of $y = \sqrt{x-2}$ 'starts' at $(2, 0)$.

105. The graph of $y = \sqrt{x+4}$ 'starts' at $(-4, 0)$.

Section 15.2

Practice Problems

1. $\sqrt{40} = \sqrt{4 \cdot 10} = \sqrt{4} \cdot \sqrt{10} = 2\sqrt{10}$

2. $\sqrt{18} = \sqrt{9 \cdot 2} = \sqrt{9} \cdot \sqrt{2} = 3\sqrt{2}$

3. $\sqrt{500} = \sqrt{100 \cdot 5} = \sqrt{100} \cdot \sqrt{5} = 10\sqrt{5}$

4. $\sqrt{15}$

The radicand 15 contains no perfect square factors other than 1. Thus $\sqrt{15}$ is in simplest form.

5. $7\sqrt{75} = 7 \cdot \sqrt{25 \cdot 3}$
$= 7 \cdot \sqrt{25} \cdot \sqrt{3}$
$= 7 \cdot 5 \cdot \sqrt{3}$
$= 35\sqrt{3}$

6. $\sqrt{\dfrac{16}{81}} = \dfrac{\sqrt{16}}{\sqrt{81}} = \dfrac{4}{9}$

7. $\sqrt{\dfrac{2}{25}} = \dfrac{\sqrt{2}}{\sqrt{25}} = \dfrac{\sqrt{2}}{5}$

8. $\sqrt{\dfrac{45}{49}} = \dfrac{\sqrt{45}}{\sqrt{49}} = \dfrac{\sqrt{9} \cdot \sqrt{5}}{7} = \dfrac{3\sqrt{5}}{7}$

9. $\sqrt{x^{11}} = \sqrt{x^{10} \cdot x} = \sqrt{x^{10}} \cdot \sqrt{x} = x^5\sqrt{x}$

10. $\sqrt{18x^4} = \sqrt{9 \cdot 2 \cdot x^4}$
$= \sqrt{9x^4 \cdot 2}$
$= \sqrt{9x^4} \cdot \sqrt{2}$
$= 3x^2\sqrt{2}$

11. $\sqrt{\dfrac{27}{x^8}} = \dfrac{\sqrt{27}}{\sqrt{x^8}} = \dfrac{\sqrt{9 \cdot 3}}{x^4} = \dfrac{\sqrt{9} \cdot \sqrt{3}}{x^4} = \dfrac{3\sqrt{3}}{x^4}$

12. $\sqrt{\dfrac{7y^7}{25}} = \dfrac{\sqrt{7y^7}}{\sqrt{25}}$
$= \dfrac{\sqrt{y^6 \cdot 7y}}{5}$
$= \dfrac{\sqrt{y^6} \cdot \sqrt{7}}{5}$
$= \dfrac{y^3\sqrt{7y}}{5}$

13. $\sqrt[3]{88} = \sqrt[3]{8 \cdot 11} = \sqrt[3]{8} \cdot \sqrt[3]{11} = 2\sqrt[3]{11}$

14. $\sqrt[3]{50}$
The number 50 contains no perfect cube factors, so $\sqrt[3]{50}$ cannot be simplified further.

15. $\sqrt[3]{\dfrac{10}{27}} = \dfrac{\sqrt[3]{10}}{\sqrt[3]{27}} = \dfrac{\sqrt[3]{10}}{3}$

16. $\sqrt[3]{\dfrac{81}{8}} = \dfrac{\sqrt[3]{81}}{\sqrt[3]{8}} = \dfrac{\sqrt[3]{27 \cdot 3}}{2} = \dfrac{\sqrt[3]{27} \cdot \sqrt[3]{3}}{2} = \dfrac{3\sqrt[3]{3}}{2}$

Vocabulary and Readiness Check

1. If $\sqrt{a}$ and $\sqrt{b}$ are real numbers, then $\sqrt{a \cdot b} = \underline{\sqrt{a} \cdot \sqrt{b}}$.

2. If $\sqrt{a}$ and $\sqrt{b}$ are real numbers, then $\sqrt{\dfrac{a}{b}} = \underline{\dfrac{\sqrt{a}}{\sqrt{b}}}$.

3. $\sqrt{16 \cdot 25} = \sqrt{\underline{16}} \cdot \sqrt{\underline{25}} = \underline{4} \cdot \underline{5} = \underline{20}$

4. $\sqrt{36 \cdot 3} = \sqrt{\underline{36}} \cdot \sqrt{\underline{3}} = \underline{6} \cdot \sqrt{\underline{3}} = \underline{6\sqrt{3}}$

5. $\sqrt{48} = 2\sqrt{12}$
$= 2\sqrt{4 \cdot 3}$
$= 2\sqrt{4} \cdot \sqrt{3}$
$= 2 \cdot 2\sqrt{3}$
$= 4\sqrt{3}$
The statement is false.

6. True; 6 has no perfect cube factors.

Exercise Set 15.2

1. $\sqrt{20} = \sqrt{4 \cdot 5} = \sqrt{4}\sqrt{5} = 2\sqrt{5}$

3. $\sqrt{50} = \sqrt{25 \cdot 2} = \sqrt{25} \cdot \sqrt{2} = 5\sqrt{2}$

5. $\sqrt{33}$ is in simplest form.

7. $\sqrt{98} = \sqrt{49 \cdot 2} = \sqrt{49} \cdot \sqrt{2} = 7\sqrt{2}$

9. $\sqrt{60} = \sqrt{4 \cdot 15} = \sqrt{4} \cdot \sqrt{15} = 2\sqrt{15}$

11. $\sqrt{180} = \sqrt{36 \cdot 5} = \sqrt{36} \cdot \sqrt{5} = 6\sqrt{5}$

13. $\sqrt{52} = \sqrt{4 \cdot 13} = \sqrt{4} \cdot \sqrt{13} = 2\sqrt{13}$

15. $3\sqrt{25} = 3 \cdot 5 = 15$

17. $7\sqrt{63} = 7\sqrt{9 \cdot 7} = 7 \cdot \sqrt{9} \cdot \sqrt{7} = 7 \cdot 3 \cdot \sqrt{7} = 21\sqrt{7}$

19. $-5\sqrt{27} = -5 \cdot \sqrt{9 \cdot 3}$
$= -5 \cdot \sqrt{9} \cdot \sqrt{3}$
$= -5 \cdot 3 \cdot \sqrt{3}$
$= -15\sqrt{3}$

21. $\sqrt{\dfrac{8}{25}} = \dfrac{\sqrt{8}}{\sqrt{25}} = \dfrac{\sqrt{4 \cdot 2}}{5} = \dfrac{\sqrt{4}\sqrt{2}}{5} = \dfrac{2\sqrt{2}}{5}$

23. $\sqrt{\dfrac{27}{121}} = \dfrac{\sqrt{27}}{\sqrt{121}} = \dfrac{\sqrt{9 \cdot 3}}{11} = \dfrac{\sqrt{9} \cdot \sqrt{3}}{11} = \dfrac{3\sqrt{3}}{11}$

25. $\sqrt{\dfrac{9}{4}} = \dfrac{\sqrt{9}}{\sqrt{4}} = \dfrac{3}{2}$

27. $\sqrt{\dfrac{125}{9}} = \dfrac{\sqrt{125}}{\sqrt{9}} = \dfrac{\sqrt{25 \cdot 5}}{3} = \dfrac{\sqrt{25} \cdot \sqrt{5}}{3} = \dfrac{5\sqrt{5}}{3}$

29. $\sqrt{\dfrac{11}{36}} = \dfrac{\sqrt{11}}{\sqrt{36}} = \dfrac{\sqrt{11}}{6}$

31. $-\sqrt{\dfrac{27}{144}} = -\dfrac{\sqrt{27}}{\sqrt{144}}$
$= -\dfrac{\sqrt{9 \cdot 3}}{12}$
$= -\dfrac{\sqrt{9} \cdot \sqrt{3}}{12}$
$= -\dfrac{3\sqrt{3}}{12}$
$= -\dfrac{\sqrt{3}}{4}$

33. $\sqrt{x^7} = \sqrt{x^6 \cdot x} = \sqrt{x^6}\sqrt{x} = x^3\sqrt{x}$

35. $\sqrt{x^{13}} = \sqrt{x^{12} \cdot x} = \sqrt{x^{12}} \cdot \sqrt{x} = x^6\sqrt{x}$

37. $\sqrt{36a^3} = \sqrt{36a^2 \cdot a} = \sqrt{36a^2}\sqrt{a} = 6a\sqrt{a}$

39. $\sqrt{96x^4} = \sqrt{16x^4 \cdot 6} = \sqrt{16x^4} \cdot \sqrt{6} = 4x^2\sqrt{6}$

41. $\sqrt{\dfrac{12}{m^2}} = \dfrac{\sqrt{12}}{\sqrt{m^2}} = \dfrac{\sqrt{4 \cdot 3}}{m} = \dfrac{\sqrt{4}\sqrt{3}}{m} = \dfrac{2\sqrt{3}}{m}$

43. $\sqrt{\dfrac{9x}{y^{10}}} = \dfrac{\sqrt{9x}}{\sqrt{y^{10}}} = \dfrac{\sqrt{9}\sqrt{x}}{y^5} = \dfrac{3\sqrt{x}}{y^5}$

45. $\sqrt{\dfrac{88}{x^{12}}} = \dfrac{\sqrt{88}}{\sqrt{x^{12}}} = \dfrac{\sqrt{4 \cdot 22}}{x^6} = \dfrac{\sqrt{4}\sqrt{22}}{x^6} = \dfrac{2\sqrt{22}}{x^6}$

47. $8\sqrt{4} = 8 \cdot 2 = 16$

49. $\sqrt{\dfrac{36}{121}} = \dfrac{\sqrt{36}}{\sqrt{121}} = \dfrac{6}{11}$

51. $\sqrt{175} = \sqrt{25 \cdot 7} = \sqrt{25} \cdot \sqrt{7} = 5\sqrt{7}$

53. $\sqrt{\dfrac{20}{9}} = \dfrac{\sqrt{20}}{\sqrt{9}} = \dfrac{\sqrt{4 \cdot 5}}{3} = \dfrac{\sqrt{4}\sqrt{5}}{3} = \dfrac{2\sqrt{5}}{3}$

55. $\sqrt{24m^7} = \sqrt{4m^6 \cdot 6m} = \sqrt{4m^6} \cdot \sqrt{6m} = 2m^3\sqrt{6m}$

57. $\sqrt{\dfrac{23y^3}{4x^6}} = \dfrac{\sqrt{23y^3}}{\sqrt{4x^6}}$
$= \dfrac{\sqrt{y^2 \cdot 23y}}{2x^3}$
$= \dfrac{\sqrt{y^2}\sqrt{23y}}{2x^3}$
$= \dfrac{y\sqrt{23y}}{2x^3}$

59. $\sqrt[3]{24} = \sqrt[3]{8 \cdot 3} = \sqrt[3]{8} \cdot \sqrt[3]{3} = 2\sqrt[3]{3}$

61. $\sqrt[3]{250} = \sqrt[3]{125 \cdot 2} = \sqrt[3]{125} \cdot \sqrt[3]{2} = 5\sqrt[3]{2}$

63. $\sqrt[3]{\dfrac{5}{64}} = \dfrac{\sqrt[3]{5}}{\sqrt[3]{64}} = \dfrac{\sqrt[3]{5}}{4}$

65. $\sqrt[3]{\dfrac{23}{8}} = \dfrac{\sqrt[3]{23}}{\sqrt[3]{8}} = \dfrac{\sqrt[3]{23}}{2}$

67. $\sqrt[3]{\dfrac{15}{64}} = \dfrac{\sqrt[3]{15}}{\sqrt[3]{64}} = \dfrac{\sqrt[3]{15}}{4}$

69. $\sqrt[3]{80} = \sqrt[3]{8 \cdot 10} = \sqrt[3]{8} \cdot \sqrt[3]{10} = 2\sqrt[3]{10}$

71. $6x + 8x = 14x$

73. $(2x+3)(x-5) = 2x^2 - 10x + 3x - 15$
$= 2x^2 - 7x - 15$

75. $9y^2 - 9y^2 = 0$

77. $\sqrt{x^6 y^3} = \sqrt{x^6 y^2 y} = \sqrt{x^6} \cdot \sqrt{y^2} \cdot \sqrt{y} = x^3 y \sqrt{y}$

79. $\sqrt{98x^5 y^4} = \sqrt{49x^4 y^4 \cdot 2x}$
$= \sqrt{49x^4 y^4} \cdot \sqrt{2x}$
$= 7x^2 y^2 \sqrt{2x}$

81. $\sqrt[3]{-8x^6} = \sqrt[3]{-8} \cdot \sqrt[3]{x^6} = -2x^3$

83. $\sqrt[3]{80} = \sqrt[3]{8 \cdot 10} = \sqrt[3]{8} \cdot \sqrt[3]{10} = 2\sqrt[3]{10}$
Each side length is $2\sqrt[3]{10}$ inches.

85. answers may vary; possible answer: let $a = 1$ and
$b = 1$ so $\sqrt{a^2 + b^2} = \sqrt{2} \neq a + b = 2$.

87. $\dfrac{\sqrt{6A}}{6} = \dfrac{\sqrt{6 \cdot 120}}{6}$
$= \dfrac{\sqrt{720}}{6}$
$= \dfrac{\sqrt{144 \cdot 5}}{6}$
$= \dfrac{\sqrt{144} \cdot \sqrt{5}}{6}$
$= \dfrac{12\sqrt{5}}{6}$
$= 2\sqrt{5}$
The length of a side is $2\sqrt{5}$ inches.

89. $\sqrt{31,329} = 177$
The roof of the Water Cube is 177 meters by 177 meters.

91. Use $\dfrac{\sqrt{6A}}{6}$ with $A = 30.375$.
$\dfrac{\sqrt{6 \cdot 30.375}}{6} = \dfrac{\sqrt{182.25}}{6} = \dfrac{13.5}{6} = 2.25$

93. $C = 100\sqrt[3]{n} + 700$
$= 100\sqrt[3]{1000} + 700$
$= 100 \cdot 10 + 700$
$= 1000 + 700$
$= 1700$
The cost is \$1700.

95. $h = 169$ and $w = 64$.
$B = \sqrt{\dfrac{hw}{3600}}$
$= \sqrt{\dfrac{169 \cdot 64}{3600}}$
$= \dfrac{\sqrt{169 \cdot 64}}{\sqrt{3600}}$
$= \dfrac{\sqrt{169}\sqrt{64}}{60}$
$= \dfrac{13 \cdot 8}{60}$
$= \dfrac{104}{60}$
$= \dfrac{26}{15} \approx 1.7$
The body surface area is about 1.7 square meters.

Section 15.3

Practice Problems

1. $6\sqrt{11} + 9\sqrt{11} = (6+9)\sqrt{11} = 15\sqrt{11}$

2. $\sqrt{7} - 3\sqrt{7} = 1\sqrt{7} - 3\sqrt{7} = (1-3)\sqrt{7} = -2\sqrt{7}$

3. $\sqrt{2} + \sqrt{2} - \sqrt{15} = 1\sqrt{2} + 1\sqrt{2} - \sqrt{15}$
$= (1+1)\sqrt{2} - \sqrt{15}$
$= 2\sqrt{2} - \sqrt{15}$

4. $3\sqrt{3} - 3\sqrt{2}$ cannot be simplified further since the radicands are not the same.

5. $\sqrt{27} + \sqrt{75} = \sqrt{9 \cdot 3} + \sqrt{25 \cdot 3}$
$= \sqrt{9} \cdot \sqrt{3} + \sqrt{25} \cdot \sqrt{3}$
$= 3\sqrt{3} + 5\sqrt{3}$
$= 8\sqrt{3}$

6. $3\sqrt{20} - 7\sqrt{45} = 3\sqrt{4 \cdot 5} - 7\sqrt{9 \cdot 5}$
$= 3\sqrt{4} \cdot \sqrt{5} - 7\sqrt{9} \cdot \sqrt{5}$
$= 3 \cdot 2\sqrt{5} - 7 \cdot 3\sqrt{5}$
$= 6\sqrt{5} - 21\sqrt{5}$
$= -15\sqrt{5}$

7. $\sqrt{36} - \sqrt{48} - 4\sqrt{3} - \sqrt{9} = 6 - \sqrt{16 \cdot 3} - 4\sqrt{3} - 3$
$= 6 - \sqrt{16} \cdot \sqrt{3} - 4\sqrt{3} - 3$
$= 6 - 4\sqrt{3} - 4\sqrt{3} - 3$
$= 3 - 8\sqrt{3}$

8. $\sqrt{9x^4} - \sqrt{36x^3} + \sqrt{x^3}$
$= 3x^2 - \sqrt{36x^2 \cdot x} + \sqrt{x^2 \cdot x}$
$= 3x^2 - \sqrt{36x^2} \cdot \sqrt{x} + \sqrt{x^2} \cdot \sqrt{x}$
$= 3x^2 - 6x\sqrt{x} + x\sqrt{x}$
$= 3x^2 - 5x\sqrt{x}$

9. $10\sqrt[3]{81p^6} - \sqrt[3]{24p^6} = 10\sqrt[3]{27p^6 \cdot 3} - \sqrt[3]{8p^6 \cdot 3}$
$= 10\sqrt[3]{27p^6} \cdot \sqrt[3]{3} - \sqrt[3]{8p^6} \cdot \sqrt[3]{3}$
$= 10 \cdot 3p^2 \sqrt[3]{3} - 2p^2 \sqrt[3]{3}$
$= 30p^2 \sqrt[3]{3} - 2p^2 \sqrt[3]{3}$
$= 28p^2 \sqrt[3]{3}$

Vocabulary and Readiness Check

1. Radicals that have the same index and same radicand are called <u>like radicals</u>.

2. The expressions $7\sqrt[3]{2x}$ and $-\sqrt[3]{2x}$ are called <u>like radicals</u>.

3. $11\sqrt{2} + 6\sqrt{2} = \underline{17\sqrt{2}}$

4. $\sqrt{5}$ is the same as $\underline{1\sqrt{5}}$.

5. $\sqrt{5} + \sqrt{5} = \underline{2\sqrt{5}}$

6. $9\sqrt{7} - \sqrt{7} = \underline{8\sqrt{7}}$

Exercise Set 15.3

1. $4\sqrt{3} - 8\sqrt{3} = (4 - 8)\sqrt{3} = -4\sqrt{3}$

3. $3\sqrt{6} + 8\sqrt{6} - 2\sqrt{6} - 5 = (3 + 8 - 2)\sqrt{6} - 5$
$= 9\sqrt{6} - 5$

5. $6\sqrt{5} - 5\sqrt{5} + \sqrt{2} = (6 - 5)\sqrt{5} + \sqrt{2} = \sqrt{5} + \sqrt{2}$

7. $2\sqrt{3} + 5\sqrt{3} - \sqrt{2} = (2 + 5)\sqrt{3} - \sqrt{2} = 7\sqrt{3} - \sqrt{2}$

9. $2\sqrt{2} - 7\sqrt{2} - 6 = (2 - 7)\sqrt{2} - 6 = -5\sqrt{2} - 6$

11. $\sqrt{12} + \sqrt{27} = \sqrt{4 \cdot 3} + \sqrt{9 \cdot 3}$
$= \sqrt{4}\sqrt{3} + \sqrt{9}\sqrt{3}$
$= 2\sqrt{3} + 3\sqrt{3}$
$= (2 + 3)\sqrt{3}$
$= 5\sqrt{3}$

13. $\sqrt{45} + 3\sqrt{20} = \sqrt{9 \cdot 5} + 3\sqrt{4 \cdot 5}$
$= \sqrt{9}\sqrt{5} + 3\sqrt{4}\sqrt{5}$
$= 3\sqrt{5} + 3 \cdot 2\sqrt{5}$
$= 3\sqrt{5} + 6\sqrt{5}$
$= (3 + 6)\sqrt{5}$
$= 9\sqrt{5}$

15. $2\sqrt{54} - \sqrt{20} + \sqrt{45} - \sqrt{24}$
$= 2\sqrt{9 \cdot 6} - \sqrt{4 \cdot 5} + \sqrt{9 \cdot 5} - \sqrt{4 \cdot 6}$
$= 2\sqrt{9}\sqrt{6} - \sqrt{4}\sqrt{5} + \sqrt{9}\sqrt{5} - \sqrt{4}\sqrt{6}$
$= 2 \cdot 3\sqrt{6} - 2\sqrt{5} + 3\sqrt{5} - 2\sqrt{6}$
$= 6\sqrt{6} - 2\sqrt{5} + 3\sqrt{5} - 2\sqrt{6}$
$= (6 - 2)\sqrt{6} + (3 - 2)\sqrt{5}$
$= 4\sqrt{6} + 1\sqrt{5}$
$= 4\sqrt{6} + \sqrt{5}$

17. $4x - 3\sqrt{x^2} + \sqrt{x} = 4x - 3x + \sqrt{x} = x + \sqrt{x}$

19. $\sqrt{25x} + \sqrt{36x} - 11\sqrt{x} = \sqrt{25}\sqrt{x} + \sqrt{36}\sqrt{x} - 11\sqrt{x}$
$= 5\sqrt{x} + 6\sqrt{x} - 11\sqrt{x}$
$= (5 + 6 - 11)\sqrt{x}$
$= 0$

21. $\sqrt{\dfrac{5}{9}} + \sqrt{\dfrac{5}{81}} = \dfrac{\sqrt{5}}{\sqrt{9}} + \dfrac{\sqrt{5}}{\sqrt{81}}$

$= \dfrac{\sqrt{5}}{3} + \dfrac{\sqrt{5}}{9}$

$= \dfrac{3\sqrt{5}}{9} + \dfrac{\sqrt{5}}{9}$

$= \left(\dfrac{3}{9} + \dfrac{1}{9}\right)\sqrt{5}$

$= \dfrac{4}{9}\sqrt{5}$

$= \dfrac{4\sqrt{5}}{9}$

23. $\sqrt{\dfrac{3}{4}} - \sqrt{\dfrac{3}{64}} = \dfrac{\sqrt{3}}{\sqrt{4}} - \dfrac{\sqrt{3}}{\sqrt{64}}$

$= \dfrac{\sqrt{3}}{2} - \dfrac{\sqrt{3}}{8}$

$= \dfrac{4\sqrt{3}}{8} - \dfrac{\sqrt{3}}{8}$

$= \left(\dfrac{4}{8} - \dfrac{1}{8}\right)\sqrt{3}$

$= \dfrac{3}{8}\sqrt{3}$

$= \dfrac{3\sqrt{3}}{8}$

25. $12\sqrt{5} - \sqrt{5} - 4\sqrt{5} = (12 - 1 - 4)\sqrt{5} = 7\sqrt{5}$

27. $\sqrt{75} + \sqrt{48} = \sqrt{25 \cdot 3} + \sqrt{16 \cdot 3}$

$= \sqrt{25}\sqrt{3} + \sqrt{16}\sqrt{3}$

$= 5\sqrt{3} + 4\sqrt{3}$

$= (5 + 4)\sqrt{3}$

$= 9\sqrt{3}$

29. $\sqrt{5} + \sqrt{15}$ is in simplest form.

31. $3\sqrt{x^3} - x\sqrt{4x} = 3\sqrt{x^2 \cdot x} - x\sqrt{4 \cdot x}$

$= 3\sqrt{x^2}\sqrt{x} - x\sqrt{4}\sqrt{x}$

$= 3x\sqrt{x} - 2x\sqrt{x}$

$= (3x - 2x)\sqrt{x}$

$= x\sqrt{x}$

33. $\sqrt{8} + \sqrt{9} + \sqrt{18} + \sqrt{81} = \sqrt{4 \cdot 2} + 3 + \sqrt{9 \cdot 2} + 9$

$= \sqrt{4}\sqrt{2} + 3 + \sqrt{9}\sqrt{2} + 9$

$= 2\sqrt{2} + 3 + 3\sqrt{2} + 9$

$= (2 + 3)\sqrt{2} + 3 + 9$

$= 5\sqrt{2} + 12$

35. $4 + 8\sqrt{2} - 9 = 8\sqrt{2} - 5$

37. $2\sqrt{45} - 2\sqrt{20} = 2\sqrt{9 \cdot 5} - 2\sqrt{4 \cdot 5}$

$= 2\sqrt{9}\sqrt{5} - 2\sqrt{4}\sqrt{5}$

$= 2 \cdot 3\sqrt{5} - 2 \cdot 2\sqrt{5}$

$= 6\sqrt{5} - 4\sqrt{5}$

$= (6 - 4)\sqrt{5}$

$= 2\sqrt{5}$

39. $\sqrt{35} - \sqrt{140} = \sqrt{35} - \sqrt{4 \cdot 35}$

$= \sqrt{35} - \sqrt{4}\sqrt{35}$

$= \sqrt{35} - 2\sqrt{35}$

$= (1 - 2)\sqrt{35}$

$= -1\sqrt{35}$

$= -\sqrt{35}$

41. $6 - 2\sqrt{3} - \sqrt{3} = 6 + (-2 - 1)\sqrt{3} = 6 - 3\sqrt{3}$

43. $3\sqrt{9x} + 2\sqrt{x} = 3\sqrt{9}\sqrt{x} + 2\sqrt{x}$

$= 3 \cdot 3\sqrt{x} + 2\sqrt{x}$

$= 9\sqrt{x} + 2\sqrt{x}$

$= (9 + 2)\sqrt{x}$

$= 11\sqrt{x}$

45. $\sqrt{9x^2} + \sqrt{81x^2} - 11\sqrt{x} = 3x + 9x - 11\sqrt{x}$

$= 12x - 11\sqrt{x}$

47. $\sqrt{3x^3} + 3x\sqrt{x} = \sqrt{x^2 \cdot 3x} + 3x\sqrt{x}$

$= \sqrt{x^2}\sqrt{3x} + 3x\sqrt{x}$

$= x\sqrt{3x} + 3x\sqrt{x}$

49. $\sqrt{32x^2} + \sqrt{32x^2} + \sqrt{4x^2}$

$= \sqrt{16x^2 \cdot 2} + \sqrt{16x^2 \cdot 2} + 2x$

$= \sqrt{16x^2}\sqrt{2} + \sqrt{16x^2}\sqrt{2} + 2x$

$= 4x\sqrt{2} + 4x\sqrt{2} + 2x$

$= (4x + 4x)\sqrt{2} + 2x$

$= 8x\sqrt{2} + 2x$

51. $\sqrt{40x} + \sqrt{40x^4} - 2\sqrt{10x} - \sqrt{5x^4}$
$= \sqrt{4 \cdot 10x} + \sqrt{4x^4 \cdot 10} - 2\sqrt{10x} - \sqrt{x^4 \cdot 5}$
$= \sqrt{4}\sqrt{10x} + \sqrt{4x^4}\sqrt{10} - 2\sqrt{10x} - \sqrt{x^4}\sqrt{5}$
$= 2\sqrt{10x} + 2x^2\sqrt{10} - 2\sqrt{10x} - x^2\sqrt{5}$
$= (2-2)\sqrt{10x} + 2x^2\sqrt{10} - x^2\sqrt{5}$
$= 0\sqrt{10x} + 2x^2\sqrt{10} - x^2\sqrt{5}$
$= 2x^2\sqrt{10} - x^2\sqrt{5}$

53. $2\sqrt[3]{9} + 5\sqrt[3]{9} - \sqrt[3]{25} = (2+5)\sqrt[3]{9} - \sqrt[3]{25}$
$\qquad\qquad\qquad\qquad\qquad = 7\sqrt[3]{9} - \sqrt[3]{25}$

55. $2\sqrt[3]{2} - 7\sqrt[3]{2} - 6 = (2-7)\sqrt[3]{2} - 6 = -5\sqrt[3]{2} - 6$

57. $\sqrt[3]{81} + \sqrt[3]{24} = \sqrt[3]{27 \cdot 3} + \sqrt[3]{8 \cdot 3}$
$\qquad\qquad\quad = \sqrt[3]{27}\sqrt[3]{3} + \sqrt[3]{8}\sqrt[3]{3}$
$\qquad\qquad\quad = 3\sqrt[3]{3} + 2\sqrt[3]{3}$
$\qquad\qquad\quad = (3+2)\sqrt[3]{3}$
$\qquad\qquad\quad = 5\sqrt[3]{3}$

59. $\sqrt[3]{8} + \sqrt[3]{54} - 5 = 2 + \sqrt[3]{27}\sqrt[3]{2} - 5 = -3 + 3\sqrt[3]{2}$

61. $2\sqrt[3]{8x^3} + 2\sqrt[3]{16x^3} = 2 \cdot 2x + 2\sqrt[3]{8x^3 \cdot 2}$
$\qquad\qquad\qquad\qquad = 4x + 2\sqrt[3]{8x^3}\sqrt[3]{2}$
$\qquad\qquad\qquad\qquad = 4x + 2 \cdot 2x\sqrt[3]{2}$
$\qquad\qquad\qquad\qquad = 4x + 4x\sqrt[3]{2}$

63. $12\sqrt[3]{y^7} - y^2\sqrt[3]{8y} = 12\sqrt[3]{y^6 \cdot y} - y^2\sqrt[3]{8}\sqrt[3]{y}$
$\qquad\qquad\qquad\qquad = 12\sqrt[3]{y^6}\sqrt[3]{y} - 2y^2\sqrt[3]{y}$
$\qquad\qquad\qquad\qquad = 12y^2\sqrt[3]{y} - 2y^2\sqrt[3]{y}$
$\qquad\qquad\qquad\qquad = (12y^2 - 2y^2)\sqrt[3]{y}$
$\qquad\qquad\qquad\qquad = 10y^2\sqrt[3]{y}$

65. $\sqrt{40x} + x\sqrt[3]{40} - 2\sqrt{10x} - x\sqrt[3]{5}$
$= \sqrt{4 \cdot 10x} + x\sqrt[3]{8 \cdot 5} - 2\sqrt{10x} - x\sqrt[3]{5}$
$= \sqrt{4}\sqrt{10x} + x\sqrt[3]{8}\sqrt[3]{5} - 2\sqrt{10x} - x\sqrt[3]{5}$
$= 2\sqrt{10x} + 2x\sqrt[3]{5} - 2\sqrt{10x} - x\sqrt[3]{5}$
$= (2-2)\sqrt{10x} + (2x-x)\sqrt[3]{5}$
$= x\sqrt[3]{5}$

67. $(x+6)^2 = (x)^2 + 2(x)(6) + (6)^2 = x^2 + 12x + 36$

69. $(2x-1)^2 = (2x)^2 - 2(2x)(1) + (1)^2 = 4x^2 - 4x + 1$

71. answers may vary

73. $P = 2l + 2w$
$\quad = 2 \cdot 3\sqrt{5} + 2 \cdot \sqrt{5}$
$\quad = 6\sqrt{5} + 2\sqrt{5}$
$\quad = (6+2)\sqrt{5}$
$\quad = 8\sqrt{5}$
The perimeter is $8\sqrt{5}$ inches.

75. Two triangular end pieces and two rectangular side panels are needed. Each side panel has area $8 \cdot 3 = 24$ square feet.

$2 \cdot 24 + 2 \cdot \dfrac{3\sqrt{27}}{4} = 48 + \dfrac{3\sqrt{9 \cdot 3}}{2}$
$\qquad\qquad\qquad\quad = 48 + \dfrac{3\sqrt{9}\sqrt{3}}{2}$
$\qquad\qquad\qquad\quad = 48 + \dfrac{3 \cdot 3\sqrt{3}}{2}$
$\qquad\qquad\qquad\quad = 48 + \dfrac{9\sqrt{3}}{2}$

The total area of wood needed is $\left(48 + \dfrac{9\sqrt{3}}{2}\right)$ square feet.

77. The expression can be simplified.
$4\sqrt{2} + 3\sqrt{2} = (4+3)\sqrt{2} = 7\sqrt{2}$

79. The expression $6 + 7\sqrt{6}$ cannot be simplified.

81. The expression can be simplified.
$\sqrt{7} + \sqrt{7} + \sqrt{7} = (1+1+1)\sqrt{7} = 3\sqrt{7}$

83. $\sqrt{\dfrac{x^3}{16}} - x\sqrt{\dfrac{9x}{25}} + \dfrac{\sqrt{81x^3}}{2}$

$= \dfrac{\sqrt{x^3}}{\sqrt{16}} - x\dfrac{\sqrt{9x}}{\sqrt{25}} + \dfrac{\sqrt{81x^3}}{2}$

$= \dfrac{\sqrt{x^2 \cdot x}}{4} - x\dfrac{\sqrt{9 \cdot x}}{5} + \dfrac{\sqrt{81x^2 \cdot x}}{2}$

$= \dfrac{\sqrt{x^2}\sqrt{x}}{4} - x\dfrac{\sqrt{9}\sqrt{x}}{5} + \dfrac{\sqrt{81x^2}\sqrt{x}}{2}$

$= \dfrac{x\sqrt{x}}{4} - \dfrac{3x\sqrt{x}}{5} + \dfrac{9x\sqrt{x}}{2}$

$= \left(\dfrac{1}{4} - \dfrac{3}{5} + \dfrac{9}{2}\right)x\sqrt{x}$

$= \left(\dfrac{5}{20} - \dfrac{12}{20} + \dfrac{90}{20}\right)x\sqrt{x}$

$= \dfrac{83}{20}x\sqrt{x}$

$= \dfrac{83x\sqrt{x}}{20}$

Section 15.4

Practice Problems

1. $\sqrt{5} \cdot \sqrt{2} = \sqrt{5 \cdot 2} = \sqrt{10}$

2. $\sqrt{7} \cdot \sqrt{7} = \sqrt{7 \cdot 7} = \sqrt{49} = 7$

3. $\sqrt{6} \cdot \sqrt{3} = \sqrt{18} = \sqrt{9 \cdot 2} = \sqrt{9} \cdot \sqrt{2} = 3\sqrt{2}$

4. $\sqrt{10x} \cdot \sqrt{2x} = \sqrt{10x \cdot 2x}$

$= \sqrt{20x^2}$

$= \sqrt{4x^2 \cdot 5}$

$= \sqrt{4x^2} \cdot \sqrt{5}$

$= 2x\sqrt{5}$

5. a. $\sqrt{7}\left(\sqrt{7} - \sqrt{3}\right) = \sqrt{7} \cdot \sqrt{7} - \sqrt{7} \cdot \sqrt{3} = 7 - \sqrt{21}$

b. $\sqrt{5x}\left(\sqrt{x} - 3\sqrt{5}\right) = \sqrt{5x} \cdot \sqrt{x} - \sqrt{5x} \cdot 3\sqrt{5}$

$= \sqrt{5x \cdot x} - 3\sqrt{5x \cdot 5}$

$= \sqrt{5 \cdot x^2} - 3\sqrt{25 \cdot x}$

$= \sqrt{5} \cdot \sqrt{x^2} - 3 \cdot \sqrt{25} \cdot \sqrt{x}$

$= x\sqrt{5} - 3 \cdot 5 \cdot \sqrt{x}$

$= x\sqrt{5} - 15\sqrt{x}$

c. $\left(\sqrt{x} + \sqrt{5}\right)\left(\sqrt{x} - \sqrt{3}\right)$

$= \sqrt{x} \cdot \sqrt{x} - \sqrt{x} \cdot \sqrt{3} + \sqrt{5} \cdot \sqrt{x} - \sqrt{5} \cdot \sqrt{3}$

$= x - \sqrt{3x} + \sqrt{5x} - \sqrt{15}$

6. a. $\left(\sqrt{3} + 8\right)\left(\sqrt{3} - 8\right) = \left(\sqrt{3}\right)^2 - 8^2$

$= 3 - 64$

$= -61$

b. $\left(\sqrt{5x} + 4\right)^2 = \left(\sqrt{5x}\right)^2 + 2\left(\sqrt{5x}\right)(4) + (4)^2$

$= 5x + 8\sqrt{5x} + 16$

7. $\dfrac{\sqrt{15}}{\sqrt{3}} = \sqrt{\dfrac{15}{3}} = \sqrt{5}$

8. $\dfrac{\sqrt{90}}{\sqrt{2}} = \sqrt{\dfrac{90}{2}} = \sqrt{45} = \sqrt{9 \cdot 5} = \sqrt{9} \cdot \sqrt{5} = 3\sqrt{5}$

9. $\dfrac{\sqrt{125x^3}}{\sqrt{5x}} = \sqrt{\dfrac{125x^3}{5x}} = \sqrt{25x^2} = 5x$

10. $\dfrac{5}{\sqrt{3}} = \dfrac{5}{\sqrt{3}} \cdot \dfrac{\sqrt{3}}{\sqrt{3}} = \dfrac{5 \cdot \sqrt{3}}{\sqrt{3} \cdot \sqrt{3}} = \dfrac{5\sqrt{3}}{3}$

11. $\dfrac{\sqrt{7}}{\sqrt{20}} = \dfrac{\sqrt{7}}{\sqrt{4 \cdot 5}}$

$= \dfrac{\sqrt{7}}{2\sqrt{5}} \cdot \dfrac{\sqrt{5}}{\sqrt{5}}$

$= \dfrac{\sqrt{7} \cdot \sqrt{5}}{2\sqrt{5} \cdot \sqrt{5}}$

$= \dfrac{\sqrt{35}}{2 \cdot 5}$

$= \dfrac{\sqrt{35}}{10}$

12. $\sqrt{\dfrac{2}{45x}} = \dfrac{\sqrt{2}}{\sqrt{45x}}$

$\qquad = \dfrac{\sqrt{2}}{\sqrt{9}\cdot\sqrt{5x}}$

$\qquad = \dfrac{\sqrt{2}}{3\sqrt{5x}}\cdot\dfrac{\sqrt{5x}}{\sqrt{5x}}$

$\qquad = \dfrac{\sqrt{2}\cdot\sqrt{5x}}{3\sqrt{5x}\cdot\sqrt{5x}}$

$\qquad = \dfrac{\sqrt{10x}}{3\cdot 5x}$

$\qquad = \dfrac{\sqrt{10x}}{15x}$

13. $\dfrac{3}{2+\sqrt{7}} = \dfrac{3\left(2-\sqrt{7}\right)}{\left(2+\sqrt{7}\right)\left(2-\sqrt{7}\right)}$

$\qquad = \dfrac{3\left(2-\sqrt{7}\right)}{2^2-\left(\sqrt{7}\right)^2}$

$\qquad = \dfrac{3\left(2-\sqrt{7}\right)}{4-7}$

$\qquad = \dfrac{3\left(2-\sqrt{7}\right)}{-3}$

$\qquad = -\dfrac{3\left(2-\sqrt{7}\right)}{3}$

$\qquad = -1\left(2-\sqrt{7}\right)$

$\qquad = -2+\sqrt{7}$

14. $\dfrac{\sqrt{2}+5}{\sqrt{2}-1} = \dfrac{\left(\sqrt{2}+5\right)\left(\sqrt{2}+1\right)}{\left(\sqrt{2}-1\right)\left(\sqrt{2}+1\right)}$

$\qquad = \dfrac{2+\sqrt{2}+5\sqrt{2}+5}{2-1}$

$\qquad = \dfrac{7+6\sqrt{2}}{1}$

$\qquad = 7+6\sqrt{2}$

15. $\dfrac{7}{2-\sqrt{x}} = \dfrac{7\left(2+\sqrt{x}\right)}{\left(2-\sqrt{x}\right)\left(2+\sqrt{x}\right)} = \dfrac{7\left(2+\sqrt{x}\right)}{4-x}$

Vocabulary and Readiness Check

1. $\sqrt{7}\cdot\sqrt{3} = \underline{\sqrt{21}}$

2. $\sqrt{10}\cdot\sqrt{10} = \underline{\sqrt{100}}$ or 10

3. $\dfrac{\sqrt{15}}{\sqrt{3}} = \underline{\sqrt{\dfrac{15}{3}}}$ or $\sqrt{5}$

4. The process of eliminating the radical in the denominator of a radical expression is called rationalizing the denominator.

5. The conjugate of $2+\sqrt{3}$ is $\underline{2-\sqrt{3}}$.

Exercise Set 15.4

1. $\sqrt{8}\cdot\sqrt{2} = \sqrt{16} = 4$

3. $\sqrt{10}\cdot\sqrt{5} = \sqrt{50} = \sqrt{25\cdot 2} = \sqrt{25}\sqrt{2} = 5\sqrt{2}$

5. $\left(\sqrt{6}\right)^2 = 6$

7. $\sqrt{2x}\cdot\sqrt{2x} = \left(\sqrt{2x}\right)^2 = 2x$

9. $\left(2\sqrt{5}\right)^2 = \left(2\sqrt{5}\right)\left(2\sqrt{5}\right) = 4\left(\sqrt{5}\right)^2 = 4\cdot 5 = 20$

11. $\left(6\sqrt{x}\right)^2 = \left(6\sqrt{x}\right)\left(6\sqrt{x}\right) = 36\left(\sqrt{x}\right)^2 = 36x$

13. $\sqrt{3x^5}\cdot\sqrt{6x} = \sqrt{3x^5\cdot 6x}$

$\qquad = \sqrt{18x^6}$

$\qquad = \sqrt{9x^6\cdot 2}$

$\qquad = \sqrt{9x^6}\sqrt{2}$

$\qquad = 3x^3\sqrt{2}$

15. $\sqrt{2xy^2}\cdot\sqrt{8xy} = \sqrt{2xy^2\cdot 8xy}$

$\qquad = \sqrt{16x^2y^3}$

$\qquad = \sqrt{16x^2y^2\cdot y}$

$\qquad = \sqrt{16x^2y^2}\sqrt{y}$

$\qquad = 4xy\sqrt{y}$

17. $\sqrt{6}\left(\sqrt{5}+\sqrt{7}\right) = \sqrt{6}\cdot\sqrt{5}+\sqrt{6}\cdot\sqrt{7} = \sqrt{30}+\sqrt{42}$

19. $\sqrt{10}\left(\sqrt{2}+\sqrt{5}\right)=\sqrt{10}\cdot\sqrt{2}+\sqrt{10}\cdot\sqrt{5}$
$$=\sqrt{20}+\sqrt{50}$$
$$=\sqrt{4\cdot5}+\sqrt{25\cdot2}$$
$$=\sqrt{4}\sqrt{5}+\sqrt{25}\sqrt{2}$$
$$=2\sqrt{5}+5\sqrt{2}$$

21. $\sqrt{7y}\left(\sqrt{y}-2\sqrt{7}\right)=\sqrt{7y}\cdot\sqrt{y}-\sqrt{7y}\cdot2\sqrt{7}$
$$=\sqrt{7y\cdot y}-2\sqrt{7y\cdot7}$$
$$=\sqrt{7y^2}-2\sqrt{49y}$$
$$=\sqrt{y^2\cdot7}-2\sqrt{49\cdot y}$$
$$=\sqrt{y^2}\sqrt{7}-2\sqrt{49}\sqrt{y}$$
$$=y\sqrt{7}-2\cdot7\sqrt{y}$$
$$=y\sqrt{7}-14\sqrt{y}$$

23. $\left(\sqrt{3}+6\right)\left(\sqrt{3}-6\right)=\left(\sqrt{3}\right)^2-6^2=3-36=-33$

25. $\left(\sqrt{3}+\sqrt{5}\right)\left(\sqrt{2}-\sqrt{5}\right)$
$$=\sqrt{3}\cdot\sqrt{2}-\sqrt{3}\sqrt{5}+\sqrt{5}\cdot\sqrt{2}-\sqrt{5}\cdot\sqrt{5}$$
$$=\sqrt{6}-\sqrt{15}+\sqrt{10}-\sqrt{25}$$
$$=\sqrt{6}-\sqrt{15}+\sqrt{10}-5$$

27. $\left(2\sqrt{11}+1\right)\left(\sqrt{11}-6\right)$
$$=2\sqrt{11}\cdot\sqrt{11}-2\sqrt{11}\cdot6+1\cdot\sqrt{11}-1\cdot6$$
$$=2\cdot11-12\sqrt{11}+\sqrt{11}-6$$
$$=22-11\sqrt{11}-6$$
$$=16-11\sqrt{11}$$

29. $\left(\sqrt{x}+6\right)\left(\sqrt{x}-6\right)=\left(\sqrt{x}\right)^2-(6)^2=x-36$

31. $\left(\sqrt{x}-7\right)^2=\left(\sqrt{x}\right)^2-2\left(\sqrt{x}\right)(7)+(7)^2$
$$=x-14\sqrt{x}+49$$

33. $\left(\sqrt{6y}+1\right)^2=\left(\sqrt{6y}\right)^2+2\left(\sqrt{6y}\right)(1)+(1)^2$
$$=6y+2\sqrt{6y}+1$$

35. $\dfrac{\sqrt{32}}{\sqrt{2}}=\sqrt{\dfrac{32}{2}}=\sqrt{16}=4$

37. $\dfrac{\sqrt{21}}{\sqrt{3}}=\sqrt{\dfrac{21}{3}}=\sqrt{7}$

39. $\dfrac{\sqrt{90}}{\sqrt{5}}=\sqrt{\dfrac{90}{5}}=\sqrt{18}=\sqrt{9\cdot2}=\sqrt{9}\sqrt{2}=3\sqrt{2}$

41. $\dfrac{\sqrt{75y^5}}{\sqrt{3y}}=\sqrt{\dfrac{75y^5}{3y}}=\sqrt{25y^4}=5y^2$

43. $\dfrac{\sqrt{150}}{\sqrt{2}}=\sqrt{\dfrac{150}{2}}=\sqrt{75}=\sqrt{25\cdot3}=\sqrt{25}\sqrt{3}=5\sqrt{3}$

45. $\dfrac{\sqrt{72y^5}}{\sqrt{3y^3}}=\sqrt{\dfrac{72y^5}{3y^3}}$
$$=\sqrt{24y^2}$$
$$=\sqrt{4y^2\cdot6}$$
$$=\sqrt{4y^2}\sqrt{6}$$
$$=2y\sqrt{6}$$

47. $\dfrac{\sqrt{24x^3y^4}}{\sqrt{2xy}}=\sqrt{\dfrac{24x^3y^4}{2xy}}$
$$=\sqrt{12x^2y^3}$$
$$=\sqrt{4x^2y^2\cdot3y}$$
$$=\sqrt{4x^2y^2}\sqrt{3y}$$
$$=2xy\sqrt{3y}$$

49. $\dfrac{\sqrt{3}}{\sqrt{5}}=\dfrac{\sqrt{3}}{\sqrt{5}}\cdot\dfrac{\sqrt{5}}{\sqrt{5}}=\dfrac{\sqrt{15}}{5}$

51. $\dfrac{7}{\sqrt{2}}=\dfrac{7}{\sqrt{2}}\cdot\dfrac{\sqrt{2}}{\sqrt{2}}=\dfrac{7\sqrt{2}}{2}$

53. $\dfrac{1}{\sqrt{6y}}=\dfrac{1}{\sqrt{6y}}\cdot\dfrac{\sqrt{6y}}{\sqrt{6y}}=\dfrac{\sqrt{6y}}{6y}$

55. $\sqrt{\dfrac{5}{18}} = \dfrac{\sqrt{5}}{\sqrt{18}}$

$= \dfrac{\sqrt{5}}{\sqrt{9 \cdot 2}}$

$= \dfrac{\sqrt{5}}{3\sqrt{2}} \cdot \dfrac{\sqrt{2}}{\sqrt{2}}$

$= \dfrac{\sqrt{5}\sqrt{2}}{3\sqrt{2} \cdot \sqrt{2}}$

$= \dfrac{\sqrt{10}}{3 \cdot 2}$

$= \dfrac{\sqrt{10}}{6}$

57. $\sqrt{\dfrac{3}{x}} = \dfrac{\sqrt{3}}{\sqrt{x}} = \dfrac{\sqrt{3}}{\sqrt{x}} \cdot \dfrac{\sqrt{x}}{\sqrt{x}} = \dfrac{\sqrt{3x}}{x}$

59. $\sqrt{\dfrac{1}{8}} = \dfrac{\sqrt{1}}{\sqrt{8}}$

$= \dfrac{1}{\sqrt{4 \cdot 2}}$

$= \dfrac{1}{2\sqrt{2}}$

$= \dfrac{1}{2\sqrt{2}} \cdot \dfrac{\sqrt{2}}{\sqrt{2}}$

$= \dfrac{\sqrt{2}}{2 \cdot 2}$

$= \dfrac{\sqrt{2}}{4}$

61. $\sqrt{\dfrac{2}{15}} = \dfrac{\sqrt{2}}{\sqrt{15}} = \dfrac{\sqrt{2}}{\sqrt{15}} \cdot \dfrac{\sqrt{15}}{\sqrt{15}} = \dfrac{\sqrt{30}}{15}$

63. $\sqrt{\dfrac{3}{20}} = \dfrac{\sqrt{3}}{\sqrt{20}}$

$= \dfrac{\sqrt{3}}{\sqrt{4 \cdot 5}}$

$= \dfrac{\sqrt{3}}{2\sqrt{5}}$

$= \dfrac{\sqrt{3}}{2\sqrt{5}} \cdot \dfrac{\sqrt{5}}{\sqrt{5}}$

$= \dfrac{\sqrt{15}}{2 \cdot 5}$

$= \dfrac{\sqrt{15}}{10}$

65. $\dfrac{3x}{\sqrt{2x}} = \dfrac{3x}{\sqrt{2x}} \cdot \dfrac{\sqrt{2x}}{\sqrt{2x}} = \dfrac{3x\sqrt{2x}}{2x} = \dfrac{3\sqrt{2x}}{2}$

67. $\dfrac{8y}{\sqrt{5}} = \dfrac{8y}{\sqrt{5}} \cdot \dfrac{\sqrt{5}}{\sqrt{5}} = \dfrac{8y\sqrt{5}}{5}$

69. $\sqrt{\dfrac{x}{36y}} = \dfrac{\sqrt{x}}{\sqrt{36y}}$

$= \dfrac{\sqrt{x}}{\sqrt{36}\sqrt{y}}$

$= \dfrac{\sqrt{x}}{6\sqrt{y}}$

$= \dfrac{\sqrt{x}}{6\sqrt{y}} \cdot \dfrac{\sqrt{y}}{\sqrt{y}}$

$= \dfrac{\sqrt{xy}}{6 \cdot y}$

$= \dfrac{\sqrt{xy}}{6y}$

71. $\sqrt{\dfrac{y}{12x}} = \dfrac{\sqrt{y}}{\sqrt{12x}}$

$= \dfrac{\sqrt{y}}{\sqrt{4}\sqrt{3x}}$

$= \dfrac{\sqrt{y}}{2\sqrt{3x}}$

$= \dfrac{\sqrt{y}}{2\sqrt{3x}} \cdot \dfrac{\sqrt{3x}}{\sqrt{3x}}$

$= \dfrac{\sqrt{3xy}}{2 \cdot 3x}$

$= \dfrac{\sqrt{3xy}}{6x}$

73. $\dfrac{3}{\sqrt{2}+1} = \dfrac{3}{\sqrt{2}+1} \cdot \dfrac{\sqrt{2}-1}{\sqrt{2}-1}$

$= \dfrac{3\left(\sqrt{2}-1\right)}{\left(\sqrt{2}\right)^2 - 1^2}$

$= \dfrac{3\sqrt{2}-3}{2-1}$

$= \dfrac{3\sqrt{2}-3}{1}$

$= 3\sqrt{2} - 3$

75. $\dfrac{4}{2-\sqrt{5}} = \dfrac{4}{2-\sqrt{5}} \cdot \dfrac{2+\sqrt{5}}{2+\sqrt{5}}$

$\qquad = \dfrac{4\left(2+\sqrt{5}\right)}{2^2 - \left(\sqrt{5}\right)^2}$

$\qquad = \dfrac{8+4\sqrt{5}}{4-5}$

$\qquad = \dfrac{8+4\sqrt{5}}{-1}$

$\qquad = -8 - 4\sqrt{5}$

77. $\dfrac{\sqrt{5}+1}{\sqrt{6}-\sqrt{5}} = \dfrac{\sqrt{5}+1}{\sqrt{6}-\sqrt{5}} \cdot \dfrac{\sqrt{6}+\sqrt{5}}{\sqrt{6}+\sqrt{5}}$

$\qquad = \dfrac{\left(\sqrt{5}+1\right)\left(\sqrt{6}+\sqrt{5}\right)}{\left(\sqrt{6}\right)^2 - \left(\sqrt{5}\right)^2}$

$\qquad = \dfrac{\sqrt{5}\sqrt{6} + \sqrt{5}\sqrt{5} + 1\cdot\sqrt{6} + 1\cdot\sqrt{5}}{6-5}$

$\qquad = \dfrac{\sqrt{30} + 5 + \sqrt{6} + \sqrt{5}}{1}$

$\qquad = \sqrt{30} + 5 + \sqrt{6} + \sqrt{5}$

79. $\dfrac{\sqrt{3}+1}{\sqrt{2}-1} = \dfrac{\sqrt{3}+1}{\sqrt{2}-1} \cdot \dfrac{\sqrt{2}+1}{\sqrt{2}+1}$

$\qquad = \dfrac{\left(\sqrt{3}+1\right)\left(\sqrt{2}+1\right)}{\left(\sqrt{2}\right)^2 - 1}$

$\qquad = \dfrac{\sqrt{3}\sqrt{2} + \sqrt{3}\cdot 1 + 1\cdot\sqrt{2} + 1^2}{2-1}$

$\qquad = \dfrac{\sqrt{6} + \sqrt{3} + \sqrt{2} + 1}{1}$

$\qquad = \sqrt{6} + \sqrt{3} + \sqrt{2} + 1$

81. $\dfrac{5}{2+\sqrt{x}} = \dfrac{5}{2+\sqrt{x}} \cdot \dfrac{2-\sqrt{x}}{2-\sqrt{x}}$

$\qquad = \dfrac{5\left(2-\sqrt{x}\right)}{2^2 - \left(\sqrt{x}\right)^2}$

$\qquad = \dfrac{10 - 5\sqrt{x}}{4-x}$

83. $\dfrac{3}{\sqrt{x}-4} = \dfrac{3}{\sqrt{x}-4} \cdot \dfrac{\sqrt{x}+4}{\sqrt{x}+4}$

$\qquad = \dfrac{3\left(\sqrt{x}+4\right)}{\left(\sqrt{x}\right)^2 - (4)^2}$

$\qquad = \dfrac{3\sqrt{x}+12}{x-16}$

85. $x+5 = 7^2$

$\qquad x = 49 - 5$

$\qquad x = 44$

87. $4z^2 + 6z - 12 = (2z)^2$

$\qquad 4z^2 + 6z - 12 = 4z^2$

$\qquad\qquad 6z - 12 = 0$

$\qquad\qquad\quad 6z = 12$

$\qquad\qquad\quad\ z = 2$

89. $9x^2 + 5x + 4 = (3x+1)^2$

$\qquad 9x^2 + 5x + 4 = 9x^2 + 6x + 1$

$\qquad\qquad 5x + 4 = 6x + 1$

$\qquad\qquad\quad\ 4 = x + 1$

$\qquad\qquad\quad\ 3 = x$

91. Area = (length)(width)

$\qquad 13\sqrt{2} \cdot 5\sqrt{6} = 13 \cdot 5 \cdot \sqrt{2} \cdot \sqrt{6}$

$\qquad\qquad\qquad = 65\sqrt{12}$

$\qquad\qquad\qquad = 65\sqrt{4}\sqrt{3}$

$\qquad\qquad\qquad = 65 \cdot 2\sqrt{3}$

$\qquad\qquad\qquad = 130\sqrt{3}$

The area is $130\sqrt{3}$ square meters.

93. $\sqrt{\dfrac{A}{\pi}} = \dfrac{\sqrt{A}}{\sqrt{\pi}} = \dfrac{\sqrt{A}}{\sqrt{\pi}} \cdot \dfrac{\sqrt{\pi}}{\sqrt{\pi}} = \dfrac{\sqrt{A\pi}}{\pi}$

95. $\sqrt{5} \cdot \sqrt{5} = \left(\sqrt{5}\right)^2 = 5$

The statement is true.

97. $\sqrt{3x} \cdot \sqrt{3x} = \left(\sqrt{3x}\right)^2 = 3x$

The statement is false.

99. $\sqrt{11} + \sqrt{2}$ cannot be simplified because the radicands are different. The statement is false.

101. answers may vary

103. answers may vary

105. $\dfrac{\sqrt{3}+1}{\sqrt{2}-1} = \dfrac{\sqrt{3}+1}{\sqrt{2}-1} \cdot \dfrac{\sqrt{3}-1}{\sqrt{3}-1}$

$\qquad = \dfrac{\left(\sqrt{3}\right)^2 - 1^2}{\left(\sqrt{2}-1\right)\left(\sqrt{3}-1\right)}$

$\qquad = \dfrac{3-1}{\sqrt{2}\sqrt{3}-1\cdot\sqrt{2}-1\cdot\sqrt{3}+1\cdot 1}$

$\qquad = \dfrac{2}{\sqrt{6}-\sqrt{2}-\sqrt{3}+1}$

Integrated Review

1. $\sqrt{36} = 6$, because $6^2 = 36$ and 6 is positive.

2. $\sqrt{48} = \sqrt{16\cdot 3} = \sqrt{16}\cdot\sqrt{3} = 4\sqrt{3}$

3. $\sqrt{x^4} = x^2$, because $(x^2)^2 = x^4$.

4. $\sqrt{y^7} = \sqrt{y^6\cdot y} = \sqrt{y^6}\sqrt{y} = y^3\sqrt{y}$

5. $\sqrt{16x^2} = 4x$, because $(4x)^2 = 16x^2$.

6. $\sqrt{18x^{11}} = \sqrt{9x^{10}\cdot 2x} = \sqrt{9x^{10}}\sqrt{2x} = 3x^5\sqrt{2x}$

7. $\sqrt[3]{8} = 2$, because $2^3 = 8$.

8. $\sqrt[4]{81} = 3$, because $3^4 = 81$.

9. $\sqrt[3]{-27} = -3$, because $(-3)^3 = -27$.

10. $\sqrt{-4}$ is not a real number.

11. $\sqrt{\dfrac{11}{9}} = \dfrac{\sqrt{11}}{\sqrt{9}} = \dfrac{\sqrt{11}}{3}$

12. $\sqrt[3]{\dfrac{7}{64}} = \dfrac{\sqrt[3]{7}}{\sqrt[3]{64}} = \dfrac{\sqrt[3]{7}}{4}$

13. $-\sqrt{16} = -4$. The negative sign indicates the negative square root of 16.

14. $-\sqrt{25} = -5$. The negative sign indicates the negative square root of 25.

15. $\sqrt{\dfrac{9}{49}} = \dfrac{\sqrt{9}}{\sqrt{49}} = \dfrac{3}{7}$

16. $\sqrt{\dfrac{1}{64}} = \dfrac{\sqrt{1}}{\sqrt{64}} = \dfrac{1}{8}$

17. $\sqrt{a^8 a^2} = \sqrt{a^8}\sqrt{b^2} = a^4 b$

18. $\sqrt{x^{10}y^{20}} = \sqrt{x^{10}}\sqrt{y^{20}} = x^5 y^{10}$

19. $\sqrt{25m^6} = \sqrt{25}\sqrt{m^6} = 5m^3$

20. $\sqrt{9n^{16}} = \sqrt{9}\sqrt{n^{16}} = 3n^8$

21. $5\sqrt{7} + \sqrt{7} = (5+1)\sqrt{7} = 6\sqrt{7}$

22. $\sqrt{50} - \sqrt{8} = \sqrt{25\cdot 2} - \sqrt{4\cdot 2}$

$\qquad = \sqrt{25}\sqrt{2} - \sqrt{4}\sqrt{2}$

$\qquad = 5\sqrt{2} - 2\sqrt{2}$

$\qquad = (5-2)\sqrt{2}$

$\qquad = 3\sqrt{2}$

23. $5\sqrt{2} - 5\sqrt{3}$ cannot be simplified.

24. $2\sqrt{x} + \sqrt{25x} - \sqrt{36x} + 3x$

$\qquad = 2\sqrt{x} + \sqrt{25}\sqrt{x} - \sqrt{36}\sqrt{x} + 3x$

$\qquad = 2\sqrt{x} + 5\sqrt{x} - 6\sqrt{x} + 3x$

$\qquad = (2+5-6)\sqrt{x} + 3x$

$\qquad = \sqrt{x} + 3x$

25. $\sqrt{2}\cdot\sqrt{15} = \sqrt{2\cdot 15} = \sqrt{30}$

26. $\sqrt{3}\cdot\sqrt{3} = \sqrt{3\cdot 3} = \sqrt{9} = 3$

27. $\left(2\sqrt{7}\right)^2 = \left(2\sqrt{7}\right)\left(2\sqrt{7}\right) = 4\left(\sqrt{7}\right)^2 = 4\cdot 7 = 28$

28. $\left(3\sqrt{5}\right)^2 = \left(3\sqrt{5}\right)\left(3\sqrt{5}\right) = 9\left(\sqrt{5}\right)^2 = 9\cdot 5 = 45$

29. $\sqrt{3}\left(\sqrt{11}+1\right) = \sqrt{3}\cdot\sqrt{11} + \sqrt{3}\cdot 1 = \sqrt{33} + \sqrt{3}$

30. $\sqrt{6}\left(\sqrt{3}-2\right) = \sqrt{6}\cdot\sqrt{3} - \sqrt{6}\cdot 2$

$\qquad = \sqrt{18} - 2\sqrt{6}$

$\qquad = \sqrt{9\cdot 2} - 2\sqrt{6}$

$\qquad = 3\sqrt{2} - 2\sqrt{6}$

31. $\sqrt{8y}\sqrt{2y} = \sqrt{8y\cdot 2y} = \sqrt{16y^2} = 4y$

32. $\sqrt{15x^2} \cdot \sqrt{3x^2} = \sqrt{15x^2 \cdot 3x^2}$
$= \sqrt{45x^4}$
$= \sqrt{9x^4 \cdot 5}$
$= 3x^2\sqrt{5}$

33. $(\sqrt{x} - 5)(\sqrt{x} + 2) = \sqrt{x} \cdot \sqrt{x} + 2\sqrt{x} - 5\sqrt{x} - 5 \cdot 2$
$= x - 3\sqrt{x} - 10$

34. $(3 + \sqrt{2})^2 = (3)^2 + 2(3)(\sqrt{2}) + (\sqrt{2})^2$
$= 9 + 6\sqrt{2} + 2$
$= 11 + 6\sqrt{2}$

35. $\dfrac{\sqrt{8}}{\sqrt{2}} = \sqrt{\dfrac{8}{2}} = \sqrt{4} = 2$

36. $\dfrac{\sqrt{45}}{\sqrt{15}} = \sqrt{\dfrac{45}{15}} = \sqrt{3}$

37. $\dfrac{\sqrt{24x^5}}{\sqrt{2x}} = \sqrt{\dfrac{24x^5}{2x}} = \sqrt{12x^4} = \sqrt{4x^4 \cdot 3} = 2x^2\sqrt{3}$

38. $\dfrac{\sqrt{75a^4b^5}}{\sqrt{5ab}} = \sqrt{\dfrac{75a^4b^5}{5ab}}$
$= \sqrt{15a^3b^4}$
$= \sqrt{a^2b^4 \cdot 15a}$
$= ab^2\sqrt{15a}$

39. $\sqrt{\dfrac{1}{6}} = \dfrac{\sqrt{1}}{\sqrt{6}} = \dfrac{1}{\sqrt{6}} = \dfrac{1}{\sqrt{6}} \cdot \dfrac{\sqrt{6}}{\sqrt{6}} = \dfrac{\sqrt{6}}{6}$

40. $\dfrac{x}{\sqrt{20}} = \dfrac{x}{\sqrt{4 \cdot 5}} = \dfrac{x}{2\sqrt{5}} = \dfrac{x}{2\sqrt{5}} \cdot \dfrac{\sqrt{5}}{\sqrt{5}} = \dfrac{x\sqrt{5}}{2 \cdot 5} = \dfrac{x\sqrt{5}}{10}$

41. $\dfrac{4}{\sqrt{6} + 1} = \dfrac{4}{\sqrt{6} + 1} \cdot \dfrac{\sqrt{6} - 1}{\sqrt{6} - 1}$
$= \dfrac{4(\sqrt{6} - 1)}{(\sqrt{6})^2 - 1^2}$
$= \dfrac{4\sqrt{6} - 4}{6 - 1}$
$= \dfrac{4\sqrt{6} - 4}{5}$

42. $\dfrac{\sqrt{2} + 1}{\sqrt{x} - 5} = \dfrac{\sqrt{2} + 1}{\sqrt{x} - 5} \cdot \dfrac{\sqrt{x} + 5}{\sqrt{x} + 5}$
$= \dfrac{(\sqrt{2} + 1)(\sqrt{x} + 5)}{(\sqrt{x})^2 - 5^2}$
$= \dfrac{\sqrt{2}\sqrt{x} + 5\sqrt{2} + 1\sqrt{x} + 1 \cdot 5}{x - 25}$
$= \dfrac{\sqrt{2x} + 5\sqrt{2} + \sqrt{x} + 5}{x - 25}$

Section 15.5

Practice Problems

1. $\sqrt{x - 2} = 7$
$(\sqrt{x - 2})^2 = 7^2$
$x - 2 = 49$
$x = 51$

2. $\sqrt{6x - 1} = \sqrt{x}$
$(\sqrt{6x - 1})^2 = (\sqrt{x})^2$
$6x - 1 = x$
$5x - 1 = 0$
$5x = 1$
$x = \dfrac{1}{5}$

3. $\sqrt{x} + 9 = 2$
$\sqrt{x} = -7$
$\sqrt{x}$ cannot equal -7. Thus, the equation has no solution.

4. $\sqrt{9y^2 + 2y - 10} = 3y$
$(\sqrt{9y^2 + 2y - 10})^2 = (3y)^2$
$9y^2 + 2y - 10 = 9y^2$
$2y - 10 = 0$
$2y = 10$
$y = 5$

5. $\sqrt{x+1} - x = -5$

$\sqrt{x+1} = x - 5$

$\left(\sqrt{x+1}\right)^2 = (x-5)^2$

$x + 1 = x^2 - 10x + 25$

$0 = x^2 - 11x + 24$

$0 = (x-8)(x-3)$

$0 = x - 8$ or $0 = x - 3$

$8 = x$ $3 = x$

Replacing x with 3 results in a false statement. 3 is an extraneous solution. The only solution is 8.

6. $\sqrt{x} + 3 = \sqrt{x+15}$

$\left(\sqrt{x}+3\right)^2 = \left(\sqrt{x+15}\right)^2$

$x + 6\sqrt{x} + 9 = x + 15$

$6\sqrt{x} = 6$

$\sqrt{x} = 1$

$x = 1$

Exercise Set 15.5

1. $\sqrt{x} = 9$

$\left(\sqrt{x}\right)^2 = 9^2$

$x = 81$

3. $\sqrt{x+5} = 2$

$\left(\sqrt{x+5}\right)^2 = 2^2$

$x + 5 = 4$

$x = -1$

5. $\sqrt{x} - 2 = 5$

$\sqrt{x} = 7$

$\left(\sqrt{x}\right)^2 = 7^2$

$x = 49$

7. $3\sqrt{x} + 5 = 2$

$3\sqrt{x} = -3$

$\sqrt{x} = -1$

$\sqrt{x}$ cannot equal -1. Thus, the equation has no solution.

9. $\sqrt{x} = \sqrt{3x-8}$

$\left(\sqrt{x}\right)^2 = \left(\sqrt{3x-8}\right)^2$

$x = 3x - 8$

$-2x = -8$

$x = 4$

11. $\sqrt{4x-3} = \sqrt{x+3}$

$\left(\sqrt{4x-3}\right)^2 = \left(\sqrt{x+3}\right)^2$

$4x - 3 = x + 3$

$3x - 3 = 3$

$3x = 6$

$x = 2$

13. $\sqrt{9x^2 + 2x - 4} = 3x$

$\left(\sqrt{9x^2 + 2x - 4}\right)^2 = (3x)^2$

$9x^2 + 2x - 4 = 9x^2$

$2x - 4 = 0$

$2x = 4$

$x = 2$

15. $\sqrt{x} = x - 6$

$\left(\sqrt{x}\right)^2 = (x-6)^2$

$x = x^2 - 12x + 36$

$0 = x^2 - 13x + 36$

$0 = (x-9)(x-4)$

$0 = x - 9$ or $0 = x - 4$

$9 = x$ $4 = x$

$x = 4$ does not check, so the solution is $x = 9$.

17. $\sqrt{x+7} = x + 5$

$\left(\sqrt{x+7}\right)^2 = (x+5)^2$

$x + 7 = x^2 + 10x + 25$

$0 = x^2 + 9x + 18$

$0 = (x+6)(x+3)$

$x + 6 = 0$ or $x + 3 = 0$

$x = -6$ $x = -3$

$x = -6$ does not check, so the solution is $x = -3$.

19. $\sqrt{3x+7} - x = 3$

$\sqrt{3x+7} = x+3$

$\left(\sqrt{3x+7}\right)^2 = (x+3)^2$

$3x+7 = x^2 + 6x + 9$

$0 = x^2 + 3x + 2$

$0 = (x+2)(x+1)$

$x+2 = 0 \quad$ or $\quad x+1 = 0$

$x = -2 \qquad\qquad x = -1$

21. $\sqrt{16x^2 + 2x + 2} = 4x$

$\left(\sqrt{16x^2 + 2x + 2}\right)^2 = (4x)^2$

$16x^2 + 2x + 2 = 16x^2$

$2x + 2 = 0$

$2x = -2$

$x = -1$

$x = -1$ does not check, so the equation has no solution.

23. $\sqrt{2x^2 + 6x + 9} = 3$

$\left(\sqrt{2x^2 + 6x + 9}\right)^2 = 3^2$

$2x^2 + 6x + 9 = 9$

$2x^2 + 6x = 0$

$2x(x+3) = 0$

$2x = 0 \quad$ or $\quad x+3 = 0$

$x = 0 \qquad\qquad x = -3$

25. $\sqrt{x-7} = \sqrt{x} - 1$

$\left(\sqrt{x-7}\right)^2 = \left(\sqrt{x} - 1\right)^2$

$x - 7 = x - 2\sqrt{x} + 1$

$2\sqrt{x} = 8$

$\sqrt{x} = 4$

$\left(\sqrt{x}\right)^2 = 4^2$

$x = 16$

27. $\sqrt{x} + 2 = \sqrt{x+24}$

$\left(\sqrt{x} + 2\right)^2 = \left(\sqrt{x+24}\right)^2$

$x + 4\sqrt{x} + 4 = x + 24$

$4\sqrt{x} = 20$

$\sqrt{x} = 5$

$\left(\sqrt{x}\right)^2 = 5^2$

$x = 25$

29. $\sqrt{x+8} = \sqrt{x} + 2$

$\left(\sqrt{x+8}\right)^2 = \left(\sqrt{x} + 2\right)^2$

$x + 8 = x + 4\sqrt{x} + 4$

$4 = 4\sqrt{x}$

$1 = \sqrt{x}$

$1^2 = \left(\sqrt{x}\right)^2$

$1 = x$

31. $\sqrt{2x+6} = 4$

$\left(\sqrt{2x+6}\right)^2 = 4^2$

$2x + 6 = 16$

$2x = 10$

$x = 5$

33. $\sqrt{x+6} + 1 = 3$

$\sqrt{x+6} = 2$

$\left(\sqrt{x+6}\right)^2 = 2^2$

$x + 6 = 4$

$x = -2$

35. $\sqrt{x+6} + 5 = 3$

$\sqrt{x+6} = -2$

$\sqrt{x+6}$ cannot equal -2. Thus, the equation has no solution.

37. $\sqrt{16x^2 - 3x + 6} = 4x$

$\left(\sqrt{16x^2 - 3x + 6}\right)^2 = (4x)^2$

$16x^2 - 3x + 6 = 16x^2$

$-3x + 6 = 0$

$-3x = -6$

$x = 2$

39. $-\sqrt{x} = -6$

$\sqrt{x} = 6$

$\left(\sqrt{x}\right)^2 = 6^2$

$x = 36$

41.
$$\sqrt{x+9} = \sqrt{x} - 3$$
$$\left(\sqrt{x+9}\right)^2 = \left(\sqrt{x} - 3\right)^2$$
$$x+9 = x - 6\sqrt{x} + 9$$
$$0 = -6\sqrt{x}$$
$$0 = \sqrt{x}$$
$$0^2 = \left(\sqrt{x}\right)^2$$
$$0 = x$$
$x = 0$ does not check, so the equation has no solution.

43.
$$\sqrt{2x+1} + 3 = 5$$
$$\sqrt{2x+1} = 2$$
$$\left(\sqrt{2x+1}\right)^2 = 2^2$$
$$2x+1 = 4$$
$$2x = 3$$
$$x = \frac{3}{2}$$

45.
$$\sqrt{x} + 3 = 7$$
$$\sqrt{x} = 4$$
$$\left(\sqrt{x}\right)^2 = 4^2$$
$$x = 16$$

47.
$$\sqrt{4x} = \sqrt{2x+6}$$
$$\left(\sqrt{4x}\right)^2 = \left(\sqrt{2x+6}\right)^2$$
$$4x = 2x + 6$$
$$2x = 6$$
$$x = 3$$

49.
$$\sqrt{2x+1} = x - 7$$
$$\left(\sqrt{2x+1}\right)^2 = (x-7)^2$$
$$2x+1 = x^2 - 14x + 49$$
$$0 = x^2 - 16x + 48$$
$$0 = (x-4)(x-12)$$
$$x - 4 = 0 \quad \text{or} \quad x - 12 = 0$$
$$x = 4 \qquad\qquad x = 12$$
$x = 4$ does not check, so the only solution is $x = 12$.

51.
$$x = \sqrt{2x-2} + 1$$
$$x - 1 = \sqrt{2x-2}$$
$$(x-1)^2 = \left(\sqrt{2x-2}\right)^2$$
$$x^2 - 2x + 1 = 2x - 2$$
$$x^2 - 4x + 3 = 0$$
$$(x-3)(x-1) = 0$$
$$x - 3 = 0 \quad \text{or} \quad x - 1 = 0$$
$$x = 3 \qquad\qquad x = 1$$

53.
$$\sqrt{1-8x} - x = 4$$
$$\sqrt{1-8x} = x + 4$$
$$\left(\sqrt{1-8x}\right)^2 = (x+4)^2$$
$$1 - 8x = x^2 + 8x + 16$$
$$0 = x^2 + 16x + 15$$
$$0 = (x+15)(x+1)$$
$$x + 15 = 0 \quad \text{or} \quad x + 1 = 0$$
$$x = -15 \qquad\qquad x = -1$$
$x = -15$ does not check, so the solution is $x = -1$.

55.
$$3x - 8 = 19$$
$$3x = 27$$
$$x = 9$$

57. Let x be the width of the rectangle, then the length is $2x$.
$$2(2x) + 2x = 24$$
$$4x + 2x = 24$$
$$6x = 24$$
$$x = 4$$
$$2x = 2(4) = 8$$
The length of the rectangle is 8 inches.

59.
$$\sqrt{x-3} + 3 = \sqrt{3x+4}$$
$$\left(\sqrt{x-3} + 3\right)^2 = \left(\sqrt{3x+4}\right)^2$$
$$x - 3 + 6\sqrt{x-3} + 9 = 3x + 4$$
$$6\sqrt{x-3} = 2x - 2$$
$$\left(6\sqrt{x-3}\right)^2 = (2x-2)^2$$
$$36(x-3) = 4x^2 - 8x + 4$$
$$36x - 108 = 4x^2 - 8x + 4$$
$$0 = 4x^2 - 44x + 112$$
$$0 = 4(x-7)(x-4)$$
$$x - 7 = 0 \quad \text{or} \quad x - 4 = 0$$
$$x = 7 \qquad\qquad x = 4$$

61. answers may vary

63. a. For $V = 20$, $b = \sqrt{\dfrac{20}{2}} = \sqrt{10} \approx 3.2$.

For $V = 200$, $b = \sqrt{\dfrac{200}{2}} = \sqrt{100} = 10$.

For $V = 2000$, $b = \sqrt{\dfrac{2000}{2}} = \sqrt{1000} \approx 31.6$.

V	20	200	2000
b	3.2	10	31.6

b. No, the volume increases by a factor of $\sqrt{10}$.

65.

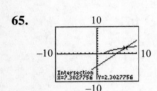

The solution of $\sqrt{x-2} = x - 5$ is $x \approx 7.30$.

67.

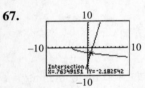

The solution of $-\sqrt{x+4} = 5x - 6$ is $x \approx 0.76$.

Section 15.6

Practice Problems

1. $a^2 + b^2 = c^2$
$3^2 + 4^2 = c^2$
$9 + 16 = c^2$
$25 = c^2$
$\sqrt{25} = c$
$5 = c$
The hypotenuse has a length of 5 centimeters.

2. $a^2 + b^2 = c^2$
$5^2 + 3^2 = c^2$
$25 + 9 = c^2$
$34 = c^2$
$\sqrt{34} = c$
$5.83 \approx c$

3. The property owner is using a right triangle with one leg measuring 40 feet and hypotenuse measuring 65 feet to find the unknown distance.
$a^2 + b^2 = c^2$
$40^2 + b^2 = 65^2$
$1600 + b^2 = 4225$
$b^2 = 2625$
$b = \sqrt{2625} = 5\sqrt{105}$
The distance across the pond is $5\sqrt{105}$ feet or approximately 51.2 feet.

4. $v = \sqrt{2gh}$
$= \sqrt{2 \cdot 32 \cdot 20}$
$= \sqrt{1280}$
$= 16\sqrt{5}$
The velocity of the object after falling 20 feet is exactly $16\sqrt{5}$ feet per second or approximately 35.8 feet per second.

Exercise Set 15.6

1. $a^2 + b^2 = c^2$
$2^2 + 3^2 = c^2$
$4 + 9 = c^2$
$13 = c^2$
$\sqrt{13} = \sqrt{c^2}$
$\sqrt{13} = c$
$c = \sqrt{13} \approx 3.61$

3. $a^2 + b^2 = c^2$
$3^2 + b^2 = 6^2$
$9 + b^2 = 36$
$b^2 = 27$
$\sqrt{b^2} = \sqrt{27}$
$b = 3\sqrt{3} \approx 5.20$

5. $a^2 + b^2 = c^2$
$7^2 + 24^2 = c^2$
$49 + 576 = c^2$
$625 = c^2$
$\sqrt{625} = \sqrt{c^2}$
$25 = c$

7. $a^2 + b^2 = c^2$

$\left(\sqrt{3}\right)^2 + b^2 = 5^2$

$3 + b^2 = 25$

$b^2 = 22$

$\sqrt{b^2} = \sqrt{22}$

$b = \sqrt{22} \approx 4.69$

9. $a^2 + b^2 = c^2$

$4^2 + b^2 = 13^2$

$16 + b^2 = 169$

$b^2 = 153$

$\sqrt{b^2} = \sqrt{153}$

$b = 3\sqrt{17}$

$b = 3\sqrt{17} \approx 12.37$

11. $a^2 + b^2 = c^2$

$4^2 + 5^2 = c^2$

$16 + 25 = c^2$

$41 = c^2$

$\sqrt{41} = \sqrt{c^2}$

$c = \sqrt{41} \approx 6.40$

13. $a^2 + b^2 = c^2$

$a^2 + 2^2 = 6^2$

$a^2 + 4 = 36$

$a^2 = 32$

$\sqrt{a^2} = \sqrt{32}$

$a = 4\sqrt{2}$

$a = 4\sqrt{2} \approx 5.66$

15. $a^2 + b^2 = c^2$

$\left(\sqrt{10}\right)^2 + b^2 = 10^2$

$10 + b^2 = 100$

$b^2 = 90$

$\sqrt{b^2} = \sqrt{90}$

$b = 3\sqrt{10} \approx 9.49$

17. The pole, wire, and ground form a right triangle with legs of 5 feet and 20 feet.

$a^2 + b^2 = c^2$

$5^2 + 20^2 = c^2$

$25 + 400 = c^2$

$425 = c^2$

$\sqrt{425} = \sqrt{c^2}$

$\sqrt{425} = c$

$c = \sqrt{425} \approx 20.6$

The length of the wire is 20.6 feet.

19. The diagonal brace is the hypotenuse of a right triangle with legs measuring 6 feet and 10 feet.

$a^2 + b^2 = c^2$

$6^2 + 10^2 = c^2$

$36 + 100 = c^2$

$136 = c^2$

$\sqrt{136} = \sqrt{c^2}$

$c = \sqrt{136} \approx 11.7$

The brace needs to be 11.7 feet.

21. $b = \sqrt{\dfrac{3V}{h}}$

$6 = \sqrt{\dfrac{3V}{2}}$

$6^2 = \left(\sqrt{\dfrac{3V}{2}}\right)^2$

$36 = \dfrac{3V}{2}$

$72 = 3V$

$24 = V$

The volume is 24 cubic feet.

23. $s = \sqrt{30fd}$

$s = \sqrt{30 \cdot 0.35 \cdot 280}$

$s = \sqrt{2940}$

$s \approx 54$

The car was moving at a speed of 54 miles per hour.

25. $v = \sqrt{2.5r}$

$v = \sqrt{2.5(300)}$

$v = \sqrt{750}$

$v \approx 27.4$

The maximum safe speed is 27 miles per hour.

27. $d = 3.5\sqrt{h}$

$d = 3.5\sqrt{285.4}$

$d \approx 59.1$

You can see a distance of 59.1 kilometers.

29. $d = 3.5\sqrt{h}$

$d = 3.5\sqrt{295.7}$

$d \approx 60.2$

You can see a distance of 60.2 kilometers.

31. $\sqrt{9} = 3$ and $-\sqrt{9} = -3$, so -3 and 3 are numbers whose square is 9.

33. $\sqrt{100} = 10$ and $-\sqrt{100} = -10$, so -10 and 10 are numbers whose square is 100.

35. $\sqrt{64} = 8$ and $-\sqrt{64} = -8$, so -8 and 8 are numbers whose square is 64.

37. First find y.

$a^2 + b^2 = c^2$

$3^2 + y^2 = 7^2$

$9 + y^2 = 49$

$y^2 = 40$

$y = \sqrt{40}$

$y = \sqrt{4 \cdot 10}$

$y = 2\sqrt{10}$

Let b be the second leg of the right triangle with hypotenuse 5.

$a^2 + b^2 = c^2$

$3^2 + b^2 = 5^2$

$9 + b^2 = 25$

$b^2 = 16$

$\sqrt{b^2} = \sqrt{16}$

$b = 4$

Now find x.

$x = y - 4$

$x = 2\sqrt{10} - 4$

39. The distance is the length of the hypotenuse of a right triangle. One leg has length $3 \cdot 30 = 90$ miles, and the other leg has length $3 \cdot 60 = 180$ miles.

$a^2 + b^2 = c^2$

$90^2 + 180^2 = c^2$

$8100 + 32,400 = c^2$

$40,500 = c^2$

$\sqrt{40,500} = \sqrt{c^2}$

$201 \approx c$

They are 201 miles apart.

41. answers may vary

Chapter 15 Vocabulary Check

1. The expressions $5\sqrt{x}$ and $7\sqrt{x}$ are examples of like radicals.

2. In the expression $\sqrt[3]{45}$ the number 3 is the index, the number 45 is the radicand, and $\sqrt{}$ is called the radical sign.

3. The conjugate of $a + b$ is $a - b$.

4. The principal square root of 25 is 5.

5. The process eliminating the radical in the denominator of a radical expression is called rationalizing the denominator.

6. The Pythagorean theorem states that for a right triangle, $(\text{leg})^2 + (\text{leg})^2 = (\text{hypotenuse})^2$.

Chapter 15 Review

1. $\sqrt{81} = 9$, because $9^2 = 81$ and 9 is positive.

2. $-\sqrt{49} = -7$. The negative indicates the negative square root of 49.

3. $\sqrt[3]{27} = 3$, because $3^3 = 27$.

4. $\sqrt[4]{81} = 3$, because $3^4 = 81$.

5. $-\sqrt{\dfrac{9}{64}} = -\dfrac{3}{8}$ because $\left(\dfrac{3}{8}\right)^2 = \dfrac{9}{64}$.

6. $\sqrt{\dfrac{36}{81}} = \dfrac{6}{9}$ because $\left(\dfrac{6}{9}\right)^2 = \dfrac{36}{81}$, and $\dfrac{6}{9} = \dfrac{2}{3}$.

7. $\sqrt[4]{16} = 2$ because $2^4 = 16$.

8. $\sqrt[3]{-8} = -2$ because $(-2)^3 = -8$.

9. c; $\sqrt{-4}$ is not a real number because the radicand is negative and the index is even.

10. a, c; $\sqrt{-5}$ and $\sqrt[4]{-5}$ are not real numbers because the radicands are negatives and the indexes are even.

11. $\sqrt{x^{12}} = x^6$, because $(x^6)^2 = x^{12}$.

12. $\sqrt{x^8} = x^4$, because $(x^4)^2 = x^8$.

13. $\sqrt{9y^2} = 3y$, because $(3y)^2 = 9y^2$.

14. $\sqrt{25x^4} = 5x^2$, because $(5x^2)^2 = 25x^4$.

15. $\sqrt{40} = \sqrt{4 \cdot 10} = \sqrt{4}\sqrt{10} = 2\sqrt{10}$

16. $\sqrt{24} = \sqrt{4 \cdot 6} = \sqrt{4}\sqrt{6} = 2\sqrt{6}$

17. $\sqrt{54} = \sqrt{9 \cdot 6} = \sqrt{9}\sqrt{6} = 3\sqrt{6}$

18. $\sqrt{88} = \sqrt{4 \cdot 22} = \sqrt{4}\sqrt{22} = 2\sqrt{22}$

19. $\sqrt{x^5} = \sqrt{x^4 \cdot x} = \sqrt{x^4}\sqrt{x} = x^2\sqrt{x}$

20. $\sqrt{y^7} = \sqrt{y^6 \cdot y} = \sqrt{y^6}\sqrt{y} = y^3\sqrt{y}$

21. $\sqrt{20x^2} = \sqrt{4x^2 \cdot 5} = \sqrt{4x^2}\sqrt{5} = 2x\sqrt{5}$

22. $\sqrt{50y^4} = \sqrt{25y^4 \cdot 2} = \sqrt{25y^4}\sqrt{2} = 5y^2\sqrt{2}$

23. $\sqrt[3]{54} = \sqrt[3]{27 \cdot 2} = \sqrt[3]{27}\sqrt[3]{2} = 3\sqrt[3]{2}$

24. $\sqrt[3]{88} = \sqrt[3]{8 \cdot 11} = \sqrt[3]{8}\sqrt[3]{11} = 2\sqrt[3]{11}$

25. $\sqrt{\dfrac{18}{25}} = \dfrac{\sqrt{18}}{\sqrt{25}} = \dfrac{\sqrt{9 \cdot 2}}{5} = \dfrac{\sqrt{9}\sqrt{2}}{5} = \dfrac{3\sqrt{2}}{5}$

26. $\sqrt{\dfrac{75}{64}} = \dfrac{\sqrt{75}}{\sqrt{64}} = \dfrac{\sqrt{25 \cdot 3}}{8} = \dfrac{\sqrt{25}\sqrt{3}}{8} = \dfrac{5\sqrt{3}}{8}$

27. $-\sqrt{\dfrac{50}{9}} = -\dfrac{\sqrt{50}}{\sqrt{9}} = -\dfrac{\sqrt{25 \cdot 2}}{3} = -\dfrac{\sqrt{25}\sqrt{2}}{3} = -\dfrac{5\sqrt{2}}{3}$

28. $-\sqrt{\dfrac{12}{49}} = -\dfrac{\sqrt{12}}{\sqrt{49}} = -\dfrac{\sqrt{4 \cdot 3}}{7} = -\dfrac{\sqrt{4}\sqrt{3}}{7} = -\dfrac{2\sqrt{3}}{7}$

29. $\sqrt{\dfrac{11}{x^2}} = \dfrac{\sqrt{11}}{\sqrt{x^2}} = \dfrac{\sqrt{11}}{x}$

30. $\sqrt{\dfrac{7}{y^4}} = \dfrac{\sqrt{7}}{\sqrt{y^4}} = \dfrac{\sqrt{7}}{y^2}$

31. $\sqrt{\dfrac{y^5}{100}} = \dfrac{\sqrt{y^5}}{\sqrt{100}} = \dfrac{\sqrt{y^4 \cdot y}}{10} = \dfrac{\sqrt{y^4}\sqrt{y}}{10} = \dfrac{y^2\sqrt{y}}{10}$

32. $\sqrt{\dfrac{x^3}{81}} = \dfrac{\sqrt{x^3}}{\sqrt{81}} = \dfrac{\sqrt{x^2 \cdot x}}{9} = \dfrac{\sqrt{x^2}\sqrt{x}}{9} = \dfrac{x\sqrt{x}}{9}$

33. $5\sqrt{8} - 8\sqrt{2} = (5-8)\sqrt{2} = -3\sqrt{2}$

34. $\sqrt{3} - 6\sqrt{3} = (1-6)\sqrt{3} = -5\sqrt{3}$

35. $6\sqrt{5} + 3\sqrt{6} - 2\sqrt{5} + \sqrt{6} = (6-2)\sqrt{5} + (3+1)\sqrt{6}$
$\phantom{6\sqrt{5} + 3\sqrt{6} - 2\sqrt{5} + \sqrt{6}} = 4\sqrt{5} + 4\sqrt{6}$

36. $-\sqrt{7} + 8\sqrt{2} - \sqrt{7} - 6\sqrt{2} = (-1-1)\sqrt{7} + (8-6)\sqrt{2}$
$\phantom{-\sqrt{7} + 8\sqrt{2} - \sqrt{7} - 6\sqrt{2}} = -2\sqrt{7} + 2\sqrt{2}$

37. $\sqrt{28} + \sqrt{63} + \sqrt{56} = \sqrt{4 \cdot 7} + \sqrt{9 \cdot 7} + \sqrt{4 \cdot 14}$
$\phantom{\sqrt{28} + \sqrt{63} + \sqrt{56}} = \sqrt{4}\sqrt{7} + \sqrt{9}\sqrt{7} + \sqrt{4}\sqrt{14}$
$\phantom{\sqrt{28} + \sqrt{63} + \sqrt{56}} = 2\sqrt{7} + 3\sqrt{7} + 2\sqrt{14}$
$\phantom{\sqrt{28} + \sqrt{63} + \sqrt{56}} = (2+3)\sqrt{7} + 2\sqrt{14}$
$\phantom{\sqrt{28} + \sqrt{63} + \sqrt{56}} = 5\sqrt{7} + 2\sqrt{14}$

38. $\sqrt{75} + \sqrt{48} - \sqrt{16} = \sqrt{25 \cdot 3} + \sqrt{16 \cdot 3} - 4$
$\phantom{\sqrt{75} + \sqrt{48} - \sqrt{16}} = \sqrt{25}\sqrt{3} + \sqrt{16}\sqrt{3} - 4$
$\phantom{\sqrt{75} + \sqrt{48} - \sqrt{16}} = 5\sqrt{3} + 4\sqrt{3} - 4$
$\phantom{\sqrt{75} + \sqrt{48} - \sqrt{16}} = (5+4)\sqrt{3} - 4$
$\phantom{\sqrt{75} + \sqrt{48} - \sqrt{16}} = 9\sqrt{3} - 4$

39.
$$\sqrt{\frac{5}{9}} - \sqrt{\frac{5}{36}} = \frac{\sqrt{5}}{\sqrt{9}} - \frac{\sqrt{5}}{\sqrt{36}}$$
$$= \frac{\sqrt{5}}{3} - \frac{\sqrt{5}}{6}$$
$$= \frac{2\sqrt{5}}{6} - \frac{\sqrt{5}}{6}$$
$$= \frac{\sqrt{5}}{6}$$

40.
$$\sqrt{\frac{11}{25}} + \sqrt{\frac{11}{16}} = \frac{\sqrt{11}}{\sqrt{25}} + \frac{\sqrt{11}}{\sqrt{16}}$$
$$= \frac{\sqrt{11}}{5} + \frac{\sqrt{11}}{4}$$
$$= \frac{4\sqrt{11}}{20} + \frac{5\sqrt{11}}{20}$$
$$= \frac{9\sqrt{11}}{20}$$

41.
$$\sqrt{45x^2} + 3\sqrt{5x^2} - 7x\sqrt{5} + 10$$
$$= \sqrt{9x^2 \cdot 5} + 3\sqrt{x^2 \cdot 5} - 7x\sqrt{5} + 10$$
$$= \sqrt{9x^2}\sqrt{5} + 3\sqrt{x^2}\sqrt{5} - 7x\sqrt{5} + 10$$
$$= 3x\sqrt{5} + 3x\sqrt{5} - 7x\sqrt{5} + 10$$
$$= (3x + 3x - 7x)\sqrt{5} + 10$$
$$= -x\sqrt{5} + 10 \text{ or } 10 - x\sqrt{5}$$

42.
$$\sqrt{50x} - 9\sqrt{2x} + \sqrt{72x} - \sqrt{3x}$$
$$= \sqrt{25 \cdot 2x} - 9\sqrt{2x} + \sqrt{36 \cdot 2x} - \sqrt{3x}$$
$$= \sqrt{25}\sqrt{2x} - 9\sqrt{2x} + \sqrt{36}\sqrt{2x} - \sqrt{3x}$$
$$= 5\sqrt{2x} - 9\sqrt{2x} + 6\sqrt{2x} - \sqrt{3x}$$
$$= (5 - 9 + 6)\sqrt{2x} - \sqrt{3x}$$
$$= 2\sqrt{2x} - \sqrt{3x}$$

43. $\sqrt{3} \cdot \sqrt{6} = \sqrt{3 \cdot 6} = \sqrt{18} = \sqrt{9 \cdot 2} = \sqrt{9} \cdot \sqrt{2} = 3\sqrt{2}$

44.
$$\sqrt{5} \cdot \sqrt{15} = \sqrt{5 \cdot 15}$$
$$= \sqrt{75}$$
$$= \sqrt{25 \cdot 3}$$
$$= \sqrt{25} \cdot \sqrt{3}$$
$$= 5\sqrt{3}$$

45. $\sqrt{2}\left(\sqrt{5} - \sqrt{7}\right) = \sqrt{2}\sqrt{5} - \sqrt{2}\sqrt{7} = \sqrt{10} - \sqrt{14}$

46. $\sqrt{5}\left(\sqrt{11} + \sqrt{3}\right) = \sqrt{5}\sqrt{11} + \sqrt{5}\sqrt{3} = \sqrt{55} + \sqrt{15}$

47.
$$\left(\sqrt{3} + 2\right)\left(\sqrt{6} - 5\right) = \sqrt{3}\sqrt{6} - 5\sqrt{3} + 2\sqrt{6} - 2 \cdot 5$$
$$= \sqrt{18} - 5\sqrt{3} + 2\sqrt{6} - 10$$
$$= \sqrt{9 \cdot 2} - 5\sqrt{3} + 2\sqrt{6} - 10$$
$$= 3\sqrt{2} - 5\sqrt{3} + 2\sqrt{6} - 10$$

48.
$$\left(\sqrt{5} + 1\right)\left(\sqrt{5} - 3\right) = \sqrt{5}\sqrt{5} - 3\sqrt{5} + 1\sqrt{5} - 1 \cdot 3$$
$$= 5 + (-3 + 1)\sqrt{5} - 3$$
$$= 2 - 2\sqrt{5}$$

49.
$$\left(\sqrt{x} - 2\right)^2 = \left(\sqrt{x}\right)^2 - 2\left(\sqrt{x}\right)(2) + 2^2$$
$$= x - 4\sqrt{x} + 4$$

50.
$$\left(\sqrt{y} + 4\right)^2 = \left(\sqrt{y}\right)^2 + 2\left(\sqrt{y}\right)(4) + 4^2$$
$$= y + 8\sqrt{y} + 16$$

51. $\dfrac{\sqrt{27}}{\sqrt{3}} = \sqrt{\dfrac{27}{3}} = \sqrt{9} = 3$

52. $\dfrac{\sqrt{20}}{\sqrt{5}} = \sqrt{\dfrac{20}{5}} = \sqrt{4} = 2$

53. $\dfrac{\sqrt{160}}{\sqrt{8}} = \sqrt{\dfrac{160}{8}} = \sqrt{20} = \sqrt{4 \cdot 5} = \sqrt{4}\sqrt{5} = 2\sqrt{5}$

54. $\dfrac{\sqrt{96}}{\sqrt{3}} = \sqrt{\dfrac{96}{3}} = \sqrt{32} = \sqrt{16 \cdot 2} = \sqrt{16}\sqrt{2} = 4\sqrt{2}$

55.
$$\frac{\sqrt{30x^6}}{\sqrt{2x^3}} = \sqrt{\frac{30x^6}{2x^3}}$$
$$= \sqrt{15x^3}$$
$$= \sqrt{x^2 \cdot 15x}$$
$$= \sqrt{x^2}\sqrt{15x}$$
$$= x\sqrt{15x}$$

56.
$$\frac{\sqrt{54x^5 y^2}}{\sqrt{3xy^2}} = \sqrt{\frac{54x^5 y^2}{3xy^2}}$$
$$= \sqrt{18x^4}$$
$$= \sqrt{9x^4 \cdot 2}$$
$$= \sqrt{9x^4}\sqrt{2}$$
$$= 3x^2\sqrt{2}$$

57. $\dfrac{\sqrt{2}}{\sqrt{11}} = \dfrac{\sqrt{2}}{\sqrt{11}} \cdot \dfrac{\sqrt{11}}{\sqrt{11}} = \dfrac{\sqrt{2 \cdot 11}}{11} = \dfrac{\sqrt{22}}{11}$

58. $\dfrac{\sqrt{3}}{\sqrt{13}} = \dfrac{\sqrt{3}}{\sqrt{13}} \cdot \dfrac{\sqrt{13}}{\sqrt{13}} = \dfrac{\sqrt{3 \cdot 13}}{13} = \dfrac{\sqrt{39}}{13}$

59. $\sqrt{\dfrac{5}{6}} = \dfrac{\sqrt{5}}{\sqrt{6}} = \dfrac{\sqrt{5}}{\sqrt{6}} \cdot \dfrac{\sqrt{6}}{\sqrt{6}} = \dfrac{\sqrt{5 \cdot 6}}{6} = \dfrac{\sqrt{30}}{6}$

60. $\sqrt{\dfrac{7}{10}} = \dfrac{\sqrt{7}}{\sqrt{10}} = \dfrac{\sqrt{7}}{\sqrt{10}} \cdot \dfrac{\sqrt{10}}{\sqrt{10}} = \dfrac{\sqrt{7 \cdot 10}}{10} = \dfrac{\sqrt{70}}{10}$

61. $\dfrac{1}{\sqrt{5x}} = \dfrac{1}{\sqrt{5x}} \cdot \dfrac{\sqrt{5x}}{\sqrt{5x}} = \dfrac{\sqrt{5x}}{5x}$

62. $\dfrac{5}{\sqrt{3y}} = \dfrac{5}{\sqrt{3y}} \cdot \dfrac{\sqrt{3y}}{\sqrt{3y}} = \dfrac{5\sqrt{3y}}{3y}$

63. $\sqrt{\dfrac{3}{x}} = \dfrac{\sqrt{3}}{\sqrt{x}} = \dfrac{\sqrt{3}}{\sqrt{x}} \cdot \dfrac{\sqrt{x}}{\sqrt{x}} = \dfrac{\sqrt{3x}}{x}$

64. $\sqrt{\dfrac{6}{y}} = \dfrac{\sqrt{6}}{\sqrt{y}} = \dfrac{\sqrt{6}}{\sqrt{y}} \cdot \dfrac{\sqrt{y}}{\sqrt{y}} = \dfrac{\sqrt{6y}}{y}$

65. $\dfrac{3}{\sqrt{5} - 2} = \dfrac{3}{\sqrt{5} - 2} \cdot \dfrac{\sqrt{5} + 2}{\sqrt{5} + 2}$

$\qquad = \dfrac{3(\sqrt{5} + 2)}{5 - 4}$

$\qquad = \dfrac{3(\sqrt{5} + 2)}{1}$

$\qquad = 3(\sqrt{5} + 2) \text{ or } 3\sqrt{5} + 6$

66. $\dfrac{8}{\sqrt{10} - 3} = \dfrac{8}{\sqrt{10} - 3} \cdot \dfrac{\sqrt{10} + 3}{\sqrt{10} + 3}$

$\qquad = \dfrac{8(\sqrt{10} + 3)}{10 - 9}$

$\qquad = \dfrac{8(\sqrt{10} + 3)}{1}$

$\qquad = 8(\sqrt{10} + 3) \text{ or } 8\sqrt{10} + 24$

67. $\dfrac{\sqrt{2} + 1}{\sqrt{3} - 1} = \dfrac{\sqrt{2} + 1}{\sqrt{3} - 1} \cdot \dfrac{\sqrt{3} + 1}{\sqrt{3} + 1}$

$\qquad = \dfrac{\sqrt{2}\sqrt{3} + 1 \cdot \sqrt{2} + 1 \cdot \sqrt{3} + 1 \cdot 1}{3 - 1}$

$\qquad = \dfrac{\sqrt{6} + \sqrt{2} + \sqrt{3} + 1}{2}$

68. $\dfrac{\sqrt{3} - 2}{\sqrt{5} + 2} = \dfrac{\sqrt{3} - 2}{\sqrt{5} + 2} \cdot \dfrac{\sqrt{5} - 2}{\sqrt{5} - 2}$

$\qquad = \dfrac{\sqrt{3}\sqrt{5} - 2\sqrt{3} - 2\sqrt{5} + 2 \cdot 2}{5 - 4}$

$\qquad = \dfrac{\sqrt{15} - 2\sqrt{3} - 2\sqrt{5} + 4}{1}$

$\qquad = \sqrt{15} - 2\sqrt{3} - 2\sqrt{5} + 4$

69. $\dfrac{10}{\sqrt{x} + 5} = \dfrac{10}{\sqrt{x} + 5} \cdot \dfrac{\sqrt{x} - 5}{\sqrt{x} - 5}$

$\qquad = \dfrac{10(\sqrt{x} - 5)}{x - 25}$

$\qquad = \dfrac{10\sqrt{x} - 50}{x - 25}$

70. $\dfrac{8}{\sqrt{x} - 1} = \dfrac{8}{\sqrt{x} - 1} \cdot \dfrac{\sqrt{x} + 1}{\sqrt{x} + 1} = \dfrac{8(\sqrt{x} + 1)}{x - 1} = \dfrac{8\sqrt{x} + 8}{x - 1}$

71. $\sqrt{2x} = 6$

$\qquad (\sqrt{2x})^2 = 6^2$

$\qquad 2x = 36$

$\qquad x = 18$

72. $\sqrt{x + 3} = 4$

$\qquad (\sqrt{x + 3})^2 = 4^2$

$\qquad x + 3 = 16$

$\qquad x = 13$

73. $\sqrt{x} + 3 = 8$

$\qquad \sqrt{x} = 5$

$\qquad (\sqrt{x})^2 = 5^2$

$\qquad x = 25$

74. $\sqrt{x} + 8 = 3$

$\qquad \sqrt{x} = -5$

$\sqrt{x}$ cannot equal -5. Thus, the equation has no solution.

75. $\sqrt{2x+1} = x - 7$

$\left(\sqrt{2x+1}\right)^2 = (x-7)^2$

$2x + 1 = x^2 - 14x + 49$

$0 = x^2 - 16x + 48$

$0 = (x-12)(x-4)$

$x - 12 = 0$ or $x - 4 = 0$

$x = 12$ $x = 4$

$x = 4$ does not check, so the solution is $x = 12$.

76. $\sqrt{3x+1} = x - 1$

$\left(\sqrt{3x+1}\right)^2 = (x-1)^2$

$3x + 1 = x^2 - 2x + 1$

$0 = x^2 - 5x$

$0 = x(x-5)$

$x = 0$ or $x - 5 = 0$

$x = 5$

$x = 0$ does not check, so the solution is $x = 5$.

77. $\sqrt{x} + 3 = \sqrt{x+15}$

$\left(\sqrt{x}+3\right)^2 = \left(\sqrt{x+15}\right)^2$

$x + 6\sqrt{x} + 9 = x + 15$

$6\sqrt{x} = 6$

$\sqrt{x} = 1$

$\left(\sqrt{x}\right)^2 = 1^2$

$x = 1$

78. $\sqrt{x-5} = \sqrt{x} - 1$

$\left(\sqrt{x-5}\right)^2 = \left(\sqrt{x}-1\right)^2$

$x - 5 = x - 2\sqrt{x} + 1$

$-6 = -2\sqrt{x}$

$3 = \sqrt{x}$

$3^2 = \left(\sqrt{x}\right)^2$

$9 = x$

79. $a^2 + b^2 = c^2$

$5^2 + b^2 = 9^2$

$25 + b^2 = 81$

$b^2 = 56$

$\sqrt{b^2} = \sqrt{56}$

$b = 2\sqrt{14} \approx 7.48$

80. $a^2 + b^2 = c^2$

$6^2 + 9^2 = c^2$

$36 + 81 = c^2$

$117 = c^2$

$\sqrt{117} = \sqrt{c^2}$

$c = 3\sqrt{13} \approx 10.82$

81. The distance between Romeo and Juliet is the length of the hypotenuse of a right triangle with legs of length 20 feet and 12 feet.

$a^2 + b^2 = c^2$

$20^2 + 12^2 = c^2$

$400 + 144 = c^2$

$544 = c^2$

$\sqrt{544} = \sqrt{c^2}$

$c = 4\sqrt{34} \approx 23.32$

The distance is exactly $4\sqrt{34}$ feet or approximately 23.32 feet.

82. The diagonal of a rectangle forms right triangles with the sides of the rectangle.

$a^2 + b^2 = c^2$

$5^2 + b^2 = 10^2$

$25 + b^2 = 100$

$b^2 = 75$

$\sqrt{b^2} = \sqrt{75}$

$b = 5\sqrt{3} \approx 8.66$

The length of the rectangle is exactly $5\sqrt{3}$ inches or approximately 8.66 inches.

83. $r = \sqrt{\dfrac{S}{4\pi}}$

$r = \sqrt{\dfrac{72}{4\pi}}$

$r \approx 2.4$

The radius is 2.4 inches.

84.
$$r = \sqrt{\frac{S}{4\pi}}$$
$$6 = \sqrt{\frac{S}{4\pi}}$$
$$6^2 = \left(\sqrt{\frac{S}{4\pi}}\right)^2$$
$$36 = \frac{S}{4\pi}$$
$$144\pi = S$$
The surface area is 144π square inches.

85. $\sqrt{144} = 12$, because $12^2 = 144$ and 12 is positive.

86. $-\sqrt[3]{64} = -4$, because $4^3 = 64$.

87. $\sqrt{16x^{16}} = 4x^8$, because $(4x^8)^2 = 16x^{16}$.

88. $\sqrt{4x^{24}} = 2x^{12}$, because $(2x^{12})^2 = 4x^{24}$.

89. $\sqrt{18x^7} = \sqrt{9x^6 \cdot 2x^1} = \sqrt{9x^6}\sqrt{2x} = 3x^3\sqrt{2x}$

90. $\sqrt{48y^6} = \sqrt{16y^6 \cdot 3} = \sqrt{16y^6}\sqrt{3} = 4y^3\sqrt{3}$

91. $\sqrt{\dfrac{y^4}{81}} = \dfrac{\sqrt{y^4}}{\sqrt{81}} = \dfrac{y^2}{9}$

92. $\sqrt{\dfrac{x^9}{9}} = \dfrac{\sqrt{x^9}}{\sqrt{9}} = \dfrac{\sqrt{x^8 \cdot x}}{3} = \dfrac{\sqrt{x^8}\sqrt{x}}{3} = \dfrac{x^4\sqrt{x}}{3}$

93.
$$\sqrt{12} + \sqrt{75} = \sqrt{4 \cdot 3} + \sqrt{25 \cdot 3}$$
$$= \sqrt{4}\sqrt{3} + \sqrt{25}\sqrt{3}$$
$$= 2\sqrt{3} + 5\sqrt{3}$$
$$= (2+5)\sqrt{3}$$
$$= 7\sqrt{3}$$

94.
$$\sqrt{63} + \sqrt{28} - \sqrt{9} = \sqrt{9 \cdot 7} + \sqrt{4 \cdot 7} - 3$$
$$= \sqrt{9}\sqrt{7} + \sqrt{4}\sqrt{7} - 3$$
$$= 3\sqrt{7} + 2\sqrt{7} - 3$$
$$= (3+2)\sqrt{7} - 3$$
$$= 5\sqrt{7} - 3$$

95.
$$\sqrt{\frac{3}{16}} - \sqrt{\frac{3}{4}} = \frac{\sqrt{3}}{\sqrt{16}} - \frac{\sqrt{3}}{\sqrt{4}}$$
$$= \frac{\sqrt{3}}{4} - \frac{\sqrt{3}}{2}$$
$$= \frac{\sqrt{3}}{4} - \frac{2\sqrt{3}}{4}$$
$$= -\frac{\sqrt{3}}{4}$$

96.
$$\sqrt{45x^3} + x\sqrt{20x} - \sqrt{5x^3}$$
$$= \sqrt{9x^2 \cdot 5x} + x\sqrt{4 \cdot 5x} - \sqrt{x^2 \cdot 5x}$$
$$= \sqrt{9x^2}\sqrt{5x} + x\sqrt{4}\sqrt{5x} - \sqrt{x^2}\sqrt{5x}$$
$$= 3x\sqrt{5x} + 2x\sqrt{5x} - x\sqrt{5x}$$
$$= (3x + 2x - x)\sqrt{5x}$$
$$= 4x\sqrt{5x}$$

97.
$$\sqrt{7} \cdot \sqrt{14} = \sqrt{7 \cdot 14}$$
$$= \sqrt{98}$$
$$= \sqrt{49 \cdot 2}$$
$$= \sqrt{49}\sqrt{2}$$
$$= 7\sqrt{2}$$

98.
$$\sqrt{3}\left(\sqrt{9} - \sqrt{2}\right) = \sqrt{3}\left(3 - \sqrt{2}\right)$$
$$= 3\sqrt{3} - \sqrt{3}\sqrt{2}$$
$$= 3\sqrt{3} - \sqrt{6}$$

99.
$$\left(\sqrt{2}+4\right)\left(\sqrt{5}-1\right) = \sqrt{2}\sqrt{5} - 1\sqrt{2} + 4\sqrt{5} - 4 \cdot 1$$
$$= \sqrt{10} - \sqrt{2} + 4\sqrt{5} - 4$$

100.
$$\left(\sqrt{x}+3\right)^2 = \left(\sqrt{x}\right)^2 + 2\left(\sqrt{x}\right)(3) + (3)^2$$
$$= x + 6\sqrt{x} + 9$$

101. $\dfrac{\sqrt{120}}{\sqrt{5}} = \sqrt{\dfrac{120}{5}} = \sqrt{24} = \sqrt{4 \cdot 6} = 2\sqrt{6}$

102. $\dfrac{\sqrt{60x^9}}{\sqrt{15x^4}} = \sqrt{\dfrac{60x^9}{15x^7}} = \sqrt{4x^2} = 2x$

103. $\sqrt{\dfrac{2}{7}} = \dfrac{\sqrt{2}}{\sqrt{7}} = \dfrac{\sqrt{2}}{\sqrt{7}} \cdot \dfrac{\sqrt{7}}{\sqrt{7}} = \dfrac{\sqrt{14}}{7}$

104. $\dfrac{3}{\sqrt{2x}} = \dfrac{3}{\sqrt{2x}} \cdot \dfrac{\sqrt{2x}}{\sqrt{2x}} = \dfrac{3\sqrt{2x}}{2x}$

105. $\dfrac{3}{\sqrt{x}-6} = \dfrac{3}{\sqrt{x}-6} \cdot \dfrac{\sqrt{x}+6}{\sqrt{x}+6}$

$\qquad = \dfrac{3\left(\sqrt{x}+6\right)}{x-36}$

$\qquad = \dfrac{3\sqrt{x}+18}{x-36}$

106. $\dfrac{\sqrt{7}-5}{\sqrt{5}+3} = \dfrac{\sqrt{7}-5}{\sqrt{5}+3} \cdot \dfrac{\sqrt{5}-3}{\sqrt{5}-3}$

$\qquad = \dfrac{\sqrt{7}\sqrt{5}-3\sqrt{7}-5\sqrt{5}+5\cdot 3}{5-9}$

$\qquad = \dfrac{\sqrt{35}-3\sqrt{7}-5\sqrt{5}+15}{-4}$

107. $\sqrt{4x} = 2$

$\quad \left(\sqrt{4x}\right)^2 = 2^2$

$\qquad 4x = 4$

$\qquad x = 1$

108. $\sqrt{x-4} = 3$

$\quad \left(\sqrt{x-4}\right)^2 = 3^2$

$\qquad x-4 = 9$

$\qquad x = 13$

109. $\sqrt{4x+8}+6 = x$

$\qquad \sqrt{4x+8} = x-6$

$\quad \left(\sqrt{4x+8}\right)^2 = (x-6)^2$

$\qquad 4x+8 = x^2-12x+36$

$\qquad 0 = x^2-16x+28$

$\qquad 0 = (x-14)(x-2)$

$x-14 = 0 \quad$ or $\quad x-2 = 0$

$\quad x = 14 \qquad\qquad x = 2$

$x = 2$ does not check, so the solution is $x = 14$.

110. $\sqrt{x-8} = \sqrt{x}-2$

$\quad \left(\sqrt{x-8}\right)^2 = \left(\sqrt{x}-2\right)^2$

$\qquad x-8 = x-4\sqrt{x}+4$

$\qquad -12 = -4\sqrt{x}$

$\qquad 3 = \sqrt{x}$

$\qquad 3^2 = \left(\sqrt{x}\right)^2$

$\qquad 9 = x$

111. $a^2+b^2 = c^2$

$\quad 3^2+7^2 = c^2$

$\quad 9+49 = c^2$

$\qquad 58 = c^2$

$\quad \sqrt{58} = \sqrt{c^2}$

$\qquad c = \sqrt{58} \approx 7.62$

112. The diagonal is the hypotenuse of a right triangle with the sides of the rectangle as its legs.

$\quad a^2+b^2 = c^2$

$\quad 2^2+b^2 = 6^2$

$\quad 4+b^2 = 36$

$\qquad b^2 = 32$

$\quad \sqrt{b^2} = \sqrt{32}$

$\qquad b = 4\sqrt{2} \approx 5.66$

The length of the rectangle is exactly $4\sqrt{2}$ inches or approximately 5.66 inches.

Chapter 15 Test

1. $\sqrt{16} = 4$, because $4^2 = 16$ and 4 is positive.

2. $\sqrt[3]{125} = 5$, because $5^3 = 125$.

3. $\sqrt[4]{81} = 3$, because $3^4 = 81$.

4. $\sqrt{\dfrac{9}{16}} = \dfrac{3}{4}$, because $\left(\dfrac{3}{4}\right)^2 = \dfrac{9}{16}$.

5. $\sqrt[4]{-81}$ is not a real number since the index 4 is even and the radicand -81 is negative.

6. $\sqrt{x^{10}} = x^5$, because $(x^5)^2 = x^{10}$.

7. $\sqrt{54} = \sqrt{9\cdot 6} = \sqrt{9}\sqrt{6} = 3\sqrt{6}$

8. $\sqrt{92} = \sqrt{4\cdot 23} = \sqrt{4}\sqrt{23} = 2\sqrt{23}$

9. $\sqrt{y^7} = \sqrt{y^6 \cdot y} = \sqrt{y^6}\sqrt{y} = y^3\sqrt{y}$

10. $\sqrt{24x^8} = \sqrt{4x^8 \cdot 6} = \sqrt{4x^8}\sqrt{6} = 2x^4\sqrt{6}$

11. $\sqrt[3]{27} = 3$

12. $\sqrt[3]{16} = \sqrt[3]{8\cdot 2} = \sqrt[3]{8}\sqrt[3]{2} = 2\sqrt[3]{2}$

13. $\sqrt{\dfrac{5}{16}} = \dfrac{\sqrt{5}}{\sqrt{16}} = \dfrac{\sqrt{5}}{4}$

14. $\sqrt{\dfrac{y^3}{25}} = \dfrac{\sqrt{y^3}}{\sqrt{25}} = \dfrac{\sqrt{y^2 \cdot y}}{5} = \dfrac{\sqrt{y^2}\sqrt{y}}{5} = \dfrac{y\sqrt{y}}{5}$

15. $\sqrt{13} + \sqrt{13} - 4\sqrt{13} = (1 + 1 - 4)\sqrt{13} = -2\sqrt{13}$

16. $\sqrt{18} - \sqrt{75} + 7\sqrt{3} - \sqrt{8}$
$= \sqrt{9 \cdot 2} - \sqrt{25 \cdot 3} + 7\sqrt{3} - \sqrt{4 \cdot 2}$
$= \sqrt{9}\sqrt{2} - \sqrt{25}\sqrt{3} + 7\sqrt{3} - \sqrt{4}\sqrt{2}$
$= 3\sqrt{2} - 5\sqrt{3} + 7\sqrt{3} - 2\sqrt{2}$
$= (3 - 2)\sqrt{2} + (-5 + 7)\sqrt{3}$
$= \sqrt{2} + 2\sqrt{3}$

17. $\sqrt{\dfrac{3}{4}} + \sqrt{\dfrac{3}{25}} = \dfrac{\sqrt{3}}{\sqrt{4}} + \dfrac{\sqrt{3}}{\sqrt{25}}$
$= \dfrac{\sqrt{3}}{2} + \dfrac{\sqrt{3}}{5}$
$= \dfrac{5\sqrt{3}}{10} + \dfrac{2\sqrt{3}}{10}$
$= \dfrac{5\sqrt{3} + 2\sqrt{3}}{10}$
$= \dfrac{(5 + 2)\sqrt{3}}{10}$
$= \dfrac{7\sqrt{3}}{10}$

18. $\sqrt{7} \cdot \sqrt{14} = \sqrt{7 \cdot 14}$
$= \sqrt{98}$
$= \sqrt{49 \cdot 2}$
$= \sqrt{49}\sqrt{2}$
$= 7\sqrt{2}$

19. $\sqrt{2}\left(\sqrt{6} - \sqrt{5}\right) = \sqrt{2}\sqrt{6} - \sqrt{2}\sqrt{5}$
$= \sqrt{12} - \sqrt{10}$
$= \sqrt{4 \cdot 3} - \sqrt{10}$
$= 2\sqrt{3} - \sqrt{10}$

20. $\left(\sqrt{x} + 2\right)\left(\sqrt{x} - 3\right) = \sqrt{x} \cdot \sqrt{x} - 3\sqrt{x} + 2\sqrt{x} - 2 \cdot 3$
$= x - 3\sqrt{x} + 2\sqrt{x} - 6$
$= x - \sqrt{x} - 6$

21. $\dfrac{\sqrt{50}}{\sqrt{10}} = \sqrt{\dfrac{50}{10}} = \sqrt{5}$

22. $\dfrac{\sqrt{40x^4}}{\sqrt{2x}} = \sqrt{\dfrac{40x^4}{2x}}$
$= \sqrt{20x^3}$
$= \sqrt{4x^2 \cdot 5x}$
$= \sqrt{4x^2}\sqrt{5x}$
$= 2x\sqrt{5x}$

23. $\sqrt{\dfrac{2}{3}} = \dfrac{\sqrt{2}}{\sqrt{3}} = \dfrac{\sqrt{2}}{\sqrt{3}} \cdot \dfrac{\sqrt{3}}{\sqrt{3}} = \dfrac{\sqrt{6}}{3}$

24. $\dfrac{8}{\sqrt{5y}} = \dfrac{8}{\sqrt{5y}} \cdot \dfrac{\sqrt{5y}}{\sqrt{5y}} = \dfrac{8\sqrt{5y}}{5y}$

25. $\dfrac{8}{\sqrt{6} + 2} = \dfrac{8}{\sqrt{6} + 2} \cdot \dfrac{\sqrt{6} - 2}{\sqrt{6} - 2}$
$= \dfrac{8\left(\sqrt{6} - 2\right)}{\left(\sqrt{6}\right)^2 - 2^2}$
$= \dfrac{8\left(\sqrt{6} - 2\right)}{6 - 4}$
$= \dfrac{8\left(\sqrt{6} - 2\right)}{2}$
$= 4\left(\sqrt{6} - 2\right)$
$= 4\sqrt{6} - 8$

26. $\dfrac{1}{3 - \sqrt{x}} = \dfrac{1}{3 - \sqrt{x}} \cdot \dfrac{3 + \sqrt{x}}{3 + \sqrt{x}} = \dfrac{1\left(3 + \sqrt{x}\right)}{3^2 - \left(\sqrt{x}\right)^2} = \dfrac{3 + \sqrt{x}}{9 - x}$

27. $\sqrt{x} + 8 = 11$
$\sqrt{x} = 3$
$\left(\sqrt{x}\right)^2 = 3^2$
$x = 9$

28. $\sqrt{3x - 6} = \sqrt{x + 4}$
$\left(\sqrt{3x - 6}\right)^2 = \left(\sqrt{x + 4}\right)^2$
$3x - 6 = x + 4$
$2x - 6 = 4$
$2x = 10$
$x = 5$

29. $\sqrt{2x-2} = x-5$

$\left(\sqrt{2x-2}\right)^2 = (x-5)^2$

$2x-2 = x^2 - 10x + 25$

$0 = x^2 - 12x + 27$

$0 = (x-3)(x-9)$

$x-3 = 0$ or $x-9 = 0$

$\qquad x = 3 \qquad\qquad x = 9$

$x = 3$ does not check, so the solution is $x = 9$.

30. $a^2 + b^2 = c^2$

$8^2 + b^2 = 12^2$

$64 + b^2 = 144$

$b^2 = 80$

$\sqrt{b^2} = \sqrt{80}$

$b = 4\sqrt{5}$

The length is $4\sqrt{5}$ inches.

31. $r = \sqrt{\dfrac{A}{\pi}}$

$r = \sqrt{\dfrac{15}{\pi}}$

$r \approx 2.19$

The radius is 2.19 meters.

Cumulative Review Chapters 1–15

1. 736.2359 rounded to the nearest tenth is 736.2.

2. 328.174 rounded to the nearest tenth is 328.2.

3. $\begin{array}{r} 23.850 \\ +\ 1.604 \\ \hline 25.454 \end{array}$

4. $\begin{array}{r} 12.762 \\ +\ 4.290 \\ \hline 17.052 \end{array}$

5. $3.7y = -3.33$

$3.7(-9) \overset{?}{=} -3.33$

$-33.3 = -3.33$ False

No, -9 is not a solution.

6. $2.8x = 16.8$

$2.8(6) \overset{?}{=} 16.8$

$16.8 = 16.8$ True

Yes, 6 is a solution.

7. $\sqrt{\dfrac{1}{36}} = \dfrac{1}{6}$ because $\left(\dfrac{1}{6}\right)^2 = \dfrac{1}{6} \cdot \dfrac{1}{6} = \dfrac{1}{36}$ and $\dfrac{1}{6}$ is positive.

8. $\sqrt{\dfrac{4}{25}} = \dfrac{2}{5}$ because $\left(\dfrac{2}{5}\right)^2 = \dfrac{2}{5} \cdot \dfrac{2}{5} = \dfrac{4}{25}$ and $\dfrac{2}{5}$ is positive.

9. $4(2x-3) + 7 = 3x + 5$

$8x - 12 + 7 = 3x + 5$

$8x - 5 = 3x + 5$

$5x - 5 = 5$

$5x = 10$

$x = 2$

10. $3(2-5x) + 24x = 12$

$6 - 15x + 24x = 12$

$6 + 9x = 12$

$9x = 6$

$x = \dfrac{6}{9} = \dfrac{2}{3}$

11. a. $1.02 \times 10^5 = 102,000$

b. $7.358 \times 10^{-3} = 0.007358$

c. $8.4 \times 10^7 = 84,000,000$

d. $3.007 \times 10^{-5} = 0.00003007$

12. a. $8.26 \times 10^4 = 82,600$

b. $9.9 \times 10^{-2} = 0.099$

c. $1.002 \times 10^5 = 100,200$

d. $8.039 \times 10^{-3} = 0.008039$

13. $(3x+2)(2x-5)$

$= (3x)(2x) - (3x)(5) + 2(2x) - 2(5)$

$= 6x^2 - 15x + 4x - 10$

$= 6x^2 - 11x - 10$

14. $(5x-1)(4x+1)$

$= (5x)(4x) + (5x)(1) + (-1)(4x) + (-1)(1)$

$= 20x^2 + 5x - 4x - 1$

$= 20x^2 + x - 1$

15. $xy + 2x + 3y + 6 = x(y+2) + 3(y+2)$
$$= (y+2)(x+3)$$

16. $16x^3 - 28x^2 + 12x - 21 = 4x^2(4x-7) + 3(4x-7)$
$$= (4x-7)(4x^2+3)$$

17. $3x^2 + 11x + 6 = (3x+2)(x+3)$

18. $9x^2 - 5x - 4 = 9x^2 - 9x + 4x - 4$
$$= 9x(x-1) + 4(x-1)$$
$$= (x-1)(9x+4)$$

19. a. The expression is undefined for $x = 3$, since the denominator, $x - 3$, is 0 when $x = 3$.

    b. The expression is undefined for $x = 2$ and $x = 1$, since the denominator, $x^2 - 3x + 2 = (x-2)(x-1)$, is 0 when $x = 2$ or $x = 1$.

    c. There are no values for which the expression is undefined, since the denominator, 3, is never 0.

20. a. The expression is undefined for $x = 0$, since the denominator, x, is 0 when $x = 0$.

    b. There are no values for which the expression is undefined, since the denominator, 5, is never 0.

    c. The expression is undefined for $x = -2$ and $x = 2$, since the denominator, $x^2 - 4 = (x+2)(x-2)$, is 0 when $x = -2$ or $x = 2$.

21. $\dfrac{x^2+4x+4}{x^2+2x} = \dfrac{(x+2)(x+2)}{x(x+2)} = \dfrac{x+2}{x}$

22. $\dfrac{16x^2-4y^2}{4x-2y} = \dfrac{4(4x^2-y^2)}{2(2x-y)}$
$$= \dfrac{2 \cdot 2(2x-y)(2x+y)}{2(2x-y)}$$
$$= 2(2x+y)$$

23. a. $\dfrac{a}{4} - \dfrac{2a}{8} = \dfrac{a}{4} - \dfrac{a}{4} = 0$

    b. $\dfrac{3}{10x^2} + \dfrac{7}{25x} = \dfrac{15}{50x^2} + \dfrac{14x}{50x^2} = \dfrac{15+14x}{50x^2}$

24. a. $\dfrac{x}{5} - \dfrac{3x}{10} = \dfrac{2x}{10} - \dfrac{3x}{10} = -\dfrac{x}{10}$

b. $\dfrac{9}{12a^2} + \dfrac{5}{16a} = \dfrac{36}{48a^2} + \dfrac{15a}{48a^2}$

$= \dfrac{36 + 15a}{48a^2}$

$= \dfrac{3(12 + 5a)}{3 \cdot 16a^2}$

$= \dfrac{12 + 5a}{16a^2}$

25. $\dfrac{4x}{x^2 + x - 30} + \dfrac{2}{x - 5} = \dfrac{1}{x + 6}$

$(x-5)(x+6)\left(\dfrac{4x}{(x-5)(x+6)} + \dfrac{2}{x-5} \right) = (x-5)(x+6)\left(\dfrac{1}{x+6} \right)$

$4x + 2(x + 6) = x - 5$

$4x + 2x + 12 = x - 5$

$6x + 12 = x - 5$

$5x + 12 = -5$

$5x = -17$

$x = -\dfrac{17}{5}$

26. $\dfrac{3}{x+3} = \dfrac{12x + 19}{x^2 + 7x + 12} - \dfrac{5}{x + 4}$

$(x+3)(x+4)\left(\dfrac{3}{x+3} \right) = (x+3)(x+4)\left(\dfrac{12x+19}{(x+3)(x+4)} - \dfrac{5}{x+4} \right)$

$3(x + 4) = 12x + 19 - 5(x + 3)$

$3x + 12 = 12x + 19 - 5x - 15$

$3x + 12 = 7x + 4$

$-4x + 12 = 4$

$-4x = -8$

$x = 2$

27.

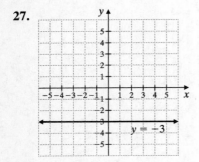

28.

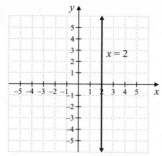

29. $\sqrt[3]{1} = 1$, because $1^3 = 1$.

30. $\sqrt[3]{8} = 2$, because $2^3 = 8$.

31. $\sqrt[3]{-27} = -3$, because $(-3)^3 = -27$.

32. $\sqrt[3]{-8} = -2$, because $(-2)^3 = -8$.

33. $\sqrt[3]{\dfrac{1}{125}} = \dfrac{1}{5}$, because $\left(\dfrac{1}{5}\right)^3 = \dfrac{1}{125}$.

34. $\sqrt[3]{\dfrac{27}{64}} = \dfrac{3}{4}$, because $\left(\dfrac{3}{4}\right)^3 = \dfrac{27}{64}$.

35. $\sqrt{54} = \sqrt{9 \cdot 6} = \sqrt{9}\sqrt{6} = 3\sqrt{6}$

36. $\sqrt{40} = \sqrt{4 \cdot 10} = \sqrt{4}\sqrt{10} = 2\sqrt{10}$

37. $\sqrt{200} = \sqrt{100 \cdot 2} = \sqrt{100}\sqrt{2} = 10\sqrt{2}$

38. $\sqrt{125} = \sqrt{25 \cdot 5} = \sqrt{25}\sqrt{5} = 5\sqrt{5}$

39. $7\sqrt{12} - 2\sqrt{75} = 7\sqrt{4 \cdot 3} - 2\sqrt{25 \cdot 3}$
$$= 7\sqrt{4}\sqrt{3} - 2\sqrt{25}\sqrt{3}$$
$$= 7 \cdot 2\sqrt{3} - 2 \cdot 5\sqrt{3}$$
$$= 14\sqrt{3} - 10\sqrt{3}$$
$$= (14 - 10)\sqrt{3}$$
$$= 4\sqrt{3}$$

40. $\sqrt{75} + \sqrt{48} = \sqrt{25 \cdot 3} + \sqrt{16 \cdot 3}$
$$= \sqrt{25}\sqrt{3} + \sqrt{16}\sqrt{3}$$
$$= 5\sqrt{3} + 4\sqrt{3}$$
$$= 9\sqrt{3}$$

41. $2\sqrt{x^2} - \sqrt{25x^5} + \sqrt{x^5}$
$$= 2x - \sqrt{25x^4 \cdot x} + \sqrt{x^4 \cdot x}$$
$$= 2x - \sqrt{25x^4}\sqrt{x} + \sqrt{x^4}\sqrt{x}$$
$$= 2x - 5x^2\sqrt{x} + x^2\sqrt{x}$$
$$= 2x + (-5x^2 + x^2)\sqrt{x}$$
$$= 2x - 4x^2\sqrt{x}$$

42. $5\sqrt{x^2} + \sqrt{36x} + \sqrt{49x^2} = 5x + \sqrt{36 \cdot x} + \sqrt{(7x)^2}$
$$= 5x + \sqrt{36}\sqrt{x} + 7x$$
$$= 5x + 6\sqrt{x} + 7x$$
$$= 12x + 6\sqrt{x}$$

43. $\dfrac{2}{\sqrt{7}} = \dfrac{2}{\sqrt{7}} \cdot \dfrac{\sqrt{7}}{\sqrt{7}} = \dfrac{2\sqrt{7}}{7}$

44. $\dfrac{4}{\sqrt{5}} = \dfrac{4}{\sqrt{5}} \cdot \dfrac{\sqrt{5}}{\sqrt{5}} = \dfrac{4\sqrt{5}}{5}$

45. $\sqrt{x} = \sqrt{5x - 2}$
$$\left(\sqrt{x}\right)^2 = \left(\sqrt{5x - 2}\right)^2$$
$$x = 5x - 2$$
$$-4x = -2$$
$$x = \dfrac{-2}{-4}$$
$$x = \dfrac{1}{2}$$

The solution is $\dfrac{1}{2}$.

46. $\sqrt{x + 5} = x - 1$
$$\left(\sqrt{x + 5}\right)^2 = (x - 1)^2$$
$$x + 5 = x^2 - 2x + 1$$
$$0 = x^2 - 3x - 4$$
$$0 = (x - 4)(x + 1)$$
$$x - 4 = 0 \quad \text{or} \quad x + 1 = 0$$
$$x = 4 \qquad\qquad x = -1$$

The possible solution $x = -1$ does not check.
The solution is 4.

Chapter 16

Practice Problems

1. $x^2 - 25 = 0$
$(x+5)(x-5) = 0$
$x + 5 = 0$ or $x - 5 = 0$
$\quad x = -5 \qquad\quad x = 5$
The solutions are -5 and 5.

2. $2x^2 - 3x = 9$
$2x^2 - 3x - 9 = 0$
$(2x+3)(x-3) = 0$
$2x + 3 = 0$ or $x - 3 = 0$
$\quad 2x = -3 \qquad\quad x = 3$
$\quad x = -\dfrac{3}{2}$

The solutions are $-\dfrac{3}{2}$ and 3.

3. $x^2 - 16 = 0$
$\quad x^2 = 16$
$x = \sqrt{16}$ or $x = -\sqrt{16}$
$x = 4 \qquad\quad x = -4$
The solutions are 4 and -4.

4. $3x^2 = 11$
$\quad x^2 = \dfrac{11}{3}$

$x = \sqrt{\dfrac{11}{3}}$ or $x = -\sqrt{\dfrac{11}{3}}$

$x = \dfrac{\sqrt{11} \cdot \sqrt{3}}{\sqrt{3} \cdot \sqrt{3}} \qquad x = -\dfrac{\sqrt{11} \cdot \sqrt{3}}{\sqrt{3} \cdot \sqrt{3}}$

$x = \dfrac{\sqrt{33}}{3} \qquad\quad x = -\dfrac{\sqrt{33}}{3}$

The solutions are $\dfrac{\sqrt{33}}{3}$ and $-\dfrac{\sqrt{33}}{3}$.

5. $(x-4)^2 = 49$
$x - 4 = \sqrt{49}$ or $x - 4 = -\sqrt{49}$
$x - 4 = 7 \qquad\quad x - 4 = -7$
$\quad x = 11 \qquad\qquad x = -3$
The solutions are 11 and -3.

6. $(x-5)^2 = 18$
$x - 5 = \sqrt{18}$ or $x - 5 = -\sqrt{18}$
$x - 5 = 3\sqrt{2} \qquad\quad x - 5 = -3\sqrt{2}$
$\quad x = 5 + 3\sqrt{2} \qquad\quad x = 5 - 3\sqrt{2}$
$x = 5 \pm 3\sqrt{2}$
The solutions are $5 \pm 3\sqrt{2}$.

7. $(x+3)^2 = -5$
This equation has no real solution because the square root of -5 is not a real number.

8. $(4x+1)^2 = 15$
$4x + 1 = \sqrt{15}$ or $4x + 1 = -\sqrt{15}$
$\quad 4x = -1 + \sqrt{15} \qquad\quad 4x = -1 - \sqrt{15}$
$\quad\quad x = \dfrac{-1 + \sqrt{15}}{4} \qquad\quad x = \dfrac{-1 - \sqrt{15}}{4}$

$x = \dfrac{-1 \pm \sqrt{15}}{4}$

The solutions are $\dfrac{-1 \pm \sqrt{15}}{4}$.

9. $h = 16t^2$
$650 = 16t^2$
$40.625 = t^2$
$6.4 = t$ or $-6.4 = t$
-6.4 is rejected because time cannot be negative.
It takes the object 6.4 seconds to fall 650 feet.

Exercise Set 16.1

1. $k^2 - 49 = 0$
$(k+7)(k-7) = 0$
$k + 7 = 0$ or $k - 7 = 0$
$\quad k = -7 \qquad\quad k = 7$
The solutions are $k = -7$ and $k = 7$.

3. $m^2 + 2m = 15$
$m^2 + 2m - 15 = 0$
$(m+5)(m-3) = 0$
$m + 5 = 0$ or $m - 3 = 0$
$\quad m = -5 \qquad\quad m = 3$
The solutions are $m = -5$ and $m = 3$.

5. $2x^2 - 32 = 0$

$2(x^2 - 16) = 0$

$2(x+4)(x-4) = 0$

$x + 4 = 0$ or $x - 4 = 0$

    $x = -4$ $x = 4$

The solutions are $x = -4$ and $x = 4$.

7. $4a^2 - 36 = 0$

$4(a^2 - 9) = 0$

$4(a-3)(a+3) = 0$

$a - 3 = 0$ or $a + 3 = 0$

    $a = 3$ $a = -3$

The solutions are $a = 3$ and $a = -3$.

9. $x^2 + 7x = -10$

$x^2 + 7x + 10 = 0$

$(x+2)(x+5) = 0$

$x + 2 = 0$ or $x + 5 = 0$

    $x = -2$ $x = -5$

The solutions are $x = -2$ and $x = -5$.

11. $x^2 = 64$

$x = \sqrt{64}$ or $x = -\sqrt{64}$

$x = 8$ $x = -8$

The solutions are $x = \pm 8$.

13. $x^2 = 21$

$x = \sqrt{21}$ or $x = -\sqrt{21}$

The solutions are $x = \pm\sqrt{21}$.

15. $x^2 = \dfrac{1}{25}$

$x = \sqrt{\dfrac{1}{25}}$ or $x = -\sqrt{\dfrac{1}{25}}$

$x = \dfrac{1}{5}$ $x = -\dfrac{1}{5}$

The solutions are $x = \pm\dfrac{1}{5}$.

17. $x^2 = -4$ has no real solution because the square root of -4 is not a real number.

19. $3x^2 = 13$

$x^2 = \dfrac{13}{3}$

$x = \sqrt{\dfrac{13}{3}}$ or $x = -\sqrt{\dfrac{13}{3}}$

$x = \dfrac{\sqrt{13}}{\sqrt{3}} \cdot \dfrac{\sqrt{3}}{\sqrt{3}}$ $x = -\dfrac{\sqrt{13}}{\sqrt{3}} \cdot \dfrac{\sqrt{3}}{\sqrt{3}}$

$x = \dfrac{\sqrt{39}}{3}$ $x = -\dfrac{\sqrt{39}}{3}$

The solutions are $x = \pm\dfrac{\sqrt{39}}{3}$.

21. $7x^2 = 4$

$x^2 = \dfrac{4}{7}$

$x = \sqrt{\dfrac{4}{7}}$ or $x = -\sqrt{\dfrac{4}{7}}$

$x = \dfrac{\sqrt{4}}{\sqrt{7}} \cdot \dfrac{\sqrt{7}}{\sqrt{7}}$ $x = -\dfrac{\sqrt{4}}{\sqrt{7}} \cdot \dfrac{\sqrt{7}}{\sqrt{7}}$

$x = \dfrac{2\sqrt{7}}{7}$ $x = -\dfrac{2\sqrt{7}}{7}$

The solutions are $x = \pm\dfrac{2\sqrt{7}}{7}$.

23. $x^2 - 2 = 0$

$x^2 = 2$

$x = \sqrt{2}$ or $x = -\sqrt{2}$

The solutions are $x = \pm\sqrt{2}$.

25. $(x-5)^2 = 49$

$x - 5 = \sqrt{49}$ or $x - 5 = -\sqrt{49}$

$x - 5 = 7$ $x - 5 = -7$

    $x = 12$ $x = -2$

The solutions are $x = -2$ and $x = 12$.

27. $(x+2)^2 = 7$

$x + 2 = \sqrt{7}$ or $x + 2 = -\sqrt{7}$

  $x = -2 + \sqrt{7}$ $x = -2 - \sqrt{7}$

The solutions are $x = -2 \pm \sqrt{7}$.

29. $\left(m - \dfrac{1}{2}\right)^2 = \dfrac{1}{4}$

$m - \dfrac{1}{2} = \sqrt{\dfrac{1}{4}}$ or $m - \dfrac{1}{2} = -\sqrt{\dfrac{1}{4}}$

$m - \dfrac{1}{2} = \dfrac{1}{2}$ $m - \dfrac{1}{2} = -\dfrac{1}{2}$

$\qquad m = 1$ $m = 0$

The solutions are $m = 0$ and $m = 1$.

31. $(p + 2)^2 = 10$

$p + 2 = \sqrt{10}$ or $p + 2 = -\sqrt{10}$

$p = -2 + \sqrt{10}$ $p = -2 - \sqrt{10}$

The solutions are $p = -2 \pm \sqrt{10}$.

33. $(3y + 2)^2 = 100$

$3y + 2 = \sqrt{100}$ or $3y + 2 = -\sqrt{100}$

$3y + 2 = 10$ $3y + 2 = -10$

$\quad 3y = 8$ $3y = -12$

$\qquad y = \dfrac{8}{3}$ $y = -4$

The solutions are $y = -4$ and $y = \dfrac{8}{3}$.

35. $(z - 4)^2 = -9$ has no real solution because the square root of -9 is not a real number.

37. $(2x - 11)^2 = 50$

$2x - 11 = \sqrt{50}$ or $2x - 11 = -\sqrt{50}$

$2x - 11 = 5\sqrt{2}$ $2x - 11 = -5\sqrt{2}$

$\quad 2x = 11 + 5\sqrt{2}$ $2x = 11 - 5\sqrt{2}$

$\qquad x = \dfrac{11 + 5\sqrt{2}}{2}$ $x = \dfrac{11 - 5\sqrt{2}}{2}$

The solutions are $x = \dfrac{11 \pm 5\sqrt{2}}{2}$.

39. $(3x - 7)^2 = 32$

$3x - 7 = \sqrt{32}$ or $3x - 7 = -\sqrt{32}$

$3x - 7 = 4\sqrt{2}$ $3x - 7 = -4\sqrt{2}$

$\quad 3x = 7 + 4\sqrt{2}$ $3x = 7 - 4\sqrt{2}$

$\qquad x = \dfrac{7 + 4\sqrt{2}}{3}$ $x = \dfrac{7 - 4\sqrt{2}}{3}$

The solutions are $x = \dfrac{7 \pm 4\sqrt{2}}{3}$.

41. $x^2 - 29 = 0$

$x^2 = 29$

$x = \sqrt{29}$ or $x = -\sqrt{29}$

The solutions are $x = \pm\sqrt{29}$.

43. $(x + 6)^2 = 24$

$x + 6 = \sqrt{24}$ or $x + 6 = -\sqrt{24}$

$x + 6 = 2\sqrt{6}$ $x + 6 = -2\sqrt{6}$

$\quad x = -6 + 2\sqrt{6}$ $x = -6 - 2\sqrt{6}$

The solutions are $x = -6 \pm 2\sqrt{6}$.

45. $\dfrac{1}{2}n^2 = 5$

$n^2 = 10$

$n = \sqrt{10}$ or $n = -\sqrt{10}$

The solutions are $n = \pm\sqrt{10}$.

47. $(4x - 1)^2 = 5$

$4x - 1 = \sqrt{5}$ or $4x - 1 = -\sqrt{5}$

$\quad 4x = 1 + \sqrt{5}$ $4x = 1 - \sqrt{5}$

$\qquad x = \dfrac{1 + \sqrt{5}}{4}$ $x = \dfrac{1 - \sqrt{5}}{4}$

The solutions are $x = \dfrac{1 \pm \sqrt{5}}{4}$.

49. $3z^2 = 36$

$z^2 = 12$

$z = \sqrt{12}$ or $z = -\sqrt{12}$

$z = 2\sqrt{3}$ $z = -2\sqrt{3}$

The solutions are $z = \pm 2\sqrt{3}$.

51. $(8 - 3x)^2 - 45 = 0$

$(8 - 3x)^2 = 45$

$8 - 3x = \sqrt{45}$ or $8 - 3x = -\sqrt{45}$

$8 - 3x = 3\sqrt{5}$ $8 - 3x = -3\sqrt{5}$

$\quad -3x = -8 + 3\sqrt{5}$ $-3x = -8 - 3\sqrt{5}$

$\qquad x = \dfrac{-8 + 3\sqrt{5}}{-3}$ $x = \dfrac{-8 - 3\sqrt{5}}{-3}$

The solutions are $x = \dfrac{-8 \pm 3\sqrt{5}}{-3}$.

53.
$$h = 16t^2$$
$$87.6 = 16t^2$$
$$\frac{87.6}{16} = t^2$$
$$5.475 = t^2$$
$$\sqrt{5.475} = t \quad \text{or} \quad -\sqrt{5.475} = t$$
$$2.3 \approx t \qquad\qquad -2.3 \approx t$$
Since the time of a dive is not a negative number, reject the solution −2.3. The dive lasted approximately 2.3 seconds.

55.
$$h = 16t^2$$
$$4000 = 16t^2$$
$$250 = t^2$$
$$\sqrt{250} = t \quad \text{or} \quad -\sqrt{250} = t$$
$$15.8 \approx t \qquad\qquad -15.8 \approx t$$
Since the time of a fall is not a negative number, reject the solution −15.8. It would take approximately 15.8 seconds for the object to reach the bottom of the canyon.

57.
$$A = \pi r^2$$
$$36\pi = \pi r^2$$
$$36 = r^2$$
$$\sqrt{36} = r \quad \text{or} \quad -\sqrt{36} = r$$
$$6 = r \qquad\qquad -6 = r$$
Since the radius does not have a negative length, reject the solution −6. The radius is 6 inches.

59.
$$A = s^2$$
$$20 = s^2$$
$$\sqrt{20} = s \quad \text{or} \quad -\sqrt{20} = s$$
$$2\sqrt{5} = s \qquad -2\sqrt{5} = s$$
Since the length of a side is not a negative number, reject the solution $-2\sqrt{5}$. The sides have length $2\sqrt{5} \approx 4.47$ inches.

61.
$$A = s^2$$
$$3039 = s^2$$
$$\sqrt{3039} = s \quad \text{or} \quad -\sqrt{3039} = s$$
$$55.13 \approx s \qquad\qquad -55.13 \approx s$$
Since the length of a side is not a negative number, reject the solution −55.13. The sides have length 55.13 feet.

63. $x^2 + 6x + 9 = (x)^2 + 2(x)(3) + (3)^2 = (x+3)^2$

65. $x^2 - 4x + 4 = x^2 - 2(x)(2) + (2)^2 = (x-2)^2$

67. answers may vary

69.
$$x^2 + 4x + 4 = 16$$
$$(x+2)^2 = 16$$
$$x + 2 = \sqrt{16} \quad \text{or} \quad x + 2 = -\sqrt{16}$$
$$x + 2 = 4 \qquad\qquad x + 2 = -4$$
$$x = 2 \qquad\qquad x = -6$$
The solutions are $x = 2$ and $x = -6$.

71.
$$x^2 = 1.78$$
$$x = \sqrt{1.78} \quad \text{or} \quad x = -\sqrt{1.78}$$
$$x \approx \pm 1.33$$
The solutions are $x = \pm 1.33$.

73.
$$y = 148(x+1.5)^2 + 589,105$$
$$605,000 = 148(x+1.5)^2 + 589,105$$
$$15,895 = 148(x+1.5)^2$$
$$\frac{15,895}{148} = (x+1.5)^2$$
$$\sqrt{\frac{15,895}{148}} = x + 1.5$$
$$-1.5 + \sqrt{\frac{15,895}{148}} = x$$
$$8.9 \approx x$$
or
$$-\sqrt{\frac{15,895}{148}} = x + 1.5$$
$$-1.5 - \sqrt{\frac{15,895}{148}} = x$$
$$-11.9 \approx x$$
Since the time will not be a negative number in this context, reject the solution of −11.9. The solution is $x \approx 9$, so the model predicts that there were 605,000 highway bridges in 2009 (2000 + 9).

Section 16.2

Practice Problems

1. $x^2 + 8x + 1 = 0$

$$x^2 + 8x = -1$$

$$x^2 + 8x + 16 = -1 + 16$$

$$(x+4)^2 = 15$$

$x + 4 = \sqrt{15}$ or $x + 4 = -\sqrt{15}$

$\quad x = -4 + \sqrt{15} \qquad x = -4 - \sqrt{15}$

The solutions are $-4 \pm \sqrt{15}$.

2. $x^2 - 14x = -32$

$$x^2 - 14x + 49 = -32 + 49$$

$$(x-7)^2 = 17$$

$x - 7 = \sqrt{17}$ or $x - 7 = -\sqrt{17}$

$\quad x = 7 + \sqrt{17} \qquad x = 7 - \sqrt{17}$

The solutions are $7 \pm \sqrt{17}$.

3. $4x^2 - 16x - 9 = 0$

$$x^2 - 4x - \frac{9}{4} = 0$$

$$x^2 - 4x = \frac{9}{4}$$

$$x^2 - 4x + 4 = \frac{9}{4} + 4$$

$$(x-2)^2 = \frac{25}{4}$$

$x - 2 = \sqrt{\dfrac{25}{4}}$ or $x - 2 = -\sqrt{\dfrac{25}{4}}$

$x - 2 = \dfrac{5}{2} \qquad\quad x - 2 = -\dfrac{5}{2}$

$x = 2 + \dfrac{5}{2} \qquad\quad x = 2 - \dfrac{5}{2}$

$x = \dfrac{9}{2} \qquad\qquad x = -\dfrac{1}{2}$

The solutions are $\dfrac{9}{2}$ and $-\dfrac{1}{2}$.

4. $2x^2 + 10x = -13$

$$x^2 + 5x = -\frac{13}{2}$$

$$x^2 + 5x + \frac{25}{4} = -\frac{13}{2} + \frac{25}{4}$$

$$\left(x + \frac{5}{2}\right)^2 = -\frac{1}{4}$$

There is no real solution to this equation since the square root of a negative number is not a real number.

5. $2x^2 = -6x + 5$

$$x^2 = -3x + \frac{5}{2}$$

$$x^2 + 3x = \frac{5}{2}$$

$$x^2 + 3x + \frac{9}{4} = \frac{5}{2} + \frac{9}{4}$$

$$\left(x + \frac{3}{2}\right)^2 = \frac{19}{4}$$

$x + \dfrac{3}{2} = \sqrt{\dfrac{19}{4}}$ or $x + \dfrac{3}{2} = -\sqrt{\dfrac{19}{4}}$

$x + \dfrac{3}{2} = \dfrac{\sqrt{19}}{2} \qquad\quad x + \dfrac{3}{2} = -\dfrac{\sqrt{19}}{2}$

$x = -\dfrac{3}{2} + \dfrac{\sqrt{19}}{2} \qquad\quad x = -\dfrac{3}{2} - \dfrac{\sqrt{19}}{2}$

The solutions are $\dfrac{-3 \pm \sqrt{19}}{2}$.

Vocabulary and Readiness Check

1. By the zero-factor property, if the product of two numbers is zero, then at least one of these two numbers must be <u>zero</u>.

2. If a is a positive number, and if $x^2 = a$, then $x = \underline{\pm\sqrt{a}}$.

3. An equation that can be written in the form $ax^2 + bx + c = 0$ where a, b, and c are real numbers and a is not zero is called a <u>quadratic equation</u>.

4. The process of solving a quadratic equation by writing it in the form $(x + a)^2 = c$ is called <u>completing the square</u>.

5. To complete the square on $x^2 + 6x$, add <u>9</u>.

6. To complete the square on $x^2 + bx$, add $\underline{\left(\dfrac{b}{2}\right)^2}$.

7. $\left(\dfrac{8}{2}\right)^2 = 4^2 = 16; \quad p^2 + 8p + \underline{16}$

8. $\left(\dfrac{6}{2}\right)^2 = 3^2 = 9; \quad p^2 + 6p + \underline{9}$

9. $\left(\dfrac{20}{2}\right)^2 = 10^2 = 100;\ x^2 + 20x + \underline{100}$

10. $\left(\dfrac{18}{2}\right)^2 = 9^2 = 81;\ x^2 + 18x + \underline{81}$

11. $\left(\dfrac{14}{2}\right)^2 = 7^2 = 49;\ y^2 + 14y + \underline{49}$

12. $\left(\dfrac{2}{2}\right)^2 = 1^2 = 1;\ y^2 + 2y + \underline{1}$

Exercise Set 16.2

1.
$$x^2 + 8x = -12$$
$$x^2 + 8x + \left(\dfrac{8}{2}\right)^2 = -12 + \left(\dfrac{8}{2}\right)^2$$
$$x^2 + 8x + 4^2 = -12 + 4^2$$
$$x^2 + 8x + 16 = -12 + 16$$
$$(x+4)^2 = 4$$
$$x + 4 = \sqrt{4} \quad \text{or} \quad x + 4 = -\sqrt{4}$$
$$x = -4 + 2 \qquad\qquad x = -4 - 2$$
$$x = -2 \qquad\qquad x = -6$$
The solutions are $x = -6$ and $x = -2$.

3.
$$x^2 + 2x - 7 = 0$$
$$x^2 + 2x = 7$$
$$x^2 + 2x + \left(\dfrac{2}{2}\right)^2 = 7 + \left(\dfrac{2}{2}\right)^2$$
$$x^2 + 2x + 1 = 7 + 1$$
$$(x+1)^2 = 8$$
$$x + 1 = \sqrt{8} \quad \text{or} \quad x + 1 = -\sqrt{8}$$
$$x + 1 = 2\sqrt{2} \qquad\quad x + 1 = -2\sqrt{2}$$
$$x = -1 + 2\sqrt{2} \qquad\quad x = -1 - 2\sqrt{2}$$
The solutions are $x = -1 \pm 2\sqrt{2}$.

5.
$$x^2 - 6x = 0$$
$$x^2 - 6x + \left(\dfrac{-6}{2}\right)^2 = 0 + \left(\dfrac{-6}{2}\right)^2$$
$$x^2 - 6x + (-3)^2 = 0 + (-3)^2$$
$$x^2 - 6x + 9 = 9$$
$$(x-3)^2 = 9$$

$$x - 3 = \sqrt{9} \quad \text{or} \quad x - 3 = -\sqrt{9}$$
$$x = 3 + 3 \qquad\qquad x = 3 - 3$$
$$x = 6 \qquad\qquad x = 0$$
The solutions are $x = 0$ and $x = 6$.

7.
$$y^2 + 5y + 4 = 0$$
$$y^2 + 5y = -4$$
$$y^2 + 5y + \left(\dfrac{5}{2}\right)^2 = -4 + \left(\dfrac{5}{2}\right)^2$$
$$\left(y + \dfrac{5}{2}\right)^2 = \dfrac{9}{4}$$
$$y + \dfrac{5}{2} = \sqrt{\dfrac{9}{4}} \quad \text{or} \quad y + \dfrac{5}{2} = -\sqrt{\dfrac{9}{4}}$$
$$y = -\dfrac{5}{2} + \dfrac{3}{2} \qquad\qquad y = -\dfrac{5}{2} - \dfrac{3}{2}$$
$$y = -\dfrac{2}{2} = -1 \qquad\qquad y = -\dfrac{8}{2} = -4$$
The solutions are $y = -1$ and $y = -4$.

9.
$$x^2 - 2x - 1 = 0$$
$$x^2 - 2x = 1$$
$$x^2 - 2x + \left(\dfrac{-2}{2}\right)^2 = 1 + \left(\dfrac{-2}{2}\right)^2$$
$$x^2 - 2x + (-1)^2 = 1 + (-1)^2$$
$$x^2 - 2x + 1 = 1 + 1$$
$$(x-1)^2 = 2$$
$$x - 1 = \sqrt{2} \quad \text{or} \quad x - 1 = -\sqrt{2}$$
$$x = 1 + \sqrt{2} \qquad\quad x = 1 - \sqrt{2}$$
The solutions are $x = 1 \pm \sqrt{2}$.

11.
$$z^2 + 5z = 7$$
$$z^2 + 5z + \left(\dfrac{5}{2}\right)^2 = 7 + \left(\dfrac{5}{2}\right)^2$$
$$z^2 + 5z + \dfrac{25}{4} = 7 + \dfrac{25}{4}$$
$$\left(z + \dfrac{5}{2}\right)^2 = \dfrac{53}{4}$$
$$z + \dfrac{5}{2} = \sqrt{\dfrac{53}{4}} \quad \text{or} \quad z + \dfrac{5}{2} = -\sqrt{\dfrac{53}{4}}$$
$$z = -\dfrac{5}{2} + \dfrac{\sqrt{53}}{2} \qquad\quad z = -\dfrac{5}{2} - \dfrac{\sqrt{53}}{2}$$
The solutions are $z = \dfrac{-5 \pm \sqrt{53}}{2}$.

13.
$$3x^2 - 6x = 24$$
$$x^2 - 2x = 8$$
$$x^2 - 2x + \left(\frac{-2}{2}\right)^2 = 8 + \left(\frac{-2}{2}\right)^2$$
$$x^2 - 2x + (-1)^2 = 8 + (-1)^2$$
$$x^2 - 2x + 1 = 8 + 1$$
$$(x-1)^2 = 9$$
$$x - 1 = \sqrt{9} \quad \text{or} \quad x - 1 = -\sqrt{9}$$
$$x = 1 + 3 \qquad\qquad x = 1 - 3$$
$$x = 4 \qquad\qquad\quad x = -2$$
The solutions are $x = -2$ and $x = 4$.

15.
$$5x^2 + 10x + 6 = 0$$
$$x^2 + 2x + \frac{6}{5} = 0$$
$$x^2 + 2x = -\frac{6}{5}$$
$$x^2 + 2x + \left(\frac{2}{2}\right)^2 = -\frac{6}{5} + \left(\frac{2}{2}\right)^2$$
$$(x+1)^2 = -\frac{1}{5}$$

This has no real solution because $\sqrt{-\frac{1}{5}}$ is not a real number.

17.
$$2x^2 = 6x + 5$$
$$2x^2 - 6x = 5$$
$$x^2 - 3x = \frac{5}{2}$$
$$x^2 - 3x + \left(\frac{-3}{2}\right)^2 = \frac{5}{2} + \left(\frac{-3}{2}\right)^2$$
$$x^2 - 3x + \frac{9}{4} = \frac{5}{2} + \frac{9}{4}$$
$$\left(x - \frac{3}{2}\right)^2 = \frac{10}{4} + \frac{9}{4}$$
$$\left(x - \frac{3}{2}\right)^2 = \frac{19}{4}$$

$$x - \frac{3}{2} = \sqrt{\frac{19}{4}} \quad \text{or} \quad x - \frac{3}{2} = -\sqrt{\frac{19}{4}}$$
$$x = \frac{3}{2} + \frac{\sqrt{19}}{2} \qquad\qquad x = \frac{3}{2} - \frac{\sqrt{19}}{2}$$
$$x = \frac{3 + \sqrt{19}}{2} \qquad\qquad x = \frac{3 - \sqrt{19}}{2}$$
The solutions are $x = \frac{3 \pm \sqrt{19}}{2}$.

19.
$$2y^2 + 8y + 5 = 0$$
$$y^2 + 4y + \frac{5}{2} = 0$$
$$y^2 + 4y = -\frac{5}{2}$$
$$y^2 + 4y + \left(\frac{4}{2}\right)^2 = -\frac{5}{2} + \left(\frac{4}{2}\right)^2$$
$$(y+2)^2 = \frac{3}{2}$$
$$y + 2 = \sqrt{\frac{3}{2}} \quad \text{or} \quad y + 2 = -\sqrt{\frac{3}{2}}$$
$$y = -2 + \frac{\sqrt{6}}{2} \qquad\qquad y = -2 - \frac{\sqrt{6}}{2}$$
The solutions are $y = -2 \pm \frac{\sqrt{6}}{2}$.

21.
$$x^2 + 6x - 25 = 0$$
$$x^2 + 6x = 25$$
$$x^2 + 6x + \left(\frac{6}{2}\right)^2 = 25 + \left(\frac{6}{2}\right)^2$$
$$x^2 + 6x + 3^2 = 25 + 3^2$$
$$x^2 + 6x + 9 = 25 + 9$$
$$(x+3)^2 = 34$$
$$x + 3 = \sqrt{34} \quad \text{or} \quad x + 3 = -\sqrt{34}$$
$$x = -3 + \sqrt{34} \qquad\qquad x = -3 - \sqrt{34}$$
The solutions are $x = -3 \pm \sqrt{34}$.

23.
$$x^2 - 3x - 3 = 0$$
$$x^2 - 3x = 3$$
$$x^2 - 3x + \left(-\frac{3}{2}\right)^2 = 3 + \left(-\frac{3}{2}\right)^2$$
$$\left(x - \frac{3}{2}\right)^2 = \frac{21}{4}$$

$$x - \frac{3}{2} = \sqrt{\frac{21}{4}} \quad \text{or} \quad x - \frac{3}{2} = -\sqrt{\frac{21}{4}}$$

$$x = \frac{3}{2} + \frac{\sqrt{21}}{2} \qquad\qquad x = \frac{3}{2} - \frac{\sqrt{21}}{2}$$

The solutions are $x = \frac{3 \pm \sqrt{21}}{2}$.

25.
$$2y^2 - 3y + 1 = 0$$
$$2y^2 - 3y = -1$$
$$y^2 - \frac{3}{2}y = -\frac{1}{2}$$
$$y^2 - \frac{3}{2}y + \left(\frac{-\frac{3}{2}}{2}\right)^2 = -\frac{1}{2} + \left(\frac{-\frac{3}{2}}{2}\right)^2$$
$$y^2 - \frac{3}{2}y + \left(-\frac{3}{4}\right)^2 = -\frac{1}{2} + \left(-\frac{3}{4}\right)^2$$
$$y^2 - \frac{3}{2}y + \frac{9}{16} = -\frac{1}{2} + \frac{9}{16}$$
$$\left(y - \frac{3}{4}\right)^2 = \frac{1}{16}$$

$$y - \frac{3}{4} = \sqrt{\frac{1}{16}} \quad \text{or} \quad y - \frac{3}{4} = -\sqrt{\frac{1}{16}}$$
$$y = \frac{3}{4} + \frac{1}{4} \qquad\qquad y = \frac{3}{4} - \frac{1}{4}$$
$$y = 1 \qquad\qquad\qquad y = \frac{1}{2}$$

The solutions are $y = \frac{1}{2}$ and $y = 1$.

27.
$$x(x+3) = 18$$
$$x^2 + 3x = 18$$
$$x^2 + 3x + \left(\frac{3}{2}\right)^2 = 18 + \left(\frac{3}{2}\right)^2$$
$$\left(x + \frac{3}{2}\right)^2 = \frac{81}{4}$$

$$x + \frac{3}{2} = \sqrt{\frac{81}{4}} \quad \text{or} \quad x + \frac{3}{2} = -\sqrt{\frac{81}{4}}$$
$$x = -\frac{3}{2} + \frac{9}{2} \qquad\qquad x = -\frac{3}{2} - \frac{9}{2}$$
$$x = \frac{6}{2} = 3 \qquad\qquad x = -\frac{12}{2} = -6$$

The solutions are $x = 3$ and $x = -6$.

29.
$$3z^2 + 6z + 4 = 0$$
$$3z^2 + 6z = -4$$
$$z^2 + 2z = -\frac{4}{3}$$
$$z^2 + 2z + \left(\frac{2}{2}\right)^2 = -\frac{4}{3} + \left(\frac{2}{2}\right)^2$$
$$z^2 + 2z + 1^2 = -\frac{4}{3} + 1^2$$
$$z^2 + 2z + 1 = -\frac{4}{3} + 1$$
$$(z+1)^2 = -\frac{1}{3}$$

The equation has no real solution, since the square root of $-\frac{1}{3}$ is not a real number.

31.
$$4x^2 + 16x = 48$$
$$x^2 + 4x = 12$$
$$x^2 + 4x + \left(\frac{4}{2}\right)^2 = 12 + \left(\frac{4}{2}\right)^2$$
$$(x+2)^2 = 16$$
$$x + 2 = \sqrt{16} \quad \text{and} \quad x + 2 = -\sqrt{16}$$
$$x = -2 + 4 \qquad\qquad x = -2 - 4$$
$$x = 2 \qquad\qquad\qquad x = -6$$

The solutions are $x = 2$ and $x = -6$.

33.
$$\frac{3}{4} - \sqrt{\frac{25}{16}} = \frac{3}{4} - \frac{\sqrt{25}}{\sqrt{16}}$$
$$= \frac{3}{4} - \frac{5}{4}$$
$$= \frac{3-5}{4}$$
$$= \frac{-2}{4}$$
$$= -\frac{1}{2}$$

35. $\frac{1}{2} + \sqrt{\frac{9}{4}} = \frac{1}{2} + \frac{3}{2} = \frac{4}{2} = 2$

37. $\frac{6 + 4\sqrt{5}}{2} = \frac{6}{2} + \frac{4\sqrt{5}}{2} = 3 + 2\sqrt{5}$

39. $\frac{3 - 9\sqrt{2}}{6} = \frac{3}{6} - \frac{9\sqrt{2}}{6} = \frac{1}{2} - \frac{3\sqrt{2}}{2} = \frac{1 - 3\sqrt{2}}{2}$

41. answers may vary

43. a. $x^2 + 6x + 9 = 11$

$(x+3)^2 = 11$

$x+3 = \sqrt{11}$ or $x+3 = -\sqrt{11}$

$x = -3 + \sqrt{11}$ $x = -3 - \sqrt{11}$

The solutions are $x = -3 \pm \sqrt{11}$.

b.   answers may vary

45. $x^2 + kx + \left(\dfrac{k}{2}\right)^2$ is a perfect square trinomial. If

$x^2 + kx + 16$ is a perfect square trinomial, then

$\left(\dfrac{k}{2}\right)^2 = 16$

$\dfrac{k}{2} = \sqrt{16}$ or $\dfrac{k}{2} = -\sqrt{16}$

$k = 2 \cdot 4$ $k = 2(-4)$

$k = 8$ $k = -8$

$x^2 + kx + 16$ is a perfect square trinomial when $k = 8$ or $k = -8$.

47.

$y = 2.5x^2 + 7.5x + 122$

$392 = 2.5x^2 + 7.5x + 122$

$270 = 2.5x^2 + 7.5x$

$108 = x^2 + 3x$

$\left(\dfrac{3}{2}\right)^2 + 108 = x^2 + 3x + \left(\dfrac{3}{2}\right)^2$

$110.25 = (x+1.5)^2$

$\sqrt{110.25} = x+1.5$ or $-\sqrt{110.25} = x+1.5$

$10.5 = x+1.5$ $-10.5 = x+1.5$

$9 = x$ $-12 = x$

Since the time will not be a negative number in this context, reject the solution -12. The solution is $x = 9$, so the model predicts that retail sales from online shopping will be $392 billion in 2011 (2002 + 9).

49. The solutions are $x = -6$ and $x = -2$.

51. The solutions are $x \approx -0.68$ and $x \approx 3.68$.

Section 16.3

Practice Problems

1. $2x^2 - x - 5 = 0$

$a = 2, b = -1, c = -5$

$x = \dfrac{-b \pm \sqrt{b^2 - 4ac}}{2a}$

$x = \dfrac{-(-1) \pm \sqrt{(-1)^2 - 4(2)(-5)}}{2(2)}$

$= \dfrac{1 \pm \sqrt{1+40}}{4}$

$= \dfrac{1 \pm \sqrt{41}}{4}$

The solutions are $\dfrac{1 \pm \sqrt{41}}{4}$.

2. $3x^2 + 8x = 3$

$3x^2 + 8x - 3 = 0$

$a = 3, b = 8, c = -3$

$x = \dfrac{-b \pm \sqrt{b^2 - 4ac}}{2a}$

$x = \dfrac{-8 \pm \sqrt{8^2 - 4(3)(-3)}}{2(3)}$

$= \dfrac{-8 \pm \sqrt{64 + 36}}{6}$

$= \dfrac{-8 \pm \sqrt{100}}{6}$

$= \dfrac{-8 \pm 10}{6}$

$x = \dfrac{-8+10}{6} = \dfrac{1}{3}$ or $\dfrac{-8-10}{6} = -3$

The solutions are $\dfrac{1}{3}$ and -3.

3. $5x^2 = 2$

$5x^2 - 2 = 0$

$a = 5, b = 0, c = -2$

$$x = \frac{-b \pm \sqrt{b^2 - 4ac}}{2a}$$

$$x = \frac{-0 \pm \sqrt{0^2 - 4(5)(-2)}}{2(5)}$$

$$= \pm \frac{\sqrt{40}}{10}$$

$$= \pm \frac{2\sqrt{10}}{10}$$

$$= \pm \frac{\sqrt{10}}{5}$$

The solutions are $\pm \dfrac{\sqrt{10}}{5}$.

4.
$$x^2 = -2x - 3$$
$$x^2 + 2x + 3 = 0$$
$$a = 1, \, b = 2, \, c = 3$$
$$x = \frac{-b \pm \sqrt{b^2 - 4ac}}{2a}$$
$$x = \frac{-2 \pm \sqrt{2^2 - 4(1)(3)}}{2(1)} = \frac{-2 \pm \sqrt{-8}}{2}$$

There is no real number solution because $\sqrt{-8}$ is not a real number.

5.
$$\frac{1}{3}x^2 - x = 1$$
$$\frac{1}{3}x^2 - x - 1 = 0$$
$$a = \frac{1}{3}, \, b = -1, \, c = -1$$
$$x = \frac{-b \pm \sqrt{b^2 - 4ac}}{2a}$$
$$x = \frac{-(-1) \pm \sqrt{(-1)^2 - 4\left(\frac{1}{3}\right)(-1)}}{2\left(\frac{1}{3}\right)}$$
$$= \frac{1 \pm \sqrt{\frac{7}{3}}}{\frac{2}{3}}$$
$$= \frac{1 \pm \frac{\sqrt{21}}{3}}{\frac{2}{3}}$$
$$= \frac{3 \pm \sqrt{21}}{2}$$

The solutions are $\dfrac{3 \pm \sqrt{21}}{2}$.

6. $\dfrac{1 + \sqrt{41}}{4} \approx 1.9$

$1 - \dfrac{\sqrt{41}}{4} \approx -1.4$

Vocabulary and Readiness Check

1. The quadratic formula is $x = \dfrac{-b \pm \sqrt{b^2 - 4ac}}{2a}$.

2. $5x^2 - 7x + 1 = 0$; $a = \underline{5}$, $b = \underline{-7}$, $c = \underline{1}$

3. $x^2 + 3x - 7 = 0$; $a = \underline{1}$, $b = \underline{3}$, $c = \underline{-7}$

4. $x^2 - 6 = 0$; $a = \underline{1}$, $b = \underline{0}$, $c = \underline{-6}$

5. $x^2 + x - 1 = 0$; $a = \underline{1}$, $b = \underline{1}$, $c = \underline{-1}$

6. $9x^2 - 4 = 0$; $a = \underline{9}$, $b = \underline{0}$, $c = \underline{-4}$

7. $\dfrac{-1 \pm \sqrt{1^2 - 4(1)(-2)}}{2(1)} = \dfrac{-1 \pm \sqrt{1 + 8}}{2}$

$$= \frac{-1 \pm \sqrt{9}}{2}$$
$$= \frac{-1 \pm 3}{2}$$

$\dfrac{-1 + 3}{2} = \dfrac{2}{2} = 1$

$\dfrac{-1 - 3}{2} = \dfrac{-4}{2} = -2$

8. $\dfrac{-(-5) \pm \sqrt{(-5)^2 - 4(2)(3)}}{2(2)} = \dfrac{5 \pm \sqrt{25 - 24}}{4}$

$$= \frac{5 \pm \sqrt{1}}{4}$$
$$= \frac{5 \pm 1}{4}$$

$\dfrac{5 + 1}{4} = \dfrac{6}{4} = \dfrac{3}{2}$

$\dfrac{5 - 1}{4} = \dfrac{4}{4} = 1$

9. $\dfrac{-5 \pm \sqrt{5^2 - 4(1)(2)}}{2(1)} = \dfrac{-5 \pm \sqrt{25 - 8}}{2} = \dfrac{-5 \pm \sqrt{17}}{2}$

10. $\dfrac{-7 \pm \sqrt{7^2 - 4(2)(1)}}{2(2)} = \dfrac{-7 \pm \sqrt{49 - 8}}{4} = \dfrac{-7 \pm \sqrt{41}}{4}$

Exercise Set 16.3

1. $x^2 - 3x + 2 = 0$
$a = 1,\ b = -3,\ c = 2$
$x = \dfrac{-b \pm \sqrt{b^2 - 4ac}}{2a}$
$x = \dfrac{-(-3) \pm \sqrt{(-3)^2 - 4(1)(2)}}{2(1)}$
$\quad = \dfrac{3 \pm \sqrt{9 - 8}}{2}$
$\quad = \dfrac{3 \pm \sqrt{1}}{2}$
$\quad = \dfrac{3 \pm 1}{2}$
$x = \dfrac{3 + 1}{2} = 2 \text{ or } x = \dfrac{3 - 1}{2} = 1$
The solutions are $x = 2$ and $x = 1$.

3. $3k^2 + 7k + 1 = 0$
$a = 3,\ b = 7,\ c = 1$
$k = \dfrac{-b \pm \sqrt{b^2 - 4ac}}{2a}$
$k = \dfrac{-7 \pm \sqrt{7^2 - 4(3)(1)}}{2(3)}$
$\quad = \dfrac{-7 \pm \sqrt{49 - 12}}{6}$
$\quad = \dfrac{-7 \pm \sqrt{37}}{6}$
The solutions are $k = \dfrac{-7 \pm \sqrt{37}}{6}$.

5. $4x^2 - 3 = 0$
$4x^2 + 0x - 3 = 0$
$a = 4,\ b = 0,\ c = -3$
$x = \dfrac{-b \pm \sqrt{b^2 - 4ac}}{2a}$

$x = \dfrac{-0 \pm \sqrt{0^2 - 4(4)(-3)}}{2(4)}$
$\quad = \dfrac{0 \pm \sqrt{0 + 48}}{8}$
$\quad = \dfrac{\pm \sqrt{48}}{8}$
$\quad = \pm \dfrac{4\sqrt{3}}{8}$
$\quad = \pm \dfrac{\sqrt{3}}{2}$
The solutions are $x = \pm \dfrac{\sqrt{3}}{2}$.

7. $5z^2 - 4z + 3 = 0$
$a = 5,\ b = -4,\ c = 3$
$z = \dfrac{-b \pm \sqrt{b^2 - 4ac}}{2a}$
$z = \dfrac{-(-4) \pm \sqrt{(-4)^2 - 4(5)(3)}}{2(5)}$
$\quad = \dfrac{4 \pm \sqrt{16 - 60}}{10}$
$\quad = \dfrac{4 \pm \sqrt{-44}}{10}$
The equation has no solution, since the square root of -44 is not a real number.

9. $y^2 = 7y + 30$
$y^2 - 7y - 30 = 0$
$a = 1,\ b = -7,\ c = -30$
$y = \dfrac{-b \pm \sqrt{b^2 - 4ac}}{2a}$
$y = \dfrac{-(-7) \pm \sqrt{(-7)^2 - 4(1)(-30)}}{2(1)}$
$\quad = \dfrac{7 \pm \sqrt{49 + 120}}{2}$
$\quad = \dfrac{7 \pm \sqrt{169}}{2}$
$\quad = \dfrac{7 \pm 13}{2}$
$y = \dfrac{7 + 13}{2} = 10 \text{ or } y = \dfrac{7 - 13}{2} = -3$
The solutions are $y = 10$ and $y = -3$.

11.
$$2x^2 = 10$$
$$2x^2 - 10 = 0$$
$$a = 2, b = 0, c = -10$$
$$x = \frac{-b \pm \sqrt{b^2 - 4ac}}{2a}$$
$$x = \frac{-0 \pm \sqrt{0^2 - 4(2)(-10)}}{2(2)}$$
$$= \frac{\pm\sqrt{80}}{4}$$
$$= \frac{\pm 4\sqrt{5}}{4}$$
$$= \pm\sqrt{5}$$
The solutions are $x = \pm\sqrt{5}$.

13.
$$m^2 - 12 = m$$
$$m^2 - m - 12 = 0$$
$$a = 1, b = -1, c = -12$$
$$m = \frac{-b \pm \sqrt{b^2 - 4ac}}{2a}$$
$$m = \frac{-(-1) \pm \sqrt{(-1)^2 - 4(1)(-12)}}{2(1)}$$
$$= \frac{1 \pm \sqrt{1 + 48}}{2}$$
$$= \frac{1 \pm \sqrt{49}}{2}$$
$$= \frac{1 \pm 7}{2}$$
$$m = \frac{1 + 7}{2} = 4 \text{ or } m = \frac{1 - 7}{2} = -3$$
The solutions are $m = 4$ and $m = -3$.

15.
$$3 - x^2 = 4x$$
$$0 = x^2 + 4x - 3$$
$$a = 1, b = 4, c = -3$$
$$x = \frac{-b \pm \sqrt{b^2 - 4ac}}{2a}$$
$$x = \frac{-4 \pm \sqrt{4^2 - 4(1)(-3)}}{2(1)}$$
$$= \frac{-4 \pm \sqrt{16 + 12}}{2}$$
$$= \frac{-4 \pm \sqrt{28}}{2}$$
$$= \frac{-4 \pm 2\sqrt{7}}{2}$$
$$= -2 \pm \sqrt{7}$$
The solutions are $x = -2 \pm \sqrt{7}$.

17.
$$6x^2 + 9x = 2$$
$$6x^2 + 9x - 2 = 0$$
$$a = 6, b = 9, c = -2$$
$$x = \frac{-b \pm \sqrt{b^2 - 4ac}}{2a}$$
$$x = \frac{-9 \pm \sqrt{9^2 - 4(6)(-2)}}{2(6)}$$
$$= \frac{-9 \pm \sqrt{81 + 48}}{12}$$
$$= \frac{-9 \pm \sqrt{129}}{12}$$
The solutions are $x = \frac{-9 \pm \sqrt{129}}{12}$.

19.
$$7p^2 + 2 = 8p$$
$$7p^2 - 8p + 2 = 0$$
$$a = 7, b = -8, c = 2$$
$$p = \frac{-b \pm \sqrt{b^2 - 4ac}}{2a}$$
$$p = \frac{-(-8) \pm \sqrt{(-8)^2 - 4(7)(2)}}{2(7)}$$
$$= \frac{8 \pm \sqrt{64 - 56}}{14}$$
$$= \frac{8 \pm \sqrt{8}}{14}$$
$$= \frac{8 \pm 2\sqrt{2}}{14}$$
$$= \frac{4 \pm \sqrt{2}}{7}$$
The solutions are $p = \frac{4 \pm \sqrt{2}}{7}$.

21. $x^2 - 6x + 2 = 0$

$a = 1, b = -6, c = 2$

$x = \dfrac{-b \pm \sqrt{b^2 - 4ac}}{2a}$

$x = \dfrac{-(-6) \pm \sqrt{(-6)^2 - 4(1)(2)}}{2(1)}$

$= \dfrac{6 \pm \sqrt{36 - 8}}{2}$

$= \dfrac{6 \pm \sqrt{28}}{2}$

$= \dfrac{6 \pm 2\sqrt{7}}{2}$

$= \dfrac{2\left(3 \pm \sqrt{7}\right)}{2}$

$= 3 \pm \sqrt{7}$

The solutions are $x = 3 \pm \sqrt{7}$.

23. $2x^2 - 6x + 3 = 0$

$a = 2, b = -6, c = 3$

$x = \dfrac{-b \pm \sqrt{b^2 - 4ac}}{2a}$

$x = \dfrac{-(-6) \pm \sqrt{(-6)^2 - 4(2)(3)}}{2(2)}$

$= \dfrac{6 \pm \sqrt{36 - 24}}{4}$

$= \dfrac{6 \pm \sqrt{12}}{4}$

$= \dfrac{6 \pm 2\sqrt{3}}{4}$

$= \dfrac{3 \pm \sqrt{3}}{2}$

The solutions are $x = \dfrac{3 \pm \sqrt{3}}{2}$.

25. $3x^2 = 1 - 2x$

$3x^2 + 2x - 1 = 0$

$a = 3, b = 2, c = -1$

$x = \dfrac{-b \pm \sqrt{b^2 - 4ac}}{2a}$

$x = \dfrac{-2 \pm \sqrt{2^2 - 4(3)(-1)}}{2(3)}$

$= \dfrac{-2 \pm \sqrt{4 + 12}}{6}$

$= \dfrac{-2 \pm \sqrt{16}}{6}$

$= \dfrac{-2 \pm 4}{6}$

$x = \dfrac{-2 + 4}{6} = \dfrac{1}{3}$ or $x = \dfrac{-2 - 4}{6} = -1$

The solutions are $x = \dfrac{1}{3}$ and $x = -1$.

27. $4y^2 = 6y + 1$

$4y^2 - 6y - 1 = 0$

$a = 4, b = -6, c = -1$

$y = \dfrac{-b \pm \sqrt{b^2 - 4ac}}{2a}$

$y = \dfrac{-(-6) \pm \sqrt{(-6)^2 - 4(4)(-1)}}{2(4)}$

$= \dfrac{6 \pm \sqrt{36 + 16}}{8}$

$= \dfrac{6 \pm \sqrt{52}}{8}$

$= \dfrac{6 \pm 2\sqrt{13}}{8}$

$= \dfrac{3 \pm \sqrt{13}}{4}$

The solutions are $y = \dfrac{3 \pm \sqrt{13}}{4}$.

29. $20y^2 = 3 - 11y$

$20y^2 + 11y - 3 = 0$

$a = 20, b = 11, c = -3$

$y = \dfrac{-b \pm \sqrt{b^2 - 4ac}}{2a}$

$y = \dfrac{-11 \pm \sqrt{11^2 - 4(20)(-3)}}{2(20)}$

$= \dfrac{-11 \pm \sqrt{121 + 240}}{40}$

$= \dfrac{-11 \pm \sqrt{361}}{40}$

$= \dfrac{-11 \pm 19}{40}$

$$y = \frac{-11+19}{40} = \frac{1}{5} \text{ or } y = \frac{-11-19}{40} = -\frac{3}{4}$$

The solutions are $y = \frac{1}{5}$ and $y = -\frac{3}{4}$.

31. $x^2 + x + 2 = 0$
$a = 1, b = 1, c = 2$

$$x = \frac{-b \pm \sqrt{b^2 - 4ac}}{2a}$$

$$x = \frac{-1 \pm \sqrt{1^2 - 4(1)(2)}}{2(1)} = \frac{-1 \pm \sqrt{1-8}}{2} = \frac{-1 \pm \sqrt{-7}}{2}$$

The equation has no solution, since the square root of -7 is not a real number.

33.
$$\frac{m^2}{2} = m + \frac{1}{2}$$

$$\frac{m^2}{2} - m - \frac{1}{2} = 0$$

$$m^2 - 2m - 1 = 0$$

$a = 1, b = -2, c = -1$

$$m = \frac{-b \pm \sqrt{b^2 - 4ac}}{2a}$$

$$m = \frac{-(-2) \pm \sqrt{(-2)^2 - 4(1)(-1)}}{2(1)}$$

$$= \frac{2 \pm \sqrt{4+4}}{2}$$

$$= \frac{2 \pm \sqrt{8}}{2}$$

$$= \frac{2 \pm 2\sqrt{2}}{2}$$

$$= \frac{2\left(1 \pm \sqrt{2}\right)}{2}$$

$$= 1 \pm \sqrt{2}$$

The solutions are $m = 1 \pm \sqrt{2}$.

35. $3p^2 - \frac{2}{3}p + 1 = 0$

$$9p^2 - 2p + 3 = 0$$

$a = 9, b = -2, c = 3$

$$p = \frac{-b \pm \sqrt{b^2 - 4ac}}{2a}$$

$$p = \frac{-(-2) \pm \sqrt{(-2)^2 - 4(9)(3)}}{2(9)}$$

$$= \frac{2 \pm \sqrt{4-108}}{18}$$

$$= \frac{2 \pm \sqrt{-104}}{18}$$

The equation has no solution, since the square root of -104 is not a real number.

37.
$$4p^2 + \frac{3}{2} = -5p$$

$$4p^2 + 5p + \frac{3}{2} = 0$$

$$8p^2 + 10p + 3 = 0$$

$a = 8, b = 10, c = 3$

$$p = \frac{-b \pm \sqrt{b^2 - 4ac}}{2a}$$

$$p = \frac{-10 \pm \sqrt{10^2 - 4(8)(3)}}{2(8)}$$

$$= \frac{-10 \pm \sqrt{100 - 96}}{16}$$

$$= \frac{-10 \pm \sqrt{4}}{16}$$

$$= \frac{-10 \pm 2}{16}$$

$$p = \frac{-10+2}{16} = -\frac{1}{2} \text{ or } p = \frac{-10-2}{16} = -\frac{3}{4}$$

The solutions are $p = -\frac{1}{2}$ and $p = -\frac{3}{4}$.

39.
$$5x^2 = \frac{7}{2}x + 1$$

$$5x^2 - \frac{7}{2}x - 1 = 0$$

$$10x^2 - 7x - 2 = 0$$

$a = 10, b = -7, c = -2$

$$x = \frac{-b \pm \sqrt{b^2 - 4ac}}{2a}$$

$$x = \frac{-(-7) \pm \sqrt{(-7)^2 - 4(10)(-2)}}{2(10)}$$

$$= \frac{7 \pm \sqrt{49 + 80}}{20}$$

$$= \frac{7 \pm \sqrt{129}}{20}$$

The solutions are $x = \frac{7 \pm \sqrt{129}}{20}$.

41. $x^2 - \frac{11}{2}x - \frac{1}{2} = 0$

$2x^2 - 11x - 1 = 0$

$a = 2,\ b = -11,\ c = -1$

$$x = \frac{-b \pm \sqrt{b^2 - 4ac}}{2a}$$

$$x = \frac{-(-11) \pm \sqrt{(-11)^2 - 4(2)(-1)}}{2(2)}$$

$$= \frac{11 \pm \sqrt{121 + 8}}{4}$$

$$= \frac{11 \pm \sqrt{129}}{4}$$

The solutions are $x = \frac{11 \pm \sqrt{129}}{4}$.

43. $5z^2 - 2z = \frac{1}{5}$

$5z^2 - 2z - \frac{1}{5} = 0$

$25z^2 - 10z - 1 = 0$

$a = 25,\ b = -10,\ c = -1$

$$z = \frac{-b \pm \sqrt{b^2 - 4ac}}{2a}$$

$$z = \frac{-(-10) \pm \sqrt{(-10)^2 - 4(25)(-1)}}{2(25)}$$

$$= \frac{10 \pm \sqrt{100 + 100}}{50}$$

$$= \frac{10 \pm \sqrt{200}}{50}$$

$$= \frac{10 \pm 10\sqrt{2}}{50}$$

$$= \frac{1 \pm \sqrt{2}}{5}$$

The solutions are $z = \frac{1 \pm \sqrt{2}}{5}$.

45. $3x^2 = 21$

$3x^2 - 21 = 0$

$3x^2 + 0x - 21 = 0$

$a = 3,\ b = 0,\ c = -21$

$$x = \frac{-b \pm \sqrt{b^2 - 4ac}}{2a}$$

$$x = \frac{-0 \pm \sqrt{0^2 - 4(3)(-21)}}{2(3)}$$

$$= \frac{\pm\sqrt{0 + 252}}{6}$$

$$= \frac{\pm\sqrt{252}}{6}$$

$$= \frac{\pm 6\sqrt{7}}{6}$$

$$= \pm\sqrt{7}$$

The solutions are $x = \pm\sqrt{7}$ or $x \approx -2.6$ and $x \approx 2.6$.

47. $x^2 + 6x + 1 = 0$

$a = 1,\ b = 6,\ c = 1$

$$x = \frac{-b \pm \sqrt{b^2 - 4ac}}{2a}$$

$$x = \frac{-6 \pm \sqrt{6^2 - 4(1)(1)}}{2(1)}$$

$$= \frac{-6 \pm \sqrt{36 - 4}}{2}$$

$$= \frac{-6 \pm \sqrt{32}}{2}$$

$$= \frac{-6 \pm 4\sqrt{2}}{2}$$

$$= -3 \pm 2\sqrt{2}$$

The solutions are $x = -3 \pm 2\sqrt{2}$ or $x \approx -5.8$ and $x \approx -0.2$.

49.
$$x^2 = 9x + 4$$
$$x^2 - 9x - 4 = 0$$
$$a = 1,\ b = -9,\ c = -4$$
$$x = \frac{-b \pm \sqrt{b^2 - 4ac}}{2a}$$
$$x = \frac{-(-9) \pm \sqrt{(-9)^2 - 4(1)(-4)}}{2(1)}$$
$$= \frac{9 \pm \sqrt{81 + 16}}{2}$$
$$= \frac{9 \pm \sqrt{97}}{2}$$

The solutions are $x = \dfrac{9 \pm \sqrt{97}}{2}$ or $x \approx 9.4$ and $x \approx -0.4$.

51. $3x^2 - 2x - 2 = 0$
$$a = 3,\ b = -2,\ c = -2$$
$$x = \frac{-b \pm \sqrt{b^2 - 4ac}}{2a}$$
$$x = \frac{-(-2) \pm \sqrt{(-2)^2 - 4(3)(-2)}}{2(3)}$$
$$= \frac{2 \pm \sqrt{4 + 24}}{6}$$
$$= \frac{2 \pm \sqrt{28}}{6}$$
$$= \frac{2 \pm 2\sqrt{7}}{6}$$
$$= \frac{1 \pm \sqrt{7}}{3}$$

The solutions are $x = \dfrac{1 \pm \sqrt{7}}{3}$ or $x \approx 1.2$ and $x \approx -0.5$.

53. $y = -3$ is a horizontal line with y-intercept $(0, -3)$.

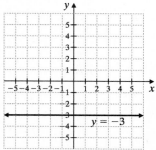

55. $y = 3x - 2$ is a line with slope of 3 and y-intercept $(0, -2)$.

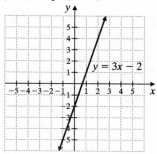

57. $5x^2 + 2 = x$
$$5x^2 - x + 2 = 0$$
$$b = -1,\ \text{which is choice c.}$$

59. $7y^2 = 3y$
$$0 = -7y^2 + 3y + 0$$
$$a = -7,\ \text{which is choice b.}$$

61. Let x be the width of the chocolate bar. Then the length is $3x - 0.6$.
$$\text{Area} = (\text{length})(\text{width})$$
$$34.65 = (3x - 0.6)(x)$$
$$34.65 = 3x^2 - 0.6x$$
$$0 = 3x^2 - 0.6x - 34.65$$
$$a = 3,\ b = -0.6,\ c = -34.65$$
$$x = \frac{-b \pm \sqrt{b^2 - 4ac}}{2a}$$
$$x = \frac{-(-0.6) \pm \sqrt{(-0.6)^2 - 4(3)(-34.65)}}{2(3)}$$
$$= \frac{0.6 \pm \sqrt{0.36 + 415.8}}{6}$$
$$= \frac{0.6 \pm \sqrt{416.16}}{6}$$
$$= \frac{0.6 \pm 20.4}{6}$$
$$x = \frac{0.6 + 20.4}{6} = \frac{21}{6} = 3.5$$
or
$$x = \frac{0.6 - 20.4}{6} = \frac{-19.8}{6} = -3.3$$

Since the width is not a negative number, discard the solution -3.3.
$$3x - 0.6 = 3(3.5) - 0.6 = 10.5 - 0.6 = 9.9$$
The width was 3.5 feet and the length was 9.9 feet.

63. $x^2 + 3\sqrt{2}x - 5 = 0$

$a = 1,\ b = 3\sqrt{2},\ c = -5$

$x = \dfrac{-b \pm \sqrt{b^2 - 4ac}}{2a}$

$x = \dfrac{-3\sqrt{2} \pm \sqrt{\left(3\sqrt{2}\right)^2 - 4(1)(-5)}}{2(1)}$

$= \dfrac{-3\sqrt{2} \pm \sqrt{18 + 20}}{2}$

$= \dfrac{-3\sqrt{2} \pm \sqrt{38}}{2}$

The solutions are $x = \dfrac{-3\sqrt{2} \pm \sqrt{38}}{2}$.

65. answers may vary

67. $7.3^2 + 5.4z - 1.1 = 0$

$a = 7.3,\ b = 5.4,\ c = -1.1$

$z = \dfrac{-b \pm \sqrt{b^2 - 4ac}}{2a}$

$z = \dfrac{-5.4 \pm \sqrt{(5.4)^2 - 4(7.3)(-1.1)}}{2(7.3)}$

$= \dfrac{-5.4 \pm \sqrt{29.16 + 32.12}}{14.6}$

$= \dfrac{-5.4 \pm \sqrt{61.28}}{14.6}$

$z = \dfrac{-5.4 + \sqrt{61.28}}{14.6} \approx 0.2$ or

$z = \dfrac{-5.4 - \sqrt{61.28}}{14.6} \approx -0.9$

The solutions are $z \approx 0.2$ and $z = -0.9$.

69. $h = -16t^2 + 120t + 80$

$0 = -16t^2 + 120t + 80$

$a = -16,\ b = 120,\ c = 80$

$t = \dfrac{-b \pm \sqrt{b^2 - 4ac}}{2a}$

$t = \dfrac{-120 \pm \sqrt{120^2 - 4(-16)(80)}}{2(-16)}$

$= \dfrac{-120 \pm \sqrt{14,400 + 5120}}{-32}$

$= \dfrac{-120 \pm \sqrt{19,520}}{-32}$

$t = \dfrac{-120 + \sqrt{19,520}}{-32} \approx -0.6$ or

$t = \dfrac{-120 - \sqrt{19,520}}{-32} \approx 8.1$

Since the time of the flight is not a negative number, discard the solution –0.6. The rocket will strike the ground approximately 8.1 seconds after it is launched.

71. $y = 0.014x^2 + 0.08x + 1.25$

$2.5 = 0.014x^2 + 0.08x + 1.25$

$0 = 0.014x^2 + 0.08x - 1.25$

$a = 0.014,\ b = 0.08,\ c = -1.25$

$x = \dfrac{-b \pm \sqrt{b^2 - 4ac}}{2a}$

$x = \dfrac{-0.08 \pm \sqrt{0.08^2 - 4(0.014)(-1.25)}}{2(0.014)}$

$= \dfrac{-0.08 \pm \sqrt{0.0064 + 0.07}}{0.028}$

$= \dfrac{-0.08 \pm \sqrt{0.0764}}{0.028}$

$x = \dfrac{-0.08 + \sqrt{0.0764}}{0.028} \approx 7$

or

$x = \dfrac{-0.08 - \sqrt{0.0764}}{0.028} \approx -13$

Since the time is not negative in this context, discard the solution –13. The solution is $x \approx 7$, so the model predicts that the average annual salary for NFL players will be $2.5 million in 2010 (2003 + 7).

Integrated Review

1. $5x^2 - 11x + 2 = 0$

$(5x - 1)(x - 2) = 0$

$5x - 1 = 0$ or $x - 2 = 0$

$5x = 1$ $x = 2$

$x = \dfrac{1}{5}$

The solutions are $x = \dfrac{1}{5}$ and $x = 2$.

2. $5x^2 + 13x - 6 = 0$

$(5x - 2)(x + 3) = 0$

$5x - 2 = 0$ or $x + 3 = 0$

      $5x = 2$ $x = -3$

        $x = \dfrac{2}{5}$

The solutions are $x = \dfrac{2}{5}$ and $x = -3$.

3. $x^2 - 1 = 2x$

$x^2 - 2x - 1 = 0$

$a = 1, b = -2, c = -1$

$x = \dfrac{-b \pm \sqrt{b^2 - 4ac}}{2a}$

$x = \dfrac{-(-2) \pm \sqrt{(-2)^2 - 4(1)(-1)}}{2(1)}$

   $= \dfrac{2 \pm \sqrt{4 + 4}}{2}$

   $= \dfrac{2 \pm \sqrt{8}}{2}$

   $= \dfrac{2 \pm 2\sqrt{2}}{2}$

   $= 1 \pm \sqrt{2}$

The solutions are $x = 1 \pm \sqrt{2}$.

4. $x^2 + 7 = 6x$

$x^2 - 6x + 7 = 0$

$a = 1, b = -6, c = 7$

$x = \dfrac{-b \pm \sqrt{b^2 - 4ac}}{2a}$

$x = \dfrac{-(-6) \pm \sqrt{(-6)^2 - 4(1)(7)}}{2(1)}$

   $= \dfrac{6 \pm \sqrt{36 - 28}}{2}$

   $= \dfrac{6 \pm \sqrt{8}}{2}$

   $= \dfrac{6 \pm 2\sqrt{2}}{2}$

   $= 3 \pm \sqrt{2}$

The solutions are $x = 3 \pm \sqrt{2}$.

5. $a^2 = 20$

     $a = \pm\sqrt{20}$

     $a = \pm 2\sqrt{5}$

The solutions are $a = \pm 2\sqrt{5}$.

6. $a^2 = 72$

     $a = \pm\sqrt{72}$

     $a = \pm 6\sqrt{2}$

The solutions are $a = \pm 6\sqrt{2}$.

7. $x^2 - x + 4 = 0$

$a = 1, b = -1, c = 4$

$x = \dfrac{-b \pm \sqrt{b^2 - 4ac}}{2a}$

$x = \dfrac{-(-1) \pm \sqrt{(-1)^2 - 4(1)(4)}}{2(1)}$

   $= \dfrac{1 \pm \sqrt{1 - 16}}{2}$

   $= \dfrac{1 \pm \sqrt{-15}}{2}$

The equation has no solution, since the square root of -15 is not a real number.

8. $x^2 - 2x + 7 = 0$

$a = 1, b = -2, c = 7$

$x = \dfrac{-b \pm \sqrt{b^2 - 4ac}}{2a}$

$x = \dfrac{-(-2) \pm \sqrt{(-2)^2 - 4(1)(7)}}{2(1)}$

   $= \dfrac{2 \pm \sqrt{4 - 28}}{2}$

   $= \dfrac{2 \pm \sqrt{-24}}{2}$

The equation has no solution, since the square root of -24 is not a real number.

9. $3x^2 - 12x + 12 = 0$

   $3(x^2 - 4x + 4) = 0$

   $3(x - 2)(x - 2) = 0$

   $x - 2 = 0$ or $x - 2 = 0$

      $x = 2$ $x = 2$

The solution is $x = 2$.

10. $5x^2 - 30x + 45 = 0$
$5(x^2 - 6x + 9) = 0$
$5(x - 3)(x - 3) = 0$
$x - 3 = 0$ or $x - 3 = 0$
$x = 3$ $\qquad x = 3$
The solution is $x = 3$.

11. $9 - 6p + p^2 = 0$
$(3 - p)(3 - p) = 0$
$3 - p = 0$ or $3 - p = 0$
$3 = p$ $\qquad 3 = p$
The solution is $p = 3$.

12. $49 - 28p + 4p^2 = 0$
$(7 - 2p)(7 - 2p) = 0$
$7 - 2p = 0$ or $7 - 2p = 0$
$7 = 2p$ $\qquad 7 = 2p$
$\dfrac{7}{2} = p$ $\qquad \dfrac{7}{2} = p$
The solution is $p = \dfrac{7}{2}$.

13. $4y^2 - 16 = 0$
$4(y^2 - 4) = 0$
$4(y - 2)(y + 2) = 0$
$y - 2 = 0$ or $\begin{array}{l} y + 2 = 0 \\ y = -2 \end{array}$
$y = 2$
The solutions are $y = \pm 2$.

14. $3y^2 - 27 = 0$
$3(y^2 - 9) = 0$
$3(y - 3)(y + 3) = 0$
$y - 3 = 0$ or $y + 3 = 0$
$y = 3$ $\qquad y = -3$
The solutions are $y = \pm 3$.

15. $x^2 - 3x + 2 = 0$
$(x - 2)(x - 1) = 0$
$x - 2 = 0$ or $x - 1 = 0$
$x = 2$ $\qquad x = 1$
The solutions are $x = 1$ and $x = 2$.

16. $x^2 + 7x + 12 = 0$
$(x + 3)(x + 4) = 0$
$x + 3 = 0$ or $x + 4 = 0$
$x = -3$ $\qquad x = -4$
The solutions are $x = -3$ and $x = -4$.

17. $(2z + 5)^2 = 25$
$2z + 5 = \sqrt{25}$ or $2z + 5 = -\sqrt{25}$
$2z + 5 = 5$ $\qquad 2z + 5 = -5$
$2z = 0$ $\qquad\quad 2z = -10$
$z = 0$ $\qquad\quad z = -5$
The solutions are $z = 0$ and $z = -5$.

18. $(3z - 4)^2 = 16$
$3z - 4 = \sqrt{16}$ or $3z - 4 = -\sqrt{16}$
$3z - 4 = 4$ $\qquad 3z - 4 = -4$
$3z = 8$ $\qquad\quad 3z = 0$
$z = \dfrac{8}{3}$ $\qquad\quad z = 0$
The solutions are $z = \dfrac{8}{3}$ and $z = 0$.

19. $30x = 25x^2 + 2$
$0 = 25x^2 - 30x + 2$
$a = 25, b = -30, c = 2$
$x = \dfrac{-b \pm \sqrt{b^2 - 4ac}}{2a}$
$x = \dfrac{-(-30) \pm \sqrt{(-30)^2 - 4(25)(2)}}{2(25)}$
$= \dfrac{30 \pm \sqrt{900 - 200}}{50}$
$= \dfrac{30 \pm \sqrt{700}}{50}$
$= \dfrac{30 \pm 10\sqrt{7}}{50}$
$= \dfrac{3 \pm \sqrt{7}}{5}$
The solutions are $x = \dfrac{3 \pm \sqrt{7}}{5}$.

20. $12x = 4x^2 + 4$
$0 = 4x^2 - 12x + 4$
$0 = 4(x^2 - 3x + 1)$
$a = 1, b = -3, c = 1$
$x = \dfrac{-b \pm \sqrt{b^2 - 4ac}}{2a}$

$$x = \frac{-(-3) \pm \sqrt{(-3)^2 - 4(1)(1)}}{2(1)}$$

$$= \frac{3 \pm \sqrt{9 - 4}}{2}$$

$$= \frac{3 \pm \sqrt{5}}{2}$$

The solutions are $x = \frac{3 \pm \sqrt{5}}{2}$.

21. $\frac{2}{3}m^2 - \frac{1}{3}m - 1 = 0$

$$2m^2 - m - 3 = 0$$
$$(2m - 3)(m + 1) = 0$$
$$2m - 3 = 0 \quad \text{or} \quad m + 1 = 0$$
$$2m = 3 \qquad\qquad m = -1$$
$$m = \frac{3}{2}$$

The solutions are $m = \frac{3}{2}$ and $m = -1$.

22. $\frac{5}{8}m^2 + m - \frac{1}{2} = 0$

$$5m^2 + 8m - 4 = 0$$
$$(5m - 2)(m + 2) = 0$$
$$5m - 2 = 0 \quad \text{or} \quad m + 2 = 0$$
$$5m = 2 \qquad\qquad m = -2$$
$$m = \frac{2}{5}$$

The solutions are $m = \frac{2}{5}$ and $m = -2$.

23. $x^2 - \frac{1}{2}x - \frac{1}{5} = 0$

$$10x^2 - 5x - 2 = 0$$
$$a = 10, \; b = -5, \; c = -2$$

$$x = \frac{-b \pm \sqrt{b^2 - 4ac}}{2a}$$

$$x = \frac{-(-5) \pm \sqrt{(-5)^2 - 4(10)(-2)}}{2(10)}$$

$$= \frac{5 \pm \sqrt{25 + 80}}{20}$$

$$= \frac{5 \pm \sqrt{105}}{20}$$

The solutions are $x = \frac{5 \pm \sqrt{105}}{20}$.

24. $x^2 + \frac{1}{2}x - \frac{1}{8} = 0$

$$8x^2 + 4x - 1 = 0$$
$$a = 8, \; b = 4, \; c = -1$$

$$x = \frac{-b \pm \sqrt{b^2 - 4ac}}{2a}$$

$$x = \frac{-4 \pm \sqrt{4^2 - 4(8)(-1)}}{2(8)}$$

$$= \frac{-4 \pm \sqrt{16 + 32}}{16}$$

$$= \frac{-4 \pm \sqrt{48}}{16}$$

$$= \frac{-4 \pm 4\sqrt{3}}{16}$$

$$= \frac{-1 \pm \sqrt{3}}{4}$$

The solutions are $\frac{-1 \pm \sqrt{3}}{4}$.

25. $4x^2 - 27x + 35 = 0$

$$(4x - 7)(x - 5) = 0$$
$$4x - 7 = 0 \quad \text{or} \quad x - 5 = 0$$
$$4x = 7 \qquad\qquad x = 5$$
$$x = \frac{7}{4}$$

The solutions are $x = \frac{7}{4}$ and $x = 5$.

26. $9x^2 - 16x + 7 = 0$

$$(9x - 7)(x - 1) = 0$$
$$9x - 7 = 0 \quad \text{or} \quad x - 1 = 0$$
$$9x = 7 \qquad\qquad x = 1$$
$$x = \frac{7}{9}$$

The solutions are $x = \frac{7}{9}$ and $x = 1$.

27. $(7 - 5x)^2 = 18$

$$7 - 5x = \sqrt{18}$$
$$-5x = -7 + 3\sqrt{2}$$
$$x = \frac{-7 + 3\sqrt{2}}{-5} = \frac{7 - 3\sqrt{2}}{5}$$

or

$$7 - 5x = -\sqrt{18}$$
$$-5x = -7 - 3\sqrt{2}$$
$$x = \frac{-7 - 3\sqrt{2}}{-5} = \frac{7 + 3\sqrt{2}}{5}$$

The solutions are $x = \dfrac{-7 \pm 3\sqrt{2}}{-5}$ or $\dfrac{7 \pm 3\sqrt{2}}{5}$.

28. $(5 - 4x)^2 = 75$

$$5 - 4x = \sqrt{75}$$
$$-4x = -5 + 5\sqrt{3}$$
$$x = \frac{-5 + 5\sqrt{3}}{-4} = \frac{5 - 5\sqrt{3}}{4}$$

or

$$5 - 4x = -\sqrt{75}$$
$$-4x = -5 - 5\sqrt{3}$$
$$x = \frac{-5 - 5\sqrt{3}}{-4} = \frac{5 + 5\sqrt{3}}{4}$$

The solutions are $x = \dfrac{-5 \pm 5\sqrt{3}}{-4}$ or $\dfrac{5 \pm 5\sqrt{3}}{4}$.

29. $3z^2 - 7z = 12$

$$3z^2 - 7z - 12 = 0$$
$$a = 3, \, b = -7, \, c = -12$$
$$z = \frac{-b \pm \sqrt{b^2 - 4ac}}{2a}$$
$$z = \frac{-(-7) \pm \sqrt{(-7)^2 - 4(3)(-12)}}{2(3)}$$
$$= \frac{7 \pm \sqrt{49 + 144}}{6}$$
$$= \frac{7 \pm \sqrt{193}}{6}$$

The solutions are $z = \dfrac{7 \pm \sqrt{193}}{6}$.

30. $6z^2 + 7z = 6$

$$6z^2 + 7z - 6 = 0$$
$$a = 6, \, b = 7, \, c = -6$$
$$z = \frac{-b \pm \sqrt{b^2 - 4ac}}{2a}$$

$$z = \frac{-7 \pm \sqrt{(7)^2 - 4(6)(-6)}}{2(6)}$$
$$= \frac{-7 \pm \sqrt{49 + 144}}{12}$$
$$= \frac{-7 \pm \sqrt{193}}{12}$$

The solutions are $z = \dfrac{-7 \pm \sqrt{193}}{12}$.

31. $x = x^2 - 110$

$$0 = x^2 - x - 110$$
$$0 = (x - 11)(x + 10)$$
$$x - 11 = 0 \quad \text{or} \quad x + 10 = 0$$
$$x = 11 \qquad\qquad x = -10$$

The solutions are $x = 11$ and $x = -10$.

32. $x = 56 - x^2$

$$0 = 56 - x - x^2$$
$$0 = (8 + x)(7 - x)$$
$$8 + x = 0 \quad \text{or} \quad 7 - x = 0$$
$$x = -8 \qquad\qquad x = 7$$

The solutions are $x = 7$ and $x = -8$.

33. $\dfrac{3}{4}x^2 - \dfrac{5}{2}x - 2 = 0$

$$3x^2 - 10x - 8 = 0$$
$$(3x + 2)(x - 4) = 0$$
$$3x + 2 = 0 \quad \text{or} \quad x - 4 = 0$$
$$3x = -2 \qquad\qquad x = 4$$
$$x = -\frac{2}{3}$$

The solutions are $x = -\dfrac{2}{3}$ and $x = 4$.

34. $x^2 - \dfrac{6}{5}x - \dfrac{8}{5} = 0$

$$5x^2 - 6x - 8 = 0$$
$$(5x + 4)(x - 2) = 0$$
$$5x + 4 = 0 \quad \text{or} \quad x - 2 = 0$$
$$5x = -4 \qquad\qquad x = 2$$
$$x = -\frac{4}{5}$$

The solutions are $x = -\dfrac{4}{5}$ and $x = 2$.

35. $x^2 - 0.6x + 0.05 = 0$
$(x - 0.5)(x - 0.1) = 0$
$x - 0.5 = 0$ or $x - 0.1 = 0$
     $x = 0.5$ $x = 0.1$
The solutions are $x = 0.5$ and $x = 0.1$.

36. $x^2 - 0.1x - 0.06 = 0$
$(x - 0.3)(x + 0.2) = 0$
$x - 0.3 = 0$ or $x + 0.2 = 0$
     $x = 0.3$ $x = -0.2$
The solutions are $x = 0.3$ and $x = -0.2$.

37. $10x^2 - 11x + 2 = 0$
$a = 10, b = -11, c = 2$
$$x = \frac{-b \pm \sqrt{b^2 - 4ac}}{2a}$$
$$x = \frac{-(-11) \pm \sqrt{(-11)^2 - 4(10)(2)}}{2(10)}$$
$$= \frac{11 \pm \sqrt{121 - 80}}{20}$$
$$= \frac{11 \pm \sqrt{41}}{20}$$
The solutions are $x = \dfrac{11 \pm \sqrt{41}}{20}$.

38. $20x^2 - 11x + 1 = 0$
$a = 20, b = -11, c = 1$
$$x = \frac{-b \pm \sqrt{b^2 - 4ac}}{2a}$$
$$x = \frac{-(-11) \pm \sqrt{(-11)^2 - 4(20)(1)}}{2(20)}$$
$$= \frac{11 \pm \sqrt{121 - 80}}{40}$$
$$= \frac{11 \pm \sqrt{41}}{40}$$
The solutions are $x = \dfrac{11 \pm \sqrt{41}}{40}$.

39. $\dfrac{1}{2}z^2 - 2z + \dfrac{3}{4} = 0$
$2z^2 - 8z + 3 = 0$
$a = 2, b = -8, c = 3$

$$z = \frac{-b \pm \sqrt{b^2 - 4ac}}{2a}$$
$$z = \frac{-(-8) \pm \sqrt{(-8)^2 - 4(2)(3)}}{2(2)}$$
$$= \frac{8 \pm \sqrt{64 - 24}}{4}$$
$$= \frac{8 \pm \sqrt{40}}{4}$$
$$= \frac{8 \pm 2\sqrt{10}}{4}$$
$$= \frac{4 \pm \sqrt{10}}{2}$$
The solutions are $z = \dfrac{4 \pm \sqrt{10}}{2}$.

40. $\dfrac{1}{5}z^2 - \dfrac{1}{2}z - 2 = 0$
$2z^2 - 5z - 20 = 0$
$a = 2, b = -5, c = -20$
$$z = \frac{-b \pm \sqrt{b^2 - 4ac}}{2a}$$
$$z = \frac{-(-5) \pm \sqrt{(-5)^2 - 4(2)(-20)}}{2(2)}$$
$$= \frac{5 \pm \sqrt{25 + 160}}{4}$$
$$= \frac{5 \pm \sqrt{185}}{4}$$
The solutions are $z = \dfrac{5 \pm \sqrt{185}}{4}$.

41. answers may vary

Section 16.4

Practice Problems

1. $y = -3x^2$

x	y
-2	-12
-1	-3
0	0
1	-3
2	-12

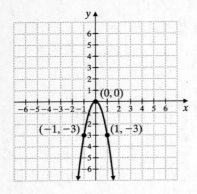

2. $y = x^2 - 9$

Let $x = 0$.

$y = 0^2 - 9 = -9$

The y-intercept is $(0, -9)$.

Let $y = 0$.

$0 = x^2 - 9$

$0 = (x - 3)(x + 3)$

$x - 3 = 0$ or $x + 3 = 0$

$x = 3$ $\qquad x = -3$

The x-intercepts are $(3, 0)$ and $(-3, 0)$.

x	y
-3	0
-2	-5
-1	-8
0	-9
1	-8
2	-5
3	0

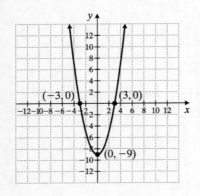

3. $y = x^2 - 2x - 3$

$a = 1, b = -2, c = -3$

$x = \dfrac{-b}{2a} = \dfrac{-(-2)}{2(1)} = \dfrac{2}{2} = 1$

$y = 1^2 - 2(1) - 3 = 1 - 2 - 3 = -4$

The vertex is $(1, -4)$.

Let $x = 0$.

$y = 0^2 - 2(0) - 3 = -3$

The y-intercept is $(0, -3)$.

Let $y = 0$.

$0 = x^2 - 2x - 3$

$0 = (x - 3)(x + 1)$

$x - 3 = 0$ or $x + 1 = 0$

$x = 3$ $\qquad x = -1$

The x-intercepts are $(3, 0)$ and $(-1, 0)$.

x	y
-1	0
0	-3
1	-4
2	-3
3	0

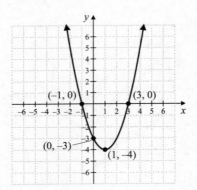

4. $y = x^2 - 4x + 1$

$a = 1, b = -4, c = 1$

$x = \dfrac{-b}{2a} = \dfrac{-(-4)}{2(1)} = \dfrac{4}{2} = 2$

$y = 2^2 - 4(2) + 1 = 4 - 8 + 1 = -3$

vertex $= (2, -3)$

$x = \dfrac{-b \pm \sqrt{b^2 - 4ac}}{2a}$

$$x = \frac{-(-4) \pm \sqrt{(-4)^2 - 4(1)(1)}}{2(1)}$$

$$= \frac{4 \pm \sqrt{16 - 4}}{2}$$

$$= \frac{4 \pm \sqrt{12}}{2}$$

$$= \frac{4 \pm 2\sqrt{3}}{2}$$

$$= 2 \pm \sqrt{3}$$

$$= 3.7 \text{ or } 0.3$$

x	y
2	-3
$2 + \sqrt{3} \approx 3.7$	0
$2 - \sqrt{3} \approx 0.3$	0
0	1
4	1

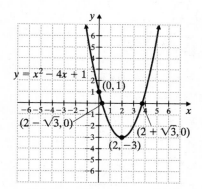

Calculator Explorations

1. $x^2 - 7x - 3 = 0$ $x \approx -0.41, 7.41$

2. $2x^2 - 11x - 1 = 0$ $x \approx -0.09, 5.59$

3. $-1.7x^2 + 5.6x - 3.7 = 0$ $x \approx 0.91, 2.38$

4. $-5.8x^2 + 2.3x - 3.9 = 0$ No real solutions

5. $5.8x^2 - 2.6x - 1.9 = 0$ $x \approx -0.39, 0.84$

6. $7.5x^2 - 3.7x - 1.1 = 0$ $x \approx -0.21, 0.70$

Exercise Set 16.4

1.

x	$y = 2x^2$
-2	$2(-2)^2 = 2(4) = 8$
-1	$2(-1)^2 = 2(1) = 2$
0	$2(0)^2 = 2(0) = 0$
1	$2(1)^2 = 2(1) = 2$
2	$2(2)^2 = 2(4) = 8$

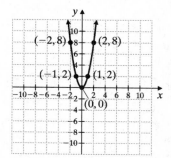

3.

x	$y = -x^2$
-2	$-(-2)^2 = -(4) = -4$
-1	$-(-1)^2 = -(1) = -1$
0	$-(0)^2 = -(0) = 0$
1	$-(1)^2 = -(1) = -1$
2	$-(2)^2 = -(4) = -4$

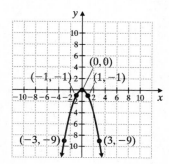

5. $y = x^2 - 1$

$y = 0$: $0 = x^2 - 1$

$1 = x^2$

$\pm\sqrt{1} = x$

$\pm 1 = x$

x-intercepts: $(-1, 0)$, $(1, 0)$

$x = 0$: $y = 0^2 - 1 = -1$

y-intercept: $(0, -1)$

$y = x^2 + 0x - 1$

$a = 1, b = 0, c = 1$

$\dfrac{-b}{2a} = \dfrac{-0}{2(1)} = \dfrac{0}{2} = 0$

$x = 0$: $y = 0^2 - 1 = -1$

The vertex is $(0, -1)$.

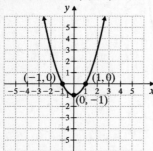

7. $y = x^2 + 4$

$y = 0$: $0 = x^2 + 4$

$-4 = x^2$

$\pm\sqrt{-4} = x$

x-intercepts: none

$x = 0$: $y = 0^2 + 4 = 4$

y-intercept: $(0, 4)$

$y = x^2 + 0x + 4$

$a = 1, b = 0, c = 4$

$\dfrac{-b}{2a} = \dfrac{-0}{2(1)} = \dfrac{0}{2} = 0$

$x = 0$: $y = 0^2 + 4 = 4$

The vertex is $(0, 4)$.

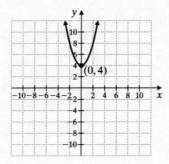

9. $y = -x^2 + 4x - 4$

$y = 0$: $0 = -x^2 + 4x - 4$

$0 = x^2 - 4x + 4$

$0 = (x - 2)^2$

$0 = x - 2$

$2 = x$

The x-intercept is $(2, 0)$.

$x = 0$: $y = -0^2 + 4(0) - 4 = -4$

The y-intercept is $(0, -4)$.

$y = -x^2 + 4x - 4$

$a = -1, b = 4, c = -4$

$\dfrac{-b}{2a} = \dfrac{-4}{2(-1)} = \dfrac{-4}{-2} = 2$

$x = 2$: $y = -(2)^2 + 4(2) - 4 = -4 + 8 - 4 = 0$

The vertex is $(2, 0)$.

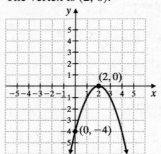

11. $y = x^2 + 5x + 4$

$y = 0$: $0 = x^2 + 5x + 4$

$0 = (x + 4)(x + 1)$

$0 = x + 4$ or $0 = x + 1$

$-4 = x$ $-1 = x$

x-intercepts: $(-4, 0)$ and $(-1, 0)$

$x = 0$: $y = 0^2 + 5(0) + 4 = 4$

y-intercept: $(0, 4)$

$y = x^2 + 5x + 4$

$a = 1, b = 5, c = 4$

$$\frac{-b}{2a} = \frac{-5}{2(1)} = \frac{-5}{2}$$

$$x = \frac{-5}{2}: \quad y = \left(-\frac{5}{2}\right)^2 + 5\left(-\frac{5}{2}\right) + 4$$

$$= \frac{25}{4} - \frac{25}{2} + 4$$

$$= \frac{25}{4} - \frac{50}{4} + \frac{16}{4}$$

$$= -\frac{9}{4}$$

The vertex is $\left(-\frac{5}{2}, -\frac{9}{4}\right)$ or $\left(-2\frac{1}{2}, -2\frac{1}{4}\right)$.

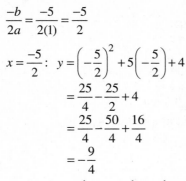

13. $y = x^2 - 4x + 5$

$y = 0: \quad 0 = x^2 - 4x + 5$

$\qquad a = 1, b = -4, c = 5$

$$y = \frac{-b \pm \sqrt{b^2 - 4ac}}{2a}$$

$$y = \frac{-(-4) \pm \sqrt{(-4)^2 - 4(1)(5)}}{2(1)}$$

$$= \frac{4 \pm \sqrt{16 - 20}}{2}$$

$$= \frac{4 \pm \sqrt{-4}}{2}$$

There are no x-intercepts, since $\sqrt{-4}$ is not a real number.

$x = 0: \quad y = 0^2 - 4(0) + 5 = 5$

y-intercept: $(0, 5)$

$y = x^2 - 4x + 5$

$a = 1, b = -4, c = 5$

$$\frac{-b}{2a} = \frac{-(-4)}{2(1)} = \frac{4}{2} = 2$$

$x = 2: \quad y = 2^2 - 4(2) + 5 = 4 - 8 + 5 = 1$

vertex: $(2, 1)$

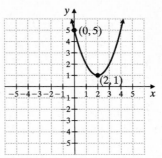

15. $y = 2 - x^2$

$y = 0: \quad 0 = 2 - x^2$

$\qquad x^2 = 2$

$\qquad x = \pm\sqrt{2}$

x-intercepts: $\left(\sqrt{2}, 0\right)$ and $\left(-\sqrt{2}, 0\right)$

$x = 0: \quad y = 2 - 0^2 = 2$

y-intercept: $(0, 2)$

$y = 2 - x^2$

$a = -1, b = 0, c = 2$

$$\frac{-b}{2a} = \frac{-0}{2(-1)} = \frac{0}{-2} = 0$$

$x = 0: \quad y = 2 - 0^2 = 2$

vertex: $(0, 2)$

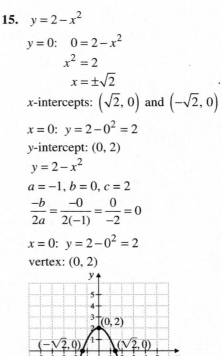

17. $y = \frac{1}{3}x^2$

$y = 0: \quad 0 = \frac{1}{3}x^2$

$\qquad 0 = x^2$

$\qquad 0 = x$

x-intercept: $(0, 0)$

The y-intercept is also $(0, 0)$.

$y = \frac{1}{3}x^2 + 0x + 0$

$a = \frac{1}{3}, \; b = 0, c = 0$

$$\frac{-b}{2a} = \frac{-0}{2\left(\frac{1}{3}\right)} = \frac{0}{\frac{2}{3}} = 0$$

$x = 0$: $y = \frac{1}{3}(0)^2 = \frac{1}{3}(0) = 0$

vertex: $(0, 0)$

For additional points, use $x = \pm 3$.

$x = -3$: $y = \frac{1}{3}(-3)^2 = \frac{1}{3}(9) = 3$

$x = 3$: $y = \frac{1}{3}(3)^2 = \frac{1}{3}(9) = 3$

$(-3, 3)$ and $(3, 3)$ are also on the graph.

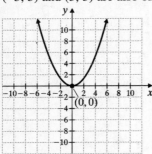

19. $y = x^2 + 6x$

$y = 0$: $0 = x^2 + 6x$

$0 = x(x + 6)$

$x = 0$ or $x + 6 = 0$

$x = -6$

x-intercepts: $(0, 0)$ and $(-6, 0)$

$x = 0$: $y = 0^2 + 6(0) = 0$

y-intercept: $(0, 0)$

$y = x^2 + 6x + 0$

$a = 1, b = 6, c = 0$

$$\frac{-b}{2a} = \frac{-6}{2(1)} = \frac{-6}{2} = -3$$

$x = -3$: $y = (-3)^2 + 6(-3) = 9 - 18 = -9$

vertex: $(-3, -9)$

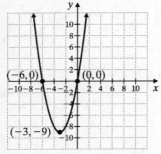

21. $y = x^2 + 2x - 8$

$y = 0$: $0 = x^2 + 2x - 8$

$0 = (x + 4)(x - 2)$

$0 = x + 4$ or $0 = x - 2$

$-4 = x$ $\qquad$ $2 = x$

x-intercepts: $(-4, 0)$, $(2, 0)$

$x = 0$: $y = 0^2 + 2(0) - 8 = -8$

y-intercept: $(0, -8)$

$y = x^2 + 2x - 8$

$a = 1, b = 2, c = -8$

$$\frac{-b}{2a} = \frac{-2}{2(1)} = \frac{-2}{2} = -1$$

$x = -1$: $y = (-1)^2 + 2(-1) - 8 = 1 - 2 - 8 = -9$

vertex: $(-1, -9)$

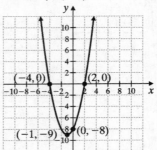

23. $y = -\frac{1}{2}x^2$

$y = 0$: $0 = -\frac{1}{2}x^2$

$0 = x^2$

$0 = x$

x-intercept: $(0, 0)$

The y-intercept is also $(0, 0)$.

$y = -\frac{1}{2}x^2 + 0x + 0$

$a = -\frac{1}{2}, b = 0, c = 0$

$$\frac{-b}{2a} = \frac{-0}{2\left(-\frac{1}{2}\right)} = \frac{0}{-1} = 0$$

$x = 0$: $y = -\frac{1}{2}(0)^2 = -\frac{1}{2}(0) = 0$

vertex: $(0, 0)$

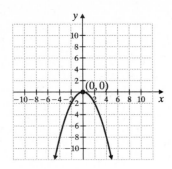

25. $y = 2x^2 - 11x + 5$

$y = 0$: $0 = 2x^2 - 11x + 5$

$\quad 0 = (2x - 1)(x - 5)$

$\quad 0 = 2x - 1$ or $0 = x - 5$

$\quad 1 = 2x \qquad\qquad 5 = x$

$\quad \dfrac{1}{2} = x$

x-intercepts: $\left(\dfrac{1}{2}, 0\right)$, $(5, 0)$

$x = 0$: $y = 2(0)^2 - 11(0) + 5 = 5$

y-intercept: $(0, 5)$

$y = 2x^2 - 11x + 5$

$a = 2, b = -11, c = 5$

$\dfrac{-b}{2a} = \dfrac{-(-11)}{2(2)} = \dfrac{11}{4}$

$x = \dfrac{11}{4}$: $\quad y = 2\left(\dfrac{11}{4}\right)^2 - 11\left(\dfrac{11}{4}\right) + 5$

$\qquad\qquad = 2\left(\dfrac{121}{16}\right) - \dfrac{121}{4} + 5$

$\qquad\qquad = \dfrac{121}{8} - \dfrac{121}{4} + 5$

$\qquad\qquad = \dfrac{121}{8} - \dfrac{242}{8} + \dfrac{40}{8}$

$\qquad\qquad = -\dfrac{81}{8}$

vertex: $\left(\dfrac{11}{4}, -\dfrac{81}{8}\right)$

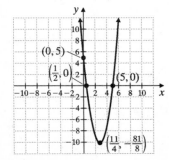

27. $y = -x^2 + 4x - 3$

$y = 0$: $0 = -x^2 + 4x - 3$

$\qquad 0 = x^2 - 4x + 3$

$\qquad 0 = (x - 3)(x - 1)$

$\qquad x - 3 = 0$ or $x - 1 = 0$

$\qquad\quad x = 3 \qquad\qquad x = 1$

x-intercepts: $(3, 0)$ and $(1, 0)$

$x = 0$: $y = -0^2 + 4(0) - 3 = -3$

y-intercept: $(0, -3)$

$y = -x^2 + 4x - 3$

$a = -1, b = 4, c = -3$

$\dfrac{-b}{2a} = \dfrac{-4}{2(-1)} = \dfrac{-4}{-2} = 2$

$x = 2$: $y = -(2)^2 + 4(2) - 3 = -4 + 8 - 3 = 1$

vertex: $(2, 1)$

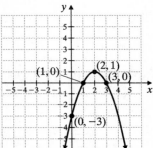

29. $\dfrac{\frac{1}{7}}{\frac{2}{5}} = \dfrac{1}{7} \div \dfrac{2}{5} = \dfrac{1}{7} \cdot \dfrac{5}{2} = \dfrac{5}{14}$

31. $\dfrac{\frac{1}{x}}{\frac{2}{x^2}} = \dfrac{1}{x} \div \dfrac{2}{x^2} = \dfrac{1}{x} \cdot \dfrac{x^2}{2} = \dfrac{x}{2}$

33. $\dfrac{2x}{1 - \frac{1}{x}} = \dfrac{x(2x)}{x\left(1 - \frac{1}{x}\right)} = \dfrac{2x^2}{x - 1}$

35. $\dfrac{\frac{a-b}{2b}}{\frac{b-a}{8b^2}} = \dfrac{a-b}{2b} \div \dfrac{b-a}{8b^2} = \dfrac{a-b}{2b} \cdot \dfrac{8b^2}{b-a} = -4b$

37. a. The maximum height appears to be about 256 feet.

b. The fireball appears to reach its maximum height when $t = 4$ seconds.

c. The fireball appears to return to the ground when $t = 8$ seconds.

39. With $a > 0$, the parabola opens upward. An upward-opening parabola that crosses the x-axis twice is graph A.

41. With $a < 0$, the parabola opens downward. A downward-opening parabola that does not touch or cross the x-axis (no x-intercept) is graph D.

43. With $a > 0$, the parabola opens upward. An upward-opening parabola that crosses the x-axis once is graph F.

Chapter 16 Vocabulary Check

1. If $x^2 = a$, then $x = \sqrt{a}$ or $x = -\sqrt{a}$. This property is called the <u>square root</u> property.

2. The graph of $y = x^2$ is called a <u>parabola</u>.

3. The formula $\dfrac{-b}{2a}$ where $y = ax^2 + bx + c$ is called the <u>vertex</u> formula.

4. The process of solving a quadratic equation by writing it in the form $(x + a)^2 = c$ is called <u>completing the square</u>.

5. The formula $x = \dfrac{-b \pm \sqrt{b^2 - 4ac}}{2a}$ is called the <u>quadratic</u> formula.

6. The lowest point on a parabola that opens upward is called the <u>vertex</u>.

7. The zero-factor property states that if the product of two numbers is zero, then at least one of the two numbers is <u>zero</u>.

Chapter 16 Review

1. $x^2 - 121 = 0$
$$x^2 = 121$$
$$x = \pm\sqrt{121}$$
$$x = \pm 11$$
The solutions are $x = \pm 11$.

2. $y^2 - 100 = 0$
$$y^2 = 100$$
$$y = \pm\sqrt{100}$$
$$y = \pm 10$$
The solutions are $y = \pm 10$.

3. $\quad 3m^2 - 5m = 2$
$$3m^2 - 5m - 2 = 0$$
$$(3m + 1)(m - 2) = 0$$
$$3m + 1 = 0 \quad \text{or} \quad m - 2 = 0$$
$$3m = -1 \qquad\qquad m = 2$$
$$m = -\frac{1}{3}$$
The solutions are $m = -\dfrac{1}{3}$ and $m = 2$.

4. $\quad 7m^2 + 2m = 5$
$$7m^2 + 2m - 5 = 0$$
$$(7m - 5)(m + 1) = 0$$
$$7m - 5 = 0 \quad \text{or} \quad m + 1 = 0$$
$$7m = 5 \qquad\qquad m = -1$$
$$m = \frac{5}{7}$$
The solutions are $m = \dfrac{5}{7}$ and $m = -1$.

5. $x^2 = 36$
$$x = \pm\sqrt{36}$$
$$x = \pm 6$$
The solutions are $x = \pm 6$.

6. $x^2 = 81$
$$x = \pm\sqrt{81}$$
$$x = \pm 9$$
The solutions are $x = \pm 9$.

7. $k^2 = 50$
$$k = \pm\sqrt{50}$$
$$k = \pm 5\sqrt{2}$$
The solutions are $k = \pm 5\sqrt{2}$.

8. $k^2 = 45$
$$k = \pm\sqrt{45}$$
$$k = \pm 3\sqrt{5}$$
The solutions are $k = \pm 3\sqrt{5}$.

9. $(x - 11)^2 = 49$
$$x - 11 = \pm\sqrt{49}$$
$$x - 11 = \pm 7$$
$$x = 11 + 7 \quad \text{or} \quad x = 11 - 7$$
$$x = 18 \qquad\qquad x = 4$$
The solutions are $x = 18$ and $x = 4$.

10. $(x+3)^2 = 100$

$$x+3 = \pm\sqrt{100}$$
$$x+3 = \pm 10$$
$$x = -3+10 \quad \text{or} \quad x = -3-10$$
$$x = 7 \qquad\qquad\quad x = -13$$

The solutions are $x = 7$ and $x = -13$.

11. $(4p+5)^2 = 41$

$$4p+5 = \pm\sqrt{41}$$
$$4p = -5 \pm \sqrt{41}$$
$$p = \frac{-5 \pm \sqrt{41}}{4}$$

The solutions are $p = \dfrac{-5 \pm \sqrt{41}}{4}$.

12. $(3p+7)^2 = 37$

$$3p+7 = \pm\sqrt{37}$$
$$3p = -7 \pm \sqrt{37}$$
$$p = \frac{-7 \pm \sqrt{37}}{3}$$

The solutions are $p = \dfrac{-7 \pm \sqrt{37}}{3}$.

13. $\quad h = 16t^2$

$$100 = 16t^2$$
$$6.25 = t^2$$
$$\pm 2.5 = t$$

Reject -2.5 because time is not negative. It will take Kara 2.5 seconds to hit the water.

14. $5 \text{ miles} \cdot \dfrac{5280 \text{ ft}}{1 \text{ mile}} = 26,400 \text{ feet}$

$$y = 16t^2$$
$$26,400 = 16t^2$$
$$1650 = t^2$$
$$\pm 40.6 = t$$

Reject -40.6 because time is not negative.
A 5-mile freefall will take 40.6 seconds.

15. $\qquad x^2 - 9x = -8$

$$x^2 - 9x + \left(-\frac{9}{2}\right)^2 = -8 + \left(-\frac{9}{2}\right)^2$$
$$\left(x - \frac{9}{2}\right)^2 = -8 + \frac{81}{4}$$
$$\left(x - \frac{9}{2}\right)^2 = \frac{49}{4}$$
$$x - \frac{9}{2} = \pm\sqrt{\frac{49}{4}}$$
$$x - \frac{9}{2} = \pm\frac{7}{2}$$
$$x = \frac{9}{2} + \frac{7}{2} = \frac{16}{2} = 8 \quad \text{or} \quad x = \frac{9}{2} - \frac{7}{2} = \frac{2}{2} = 1$$

The solutions are $x = 8$ and $x = 1$.

16. $\qquad x^2 + 8x = 20$

$$x^2 + 8x + \left(\frac{8}{2}\right)^2 = 20 + \left(\frac{8}{2}\right)^2$$
$$(x+4)^2 = 36$$
$$x+4 = \pm\sqrt{36}$$
$$x+4 = \pm 6$$
$$x = -4+6 = 2 \quad \text{or} \quad x = -4-6 = -10$$

The solutions are $x = 7$ and $x = -10$.

17. $\qquad x^2 + 4x = 1$

$$x^2 + 4x + \left(\frac{4}{2}\right)^2 = 1 + \left(\frac{4}{2}\right)^2$$
$$(x+2)^2 = 5$$
$$x+2 = \pm\sqrt{5}$$
$$x = -2 \pm \sqrt{5}$$

The solutions are $x = -2 \pm \sqrt{5}$.

18. $\qquad x^2 - 8x = 3$

$$x^2 - 8x + \left(-\frac{8}{2}\right)^2 = 3 + \left(-\frac{8}{2}\right)^2$$
$$(x-4)^2 = 19$$
$$x-4 = \pm\sqrt{19}$$
$$x = 4 \pm \sqrt{19}$$

The solutions are $x = 4 \pm \sqrt{19}$.

19.
$$x^2 - 6x + 7 = 0$$
$$x^2 - 6x = -7$$
$$x^2 - 6x + \left(-\frac{6}{2}\right)^2 = -7 + \left(-\frac{6}{2}\right)^2$$
$$(x-3)^2 = 2$$
$$x - 3 = \pm\sqrt{2}$$
$$x = 3 \pm \sqrt{2}$$
The solutions are $3 \pm \sqrt{2}$.

20.
$$x^2 + 6x + 7 = 0$$
$$x^2 + 6x = -7$$
$$x^2 + 6x + \left(\frac{6}{2}\right)^2 = -7 + \left(\frac{6}{2}\right)^2$$
$$(x+3)^2 = 2$$
$$x + 3 = \pm\sqrt{2}$$
$$x = -3 \pm \sqrt{2}$$
The solutions are $-3 \pm \sqrt{2}$.

21.
$$2y^2 + y - 1 = 0$$
$$2y^2 + y = 1$$
$$y^2 + \frac{1}{2}y = \frac{1}{2}$$
$$y^2 + \frac{1}{2}y + \left(\frac{1}{4}\right)^2 = \frac{1}{2} + \left(\frac{1}{4}\right)^2$$
$$\left(y + \frac{1}{4}\right)^2 = \frac{9}{16}$$
$$y + \frac{1}{4} = \pm\sqrt{\frac{9}{16}}$$
$$y + \frac{1}{4} = \pm\frac{3}{4}$$
$$y = -\frac{1}{4} + \frac{3}{4} = \frac{2}{4} = \frac{1}{2} \quad \text{or}$$
$$y = -\frac{1}{4} - \frac{3}{4} = -\frac{4}{4} = -1$$
The solutions are $y = \frac{1}{2}$ and $y = -1$.

22.
$$4y^2 + 3y - 1 = 0$$
$$4y^2 + 3y = 1$$
$$y^2 + \frac{3}{4}y = \frac{1}{4}$$
$$y^2 + \frac{3}{4}y + \left(\frac{3}{8}\right)^2 = \frac{1}{4} + \left(\frac{3}{8}\right)^2$$
$$\left(y + \frac{3}{8}\right)^2 = \frac{25}{64}$$
$$y + \frac{3}{8} = \pm\sqrt{\frac{25}{64}}$$
$$y + \frac{3}{8} = \pm\frac{5}{8}$$
$$y = -\frac{3}{8} + \frac{5}{8} = \frac{2}{8} = \frac{1}{4} \quad \text{or} \quad y = -\frac{3}{8} - \frac{5}{8} = -\frac{8}{8} = -1$$
The solutions are $y = \frac{1}{4}$ and $y = -1$.

23. $9x^2 + 30x + 25 = 0$
$a = 9, b = 30, c = 25$
$$x = \frac{-b \pm \sqrt{b^2 - 4ac}}{2a}$$
$$x = \frac{-30 \pm \sqrt{30^2 - 4(9)(25)}}{2(9)}$$
$$= \frac{-30 \pm \sqrt{900 - 900}}{18}$$
$$= \frac{-30 \pm \sqrt{0}}{18}$$
$$= \frac{-30}{18}$$
$$= -\frac{5}{3}$$
The solution is $x = -\frac{5}{3}$.

24. $16x^2 - 72x + 81 = 0$
$a = 16, b = -72, c = 81$
$$x = \frac{-b \pm \sqrt{b^2 - 4ac}}{2a}$$

$$x = \frac{-(-72) \pm \sqrt{(-72)^2 - 4(16)(81)}}{2(16)}$$

$$= \frac{72 \pm \sqrt{5184 - 5184}}{32}$$

$$= \frac{72 \pm \sqrt{0}}{32}$$

$$= \frac{72}{32}$$

$$= \frac{9}{4}$$

The solution is $x = \frac{9}{4}$.

25.
$$7x^2 = 35$$
$$7x^2 - 35 = 0$$
$$a = 7, b = 0, c = -35$$
$$x = \frac{-b \pm \sqrt{b^2 - 4ac}}{2a}$$
$$x = \frac{-0 \pm \sqrt{0^2 - 4(7)(-35)}}{2(7)}$$
$$= \frac{\pm\sqrt{980}}{14}$$
$$= \frac{\pm 14\sqrt{5}}{14}$$
$$= \pm\sqrt{5}$$

The solutions are $x = \pm\sqrt{5}$.

26.
$$11x^2 = 33$$
$$11x^2 - 33 = 0$$
$$a = 11, b = 0, c = -33$$
$$x = \frac{-b \pm \sqrt{b^2 - 4ac}}{2a}$$
$$x = \frac{-0 \pm \sqrt{0^2 - 4(11)(-33)}}{2(11)}$$
$$= \frac{\pm\sqrt{1452}}{22}$$
$$= \frac{\pm 22\sqrt{3}}{22}$$
$$= \pm\sqrt{3}$$

The solutions are $x = \pm\sqrt{3}$.

27. $x^2 - 10x + 7 = 0$
$$a = 1, b = -10, c = 7$$
$$x = \frac{-b \pm \sqrt{b^2 - 4ac}}{2a}$$
$$x = \frac{-(-10) \pm \sqrt{(-10)^2 - 4(1)(7)}}{2(1)}$$
$$= \frac{10 \pm \sqrt{100 - 28}}{2}$$
$$= \frac{10 \pm \sqrt{72}}{2}$$
$$= \frac{10 \pm 6\sqrt{2}}{2}$$
$$= 5 \pm 3\sqrt{2}$$

The solutions are $x = 5 \pm 3\sqrt{2}$.

28. $x^2 + 4x - 7 = 0$
$$a = 1, b = 4, c = -7$$
$$x = \frac{-b \pm \sqrt{b^2 - 4ac}}{2a}$$
$$x = \frac{-4 \pm \sqrt{4^2 - 4(1)(-7)}}{2(1)}$$
$$= \frac{-4 \pm \sqrt{16 + 28}}{2}$$
$$= \frac{-4 \pm \sqrt{44}}{2}$$
$$= \frac{-4 \pm 2\sqrt{11}}{2}$$
$$= -2 \pm \sqrt{11}$$

The solutions are $x = -2 \pm \sqrt{11}$.

29. $3x^2 + x - 1 = 0$
$$a = 3, b = 1, c = -1$$
$$x = \frac{-b \pm \sqrt{b^2 - 4ac}}{2a}$$
$$x = \frac{-1 \pm \sqrt{(1)^2 - 4(3)(-1)}}{2(3)}$$
$$= \frac{-1 \pm \sqrt{1 + 12}}{6}$$
$$= \frac{-1 \pm \sqrt{13}}{6}$$

The solutions are $x = \frac{-1 \pm \sqrt{13}}{6}$.

30. $x^2 + 3x - 1 = 0$

$a = 1, b = 3, c = -1$

$$x = \frac{-b \pm \sqrt{b^2 - 4ac}}{2a}$$

$$x = \frac{-3 \pm \sqrt{3^2 - 4(1)(-1)}}{2(1)}$$

$$= \frac{-3 \pm \sqrt{9 + 4}}{2}$$

$$= \frac{-3 \pm \sqrt{13}}{2}$$

The solutions are $x = \dfrac{-3 \pm \sqrt{13}}{2}$.

31. $2x^2 + x + 5 = 0$

$a = 2, b = 1, c = 5$

$$x = \frac{-b \pm \sqrt{b^2 - 4ac}}{2a}$$

$$x = \frac{-1 \pm \sqrt{1^2 - 4(2)(5)}}{2(2)}$$

$$= \frac{-1 \pm \sqrt{1 - 40}}{4}$$

$$= \frac{-1 \pm \sqrt{-39}}{4}$$

The equation has no solution, since the square root of -39 is not a real number.

32. $7x^2 - 3x + 1 = 0$

$a = 7, b = -3, c = 1$

$$x = \frac{-b \pm \sqrt{b^2 - 4ac}}{2a}$$

$$x = \frac{-(-3) \pm \sqrt{(-3)^2 - 4(7)(1)}}{2(7)}$$

$$= \frac{3 \pm \sqrt{9 - 28}}{14}$$

$$= \frac{3 \pm \sqrt{-19}}{14}$$

The equation has no solution since the square root of -19 is not a real number.

33. $x = \dfrac{-1 + \sqrt{13}}{6} \approx 0.4$ or $x = \dfrac{-1 - \sqrt{13}}{6} \approx -0.8$

34. $x = \dfrac{-3 + \sqrt{13}}{2} \approx 0.3$ or $x = \dfrac{-3 - \sqrt{13}}{2} \approx -3.3$

35. $y = 8x^2 + 109x + 700$

$2590 = 8x^2 + 109x + 700$

$0 = 8x^2 + 109x - 1890$

$a = 8, b = 109, c = -1890$

$$x = \frac{-b \pm \sqrt{b^2 - 4ac}}{2a}$$

$$x = \frac{-109 \pm \sqrt{109^2 - 4(8)(-1890)}}{2(8)}$$

$$= \frac{-109 \pm \sqrt{11,881 + 60,480}}{16}$$

$$= \frac{-109 \pm \sqrt{72,361}}{16}$$

$$= \frac{-109 \pm 269}{16}$$

$$x = \frac{-109 + 269}{16} = \frac{160}{16} = 10$$

or

$$x = \frac{-109 - 269}{16} = \frac{-378}{16} = -23.625$$

Since time will not be a negative number in this context, discard the solution -23.625. The solution is $x = 10$, so the model predicts that the price of platinum will be $2590 per ounce in 2013 (2003 + 10).

36. $y = 26x^2 + 115x + 493$

$3077 = 26x^2 + 115x + 493$

$0 = 26x^2 + 115x - 2584$

$a = 26, b = 115, c = -2584$

$$x = \frac{-b \pm \sqrt{b^2 - 4ac}}{2a}$$

$$x = \frac{-115 \pm \sqrt{115^2 - 4(26)(-2584)}}{2(26)}$$

$$= \frac{-115 \pm \sqrt{13,225 + 268,736}}{52}$$

$$= \frac{-115 \pm \sqrt{281,961}}{52}$$

$$= \frac{-115 \pm 531}{52}$$

$$x = \frac{-115 + 531}{52} = \frac{416}{52} = 8$$

or

$$x = \frac{-115 - 531}{52} = \frac{-646}{52} \approx -12.4$$

Since time will not be a negative number in this

context, discard the solution –12.4. The solution is $x = 8$, so the model predicts that the price of silver will be 3077 cents per ounce in 2011 (2003 + 8).

37. $y = 5x^2$

$y = 0$: $\quad 0 = 5x^2$

$\qquad\quad 0 = x^2$

$\qquad\quad 0 = x$

x-intercept: (0, 0)

The y-intercept is also (0, 0).

x	$y = 5x^2$
–2	$5(-2)^2 = 5(4) = 20$
–1	$5(-1)^2 = 5(1) = 5$
0	$5(0)^2 = 5(0) = 0$
1	$5(1)^2 = 5(1) = 5$
2	$5(2)^2 = 5(4) = 20$

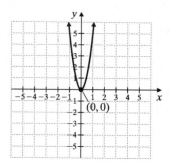

38. $y = -\dfrac{1}{2}x^2$

$y = 0$: $\quad 0 = -\dfrac{1}{2}x^2$

$\qquad\quad 0 = x^2$

$\qquad\quad 0 = x$

x-intercept: (0, 0)

The y-intercept is also (0, 0).

x	$y = -\dfrac{1}{2}x^2$
–2	$-\dfrac{1}{2}(-2)^2 = -\dfrac{1}{2}(4) = -2$
–1	$-\dfrac{1}{2}(-1)^2 = -\dfrac{1}{2}(1) = -\dfrac{1}{2}$
0	$-\dfrac{1}{2}(0)^2 = -\dfrac{1}{2}(0) = 0$
1	$-\dfrac{1}{2}(1)^2 = -\dfrac{1}{2}(1) = -\dfrac{1}{2}$
2	$-\dfrac{1}{2}(2)^2 = -\dfrac{1}{2}(4) = -2$

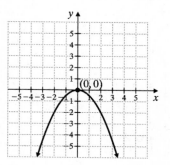

39. $y = x^2 - 25$

$y = 0$: $\qquad 0 = x^2 - 25$

$\qquad\qquad 25 = x^2$

$\qquad\quad \pm\sqrt{25} = x$

$\qquad\qquad \pm 5 = x$

x-intercepts: (5, 0) and (–5, 0)

$x = 0$: $\ y = 0^2 - 25 = -25$

y-intercept: (0, –25)

$y = x^2 + 0x - 25$

$a = 1$, $b = 0$, $c = -25$

$\dfrac{-b}{2a} = \dfrac{-0}{2(1)} = \dfrac{0}{2} = 0$

$x = 0$: $\ y = 0^2 - 25 = -25$

vertex: (0, –25)

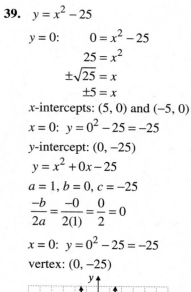

40. $y = x^2 - 36$

$y = 0$: $\quad 0 = x^2 - 36$

$\qquad\qquad 36 = x^2$

$\qquad\quad \pm\sqrt{36} = x$

$\qquad\qquad \pm 6 = x$

x-intercepts: $(6, 0)$ and $(-6, 0)$

$x = 0$: $y = 0^2 - 36 = -36$

y-intercept: $(0, -36)$

$y = x^2 + 0x - 36$

$a = 1, b = 0, c = -36$

$\dfrac{-b}{2a} = \dfrac{-0}{2(1)} = \dfrac{0}{2} = 0$

$x = 0$: $y = 0^2 - 36 = -36$

vertex: $(0, -36)$

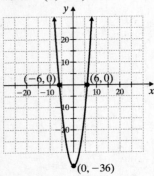

41. $y = x^2 + 3$

$y = 0$: $\quad 0 = x^2 + 3$

$\qquad\qquad -3 = x^2$

$\qquad\quad \pm\sqrt{-3} = x$

x-intercepts: none

$x = 0$: $y = 0^2 + 3 = 3$

y-intercept: $(0, 3)$

$y = x^2 + 0x + 3$

$a = 1, b = 0, c = 3$

$\dfrac{-b}{2a} = \dfrac{-0}{2(1)} = \dfrac{0}{2} = 0$

$x = 0$: $y = 0^2 + 3 = 3$

vertex: $(0, 3)$

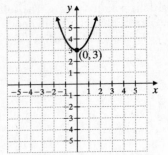

42. $y = x^2 + 8$

$y = 0$: $\qquad 0 = x^2 + 8$

$\qquad\qquad -8 = x^2$

$\qquad\quad \pm\sqrt{-8} = x$

x-intercepts: none

$x = 0$: $y = 0^2 + 8 = 8$

y-intercept: $(0, 8)$

$y = x^2 + 0x + 8$

$a = 1, b = 0, c = 8$

$\dfrac{-b}{2a} = \dfrac{0}{2(1)} = \dfrac{0}{2} = 0$

$x = 0$: $y = 0^2 + 8 = 8$

vertex: $(0, 8)$

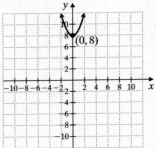

43. $y = -4x^2 + 8$

$y = 0$: $\qquad 0 = -4x^2 + 8$

$\qquad\qquad 0 = -4(x^2 - 2)$

$\qquad\qquad 0 = x^2 - 2$

$\qquad\qquad 2 = x^2$

$\qquad\quad \pm\sqrt{2} = x$

x-intercepts: $\left(\sqrt{2}, 0\right)$ and $\left(-\sqrt{2}, 0\right)$

$x = 0$: $y = -4(0)^2 + 8 = 8$

y-intercept: $(0, 8)$

$y = -4x^2 + 0x + 8$

$a = -4, b = 0, c = 8$

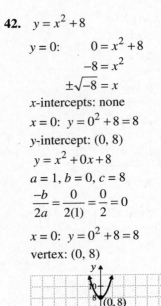

$$\frac{-b}{2a} = \frac{-0}{2(-4)} = \frac{0}{-8} = 0$$

$x = 0$: $y = -4(0)^2 + 8 = 8$

vertex: $(0, 8)$

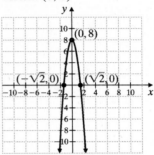

44. $y = -3x^2 + 9$

$y = 0$: $0 = -3x^2 + 9$

           $0 = -3(x^2 - 3)$

           $0 = x^2 - 3$

           $3 = x^2$

           $\pm\sqrt{3} = x$

x-intercepts: $\left(\sqrt{3}, 0\right)$ and $\left(-\sqrt{3}, 0\right)$

$x = 0$: $y = -3(0)^2 + 9 = 9$

y-intercept: $(0, 9)$

$y = -3x^2 + 0x + 9$

$a = -3$, $b = 0$, $c = 8$

$$\frac{-b}{2a} = \frac{-0}{2(-3)} = \frac{0}{-6} = 0$$

$x = 0$: $y = -3(0)^2 + 9 = 9$

vertex: $(0, 9)$

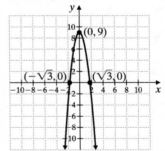

45. $y = x^2 + 3x - 10$

$y = 0$: $0 = x^2 + 3x - 10$

         $0 = (x + 5)(x - 2)$

           $0 = x + 5$ or $0 = x - 2$

         $-5 = x$ $2 = x$

x-intercepts: $(-5, 0)$ and $(2, 0)$

$x = 0$: $y = 0^2 + 3(0) - 10 = -10$

y-intercept: $(0, -10)$

$y = x^2 + 3x - 10$

$a = 1$, $b = 3$, $c = -10$

$$\frac{-b}{2a} = \frac{-3}{2(1)} = -\frac{3}{2}$$

$x = -\dfrac{3}{2}$: $y = \left(-\dfrac{3}{2}\right)^2 + 3\left(-\dfrac{3}{2}\right) - 10$

               $= \dfrac{9}{4} - \dfrac{9}{2} - 10$

               $= \dfrac{9}{4} - \dfrac{18}{4} - \dfrac{40}{4}$

               $= -\dfrac{49}{4}$

vertex: $\left(-\dfrac{3}{2}, -\dfrac{49}{4}\right)$

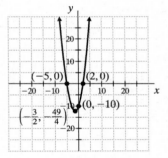

46. $y = x^2 + 3x - 4$

$y = 0$: $0 = x^2 + 3x - 4$

         $0 = (x + 4)(x - 1)$

           $0 = x + 4$ or $0 = x - 1$

         $-4 = x$ $1 = x$

x-intercepts: $(-4, 0)$ and $(1, 0)$

$x = 0$: $y = 0^2 + 3(0) - 4 = -4$

y-intercept: $(0, -4)$

$y = x^2 + 3x - 4$

$a = 1$, $b = 3$, $c = -4$

$$\frac{-b}{2a} = \frac{-3}{2(1)} = \frac{-3}{2}$$

$$x = -\frac{3}{2}: \quad y = \left(-\frac{3}{2}\right)^2 + 3\left(-\frac{3}{2}\right) - 4$$

$$= \frac{9}{4} - \frac{9}{2} - 4$$

$$= \frac{9}{4} - \frac{18}{4} - \frac{16}{4}$$

$$= -\frac{25}{4}$$

vertex: $\left(-\frac{3}{2}, -\frac{25}{4}\right)$

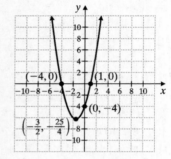

47. $y = -x^2 - 5x - 6$

$y = 0: \quad 0 = -x^2 - 5x - 6$

$\qquad 0 = x^2 + 5x + 6$

$\qquad 0 = (x+3)(x+2)$

$\qquad 0 = x+3 \quad \text{or} \quad 0 = x+2$

$\qquad -3 = x \qquad\qquad -2 = x$

x-intercepts: $(-3, 0)$ and $(-2, 0)$

$x = 0: \quad y = -0^2 - 5(0) - 6 = -6$

y-intercept: $(0, -6)$

$y = -x^2 - 5x - 6$

$a = -1, b = -5, c = -6$

$\dfrac{-b}{2a} = \dfrac{-(-5)}{2(-1)} = \dfrac{5}{-2} = -\dfrac{5}{2}$

$$x = -\frac{5}{2}: \quad y = -\left(-\frac{5}{2}\right)^2 - 5\left(-\frac{5}{2}\right) - 6$$

$$y = -\frac{25}{4} + \frac{25}{2} - 6$$

$$y = -\frac{25}{4} + \frac{50}{4} - \frac{24}{4}$$

$$y = \frac{1}{4}$$

vertex: $\left(-\frac{5}{2}, \frac{1}{4}\right)$

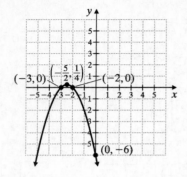

48. $y = 3x^2 - x - 2$

$y = 0: \quad 0 = 3x^2 - x - 2$

$\qquad 0 = (3x+2)(x-1)$

$\qquad 0 = 3x+2 \quad \text{or} \quad 0 = x-1$

$\qquad -2 = 3x \qquad\qquad 1 = x$

$\qquad -\dfrac{2}{3} = x$

x-intercepts: $\left(-\dfrac{2}{3}, 0\right)$ and $(1, 0)$

$x = 0: \quad y = 3(0)^2 - 0 - 2 = -2$

y-intercept: $(0, -2)$

$y = 3x^2 - x - 2$

$a = 3, b = -1, c = -2$

$\dfrac{-b}{2a} = \dfrac{-(-1)}{2(3)} = \dfrac{1}{6}$

$$x = \frac{1}{6}: \quad y = 3\left(\frac{1}{6}\right)^2 - \frac{1}{6} - 2$$

$$y = \frac{3}{36} - \frac{1}{6} - 2$$

$$y = \frac{3}{36} - \frac{6}{36} - \frac{72}{36}$$

$$y = -\frac{75}{36} = -\frac{25}{12}$$

vertex: $\left(\dfrac{1}{6}, -\dfrac{25}{12}\right)$

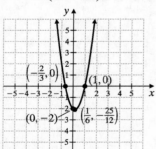

49. $y = 2x^2 - 11x - 6$

$y = 0$: $0 = 2x^2 - 11x - 6$

$\quad\quad 0 = (2x+1)(x-6)$

$\quad\quad\quad 0 = 2x+1 \quad$ or $\quad 0 = x-6$

$\quad\quad\quad -1 = 2x \quad\quad\quad\quad 6 = x$

$\quad\quad\quad -\dfrac{1}{2} = x$

x-intercepts: $\left(-\dfrac{1}{2}, 0\right)$ and $(6, 0)$

$x = 0$: $y = 2(0)^2 - 11(0) - 6 = -6$

y-intercept: $(0, -6)$

$y = 2x^2 - 11x - 6$

$a = 2$, $b = -11$, $c = -6$

$\dfrac{-b}{2a} = \dfrac{-(-11)}{2(2)} = \dfrac{11}{4}$

$x = \dfrac{11}{4}$: $y = 2\left(\dfrac{11}{4}\right)^2 - 11\left(\dfrac{11}{4}\right) - 6$

$\quad\quad\quad y = \dfrac{242}{16} - \dfrac{121}{4} - 6$

$\quad\quad\quad y = \dfrac{242}{16} - \dfrac{484}{16} - \dfrac{96}{16}$

$\quad\quad\quad y = -\dfrac{338}{16} = -\dfrac{169}{8}$

vertex: $\left(\dfrac{11}{4}, -\dfrac{169}{8}\right)$

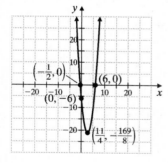

50. $y = -x^2 + 4x + 8$

$y = 0$: $0 = -x^2 + 4x + 8$

$a = -1$, $b = 4$, $c = 8$

$x = \dfrac{-b \pm \sqrt{b^2 - 4ac}}{2a}$

$x = \dfrac{-4 \pm \sqrt{4^2 - 4(-1)(8)}}{2(-1)}$

$\quad = \dfrac{-4 \pm \sqrt{16 + 32}}{2}$

$\quad = \dfrac{-4 \pm \sqrt{48}}{-2}$

$\quad = \dfrac{-4 \pm 4\sqrt{3}}{-2}$

$\quad = 2 \pm 2\sqrt{3}$

x-intercepts: $\left(2 + 2\sqrt{3}, 0\right)$ and $\left(2 - 2\sqrt{3}, 0\right)$

$x = 0$: $y = -0^2 + 4(0) + 8 = 8$

y-intercept: $(0, 8)$

$y = -x^2 + 4x + 8$

$a = -1$, $b = 4$, $c = 8$

$\dfrac{-b}{2a} = \dfrac{-4}{2(-1)} = \dfrac{-4}{-2} = 2$

$x = 2$: $y = -(2)^2 + 4(2) + 8 = -4 + 8 + 8 = 12$

vertex: $(2, 12)$

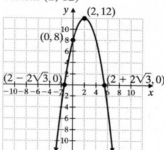

51. $y = 2x^2$ matches with graph A.

52. $y = -x^2$ matches with graph D.

53. $y = x^2 + 4x + 4$ matches with graph B.

54. $y = x^2 + 5x + 4$ matches with graph C.

55. The graph crosses the x-axis once so there is one real solution.

56. The graph crosses the x-axis twice so there are two real solutions.

57. The graph doesn't cross the x-axis so there are no real solutions.

58. The graph crosses the x-axis twice so there are two real solutions.

59. $x^2 = 49$

$x = \pm\sqrt{49}$

$x = \pm 7$

The solutions are $x = \pm 7$.

60. $y^2 = 75$

$y = \pm\sqrt{75}$

$y = \pm 5\sqrt{3}$

The solutions are $y = \pm 5\sqrt{3}$.

61. $(x-7)^2 = 64$

$x - 7 = \pm\sqrt{64}$

$x - 7 = \pm 8$

$x - 7 = 8$ or $x - 7 = -8$

$x = 15$ $x = -1$

The solutions are $x = 15$ and $x = -1$.

62. $\qquad x^2 + 4x = 6$

$x^2 + 4x + \left(\dfrac{4}{2}\right)^2 = 6 + \left(\dfrac{4}{2}\right)^2$

$(x+2)^2 = 10$

$x + 2 = \pm\sqrt{10}$

$x = -2 \pm \sqrt{10}$

The solutions are $x = -2 \pm \sqrt{10}$.

63. $\qquad 3x^2 + x = 2$

$x^2 + \dfrac{1}{3}x = \dfrac{2}{3}$

$x^2 + \dfrac{1}{3}x + \left(\dfrac{1}{6}\right)^2 = \dfrac{2}{3} + \left(\dfrac{1}{6}\right)^2$

$\left(x + \dfrac{1}{6}\right)^2 = \dfrac{25}{36}$

$x + \dfrac{1}{6} = \pm\sqrt{\dfrac{25}{36}}$

$x + \dfrac{1}{6} = \pm\dfrac{5}{6}$

$x = -\dfrac{1}{6} \pm \dfrac{5}{6}$

$x = -\dfrac{1}{6} + \dfrac{5}{6} = \dfrac{4}{6} = \dfrac{2}{3}$ or $x = -\dfrac{1}{6} - \dfrac{5}{6} = -\dfrac{6}{6} = -1$

The solutions are $x = \dfrac{2}{3}$ and $x = -1$.

64. $\qquad 4x^2 - x - 2 = 0$

$x^2 - \dfrac{1}{4}x - \dfrac{1}{2} = 0$

$x^2 - \dfrac{1}{4}x = \dfrac{1}{2}$

$x^2 - \dfrac{1}{4}x + \left(-\dfrac{1}{8}\right)^2 = \dfrac{1}{2} + \left(-\dfrac{1}{8}\right)^2$

$\left(x - \dfrac{1}{8}\right)^2 = \dfrac{33}{64}$

$x - \dfrac{1}{8} = \pm\sqrt{\dfrac{33}{64}}$

$x - \dfrac{1}{8} = \pm\dfrac{\sqrt{33}}{8}$

$x = \dfrac{1}{8} \pm \dfrac{\sqrt{33}}{8}$

$x = \dfrac{1 \pm \sqrt{33}}{8}$

The solutions are $x = \dfrac{1 \pm \sqrt{33}}{8}$.

65. $4x^2 - 3x - 2 = 0$

$a = 4,\ b = -3,\ c = -2$

$x = \dfrac{-b \pm \sqrt{b^2 - 4ac}}{2a}$

$x = \dfrac{-(-3) \pm \sqrt{(-3)^2 - 4(4)(-2)}}{2(4)}$

$= \dfrac{3 \pm \sqrt{9 + 32}}{8}$

$= \dfrac{3 \pm \sqrt{41}}{8}$

The solutions are $x = \dfrac{3 \pm \sqrt{41}}{8}$.

66. $5x^2 + x - 2 = 0$

$a = 5,\ b = 1,\ c = -2$

$x = \dfrac{-b \pm \sqrt{b^2 - 4ac}}{2a}$

$$x = \frac{-1 \pm \sqrt{1^2 - 4(5)(-2)}}{2(5)}$$

$$= \frac{-1 \pm \sqrt{1 + 40}}{10}$$

$$= \frac{-1 \pm \sqrt{41}}{10}$$

The solutions are $x = \dfrac{-1 \pm \sqrt{41}}{10}$.

67. $4x^2 + 12x + 9 = 0$
$a = 4, b = 12, c = 9$

$$x = \frac{-b \pm \sqrt{b^2 - 4ac}}{2a}$$

$$x = \frac{-12 \pm \sqrt{12^2 - 4(4)(9)}}{2(4)}$$

$$= \frac{-12 \pm \sqrt{144 - 144}}{8}$$

$$= \frac{-12 \pm \sqrt{0}}{8}$$

$$= -\frac{12}{8}$$

$$= -\frac{3}{2}$$

The solution is $x = -\dfrac{3}{2}$.

68. $2x^2 + x + 4 = 0$
$a = 2, b = 1, c = 4$

$$x = \frac{-b \pm \sqrt{b^2 - 4ac}}{2a}$$

$$x = \frac{-1 \pm \sqrt{1^2 - 4(2)(4)}}{2(2)}$$

$$= \frac{-1 \pm \sqrt{1 - 32}}{4}$$

$$= \frac{-1 \pm \sqrt{-31}}{4}$$

The equation has no solution, since the square root of -31 is not a real number.

69. $y = 4 - x^2$

$y = 0$: $0 = 4 - x^2$
$$x^2 = 4$$
$$x = \pm\sqrt{4}$$
$$x = \pm 2$$

x-intercepts: (2, 0) and (−2, 0)

$x = 0$: $y = 4 - 0^2 = 4$

y-intercept: (0, 4)

$$y = 4 + 0x - x^2$$
$a = -1, b = 0, c = 4$

$$\frac{-b}{2a} = \frac{-0}{2(-1)} = \frac{0}{-2} = 0$$

$x = 0$: $y = 4 - 0^2 = 4$

vertex: (0, 4)

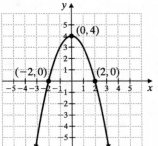

70. $y = x^2 + 4$

$y = 0$: $0 = x^2 + 4$
$$-4 = x^2$$
$$\pm\sqrt{-4} = x$$

x-intercepts: none

$x = 0$: $y = 0^2 + 4 = 4$

y-intercept: (0, 4)

$$y = x^2 + 0x + 4$$
$a = 1, b = 0, c = 4$

$$\frac{-b}{2a} = \frac{-0}{2(1)} = \frac{0}{2} = 0$$

$x = 0$: $y = 0^2 + 4 = 4$

vertex: (0, 4)

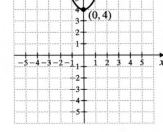

71. $y = x^2 + 6x + 8$

$y = 0$: $0 = x^2 + 6x + 8$
$$0 = (x + 4)(x + 2)$$

$$x + 4 = 0 \quad \text{or} \quad x + 2 = 0$$
$$x = -4 \qquad\qquad x = -2$$

x-intercepts: $(-4, 0)$ and $(-2, 0)$

$x = 0:\ y = 0^2 + 6(0) + 8 = 8$

y-intercept: $(0, 8)$

$y = x^2 + 6x + 8$

$a = 1,\ b = 6,\ c = 8$

$$\frac{-b}{2a} = \frac{-6}{2(1)} = \frac{-6}{2} = -3$$

$x = -3:\ y = (-3)^2 + 6(-3) + 8 = 9 - 18 + 8 = -1$

vertex: $(-3, -1)$

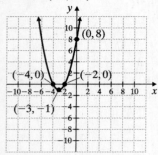

72. $y = x^2 - 2x - 4$

$y = 0:\ 0 = x^2 - 2x - 4$

$a = 1,\ b = -2,\ c = -4$

$$x = \frac{-b \pm \sqrt{b^2 - 4ac}}{2a}$$

$$x = \frac{-(-2) \pm \sqrt{(-2)^2 - 4(1)(-4)}}{2(1)}$$

$$= \frac{2 \pm \sqrt{4 + 16}}{2}$$

$$= \frac{2 \pm \sqrt{20}}{2}$$

$$= \frac{2 \pm 2\sqrt{5}}{2}$$

$$= 1 \pm \sqrt{5}$$

x-intercepts: $\left(1 + \sqrt{5},\ 0\right)$ and $\left(1 - \sqrt{5},\ 0\right)$

$x = 0:\ y = 0^2 - 2(0) - 4 = -4$

x-intercept: $(0, -4)$

$y = x^2 - 2x - 4$

$a = 1,\ b = -2,\ c = -4$

$$\frac{-b}{2a} = \frac{-(-2)}{2(1)} = \frac{2}{2} = 1$$

$x = 1:\ y = 1^2 - 2(1) - 4 = 1 - 2 - 4 = -5$

vertex: $(1, -5)$

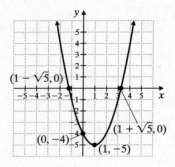

Chapter 16 Test

1. $\qquad x^2 - 400 = 0$

$(x + 20)(x - 20) = 0$

$x + 20 = 0 \quad \text{or} \quad x - 20 = 0$

$\qquad x = -20 \qquad\qquad x = 20$

The solutions are $x = \pm 20$.

2. $\qquad 2x^2 - 11x = 21$

$2x^2 - 11x - 21 = 0$

$(2x + 3)(x - 7) = 0$

$2x + 3 = 0 \quad \text{or} \quad x - 7 = 0$

$\quad 2x = -3 \qquad\qquad x = 7$

$$x = -\frac{3}{2}$$

The solutions are $x = -\dfrac{3}{2}$ and $x = 7$.

3. $5k^2 = 80$

$k^2 = 16$

$k = \pm\sqrt{16}$

$k = \pm 4$

The solutions are $k = \pm 4$.

4. $(3m - 5)^2 = 8$

$3m - 5 = \pm\sqrt{8}$

$3m - 5 = \pm 2\sqrt{2}$

$3m = 5 \pm 2\sqrt{2}$

$$m = \frac{5 \pm 2\sqrt{2}}{3}$$

The solutions are $m = \dfrac{5 \pm 2\sqrt{2}}{3}$.

5.
$$x^2 - 26x + 160 = 0$$
$$x^2 - 26x = -160$$
$$x^2 - 26x + \left(\frac{-26}{2}\right)^2 = -160 + \left(\frac{-26}{2}\right)^2$$
$$x^2 - 26x + (-13)^2 = -160 + (-13)^2$$
$$x^2 - 26x + 169 = -160 + 169$$
$$(x - 13)^2 = 9$$
$$x - 13 = \sqrt{9} \text{ or } x - 13 = -\sqrt{9}$$
$$x - 13 = 3 \qquad x - 13 = -3$$
$$x = 16 \qquad\quad x = 10$$
The solutions are $x = 10$ and $x = 16$.

6.
$$3x^2 + 12x - 4 = 0$$
$$x^2 + 4x - \frac{4}{3} = 0$$
$$x^2 + 4x = \frac{4}{3}$$
$$x^2 + 4x + \left(\frac{4}{2}\right)^2 = \frac{4}{3} + \left(\frac{4}{2}\right)^2$$
$$x^2 + 4x + (2)^2 = \frac{4}{3} + 2^2$$
$$(x + 2)^2 = \frac{16}{3}$$
$$x + 2 = \pm\sqrt{\frac{16}{3}}$$
$$x + 2 = \pm\sqrt{\frac{16}{3}} \cdot \sqrt{\frac{3}{3}}$$
$$x + 2 = \pm\frac{4\sqrt{3}}{3}$$
$$x = -2 \pm \frac{4\sqrt{3}}{3}$$

The solutions are $x = -2 \pm \dfrac{4\sqrt{3}}{3}$.

7. $x^2 - 3x - 10 = 0$
$$a = 1, b = -3, c = -10$$
$$x = \frac{-b \pm \sqrt{b^2 - 4ac}}{2a}$$

$$x = \frac{-(-3) \pm \sqrt{(-3)^2 - 4(1)(-10)}}{2(1)}$$
$$= \frac{3 \pm \sqrt{9 + 40}}{2}$$
$$= \frac{3 \pm \sqrt{49}}{2}$$
$$= \frac{3 \pm 7}{2}$$
$$x = \frac{3 + 7}{2} = \frac{10}{2} = 5 \text{ or } x = \frac{3 - 7}{2} = \frac{-4}{2} = -2$$
The solutions are $x = 5$ and $x = -2$.

8. $p^2 - \dfrac{5}{3}p - \dfrac{1}{3} = 0$
$$a = 1, \; b = -\frac{5}{3}, \; c = -\frac{1}{3}$$
$$p = \frac{-b \pm \sqrt{b^2 - 4ac}}{2a}$$
$$p = \frac{-\left(-\frac{5}{3}\right) \pm \sqrt{\left(-\frac{5}{3}\right)^2 - 4(1)\left(-\frac{1}{3}\right)}}{2(1)}$$
$$= \frac{\frac{5}{3} \pm \sqrt{\frac{25}{9} + \frac{4}{3}}}{2}$$
$$= \frac{\frac{5}{3} \pm \sqrt{\frac{25}{9} + \frac{12}{9}}}{2}$$
$$= \frac{\frac{5}{3} \pm \sqrt{\frac{37}{9}}}{2}$$
$$= \frac{\frac{5}{3} \pm \frac{\sqrt{37}}{3}}{2}$$
$$= \frac{5 \pm \sqrt{37}}{6}$$

The solutions are $p = \dfrac{5 \pm \sqrt{37}}{6}$.

9.
$$(3x - 5)(x + 2) = -6$$
$$3x^2 + 6x - 5x - 10 = -6$$
$$3x^2 + x - 10 = -6$$
$$3x^2 + x - 4 = 0$$
$$a = 3, b = 1, c = -4$$
$$x = \frac{-b \pm \sqrt{b^2 - 4ac}}{2a}$$

$$x = \frac{-1 \pm \sqrt{1^2 - 4(3)(-4)}}{2(3)}$$

$$= \frac{-1 \pm \sqrt{1 + 48}}{6}$$

$$= \frac{-1 \pm \sqrt{49}}{6}$$

$$= \frac{-1 \pm 7}{6}$$

$$x = \frac{-1 + 7}{6} = 1 \text{ or } x = \frac{-1 - 7}{6} = -\frac{4}{3}$$

The solutions are $x = 1$ and $x = -\frac{4}{3}$.

10. $(3x - 1)^2 = 16$

$$3x - 1 = \pm\sqrt{16}$$

$$3x - 1 = \pm 4$$

$$3x = 1 \pm 4$$

$$x = \frac{1 \pm 4}{3}$$

$$x = \frac{1 + 4}{3} = \frac{5}{3} \text{ or } x = \frac{1 - 4}{3} = \frac{-3}{3} = -1$$

The solutions are $x = \frac{5}{3}$ and $x = -1$.

11. $3x^2 - 7x - 2 = 0$

$a = 3, b = -7, c = -2$

$$x = \frac{-b \pm \sqrt{b^2 - 4ac}}{2a}$$

$$x = \frac{-(-7) \pm \sqrt{(-7)^2 - 4(3)(-2)}}{2(3)}$$

$$= \frac{7 \pm \sqrt{49 + 24}}{6}$$

$$= \frac{7 \pm \sqrt{73}}{6}$$

The solutions are $x = \frac{7 \pm \sqrt{73}}{6}$.

12. $x^2 - 4x - 5 = 0$

$(x - 5)(x + 1) = 0$

$x - 5 = 0$ or $x + 1 = 0$

$\quad x = 5 \qquad\qquad x = -1$

The solutions are $x = 5$ and $x = -1$.

13. $3x^2 - 7x + 2 = 0$

$a = 3, b = -7, c = 2$

$$x = \frac{-b \pm \sqrt{b^2 - 4ac}}{2a}$$

$$x = \frac{-(-7) \pm \sqrt{(-7)^2 - 4(3)(2)}}{2(3)}$$

$$= \frac{7 \pm \sqrt{49 - 24}}{6}$$

$$= \frac{7 \pm \sqrt{25}}{6}$$

$$= \frac{7 \pm 5}{6}$$

$$x = \frac{7 + 5}{6} = 2 \text{ or } x = \frac{7 - 5}{6} = \frac{1}{3}$$

The solutions are $x = \frac{1}{3}$ and $x = 2$.

14. $2x^2 - 6x + 1 = 0$

$a = 2, b = -6, c = 1$

$$x = \frac{-b \pm \sqrt{b^2 - 4ac}}{2a}$$

$$x = \frac{-(-6) \pm \sqrt{(-6)^2 - 4(2)(1)}}{2(2)}$$

$$= \frac{6 \pm \sqrt{36 - 8}}{4}$$

$$= \frac{6 \pm \sqrt{28}}{4}$$

$$= \frac{6 \pm 2\sqrt{7}}{4}$$

$$= \frac{3 \pm \sqrt{7}}{2}$$

The solutions are $x = \frac{3 \pm \sqrt{7}}{2}$.

15. Let $x =$ the length of the base.

$4x =$ height

$$A = \frac{1}{2}bh$$

$$18 = \frac{1}{2}(x)(4x)$$

$$36 = 4x^2$$

$$9 = x^2$$

$$\pm\sqrt{9} = x$$

$$\pm 3 = x$$

$$4x = 4(3) = 12$$

The base is 3 feet. The height is 12 feet.

16. $y = -5x^2$

$\quad y = 0:\ 0 = -5x^2$

$\qquad\qquad 0 = x^2$

$\qquad\qquad 0 = x$

$\quad$ *x*-intercept: (0, 0)

$\quad$ The *y*-intercept is also (0, 0).

$\quad y = -5x^2 + 0x + 0$

$\quad a = -5,\ b = 0,\ c = 0$

$\quad \dfrac{-b}{2a} = \dfrac{-0}{2(-5)} = \dfrac{0}{-10} = 0$

$\quad x = 0:\ y = -5(0)^2 = 0$

$\quad$ vertex: (0, 0)

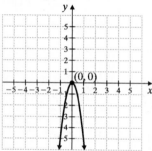

17. $y = x^2 - 4$

$\quad y = 0:\ 0 = x^2 - 4$

$\qquad\qquad 0 = (x+2)(x-2)$

$\qquad\quad 0 = x+2 \quad$ or $\quad 0 = x-2$

$\qquad\quad -2 = x \qquad\qquad\quad 2 = x$

$\quad$ *x*-intercepts: (−2, 0), (2, 0)

$\quad x = 0:\ y = 0^2 - 4 = -4$

$\quad$ *y*-intercept: (0, −4)

$\quad y = x^2 + 0x - 4$

$\quad a = 1,\ b = 0,\ c = -4$

$\quad \dfrac{-b}{2a} = \dfrac{-0}{2(1)} = \dfrac{0}{2} = 0$

$\quad x = 0:\ y = 0^2 - 4 = -4$

$\quad$ vertex: (0, −4)

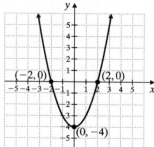

18. $y = x^2 - 7x + 10$

$\quad y = 0:\ 0 = x^2 - 7x + 10$

$\qquad\qquad 0 = (x-5)(x-2)$

$\qquad\quad x - 5 = 0 \quad$ or $\quad x - 2 = 0$

$\qquad\qquad x = 5 \qquad\qquad\quad x = 2$

$\quad$ *x*-intercepts: (5, 0) and (2, 0)

$\quad x = 0:\ y = 0^2 - 7(0) + 10 = 10$

$\quad$ *y*-intercept: (0, 10)

$\quad y = x^2 - 7x + 10$

$\quad a = 1,\ b = -7,\ c = 10$

$\quad \dfrac{-b}{2a} = \dfrac{-(-7)}{2(1)} = \dfrac{7}{2}$

$\quad x = \dfrac{7}{2}:\ y = \left(\dfrac{7}{2}\right)^2 - 7\left(\dfrac{7}{2}\right) + 10$

$\qquad\qquad = \dfrac{49}{4} - \dfrac{49}{2} + 10$

$\qquad\qquad = \dfrac{49}{4} - \dfrac{98}{4} + \dfrac{40}{4}$

$\qquad\qquad = -\dfrac{9}{4}$

$\quad$ vertex: $\left(\dfrac{7}{2}, -\dfrac{9}{4}\right)$

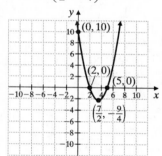

19. $y = 2x^2 + 4x - 1$

$\quad y = 0:\ 0 = 2x^2 + 4x - 1$

$\quad a = 2,\ b = 4,\ c = -1$

$\quad x = \dfrac{-b \pm \sqrt{b^2 - 4ac}}{2a}$

$$x = \frac{-4 \pm \sqrt{4^2 - 4(2)(-1)}}{2(2)}$$

$$= \frac{-4 \pm \sqrt{16 + 8}}{4}$$

$$= \frac{-4 \pm \sqrt{24}}{4}$$

$$= \frac{-4 \pm 2\sqrt{6}}{4}$$

$$= \frac{-2 \pm \sqrt{6}}{2}$$

x-intercepts: $\left(\dfrac{-2 - \sqrt{6}}{2}, 0\right)$ and $\left(\dfrac{-2 + \sqrt{6}}{2}, 0\right)$

$x = 0$: $y = 2(0)^2 + 4(0) - 1 = -1$

y-intercept: $(0, -1)$

$$y = 2x^2 + 4x - 1$$

$a = 2, b = 4, c = -1$

$$\frac{-b}{2a} = \frac{-4}{2(2)} = \frac{-4}{4} = -1$$

$x = -1$: $y = 2(-1)^2 + 4(-1) - 1 = 2 - 4 - 1 = -3$

vertex: $(-1, -3)$

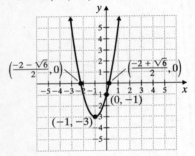

20. $d = \dfrac{n^2 - 3n}{2}$

$$9 = \frac{n^2 - 3n}{2}$$

$$18 = n^2 - 3n$$

$$0 = n^2 - 3n - 18$$

$$0 = (n - 6)(n + 3)$$

$n - 6 = 0$ or $n + 3 = 0$
$\quad n = 6 \qquad\quad n = -3$

A 6-sided polygon has 9 diagonals.

21.
$$h = 16t^2$$
$$120.75 = 16t^2$$
$$\frac{120.75}{16} = t^2$$
$$7.546875 = t^2$$
$$\sqrt{7.546875} = t \text{ or } -\sqrt{7.546875} = t$$
$$2.7 \approx t \qquad\qquad -2.7 \approx t$$

Since the time of the dive is not a negative number, discard the solution $t \approx -2.7$. The dive took approximately 2.7 seconds.

Cumulative Review Chapters 1–16

1. $\dfrac{786.1}{1000} = 0.7861$

2. $\dfrac{818}{1000} = 0.818$

3. $-\dfrac{0.12}{10} = -0.012$

4. $-\dfrac{5.03}{100} = -0.0503$

5. Add the percentages for Mexico and Canada:
$25\% + 32\% = 59\%$
59% of the visitors to the U.S. were from Mexico or Canada.

6. Add the percentages for Europe, Asia, and South America: $20\% + 11\% + 4\% = 35\%$
35% of the visitors to the U.S. were from Europe, Asia, or South America.

7. Perimeter = 11 + 3 + 11 + 3 = 28
The perimeter is 28 inches.

8. Perimeter = 6 + 8 + 11 = 25
The perimeter is 25 feet.

9. Area = bh = (3.4 mi)(1.5 mi) = 5.1 sq mi
The area is 5.1 square miles.

10. Area = $\dfrac{1}{2}bh = \dfrac{1}{2}$(17 in.)(8 in.) = 68 sq in.
The area is 68 square inches.

11. 3210 ml = $\dfrac{3210 \text{ ml}}{1} \cdot \dfrac{1 \text{ L}}{1000 \text{ ml}} = \dfrac{3210}{1000}$ L = 3.21 L

12. $4321 \text{ cl} = \dfrac{4321 \text{ cl}}{1} \cdot \dfrac{1 \text{ L}}{100 \text{ cl}} = \dfrac{4321}{100} \text{ L} = 43.21 \text{ L}$

13. $8(2-t) = -5t$
$16 - 8t = -5t$
$16 = 3t$
$\dfrac{16}{3} = t$

14. $\dfrac{5}{2}x - 1 = x + \dfrac{1}{4}$
$4\left(\dfrac{5}{2}x - 1\right) = 4\left(x + \dfrac{1}{4}\right)$
$10x - 4 = 4x + 1$
$6x - 4 = 1$
$6x = 5$
$x = \dfrac{5}{6}$

15. $3^0 = 1$

16. $-2^0 = -(2^0) = -1$

17. $r^2 - r - 42 = (r-7)(r+6)$

18. $y^2 + 3y - 70 = (y-7)(y+10)$

19. $10x^2 - 13xy - 3y^2 = (2x - 3y)(5x + y)$

20. $72x^2 - 35xy + 3y^2 = (9x - y)(8x - 3y)$

21. $8x^2 - 14x + 5 = 8x^2 - 4x - 10x + 5$
$= 4x(2x-1) - 5(2x-1)$
$= (2x-1)(4x-5)$

22. $15x^2 - 4x - 4 = 15x^2 - 10x + 6x - 4$
$= 5x(3x-2) + 2(3x-2)$
$= (3x-2)(5x+2)$

23. a. $4x^3 - 49x = x(4x^2 - 49) = x(2x-7)(2x+7)$

    b. $162x^4 - 2 = 2(81x^4 - 1)$
$= 2(9x^2 - 1)(9x^2 + 1)$
$= 2(9x^2 + 1)(3x-1)(3x+1)$

24. a. $9x^3 - x = x(9x^2 - 1) = x(3x-1)(3x+1)$

    b. $5x^4 - 5 = 5(x^4 - 1)$
$= 5(x^2 + 1)(x^2 - 1)$
$= 5(x^2 + 1)(x+1)(x-1)$

25. $(5x-1)(2x^2 + 15x + 18) = 0$
$(5x-1)(2x+3)(x+6) = 0$
$5x - 1 = 0 \quad \text{or} \quad 2x + 3 = 0 \quad \text{or} \quad x + 6 = 0$
$5x = 1 \qquad\qquad 2x = -3 \qquad\qquad x = -6$
$x = \dfrac{1}{5} \qquad\qquad x = -\dfrac{3}{2}$
The solutions are $x = \dfrac{1}{5}$, $x = -\dfrac{3}{2}$, and $x = -6$.

26. $(x+4)(40x^2 - 34x + 3) = 0$
$(x+4)(4x-3)(10x-1) = 0$
$x + 4 = 0 \quad \text{or} \quad 4x - 3 = 0 \quad \text{or} \quad 10x - 1 = 0$
$x = -4 \qquad\qquad 4x = 3 \qquad\qquad 10x = 1$
$x = \dfrac{3}{4} \qquad\qquad x = \dfrac{1}{10}$
The solutions are $x = -4$, $x = \dfrac{3}{4}$, and $x = \dfrac{1}{10}$.

27. $\dfrac{x^2 + 8x + 7}{x^2 - 4x - 5} = \dfrac{(x+7)(x+1)}{(x-5)(x+1)} = \dfrac{x+7}{x-5}$

28. $\dfrac{x^2 - 6x + 5}{x^2 + 6x - 7} = \dfrac{(x-1)(x-5)}{(x-1)(x+7)} = \dfrac{x-5}{x+7}$

29. $\dfrac{n}{6} - \dfrac{5}{3} = \dfrac{n}{2}$
$6\left(\dfrac{n}{6} - \dfrac{5}{3}\right) = 6\left(\dfrac{n}{2}\right)$
$n - 10 = 3n$
$-10 = 2n$
$-5 = n$
The number is -5.

30. $\dfrac{4n+5}{6} = \dfrac{7}{2}$
$6\left(\dfrac{4n+5}{6}\right) = 6\left(\dfrac{7}{2}\right)$
$4n + 5 = 21$
$4n = 16$
$n = 4$
The number is 4.

31.

	x	$y = 3x$
a.	-1	-3
b.	0	0
c.	-3	-9

32.

	$x = \frac{y-7}{-2}$	$y = -2x + 7$
a.	0	7
b.	$\frac{7}{2}$	0
c.	5	-3

33. a.
$$y = -\frac{1}{5}x + 1$$
$$2x + 10y = 3$$
$$10y = -2x + 3$$
$$y = \frac{-2}{10}x + \frac{3}{10}$$
$$y = -\frac{1}{5}x + \frac{3}{10}$$
These two equations have the same slope, therefore they are parallel.

b.
$$x + y = 3 \Rightarrow y = -x + 3$$
$$-x + y = 4 \Rightarrow y = x + 4$$
These two equations have slopes whose product is -1, therefore they are perpendicular.

c.
$$3x + y = 5 \Rightarrow y = -3x + 5$$
$$2x + 3y = 6 \Rightarrow 3y = -2x + 6$$
$$\Rightarrow y = -\frac{2}{3}x + 2$$
These two equations have different slopes (and their product is $\neq -1$), so they are neither parallel nor perpendicular.

34. a.
$$y = -2x + 3$$
$$y = -2x + 5$$
These two equations have the same slope, therefore they are parallel.

b. $-2x + y = 3 \Rightarrow y = 2x + 3$
$$x + 2y = 9 \Rightarrow 2y = -x + 9 \Rightarrow y = -\frac{1}{2}x + \frac{9}{2}$$
These two equations have slopes whose product is -1, therefore they are perpendicular.

c. $3x - 2y = -8 \Rightarrow -2y = -3x - 8$
$$\Rightarrow y = \frac{3}{2}x + 4$$
$$3x + 2y = 1 \Rightarrow 2y = -3x + 1$$
$$\Rightarrow y = -\frac{3}{2}x + \frac{1}{2}$$
These two lines have different slopes (and their product is $\neq -1$), so they are neither parallel nor perpendicular.

35. a. $\{(-1, 1), (2, 3), (7, 3), (8, 6)\}$
This is a function because each x-value is assigned to only one y-value.

b. $\{(0, -2), (1, 5), (0, 3), (7, 7)\}$
This is not a function because the x-value 0 is paired with two different y-values.

36. a. $\{(-2, 3), (-5, 7), (9, 3), (0, 0)\}$
This is a function because each x-value is assigned to only one y-value.

b. $\left\{(9, -1), \left(0, \frac{1}{2}\right), (2, -1), (9, 0)\right\}$
This is not a function because the x-value 9 is paired with two different y-values.

37. $\begin{cases} 2x + y = 10 \\ x = y + 2 \end{cases}$
Substitute $y + 2$ for x in the first equation.
$$2(y + 2) + y = 10$$
$$2y + 4 + y = 10$$
$$3y = 6$$
$$y = 2$$
Solve for x.
$$x = y + 2 = 2 + 2 = 4$$
The solution for this system is (4, 2).

38. $\begin{cases} 8x - 3y = -4 \\ y = 7x - 3 \end{cases}$
Substitute $7x - 3$ for y in the first equation.
$$8x - 3(7x - 3) = -4$$
$$8x - 21x + 9 = -4$$
$$-13x + 9 = -4$$
$$-13x = -13$$
$$x = 1$$
Solve for y.
$$y = 7x - 3 = 7(1) - 3 = 7 - 3 = 4$$
The solution for this system is (1, 4).

39. $\sqrt{36} = 6$ because $6^2 = 36$.

40. $\sqrt{81} = 9$ because $9^2 = 81$.

41. $\sqrt{\dfrac{9}{100}} = \dfrac{3}{10}$ because $\left(\dfrac{3}{10}\right)^2 = \dfrac{9}{100}$.

42. $\sqrt{\dfrac{16}{25}} = \dfrac{4}{5}$ because $\left(\dfrac{4}{5}\right)^2 = \dfrac{16}{25}$.

43. $\dfrac{2}{1+\sqrt{3}} \cdot \dfrac{1-\sqrt{3}}{1-\sqrt{3}} = \dfrac{2-2\sqrt{3}}{1-3} = \dfrac{2-2\sqrt{3}}{-2} = -1+\sqrt{3}$

44. $\dfrac{7}{\sqrt{5}-2} \cdot \dfrac{\sqrt{5}+2}{\sqrt{5}+2} = \dfrac{7\left(\sqrt{5}+2\right)}{5-4}$

$\qquad\qquad\qquad = \dfrac{7\left(\sqrt{5}+2\right)}{1}$

$\qquad\qquad\qquad = 7\left(\sqrt{5}+2\right)$

45. $(x-3)^2 = 16$

$\qquad x-3 = \pm\sqrt{16}$

$\qquad x-3 = \pm 4$

$\qquad\quad x = 3 \pm 4$

$x = 3 + 4 = 7 \quad$ or $\quad x = 3 - 4 = -1$

The solutions are $x = 7$ and $x = -1$.

46. $(x+4)^2 = 9$

$\qquad x+4 = \pm\sqrt{9}$

$\qquad x+4 = \pm 3$

$\qquad\quad x = -4 \pm 3$

$x = -4 + 3 = -1$ or $x = -4 - 3 = -7$

The solutions are $x = -1$ and $x = -7$.

47. $\qquad \dfrac{1}{2}x^2 - x = 2$

$\qquad \dfrac{1}{2}x^2 - x - 2 = 0$

$\qquad a = \dfrac{1}{2},\ b = -1,\ c = -2$

$\qquad x = \dfrac{-b \pm \sqrt{b^2 - 4ac}}{2a}$

$\qquad x = \dfrac{-(-1) \pm \sqrt{(-1)^2 - 4\left(\frac{1}{2}\right)(-2)}}{2\left(\frac{1}{2}\right)}$

$\qquad\ = \dfrac{1 \pm \sqrt{1+4}}{1}$

$\qquad\ = 1 \pm \sqrt{5}$

The solutions are $x = 1 \pm \sqrt{5}$.

48. $\qquad 2x^2 = \dfrac{5}{2}x + \dfrac{7}{2}$

$\qquad 2(2x^2) = 2\left(\dfrac{5}{2}x + \dfrac{7}{2}\right)$

$\qquad\quad 4x^2 = 5x + 7$

$4x^2 - 5x - 7 = 0$

$a = 4,\ b = -5,\ c = -7$

$\qquad x = \dfrac{-b \pm \sqrt{b^2 - 4ac}}{2a}$

$\qquad x = \dfrac{-(-5) \pm \sqrt{(-5)^2 - 4(4)(-7)}}{2(4)}$

$\qquad\ = \dfrac{5 \pm \sqrt{25 + 112}}{8}$

$\qquad\ = \dfrac{5 \pm \sqrt{137}}{8}$

The solutions are $x = \dfrac{5 \pm \sqrt{137}}{8}$.

Appendix

1. $a^3 + 27 = a^3 + 3^3$
$$= (a+3)[a^2 - (a)(3) + 3^2]$$
$$= (a+3)(a^2 - 3a + 9)$$

3. $8a^3 + 1 = (2a)^3 + 1^3$
$$= (2a+1)[(2a)^2 - (2a)(1) + 1^2]$$
$$= (2a+1)(4a^2 - 2a + 1)$$

5. $5k^3 + 40 = 5(k^3 + 8)$
$$= 5(k^3 + 2^3)$$
$$= 5(k+2)[k^2 - (k)(2) + 2^2]$$
$$= 5(k+2)(k^2 - 2k + 4)$$

7. $x^3y^3 - 64 = (xy)^3 - 4^3$
$$= (xy-4)[(xy)^2 + (xy)(4) + 4^2]$$
$$= (xy-4)(x^2y^2 + 4xy + 16)$$

9. $x^3 + 125 = x^3 + 5^3$
$$= (x+5)[x^2 - (x)(5) + 5^2]$$
$$= (x+5)(x^2 - 5x + 25)$$

11. $24x^4 - 81xy^3$
$$= 3x(8x^3 - 27y^3)$$
$$= 3x[(2x)^3 - (3y)^3]$$
$$= 3x(2x - 3y)[(2x)^2 + (2x)(3y) + (3y)^2]$$
$$= 3x(2x - 3y)(4x^2 + 6xy + 9y^2)$$

13. $27 - t^3 = 3^3 - t^3$
$$= (3-t)[3^2 + (3)(t) + t^2]$$
$$= (3-t)(9 + 3t + t^2)$$

15. $8r^3 - 64 = 8(r^3 - 8)$
$$= 8(r^3 - 2^3)$$
$$= 8(r-2)[r^2 + (r)(2) + 2^2]$$
$$= 8(r-2)(r^2 + 2r + 4)$$

17. $t^3 - 343 = t^3 - 7^3$
$$= (t-7)[t^2 + (t)(7) + 7^2]$$
$$= (t-7)(t^2 + 7t + 49)$$

19. $s^3 - 64t^3 = s^3 - (4t)^3$
$$= (s-4t)[s^2 + (s)(4t) + (4t)^2]$$
$$= (s-4t)(s^2 + 4st + 16t^2)$$

Appendix C

Practice Problems

1. Let x represent the liters of 20% solution.

	Number of Liters	Dye Strength	Amount
20% solution	x	20%	$0.2x$
50% solution	$6 - x$	50%	$0.5(6-x)$
40% solution	6	40%	$0.4(6)$

$$0.2x + 0.5(6+x) = 0.4(6)$$
$$0.2x + 3 - 0.5x = 2.4$$
$$-0.3x + 3 = 2.4$$
$$-0.3x = -0.6$$
$$x = 2$$

$6 - x = 6 - 2 = 4$
2 liters of the 20% solution should be mixed with 4 liters of the 50% solution.

2. Let x represent the number of $5 bills.

Denomination	Number of Bills	Value of Bills (in dollars)
$5 bills	x	$5x$
$20 bills	$x - 47$	$20(x-47)$

The total value was $1710.
$$5x + 20(x - 47) = 1710$$
$$5x + 20x - 940 = 1710$$
$$25x - 940 = 1710$$
$$25x = 2650$$
$$x = 106$$

$x - 47 = 106 - 47 = 59$
There were 106 $5 bills and 59 $20 bills.

3. Let x represent the time it took to hike up the mountain.

	Rate ·	Time =	Distance
Up	1.5	x	$1.5x$
Down	4	$x - 1$	$4(x-1)$

The distance up is the same as the distance down.
$$1.5x = 4(x-1)$$
$$1.5x = 4x - 4$$
$$-2.5x = -4$$
$$x = 1.6$$
$$x - 1 = 1.6 - 1 = 0.6$$
The total time is $1.6 + 0.6 = 2.2$ hours.

4. Let x represent the speed of the eastbound train.

	r ·	t =	d
East Train	x	1.5	$1.5x$
West Train	$x - 10$	1.5	$1.5(x-10)$

The total distance after 1.5 hours is 171 miles.
$$1.5x + 1.5(x-10) = 171$$
$$1.5x + 1.5x - 15 = 171$$
$$3x - 15 = 171$$
$$3x = 186$$
$$x = 62$$
$$x - 10 = 62 - 10 = 52$$
The eastbound train is going 62 miles per hour and the westbound train is going 52 miles per hour.

Appendix C Exercise Set

1. Let x represent the amount of pure acid.

	Number of Gallons ·	Acid Strength =	Amount of Acid
Pure Acid	x	100%	$1.00x$
40% Acid Solution	2	40%	$0.40(2)$
70% Acid Solution	$x + 2$	70%	$0.70(x+2)$

$$1.00x + 0.40(2) = 0.70(x+2)$$
$$x + 0.8 = 0.7x + 1.4$$
$$0.3x + 0.8 = 1.4$$
$$0.3x = 0.6$$
$$x = 2$$
2 gallons of pure acid are needed.

3. Let x represent the amount of $7 per pound coffee.

	Number of Pounds ·	Cost per Pound =	Value
$7 per lb	x	7	$7x$
$4 per lb	14	4	$4(14)$
$5 per lb	$x + 14$	5	$5(x+14)$

$$7x + 4(14) = 5(x+14)$$
$$7x + 56 = 5x + 70$$
$$2x + 56 = 70$$
$$2x = 14$$
$$x = 7$$
7 pounds of the $7 per pound coffee should be used.

		Number of Coins or Bills	Value of Coins or Bills (in dollars)
5.	dimes	y	$0.10y$
7.	nickels	$(x+7)$	$0.05(x+7)$
9.	$20 bills	$4y$	$20(4y)$ or $80y$
11.	$50 bills	$(35-x)$	$50(35-x)$

13. Let x represent the number of $10 bills.

	Number of Bills	Value of Bills
$5 bills	$x + 20$	$5(x+20)$
$10 bills	x	$10x$
Total		280

$$5(x+20) + 10x = 280$$
$$5x + 100 + 10x = 280$$
$$15x + 100 = 280$$
$$15x = 180$$
$$x = 12$$
$$x + 20 = 12 + 20 = 32$$
There were 12 $10 bills and 32 $5 bills.

15. Let x represent the amount of the 20% copper alloy.
$$0.20x + 0.50(200) = 0.30(x + 200)$$
$$0.2x + 100 = 0.3x + 60$$
$$100 = 0.1x + 60$$
$$40 = 0.1x$$
$$400 = x$$
400 ounces of the 20% copper alloy should be used.

17. Let x represent the amount of self-tanning lotion used.
$$3x + 0.30(800) = 1.20(x + 800)$$
$$3x + 240 = 1.2x + 960$$
$$1.8x + 240 = 960$$
$$1.8x = 720$$
$$x = 400$$
400 ounces of the self-tanning lotion should be used.

19. Let x be the amount of time each car drives.
$$56x + 47x = 206$$
$$103x = 206$$
$$x = 2$$
The cars will be 206 miles apart after 2 hours.

21. Let x represent the speed of the slower train.
$$2.5x + 2.5(x + 10) = 205$$
$$2.5x + 2.5x + 25 = 205$$
$$5x + 25 = 205$$
$$5x = 180$$
$$x = 36$$
$x + 10 = 36 + 10 = 46$
The slower train is going 36 miles per hour and the faster train is going 46 miles per hour.

23. Let x represent the amount of time that the truck and van are traveling.
$$52x + 63x = 460$$
$$115x = 460$$
$$x = 4$$
They will be 460 miles apart after 4 hours.

25. Let x represent the amount of time the cars are traveling.
$$70x - 58x = 30$$
$$12x = 30$$
$$x = 2.5$$
The cars will be 30 miles apart after $2\frac{1}{2}$ hours.

27. Let x be the amount of time that the jet travels.
$$500x = 200(x + 2)$$
$$500x = 200x + 400$$
$$300x = 400$$
$$x = \frac{4}{3}$$
$$500x = 500\left(\frac{4}{3}\right) = 666\frac{2}{3}$$
The planes are $666\frac{2}{3}$ miles from the starting point.

29. Let x represent the speed of the bus on the winding road.
$$4x + 3(x + 20) = 305$$
$$4x + 3x + 60 = 305$$
$$7x + 60 = 305$$
$$7x = 245$$
$$x = 35$$
$x + 20 = 35 + 20 = 55$
The average speed of the bus on the level road was 55 miles per hour.

31. Let x represent the time both men bicycle.
$$5.5x + 6.5x = 35$$
$$12x = 35$$
$$x = \frac{35}{12} = 2\frac{11}{12}$$
$$\left(\frac{11}{12}\text{ hour}\right)\left(\frac{60\text{ minutes}}{1\text{ hour}}\right) = 55\text{ minutes}$$
They will be able to talk for 2 hours 55 minutes.

33. Let x represent the speed of the slower hiker.
$$2x + 2(x + 1.1) = 11$$
$$2x + 2x + 2.2 = 11$$
$$4x + 2.2 = 11$$
$$4x = 8.8$$
$$x = 2.2$$
$x + 1.1 = 2.2 + 1.1 = 3.3$
The slower hiker walks 2.2 miles per hour and the faster hiker walks 3.3 miles per hour.

35. Let x represent the time that Mark rows upstream.
$$5x = 11(4 - x)$$
$$5x = 44 - 11x$$
$$16x = 44$$
$$x = 2.75$$
$5x = 5(2.75) = 13.75$
Mark rowed 13.75 miles upstream and the same distance downstream, so he rowed a total of $13.75 + 13.75 = 27.5$ miles.

37. Let x represent the number of $100 bills. Then there are $(x + 46)$ $50 bills and $7x$ $20 bills.

$$20(7x) + 50(x + 46) + 100x = 9550$$
$$140x + 50x + 2300 + 100x = 9550$$
$$290x + 2300 = 9550$$
$$290x = 7250$$
$$x = 25$$

$x + 46 = 25 + 46 = 71$
$7x = 7(25) = 175$
There were 175 $20 bills, 71 $50 bills, and 25 $100 bills.

Appendix D Exercise Set

1. $\begin{cases} y \geq x+1 \\ y \geq 3-x \end{cases}$

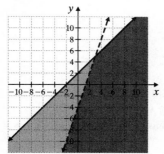

3. $\begin{cases} y < 3x-4 \\ y \leq x+2 \end{cases}$

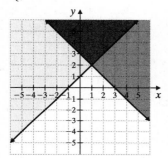

5. $\begin{cases} y < -2x-2 \\ y > x+4 \end{cases}$

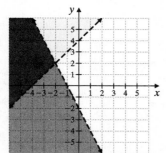

7. $\begin{cases} y \geq -x+2 \\ y \leq 2x+5 \end{cases}$

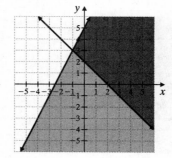

9. $\begin{cases} x \geq 3y \\ x+3y \leq 6 \end{cases}$

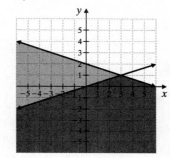

11. $\begin{cases} y+2x \geq 0 \\ 5x-3y \leq 12 \end{cases}$

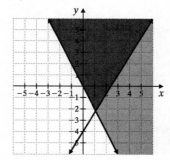

13. $\begin{cases} 3x-4y \geq -6 \\ 2x+y \leq 7 \end{cases}$

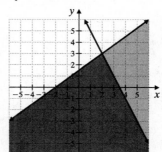

15. $\begin{cases} x \le 2 \\ y \ge -3 \end{cases}$

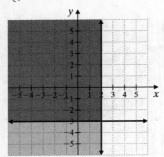

17. $\begin{cases} y \ge 1 \\ x < -3 \end{cases}$

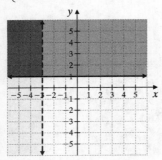

19. $\begin{cases} 2x + 3y < -8 \\ x \ge -4 \end{cases}$

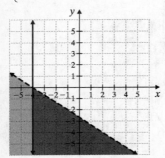

21. $\begin{cases} 2x - 5y \le 9 \\ y \le -3 \end{cases}$

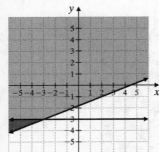

23. $\begin{cases} y \ge \dfrac{1}{2}x + 2 \\ y \le \dfrac{1}{2}x - 3 \end{cases}$

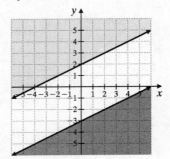

25. The graph of the system $\begin{cases} y < 5 \\ x > 3 \end{cases}$ is graph C.

27. The graph of the system $\begin{cases} y \le 5 \\ x < 3 \end{cases}$ is graph D.

Practice Final Exam

Chapters 1–8

1. $2^3 \cdot 5^2 = 2 \cdot 2 \cdot 2 \cdot 5 \cdot 5 = 200$

2. $16 + 9 \div 3 \cdot 4 - 7 = 16 + 3 \cdot 4 - 7$
$= 16 + 12 - 7$
$= 28 - 7$
$= 21$

3. $18 - 24 = 18 + (-24) = -6$

4. $5 \cdot (-20) = -100$

5. $\sqrt{49} = 7$ because $7^2 = 49$.

6. $(-5)^3 - 24 \div (-3) = -125 - 24 \div (-3)$
$= -125 - (-8)$
$= -125 + 8$
$= -117$

7. $0 \div 49 = 0$

8. $62 \div 0$ is undefined.

9. $-\dfrac{8}{15y} - \dfrac{2}{15y} = \dfrac{-8 - 2}{15y} = \dfrac{-10}{15y} = -\dfrac{2 \cdot 5}{3 \cdot 5 \cdot y} = -\dfrac{2}{3y}$

10. $\dfrac{11}{12} - \dfrac{3}{8} + \dfrac{5}{24} = \dfrac{11 \cdot 2}{12 \cdot 2} - \dfrac{3 \cdot 3}{8 \cdot 3} + \dfrac{5}{24}$

$\phantom{\dfrac{11}{12} - \dfrac{3}{8} + \dfrac{5}{24}} = \dfrac{22}{24} - \dfrac{9}{24} + \dfrac{5}{24}$

$\phantom{\dfrac{11}{12} - \dfrac{3}{8} + \dfrac{5}{24}} = \dfrac{22 - 9 + 5}{24}$

$\phantom{\dfrac{11}{12} - \dfrac{3}{8} + \dfrac{5}{24}} = \dfrac{18}{24}$

$\phantom{\dfrac{11}{12} - \dfrac{3}{8} + \dfrac{5}{24}} = \dfrac{3 \cdot 6}{4 \cdot 6}$

$\phantom{\dfrac{11}{12} - \dfrac{3}{8} + \dfrac{5}{24}} = \dfrac{3}{4}$

11. $\dfrac{3a}{8} \cdot \dfrac{16}{6a^3} = \dfrac{3a \cdot 16}{8 \cdot 6a^3} = \dfrac{3 \cdot a \cdot 8 \cdot 2}{8 \cdot 2 \cdot 3 \cdot a \cdot a \cdot a} = \dfrac{1}{a \cdot a} = \dfrac{1}{a^2}$

12. $-\dfrac{16}{3} \div -\dfrac{3}{12} = -\dfrac{16}{3} \cdot -\dfrac{12}{3}$

$\phantom{-\dfrac{16}{3} \div -\dfrac{3}{12}} = \dfrac{16 \cdot 12}{3 \cdot 3}$

$\phantom{-\dfrac{16}{3} \div -\dfrac{3}{12}} = \dfrac{16 \cdot 3 \cdot 4}{3 \cdot 3}$

$\phantom{-\dfrac{16}{3} \div -\dfrac{3}{12}} = \dfrac{64}{3}$ or $21\dfrac{1}{3}$

13.

$\begin{array}{r} 19 \\ -\,2\dfrac{3}{11} \\ \hline \end{array}$
$\qquad$
$\begin{array}{r} 18\dfrac{11}{11} \\ -\,2\dfrac{3}{11} \\ \hline 16\dfrac{8}{11} \end{array}$

14. $\dfrac{0.23 + 1.63}{-0.3} = \dfrac{1.86}{-0.3} = -6.2$

15.
$\begin{array}{r} 10.2 \\ \times\ \ 4.01 \\ \hline 102 \\ 40\ 800 \\ \hline 40.902 \end{array}$
$\quad$
1 decimal place
2 decimal places

$1 + 2 = 3$ decimal places

16. $0.6\% = 0.6(0.01) = 0.006$

17. $6.1 = 6.1(100\%) = 610\%$

18. $\dfrac{3}{8} = \dfrac{3}{8} \cdot \dfrac{100}{1}\% = \dfrac{300}{8}\% = 37.5\%$

19. $0.345 = \dfrac{345}{1000} = \dfrac{5 \cdot 69}{5 \cdot 200} = \dfrac{69}{200}$

20. $-\dfrac{13}{26} = -\dfrac{1 \cdot 13}{2 \cdot 13} = -\dfrac{1}{2} = -\dfrac{1 \cdot 5}{2 \cdot 5} = -\dfrac{5}{10} = -0.5$

21. 34.8923 rounded to the nearest tenth is 34.9.

22. Let x be 2.

$5(x^3 - 2) = 5(2^3 - 2) = 5(8 - 2) = 5(6) = 30$

23. $10 - y^2 = 10 - (-3)^2 = 10 - 9 = 1$

24. $x \div y = \dfrac{1}{2} \div 3\dfrac{7}{8}$

$ = \dfrac{1}{2} \div \dfrac{31}{8}$

$ = \dfrac{1}{2} \cdot \dfrac{8}{31}$

$ = \dfrac{1 \cdot 8}{2 \cdot 31}$

$ = \dfrac{1 \cdot 2 \cdot 4}{2 \cdot 31}$

$ = \dfrac{4}{31}$

25. $-(3z + 2) - 5z - 18 = -1(3z + 2) - 5z - 18$

$ = -1 \cdot 3z + (-1) \cdot 2 - 5z - 18$

$ = -3z - 2 - 5z - 18$

$ = -3z - 5z - 2 - 18$

$ = -8z - 20$

26. perimeter $= 3(5x + 5) = 3 \cdot 5x + 3 \cdot 5 = 15x + 15$
The perimeter is $(15x + 15)$ inches.

27. $\dfrac{n}{-7} = 4$

$-7 \cdot \dfrac{n}{-7} = -7 \cdot 4$

$\dfrac{-7}{-7} \cdot n = -7 \cdot 4$

$n = -28$

The solution is -28.

28. $-4x + 7 = 15$

$-4x + 7 - 7 = 15 - 7$

$-4x = 8$

$\dfrac{-4x}{-4} = \dfrac{8}{-4}$

$x = -2$

29.
$$-4(x-11)-34=10-12$$
$$-4x+44-34=10-12$$
$$-4x+10=-2$$
$$-4x+10-10=-2-10$$
$$-4x=-12$$
$$\frac{-4x}{-4}=\frac{-12}{-4}$$
$$x=3$$

30.
$$\frac{x}{5}+x=-\frac{24}{5}$$
$$5\left(\frac{x}{5}+x\right)=5\left(-\frac{24}{5}\right)$$
$$5\cdot\frac{x}{5}+5\cdot x=-24$$
$$x+5x=-24$$
$$6x=-24$$
$$\frac{6x}{6}=\frac{-24}{6}$$
$$x=-4$$

31.
$$2(x+5.7)=6x-3.4$$
$$2x+11.4=6x-3.4$$
$$2x+11.4-11.4=6x-3.4-11.4$$
$$2x=6x-14.8$$
$$2x-6x=6x-6x-14.8$$
$$-4x=-14.8$$
$$\frac{-4x}{-4}=\frac{-14.8}{-4}$$
$$x=3.7$$

32.
$$\frac{5}{y+1}=\frac{4}{y+2}$$
$$5(y+2)=4(y+1)$$
$$5y+10=4y+4$$
$$y+10=4$$
$$y=-6$$

33. Perimeter $=(20+10+20+10)$ yards $=60$ yards

Area $=$ (length)(width)
$$=(20 \text{ yards})(10 \text{ yards})$$
$$=200 \text{ square yards}$$

34. average $=\dfrac{-12+(-13)+0+9}{4}=\dfrac{-16}{4}=-4$

35. The difference of three times a number and five times the same number is 4 translates to
$$3x-5x=4$$
$$-2x=4$$
$$\frac{-2x}{-2}=\frac{4}{-2}$$
$$x=-2$$
The number is -2.

36. $258\div10\dfrac{3}{4}=\dfrac{258}{1}\div\dfrac{43}{4}=\dfrac{258}{1}\cdot\dfrac{4}{43}=\dfrac{43\cdot6\cdot4}{1\cdot43}=24$

Expect to travel 24 miles on 1 gallon of gas.

37. Let x be the number of women runners entered in the race. Since the number of men entered in the race is 112 more than the number of women, the number of men is $x + 112$. Since the total number of runners in the race is 600, the sum of x and $x + 112$ is 600.
$$x+x+112=600$$
$$2x+112=600$$
$$2x+112-112=600-112$$
$$2x=488$$
$$\frac{2x}{2}=\frac{488}{2}$$
$$x=244$$
244 women entered the race.

38. Let x be the number of defective bulbs out of 510 bulbs.
$$\text{defective}\rightarrow\frac{3}{85}=\frac{x}{510}\leftarrow\text{defective}$$
$$\text{bulbs}\rightarrow\qquad\qquad\leftarrow\text{bulbs}$$
$$3\cdot510=85\cdot x$$
$$1530=85x$$
$$\frac{1530}{85}=\frac{85x}{85}$$
$$18=x$$
There should be 18 defective bulbs in 510.

39. Amount of discount $=15\%\cdot\$120$
$$=0.15\cdot\$120$$
$$=\$18$$
Sale price $=\$120-\$18=\$102$
The amount of the discount is $18; the sale price is $102.

40. hypotenuse $=\sqrt{(\text{leg})^2+(\text{other leg})^2}$
$$=\sqrt{4^2+4^2}$$
$$=\sqrt{16+16}$$
$$=\sqrt{32}$$
$$\approx5.66$$
The hypotenuse is 5.66 centimeters.

41. The complement of an angle that measures 78° is an angle that measures 90° − 78° = 12°.

42. $\angle x$ and the angle marked 73° are vertical angles, so $m\angle x = 73°$.

$\angle x$ and $\angle y$ are alternate interior angles, so $m\angle y = m\angle x = 73°$.

$\angle x$ and $\angle z$ are corresponding angles, so $m\angle z = m\angle x = 73°$.

43. The unmarked vertical side has length 11 in. − 7 in. = 4 in. The unmarked horizontal side has length 23 in. − 6 in. = 17 in.
$P = (6 + 4 + 17 + 7 + 23 + 11)$ in. = 68 in.
Extending the unmarked vertical side downward divides the region into two rectangles. The region's area is the sum of the areas of these:
$A = 11$ in.$\cdot 6$ in.$+ 7$ in.$\cdot 17$ in.
$\quad = 66$ sq in.$+ 119$ sq in.
$\quad = 185$ sq in.

44. Circumference:
$C = 2 \cdot \pi \cdot r$
$\quad = 2 \cdot \pi \cdot 9$ in.
$\quad = 18\pi$ in.
$\quad \approx 56.52$ in.
Area:
$A = \pi r^2$
$\quad = \pi(9 \text{ in.})^2$
$\quad = 81\pi$ sq in.
$\quad \approx 254.34$ sq in.

45. $2\frac{1}{2}$ gal $= \dfrac{2\frac{1}{2} \text{ gal}}{1} \cdot \dfrac{4 \text{ qt}}{1 \text{ gal}} = 2\frac{1}{2} \cdot 4$ qt $= 10$ qt

46. 2.4 kg $= \dfrac{2.4 \text{ kg}}{1} \cdot \dfrac{1000 \text{ g}}{1 \text{ kg}} = 2.4 \cdot 1000$ g $= 2400$ g

Chapters 9–16

47. $-3^4 = -(3 \cdot 3 \cdot 3 \cdot 3) = -81$

48. $4^{-3} = \dfrac{1}{4^3} = \dfrac{1}{64}$

49. $7 + 2(5y - 3) = 7 + 10y - 6$
$\quad = 7 - 6 + 10y$
$\quad = 1 + 10y$
$\quad = 10y + 1$

50.
$$\begin{array}{r} 5x^3 + x^2 + 5x - 2 \\ - (8x^3 - 4x^2 + x - 7) \\ \hline \end{array} \qquad \begin{array}{r} 5x^3 + x^2 + 5x - 2 \\ -8x^3 + 4x^2 - x + 7 \\ \hline -3x^3 + 5x^2 + 4x + 5 \end{array}$$

51. $(4x - 2)^2 = (4x)^2 - 2(4x)(2) + 2^2$
$\quad = 16x^2 - 16x + 4$

52. $(3x + 7)(x^2 + 5x + 2)$
$\quad = 3x(x^2 + 5x + 2) + 7(x^2 + 5x + 2)$
$\quad = 3x(x^2) + 3x(5x) + 3x(2) + 7(x^2) + 7(5x) + 7(2)$
$\quad = 3x^3 + 15x^2 + 6x + 7x^2 + 35x + 14$
$\quad = 3x^3 + 22x^2 + 41x + 14$

53. $6t^2 - t - 5 = 6t^2 + 5t - 6t - 5$
$\quad = t(6t + 5) - 1(6t + 5)$
$\quad = (6t + 5)(t - 1)$

54. $180 - 5x^2 = 5(36 - x^2)$
$\quad = 5(6^2 - x^2)$
$\quad = 5(6 - x)(6 + x)$

55. $3a^2 + 3ab - 7a - 7b = 3a(a + b) - 7(a + b)$
$\quad = (a + b)(3a - 7)$

56. $3x^3 - 21x^2 + 30x = 3x(x^2 - 7x + 10)$
$\quad = 3x(x - 5)(x - 2)$

57. $\left(\dfrac{4x^2 y^3}{x^3 y^{-4}}\right)^2 = \dfrac{4^2 x^{2 \cdot 2} y^{3 \cdot 2}}{x^{3 \cdot 2} y^{-4 \cdot 2}}$
$\quad = \dfrac{16x^4 y^6}{x^6 y^{-8}}$
$\quad = 16x^{4-6} y^{6-(-8)}$
$\quad = 16x^{-2} y^{14}$
$\quad = \dfrac{16 y^{14}}{x^2}$

58. $\dfrac{5 - \frac{1}{y^2}}{\frac{1}{y} + \frac{2}{y^2}} = \dfrac{y^2 \left(5 - \frac{1}{y^2}\right)}{y^2 \left(\frac{1}{y} + \frac{2}{y^2}\right)} = \dfrac{5y^2 - 1}{y + 2}$

59. $\dfrac{x^2-9}{x^2-3x} \div \dfrac{x^2+4x+1}{2x+10} = \dfrac{x^2-9}{x^2-3x} \cdot \dfrac{2x+10}{x^2+4x+1}$

$= \dfrac{(x-3)(x+3)}{x(x-3)} \cdot \dfrac{2(x+5)}{x^2+4x+1}$

$= \dfrac{2(x+3)(x+5)}{x(x^2+4x+1)}$

60. $\dfrac{5a}{a^2-a-6} - \dfrac{2}{a-3}$

$= \dfrac{5a}{(a-3)(a+2)} - \dfrac{2}{a-3}$

$= \dfrac{5a}{(a-3)(a+2)} - \dfrac{2(a+2)}{(a-3)(a+2)}$

$= \dfrac{5a-2(a+2)}{(a-3)(a+2)}$

$= \dfrac{5a-2a-4}{(a-3)(a+2)}$

$= \dfrac{3a-4}{(a-3)(a+2)}$

61.
$$
\begin{array}{r}
x+2 \\
x+5 \overline{\smash{)}\, x^2+7x+10} \\
\underline{x^2+5x} \\
2x+10 \\
\underline{2x+10} \\
0
\end{array}
$$

$\dfrac{x^2+7x+10}{x+5} = x+2$

62. $\quad 4(n-5) = -(4-2n)$

$4n-20 = -4+2n$

$4n-20-2n = -4+2n-2n$

$2n-20 = -4$

$2n-20+20 = -4+20$

$2n = 16$

$\dfrac{2n}{2} = \dfrac{16}{2}$

$n = 8$

63. $\quad (3x-5)(x+2) = -6$

$3x^2+6x-5x-10 = -6$

$3x^2+x-10 = -6$

$3x^2+x-4 = 0$

$a=3,\, b=1,\, c=-4$

$x = \dfrac{-b \pm \sqrt{b^2-4ac}}{2a}$

$x = \dfrac{-1 \pm \sqrt{1^2 - 4(3)(-4)}}{2(3)}$

$= \dfrac{-1 \pm \sqrt{1+48}}{6}$

$= \dfrac{-1 \pm \sqrt{49}}{6}$

$= \dfrac{-1 \pm 7}{6}$

$x = \dfrac{-1+7}{6} = 1$ or $x = \dfrac{-1-7}{6} = -\dfrac{4}{3}$

The solutions are $x = 1$ and $x = -\dfrac{4}{3}$.

64. $\quad -5(x-1)+6 \le -3(x+4)+1$

$-5x+5+6 \le -3x-12+1$

$-5x+11 \le -3x-11$

$-5x+11+3x \le -3x-11+3x$

$-2x+11 \le -11$

$-2x+11-11 \le -11-11$

$-2x \le -22$

$\dfrac{-2x}{-2} \ge \dfrac{-22}{-2}$

$x \ge 11$

$\{x | x \ge 11\}$

65. $\quad 2x^2-6x+1 = 0$

$a=2,\, b=-6,\, c=1$

$x = \dfrac{-b \pm \sqrt{b^2-4ac}}{2a}$

$x = \dfrac{-(-6) \pm \sqrt{(-6)^2 - 4(2)(1)}}{2(2)}$

$= \dfrac{6 \pm \sqrt{36-8}}{4}$

$= \dfrac{6 \pm \sqrt{28}}{4}$

$= \dfrac{6 \pm 2\sqrt{7}}{4}$

$= \dfrac{3 \pm \sqrt{7}}{2}$

The solutions are $x = \dfrac{3 \pm \sqrt{7}}{2}$.

66. The LCD is $3 \cdot 5 \cdot y = 15y$.

$$\frac{4}{y} - \frac{5}{3} = -\frac{1}{5}$$

$$15y\left(\frac{4}{y} - \frac{5}{3}\right) = 15y\left(-\frac{1}{5}\right)$$

$$60 - 25y = -3y$$

$$60 = 22y$$

$$\frac{60}{22} = y$$

$$\frac{30}{11} = y$$

The solution is $\frac{30}{11}$.

67. The LCD is $2(a - 3)$.

$$\frac{a}{a-3} = \frac{3}{a-3} - \frac{3}{2}$$

$$2(a-3)\left(\frac{a}{a-3}\right) = 2(a-3)\left(\frac{3}{a-3} - \frac{3}{2}\right)$$

$$2a = 6 - 3(a - 3)$$

$$2a = 6 - 3a + 9$$

$$5a = 15$$

$$a = 3$$

Since $a = 3$ causes the denominator $a - 3$ to be 0, the equation has no solution.

68.

$$\sqrt{2x - 2} = x - 5$$

$$\left(\sqrt{2x-2}\right)^2 = (x-5)^2$$

$$2x - 2 = x^2 - 10x + 25$$

$$0 = x^2 - 12x + 27$$

$$0 = (x-3)(x-9)$$

$$x - 3 = 0 \quad \text{or} \quad x - 9 = 0$$

$$x = 3 \qquad x = 9$$

$x = 3$ does not check, so the solution is $x = 9$.

69. $5x - 7y = 10$

$y = 0$: $5x - 7(0) = 10$

$$5x - 0 = 10$$

$$5x = 10$$

$$x = 2$$

x-intercept: $(2, 0)$

$x = 0$: $5(0) - 7y = 10$

$$0 - 7y = 10$$

$$-7y = 10$$

$$y = -\frac{10}{7}$$

y-intercept: $\left(0, -\frac{10}{7}\right)$

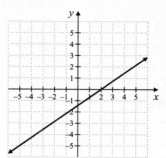

70. The graph of $y = -1$ is a horizontal line with a y-intercept of $(0, -1)$.

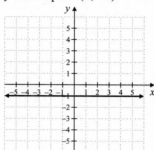

71. Graph the boundary line, $y = -4x$, with a solid line.

Test $(1, 1)$: $y \geq -4x$

$$1 \geq -4(1)$$

$$1 \geq -4 \quad \text{True}$$

Shade the half-plane containing $(1, 1)$.

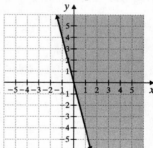

72. $m = \dfrac{y_2 - y_1}{x_2 - x_1} = \dfrac{2 - (-5)}{-1 - 6} = \dfrac{7}{-7} = -1$

73. $y = mx + b$

$$-3x + y = 5$$

$$y = 3x + 5$$

$$m = 3$$

675

74. $m = \dfrac{y_2 - y_1}{x_2 - x_1} = \dfrac{3 - (-5)}{1 - 2} = \dfrac{3 + 5}{-1} = -8$

$$y - y_1 = m(x - x_1)$$
$$y - (-5) = -8(x - 2)$$
$$y + 5 = -8x + 16$$
$$y = -8x + 11$$
$$8x + y = 11$$

75. $m = \dfrac{1}{8};\ b = 12$

$$y = \dfrac{1}{8}x + 12$$
$$8y = x + 8(12)$$
$$8y = x + 96$$
$$x - 8y = -96$$

76. $\begin{cases} 3x - 2y = -14 \\ y = x + 5 \end{cases}$

Substitute $x + 5$ for y in the first equation and solve for x.
$$3x - 2y = -14$$
$$3x - 2(x + 5) = -14$$
$$3x - 2x - 10 = -14$$
$$x - 10 = -14$$
$$x = -4$$
$$y = x + 5 = -4 + 5 = 1$$
The solution of the system is $(-4, 1)$.

77. $\begin{cases} 4x - 6y = 7 \\ -2x + 3y = 0 \end{cases}$

Multiply the second equation by 2.
$$\begin{cases} 4x - 6y = 7 \\ 2(-2x + 3y) = 2(0) \end{cases} \rightarrow \begin{cases} 4x - 6y = 7 \\ -4x + 6y = 0 \end{cases}$$

Add the equations to eliminate x.
$$\begin{array}{r} 4x - 6y = 7 \\ -4x + 6y = 0 \\ \hline 0 = 7 \end{array}$$

Since the statement $0 = 7$ is false, the system has no solution.

78. $f(x) = x^3 - x$

   a. $f(-1) = (-1)^3 - (-1) = -1 + 1 = 0$

   b. $f(0) = 0^3 - 0 = 0 - 0 = 0$

   c. $f(4) = 4^3 - 4 = 64 - 4 = 60$

79. The x-value -3 is assigned to two y-values, -3 and 2, so the relation is not a function. Note that the x-value 0 is also assigned to two y-values, 5 and 0.

80. $\sqrt{54} = \sqrt{9 \cdot 6} = \sqrt{9}\sqrt{6} = 3\sqrt{6}$

81. $\sqrt{24x^8} = \sqrt{4x^8 \cdot 6} = \sqrt{4x^8}\sqrt{6} = 2x^4\sqrt{6}$

82. $\sqrt{18} - \sqrt{75} + 7\sqrt{3} - \sqrt{8}$
$$= \sqrt{9 \cdot 2} - \sqrt{25 \cdot 3} + 7\sqrt{3} - \sqrt{4 \cdot 2}$$
$$= \sqrt{9}\sqrt{2} - \sqrt{25}\sqrt{3} + 7\sqrt{3} - \sqrt{4}\sqrt{2}$$
$$= 3\sqrt{2} - 5\sqrt{3} + 7\sqrt{3} - 2\sqrt{2}$$
$$= (3 - 2)\sqrt{2} + (-5 + 7)\sqrt{3}$$
$$= \sqrt{2} + 2\sqrt{3}$$

83. $\dfrac{\sqrt{40x^4}}{\sqrt{2x}} = \sqrt{\dfrac{40x^4}{2x}}$
$$= \sqrt{20x^3}$$
$$= \sqrt{4x^2 \cdot 5x}$$
$$= \sqrt{4x^2}\sqrt{5x}$$
$$= 2x\sqrt{5x}$$

84. $\sqrt{2}\left(\sqrt{6} - \sqrt{5}\right) = \sqrt{2}\sqrt{6} - \sqrt{2}\sqrt{5}$
$$= \sqrt{12} - \sqrt{10}$$
$$= \sqrt{4 \cdot 3} - \sqrt{10}$$
$$= 2\sqrt{3} - \sqrt{10}$$

85. $\dfrac{8}{\sqrt{5y}} = \dfrac{8}{\sqrt{5y}} \cdot \dfrac{\sqrt{5y}}{\sqrt{5y}} = \dfrac{8\sqrt{5y}}{5y}$

86. $\dfrac{8}{\sqrt{6} + 2} = \dfrac{8}{\sqrt{6} + 2} \cdot \dfrac{\sqrt{6} - 2}{\sqrt{6} - 2}$
$$= \dfrac{8\left(\sqrt{6} - 2\right)}{\left(\sqrt{6}\right)^2 - 2^2}$$
$$= \dfrac{8\left(\sqrt{6} - 2\right)}{6 - 4}$$
$$= \dfrac{8\left(\sqrt{6} - 2\right)}{2}$$
$$= 4\left(\sqrt{6} - 2\right)$$
$$= 4\sqrt{6} - 8$$

87. $y = x^2 - 7x + 10$

$y = 0$: $0 = x^2 - 7x + 10$

$\qquad 0 = (x-5)(x-2)$

$\qquad x - 5 = 0 \quad \text{or} \quad x - 2 = 0$

$\qquad\qquad x = 5 \qquad\qquad x = 2$

x-intercepts: (5, 0) and (2, 0)

$x = 0$: $y = 0^2 - 7(0) + 10 = 10$

y-intercept: (0, 10)

$y = x^2 - 7x + 10$

$a = 1, b = -7, c = 10$

$\dfrac{-b}{2a} = \dfrac{-(-7)}{2(1)} = \dfrac{7}{2}$

$x = \dfrac{7}{2}$: $y = \left(\dfrac{7}{2}\right)^2 - 7\left(\dfrac{7}{2}\right) + 10$

$\qquad\qquad = \dfrac{49}{4} - \dfrac{49}{2} + 10$

$\qquad\qquad = \dfrac{49}{4} - \dfrac{98}{4} + \dfrac{40}{4}$

$\qquad\qquad = -\dfrac{9}{4}$

vertex: $\left(\dfrac{7}{2}, -\dfrac{9}{4}\right)$

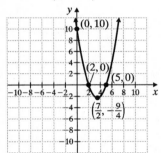

88. Let n be the number.

$n + 5\left(\dfrac{1}{n}\right) = 6$

$n + \dfrac{5}{n} = 6$

$n\left(n + \dfrac{5}{n}\right) = n(6)$

$n^2 + 5 = 6n$

$n^2 - 6n + 5 = 0$

$(n-5)(n-1) = 0$

$n - 5 = 0 \quad \text{or} \quad n - 1 = 0$

$\quad n = 5 \qquad\qquad n = 1$

The number is 1 or 5.

89. Let x be the number.

$x + \dfrac{2}{3}x = 35$

$\dfrac{3}{3}x + \dfrac{2}{3}x = 35$

$\dfrac{5}{3}x = 35$

$\dfrac{3}{5} \cdot \dfrac{5}{3}x = \dfrac{3}{5} \cdot 35$

$x = 21$

The number is 21.

90. Let x represent the number of public libraries in Indiana. Then there are $x + 650$ public libraries in New York.

$x + x + 650 = 1504$

$2x + 650 = 1504$

$2x + 650 - 650 = 1504 - 650$

$2x = 854$

$\dfrac{2x}{2} = \dfrac{854}{2}$

$x = 427$

$x + 650 = 427 + 650 = 1077$

Indiana has 427 public libraries and New York has 1077.

91. Let x be the speed of the boat in still water. Let $x + 2$ be the speed of the boat going downstream. Let $x - 2$ be the speed of the boat going upstream.

	distance	=	rate	·	time
Upstream	14		$x - 2$		$\frac{14}{x-2}$
Downstream	16		$x + 2$		$\frac{16}{x+2}$

$\dfrac{14}{x-2} = \dfrac{16}{x+2}$

$14(x+2) = 16(x-2)$

$14x + 28 = 16x - 32$

$60 = 2x$

$30 = x$

The speed of the boat in still water is 30 mph.